QUANTUM CHEMISTRY

Student Edition

QUANTUM CHEMISTRY

Student Edition

JOHN P. LOWE

THE PENNSYLVANIA STATE UNIVERSITY

ACADEMIC PRESS New York San Francisco London

A Subsidiary of Harcourt Brace Jovanovich, Publishers

ACADEMIC PRESS, INC.
111 Fifth Avenue, New York, New York 10003

United Kingdom Edition published by
ACADEMIC PRESS, INC. (LONDON) LTD.
24/28 Oval Road, London NW1

LIBRARY OF CONGRESS CATALOG CARD NUMBER: 77-6602
ISBN 0-12-457552-8

PRINTED IN THE UNITED STATES OF AMERICA

80 81 82   9 8 7 6 5 4 3 2

To
ARTHUR A. FROST

THE MOLECULAR CHALLENGE

Sir Ethylene, to scientists fair prey,
(Who dig and delve and peek and push and pry,
And prove their findings with equations sly)
Smoothed out his ruffled orbitals, to say:
"I stand in symmetry. Mine is a way
Of mystery and magic. Ancient, I
Am also deemed immortal. Should I die,
Pi would be in the sky, and Judgement Day
Would be upon us. For all things must fail,
That hold our universe together, when
Bonds such as bind me fail, and fall asunder.
Hence, stand I firm against the endless hail
Of scientific blows. I yield not." Men
And their computers stand and stare and wonder.

W. G. LOWE

CONTENTS

PREFACE xv

Chapter 1 **Classical Waves and the Time-Independent Schrödinger Wave Equation**

1-1 Introduction 1
1-2 Waves 1
1-3 The Classical Wave Equation 5
1-4 Standing Waves in a Clamped String 7
1-5 Light as an Electromagnetic Wave 9
1-6 The Photoelectric Effect 11
1-7 The Wave Nature of Matter 15
1-8 A Diffraction Experiment with Electrons 16
1-9 Schrödinger's Time-Independent Wave Equation 19
1-10 Conditions on ψ 21
1-11 Some Insight into the Schrödinger Equation 23
1-12 Summary 23
Problems 24

Chapter 2 **Quantum Mechanics of Some Simple Systems**

2-1 The Particle in a One-Dimensional "Box" 27
2-2 Detailed Examination of Particle-in-a-Box Solutions 30
2-3 The Particle in a One-Dimensional "Box" with One Finite Wall 38
2-4 The Particle in an Infinite "Box" with a Finite Central Barrier 44
2-5 The Free Particle in One Dimension 49
2-6 The Particle in a Ring of Constant Potential 50
2-7 The Particle in a Three-Dimensional Box: Separation of Variables 52
2-8 Summary 56
Problems 57
Reference 59

Chapter 3 **The One-Dimensional Harmonic Oscillator**

3-1 Introduction 60
3-2 Some Characteristics of the Classical One-Dimensional Harmonic Oscillator 60

3-3 The Quantum-Mechanical Harmonic Oscillator 63
3-4 Solution of the Harmonic Oscillator Schrödinger Equation 65
3-5 Quantum-Mechanical Average Value of the Potential Energy 73
Problems 74

Chapter 4 The Hydrogenlike Ion

4-1 The Schrödinger Equation and the Nature of Its Solutions 76
4-2 Separation of Variables 92
4-3 Solution of the R, Θ, and Φ Equations 93
4-4 Atomic Units 96
4-5 Angular Momentum and Spherical Harmonics 97
4-6 Summary 103
Problems 104
References 106

Chapter 5 Many-Electron Atoms

5-1 The Independent Electron Approximation 107
5-2 Simple Products and Electron Exchange Symmetry 109
5-3 Electron Spin and the Exclusion Principle 112
5-4 Slater Determinants and the Pauli Principle 117
5-5 Singlet and Triplet States for the 1s2s Configuration of Helium 119
5-6 The Self-Consistent Field, Slater-Type Orbitals, and the Aufbau Principle 127
Problems 132
References 134

Chapter 6 Postulates and Theorems of Quantum Mechanics

6-1 Introduction 135
6-2 The Wavefunction Postulate 135
6-3 The Postulate for Constructing Operators 136
6-4 The Time-Dependent Schrödinger Equation Postulate 137
6-5 The Postulate Relating Measured Values to Eigenvalues 138
6-6 The Postulate for Average Values 139
6-7 Hermitian Operators 140
6-8 Proof That Eigenvalues of Hermitian Operators Are Real 141
6-9 Proof That Eigenfunctions of an Hermitian Operator Form an Orthonormal Set 142
6-10 Proof That Commuting Operators Have Simultaneous Eigenfunctions 143
6-11 Completeness of Eigenfunctions of an Hermitian Operator 144
6-12 The Variation Principle 145
6-13 Measurement, Commutators, and Uncertainty 146
6-14 Summary 147
Problems 148
References 149

Chapter 7 The Variation Method

7-1 The Spirit of the Method 150
7-2 Nonlinear Variation: The Hydrogen Atom 151
7-3 Nonlinear Variation: The Helium Atom 155
7-4 Linear Variation: The Polarizability of the Hydrogen Atom 157
7-5 Linear Combination of Atomic Orbitals: The H_2^+ Molecule-Ion 167
7-6 Molecular Orbitals of Homonuclear Diatomic Molecules 181
7-7 Basis Set Choice and the Variational Wavefunction 192
7-8 Beyond the Orbital Approximation 195
Problems 197
References 200

Chapter 8 The Simple Hückel Method and Applications

8-1 The Importance of Symmetry 202
8-2 The Assumption of σ–π Separability 202
8-3 The Independent π-Electron Assumption 204
8-4 Setting up the Hückel Determinant 205
8-5 Solving the HMO Determinantal Equation for Orbital Energies 209
8-6 Solving for the Molecular Orbitals 209
8-7 The Cyclopropenyl System: Handling Degeneracies 211
8-8 Charge Distributions from HMOs 214
8-9 Some Simplifying Generalizations 217
8-10 HMO Calculations on Some Simple Molecules 222
8-11 Summary: The Simple HMO Method for Hydrocarbons 227
8-12 Relation between Bond Order and Bond Length 228
8-13 π-Electron Densities and Electron Spin Resonance Hyperfine Splitting Constants 231
8-14 Orbital Energies and Oxidation–Reduction Potentials 234
8-15 Orbital Energies and Ionization Potentials 236
8-16 π-Electron Energy and Aromaticity 239
8-17 Extension to Heteroatomic Molecules 245
8-18 Self-Consistent Variations of α and β 248
8-19 HMO Reaction Indices 250
8-20 Conclusions 257
Problems 258
References 266

Chapter 9 Matrix Formulation of the Linear Variation Method

9-1 Introduction 267
9-2 Matrices and Vectors 267
9-3 Matrix Formulation of the Linear Variation Method 275
9-4 Solving the Matrix Equation 277
9-5 Summary 280
Problems 280
References 282

Chapter 10 The Extended Hückel Method

10-1 The Extended Hückel Method 283
10-2 Mulliken Populations 295
10-3 Extended Hückel Energies and Mulliken Populations 298
10-4 Extended Hückel Energies and Experimental Energies 301
Problems 304
References 308

Chapter 11 The SCF–LCAO–MO Method and Extensions

11-1 *Ab Initio* Calculations 309
11-2 The Molecular Hamiltonian 310
11-3 The Form of the Wavefunction 310
11-4 The Nature of the Basis Set 311
11-5 The LCAO–MO–SCF Equation 311
11-6 Interpretation of the LCAO–MO–SCF Eigenvalues 313
11-7 The SCF Total Electronic Energy 314
11-8 Basis Sets 315
11-9 The Hartree–Fock Limit 318
11-10 Correlation Energy 319
11-11 Koopmans' Theorem 320
11-12 Configuration Interaction 322
11-13 Examples of *Ab Initio* Calculations 328
11-14 Approximate SCF–MO Methods 342
Problems 344
References 345

Chapter 12 Time-Independent Rayleigh–Schrödinger Perturbation Theory

12-1 An Introductory Example 347
12-2 Formal Development of the Theory for Nondegenerate States 347
12-3 A Uniform Electrostatic Perturbation of an Electron in a "Wire" 352
12-4 The Ground-State Energy to First Order of Heliumlike Systems 359
12-5 Perturbation at an Atom in the Simple Hückel MO Method 361
12-6 Perturbation Theory for a Degenerate State 364
12-7 Polarizability of the Hydrogen Atom in the $n = 2$ States 365
12-8 Interaction between Two Orbitals: An Important Chemical Model 368
12-9 Connection between Time-Independent Perturbation Theory and Spectroscopic Selection Rules 371
Problems 374
References 380

Chapter 13 Group Theory

13-1 Introduction 381
13-2 An Elementary Example 381

13-3 Symmetry Point Groups 383
13-4 The Concept of Class 386
13-5 Symmetry Elements and Their Notation 389
13-6 Identifying the Point Group of a Molecule 395
13-7 Representations for Groups 396
13-8 Generating Representations from Basis Functions 399
13-9 Labels for Representations 405
13-10 Some Connections between the Representation Table and Molecular Orbitals 406
13-11 Representations for Cyclic and Related Groups 408
13-12 Orthogonality in Irreducible Inequivalent Representations 411
13-13 Characters and Character Tables 413
13-14 Using Characters to Resolve Reducible Representations 417
13-15 Identifying Molecular Orbital Symmetries 418
13-16 Determining in Which Molecular Orbital an Atomic Orbital Will Appear 421
13-17 Generating Symmetry Orbitals 422
13-18 Hybrid Orbitals and Localized Orbitals 425
13-19 Symmetry and Integration 428
Problems 431
References 436

Chapter 14 **Qualitative Molecular Orbital Theory**

14-1 The Need for a Qualitative Theory 437
14-2 Hierarchy in Molecular Structure and in Molecular Orbitals 437
14-3 H_2^+ Revisited 438
14-4 H_2: Comparisons with H_2^+ 441
14-5 Rules for Qualitative Molecular Orbital Theory 443
14-6 Application of QMOT Rules to Homonuclear Diatomic Molecules 444
14-7 Shapes of Polyatomic Molecules: Walsh Diagrams 447
14-8 Frontier Orbitals 461
14-9 Qualitative Molecular Orbital Theory of Reactions 464
Problems 480
References 482

Appendix 1 **Useful Integrals** 483

Appendix 2 **Determinants** 485

Appendix 3 **Evaluation of the Coulomb Repulsion Integral over 1s AOs** 488

Appendix 4 **Some Characteristics of Solutions of the Linear Variation Procedure** 493

Appendix 5 **The Pairing Theorem** 498

Appendix 6 **Hückel Molecular Orbital Energies, Coefficients, Electron Densities, and Bond Orders for Some Simple Molecules** 500

Appendix 7 **Derivation of the Hartree–Fock Equation** 509

Appendix 8 **The Virial Theorem for Atoms and Diatomic Molecules** 520

Appendix 9 **Details of the Solution of the Matrix Equation HC=SCE** 525

Appendix 10 **Computer Program Listings** 538

Appendix 11 **Bra–Ket Notation** 552

Appendix 12 **Values of Some Useful Constants and Conversion Factors** 554

Appendix 13 **Group Theoretical Charts and Tables** 558

Appendix 14 **Hints for Solving Selected Problems** 572

Appendix 15 **Answers to Selected Problems** 574

INDEX 595

PREFACE

My aim in this book is to present a reasonably rigorous treatment of molecular orbital theory, embracing subjects that are of practical interest to organic and inorganic as well as physical chemists. My approach here has been to rely on physical intuition as much as possible, first solving a number of specific problems in order to develop sufficient insight and familiarity to make the formal treatment of Chapter 6 more palatable. My own experience suggests that most chemists find this route the most natural.

I have assumed that the reader has at some time learned calculus and elementary physics, but I have not assumed that this material is fresh in his or her mind. Other mathematics is developed as it is needed. The book could be used as a text for undergraduate or graduate students in a half or full year course. The level of rigor of the book is somewhat adjustable. For example, Chapters 3 and 4, on the harmonic oscillator and hydrogen atom, can be truncated if one wishes to know the nature of the solutions, but not the mathematical details of how they are produced.

I have made use of appendixes for certain of the more complicated derivations or proofs. This is done in order to avoid having the development of major ideas in the text interrupted or obscured. Certain of the appendixes will interest only the more theoretically inclined student. Also, because I anticipate that some readers may wish to skip certain chapters or parts of chapters, I have occasionally repeated information so that a given chapter will be less dependent on its predecessors. This may seem inelegant at times, but most students will more readily forgive repetition of something they already know than an overly terse presentation.

I have avoided early usage of bra-ket notation. I believe that simultaneous introduction of new concepts and unfamiliar notation is poor pedagogy. Bra-ket notation is used only after the ideas have had a chance to jell.

Problem solving is extremely important in acquiring an understanding of quantum chemistry. I have included a fair number of problems with hints for a few of them in Appendix 14 and answers for almost all of them in Appendix 15.

It is inevitable that one be selective in choosing topics for a book such as this. This book emphasizes ground state MO theory of molecules more than do most introductory texts, with rather less emphasis on spectroscopy than is usual. Angular momentum is treated at a fairly elementary level at various appropriate places in the text, but it is never given a full-blown formal development using operator commutation relations. Time-dependent phenomena are not included. Thus, scattering theory is absent, although selection rules and the transition dipole are discussed in the chapter on time-independent perturbation theory. Valence-bond theory is completely absent. If I have succeeded in my effort to provide a clear and meaningful treatment of topics relevant to modern molecular orbital theory, it should not be difficult for an instructor to provide for excursions into related topics not covered in the text.

Over the years, many colleagues have been kind enough to read sections of the evolving manuscript and provide corrections and advice. I especially thank L. P. Gold and O. H. Crawford, who cheerfully bore the brunt of this task.

Finally, I would like to thank my father, Wesley G. Lowe, for allowing me to include his sonnet, "The Molecular Challenge."

QUANTUM CHEMISTRY

Student Edition

CHAPTER 1

CLASSICAL WAVES AND THE TIME-INDEPENDENT SCHRÖDINGER WAVE EQUATION

1-1 Introduction

The application of quantum-mechanical principles to chemical problems has revolutionized the field of chemistry. Today our understanding of chemical bonding, spectral phenomena, molecular reactivities, and various other fundamental chemical problems rests heavily on our knowledge of the detailed behavior of electrons in atoms and molecules. In this book we shall describe in detail some of the basic principles, methods, and results of quantum chemistry that lead to our understanding of electron behavior.

In the first few chapters we shall discuss some simple, but important, particle systems. This will allow us to introduce many basic concepts and definitions in a fairly physical way. Thus, some background will be prepared for the more formal general development of Chapter 6. In this first chapter, we review briefly some of the concepts of classical physics as well as some early indications that classical physics is not sufficient to explain all phenomena. (Those readers who are already familiar with the physics of classical waves and with early atomic physics may prefer to jump ahead to Section 1-7.)

1-2 Waves

A. Traveling Waves

A very simple example of a traveling wave is provided by cracking a whip. A pulse of energy is imparted to the whipcord by a single oscillation of the handle. This results in a wave which travels down the cord, transferring the energy to the "popper" at the end of the whip. In Fig. 1-1, an idealization of the process is sketched. The shape of the disturbance in the whip is called the *wave profile* and is usually symbolized $\psi(x)$. The wave profile for the traveling wave in Fig. 1-1 shows where the energy is located at a given instant. It also contains the information needed to tell how much energy is being transmitted,

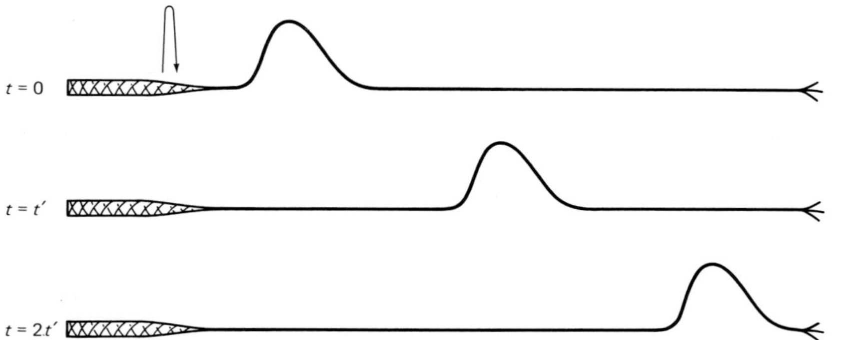

FIG. 1-1 Cracking the whip. As time passes, the disturbance moves from left to right along the extended whip cord. Each segment of the cord oscillates up and down as the disturbance passes by, ultimately returning to its equilibrium position.

because the height and shape of the wave reflect the vigor with which the handle was oscillated.

The feature common to all traveling waves in classical physics is that energy is transmitted through a medium. The medium itself undergoes no permanent displacement; it merely undergoes local oscillations as the disturbance passes through.

One of the most important kinds of wave in physics is the *harmonic* wave, for which the wave profile is a sinusoidal function. A harmonic wave, at a particular instant in time, is sketched in Fig. 1-2. The maximum displacement of the wave from the rest position is the *amplitude* of the wave, and the *wavelength* λ is the distance required to enclose one complete oscillation. Such a wave would result from a harmonic[1] oscillation at one end of a taut string. Analogous waves would be produced on the surface of a quiet pool by a vibrating bob, or in air by a vibrating tuning fork.

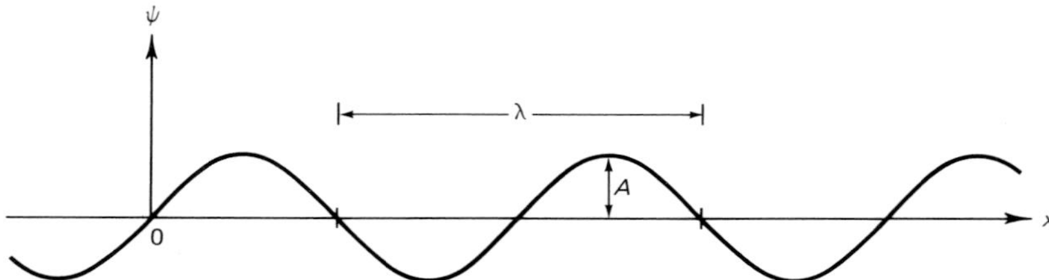

FIG. 1-2 A harmonic wave at a particular instant in time. A is the amplitude and λ is the wavelength.

At the instant depicted in Fig. 1-2, the profile is described by the function

$$\psi(x) = A \sin(2\pi x/\lambda) \tag{1-1}$$

[1] A harmonic oscillation is one whose equation of motion has a sine or cosine dependence on time.

($\psi = 0$ when $x = 0$, and the argument of the sine function goes from 0 to 2π, encompassing one complete oscillation as x goes from 0 to λ.) Let us suppose that the situation in Fig. 1-2 pertains at the time $t = 0$, and let the velocity of the disturbance through the medium be c. Then, after time t, the distance traveled is ct, the profile is shifted to the right by ct and is now given by

$$\Psi(x, t) = A \sin[(2\pi/\lambda)(x - ct)] \tag{1-2}$$

A capital Ψ is used to distinguish the time-dependent function (1-2) from the time-independent function (1-1).

The *frequency* ν of a wave is the number of individual repeating wave units passing a point per unit time. For our harmonic wave, this is the distance traveled in unit time c divided by the length of a wave unit λ. Hence,

$$\nu = c/\lambda \tag{1-3}$$

Note that the wave described by the formula

$$\Psi'(x, t) = A \sin[(2\pi/\lambda)(x - ct) + \epsilon] \tag{1-4}$$

is similar to Ψ of Eq. (1-2) except for being displaced. If we compare the two waves at the same instant in time, we find Ψ' to be shifted to the left of Ψ by $\epsilon\lambda/2\pi$. If $\epsilon = \pi, 3\pi, \ldots$, then Ψ' is shifted by $\lambda/2, 3\lambda/2, \ldots$ and the two functions are said to be exactly out of phase. If $\epsilon = 2\pi, 4\pi, \ldots$, the shift is by $\lambda, 2\lambda, \ldots$, and the two waves are exactly in phase. ϵ is the *phase factor* for Ψ' relative to Ψ. Alternatively, we can compare the two waves at the same point in x, in which case the phase factor causes the two waves to be displaced from each other in time.

B. Standing Waves

In problems of physical interest, the medium is usually subject to constraints. For example, a string will have ends, and these may be clamped, as in a violin, so that they cannot oscillate when the disturbance reaches them. Under such circumstances, the energy pulse is unable to progress further. It cannot be absorbed by the clamping mechanism if it is perfectly rigid, and it has no choice but to travel back along the string in the opposite direction. The reflected wave is now moving into the face of the primary wave, and the motion of the string is in response to the demands placed on it by the two simultaneous waves:

$$\Psi(x, t) = \Psi_{\text{primary}}(x, t) + \Psi_{\text{reflected}}(x, t) \tag{1-5}$$

When the primary and reflected waves have the same amplitude and speed, we can write

$$\begin{aligned}\Psi(x, t) &= A \sin[(2\pi/\lambda)(x - ct)] + A \sin[(2\pi/\lambda)(x + ct)] \\ &= 2A \sin(2\pi x/\lambda) \cos(2\pi ct/\lambda)\end{aligned} \tag{1-6}$$

This formula describes a *standing wave*—a wave that does not appear to travel through the medium, but appears to vibrate "in place." The first part of the function depends only on the x variable. Wherever the sine function vanishes, Ψ will vanish, regardless of the value of t. This means that there are places where the medium does not ever vibrate. Such places are called *nodes*. Between the nodes, $\sin(2\pi x/\lambda)$ is finite. As time passes, the cosine function oscillates between plus and minus unity. This means that Ψ oscillates between plus and minus the value of $\sin(2\pi x/\lambda)$. We say that the x-dependent part of the function gives the maximum displacement of the standing wave, and the t-dependent part governs the motion of the medium back and forth between these extremes of maximum displacement. A standing wave with a central node is shown in Fig. 1-3.

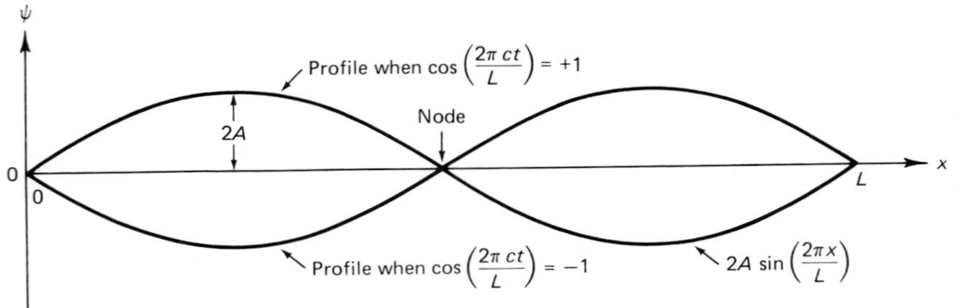

FIG. 1-3 A standing wave in a string clamped at $x = 0$ and $x = L$. The wavelength λ is equal to L.

Equation (1-6) is often written as

$$\Psi(x, t) = \psi(x)\cos(\omega t) \tag{1-7}$$

where

$$\omega = 2\pi c/\lambda \tag{1-8}$$

The profile $\psi(x)$ is often called the *amplitude function* and ω is the *frequency factor*.

Let us consider how the energy is stored in the vibrating string depicted in Fig. 1-3. The string segments at the central node and at the clamped endpoints of the string do not move. Hence, their kinetic energies are zero at all times. Furthermore, since they are never displaced from their equilibrium positions, their potential energies are likewise always zero. Therefore, the total energy stored at these segments is always zero as long as the string continues to vibrate in the mode shown. The maximum kinetic and potential energies are associated with those segments located at the wave peaks and valleys (called the *antinodes*) because these segments have the greatest average velocity and displacement from the equilibrium position. A more detailed mathematical treatment would show that the total energy of any string segment is proportional to $\psi(x)^2$ (Problem 1-7).

1-3 The Classical Wave Equation

It is one thing to draw a picture of a wave and describe its properties, and quite another to predict what sort of wave will result from disturbing a particular system. To make such predictions, we must consider the physical laws that the medium must obey. One condition is that the medium must obey Newton's laws of motion. For example, any segment of string of mass m subjected to a force F must undergo an acceleration of F/m in accord with Newton's second law. In this regard, wave motion is perfectly consistent with ordinary particle motion. Another condition, however, peculiar to waves, is that each segment of the medium is "attached" to the neighboring segments so that, as it is displaced, it drags along its neighbor, which in turn drags along *its* neighbor, etc. This provides the mechanism whereby the disturbance is propagated along the medium.[2]

Let us consider a string under a tensile force T. When the string is displaced from its equilibrium position, this tension is responsible for exerting a restoring force. For example, observe the string segment associated with the region x to $x + dx$ in Fig. 1-4. Note that the tension exerted at either end of this segment can be decomposed into components parallel and perpendicular to the x axis. The parallel component tends to stretch the string (which, however, we assume to be unstretchable), the perpendicular component acts to accelerate the segment toward or away from the rest position. At the right end of the segment, the perpendicular component F divided by the horizontal component

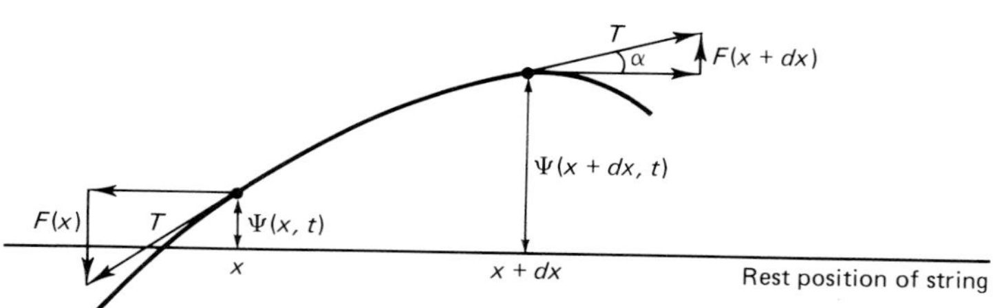

FIG. 1-4 A segment of string under tension T. The forces at each end of the segment are decomposed into forces perpendicular and parallel to x.

[2] Fluids are of relatively low viscosity, so the tendency of one segment to drag along its neighbor is weak. For this reason fluids are poor transmitters of *transverse* waves (waves in which the medium oscillates in a direction perpendicular to the direction of propagation). In *compression* waves, one segment displaces the next by pushing it. Here the requirement is that the medium possess elasticity for compression. Solids and fluids often meet this requirement well enough to transmit compression waves. The ability of rigid solids to transmit both wave types while fluids transmit only one type is the basis for using earthquake-induced waves to determine how deep the solid part of the earth's mantle extends.

gives the slope of T. However, for small deviations of the string from equilibrium (that is, for small angle α) the horizontal component is nearly equal in length to the vector T. This means that it is a good approximation to write

$$\text{slope of vector } T = F/T \qquad \text{at} \quad x + dx \tag{1-9}$$

But the slope is also given by the derivative of Ψ, and so we can write

$$F_{x+dx} = T(\partial\Psi/\partial x)_{x+dx} \tag{1-10}$$

At the other end of the segment the tensile force acts in the opposite direction, and we have

$$F_x = -T(\partial\Psi/\partial x)_x \tag{1-11}$$

The net perpendicular force on our string segment is the resultant of these two:

$$F = T[(\partial\Psi/\partial x)_{x+dx} - (\partial\Psi/\partial x)_x] \tag{1-12}$$

The difference in slope at two infinitesimally separated points, divided by dx, is by definition the second derivative of a function. Therefore,

$$F = T\,\partial^2\Psi/\partial x^2\,dx \tag{1-13}$$

Equation (1-13) gives the force on our string segment. If the string has mass m per unit length, then the segment has mass $m\,dx$, and Newton's equation $F = ma$ may be written

$$T\,\partial^2\Psi/\partial x^2 = m\,\partial^2\Psi/\partial t^2 \tag{1-14}$$

where we recall that acceleration is the second derivative of position with respect to time.

Equation (1-14) is the wave equation for motion in a string of uniform density under tension T. It should be evident that its derivation involves nothing fundamental beyond Newton's second law and the fact that the two ends of the segment are linked to each other and to a common tensile force. Generalizing this equation to waves in three-dimensional media gives

$$\left(\frac{\partial^2}{\partial x^2} + \frac{\partial^2}{\partial y^2} + \frac{\partial^2}{\partial z^2}\right)\Psi(x, y, z, t) = \beta\frac{\partial^2\Psi(x, y, z, t)}{\partial t^2} \tag{1-15}$$

where β is a composite of physical quantities (analogous to m/T) for the particular system.

Returning to our string example, we have in Eq. (1-14) a *time-dependent* differential equation. Suppose we wish to limit our consideration to standing waves that can be separated into a space-dependent amplitude function and a harmonic time-dependent function. Then

$$\Psi(x, t) = \psi(x)\cos(\omega t) \tag{1-16}$$

and the differential equation becomes

$$\cos(\omega t)\frac{d^2\psi(x)}{dx^2} = \frac{m}{T}\psi(x)\frac{d^2\cos(\omega t)}{dt^2} = -\frac{m}{T}\psi(x)\cos(\omega t) \qquad (1\text{-}17)$$

or, dividing by $\cos(\omega t)$,

$$d^2\psi(x)/dx^2 = -(\omega^2 m/T)\psi(x) \qquad (1\text{-}18)$$

This is the classical *time-independent* wave equation for a string.

We can see by inspection what kind of function $\psi(x)$ must be to satisfy Eq. (1-18). ψ is a function that, when twice differentiated, is reproduced with a coefficient of $-\omega^2 m/T$. One solution is

$$\psi = A\sin(\omega\sqrt{m/T}\,x) \qquad (1\text{-}19)$$

This illustrates that Eq. (1-18) has sinusoidally varying solutions such as those discussed in Section 1-2. Comparing Eq. (1-19) with (1-1) indicates that $2\pi/\lambda = \omega\sqrt{m/T}$. Substituting this relation into Eq. (1-18) gives

$$d^2\psi(x)/dx^2 = -(2\pi/\lambda)^2\psi(x) \qquad (1\text{-}20)$$

For three-dimensional systems, the classical time-independent wave equation for an isotropic and uniform medium is

$$(\partial^2/\partial x^2 + \partial^2/\partial y^2 + \partial^2/\partial z^2)\psi(x, y, z) = -(2\pi/\lambda)^2\psi(x, y, z) \qquad (1\text{-}21)$$

where λ depends on the elasticity of the medium. The combination of partial derivatives on the left-hand side of Eq. (1-21) is called the Laplacian, and is often given the short-hand symbol ∇^2 (del squared). This would give for Eq. (1-21)

$$\nabla^2\psi(x, y, z) = -(2\pi/\lambda)^2\psi(x, y, z) \qquad (1\text{-}22)$$

1-4 Standing Waves in a Clamped String

We now demonstrate how Eq. (1-20) can be used to predict the nature of standing waves in a string. Suppose that the string is clamped at $x = 0$ and L. This means that the string cannot oscillate at these points. Mathematically this means that

$$\psi(0) = \psi(L) = 0 \qquad (1\text{-}23)$$

Conditions such as these are called *boundary conditions*. Our question is, "What functions ψ satisfy Eq. (1-20) and also Eq. (1-23)?" We begin by trying to find the most general equation that can satisfy Eq. (1-20). We have already seen that $A\sin(2\pi x/\lambda)$ is a solution, but it is easy to show that $A\cos(2\pi x/\lambda)$ is also a solution. More general than either of these is the linear combination[3]

$$\psi(x) = A\sin(2\pi x/\lambda) + B\cos(2\pi x/\lambda) \qquad (1\text{-}24)$$

By varying A and B, we can get different functions ψ.

[3] Given functions $f_1, f_2, f_3, \ldots$. A *linear combination* of these functions is $c_1 f_1 + c_2 f_2 + c_3 f_3 + \cdots$, where $c_1, c_2, c_3, \ldots$ are numbers (which need not be real).

There are two remarks to be made at this point. First, some readers will have noticed that other functions exist that satisfy Eq. (1-20). These are $A \exp(2\pi ix/\lambda)$ and $A \exp(-2\pi ix/\lambda)$, where $i = \sqrt{-1}$. The reason we have not included these in the general function (1-24) is that these two exponential functions are mathematically equivalent to the trigonometric functions. The relationship is

$$\exp(\pm ikx) = \cos(kx) \pm i \sin(kx) \tag{1-25}$$

This means that any trigonometric function may be expressed in terms of such exponentials and vice versa. Hence, the set of trigonometric functions and the set of exponentials is redundant, and no additional flexibility would result by including exponentials in Eq. (1-24) (see Problem 1-1). The two sets of functions are *linearly dependent*.[4]

The second remark is that for a given A and B the function described by Eq. (1-24) is a single sinusoidal wave with wavelength λ. By altering the ratio of A to B, we cause the wave to shift to the left or right with respect to the origin. If $A = 1$ and $B = 0$, the wave has a node at $x = 0$. If $A = 0$ and $B = 1$, the wave has an antinode at $x = 0$.

We now proceed by letting the boundary conditions determine the constants A and B. The condition at $x = 0$ gives

$$\psi(0) = A \sin(0) + B \cos(0) = 0 \tag{1-26}$$

However, since $\sin(0) = 0$ and $\cos(0) = 1$, this gives

$$B = 0 \tag{1-27}$$

Therefore, our first boundary condition forces B to be zero and leaves us with

$$\psi(x) = A \sin(2\pi x/\lambda) \tag{1-28}$$

Our second boundary condition, at $x = L$, gives

$$\psi(L) = A \sin(2\pi L/\lambda) = 0 \tag{1-29}$$

One solution is provided by setting A equal to zero. This gives $\psi = 0$, which corresponds to no wave at all in the string. This is possible, but not very interesting. The other possibility is for $2\pi L/\lambda$ to be equal to $0, \pm\pi, \pm 2\pi, \ldots, \pm n\pi, \ldots$ since the sine function vanishes then. This gives the relation

$$2\pi L/\lambda = n\pi, \qquad n = 0, \pm 1, \pm 2, \ldots \tag{1-30}$$

or

$$\lambda = 2L/n, \qquad n = 0, \pm 1, \pm 2, \ldots \tag{1-31}$$

[4] If one member of a set of functions $(f_1, f_2, f_3, \ldots)$ can be expressed as a linear combination of the remaining functions (i.e., if $f_1 = c_2 f_2 + c_3 f_3 + \cdots$), the set of functions is said to be linearly dependent. Otherwise, they are linearly independent.

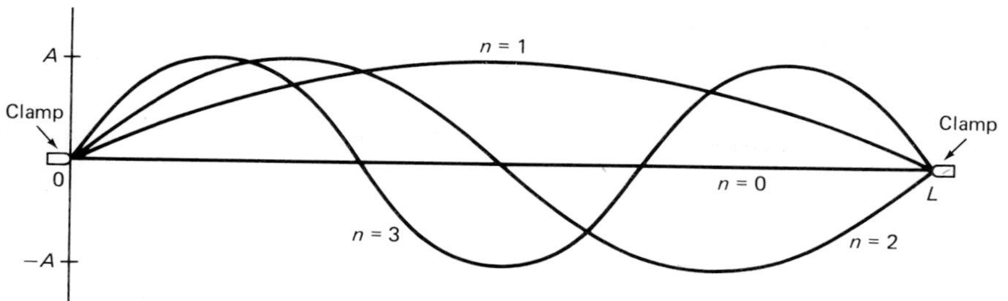

FIG. 1-5 Solutions for the time-independent wave equation in one dimension with boundary conditions $\psi(0) = \psi(L) = 0$.

Substituting this expression for λ into Eq. (1-28) gives

$$\psi(x) = A \sin(n\pi x/L), \qquad n = 0, \pm 1, \pm 2, \ldots \tag{1-32}$$

Some of these solutions are sketched in Fig. 1-5. The solution for $n = 0$ is again the uninteresting $\psi = 0$ case. Furthermore, since $\sin(-x)$ equals $-\sin(x)$, it is clear that the set of functions produced by positive integers n is not physically different from the set produced by negative n, so we may arbitrarily restrict our attention to solutions with positive n. (The two sets are linearly dependent.) The constant A is still undetermined. It affects the amplitude of the wave. To determine A would require knowing how much energy is stored in the wave, that is, how hard the string was plucked.

It is evident that there are an infinite number of acceptable solutions, each one corresponding to a different number of half-waves fitting between 0 and L. But an even larger infinity of waves has been excluded by the boundary conditions—namely, all waves having wavelengths not divisible into $2L$ an integral number of times. The result of applying boundary conditions has been to restrict the allowed wavelengths to certain discrete values. As we shall see, this behavior is closely related to the quantization of energies in quantum mechanics.

The example worked out above is an extremely simple one. Nevertheless, it demonstrates how a differential equation and boundary conditions are used to define the allowed states for a system. One could have arrived at solutions for this case by simple physical argument, but this is usually not possible in more complicated cases. The differential equation provides a systematic approach for finding solutions when physical intuition is not enough.

1-5 Light as an Electromagnetic Wave

Suppose a charged particle is caused to oscillate harmonically on the z axis. If there is another charged particle some distance away and initially at rest in the xy plane, this second particle will commence oscillating harmonically too.

Thus, energy is being transferred from the first particle to the second, which indicates that there is an oscillating electric field emanating from the first particle. We can plot the magnitude of this electric field at a given instant as it would be felt by a series of imaginary test charges stationed along a line emanating from the source and perpendicular to the axis of vibration (Fig. 1-6). The wave is coplanar with that axis and travels in directions perpendicular to it.

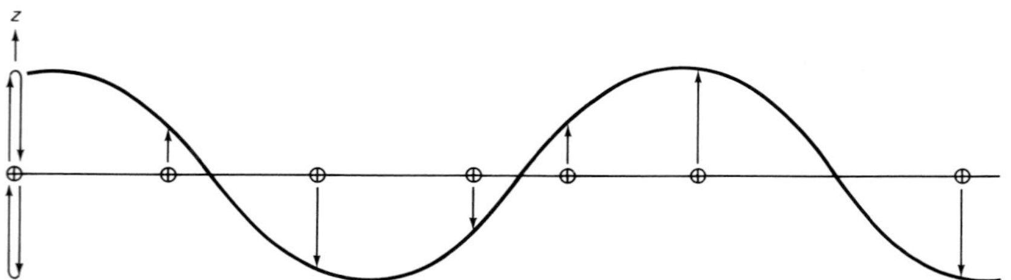

FIG. 1-6 A harmonic electric-field wave emanating from a vibrating electric charge. The wave magnitude is proportional to the force felt by the test charges. The charges are only imaginary; if they actually existed, they would possess mass and under acceleration would absorb energy from the wave, causing it to attenuate. The field radiates isotropically in the *xy* plane.

If there are some magnetic compasses in the neighborhood of the oscillating charge, these will be found to swing back and forth in response to the disturbance. This means that an oscillating *magnetic* field is produced by the charge too. Varying the placement of the compasses will show that this field oscillates in a plane perpendicular to the axis of vibration of the charged particle. The combined electric and magnetic fields traveling along one ray in the *xy* plane appear in Fig. 1-7.

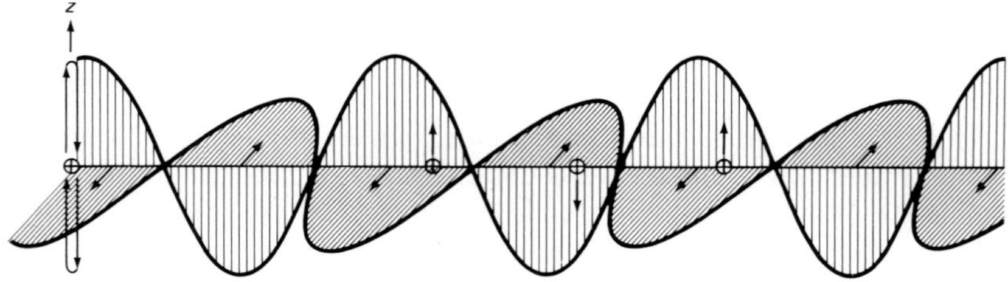

FIG. 1-7 A harmonic electromagnetic field produced by an oscillating electric charge. The arrows without attached charges show the direction in which the north pole of a magnet would be attracted. The magnetic field is oriented perpendicular to the electric field.

The changes in electric and magnetic fields propagate outward with a characteristic velocity c, and are describable as a traveling wave, called an electromagnetic wave. Its frequency ν is the same as the oscillation frequency of the vibrating charge. Its wavelength is $\lambda = c/\nu$. Visible light, infrared radiation, radio waves, microwaves, ultraviolet radiation, X rays, and γ rays are all forms of electromagnetic radiation, their only difference being their frequencies ν. We shall continue the discussion in the context of light, understanding that it applies to all forms of electromagnetic radiation.

If a beam of light is produced so that the orientation of the electric field wave is always in the same plane, the light is said to be plane (or linearly) polarized. The plane-polarized light shown in Fig. 1-7 is said to be z polarized. If the plane of orientation of the electric field wave rotates clockwise or counterclockwise about the axis of travel (i.e., if the electric field wave "corkscrews" through space), the light is said to be right or left circularly polarized. If the light is a composite of waves having random field orientations so that there is no resultant orientation, the light is unpolarized.

Experiments with light in the nineteenth century and earlier were consistent with the view that light is a wave phenomenon. One of the more obvious experimental verifications of this is provided by the interference pattern produced when light from a point source is allowed to pass through a pair of slits and then to fall on a screen. The resulting interference patterns are understandable only in terms of the constructive and destructive interference of waves. The differential equations of Maxwell, which provided the connection between electromagnetic radiation and the basic laws of physics, also indicated that light is a wave.

But there remained several problems that prevented physicists from closing the book on this subject. One was the inability of classical physical theory to explain the intensity and wavelength characteristics of light emitted by a glowing "blackbody." This problem was studied by Planck, who was forced to conclude that the vibrating charged particles producing the light can exist only in certain "discrete" (separated) energy states. We shall not discuss this problem. Another problem had to do with the interpretation of a phenomenon discovered in the late 1800s, called the *photoelectric effect*.

1-6 The Photoelectric Effect

This phenomenon occurs when the exposure of some material to light causes it to eject electrons. Many metals do this quite readily. A simple apparatus that could be used to study this behavior is drawn schematically in Fig. 1-8. Incident light strikes the metal dish in the evacuated chamber. If electrons are ejected, some of them will strike the collecting wire, giving rise to a deflection of the galvanometer. In this apparatus, one can vary the potential difference between the metal dish and the collecting wire, and also the intensity and frequency of the incident light.

Suppose that the potential difference is set at zero and a current is detected when light of a certain intensity and frequency strikes the dish. This means that electrons are being emitted from the dish with finite kinetic energy, enabling

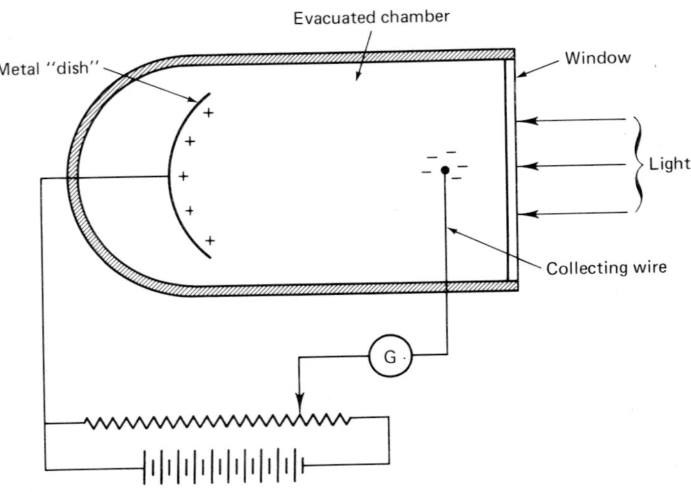

FIG. 1-8 A phototube.

them to travel to the wire. If a retarding potential is now applied, electrons that are emitted with only a small kinetic energy will have insufficient energy to overcome the retarding potential and will not travel to the wire. Hence, the current being detected will decrease. The retarding potential can be increased gradually until finally even the most energetic photoelectrons cannot make it to the collecting wire. This enables one to calculate the maximum kinetic energy for photoelectrons produced by the incident light on the metal in question.

The observations from experiments of this sort can be summarized as follows:

(1) Below a certain "cutoff" frequency of incident light, no photoelectrons are ejected, no matter how intense the light.

(2) Above the cutoff frequency, the number of photoelectrons is directly proportional to the intensity of the light.

(3) As the frequency of the incident light is increased, the maximum velocity of the photoelectrons increases.

(4) In cases where the radiation intensity is extremely low (but frequency is above the cutoff value) photoelectrons are emitted from the metal without any time lag.

Some of these results are summarized graphically in Fig. 1-9. Apparently, the kinetic energy of the photoelectron is given by

$$\text{kinetic energy} = h(\nu - \nu_0) \tag{1-33}$$

where h is a constant. The cutoff frequency ν_0 depends on the metal being studied (and also its temperature), but the slope h is the same for all substances.

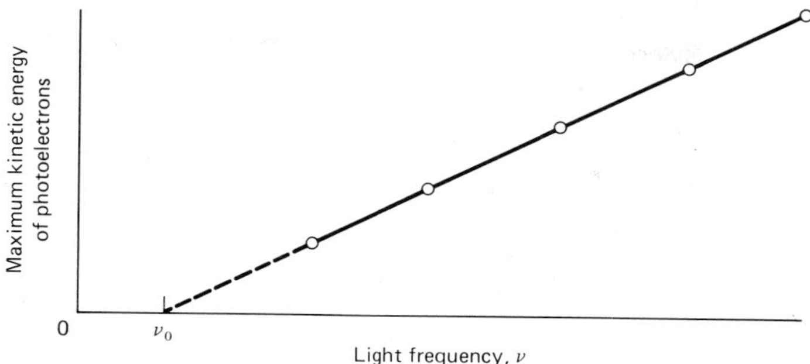

FIG. 1-9 Maximum kinetic energy of photoelectrons as a function of incident light frequency, where ν_0 is the minimum frequency for which photoelectrons are ejected from the metal in the absence of any retarding or accelerating potential.

We can also write the kinetic energy as

$$\text{kinetic energy} = \text{energy of light} - \text{energy needed to escape surface} \tag{1-34}$$

The last quantity in Eq. (1-34) is often referred to as the *work function W* of the metal. Equating Eq. (1-33) with (1-34) gives

$$\text{energy of light} - W = h\nu - h\nu_0 \tag{1-35}$$

The material-dependent term W is identified with the material-dependent term $h\nu_0$, yielding

$$\text{energy of light} \equiv E = h\nu \tag{1-36}$$

where the value of h has been determined to be 6.626176×10^{-34} J sec. (See Appendix 12 for units and conversion factors.)

Physicists found it difficult to reconcile these observations with the classical electromagnetic field theory of light. For example, if light of a certain frequency and intensity causes emission of electrons having a certain maximum kinetic energy, one would expect increased light *intensity* (corresponding classically to a greater electromagnetic field amplitude and hence greater energy density) to produce photoelectrons of higher kinetic energy. However, it only produces more photoelectrons and does not affect their energies. Again, if light is a wave, the energy is distributed over the entire wavefront and this means that a low light intensity would impart energy at a very low rate to an area of surface occupied by one atom. One can calculate that it would take years for an individual atom to collect sufficient energy to eject an electron under such conditions. No such induction period is observed.

An explanation for these results was suggested in 1905 by Einstein, who proposed that the incident light be viewed as being comprised of discrete units of energy. Each such unit, or *photon*, would have an associated energy of $h\nu$, where ν is the frequency of the oscillating emitter. Increasing the intensity of the light would correspond to increasing the number of photons, whereas increasing the frequency of the light would increase the energy of the photons. If we envision each emitted photoelectron as resulting from a photon striking the surface of the metal, it is quite easy to see that Einstein's proposal accords with observation. But it creates a new problem: If we are to visualize light as a stream of photons, how can we explain the wave properties of light, such as the double-slit diffraction pattern? What is the physical meaning of the electromagnetic wave?

Essentially, the problem is that in the classical view, the square of the electromagnetic wave at any point in space is a measure of the energy density at that point. Now the square of the electromagnetic wave is a continuous and smoothly varying function, and if energy is continuous and infinitely divisible, there is no problem with this theory. But if the energy cannot be divided into amounts smaller than a photon—if it has a particulate rather than a continuous nature—then the classical interpretation cannot apply, for it is not possible to produce a smoothly varying energy distribution from energy *particles* any more than it is possible to produce, at the microscopic level, a smooth density distribution in gas made from *atoms* of matter. Einstein suggested that the square of the electromagnetic wave at some point (that is, the sum of the squares of the electric and magnetic field magnitudes) be taken as the *probability density* for finding a photon in the volume element around that point. The greater the square of the wave in some region, the greater is the probability for finding the photon in that region. Thus, the classical notion of energy having a definite and smoothly varying distribution is replaced by the idea of a smoothly varying probability density for finding an atomistic packet of energy.

Let us explore this probabilistic interpretation within the context of the two-slit interference experiment. We know that the pattern of light and darkness observed on the screen agrees with the classical picture of interference of waves. Suppose we carry out the experiment in the usual way, except we use a light source (of frequency ν) so weak that only $h\nu$ units of energy per second pass through the apparatus and strike the screen. According to the classical picture, this tiny amount of energy should strike the screen in a delocalized manner, producing an extremely faint image of the entire diffraction pattern. Over a period of many seconds, this pattern could be accumulated (on a photographic plate, say) and would become more intense. According to Einstein's view, our experiment corresponds to transmission of one photon per second and each photon strikes the screen at a localized point. Each photon strikes a new spot (not to imply the same spot cannot be struck more than once) and, over a long period of time, they build up the observed diffraction pattern. If we wish to state in advance where the next photon will appear, we are unable to do so. The best we can do is to say that the next photon is more likely to strike in one area than in another, the relative probabilities being quantitatively described by the square of the electromagnetic wave.

The interpretation of electromagnetic waves as probability waves often leaves one with some feelings of unreality. If the wave only tells us relative probabilities for finding a photon at one point or another, one is entitled to ask whether the wave has "physical reality," or if it is merely a mathematical device which allows us to analyze photon distribution, the photons being the "physical reality." We will defer discussion of this question until a later section on electron diffraction.

1-7 The Wave Nature of Matter

Evidently light has wave and particle aspects, and we can describe it in terms of photons, which are associated with waves of frequency $\nu = E/h$. Now photons are rather peculiar particles in that they have zero rest mass. In fact, they can exist only when traveling at the speed of light. The more normal particles in our experience have nonzero rest masses and can exist at any velocity up to the speed-of-light limit. Are there also waves associated with such normal particles?

Imagine a particle having a finite rest mass that somehow can be made lighter and lighter, approaching zero in a continuous way. It seems reasonable that the existence of a wave associated with the motion of the particle should become more and more apparent, rather than the wave coming into existence abruptly when $m = 0$. De Broglie proposed that all material particles were associated with waves, which he called "matter waves," but that the existence of these waves was likely to be observable only in the behaviors of extremely light particles.

De Broglie's relation can be reached as follows. Einstein's relation for photons is

$$E = h\nu \tag{1-37}$$

But a photon carrying energy E has a relativistic mass given by

$$E = mc^2 \tag{1-38}$$

Equating these two equations gives

$$E = mc^2 = h\nu = hc/\lambda \tag{1-39}$$

or

$$mc = h/\lambda \tag{1-40}$$

A normal particle, with nonzero rest mass, travels at a velocity v. If we regard Eq. (1-40) as merely the high-velocity limit of a more general expression, we arrive at an equation relating particle momentum p and associated wavelength λ:

$$mv = p = h/\lambda \tag{1-41}$$

or

$$\lambda = h/p \tag{1-42}$$

Here, m refers to the rest mass of the particle plus the relativistic correction, bu the latter is usually negligible in comparison to the former.

This relation, proposed by de Broglie in 1922, was demonstrated to b correct shortly thereafter when Davisson and Germer showed that a beam o electrons impinging on a nickel target produced the scattering patterns on expects from interfering waves. These "electron waves" were observed to hav wavelengths related to electron momentum in just the manner proposed by d Broglie.

Equation (1-42) relates the de Broglie wavelength λ of a matter wave to th momentum p of the particle. A higher momentum corresponds to a shorte wavelength. Since

$$\text{kinetic energy} \equiv T = \tfrac{1}{2}mv^2 = (1/2m)(m^2v^2) = p^2/2m \tag{1-43}$$

it follows that

$$p = \sqrt{2mT} \tag{1-44}$$

Furthermore, since $E = T + V$, where E is the total energy and V is the poten tial energy, we can rewrite the de Broglie wavelength as

$$\lambda = h/\sqrt{2m(E - V)} \tag{1-45}$$

Equation (1-45) is useful for understanding the way in which λ will chang for a particle moving with constant total energy in a varying potential. Fo example, if the particle enters a region where its potential energy increases (e.g an electron approaches a negatively charged plate), $E - V$ decreases and increases (i.e., the particle slows down, so its momentum decreases and it associated wavelength increases). We shall see examples of this behavior i future chapters.

Observe that, if $E \geq V$, λ as given by Eq. (1-45) is real. However, if $E < V$ λ becomes imaginary. Classically, we never encounter such a situation, but w will find it is necessary to consider this possibility in quantum mechanics.

1-8 A Diffraction Experiment with Electrons

In order to gain a better understanding of the meaning of matter waves we now consider a set of simple experiments. Suppose that we have a source o a beam of monoenergetic electrons and a pair of slits, as indicated schematicall in Fig. 1-10. Any electron arriving at the phosphorescent screen produces a flash of light, just as in a television set. For the moment we ignore the ligh source near the slits (assume that it is turned off) and inquire as to the nature o the image on the phosphorescent screen when the electron beam is directed a the slits. The observation, consistent with the observations of Davisson an

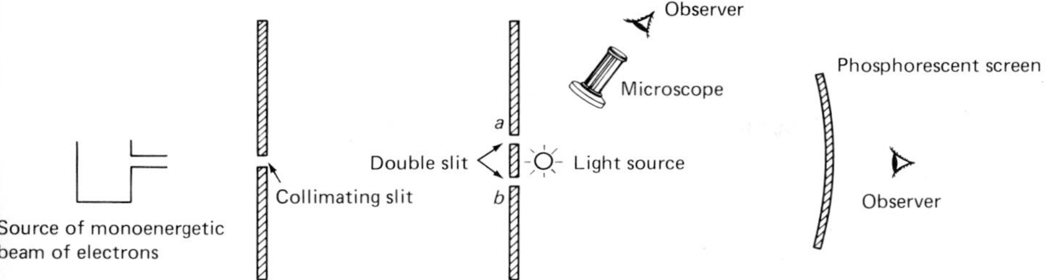

FIG. 1-10 The electron source produces a beam of electrons, some of which pass through slits *a* and/or *b* to be detected as flashes of light on the phosphorescent screen.

Germer already mentioned, is that there are alternating bands of light and dark, indicating that the electron beam is being diffracted by the slits. Furthermore, the distance separating the bands is consistent with the de Broglie wavelength corresponding to the energy of the electrons. The variation in light intensity observed on the screen is depicted in Fig. 1-11a.

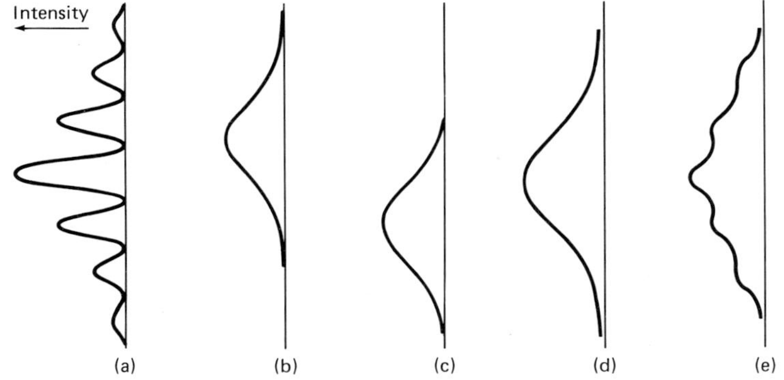

FIG. 1-11 Light intensity at phosphorescent screen under various conditions: (a) *a* and *b* open, light off; (b) *a* open, *b* closed, light off; (c) *a* closed, *b* open, light off; (d) *a* and *b* open, light on, λ short; (e) *a* and *b* open, light on, λ longer.

Evidently, the electrons in this experiment are displaying wave behavior. Does this mean that the electrons are spread out like waves when they are detected at the screen? We test this by reducing our beam intensity to let only one electron per second through the apparatus and observe that each electron gives a localized pinpoint of light, the entire diffraction pattern building up gradually by the accumulation of many points. Thus, the square of de Broglie's matter wave has the same kind of statistical significance that Einstein proposed for electromagnetic waves and photons, and the electrons really are localized particles, at least when they are detected at the screen.

However, if they are really particles, it is hard to see how they can be diffracted. Consider what happens when slit *b* is closed. Then all the electrons striking the screen must have come through slit *a*. We observe the result to be a single area of light on the screen (Fig. 1-11b). Closing slit *a* and opening *b* gives a similar (but displaced) light area, as shown in Fig. 1-11c. These patterns are just what we would expect for particles. Now, with both slits open, we expect half the particles to pass through slit *a* and half through slit *b*, the resulting pattern being the *sum* of the results just described. Instead we obtain the diffraction pattern (Fig. 1-11a). How can this happen? It seems that, somehow, an electron passing through the apparatus can sense whether one or both slits are open, even though as a particle it can explore only one slit or the other. One might suppose that we are seeing the result of simultaneous traversal of the two slits by two electrons, the path of each electron being affected by the presence of an electron in the other slit. This would explain how an electron passing through slit *a* would "know" whether slit *b* was open or closed. But the fact that the pattern builds up even when electrons pass through at the rate of one per second indicates that this argument will not do. Could an electron be coming through both slits at once?

To test this question, we need to have detailed information about the positions of the electrons as they pass through the slits. We can get such data by turning on the light source and aiming a microscope at the slits. Then photons will bounce off each electron as it passes the slits and will be observed through the microscope. The observer thus can tell through which slit each electron has passed, and also record its final position on the phosphorescent screen. In this experiment, it is necessary to use light having a wavelength short in comparison to the interslit distance; otherwise the microscope cannot resolve a flash well enough to tell which slit it is nearest. When this experiment is performed, we indeed detect each electron as coming through one slit or the other, and not both, but we also find that the diffraction pattern on the screen has been lost and that we have the broad, featureless distribution shown in Fig. 1-11d, which is basically the sum of the single-slit experiments. What has happened is that the photons from our light source, in bouncing off the electrons as they emerge from the slits, have affected the momenta of the electrons and changed their paths from what they were in the absence of light. We can try to counteract this by using photons with lower momentum; but this means using photons of lower E, hence longer λ. As a result, the images of the electrons in the microscope get broader, and it becomes more and more ambiguous as to which slit a given electron has passed through or that it really passed through only one slit. As we become more and more uncertain about the path of each electron as it moves past the slits, the accumulating diffraction pattern becomes more and more pronounced (Fig. 1-11e). (Since this is a "thought experiment," we can ignore the inconvenient fact that our "light" source must produce X rays or γ rays in order to have a wavelength short in comparison to the appropriate interslit distance.)

This conceptual experiment illustrates a basic feature of microscopic systems—we cannot measure properties of the system without affecting the future development of the system in a nontrivial way. The system with the light turned off is significantly different from the system with the light turned on (with short λ), and so the electrons arrive at the screen with different distributions. No matter how cleverly one devises his experiment, there is some minimum necessary disturbance involved in any measurement. In this example with the light off, the problem is that we know the momentum of each electron quite accurately (since the beam is monoenergetic and collimated), but we do not know anything about the way the electrons traverse the slits. With the light on, we obtain information about electron position just beyond the slits but we change the momentum of each electron in an unknown way. The measurement of particle position leads to loss of knowledge about particle momentum. This is an example of the *uncertainty principle* of Heisenberg, who stated that the product of the simultaneous uncertainties in "conjugate variables," a and b, can never be smaller than a number on the order of Planck's constant h:

$$\Delta a \cdot \Delta b \gtrsim h = 6.626176 \times 10^{-34} \quad \text{J sec} \tag{1-46}$$

Here, Δa is a measure of the uncertainty in the variable a, etc. (The easiest way to recognize conjugate variables is to note that their dimensions must multiply to joule seconds. Linear momentum and linear position satisfies this requirement. Two other important pairs of conjugate variables are energy–time and angular momentum–angular position.) In this example with the light off, our uncertainty in momentum is small and our uncertainty in position is unacceptably large, since we cannot say which slit each electron traverses. With the light on, we reduce our uncertainty in position to an acceptable size, but subsequent to the position of each electron being observed, we have much greater uncertainty in momentum.

Thus, we see that the appearance of an electron (or a photon) as a particle or a wave depends on our experiment. Because *any* observation on so small a particle involves a significant perturbation of its state, it is proper to think of the electron plus apparatus as a single system. The question, "Is the electron a particle or a wave?" becomes meaningful only when the apparatus is defined on which we plan a measurement. In some experiments, the apparatus and electrons interact in a way suggestive of the electron being a wave, in others, a particle. The question, "What is the electron when we're not looking?," cannot be answered experimentally, since an experiment *is* a "look" at the electron.

1-9 Schrödinger's Time-Independent Wave Equation

Earlier we saw that we needed a wave equation in order to solve for the standing waves pertaining to a particular classical system and its set of boundary conditions. The same need exists for a wave equation to solve for matter waves.

Schrödinger obtained such an equation by taking the classical time-independent wave equation and substituting de Broglie's relation for λ. Thus, if

$$\nabla^2\psi = -(2\pi/\lambda)^2\psi \tag{1-47}$$

and

$$\lambda = h/\sqrt{2m(E - V)} \tag{1-48}$$

then

$$[-(h^2/8\pi^2 m)\nabla^2 + V(x, y, z)]\psi(x, y, z) = E\psi(x, y, z) \tag{1-49}$$

Equation (1-49) is Schrödinger's time-independent wave equation for a single particle of mass m moving in the three-dimensional potential field V.

In classical mechanics we have separate equations for wave motion and particle motion, whereas in quantum mechanics, in which the distinction between particles and waves is not clear-cut, we have a single equation—the Schrödinger equation. We have seen that the link between the Schrödinger equation and the classical *wave* equation is the de Broglie relation. Let us now compare Schrödinger's equation with the classical equation for *particle* motion.

Classically, for a particle moving in three dimensions, the total energy is the sum of kinetic and potential energies:

$$(1/2m)(p_x{}^2 + p_y{}^2 + p_z{}^2) + V = E \tag{1-50}$$

where p_x is the momentum in the x coordinate, etc. We have just seen that the analogous Schrödinger equation is [writing out Eq. (1-49)]

$$\left[\frac{-h^2}{8\pi^2 m}\left(\frac{\partial^2}{\partial x^2} + \frac{\partial^2}{\partial y^2} + \frac{\partial^2}{\partial z^2}\right) + V(x, y, z)\right]\psi(x, y, z) = E\psi(x, y, z) \tag{1-51}$$

It is easily seen that Eq. (1-50) is linked to the quantity in brackets of Eq. (1-51) by a relation associating classical momentum with a partial differential operator:

$$p_x \leftrightarrow (h/2\pi i)(\partial/\partial x) \tag{1-52}$$

and similarly for p_y and p_z. The relations (1-52) will be seen later to be an important postulate in a formal development of quantum mechanics.

The left-hand side of Eq. (1-50) is called the hamiltonian for the system. For this reason the operator in square brackets on the LHS of Eq. (1-51) is called the *hamiltonian operator*[5] H. For a given system, we shall see that the construction of H is not difficult. The difficulty comes in solving Schrödinger's equation, often written as

$$H\psi = E\psi \tag{1-53}$$

[5] An *operator* is a symbol telling us to carry out a certain mathematical operation. Thus, d/dx is a differential *operator* telling us to differentiate anything following it with respect to x. The function $1/x$ may be viewed as a multiplicative operator. Any function combined with it gets multiplied by $1/x$.

The classical and quantum-mechanical wave equations that we have discussed are members of a special class of equations called *eigenvalue equations.* Such equations have the format

$$\mathrm{Op} f = cf \tag{1-54}$$

where Op is an operator, f is a function, and c is a constant. Thus, eigenvalue equations have the property that operating on a function regenerates the *same function* times a constant. The function f that satisfies Eq. (1-54) is called an *eigenfunction* of the operator. The constant c is called the *eigenvalue* associated with the eigenfunction f. Often, an operator will have a large number of eigenfunctions and eigenvalues of interest associated with it, and so an index is necessary to keep them sorted, viz.

$$\mathrm{Op} f_i = c_i f_i \tag{1-55}$$

We have already seen an example of this sort of equation, Eq. (1-19) being an eigenfunction for Eq. (1-18), with eigenvalue $-\omega^2 m/T$.

The solutions ψ for Schrödinger's equation (1-53), are referred to as eigenfunctions, wavefunctions, or state functions.

1-10 Conditions on ψ

We have already indicated that ψ^2 is interpreted as the probability density function for finding the particle at various places in space. Thus, in a one-dimensional problem (for example, a particle constrained to move on a line), the probability that the particle will be found in the interval dx around the point x_1 is taken to be $\psi^2(x_1)\,dx$. If ψ is a complex function, then the *absolute square,* $|\psi|^2 \equiv \psi^*\psi$ is used instead of ψ^2.[6] This makes it mathematically impossible for the average mass distribution to be negative in any region.

If an eigenfunction ψ has been found for Eq. (1-53), it is easy to see that $c\psi$ will also be an eigenfunction, for any constant c. This is due to the fact that a multiplicative constant commutes[7] with the operator H, that is,

$$H(c\psi) = cH\psi = cE\psi = E(c\psi) \tag{1-56}$$

The equality of the first and last terms is a statement of the fact that $c\psi$ is an eigenfunction of H. The question of which constant to use for the wavefunction is resolved by appeal to the probability interpretation of $|\psi|^2$. For a particle moving on the x axis, the probability that the particle is between $x = -\infty$ and $x = +\infty$ is unity, that is, a certainty. This probability is also equal to the sum of the probabilities for finding the particle in each and every infinitesimal interval along x, so this sum (an integral) must equal unity:

$$c^*c \int_{-\infty}^{+\infty} \psi^*(x)\psi(x)\,dx = 1 \tag{1-57}$$

[6] If $f = u + iv$, then f^*, the complex conjugate of f, is given by $u - iv$, where u and v are real functions.

[7] a and b are said to *commute* if $ab = ba$.

If the selection of the constant multiplier c is made so that Eq. (1-57) is satisfied, the wavefunction $\psi' = c\psi$ is said to be *normalized.* For a three-dimensional function, $c\psi(x, y, z)$, the normalization requirement is

$$c^*c \int_{-\infty}^{+\infty} \int_{-\infty}^{+\infty} \int_{-\infty}^{+\infty} \psi^*(x, y, z)\psi(x, y, z)\, dx\, dy\, dz \equiv |c|^2 \int_{\text{all space}} |\psi|^2\, dv = 1 \tag{1-58}$$

As a result of our physical interpretation of $|\psi|^2$ plus the fact that ψ must be an eigenfunction of the hamiltonian operator H, we can reach some general conclusions about what sort of mathematical properties ψ can or cannot have. First, we require that ψ be a *single-valued* function because we want $|\psi|^2$ to give an unambiguous probability for finding a particle in a given region (see Fig. 1-12). Also, we reject functions that are infinite in any region of space because such an infinity will always be infinitely greater than any finite region, and $|\psi|^2$ will be useless as a measure of comparative probabilities.[8] In order for $H\psi$ to be defined

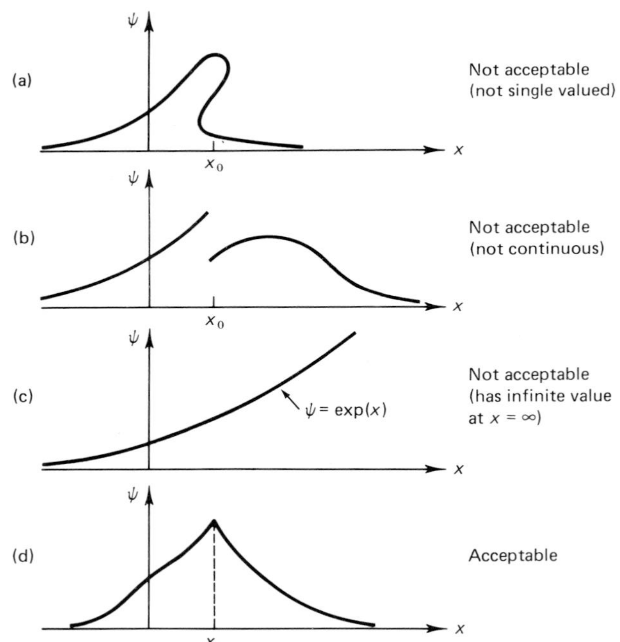

FIG. 1-12 (a) ψ is triple valued at x_0. (b) ψ is discontinuous at x_0. (c) ψ grows without limit as x approaches $+\infty$ (i.e., ψ "blows up," or "explodes"). (d) ψ is continuous and has a "cusp" at x_0. Hence, first derivative of ψ is discontinuous at x_0 and is only piecewise continuous. This does not prevent ψ from being acceptable.

[8] There are cases, particularly in relativistic treatments, where ψ is infinite at *single points* of zero measure, so that $|\psi|^2\, dx$ remains finite. Normally we do not encounter such situations in quantum chemistry.

everywhere, it is necessary that the second derivative of ψ be defined everywhere. This requires that the first derivative of ψ be *piecewise continuous* and that ψ itself be *continuous*. (We shall see an example of this shortly.)

Functions that are single-valued, continuous, nowhere infinite, and have piecewise continuous first derivatives will be referred to as *acceptable* functions. The meanings of these terms are illustrated by some sample functions in Fig. 1-12.

In most cases, there is one more general restriction we place on ψ, namely, that it be a normalizable function. This means that the integral of $|\psi|^2$ over all space must not be equal to zero or infinity. A function satisfying this condition is said to be *square-integrable*.

1-11 Some Insight into the Schrödinger Equation

There is a fairly simple way to view the physical meaning of the Schrödinger equation (1-49). The equation essentially states that E in $H\psi = E\psi$ depends on two things, V and the second derivatives of ψ. Since V is the potential energy, the second derivatives of ψ must be related to the kinetic energy. Now the second derivative of ψ with respect to a given direction is a measure of the rate of change of slope (i.e., the curvature, or "wiggliness") of ψ in that direction. Hence, we see that a more wiggly wavefunction leads, through the Schrödinger equation, to a higher kinetic energy. This is in accord with the spirit of de Broglie's relation, since a shorter wavelength function is a more wiggly function. But the Schrödinger equation is more generally applicable because we can take second derivatives of any acceptable function, whereas wavelength is defined only for periodic functions. Since E is a constant, the solutions of the Schrödinger equation must be more wiggly in regions where V is low and less wiggly where V is high. Examples for some one-dimensional cases are shown in Fig. 1-13.

In the next chapter we use some fairly simple examples to illustrate the ideas that we have already introduced and to bring out some additional points.

1-12 Summary

In closing this chapter, we collect and summarize the major points to be used in future discussions.

(1) Associated with any particle is a wavefunction having wavelength related to particle momentum by $\lambda = h/p = h/\sqrt{2m(E - V)}$.

(2) The wavefunction has the following physical meaning; its absolute square is proportional to the probability density for finding the particle. If the wavefunction is normalized, its square is *equal* to the probability density.

(3) The wavefunctions ψ for time-independent states are eigenfunctions of Schrödinger's equation, which can be constructed from the classical wave

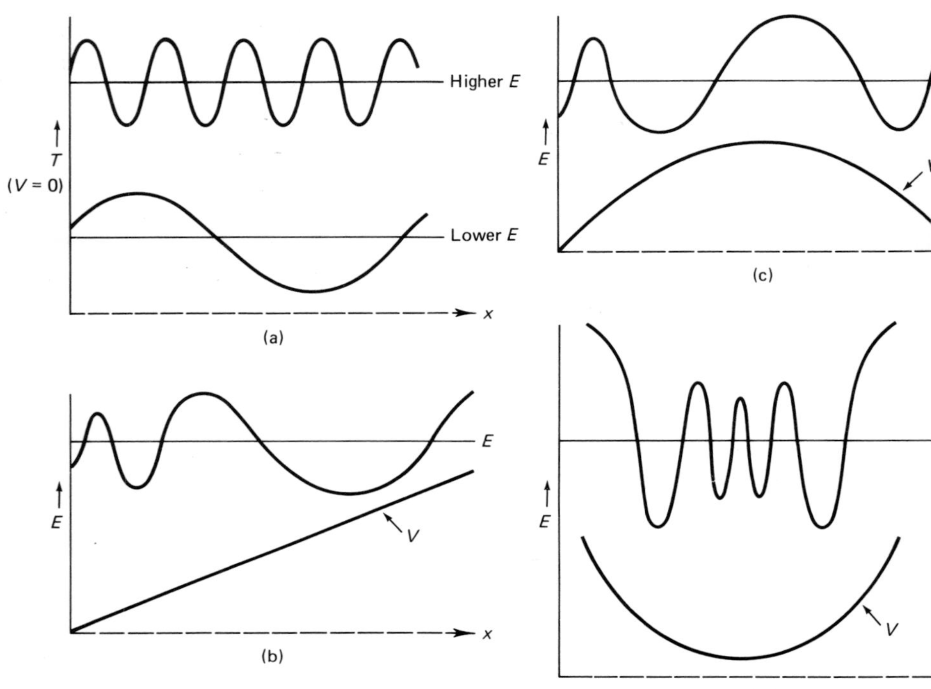

FIG. 1-13 (a) For free particle, $V = 0$ and so $E = T$. For higher T, ψ is more wiggly, which means that λ is shorter. (Since ψ is periodic for a free particle, λ is defined.) (b) As V increases from left to right, ψ becomes less wiggly. (c)–(d) ψ is most wiggly where V is lowest and T is greatest.

equation by requiring $\lambda = h/\sqrt{2m(E - V)}$, or from the classical particle equation by replacing p_k with $-(h/2\pi i)\,\partial/\partial k$, $k = x, y, z$.

(4) For ψ to be acceptable, it must be single-valued, continuous, nowhere infinite, with a piecewise continuous first derivative. For most situations, we also require ψ to be square-integrable.

(5) The wavefunction for a particle in a varying potential oscillates most rapidly where V is low, giving a high T in this region. The low V plus high T equals E. In another region, where V is high, the wavefunction oscillates more slowly, giving a low T, which, with the high V, equals the same E as in the first region.

PROBLEMS

1-1 Express $A\cos(kx) + B\sin(kx) + C\exp(ikx) + D\exp(-ikx)$ purely in terms of $\cos(kx)$ and $\sin(kx)$.

1-2 Repeat the standing-wave-in-a-string problem worked out in Section 1-4, but clamp the string at $x = +L/2$ and $-L/2$ instead of at 0 and L.
1-3 Find the condition that must be satisfied by α and β in order that $\psi(x) = A \sin(\alpha x) + B \cos(\beta x)$ satisfy Eq. (1-20).
1-4 The apparatus sketched in Fig. 1-8 is used with a dish plated with zinc and also with a dish plated with cesium. The wavelengths of the incident light and the corresponding retarding potentials needed to just prevent the photoelectrons from reaching the collecting wire are given in Table P1-4. Plot incident light frequency versus retarding potential for these two metals. Evaluate their work functions (in eV) and the proportionality constant h (in eV sec).

TABLE P1-4

	Retarding potential (V)	
λ(Å)	Cs	Zn
6000	0.167	—
3000	2.235	0.435
2000	4.302	2.502
1500	6.369	4.567
1200	8.436	6.636

1-5 Calculate the de Broglie wavelength in nanometers for each of the following:
(a) An electron that has been accelerated from rest through a potential change of 500 V.
(b) A bullet weighing 5 gm and traveling at 400 m/sec^{-1}.
1-6 Consider the two operators $A \equiv x\, d/dx$ and $B \equiv x^2\, d^2/dx^2$. Do these operators commute (that is, does $AB = BA$)?
1-7 The equation for a standing wave in a string has the form

$$\Psi(x, t) = \psi(x) \cos(\omega t)$$

(a) Calculate the time-averaged potential energy (PE) for this motion. [*Hint:* Use PE $= -\int F\, d\Psi$; $F = ma$; $a = \partial^2\Psi/\partial t^2$.]
(b) Calculate the time-averaged kinetic energy (KE) for this motion. [*Hint:* Use KE $= \frac{1}{2}mv^2$ and $v = \partial\Psi/\partial t$.]
(c) Show that this harmonically vibrating string stores its energy *on the average* half as kinetic and half as potential energy, and that $E(x)_{\text{av}} \propto \psi^2(x)$.
1-8 Indicate which of the following functions are "acceptable." If one is not, give a reason.
(a) $\psi = x$ (b) $\psi = x^2$ (c) $\psi = \sin x$
(d) $\psi = \exp(-x)$ (e) $\psi = \exp(-x^2)$
1-9 An acceptable function is never infinite. Does this mean that an acceptable function must be square integrable? If you think these are not the same, try to find an example of a function (other than zero) that is never infinite but is not square integrable.

1-10 Explain why the fact that $\sin(x) = -\sin(-x)$ means that we can restrict Eq. (1-32) to nonnegative n without loss of physical content.

1-11 Which of the following are eigenfunctions for d/dx?

(a) x^2 (b) $\exp(-3.4x^2)$ (c) 37
(d) $\exp(x)$ (e) $\sin(ax)$ (f) $\cos(4x) + i\sin(4x)$

CHAPTER 2

QUANTUM MECHANICS OF SOME SIMPLE SYSTEMS

2-1 The Particle in a One-Dimensional "Box"

Imagine that a particle of mass m is free to move along the x axis between $x = 0$ and $x = L$, with no change in potential (set $V = 0$ for $0 < x < L$). At $x = 0$ and L and at all points beyond these limits the particle encounters an infinitely repulsive barrier ($V = \infty$ for $x \leq 0$, $x \geq L$). The situation is illustrated in Fig. 2-1. Because of the shape of this potential, this problem is often referred to as a "particle in a square well" or a "particle in a box" problem. It is well to bear in mind, however, that the situation is really like that of a particle confined to movement along a finite length of wire.

When the potential is discontinuous, as it is here, it is convenient to write a wave equation for each region. For the two regions beyond the ends of the box

$$\frac{-h^2}{8\pi^2 m}\frac{d^2\psi}{dx^2} + \infty\psi = E\psi, \qquad x \leq 0, \quad x \geq L \tag{2-1}$$

Within the box, ψ must satisfy the equation

$$\frac{-h^2}{8\pi^2 m}\frac{d^2\psi}{dx^2} = E\psi, \qquad 0 < x < L \tag{2-2}$$

It should be realized that E must take on the same values for both of these equations; the eigenvalue E pertains to the *entire* range of the particle and is not influenced by divisions we make for mathematical convenience.

Let us examine Eq. (2-1) first. Suppose that, at some point within the infinite barrier, say $x = L + dx$, ψ is finite. Then the second term on the left-hand side of Eq. (2-1) will be infinite. If the first term on the left-hand side is finite or zero, it follows immediately that E is infinite at the point $L + dx$ (and hence everywhere in the system). Is it possible that a solution exists such that E is finite? One possibility is that $\psi = 0$ at all points where $V = \infty$. The other possibility is that the first term on the left-hand side of Eq. (2-1) can be made to cancel the infinite second term. This might happen if the second derivative of the wavefunction is infinite at all points where $V = \infty$ and $\psi \neq 0$. For the

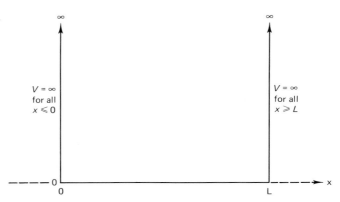

FIG. 2-1 The potential felt by a particle as a function of its x coordinate.

second derivative to be infinite, the first derivative must be discontinuous, and so ψ itself must be nonsmooth (i.e., it must have a sharp "corner"; see Fig. 2-2). Thus, we see that it may be possible to obtain a finite value for both E and ψ at $x = L + dx$, provided that ψ is nonsmooth there. But what about the next point, $x = L + 2\,dx$, and all the other points outside the "box"? If we try to use the same device, we end up with the requirement that ψ be nonsmooth at every point where $V = \infty$. A function that is continuous but which has a pointwise discontinuous first derivative is a contradiction in terms (i.e., a continuous f cannot be 100% corners. To have recognizable corners, we must have some (continuous) edges. We say that the first derivative of ψ must be *piecewise continuous*.) Hence, if $V = \infty$ *at a single point*, we might find a solution ψ which is finite at that point, with finite energy. If $V = \infty$ over a finite range of connected points, however, either E for the system is infinite, and ψ is finite over this region or E is not infinite (but is indeterminate) and ψ is zero over this region.

We are not concerned with particles of infinite energy, and so we will say that the solution to Eq. (2-1) is $\psi = 0$.[1]

Turning now to Eq. (2-2) we ask what solutions ψ exist in the box having associated eigenvalues E which are finite and positive. Any function that when twice differentiated yields a negative constant times the selfsame function is a possible candidate for ψ. Such functions are $\sin(kx)$, $\cos(kx)$, and $\exp(\pm ikx)$. But these functions are not all independent since, as we noted in Chapter 1,

$$\exp(\pm ikx) = \cos(kx) \pm i\sin(kx) \tag{2-3}$$

We thus are free to express ψ in terms of $\exp(\pm ikx)$ or else in terms of $\sin(kx)$ and $\cos(kx)$. We choose the latter because of their greater familiarity, although the final answer must be independent of this choice.

[1] Thus, the particle never gets into these regions. It is meaningless to talk of the energy of the particle in such regions, and our earlier statement that E must be identical in Eqs. (2-1) and (2-2) must be modified; E is constant in all regions where ψ is finite.

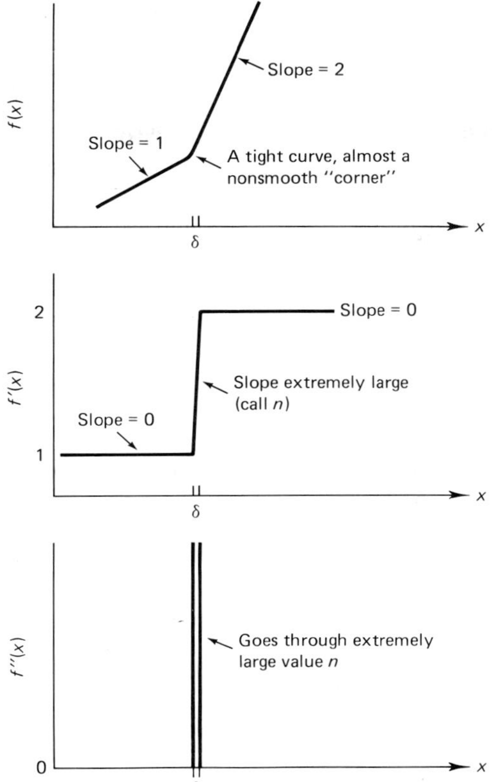

FIG. 2-2 As the function $f(x)$ approaches being nonsmooth, δ approaches zero (the width of one point) and n approaches infinity.

The most general form for the solution is

$$\psi(x) = A\sin(kx) + B\cos(kx) \tag{2-4}$$

where A, B, and k remain to be determined. As we have already shown, ψ is zero at $x \leq 0 \geq L$, and so we have as boundary conditions

$$\psi(0) = 0 \tag{2-5}$$

$$\psi(L) = 0 \tag{2-6}$$

Mathematically, this is precisely the same problem we have already solved in Chapter 1 for the standing waves in a clamped string. The solutions are

$$\begin{aligned} \psi(x) &= A\sin(n\pi x/L), \qquad n = 1, 2, \ldots, \quad 0 < x < L \\ \psi(x) &= 0, \qquad 0 \geq x \geq L \end{aligned} \tag{2-7}$$

One difference between Eq. (2-7) and the string solutions is that we have rejected the $n = 0$ solution in Eq. (2-7). For the string, this solution was for no vibration at all—a physically realizable circumstance. For the particle-in-a-box problem, this solution is rejected because it is not square-integrable. (It gives $\psi = 0$, which means *no* particle on the x axis, contradicting our starting premise. One could also reject this solution for the classical case since it means no energy in the string, which might contradict a starting premise depending on how the problem is worded.)

Let us check to be sure these functions satisfy Schrödinger's equation:

$$H\psi(x) = \frac{-h^2}{8\pi^2 m} \frac{d^2[A \sin(n\pi x/L)]}{dx^2} = \frac{-h^2}{8\pi^2 m}\left[-A\frac{n^2\pi^2}{L^2}\sin\left(\frac{n\pi x}{L}\right)\right]$$

$$= \frac{n^2h^2}{8mL^2}\left[A \sin\left(\frac{n\pi x}{L}\right)\right] = E\psi(x) \qquad (2\text{-}8)$$

This shows that the functions (2-7) are indeed eigenfunctions of H. We note in passing that these functions are acceptable in the sense of Chapter 1.

The only remaining parameter is the constant A. We set this to make the probability of finding the particle in the well equal to unity:

$$\int_0^L \psi^2(x)\, dx = A^2 \int_0^L \sin^2(n\pi x/L)\, dx = 1 \qquad (2\text{-}9)$$

This leads to (Problem 2-2)

$$A = \sqrt{2/L} \qquad (2\text{-}10)$$

which completes the solving of Schrödinger's time-independent equation for the problem. Our results are the normalized eigenfunctions

$$\psi_n(x) = \sqrt{(2/L)}\, \sin(n\pi x/L), \qquad n = 1, 2, 3, \ldots \qquad (2\text{-}11)$$

and the corresponding eigenvalues, from Eq. (2-8),

$$E_n = n^2h^2/8mL^2, \qquad n = 1, 2, 3, \ldots \qquad (2\text{-}12)$$

Each different value of n corresponds to a different *stationary state* of this system.

2-2 Detailed Examination of Particle-in-a-Box Solutions

Having solved the Schrödinger equation for the particle in the infinitely deep square-well potential, we now examine the results in more detail. Let us first consider the nature of the eigenvalues E_n.

The most obvious feature of the energies is that, as we move through the allowed states ($n = 1, 2, 3, \ldots$), E skips from one discrete, well-separated value to another (1, 4, 9 in units of $h^2/8mL^2$). Thus, the particle can have only certain discrete energies—the energy is *quantized*. This situation is normally indicated

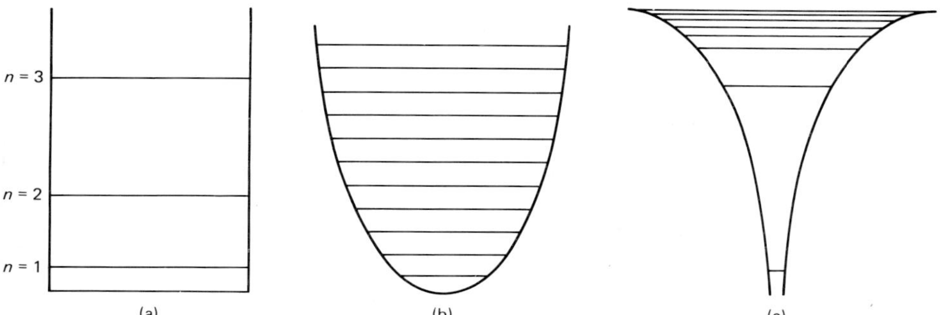

FIG. 2-3 Allowed energies for a particle in various one-dimensional potentials. (a) "box" with infinite walls. (b) quadratic potential, $V = \frac{1}{2}kx^2$. (c) $V = -1/|x|$. Tendency for higher levels in (b) and (c) not to diverge as in (a) is due to larger "effective box size" for higher energies in (b) and (c).

by sketching the allowed *energy levels* as horizontal lines superimposed on the potential energy sketch, as in Fig. 2-3a. The fact that each energy level is a horizontal line emphasizes the fact that E is a *constant* and is the same regardless of the x coordinate of the particle. For this reason, E is called a *constant of motion*. The dependence of E on n^2 is displayed in the increased spacing between levels with increasing n in Fig. 2-3a. The number n is called a *quantum number*.

We note also that E is proportional to L^{-2}. This means that the more tightly a particle is confined, the greater is the spacing between the allowed energy levels. Alternatively, as the box is made wider, the separation between energies decreases and, in the limit of an infinitely wide box, disappears entirely. Thus, we associate quantized energies with spatial confinement.

For some systems, the degree of confinement of a particle depends on its total energy. For example, a pendulum swings over a longer trajectory if it has higher energy. The potential energy for a pendulum is given by $V = \frac{1}{2}kx^2$ and is given in Fig. 2-3b. If one solves the Schrödinger equation for this system (see Chapter 3), one finds that the energies are proportional to n rather than n^2. We can rationalize this by thinking of the particle as occupying successively bigger boxes as we go to higher energies. This counteracts the n^2 increase in energy levels found for constant box width. For the potential $V = -1/|x|$ (which is the one-dimensional analog of a hydrogen atom) E varies as $1/n^2$ (Fig. 2-3c), and this is also consistent with the effective increase in L with increasing E.

The energy is proportional to $1/m$. This means that the separation between allowed energy levels decreases as m increases. Ultimately, for a macroscopic object, m is so large that the levels are too closely spaced to be distinguished from the continuum of levels expected in classical mechanics. This is an example of the *correspondence principle*, which, in its most general form, states that the predictions of quantum mechanics must pass smoothly into those of classical mechanics whenever we progress in a continuous way from the microscopic to the macroscopic realm.

Notice that the lowest possible energy for this system occurs for $n = 1$ and is $E = h^2/8mL^2$. This remarkable result means that a constrained particle (i.e., L not infinite) can *never* have an energy of zero. Evidently, the particle continues to move about in the region 0 to L, even at a temperature of absolute zero. For this reason, $h^2/8mL^2$ is called the *zero-point energy* for this system. In general, a finite zero-point energy occurs in any system having a restriction for motion in any coordinate.

It is possible to show that, for $L \neq \infty$, our particle in a box would have to violate the Heisenberg uncertainty principle to achieve an energy of zero. For, suppose the energy *is* precisely zero. Then the momentum must be precisely zero too. (In this system, all energy of the particle is kinetic since $V = 0$ in the box.) If the momentum p_x is *precisely* zero, however, our *uncertainty* in the value of the momentum Δp_x is also zero. If Δp_x is zero, the uncertainty principle [Eq. (1-46)] requires that the uncertainty in position Δx be infinite. But we know that the particle is between $x = 0$ and $x = L$. Hence, our uncertainty is on the order of L, not infinity, and the uncertainty principle is not satisfied. However, when $L = \infty$ (the particle is unconstrained), it *is* possible for the uncertainty principle to be satisfied simultaneously with having $E = 0$, and this is in satisfying accord with the fact that $E = h^2/8mL^2$ goes to zero as L approaches infinity.

Finally, we note that each separate value of n leads to a different energy. Thus, no two states have the same energy, and the states are said to be *nondegenerate* with respect to energy.

We turn now to the eigenfunctions (2-11) for this problem. These are typically displayed by superimposing them on the energy levels as shown in

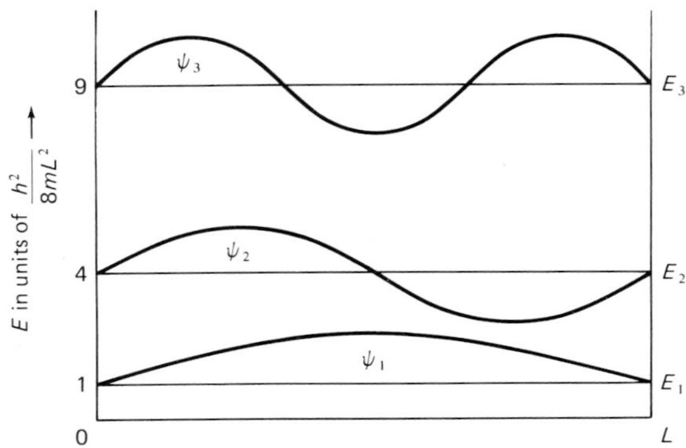

FIG. 2-4 The eigenfunctions corresponding to $n = 1, 2, 3$, plotted on the corresponding energy levels. The energy units of the ordinate do not refer to the wavefunctions ψ. Each wavefunction has a zero value wherever it intersects its own energy level, and a maximum value of $\sqrt{2/L}$.

Fig. 2-4 for the three lowest-energy wavefunctions. (It should be recognized that the energy units of the vertical axis do *not* pertain to the amplitudes of the wavefunctions.)

It is apparent from Fig. 2-4 that the allowed wavefunctions for this system could have been produced merely by placing an integral number of half sine waves in the range 0–L. The resulting wavelengths would then yield the energy of each state through application of de Broglie's relation (1-42). Thus, by inspection of Fig. 2-4, the allowed wavelengths are

$$\lambda = 2L/n, \qquad n = 1, 2, 3, \ldots \tag{2-13}$$

Therefore

$$p = h/\lambda = nh/2L \tag{2-14}$$

and

$$E = p^2/2m = n^2h^2/8mL^2 \tag{2-15}$$

in agreement with Eq. (2-12). As pointed out in Section 1-11, the wavefunctions having higher kinetic energy oscillate more rapidly. (Here $V = 0$, and E is all kinetic energy.)

Let us now consider the physical meaning of the eigenfunctions ψ. According to our earlier discussion, ψ^2 summarizes the results of many determinations of the position of the particle. Suppose that we had a particle-in-a-box system that we had somehow prepared in such a way that we knew it to be in the state with $n = 1$. We can imagine some sort of experiment, such as flashing a powerful γ-ray flashbulb and taking an instantaneous photograph, which tells us where the particle was at the instant of the flash. Now, suppose we wish to determine the position of the particle again. We want this second determination to be for the $n = 1$ state also, but we cannot use our original system for this because we have "spoiled" it by our first measurement process. Hitting the particle with one or more γ-ray photons has knocked it into some other state, and we do not even know which one. Therefore, we must either reprepare our system, or else use a separate system whose preparation is identical to that of the first system. In general we shall assume that we have an inexhaustible supply of identically prepared systems. Therefore, we take a second photograph (on our second system) using the same photographic plate. Then we photograph a third system, a fourth, etc., until we have amassed a large number of images of the particle on the film. The distribution of these images is given by $\psi_1{}^2$. (Since ψ is always a real function for this system, we do not need to bother with $\psi^*\psi$.) Other states, like ψ_2, ψ_3, will lead to different distributions of images. The results for the several states are depicted in Fig. 2-5.

The probability for finding the particle at the midpoint of the "wire" in the $n = 2$ state approaches zero in the limit of our measurement becoming precise enough to observe a single point. This troubles many students at first

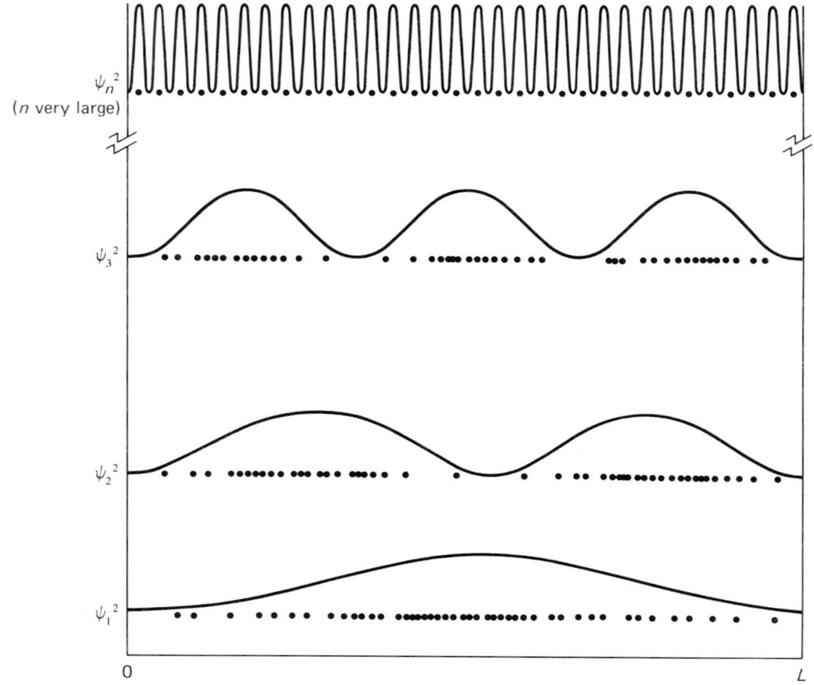

FIG. 2-5 ψ^2 and observed particle distribution for the three lowest-energy and one high-energy state of the particle in a one-dimensional box.

encounter because they worry about how the particle can get from one side of the box to the other in the $n = 2$ state. In fact, this question can be raised for any state whose wavefunction has any nodes. However, our discussion in the preceding paragraph shows that this question, like the question, "Is an electron a particle or a wave when we are not looking?" has no meaningful answer because no experiment can be conceived that would answer it. To test whether or not the particle does travel from one side of the "box" to the other, we would have to prepare the system in the $n = 2$ state and measure the position of the particle enough times so that we either (a) always find it on the same side (requires many measurements for confidence), or (b) find it on different sides (requires at least two measurements). But for our question to be answered, the system must be in the $n = 2$ state throughout this entire experiment, and we have seen that the process of measuring particle position prevents this. (If we find the particle first on the left and later on the right, we cannot be sure it did not travel across the midpoint while the system was perturbed by the first measurement.) Thus, the sketches in Fig. 2-5 are most safely regarded as a summary of the results of measurements on an *ensemble* of systems.

Classically, since the particle has constant energy, hence constant speed, we would expect the particle to spend equal time in each line segment dx between 0 and L, but Fig. 2-5 shows that the quantum system with $n = 1$ predicts that the particle spends more time in segments near the center. It is characteristic of lower-energy states of quantum-mechanical systems to display "anti-classical" distributions. With higher quantum numbers, the distribution evens out for the quantum system, approaching the classical distribution as a limit (see Fig. 2-5). This is another example of the tendency of quantum-mechanical predictions to approach classical predictions when one goes toward the macroscopic realm (here large n and therefore large E).

Inspection of Fig. 2-5 shows that the particle has equal probabilities for being observed in the left half and right half of the "box," regardless of state. This seems reasonable because there is no physical factor discriminating between these halves. We shall now show that the hamiltonian operator is invariant for a reflection through the "box" center, and that a necessary consequence of this is that ψ has certain symmetry properties.

First, we show that H is invariant. Reflection through the "box" center is accomplished by replacing x by $-x + L$. We can define a reflection operator R such that $Rf(x) = f(-x + L)$; i.e., R reflects any function through a plane normal to x at $x = L/2$ (see Fig. 2-6).

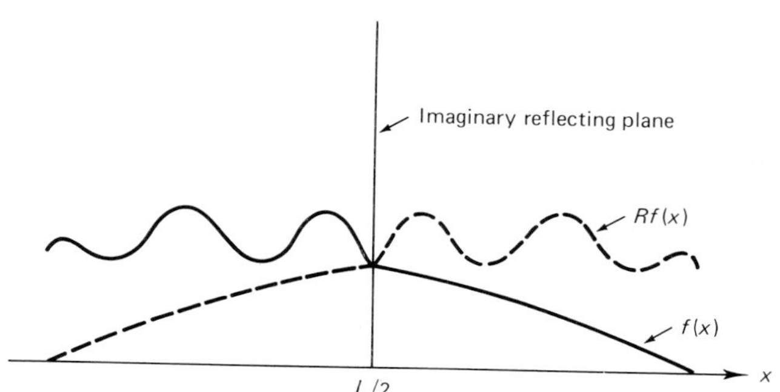

FIG. 2-6 A function $f(x)$ and its mirror image reflected at $x = L/2$.

The kinetic part of the hamiltonian T is unchanged by R:

$$RT = R\left[-\frac{h^2}{8\pi^2 m}\frac{d^2}{dx^2}\right] = \frac{-h^2}{8\pi^2 m}\frac{d^2}{d(-x + L)^2} = \frac{-h^2}{8\pi^2 m}\frac{d^2}{dx^2} = T \qquad (2\text{-}16)$$

where we have used the fact that L is constant and $d/d(-x) = -d/dx$. That the potential part of H is unchanged by reflection through $L/2$ is easily seen; the identical infinite barriers merely interchange position. Therefore, $RT = T$ and $RV = V$, and $RH = R(T + V) = RT + RV = T + V = H$.

Now let us see what this means for eigenfunctions of H.

Assume we have a normalized eigenfunction ψ

$$H\psi = E\psi \tag{2-17}$$

The two sides of Eq. (2-17) will still be equal if we reflect our coordinate system *throughout the equation*. (If two functions are identical in one coordinate system, say a right handed system, then they are identical in any coordinate system.) Therefore,[2]

$$(RH)(R\psi) = (RE)(R\psi) \tag{2-18}$$

But E is simply a constant, and so it is immune to R. Furthermore, we have just seen that $RH = H$. Therefore,

$$H(R\psi) = E(R\psi) \tag{2-19}$$

which shows that the function $R\psi$ is an eigenfunction of H with the same eigenvalue as ψ.

We have already mentioned that the eigenfunctions of this system are nondegenerate with respect to energy. This is equivalent to saying that no two linearly independent eigenfunctions having the same eigenvalue exist for this system. But we have just shown that ψ and $R\psi$ are both eigenfunctions having the same eigenvalue E. Therefore, we are forced to conclude that ψ and $R\psi$ are linearly dependent, that is,

$$R\psi = c\psi \tag{2-20}$$

where c is a constant. A moment's thought shows that $R\psi$ must still be normalized (since reflecting a function does not change its area or the area under its square), and it also must still be real (since reflecting a real function does not introduce imaginary character). Therefore,

$$\int_0^L (R\psi)^2\,dx = 1 = \int_0^L (c\psi)^2\,dx = c^2 \int_0^L \psi^2\,dx = c^2 \tag{2-21}$$

where we have made use of the fact that ψ is normalized. If $c^2 = 1$, then $c = \pm 1$, and

$$R\psi = \pm\psi \tag{2-22}$$

When $R\psi = +\psi$, as is the case for ψ_1 or ψ_3 (Fig. 2-4), ψ is said to be *symmetric*, or *even*, for reflection. If $R\psi = -\psi$, as for ψ_2, ψ is said to be *antisymmetric*, or *odd*. (A function that is neither symmetric nor antisymmetric is said to be *unsymmetric*, or *asymmetric*. Be careful to avoid confusing "asymmetric" with "antisymmetric.")

We have proved a very important property of wavefunctions. *In general, if*

[2] The parentheses in Eq. (2-18) are meant to restrict the extent of operation of R. This is a departure from the usual mathematical convention, but it is hoped that this temporary departure results in greater clarity for the student.

ψ is the wavefunction for a nondegenerate state, it must be symmetric or antisymmetric under any transformation that leaves H unchanged.

It is possible to show that integration over the product of two *different* eigenfunctions, ψ_n and ψ_m, must give zero as the result:

$$\int_0^L \psi_n \psi_m \, dx = 0, \qquad n \neq m \tag{2-23}$$

The wavefunctions then are said to be *orthogonal*. For many choices of n and m it is possible to use symmetry to demonstrate orthogonality. Take, for example, ψ_1 and ψ_2. Figure 2-7 shows that, since ψ_1 is symmetric and ψ_2 is antisymmetric for reflection, the product of these functions is antisymmetric. (In fact, it is not difficult to show in general that the product of two symmetric or of two antisymmetric functions is symmetric, and that an antisymmetric function times a symmetric function gives an antisymmetric product. See Problem 2-4.) Integration over an antisymmetric function *must give zero* as the result since an antisymmetric function has to have equal amounts of positive and negative area. Therefore, ψ_1 and ψ_2 are orthogonal "by symmetry" as, indeed, are all the symmetric–antisymmetric pairs of wavefunctions. Since all ψ's having odd quantum number n are symmetric, and all ψ's having even n are antisymmetric, we have used symmetry to prove ψ_n and ψ_m orthogonal for n even and m odd. To show orthogonality for n and m both even or both odd requires doing the integral out explicitly (Problem 2-3).

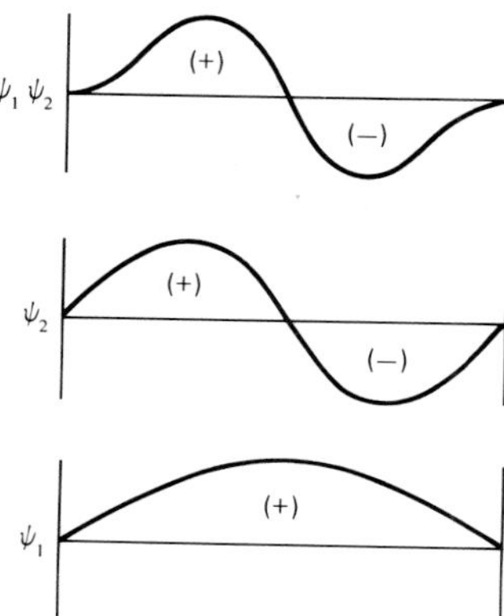

FIG. 2-7 ψ_1 is even, ψ_2 is odd, and $\psi_1\psi_2$ is odd. The total signed area bounded by the odd functions is zero since complete cancellation of positive and negative components occurs.

The eigenfunctions (2-11) are orthogonal to each other and individually normalized, and we refer to them as *orthonormal* functions. Mathematically, this is summarized as

$$\int_0^L \psi_n \psi_m \, dx = \begin{Bmatrix} 0, \ldots \; n \neq m \\ 1, \ldots \; n = m \end{Bmatrix} \equiv \delta_{n,m} \tag{2-24}$$

The quantity $\delta_{n,m}$ is called the *Kronecker delta function*, and it is merely a convenient shorthand for the information in the braces.

2-3 The Particle in a One-Dimensional "Box" with One Finite Wall

Let us now modify the system just discussed by lowering the potential on one side of the "box" to some finite value U. The resulting potential is shown in Fig. 2-8. We can think of a bead on a wire encountering infinite repulsion at $x = 0$ and finite repulsion for $x \geq L$. As before, it is convenient to break up the problem into separate regions of x. For the region $x \leq 0$, where V is infinite, ψ must be zero for the same reasons as before (Section 2-1).

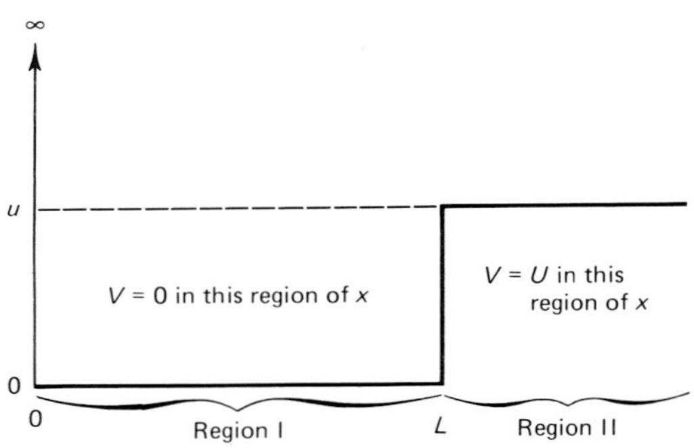

FIG. 2-8 The potential for a one-dimensional "box" with one infinite barrier at $x \leq 0$, and a barrier of $V = U$ at $x \geq L$.

When the particle is in Region I of Fig. 2-8, $V = 0$ and all is identical to our earlier "box." Therefore, in this region we will have harmonic waves of the general form

$$\psi_{\mathrm{I}} = A_{\mathrm{I}} \sin(2\pi x/\lambda_{\mathrm{I}}) + B_{\mathrm{I}} \cos(2\pi x/\lambda_{\mathrm{I}}) \tag{2-25}$$

where we have used the form (1-24) in which the wavelength appears explicitly. As before, the boundary condition that ψ vanish at $x = 0$ forces B_{I} to vanish, leaving

$$\psi_{\mathrm{I}} = A_{\mathrm{I}} \sin(2\pi x/\lambda_{\mathrm{I}}) \tag{2-26}$$

For the moment, we have no other boundary condition on ψ_{I} because we do not know that ψ equals zero at the finite barrier. We do know, however, that the wavelength λ_{I}, whatever it turns out to be, will be related to the energy through

$$\lambda_{\mathrm{I}} = h/\sqrt{2m(E - V_{\mathrm{I}})} \tag{2-27}$$

and, since $V_{\mathrm{I}} = 0$ (in region I),

$$\lambda_{\mathrm{I}} = h/\sqrt{2mE} \tag{2-28}$$

which is a real number for positive E.

We now turn to region II. Here we must examine two possibilities: $E > U$ and $E < U$. The second of these corresponds to the classical situation where the particle has insufficient energy to escape from the "box."

Since V is constant in region II, ψ will again be a harmonic wave. Therefore, it has the general form

$$\psi_{\mathrm{II}} = A_{\mathrm{II}} \sin(2\pi x/\lambda_{\mathrm{II}}) + B_{\mathrm{II}} \cos(2\pi x/\lambda_{\mathrm{II}}) \tag{2-29}$$

As mentioned in Section 1-3, this can be written in the equivalent form

$$\psi_{\mathrm{II}} = C_{\mathrm{II}} \exp(+2\pi ix/\lambda_{\mathrm{II}}) + D_{\mathrm{II}} \exp(-2\pi ix/\lambda_{\mathrm{II}}) \tag{2-30}$$

Let us consider first the case where $E < U$ and the particle is classically unable to get into region II. For this case, λ_{II} is imaginary since

$$\lambda_{\mathrm{II}} = h/\sqrt{2m(E - U)} \tag{2-31}$$

and $E - U$ is negative. Because λ_{II} is imaginary, it is more convenient to use the general form (2-30) because then the i in the exponential argument can combine with the i of λ_{II} to produce a real argument. Let us assume that λ_{II} is equal to i times a *positive* number. (This will not affect our results.)

Let us now examine the properties of the two exponential functions in Eq. (2-30). The first exponential has an argument that is *real* (because the i's cancel) and *positive* (because of our above assumption). As x increases, this exponential increases rapidly, approaching infinity. Since acceptable functions do not blow up like this, we set C_{II} equal to zero to prevent it. The second exponential has a negative, real argument, so it decays exponentially toward zero as x approaches infinity. This is acceptable behavior, and we are left with

$$\psi_{\mathrm{II}} = D_{\mathrm{II}} \exp(-2\pi ix/\lambda_{\mathrm{II}}) \tag{2-32}$$

We now have formulas describing fragments of the wavefunction for the two regions. All that remains is to join these together at $x = L$ in such a way that the resulting wavefunction is continuous at $x = L$ and has a continuous first derivative there. (Recall that this second requirement results from the fact that the potential is finite at $x = L$. Hence, ψ must be smooth at $x = L$.)

The continuity requirement gives

$$A_{\mathrm{I}} \sin(2\pi L/\lambda_{\mathrm{I}}) = D_{\mathrm{II}} \exp(-2\pi iL/\lambda_{\mathrm{II}}) \tag{2-33}$$

Taking the derivatives of ψ_{I} and ψ_{II} and setting these equal at $x = L$ (to force smoothness) gives

$$(2\pi/\lambda_{\mathrm{I}})\, A_{\mathrm{I}} \cos(2\pi L/\lambda_{\mathrm{I}}) = (-2\pi i/\lambda_{\mathrm{II}})\, D_{\mathrm{II}} \exp(-2\pi iL/\lambda_{\mathrm{II}}) \tag{2-34}$$

The exponential term is common to both Eqs. (2-33) and (2-34), providing the basis for another equality:

$$A_{\mathrm{I}} \sin(2\pi L/\lambda_{\mathrm{I}}) = (-A_{\mathrm{I}}\lambda_{\mathrm{II}}/i\lambda_{\mathrm{I}}) \cos(2\pi L/\lambda_{\mathrm{I}}) \tag{2-35}$$

or

$$\tan(2\pi L/\lambda_{\mathrm{I}}) = i\lambda_{\mathrm{II}}/\lambda_{\mathrm{I}} \tag{2-36}$$

Substituting for λ_{I} and λ_{II} as indicated by Eqs. (2-28) and (2-31) gives

$$\tan(2\pi L\sqrt{2mE}/h) = -\sqrt{E}/\sqrt{U - E} \tag{2-37}$$

The only unknown in Eq. (2-37) is the total energy E. For given values of L, m, and U, only certain values of $E < U$ will satisfy Eq. (2-37). Thus, the particle can have only certain energies when it is trapped in the "box." These allowed energies can be found by graphing the left-hand side and right-hand side of Eq. (2-37) as functions of E. The values of E where the plots intersect satisfy Eq. (2-37). Figure 2-9 illustrates the graphical solution of Eq. (2-37) for a particular set of values for L, m, and U.

Once a value of E is selected, λ_{I} and λ_{II} are known [from Eqs. (2-28) and (2-31)] and it remains only to find A_{I} and D_{II}. The ratio $A_{\mathrm{I}}/D_{\mathrm{II}}$ may be found from Eq. (2-33). The numerical values of A_{I} and D_{II} will then be obtainable if

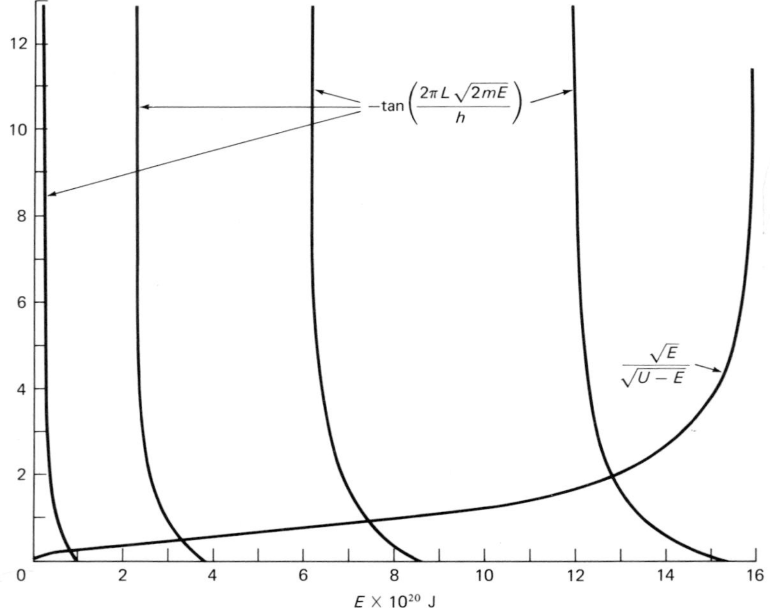

FIG. 2-9 Graphical solution of the equation $-\tan(2\pi L\sqrt{2mE}/h) = \sqrt{E}/\sqrt{U - E}$. Here $L = 25$ Å, $m = 9.11 \times 10^{-28}$ gm, $U = 1$ eV $= 16.02 \times 10^{-20}$ J. Intersections occur at $E = 0.82815 \times 10^{-20}$ J, 3.29869×10^{-20} J, 7.35730×10^{-20} J and 12.82153×10^{-20} J.

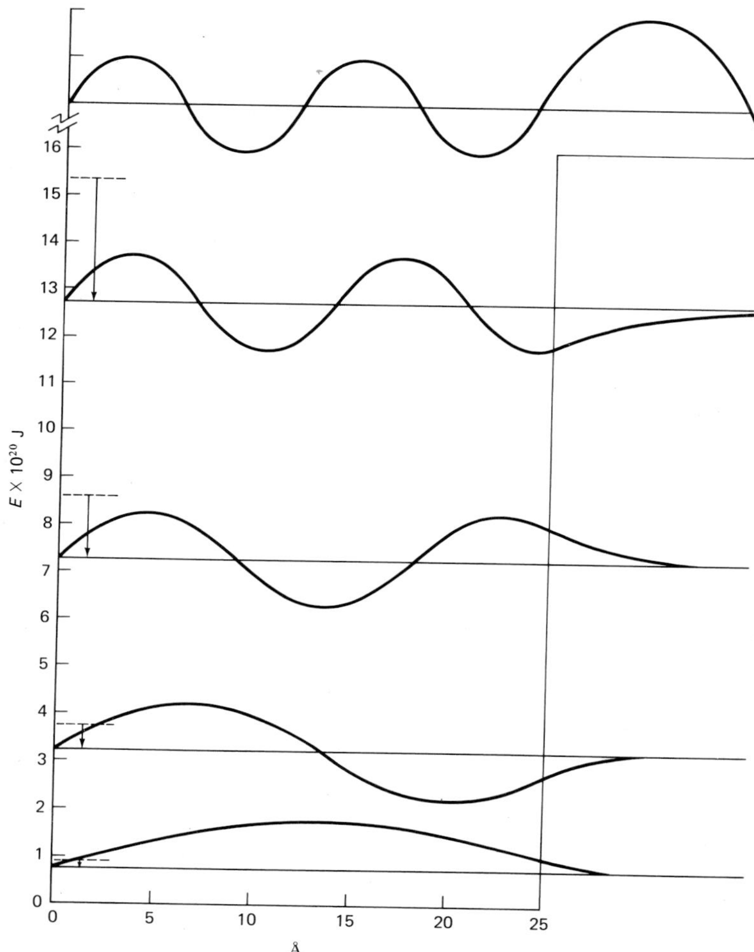

FIG. 2-10 Solutions for particle in well with one finite wall (see Fig. 2-9 for details). Dotted lines correspond to energy levels which would exist if $U = \infty$.

we require that the wavefunction be normalized. A set of such solutions is shown in Fig. 2-10.

Before solving for the case where $E > U$, let us discuss in detail the results just obtained.

In the first place, the energies are quantized, much as they were in the infinitely deep square well. There is some difference, however. In the infinitely deep well or "box," the energy levels increased with the square of the quantum number n. Here they increase less rapidly (the dotted lines in Fig. 2-10 show the allowed energy levels which result when $U = \infty$) because the barrier becomes effectively less restrictive for particles with higher energies (see the following). For the lowest solution, for example, slightly less than one-half a sine wave is needed in one box width of distance. Thus, the wavelength here is slightly longer than in an infinitely deep well of equal width, and so, by de Broglie's relation the energy is slightly lower. Notice that the effect of lowering the height of one wall is least for the levels lying deepest in the well.

The solutions sketched in Fig. 2-10 indicate that there is a finite probability for finding the particle in the region $x > L$ even though it must have a negative kinetic energy there. Thus, quantum mechanics allows the particle to penetrate into regions where classical mechanics claims it cannot go. Notice that the penetration becomes more appreciable as the energy of the particle approaches that of the barrier. This results from the fact that $E - U$ determines the rate at which the exponential in ψ_{II} decays [see Eqs. (2-31) and (2-32)]. In the limit that $U \to \infty$, the wavefunction vanishes at the barrier, in agreement with the results of the infinite square well of Section 2-1.

If the barrier in Fig. 2-8 has finite thickness (V becomes zero again at, say, $x = 2L$), then there is a finite probability that a particle in the well will penetrate through the barrier and appear on the other side. This phenomenon is called *quantum-mechanical tunneling*, and this is the way, for example, an α particle escapes from a nucleus even though it classically lacks sufficient energy to overcome the nuclear forces. We emphasize that the tunneling referred to in this example is really not a stationary state phenomenon. We have an *initial* condition (particle in the well) and ask what the half-life is for the escape of the particle—a time-dependent problem.

We saw earlier that the energy quantization for the particle in the infinitely deep well could be thought of as resulting from fitting integral numbers of half sine waves into a fixed width. Most sine waves just will not fit perfectly, and so most energies are not allowed. In this problem the waves are allowed to leak past one of the well walls, but we can still see why only certain energies are allowed. Suppose that we pick some arbitrary energy E for the particle. We know that ψ must be zero at the left wall of the well where $V = \infty$. Starting there, we can draw a sine wave of *wavelength determined by E* across the well to the right wall, as shown in Fig. 2-11. When the wave hits the right wall, it must join on smoothly to a decaying exponential, which also depends on E. Most of the time, it will be impossible to effect a smooth junction, and that particular value of E will be disallowed.

Let us now consider the case where $E > U$. In region I, the considerations are the same as before. Then, ψ_{I} is a sine wave that can be drawn from the left wall and has a wavelength determined by $E(= T)$ from de Broglie's relation. This sine wave arrives at $x = L$ with a certain magnitude and a certain derivative (assuming that the multiplier A_{I} has been fixed at some arbitrary value). In region II, we also have a solution of the usual form

$$\psi_{\text{II}}(x) = A_{\text{II}} \sin(2\pi x/\lambda_{\text{II}}) + B_{\text{II}} \cos(2\pi x/\lambda_{\text{II}}) \tag{2-38}$$

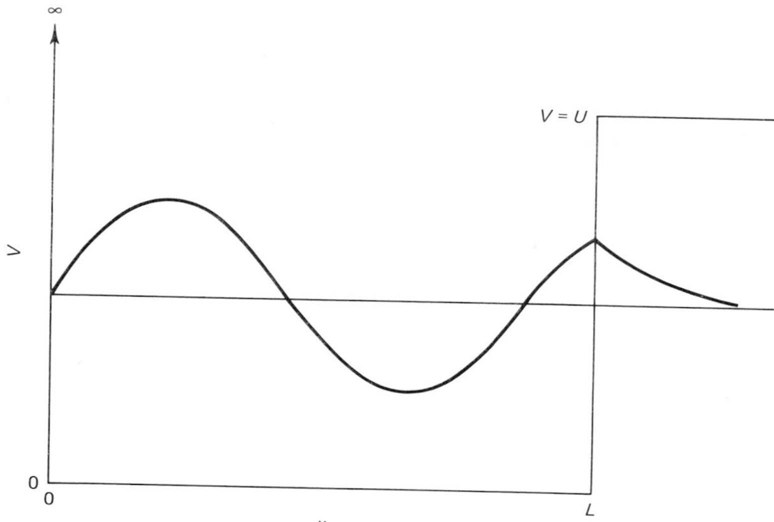

FIG. 2-11 An example of partial wavefunctions for an arbitrary energy E. These functions cannot be joined smoothly at $x = L$ and so this value of E is not allowed.

where λ_{II} is real and determined by $E - U$, which is now positive. The question is, can we always adjust ψ_{II} (by changing A_{II} and B_{II}) so that it has the same value and slope at $x = L$ that ψ_{I} has? A little thought shows that such adjustment is indeed always possible. The two adjustments allowed in ψ_{II} correspond to a change of *phase* for ψ_{II} (a shift in the horizontal direction) and a change in *amplitude* for ψ_{II}. The only thing about ψ_{II} we cannot change is the wavelength, since this is determined by $E - U$. This is just a physical description of the mathematical circumstance in which we have two adjustable parameters and two requirements to fit—a soluble problem. The essential difference between this case and that of the trapped particle is that here we have fewer boundary conditions. Before, our square-integrability requirement was used to remove a positive exponential term. That requirement is, in effect, a boundary condition—ψ must vanish at $x = \infty$—and it led to energy quantization. Then we used the normality requirement to achieve unique values for A_{I} and D_{II}. In this case we cannot get a square-integrable solution. ψ_{II} goes on oscillating as $x \to \infty$, and so we have no boundary condition there. As a result, E is not quantized and ψ is not normalizable, so that only ratios of A_{I}, A_{II}, and B_{II} are obtainable.

The energy scheme for the particle in the potential well with one finite wall, then, is discrete when $E < U$, and continuous when $E > U$.

Notice the way in which the wavelengths vary in Fig. 2-10. We have already seen that the time-independent Schrödinger equation states that the total energy for a particle in a stationary state is the same at all particle positions (i.e., a "constant of motion"). The kinetic and potential energies must vary together, then, in such a way that their sum is constant. This is reflected by the fact that the wavelength of an unbound solution is shorter in region I than it is in region II. In region I, $V = 0$, so that all energy of the particle is kinetic ($T = E$). In region II, $V > 0$, so that the kinetic energy ($T = E - V$) is less than it was in region I. Therefore, the de Broglie wavelength, which is related to *kinetic* energy, must be greater in region II.

2-4 The Particle in an Infinite "Box" with a Finite Central Barrier

Another example of barrier penetration in a stationary state of a system is provided by inserting a barrier of finite height and thickness at the midpoint of the infinite square well of Section 2-1 (see Fig. 2-12).

The boundary conditions for this problem are easily obtained by obvious extensions of the considerations already discussed. Rather than solve this case directly, we shall make use of our insights from previous systems to deduce the main characteristics of the solutions. Let us begin by considering the case where the barrier is infinitely high. Then the problem becomes merely that of two isolated infinite square wells, each well having solutions as described in Sections 2-1 and 2-2.

Now, as the height of the barrier is lowered from infinity, what happens? The levels lying deepest in the two sections should be least affected by the change. They must still vanish at the outer walls but now they can penetrate slightly into the finite barrier. Thus, the lowest state in, say, the left-hand section of the well will begin to look as given in Fig. 2-12b. The solution on the right side will do likewise, of course. As this happens, their energies will decrease slightly since their wavelengths increase. However, since the two wells are no longer separated by an infinite barrier, they are no longer independent. We can no longer talk about separate solutions for the two halves. Each solution for the Schrödinger equation is now a solution for the whole system from $x = -L$ to $+L$. Furthermore, symmetry arguments state that, since the hamiltonian for this problem is symmetric for reflection through $x = 0$, the solutions, if nondegenerate, must be either symmetric or antisymmetric through $x = 0$.

This requirement must be reconciled with the behavior indicated by Fig. 2-12b, which is also occurring. One way to accomplish this is by summing the two half waves as shown in Fig. 2-12c, giving a symmetric wavefunction. Alternatively, subtraction gives the antisymmetric form shown in Fig. 2-12d. Both of these solutions will be lower in energy than their infinite-well counterparts. Will their energies be equal to each other? Not quite. By close inspection, we can figure out which solution will have the lower energy. In Figs. 2-12b to 2-12d, the slopes of the half wave, the symmetric, and the antisymmetric combinations at the finite barrier are labeled respectively m, m', and m''.

What can we say about their relative values? The slope m' should be less

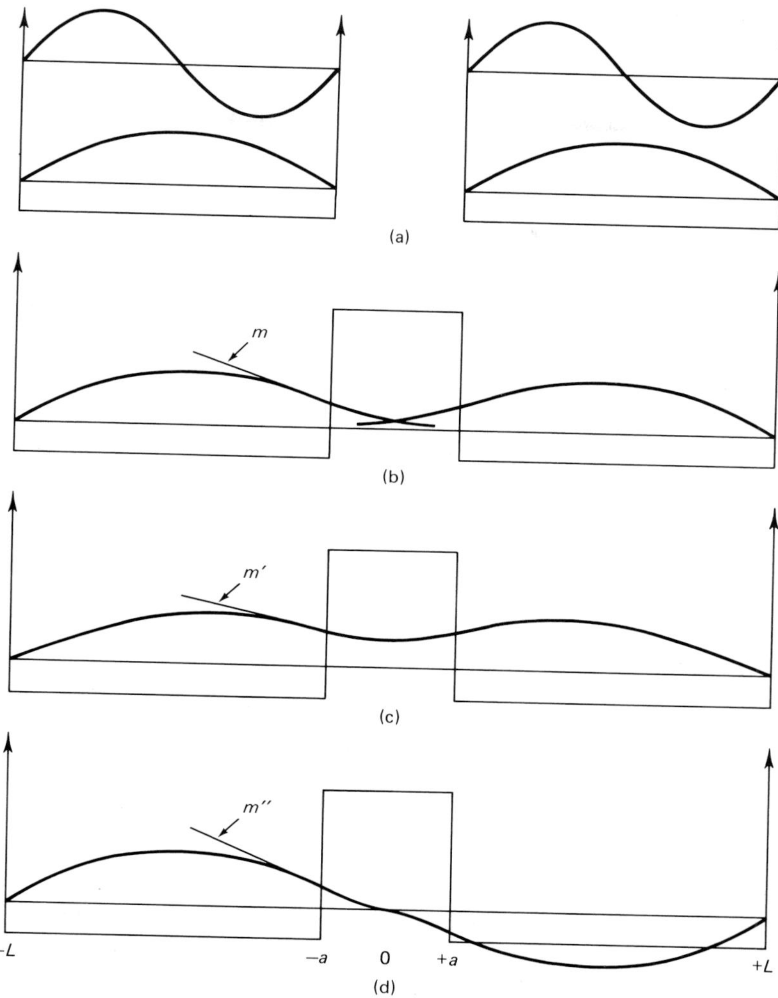

FIG. 2-12 (a) Solutions for identical infinite square wells. (b) Effect of finite partition on half waves. (c) Symmetric combination of half waves. (d) Antisymmetric combination of half waves.

negative than m because the decaying exponential producing m has an increasing exponential added to it in when producing m'. Slope m'' should be more negative than m since the decaying exponential has an increasing exponential subtracted from it in case *d*, causing it to decay faster. This means that the sine curve on the left-hand side of Fig. 2-12c cannot be identical with that of the left side of Fig. 2-12d since they must arrive at the barrier with different slopes. (The same is true for the right-hand sides, of course.) How can we make the sine wave arrive with a less negative slope m'?—by increasing the wavelength slightly so that not quite so much of the sine wave fits into the left well (see Fig. 2-13a). Increasing the wavelength slightly means, by de Broglie's relation, that the energy of the particle is decreased. Similarly, the sine curve in Fig. 2-12d must be shortened so that it will arrive at the barrier with slope m'', which corresponds to an energy increase. Of course, now that the energy has changed outside the barrier, it must change inside the barrier too. This would require going back and modifying the exponentials inside the barrier. But the first step is sufficient to indicate the qualitative results. The symmetric solution has lower energy. In Fig. 2-13a is a detailed sketch of the final solution for the two lowest states.

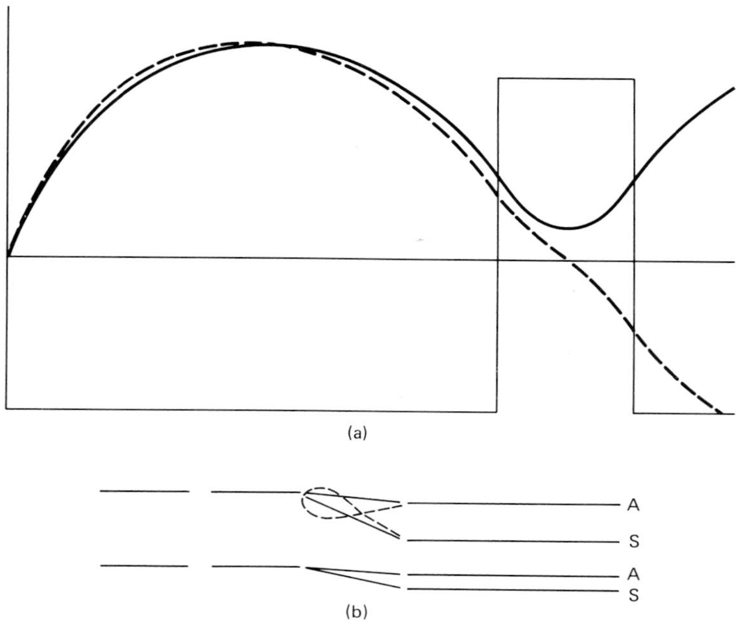

FIG. 2-13 (a) Detailed sketch of the two lowest solutions for the infinite square-well divided by a finite barrier at the midpoint. The waves are sketched from a common energy value for ease of comparison. Actually, the symmetric wave has a lower energy. (b) A correlation diagram relating energies when the barrier is infinite (left side) with those when the barrier vanishes. Letters A and S refer to antisymmetric and symmetric solutions, respectively.

There is a simpler way to decide that the symmetric solution has lower energy. As the barrier height becomes lower and lower, the two solutions become more and more separated in energy, but they always remain symmetric or antisymmetric with respect to reflection since the hamiltonian always has reflection symmetry. In the limit when the barrier completely disappears we have a simple square well again (but larger), the lowest solution of which is symmetric. This lowest symmetric solution must "come from" the symmetric combination sketched in Fig. 2-12a; similarly, the second lowest, antisymmetric solution of the large well "correlates" with the antisymmetric combination (Fig. 2-12d). A correlation diagram for this process is sketched in Fig. 2-13b. This shows that, when the barrier vanishes, the symmetric state has the lowest energy. It is reasonable that, at intermediate barrier heights, the same should hold true. (In many physical situations, lines in correlation diagrams are strongly curved and straight line diagrams can be misleading. Thus, there is nothing in principle to prevent the lines from crossing in the manner depicted by dotted lines in Fig. 2-13b. However, in the case at hand, there is no physical subtlety operating to produce such behavior.) We shall see that the correlation of wavefunction symmetries in such a manner as this is a powerful technique in understanding and predicting chemical behavior.

The next pair of states is produced essentially from symmetric and antisymmetric combinations of the second states of the infinite square wells. These states are closer to the top of the barrier, so they will exhibit more penetration. This results in greater differences between slopes m, m', and m'' and ultimately a greater splitting between the symmetric and antisymmetric state energy levels.

The kind of energy level splitting just described is an extremely pervasive phenomenon in quantum chemistry. When two atoms interact to form a molecule, the original atomic wavefunctions combine to form molecular wavefunctions in much the same way as was just described. One of these molecular wavefunctions may have an energy markedly lower than those in the corresponding atoms. Electrons having such a wavefunction will stabilize the molecule relative to the separated atoms.

Another case in which energy level splitting occurs is in the ammonia molecule. Ammonia is most stable in a pyramidal configuration, but is capable of inverting through a higher-energy planar configuration into an equivalent "mirror image" pyramid. Thus, vibrations tending to flatten out the ammonia molecule occur in a potential similar to the double well, except that in ammonia the potential is not discontinuous. The lowest vibrational energy levels are not sufficiently high to allow classical inversion of ammonia. However, these vibrational levels are split by interaction through barrier penetration just as quantum mechanics predicts. The energy required to excite ammonia from the lowest of these sublevels to its associated sublevel can be accurately measured through microwave spectroscopy. Knowledge of the level splittings in turn allows a precise determination of the height of the barrier to inversion in ammonia (see Fig. 2-14).

It is easy to anticipate the appearance of the solutions for the square well with central barrier for energies greater than the partition height. They will be sinusoidal waves, symmetric or antisymmetric in the well, and vanishing at the walls. Their wavelengths will be somewhat longer in the region of the partition

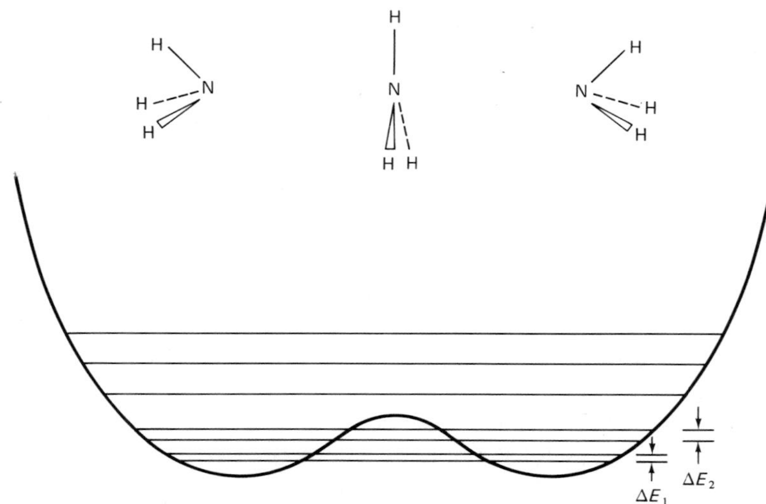

FIG. 2-14 Sketch of potential for breathing vibrational mode in ammonia. The lowest levels are split by tunneling. The low energy transition ΔE_1 is visible in the microwave region whereas the second transition ΔE_2 is visible in the infrared (Problem 2-9). $\Delta E_1 = 0.16 \times 10^{-22}$ J; $\Delta E_2 = 7.15 \times 10^{-22}$ J.

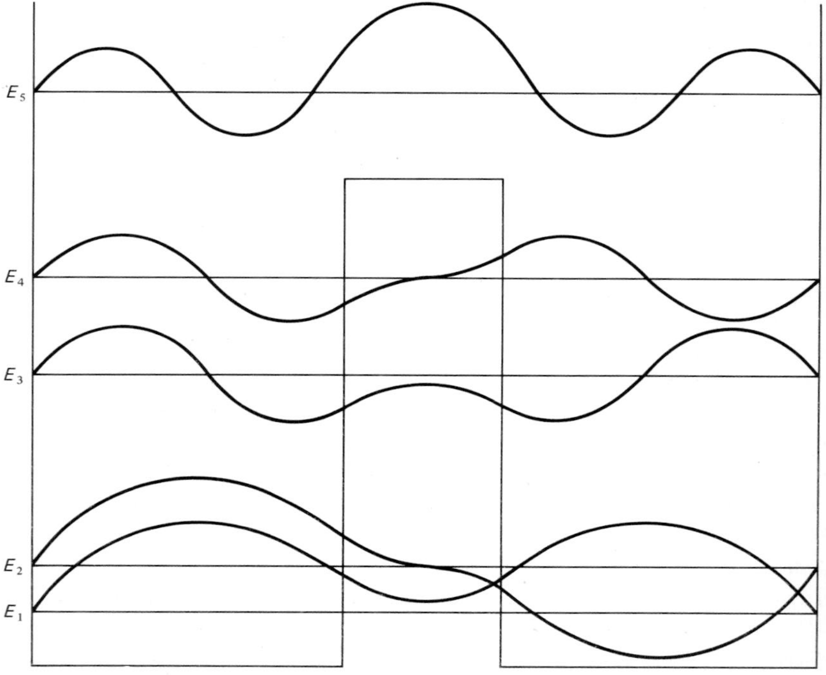

FIG. 2-15 Wavefunctions for the infinite square well with finite partition.

than elsewhere because some of the kinetic energy of the particle is transformed to potential energy there. A sketch of the final results is given in Fig. 2-15.

2-5 The Free Particle in One Dimension

Suppose a particle of mass m moves in one dimension in a potential that is everywhere zero. The Schrödinger equation becomes

$$\frac{-h^2}{8\pi^2 m}\frac{d^2\psi}{dx^2} = E\psi \tag{2-39}$$

which has as solutions

$$\psi = A\exp(\pm 2\pi i\sqrt{2mE}x/h) \tag{2-40}$$

or alternatively, trigonometric solutions

$$\psi = A'\sin(2\pi\sqrt{2mE}x/h), \qquad \psi = A'\cos(2\pi\sqrt{2mE}x/h) \tag{2-41}$$

As is most easily seen from the exponential forms (2-40), if E is negative, ψ will blow up at either $+\infty$ or $-\infty$, and so we reject negative energies. Since there are no boundary conditions, it follows that E can take on any positive value; the energies of the free particle are not quantized. This result would be expected from our earlier results on constrained particles. There we saw that quantization resulted from spatial constraints, and here we have none.

The constants A and A' of Eqs. (2-40) and (2-41) cannot be evaluated in the usual way, since the solutions do not vanish at $x = \pm\infty$. Sometimes it is convenient to evaluate them to correspond to some experimental situation. For instance, suppose that one was working with a monoenergetic beam of electrons having an intensity of one electron every 10^{-4} cm. Then we could normalize ψ so that

$$\int_0^{10^{-4}\,\text{cm}} |\psi|^2\,dx = 1$$

Notice that the first expressions (2-40) for ψ differ in their predicted charge distributions from expressions (2-41). The absolute square $\psi^*\psi$ of the exponentials is a constant (A^*A), whereas the squares of the trigonometric functions are fluctuating functions of x. It seems absurd that a particle having no restriction whatsoever on it should have varying degrees of probability of being found at different positions along x. This seems to violate the translational symmetry of the problem, which admits no privileged point in space from which to refer our coordinate axis. This apparent paradox results from the fact that we have two independent solutions for each allowed value of E (except for $E = 0$, which has but one solution, $\psi =$ constant). This double degeneracy with respect to energy means that from a degenerate pair, ψ and ψ', one can produce any number of new eigenfunctions, $\psi'' = a\psi + b\psi'$ (Problem 2-10). In such a situation, the symmetry proof of Section 2-2 does not hold. However, there will always be an independent pair of degenerate wavefunctions that *will* satisfy certain symmetry requirements. Thus, in the problem at hand, we have one pair of solutions, the exponentials, which do have the proper symmetry since their absolute squares are constant. From this pair we can produce any number of linear combinations [one set being given by Eq. (2-41)], but these need not display the symmetry properties anymore.

The exponential solutions have another special attribute: A particle whose state is described by one of the exponentials has a definite linear momentum, whereas, when described by a trigonometric function, it does not. In Section 1-9, it was shown that the connection between classical and wave mechanics could be made if one related the classical momentum, p_x with a quantum mechanical operator $(h/2\pi i)\, d/dx$. Now, for a particle to have a definite (sharp) value p_0 for its momentum really means that, if we measure the momentum at some instant, there is no possibility of getting any value other than p_0. This means that the particle in the state described by ψ *always* has momentum p_0, no matter where it is in x; i.e., its momentum is a constant of motion, just as its energy is. This corresponds to saying that there is an eigenvalue equation for momentum, just as for energy. Thus

$$\frac{h}{2\pi i}\frac{d\psi}{dx} = p_0\psi \tag{2-42}$$

The statement made earlier, that the exponential solutions correspond to the particle having sharp momentum, means that the exponentials (2-40) must be solutions to Eq. (2-42). This is easily verified:

$$\frac{h}{2\pi i}\frac{d}{dx}\left[A\exp\left(\frac{\pm 2\pi i\sqrt{2mE}x}{h}\right)\right] = \pm\sqrt{2mE}\left[A\exp\left(\frac{\pm 2\pi i\sqrt{2mE}x}{h}\right)\right]$$

Thus, the positive and negative exponential solutions correspond to momentum values of $+\sqrt{2mE}$ and $-\sqrt{2mE}$, respectively, and are interpreted as referring to particle motion toward $+\infty$ and $-\infty$ respectively. Since energy is related to the square of the momentum, these two solutions have identical energies. (The solution for $E = 0$ corresponds to no momentum at all, and the directional degeneracy is removed.) A mixture of these states contains contributions from two different momenta but only one energy, so linear combinations of the exponentials fail to maintain a sharp value for momentum but do maintain a sharp value for energy.

2-6 The Particle in a Ring of Constant Potential

Suppose that a particle of mass m is free to move around a ring of radius r and zero potential, but that it requires infinite energy to get off the ring. This system has only one variable coordinate—the angle ϕ. In classical mechanics, the useful quantities and relationships for describing such circular motion are those given in Table 2-1.

TABLE 2-1

Quantity	Formula	Units
Moment of inertia	$I = mr^2$	g cm^2 or kg m^2
Angular velocity	$\omega = \Delta\phi/\Delta t = v/r$	sec^{-1}
Angular momentum (linear momentum times orbit radius)	$mvr = I\omega$	g cm^2/sec or erg sec or J sec

Comparing formulas for linear momentum and angular momentum reveals that the variables mass and linear velocity are analogous to moment of inertia and angular velocity in circular motion, where the coordinate ϕ replaces x. The Schrödinger equation for circular motion, then, is

$$\frac{-h^2}{8\pi^2 I}\frac{d^2\psi(\phi)}{d\phi^2} = E\psi(\phi) \tag{2-43}$$

which has, as solutions

$$A \exp(\pm ik\phi) \tag{2-44}$$

or alternatively

$$A' \sin(k\phi) \tag{2-45}$$

and

$$A' \cos(k\phi) \tag{2-46}$$

where

$$k = 2\pi\sqrt{2IE}/h \tag{2-47}$$

Let us solve the problem first with the trigonometric functions. Starting at some arbitrary point on the ring and moving around the circumference with a sinusoidal function, we shall eventually reencounter the initial point. In order that our wavefunction be single valued, it is necessary that the sinusoidal function connect smoothly onto itself, head to tail, at this point. Thus, ψ and $d\psi/d\phi$ must be equal for the head and the tail. This is equivalent to saying that ψ and $d\psi/d\phi$ must repeat themselves every time ϕ changes by 2π radians. Thus, for ψ given by Eq. (2-45),

$$\sin(k\phi) = \sin[k(\phi + 2\pi)] \tag{2-48}$$

and for $d\psi/d\phi$

$$k\cos(k\phi) = k\cos(k\phi + 2k\pi) \tag{2-49}$$

These relations are satisfied only if k is an integer. The same result comes from ψ as given by Eq. (2-46). The case in which $k = 0$ is not allowed for the sine function since it then vanishes everywhere and is unsuitable. However, $k = 0$ is allowed for the cosine form. The normalized solutions are, then,

$$\psi = (1/\sqrt{\pi})\sin(k\phi), \qquad k = 1, 2, 3, \ldots$$

$$\psi = (1/\sqrt{\pi})\cos(k\phi) \qquad k = 1, 2, 3, \ldots \tag{2-50}$$

$$\psi = (1/\sqrt{2\pi}) \qquad \text{(from the } k = 0 \text{ case for the cosine)}$$

Now let us examine the exponential form of ψ (Eq. 2-44). The requirement that ψ repeat itself for $\phi \to \phi + 2\pi$ gives

$$A \exp(\pm ik\phi) = A \exp[\pm ik(\phi + 2\pi)] = A[\exp(\pm ik\phi) \exp(\pm 2\pi ik)]$$

or

$$\exp(\pm 2\pi ik) = 1$$

Taking the positive case and utilizing Eq. (2-3), we obtain

$$\cos(2\pi k) + i \sin(2\pi k) = 1 \quad \text{or} \quad \cos(2\pi k) = 1 \quad \text{and} \quad \sin(2\pi k) = 0$$

Again, k must be an integer. (The same result arises by requiring that $d\psi/d\phi$ repeat for $\phi \to \phi + 2\pi$.) Thus, an alternative set of solutions is

$$\psi = (1/\sqrt{2\pi}) \exp(\pm ik\phi), \qquad k = 0, 1, 2, 3, \ldots \tag{2-51}$$

The energies for the particle in the ring are easily obtained from Eq. (2-47):

$$E = k^2h^2/8\pi^2I, \qquad k = 0, 1, 2, 3, \ldots \tag{2-52}$$

The energies increase with the square of k, just as in the case of the infinite square well potential. Here we have a single state with $E = 0$, and doubly degenerate states above, whereas, in the square well, we had no solution at $E = 0$, and all solutions were nondegenerate. The solution at $E = 0$ means that there is no finite zero point energy to be associated with free rotation, and this is in accord with uncertainty principle arguments since there is no constraint in the coordinate ϕ.

The similarity between the particle in a ring and the free particle problems is striking. Aside from the fact that in the ring the energies are quantized and the solutions are normalizable, there are few differences. The exponential solutions (2-51) are eigenfunctions for the angular momentum operator $(h/2\pi i)\, d/d\phi$. The two momenta for a pair of degenerate solutions correspond to particle motion clockwise or counterclockwise in the ring. (The nondegenerate solution for $E = 0$ has no momentum, hence no ability to achieve degeneracy through directional behavior.) The particle density predicted by the exponentials is uniform in the ring, while that for the trigonometric solutions is not. Since the trigonometric functions tend to localize the particle into part of the ring, thereby causing $\Delta\phi \neq \infty$, it is consistent that they are impure momentum states ($\Delta p_\phi \neq 0$). (Infinite uncertainty in the coordinate ϕ means that all values of ϕ in the range 0–2π are equally likely.)

2-7 The Particle in a Three-Dimensional Box: Separation of Variables

Let us now consider the three-dimensional analog of the square well of Section 2-1. This would be a three-dimensional box with zero potential inside and infinite potential outside. As before, the particle has no probability for penetrating beyond the box. Therefore, the Schrödinger equation is just

$$\frac{-h^2}{8\pi^2 m}\left(\frac{\partial^2}{\partial x^2} + \frac{\partial^2}{\partial y^2} + \frac{\partial^2}{\partial z^2}\right)\psi = E\psi \tag{2-53}$$

and ψ vanishes at the box edges.

The hamiltonian operator on the left side of Eq. (2-53) can be written as a sum of operators, one in each variable (e.g., $H_x = (-h^2/8\pi^2 m)\,\partial^2/\partial x^2$). Let us assume for the moment that ψ can be written as a product of three functions, each one being a function of a different variable, x, y, or z (i.e., $\psi = X(x)Y(y)Z(z)$). If we can show that such a ψ satisfies Eq. (2-53), we will have a much simpler problem to solve. Using this assumption, Eq. (2-53) becomes

$$(H_x + H_y + H_z)XYZ = EXYZ \tag{2-54}$$

This can be expanded and then divided through by XYZ to obtain

$$\frac{H_x XYZ}{XYZ} + \frac{H_y XYZ}{XYZ} + \frac{H_z XYZ}{XYZ} = E \qquad \text{(a constant)} \tag{2-55}$$

Now, since H_x, for example, operates only on functions of x, but not y or z, we can carry out some limited cancellation. Those functions that are *not* operated on in a numerator can be canceled against the denominator. Those that *are* operated on cannot be canceled since these are differential operators [e.g., in $(1/x)\,dx^2/dx$ it is not permissible to cancel $1/x$ against x^2 before differentiating: $(1/x)\,dx^2/dx \neq dx/dx$]. Such cancellation gives

$$\frac{H_x X}{X} + \frac{H_y Y}{Y} + \frac{H_z Z}{Z} = E \qquad \text{(a constant)} \tag{2-56}$$

Now, suppose the particle is moving in the box parallel to the x axis so that the variables y and z are not changing. Then, of course, the functions Y and Z are also not changing, so $H_y Y/Y$ and $H_z Z/Z$ are both constant. Only $H_x X/X$ can vary—but does it vary? Not according to Eq. (2-56), which reduces under these conditions to

$$\frac{H_x X}{X} + \text{constant} + \text{constant} = E \qquad \text{(a constant)} \tag{2-57}$$

Therefore, even though the particle is moving in the x direction, $H_x X/X$ must also be a constant, which we shall call E_x. Similar reasoning leads to analogous constants E_y and E_z. Furthermore, the behavior of $H_x X/X$ must really be independent of whether the particle is moving parallel to the y and z axes. Even if y and z do change, they do not appear in the quantity $H_x X/X$ anyway. Thus we may write, without restriction,

$$\frac{H_x X}{X} = E_x, \qquad \frac{H_y Y}{Y} = E_y, \qquad \frac{H_z Z}{Z} = E_z \tag{2-58}$$

and, from Eq. (2-56),

$$E_x + E_y + E_z = E \tag{2-59}$$

Our original equation in three variables has been separated into three equations, one in each variable. The first of these equations may be rewritten

$$H_x X = E_x X \tag{2-60}$$

which is just the Schrödinger equation for the particle in the one-dimensional square well, which we have already solved. For a rectangular box with $L_x \neq L_y \neq L_z$ we have the general solution

$$\psi = XYZ = \sqrt{2/L_x}\sin(n_x \pi x/L_x)\sqrt{2/L_y}\sin(n_y \pi y/L_y)\sqrt{2/L_z}\sin(n_z \pi z/L_z) \tag{2-61}$$

and

$$E = E_x + E_y + E_z = (h^2/8m)(n_x{}^2/L_x{}^2 + n_y{}^2/L_y{}^2 + n_z{}^2/L_z{}^2) \tag{2-62}$$

For a cubical box, $L_x = L_y = L_z = L$, and the energy expression simplifies to

$$E = (h^2/8mL^2)(n_x{}^2 + n_y{}^2 + n_z{}^2) \tag{2-63}$$

The lowest energy occurs when $n_x = n_y = n_z = 1$, and so

$$E_1(1) = 3h^2/8mL^2 \tag{2-64}$$

Thus, the cubical box has three times the zero point energy of the corresponding one-dimensional well, one-third coming from each independent coordinate for motion (i.e., "degree of freedom"). The "one" in parentheses indicates that this level is nondegenerate. The next level is produced when one of the quantum numbers n has a value of two while the others have values of one. There are three independent ways of doing this; therefore, the second level is triply degenerate, and $E_2(3) = 6h^2/8mL^2$. Proceeding, $E_3(3) = 9h^2/8mL^2$, $E_4(3) = 11h^2/8mL^2$, $E_5(1) = 12h^2/8mL^2$, $E_6(6) = 14h^2/8mL^2$, etc. Apparently, the energy level scheme and degeneracies of these levels do not proceed in the regular manner which is found in the one-dimensional cases we have studied.

We shall now briefly consider what probability distributions for the particle are predicted by these solutions. The lowest-energy solution has its largest value at the box center where all three sine functions are simultaneously largest. The particle distribution is sketched in Fig. 2-16a. The second level may be produced by setting $n_x = 2$, and $n_y = n_z = 1$. Then there will be a nodal plane running through the box perpendicular to the x axis, producing the split distribution shown in Fig. 2-16b. Since there are three ways this node can be oriented to produce distinct but energetically equal distributions, this energy level is triply degenerate. The particle distribution for the state where $n_x = n_y = n_z = 2$ is sketched in Fig. 2-16c. It is apparent that, in the high energy limit, the particle

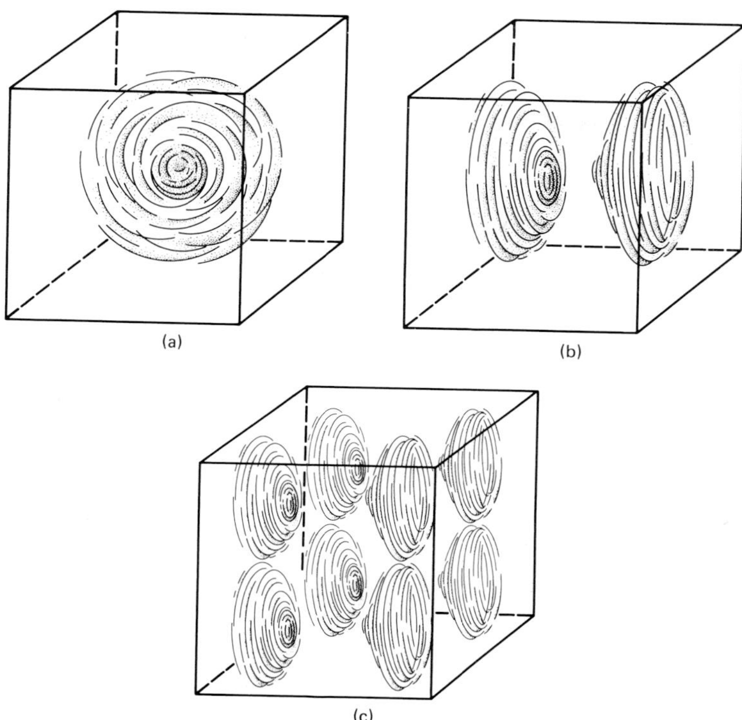

FIG. 2-16 Sketches of particle probability distributions for a particle in a cubical box. (a) $n_x = n_y = n_z = 1$. (b) $n_x = 2$, $n_y = n_z = 1$. (c) $n_x = n_y = n_z = 2$.

distribution becomes spread out uniformly throughout the box in accord with the classical prediction.

The separation of variables technique which we have used to convert our three-dimensional problem into three independent one-dimensional problems will recur in other quantum-chemical applications. Reviewing the procedure makes it apparent that this technique will work whenever the hamiltonian operator can be cleanly broken into parts dependent on completely different coordinates. This is always possible for the kinetic energy operator in cartesian coordinates. However, the potential energy operator often prevents separation of variables in physical systems of interest.

It is useful to state the general results of separation of variables. Suppose we have a hamiltonian operator, with associated eigenfunctions and eigenvalues:

$$H\psi_i = E_i\psi_i \tag{2-65}$$

Suppose this hamiltonian can be separated, for example,

$$H(\alpha, \beta) = H_\alpha(\alpha) + H_\beta(\beta) \tag{2-66}$$

where α and β stand for two different coordinates or groups of coordinates. Then it follows that

$$\psi_{j,k} = f_j(\alpha)g_k(\beta) \tag{2-67}$$

where

$$H_\alpha f_j = a_j f_j \tag{2-68}$$

and

$$H_\beta g_k = b_k g_k \tag{2-69}$$

Furthermore,

$$E_{j,k} = a_j + b_k \tag{2-70}$$

In other words, if a hamiltonian is separable, then the eigenfunctions will be *products* of eigenfunctions of the subhamiltonians, and the eigenvalues will be *sums* of the subeigenvalues.

2-8 Summary

In this chapter we have discussed the following points:

(1) A particle constrained in the classical sense (i.e., lacking the energy to overcome barriers preventing its motion over the entire coordinate range) will have quantized energy levels and a finite zero-point energy. In the mathematical analysis, this arises from requirements on ψ at boundaries.

(2) ψ can be nonsmooth, or "cusped," where V is infinite at a point. If V is infinite over a finite range, ψ must be zero there.

(3) Nondegenerate eigenfunctions of H must be symmetric or antisymmetric for any operation that leaves H unchanged.

(4) $|\psi|^2$ must be regarded as a statistical measure—a summary of many measurements of position on independent, but identically prepared, systems.

(5) Quantum-mechanical predictions must approach classical predictions in the limits of large E, or large mass, or very high quantum number values.

(6) Integrals with antisymmetric integrands must vanish.

(7) $|\psi|^2$ does not vanish in regions where $V > E$ if V is finite. This is called "barrier penetration."

(8) One-dimensional motion of a free particle has a continuum of energy levels. Except for $E = 0$, the states are doubly degenerate. Therefore, any mixture of such a pair of states is still an eigenfunction of H. But only two eigenfunctions (for a given $E \neq 0$) are also eigenfunctions for $\hat{p}_x$, the momentum operator. These are the exponential functions. Since they correspond to different momenta, mixing them produces functions that are not eigenfunctions for $\hat{p}_x$.

(9) Motion of a particle on a ring has quantum-mechanical solutions very similar to those for free-particle motion in one dimension. In both cases,

there is no zero-point energy. Both are doubly degenerate for $E > 0$ because of directional degeneracy. Both have a set of exponential solutions which are eigenfunctions for momentum. The main difference is that the particle-in-a-ring energies are quantized due to head-to-tail "joining conditions" on ψ.

PROBLEMS

2-1 Ascertain that the expression (2-12) for energy has the proper dimensions.

2-2 Solve Eq. (2-9) for A.

2-3 Verify Eq. (2-23) for the *general* case $n \neq m$ by explicit integration.

2-4 Let S and A be respectively symmetric and antisymmetric functions for the operator R. Evaluate the following:

(a) RS (b) RA (c) RSS (d) RAA
(e) RAS (f) $RAASASSA$ (g) $RAASASAA$

Can you think of a simple general rule for telling when a product of symmetric and antisymmetric functions will be antisymmetric?

2-5 Using the concept of odd and even functions, ascertain *by inspection* whether the following need be identically zero:

(a) $\int_0^{\pi} \sin\theta\cos\theta\, d\theta$ (b) $\int_{-\pi}^{\pi} \sin\theta\cos\theta\, d\theta$

(c) $\int_{-1}^{1} x\cos x\, dx$ (d) $\int_{-a}^{a} \cos y \sin^2 y\, dy$

(e) $\int_0^{\pi} \sin^3\theta\cos^2\theta\, d\theta$ (f) $\int_0^{\pi} \sin^2\theta\cos^3\theta\, d\theta$

(g) $\int_{-1}^{1}\int_{-1}^{1} x^2 y\, dx\, dy$ (h) $\int_{-\pi}^{\pi} x \sin x \cos x\, dx$

2-6 Verify that, as U approaches infinity in Fig. 2-8, the penetration of the particle past $x = L$ becomes infinitesimal [Eqs. (2-31) and (2-32)].

2-7 For the potential of Fig. 2-8, when $E < U$ the energies are discrete, and when $E > U$, they are continuous. Is there a solution with $E = U$? What special requirements are there, if any, for such a solution to exist?

2-8 Evaluate the probability for finding a particle in the middle third of a one-dimensional "box" in states with $n = 1, 2, 3$. Compare your answers with the sketches in Fig. 2-5 to see if they are reasonable.

2-9 Referring to Fig. 2-14, calculate the wavelengths in angstroms for radiation corresponding to the energies ΔE_1 and ΔE_2.

2-10 Prove the following statement: any linear combination of degenerate eigenfunctions of H is also an eigenfunction of H.

2-11 Explain why $(2\pi)^{-1/2}\exp(i\sqrt{2}\phi)$ is unacceptable as a wavefunction for the particle in a ring.

2-12 In a few words, indicate what is wrong with the wavefunctions sketched in the potentials shown in Fig. P2-12. If the solution appears to be acceptable, indicate this fact.

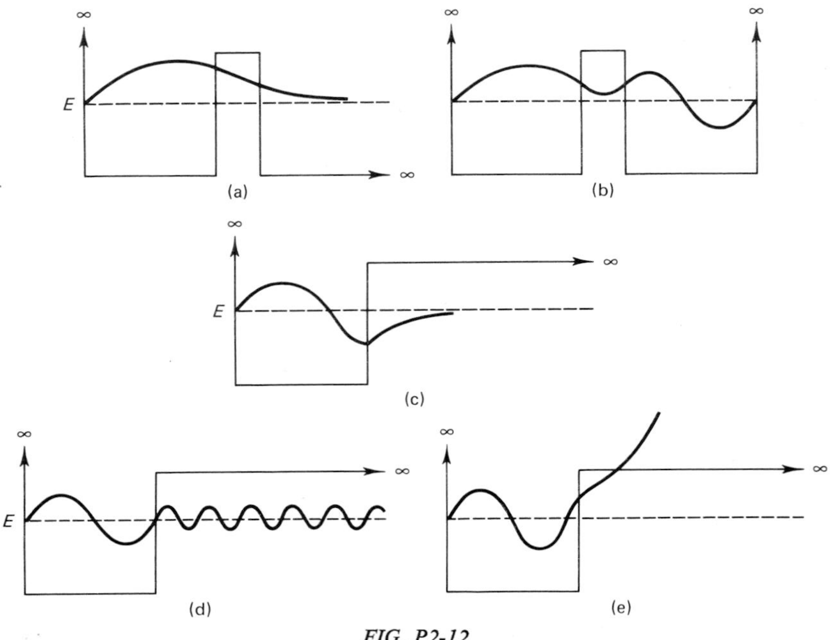

FIG. P2-12

2-13 Consider the particle in a three-dimensional rectangular box with $L_x = L_y = L_z/2$. What would be the energy when $n_x = 1$, $n_y = 2$, $n_z = 2$? For $n_x = 1$, $n_y = 1$, $n_z = 4$? Can you guess the meaning of the term "accidental degeneracy?"

2-14 Kuhn [1] has suggested that the mobile π electrons in polymethine dyes can be modeled after the one-dimensional box. Consider the symmetric carbocyanine dyes (I) where the positive charge "resonates" between the two nitrogen atoms. The zigzag polymethine "path" along which the π electrons are relatively free to move extends along the conjugated system between the two nitrogens. Kuhn assumed a

(I)

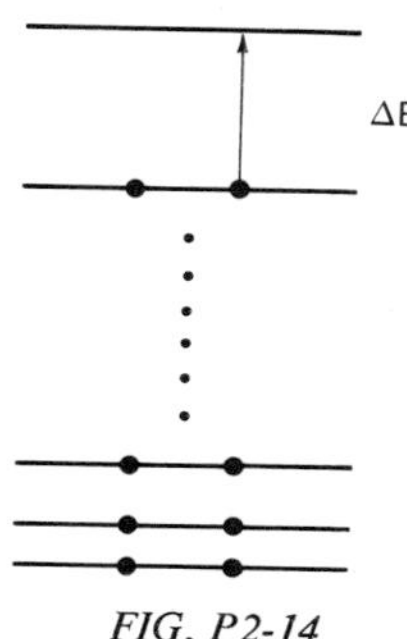

FIG. P2-14

box length L equal to this path length plus one extra bond length on each end (so that the nitrogens would not be at the very edge of the box where they would be prevented from having any π-electron charge). This gives $L = (2n + 10)\, l$ where l is 1.39 Å, the bond length of an intermediate (i.e., between single and double) C–C bond. The number of π electrons in the polymethine region is $2n + 10$. Assume that each energy level in the box is capable of holding no more than two electrons and that the electronic transition responsible for the dye color corresponds to the promotion of an electron from the highest filled to the lowest empty level, the levels having initially been filled starting with the lowest, as shown in Fig. P2-14. Calculate ΔE and λ for the cases $n = 0, 1, 2, 3$ and compare with the observed λ values of maximum absorption of about 5750, 7150, 8180, and 9250 Å, respectively.

REFERENCE

[1] H. Kuhn, *J. Chem. Phys.* **17**, 1198 (1949).

CHAPTER 3

THE ONE-DIMENSIONAL HARMONIC OSCILLATOR

3-1 Introduction

In Chapter 2 we examined several systems with discontinuous potential energies. In this chapter we consider the simple harmonic oscillator—a system with a continuously varying potential. There are several reasons for studying this problem in detail. First, the quantum-mechanical harmonic oscillator plays an essential role in our understanding of molecular vibrations, their spectra, and their influence on thermodynamic properties. Second, the qualitative results of the problem exemplify the concepts we have presented in Chapters 1 and 2. Finally, the problem provides a good demonstration of mathematical techniques that are important in quantum chemistry. Since many chemists are not overly familiar with some of these mathematical concepts, we shall deal with them in detail in the context of this problem.

3-2 Some Characteristics of the Classical One-Dimensional Harmonic Oscillator

A pendulum consisting of a large mass hanging by an almost weightless wire, and swinging through a very small angle, is a close approximation to a classical harmonic oscillator. It is an oscillator since its motion is back and forth over the same path. It is harmonic to the extent that the restoring force on the mass is proportional to the horizontal component of the displacement of the mass from its rest position. This force law, known as Hooke's law, is the common first approximation made in the analysis of a system vibrating about an equilibrium position. If we let the x axis be the coordinate of displacement of the mass, with $x = 0$ as the rest position, then we may write the restoring force as

$$F = -kx, \tag{3-1}$$

where k is the *force constant*. The minus sign assures that the force on the displaced mass is always directed toward the rest position.

We can use this force expression to determine an *equation of motion* for the mass, that is, an expression for its position x as a function of time t:

$$F = -kx(t) = ma = m\frac{d^2x(t)}{dt^2} \tag{3-2}$$

or

$$\frac{d^2x(t)}{dt^2} = (-k/m)x(t). \tag{3-3}$$

The solution $x(t)$ is a function that, when differentiated twice, is regenerated with the multiplier $-k/m$. A general solution is

$$x(t) = a\sin(\sqrt{k/m}t) + b\cos(\sqrt{k/m}t) \tag{3-4}$$

If we require that $x(t)$ be at its maximum value L at $t = 0$ (the pendulum is held at its position of maximum displacement and then released at $t = 0$), then it follows that $b = L$. Since the pendulum is also motionless at $t = 0$, $(dx(t)/dt)_{t=0} = 0$, and so $a = 0$. Hence,

$$x(t) = L\cos(\sqrt{k/m}t) \tag{3-5}$$

Thus, our equation of motion has the trigonometric time dependence characteristic of *harmonic* motion. From this expression, we see that $x(t)$ repeats itself whenever the argument of the cosine increases by 2π. This will require a certain time interval t'. Thus, the pendulum makes one complete back and forth motion in a time t' given by

$$\sqrt{k/m}t' = 2\pi \qquad t' = 2\pi\sqrt{m/k} \tag{3-6}$$

so the *frequency* of the oscillation ν is

$$\nu = 1/t' = (1/2\pi)\sqrt{k/m} \tag{3-7}$$

Suppose that one were to take a multiflash photograph of a swinging pendulum from above. The result would look as shown in Fig. 3-1a, the number of images being much greater near the termini of the swing (called the "turning points") than at the middle because the pendulum is moving fastest as it crosses the middle. This, in turn, results from the fact that all the potential energy of the mass has been converted to kinetic energy at that point. We thus arrive at a classical prediction for the time-averaged distribution of the projection of the harmonic oscillator in the displacement coordinate: This *distribution function* is greatest in regions where the potential energy is highest (Fig. 3-1b) (Problem 3-1).

Let us calculate and compare the time-averaged potential and kinetic energies for the classical harmonic oscillator. When the particle is at some instantaneous displacement x', its potential energy is

$$V(x') = (\text{force times distance to return to } x = 0)$$

$$= \int_0^{x'} kx\,dx = \tfrac{1}{2}kx'^2 \tag{3-8}$$

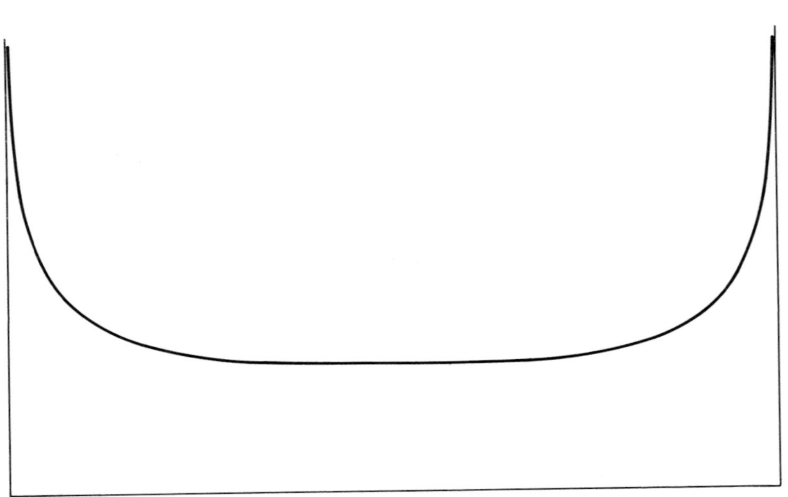

(a)

(b)

FIG. 3-1 (a) Results of a uniform multiflash photograph of a swinging pendulum as photographed from above. (b) Distribution function corresponding to the continuous limit of discrete distribution shown in (a).

The cumulative value of the potential energy over one complete oscillation V_c is given by the integral

$$V_c(t' - 0) = \int_0^{t'} V(t)\,dt = \tfrac{1}{2}k \int_0^{t'} x(t)^2\,dt \tag{3-9}$$

Substituting for $x(t)$ as indicated in Eq. (3-5)

$$\begin{aligned} V_c(t' - 0) &= \tfrac{1}{2}kL^2 \int_0^{t'} \cos^2(\sqrt{k/m}t)\,dt \\ &= \tfrac{1}{2}kL^2\sqrt{m/k} \int_0^{t'} \cos^2(\sqrt{k/m}t)\,d(\sqrt{k/m}t) \end{aligned} \tag{3-10}$$

When $t = t'$, $\sqrt{k/m}t = 2\pi$, and we may rewrite Eq. (3-10) as

$$V_c(t' - 0) = \tfrac{1}{2}kL^2\sqrt{m/k} \int_0^{2\pi} \cos^2 y\,dy = (\pi/2)kL^2\sqrt{m/k} \tag{3-11}$$

If we now divide by t' to get the average potential energy per unit time, we find

$$\overline{V} = \frac{V_c(t' - 0)}{t'} = \frac{(\pi/2)kL^2\sqrt{m/k}}{2\pi\sqrt{m/k}} = \frac{kL^2}{4} \tag{3-12}$$

The total energy for the system E is a constant of motion, so if we know it at one instant, we know it for all time. We can evaluate E by recognizing that, at the moment of release ($t = 0$ and $x = L$), the mass is motionless so that the total energy is identical to the potential energy:

$$E = \tfrac{1}{2}kL^2 \tag{3-13}$$

Comparing Eqs. (3-12) and (3-13) we see that, on the average, the classical harmonic oscillator stores half of its total energy as potential energy and half as kinetic energy.

3-3 The Quantum-Mechanical Harmonic Oscillator

We have already seen [Eq. (3-8)] that the potential energy of a harmonic oscillator is given by

$$V(x) = \tfrac{1}{2}kx^2 \tag{3-14}$$

and we can immediately write down the one-dimensional Schrödinger equation for the harmonic oscillator:

$$[(-h^2/8\pi^2 m)(d^2/dx^2) + \tfrac{1}{2}kx^2]\psi(x) = E\psi(x) \tag{3-15}$$

We can guess a great deal about the nature of the solutions to this equation by analogy with the systems studied in Chapter 2. In Fig. 3-2 the potential, the eigenvalues and the wavefunctions for the harmonic oscillator and for the particle in the infinite square well are shown. [We shall defer the detailed solution of Eq. (3-15) until the next section.] We can think of the harmonic oscillator potential as being produced by a continuous deformation of the square well potential and ask how the square well energies and wavefunctions will be influenced by the change. As mentioned in Chapter 2, we expect the energy levels for the harmonic oscillator to diverge less rapidly than those for the square well because the higher energy states in the harmonic oscillator have effectively larger "boxes" than do the lower states (that is, the more energetic the oscillator, the more widely separated are its classical turning points). We show later that the energy level spacing for the harmonic oscillator is in fact constant.

The nondegeneracy of the levels in the square well remains when we go over to the harmonic oscillator and there is no reason for expecting otherwise since the symmetry of the problem remains unaffected. It follows that solutions in the harmonic oscillator problem must be symmetric or antisymmetric with respect

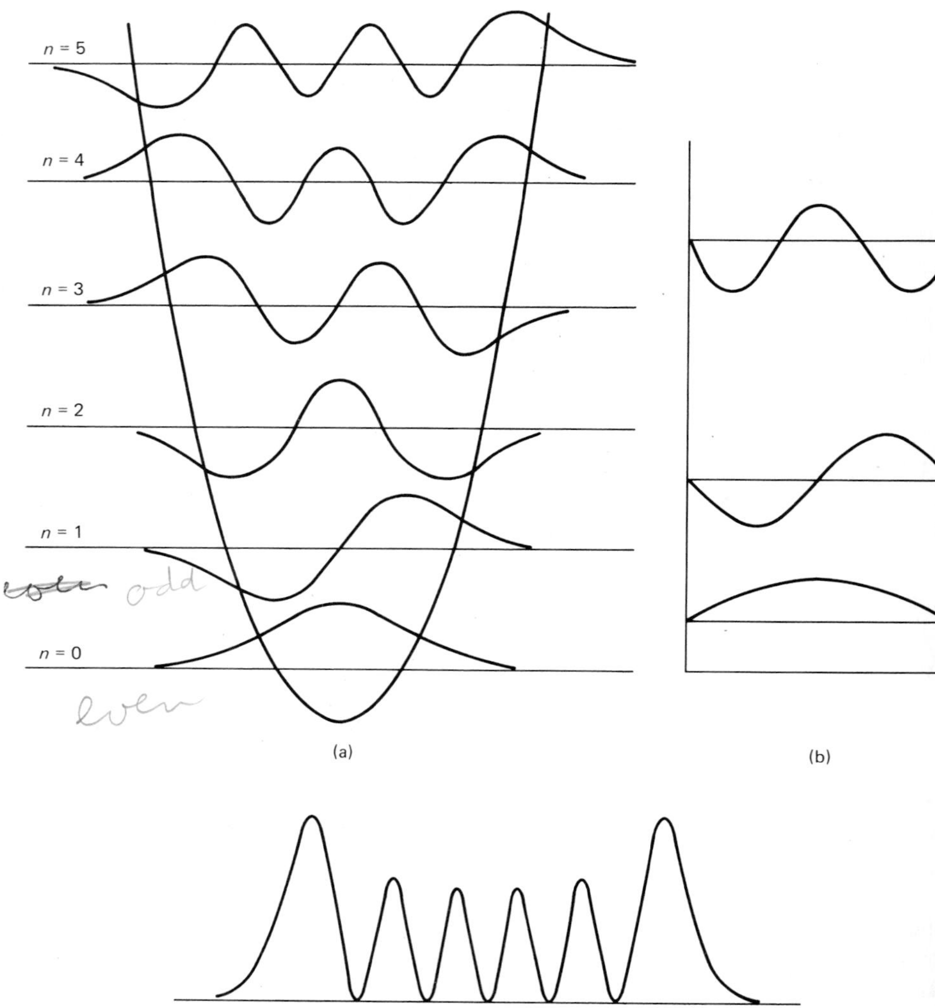

FIG. 3-2 The potential function, energy levels, and wavefunctions for (a) the harmonic oscillator, (b) the particle in the infinitely deep square well. (c) ψ^2 for the harmonic oscillator in the state $n = 5$.

to reflection through $x = 0$. Symmetric wavefunctions are automatically orthogonal to antisymmetric wavefunctions, as discussed earlier. (Actually, all the wavefunctions are orthogonal to each other. This is proved in Section 3-4.)

The harmonic oscillator has a finite zero-point energy. This is expected since the change from square well to parabolic well does not remove the restrictions on particle position; it merely changes them.

The particle has a finite probability of being found beyond the classical turning points; it penetrates the barrier. This is to be expected on the basis of earlier considerations since the barrier is not infinite at the turning point. (The potential becomes infinite only at $x = \pm\infty$.)

Finally, we note that in the lowest state the probability distribution favors the particle being in the low-potential central region of the well, while at higher energies the distribution approaches more nearly the classical result of favoring the higher potential regions (Fig. 3-2c).

3-4 Solution of the Harmonic Oscillator Schrödinger Equation

A. *Simplifying the Schrödinger Equation*

Equation (3-15) is simplified by substituting in the following relations:

$$\alpha \equiv 8\pi^2 mE/h^2 \qquad (3\text{-}16)$$

$$\beta^2 \equiv 4\pi^2 mk/h^2 \qquad (3\text{-}17)$$

The quantities α and β have units of cm^{-2}. We will assume that β is the positive root of β^2. The quantity α is necessarily positive. The Schrödinger equation now can be written

$$\frac{d^2\psi(x)}{dx^2} + (\alpha - \beta^2x^2)\psi(x) = 0 \qquad (3\text{-}18)$$

B. *Establishing the Correct Asymptotic Behavior*

At very large values of $|x|$, the quantity α (which is a constant since E is a constant) becomes negligible compared to β^2x^2. That is, the Schrödinger equation (3-18) approaches more and more closely the asymptotic form

$$d^2\psi(x)/dx^2 = \beta^2x^2\psi(x), \qquad |x| \to \infty \qquad (3\text{-}19)$$

What we need, then, are solutions $\psi(x)$ which approach the solutions of Eq. (3-19) at large values of $|x|$. The solutions for Eq. (3-19) can be figured out from the general rule for differentiating exponentials:

$$(d/dx)\exp(u(x)) = \exp(u(x))\, du(x)/dx \qquad (3\text{-}20)$$

Then

$$(d^2/dx^2)\exp(u(x)) = [(du(x)/dx)^2 + d^2u(x)/dx^2]\exp(u(x)) \qquad (3\text{-}21)$$

We want the term in square brackets to equal β^2x^2 for large $|x|$. If

$$u(x) = \pm\beta x^2/2 \qquad (3\text{-}22)$$

then

$$(d^2/dx^2)\exp(u(x)) = (\beta^2x^2 \pm \beta)\exp(\pm\beta x^2/2) \qquad (3\text{-}23)$$

At large values of $|x|$, β is negligible compared to β^2x^2, and so $\exp(\pm\beta x^2/2)$ are asymptotic solutions for Eq. (3-19). As $|x|$ increases, the positive exponential increases rapidly whereas the negative exponential dies away. We have seen that, for the wavefunction to be physically meaningful, we must reject the solution that blows up at large $|x|$. On the basis of these considerations, we can say that, if ψ contains $\exp(-\beta x^2/2)$, it will have the correct asymptotic behavior if no other term is present that dominates at large $|x|$. Therefore,

$$\psi(x) = q(x)\exp(-\beta x^2/2) \tag{3-24}$$

and it remains to find the function $q(x)$.

C. *The Differential Equation for $q(x)$*

Substituting Eq. (3-24) into the Schrödinger equation (3-18) gives

$$\exp(-\beta x^2/2)\left[-\beta q(x) - 2\beta x\frac{dq(x)}{dx} + \frac{d^2q(x)}{dx^2} + \alpha q(x)\right] = 0 \tag{3-25}$$

This equation is satisfied only if the term in brackets is zero:

$$\frac{d^2q(x)}{dx^2} - 2\beta x\frac{dq(x)}{dx} + (\alpha - \beta)q(x) = 0 \tag{3-26}$$

Thus, we have a differential equation for $q(x)$.

At this point it is convenient to transform variables to put the equation into a simpler form. Let

$$y = \sqrt{\beta}x \tag{3-27}$$

Then

$$d/dy = d/d(\sqrt{\beta}x) = (1/\sqrt{\beta})\,d/dx \tag{3-28}$$

so that

$$d/dx = \sqrt{\beta}\,d/dy \tag{3-29}$$

Similarly

$$d^2/dx^2 = \beta\,d^2/dy^2 \tag{3-30}$$

and

$$x = y/\sqrt{\beta} \tag{3-31}$$

Substituting Eqs. (3-29)–(3-31) into (3-26), and defining $f(y)$ as

$$f(y) \equiv f(\sqrt{\beta}x) = q(x) \tag{3-32}$$

we obtain (after dividing by β)

$$\frac{d^2f(y)}{dy^2} - 2y\frac{df(y)}{dy} + [(\alpha/\beta) - 1]f(y) = 0 \tag{3-33}$$

D. *Representing f as a Power Series*

Now $f(y)$ is some function of y that must be single valued, continuous, and smooth (i.e., have a continuous first derivative), if ψ is to be properly behaved. Can we think of any functions which satisfy these properties? Of course, we can think of a limitless number of them. For example, 1, y, y^2, y^3, y^4, etc., are all single valued, continuous, and have continuous derivatives, and so is any linear combination of such functions (e.g., $4y^3 - y + 3$). Other examples are $\sin(y)$ and $\exp(y)$. These functions can be expressed as infinite sums of powers of y, however, and so they are included, in principle in the first example. Thus

$$\sin(y) = y - y^3/3! + y^5/5! - y^7/7! + \cdots \tag{3-34}$$

and

$$\exp(y) = \sum_{n=0}^{\infty} y^n/n! \tag{3-35}$$

that is, $\sin(y)$ and the set of all positive powers of y are *linearly dependent*. Because the powers of y can be combined linearly to reproduce certain other functions, the powers of y are called a *complete set* of functions. However, we must exercise some care with the concept of completeness. The positive powers of y cannot be used to reproduce a discontinuous function, or a function with discontinuous derivatives. Hence, there are certain restrictions on the nature of functions $g(y)$, which satisfy the relation

$$g(y) = \sum_{n=0}^{\infty} c_n y^n \tag{3-36}$$

These restrictions define a class of functions, and the *powers of y are a complete set only within this class*. The positive powers of y, then, form a complete set, but if we remove one of the members of the set, say 1 (the zero power of y), then the set is no longer complete. This means that the remaining members of the set cannot compensate for the role played by the missing member. In other words, the missing member cannot be expressed as a linear combination of the remaining members. In this example

$$1 \neq \sum_{n=1}^{\infty} c_n y^n \tag{3-37}$$

This is easily demonstrated to be true since the left-hand side of Eq. (3-37) is unity whereas the right-hand side must be zero when $y = 0$ for any choice of coefficients. Thus, the powers of y are *linearly independent* functions (no one of them can be expressed as a linear combination of all the others).

The function $f(y)$ involved in ψ should be a member of the class of functions for which the powers of y form a complete set. Therefore, we may write

$$f(y) = \sum_{n=0}^{\infty} c_n y^n \tag{3-38}$$

and seek an expression for the unknown multipliers c_n.

E. *Establishing a Recursion Relation for f*

Notice that if

$$f(y) = c_0 + c_1 y + c_2 y^2 + c_3 y^3 + c_4 y^4 + \cdots \tag{3-39}$$

then

$$df(y)/dy = c_1 + 2c_2 y + 3c_3 y^2 + 4c_4 y^3 + \cdots \tag{3-40}$$

and

$$d^2 f(y)/dy^2 = 2c_2 + 2\cdot 3y + 3\cdot 4y^2 + \cdots \tag{3-41}$$

Thus, substituting Eq. (3-38) into (3-33) gives

$$\begin{aligned} 1\cdot 2c_2 + 2\cdot 3c_3 y + 3\cdot 4c_4 y^2 + \cdots - 2c_1 y - 2\cdot 2c_2 y^2 - 2\cdot 3c_3 y^3 - \cdots \\ + [(\alpha/\beta) - 1]c_0 + [(\alpha/\beta) - 1]c_1 y + [(\alpha/\beta) - 1]c_2 y^2 + \cdots = 0 \end{aligned} \tag{3-42}$$

Now we will take advantage of the fact that the various powers of x form a linearly independent set. Equation (3-42) states that the expression on the LHS equals zero for all values of y. There are two ways this might happen. One of these is that minus the constant part of the expression is always exactly equal to the y-dependent part, no matter what the value of y. This would require a relationship like Eq. (3-37) (except with an equality), which we have seen is not possible for independent functions. The remaining possibility is that the various independent parts of Eq. (3-42) are individually equal to zero—the constant is zero, the coefficient for y is zero, etc. This gives us a whole set of equations. Setting the constant term equal to zero gives

$$2c_2 + [(\alpha/\beta) - 1]c_0 = 0 \cdots \qquad m = 0 \tag{3-43}$$

Setting the coefficient for the first power of y to zero gives

$$2\cdot 3c_3 - 2c_1 + [(\alpha/\beta) - 1]c_1 = 0 \cdots \qquad m = 1 \tag{3-44}$$

The y^2 term gives

$$3\cdot 4c_4 - 2\cdot 2c_2 + [(\alpha/\beta) - 1]c_2 = 0 \cdots \qquad m = 2 \tag{3-45}$$

By inspecting this series, we can arrive at the general result

$$(m + 1)(m + 2)c_{m+2} + [(\alpha/\beta) - 1 - 2m]c_m = 0 \tag{3-46}$$

or

$$c_{m+2} = \frac{-[(\alpha/\beta) - 2m - 1]}{(m + 1)(m + 2)}\, c_m \tag{3-47}$$

Equation (3-47) is called a *recursion relation*. If we knew c_0, we could produce c_2, c_4, c_6, etc., by continued application of Eq. (3-47). Similarly, knowledge of c_1 would lead to c_3, c_5, etc. Thus, it appears that the coefficients for even powers of x and those for odd powers of x form separate sets. Choosing c_0 determines one set, and choosing c_1 determines the other, and the choices for c_0 and c_1 seem independent. This separation into two sets is reasonable when we recall that our final solutions must be symmetric or antisymmetric in x. The asymptotic part of ψ, $\exp(-\beta x^2/2)$, is symmetric about $x = 0$, and so we expect the remainder of ψ, $f(y)$, to be either symmetric (even powers of $y = \sqrt{\beta}x$) or antisymmetric (odd powers). Thus, we can anticipate that some of our solutions will have $c_0 \neq 0$, $c_2 \neq 0$, $c_4 \neq 0, \ldots$ and $c_1 = c_3 = c_5 = \cdots = 0$. This will produce, by Eq. (3-47), symmetric solutions. The remaining solutions will have $c_0 = c_2 = c_4 = \cdots = 0$ and $c_1 \neq 0$, $c_3 \neq 0, \ldots$, and be antisymmetric.

F. *Preventing f(y) from Dominating the Asymptotic Behavior*

We now examine the asymptotic behavior of $f(y)$. Recall that, at very large values of $|y|$, $f(y)$ must become insignificant compared to $\exp(-\beta x^2/2) = \exp(-y^2/2)$. We will show that $f(y)$ fails to have this behavior if its power series expression is infinitely long.

We know that the series expression for $\exp(y^2)$ is

$$\exp(y^2) = 1 + y^2 + \frac{y^4}{2!} + \frac{y^6}{3!} + \cdots + \frac{y^n}{(n/2)!} + \frac{y^{n+2}}{[(n/2)+1]!} + \cdots \tag{3-48}$$

The series for $f(y)$ has terms

$$\cdots + c_n y^n + c_{n+2} y^{n+2} + c_{n+4} y^{n+4} + \cdots \tag{3-49}$$

The ratio between coefficients for two adjacent terms high up in the series (large n) is for $\exp(y^2)$, from Eq. (3-48)

$$\frac{\text{coeff for } y^{n+2}}{\text{coeff for } y^n} = \frac{(n/2)!}{[(n/2)+1]!} = \frac{1}{(n/2)+1} \xrightarrow{\text{large } n} \frac{2}{n} \tag{3-50}$$

and for $f(y)$ it is, from Eqs. (3-49) and (3-47),

$$\frac{\text{coeff for } y^{n+2}}{\text{coeff for } y^n} = \frac{c_{n+2}}{c_n} = \frac{-(\alpha/\beta) + 1 + 2n}{n^2 + 3n + 2} \xrightarrow{\text{large } n} \frac{2}{n} \tag{3-51}$$

This means that, at large values of y, when the higher-order terms in the series dominate, $f(y)$ behaves like $\exp(y^2)$. Then

$$\lim_{y\to\infty} \psi(y) = \lim_{y\to\infty} f(y)\exp(-y^2/2) = \exp(y^2/2) \to \infty \tag{3-52}$$

The asymptotic behavior of ψ is ruined. We can overcome this problem by requiring the series for $f(y)$ to terminate at some finite power: $f(y)$ must be a polynomial. This condition is automatically fulfilled if any one of the coefficients in a given series (odd or even) is zero since Eq. (3-47) guarantees that all the higher coefficients in that series will then vanish. Therefore, we require that some coefficient vanish:

$$c_{n+2} = 0 \tag{3-53}$$

Assuming that this is the lowest zero coefficient (i.e., $c_n \neq 0$), Eq. (3-47) gives

$$(\alpha/\beta) - 2n - 1 = 0 \tag{3-54}$$

or

$$\alpha = \beta(2n + 1) \tag{3-55}$$

G. *The Nature of the Energy Spectrum*

Now we have a recipe for producing acceptable solutions for the Schrödinger equation for the harmonic oscillator. If we desire a symmetric solution, we set $c_1 = 0$ and $c_0 = 1$. If we want the polynomial to terminate at y^n, we require that α and β be related as in Eq. (3-55). In this way we can generate an unlimited number of symmetric solutions. Similarly, an unlimited set of antisymmetric solutions results from setting $c_0 = 0$ and $c_1 = 1$ and allowing n to take on various odd integer values.

Since we now know that an acceptable solution satisfies Eq. (3-55), we can examine the energy spectrum. Substituting into Eq. (3-55) the expressions for α and β [Eqs. (3-16) and (3-17)], we obtain

$$8\pi^2 mE/h^2 = (2\pi\sqrt{mk}/h)(2n + 1) \tag{3-56}$$

or

$$E = h(n + \tfrac{1}{2})(1/2\pi)\sqrt{k/m} = (n + \tfrac{1}{2})h\nu \tag{3-57}$$

where the classical definition of ν [Eq. (3-7)] has been used.

This result shows that, whenever n increases by unity, the energy increases by $h\nu$, so the energy levels are evenly spaced as shown in Fig. 3-2. At absolute zero, the system will lose its energy to its surroundings insofar as possible. However, since $n = 0$ in the lowest permissible state for the system, there will remain a zero-point energy of $\frac{1}{2}h\nu$.

H. *Nature of the Wavefunctions*

The lowest energy solution corresponds to $n = 0$. This means that c_0 is the highest nonzero coefficient in the power series expansion for $f(y)$. Hence, we must set $c_1 = c_2 = 0$. Thus, for $n = 0$, we can write the unnormalized wavefunction as [from Eq. (3-24)]

$$\psi_0 = c_0 \exp(-y^2/2) = c_0 \exp(-\beta x^2/2) \tag{3-58}$$

This is just a constant times a Gauss error function or simple "gaussian-type" function. This wavefunction is sketched in Fig. 3-2 and is obviously symmetric.

The next solution has $n = 1$, $c_1 \neq 0$ but $c_3 = c_5 = \cdots = 0$. (The even-powered series coefficients are all zero for this case.) The unnormalized wavefunction for $n = 1$ is then

$$\psi_1(y) = c_1 y \exp(-y^2/2) \tag{3-59}$$

The exponential is symmetric and y is antisymmetric, and so their product, $\psi_1(y)$, is antisymmetric (Fig. 3-2).

To get ψ_2 we need to use the recursion relation (3-47). We know that odd-index coefficients are all zero and that only c_0 and c_2 of the even-index coefficients are nonzero. Assuming $c_0 = 1$, we have (using (Eq. 3-47) with $m = 0$)

$$c_2 = \frac{-[(\alpha/\beta) - 2\cdot 0 - 1]}{(1)(2)} = -\frac{(\alpha/\beta) - 1}{2} \tag{3-60}$$

But the ratio α/β is determined by the requirement that $c_4 = 0$. Referring to Eq. (3-55), this gives (for $n = 2$) $\alpha/\beta = 5$, and so

$$c_2 = -4/2 = -2 \tag{3-61}$$

and the unnormalized wavefunction is

$$\psi_2(y) = (1 - 2y^2)\exp(-y^2/2) \tag{3-62}$$

These polynomials, which are solutions to the differential equation (3-33), are known as Hermite (Her·*meet*) polynomials, $H_n(y)$. In addition to the recursion relation (3-47), which we have derived, other definitions are known. One of these involves successive differentiation:

$$H_n(y) = (-1)^n \exp(y^2)\,\frac{d^n \exp(-y^2)}{dy^n} \tag{3-63}$$

Thus, if we want $H_2(y)$, we just set $n = 2$ in Eq. (3-63) and evaluate that expression to get

$$H_2(y) = 4y^2 - 2 \tag{3-64}$$

which differs from our earlier result by a factor of -2. Yet another means of producing Hermite polynomials is by using the generating function

$$G(y, u) = \exp[y^2 - (u - y)^2] \equiv \sum_{n=0}^{\infty} (H_n(y)/n!)u^n \tag{3-65}$$

We use this expression as follows:

(1) Express the exponential in terms of its power series, writing down a few of the leading terms. There will exist, then, various powers of u and y and factorial coefficients.

(2) Collect together all the terms containing u^2.
(3) The coefficient for this term will be equal to $H_2(y)/2!$.

This is a fairly clumsy procedure for producing polynomials, but Eq. (3-65) is useful in determining general mathematical properties of these polynomials. For instance, Eq. (3-65) will be used in showing that the harmonic oscillator wavefunctions are orthogonal.

I. *Orthogonality and Normalization*

We will now show that the harmonic oscillator wavefunctions are orthogonal, i.e., that

$$\int_{-\infty}^{+\infty} \psi_n(y)\psi_m(y)\, dy = \int_{-\infty}^{+\infty} H_n(y)H_m(y) \exp(-y^2)\, dy = 0 \cdots \qquad n \neq m \tag{3-66}$$

Consider the integral involving two generating functions and the exponential of y^2:

$$\int_{-\infty}^{+\infty} G(y, u)G(y, v) \exp(-y^2)\, dy = \sum_n \sum_m u^n v^m \underbrace{\int_{-\infty}^{+\infty} \frac{H_n(y)H_m(y)}{n!m!} \exp(-y^2)\, dy}_{c_{nm}} \tag{3-67}$$

where we label the integral c_{nm} for convenience. The left-hand side of Eq. (3-67) may also be written as [using Eq. (3-65)]

$$\int_{-\infty}^{+\infty} \exp[-(y - u - v)^2] \exp(2uv)\, dy = \exp(2uv) \int_{-\infty}^{+\infty} \exp[-(y - u - v)^2]\, dy \tag{3-68}$$

However, we can add constants to the differential element without affecting the integral value, and u and v are constants when only y varies. Therefore, (3-68) becomes (see Appendix 1 for a table of useful integrals)

$$\begin{aligned} \exp(2uv) \int_{-\infty}^{+\infty} \exp[-(y - u - v)^2]\, d(y - u - v) &= \exp(2uv)\sqrt{\pi} \\ &= \sqrt{\pi}\{1 + 2uv + 4u^2v^2/2! + 8u^3v^3/3! + \cdots + 2^n u^n v^n/n! + \cdots\} \end{aligned} \tag{3-69}$$

This expression is equal to the right-hand side of Eq. (3-67). Comparing Eq. (3-67) with (3-69), we see that $c_{11} = 2\sqrt{\pi}$ since the term u^1v^1 is multiplied by $2\sqrt{\pi}$ in Eq. (3-69) and by c_{11} in Eq. (3-67). Similarly $c_{22} = 4\sqrt{\pi}/2!$. But $c_{12} = 0$. Hence, we arrive at the result

$$c_{nm} = \int_{-\infty}^{+\infty} \frac{H_n(y)H_m(y)}{n!m!} \exp(-y^2)\, dy = \sqrt{\pi}(2^n/n!)\, \delta_{n,m} \tag{3-70}$$

($\delta_{n,m}$ is the "Kronecker" delta. It is a discontinuous function having a value of unity when $n = m$ but zero when $n \neq m$.) So

$$\int_{-\infty}^{+\infty} \psi_n(y)\psi_m(y)\, dy = \sqrt{\pi} m!\, 2^n\, \delta_{n,m} \tag{3-71}$$

This proves the wavefunctions to be orthogonal and also provides us with a normalizing factor. Normality refers to integration in x, rather than in $y = \sqrt{\beta}x$, so we must change the differential element in Eq. (3-71):

$$\int_{-\infty}^{+\infty} \psi_n^2(y)\, dy = \sqrt{\beta} \int_{-\infty}^{+\infty} \psi_n^2(y)\, dx = \sqrt{\pi} n!\, 2^n \tag{3-72}$$

Requiring that $\int_{-\infty}^{+\infty} \psi_n^2(y)\, dx = 1$ leads to the expression for the normalized wavefunctions:

$$\psi_n(y) = (\sqrt{\beta/\pi}\; 1/2^n n!)^{1/2} H_n(y) \exp(-y^2/2) \cdots y = \sqrt{\beta}x, \qquad n = 0, 1, 2, \ldots \tag{3-73}$$

The first members of the set of Hermite polynomials are

$$H_0(y) = 1, \quad H_1(y) = 2y, \quad H_2(y) = 4y^2 - 2, \quad H_3(y) = 8y^3 - 12y$$
$$H_4(y) = 16y^4 - 48y^2 + 12, \quad H_5(y) = 32y^5 + 160y^3 + 120y \tag{3-74}$$

J. Summary of Solution of Harmonic-Oscillator Schrödinger Equation

The detailed solution is so long that the reader may have lost the broad outline.

The basic steps were:

(1) Determine the asymptotic behavior of the Schrödinger equation and of ψ. This produces a gaussian factor $\exp(-y^2/2)$ times a function of y, $f(y)$.

(2) Obtain a differential equation for the rest of the wavefunction, $f(y)$.

(3) Represent $f(y)$ as a power series in y, and find a recursion relation for the coefficients in the series. The symmetries of the wavefunctions are linked to the symmetries of the series.

(4) Force the power series to be finite (i.e., polynomials) so as not to spoil the asymptotic behavior of the wavefunctions. This leads to a relation between α and β that produces uniformly spaced, quantized energy levels.

(5) Recognize the polynomials as being Hermite polynomials, and utilize some of the known properties of these functions to establish orthogonality and normalization constants for the wavefunctions.

3-5 Quantum-Mechanical Average Value of the Potential Energy

We showed in Section 3-2 that the classical harmonic oscillator stores, on the average, half of its energy as kinetic energy, and half as potential. We now make the analogous comparison in the quantum-mechanical system for the ground ($n = 0$) state.

The wavefunction is

$$\psi_0(x) = (\beta/\pi)^{1/4} \exp(-\beta x^2/2) \tag{3-75}$$

and the distribution of the particle along the x coordinate is given by $\psi_0^2(x)$. The total energy is constant and equal to

$$E_0 = \tfrac{1}{2}h\nu = (h/4\pi)\sqrt{k/m} \tag{3-76}$$

and the potential energy as a function of x is

$$V(x) = \tfrac{1}{2}kx^2 \tag{3-77}$$

The fraction of time that the oscillating particle spends in the line element dx around some point x_1 is $\psi_0^2(x_1)\,dx$, since ψ_0 of Eq. (3-75) is normalized. Hence, the average value for the potential energy is just the sum of all the potential energies due to all the elements dx, each weighted by the fraction of time the particle is in dx:

$$\overline{V} = \int_{-\infty}^{+\infty} \psi_0^2(x)V(x)\,dx \tag{3-78}$$

This is

$$\overline{V} = (\beta/\pi)^{1/2}\cdot\tfrac{1}{2}k\int_{-\infty}^{+\infty} \exp(-\beta x^2)x^2\,dx = \sqrt{\beta/\pi}\cdot\tfrac{1}{2}k\cdot\tfrac{1}{2}\sqrt{\pi/\beta^3} \tag{3-79}$$

where we have referred to Appendix 1 to evaluate the integral. Using the definition of β^2 (Eq. 3-17) we have

$$\overline{V} = k/4\beta = (k/4)\cdot h/2\pi\sqrt{mk} = (h/8\pi)\sqrt{k/m} \tag{3-80}$$

which is just one half of the total energy [Eq. (3-76)]. We thus arrive at the important result that the ratio of average potential and kinetic energies is the same in the classical harmonic oscillator and the ground state of the quantum-mechanical system. This result is also true for the higher states. For other kinds of potential, the storage need not be half and half, but whatever it is, it will be the same for the classical and quantum-mechanical treatments of the system. We discuss this point in more detail later when we examine the virial theorem (Chapter 11 and Appendix 8).

PROBLEMS

3-1 From the equation of motion (3-5) show that the classical distribution function is proportional to $(1 - x^2/L^2)^{-1/2}$.

3-2 Use the differential expression (3-63) for Hermite polynomials to produce $H_2(y)$.

3-3 Use the generating function (3-65) to produce $H_2(y)$.

3-4 Give a simple reason why $(2 + y - 3y^2)\exp(-y^2/2)$ cannot be a satisfactory wavefunction for the harmonic oscillator. What about $2y\exp(+y^2/2)$? You should be able to answer by inspection, without calculation and without reference to tabulations.

3-5 Write down the Schrödinger equation for a three-dimensional (isotropic) harmonic oscillator. Separate variables. What will be the zero-point energy for this system? What will be the degeneracy of the energy level having a value of $(\frac{9}{2})h\nu$? $(\frac{5}{2})h\nu$? Sketch (roughly) each of the solutions for the latter case and note their similarity to Case (b) in Fig. 2-16.

3-6 Suppose $V(x) = \frac{1}{2}kx^2$ for $x \geq 0$, and ∞ for $x < 0$. What can you say about the eigenfunctions and eigenvalues for this system?

CHAPTER 4

THE HYDROGENLIKE ION

4-1 The Schrödinger Equation and the Nature of Its Solutions

A. The Schrödinger Equation

Consider the two-particle system composed of an electron (charge $-e$) and a nucleus having atomic number Z and charge Ze. (See Appendix 12 for values of physical constants, such as e.) Let x_1, y_1, z_1 be the coordinates of the nucleus and x_2, y_2, z_2 be those for the electron. The distance between the particles is, then, $[(x_1 - x_2)^2 + (y_1 - y_2)^2 + (z_1 - z_2)^2]^{1/2}$. The potential energy is given by the product of the charges divided by the distance between them:

$$V = \frac{-Ze^2}{[(x_1 - x_2)^2 + (y_1 - y_2)^2 + (z_1 - z_2)^2]^{1/2}} \tag{4-1}$$

The time-independent Schrödinger equation for this system is

$$\begin{aligned}\Bigg[\frac{-h^2}{8\pi^2 M}\left(\frac{\partial^2}{\partial x_1{}^2} + \frac{\partial^2}{\partial y_1{}^2} + \frac{\partial^2}{\partial z_1{}^2}\right) - \frac{h^2}{8\pi^2 m_e}\left(\frac{\partial^2}{\partial x_2{}^2} + \frac{\partial^2}{\partial y_2{}^2} + \frac{\partial^2}{\partial z_2{}^2}\right)& \\ - \frac{Ze^2}{[(x_1 - x_2)^2 + (y_1 - y_2)^2 + (z_1 - z_2)^2]^{1/2}}\Bigg]\psi(x_1, y_1, z_1, x_2, y_2, z_2)& \\ = E\psi(x_1, y_1, z_1, x_2, y_2, z_2)&\end{aligned} \tag{4-2}$$

where M and m_e are the masses of the nucleus and electron, respectively. The hamiltonian operator in brackets in Eq. (4-2) has three terms, corresponding to a kinetic energy operator for the nucleus, a kinetic energy operator for the electron, and a potential term for the pair of particles.

Equation (4-2) has eigenfunctions ψ that are dependent on the positions of both the electron and the nucleus. It is possible to convert to center-of-mass coordinates and then to separate Eq. (4-2) into two equations, one for the motion of the center of mass and *one for a particle of reduced mass moving around a fixed center to which it is attracted in exactly the same way the electron is attracted to the nucleus*. Because this conversion is rather tedious, we will not perform it in this book,[1] but merely discuss the results. The first of the two resulting equations treats the center of mass as a free particle moving through field-free space; its eigenvalues are simply *translational* energies of the ion. For us, the interesting equation is the second one, which is

$$\left\{\frac{-h^2}{8\pi^2\mu}\left(\frac{\partial^2}{\partial x^2}+\frac{\partial^2}{\partial y^2}+\frac{\partial^2}{\partial z^2}\right)-\frac{Ze^2}{(x^2+y^2+z^2)^{1/2}}\right\}\psi(x, y, z) = E\psi(x, y, z) \tag{4-3}$$

The quantity μ is the *reduced mass* for the particle in our center-of-mass system, and is given by

$$\mu = m_e M/(m_e + M) \tag{4-4}$$

The coordinates x, y, and z are the coordinates of the reduced-mass particle *with respect to the center of mass of the system.*

Even without going through the detailed procedure of converting to center-of-mass coordinates, we can show that Eq. (4-3) makes sense. In the idealized case in which M is infinitely greater than m_e, μ equals m_e, and Eq. (4-3) becomes just the Schrödinger equation for the motion of an electron about a *fixed* nucleus at the coordinate origin. This would not be a bad approximation because, even in the case of the lightest nucleus (i.e., the hydrogen atom), M is nearly 2000 times m_e, and so μ is very close to m_e, and the center of mass is very near the nucleus. Therefore, the result of using center-of-mass coordinates to separate the Schrödinger equation is almost identical to making the assumption at the outset that the nucleus is fixed, and simply writing down the one-particle Schrödinger equation:

$$\left\{\frac{-h^2}{8\pi^2 m_e}\left(\frac{\partial^2}{\partial x^2}+\frac{\partial^2}{\partial y^2}+\frac{\partial^2}{\partial z^2}\right)-\frac{Ze^2}{(x^2+y^2+z^2)^{1/2}}\right\}\psi(x, y, z) = E\psi(x, y, z) \tag{4-5}$$

The use of m_e instead of μ [i.e., Eq. (4-5) instead of (4-3)] has no effect on the qualitative nature of the solutions. However, it does produce small errors in eigenvalues—errors that are significant in the very precise measurements and calculations of atomic spectroscopy (Problem 4-1). In what follows we shall use μ, but for purposes of discussion we will pretend that the nucleus and center of mass coincide.

Equation (4-3) can be transformed into spherical polar coordinates. (Some important relationships between spherical polar and cartesian coordinates are given in Fig. 4-1.) The result is

$$[(-h^2/8\pi^2\mu)\nabla^2 - (Ze^2/r)]\psi(r, \theta, \phi) = E\psi(r, \theta, \phi) \tag{4-6}$$

[1] See, for example, Eyring *et al.* [1, Chapter VI] or Levine [2, pp. 90–95].

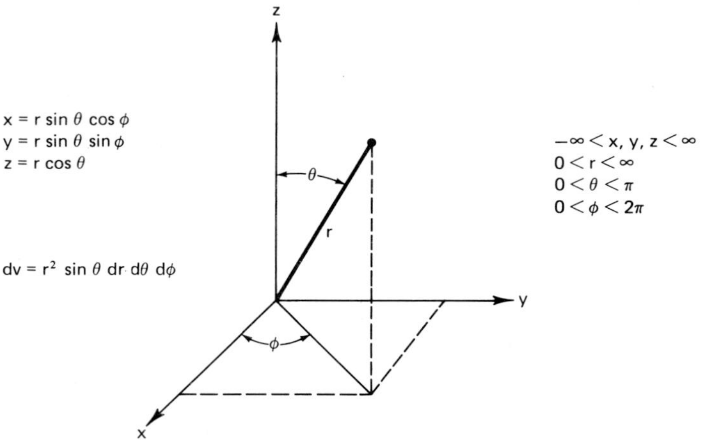

FIG. 4-1 The spherical polar coordinate system. The angle ϕ is called the azimuthal angle. Notice that the differential volume element is *not* equal to $dr\, d\theta\, d\phi$ and that the ranges of values for r, θ, ϕ are *not* $-\infty$ to $+\infty$.

Here ∇^2 is understood to be in spherical polar coordinates. In these coordinates it looks quite complicated[2]:

$$\nabla^2 = \frac{1}{r^2}\frac{\partial}{\partial r}\left(r^2\frac{\partial}{\partial r}\right) + \frac{1}{r^2 \sin\theta}\frac{\partial}{\partial\theta}\left(\sin\theta\frac{\partial}{\partial\theta}\right) + \frac{1}{r^2\sin^2\theta}\frac{\partial^2}{\partial\phi^2} \tag{4-7}$$

However, this coordinate system is the natural one for this system and leads to the easiest solution despite this rather formidable looking operator.

Notice that the potential term, $-Ze^2/r$, has no θ or ϕ dependence. The potential is *spherically symmetric.* However, θ and ϕ dependence does enter the hamiltonian through ∇^2, so the eigenfunctions ψ may be expected to show angular dependence.

Next we describe the solutions of the Schrödinger equation (4-6), relegating to later sections the mathematical details of how the solutions are obtained.

B. *The Nature of the Eigenvalues*

The potential energy, $-Ze^2/r$, becomes negatively infinite when $r = 0$ and approaches zero as r becomes very large. A cross-sectional view of this potential is sketched in Fig. 4-2 for the case in which $Z = 1$. We expect the energy levels to diverge less rapidly here than was the case for the harmonic oscillator since the "effective box size" increases more rapidly with increasing energy in this case than in the harmonic oscillator case. (See Fig. 2-3 for the one-dimensional analogs.) Since the harmonic oscillator levels are separated by a *constant* ($h\nu$, for one- *or* three-dimensional cases), the hydrogenlike ion

[2] See, e.g., Eyring *et al.* [1, Appendix III].

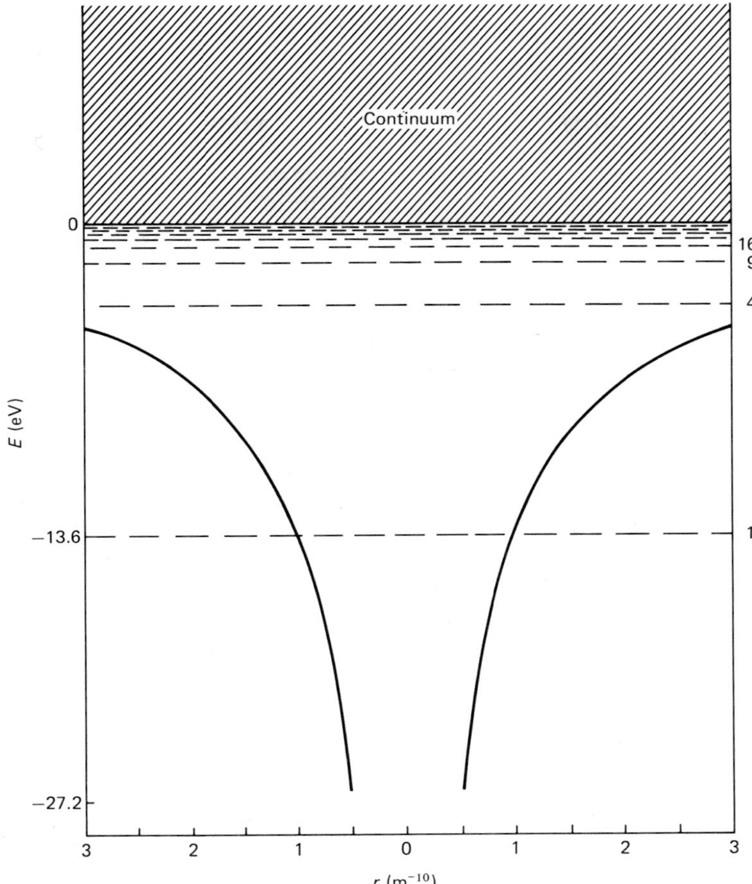

FIG. 4-2 A cross section of the potential function $V = -e^2/r$ with eigenvalues superimposed (dashed lines). Degeneracies for the first few levels are noted on the right. (Note that we have plotted r in two directions, putting the nuclear position in the middle of the plot rather than at one side. This is a little inelegant, but seems more natural to chemists.)

levels should *converge* at higher energies. Figure 4-2 shows that this is indeed the case. Furthermore, by analogy with the case of the particle in a box with one finite wall, we expect the allowed energies to form a discrete set for the classically trapped electron ($E < 0$) and a continuum for the unbound cases ($E > 0$). Thus, the spectrum of eigenvalues sketched in Fig. 4-2 is in qualitative accord with understandings developed earlier.

The lowest allowed energy for the system is far above the bottom of the potential well. This corresponds to the finite zero point energy which we have seen in other systems where particle motion is constrained. Here it means that, at absolute zero, the electron does not fall into the nucleus, but rather continues to move about with a finite total energy.

All of the energy levels of Fig. 4-2 are degenerate except for the lowest one. The order of the degeneracy is listed next to each of the lowest few levels in Fig. 4-2. This degeneracy is not surprising since we are dealing here with a three-dimensional system, and we have earlier seen that, in such cases (e.g., the cubic box), the physical equivalence of different directions in space can produce degeneracies (called "spatial degeneracies"). We shall see later that some of the degeneracies in this system *are* a result of directional equivalence (here, spherical symmetry), whereas others are not.

The discrete, negative eigenvalues are given by the formula

$$E_n = -2\pi^2 \mu Z^2 e^4 / h^2 n^2, \qquad n = 1, 2, 3, \ldots \tag{4-8}$$

C. *The Lowest-Energy Wavefunction*

We will now discuss the lowest-energy eigenfunction of Eq. (4-6) in some detail, since an understanding of atomic wavefunctions is crucial in quantum chemistry. The derivation of formulas for this and other wavefunctions will be discussed in later sections, but it is not necessary to labor through the mathematical details of the exact solution of Eq. (4-6) to be able to understand most of the essential features of the eigenfunctions.

The formula for the normalized, lowest-energy solution of Eq. (4-6) is

$$\psi(r) = (1/\sqrt{\pi})(Z/a_0)^{3/2} \exp(-Zr/a_0) \tag{4-9}$$

where $a_0 = 5.2917706 \times 10^{-11}\, m$ (called the "Bohr radius") and Ze is the nuclear charge. A sketch of ψ versus r for $Z = 1$ is superimposed on the potential function in Fig. 4-3a. It is apparent that the electron penetrates the potential barrier (Problem 4-1).

The square of the wavefunction (4-9) tells us how the electron is distributed about the nucleus. In Fig. 4-3b is plotted $\psi^2(r)$ as a function of r. We refer to ψ^2 as the *electron probability density function.* In this case, the probability density is greatest at the nucleus ($r = 0$) and decays to zero as r becomes infinite.

It is important for the chemist to be able to visualize the electron distributions, or charge "clouds," in atoms and molecules, and various methods of depicting electronic distributions have been devised. In Fig. 4-3 a few of these are presented for the lowest-energy wavefunction. The dot picture (Fig. 4-3c) represents what one would expect if one took a multiflash photograph of a magnified, slowed-down hydrogenlike ion (assuming no disturbance of the ion by the photographing process). Each dot represents an instantaneous electron position, and the density of these dots is greatest at the nucleus. An alternative way of picturing the charge is to draw a contour diagram, each contour indicating that the density has increased or decreased by a certain amount (Fig. 4-3d). Even simpler is to sketch a surface that follows a contour and encloses a certain

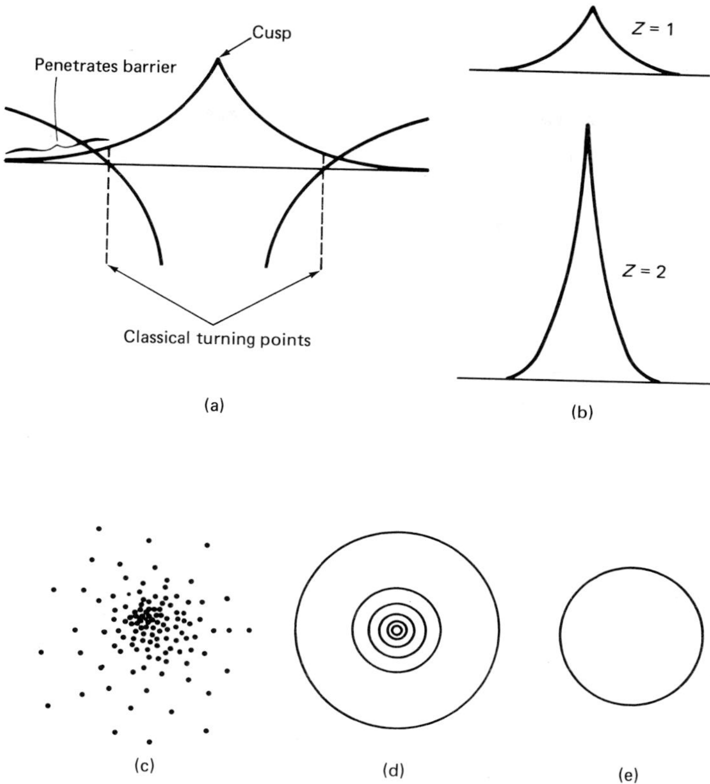

FIG. 4-3 (a) H-atom wavefunction superposed on $-e^2/r$ potential curve. (b) Wavefunction squared for H and He^+. (c) Dot picture of electronic distribution. (d) Contour diagram of electron distribution. (e) Sphere model of electron distribution.

amount (say 90%) of the charge (Fig. 4-3e). (We have been describing the electron as a point charge moving rapidly about the nucleus. However, for most purposes it is just as convenient to picture the electron as being smeared out into a charge cloud like those sketched in Fig. 4-3. Thus, the statements "the electron spends 90% of its time inside this surface," and "90% of the electronic charge is contained within this surface," are equivalent.)

The multiflash "photograph" sketched in Fig. 4-3c shows the electron probability density to be greatest at the nucleus. Suppose that we were just to take a single flash photograph. Then the electron would appear as a single dot. At what distance from the nucleus would this dot be most likely to occur? The answer is not zero. Although the *probability density* is a maximum at $r = 0$, the *probability* for finding the electron in a volume element at the nucleus approaches zero. This is because the probability density is the measure of the probability *per unit volume* for the electron being at various distances from the nucleus. When we compare a tiny volume element near the nucleus with an identical one farther out, we see from Fig. 4-3 that there is indeed more likelihood for the electron being in the volume element nearer the nucleus. *But there are more volume elements associated with the larger distance.* (The number of *identical* volume elements varies as the area of the surface of the sphere, $4\pi r^2$.) Hence, the probability for the electron being in a radial element dr at a given *distance* r from the nucleus is given by the number of volume elements at r times the probability density per unit volume element. The reason for the near-zero probability for finding the electron in a volume element at the nucleus is that the number of volume elements associated with $r = 0$ is vanishingly small compared to the number associated with larger r values. Figure 4-4 is a graph of $4\pi r^2\psi^2$, the *volume-weighted probability density*. It is apparent that the *most probable* value of r, r_{mp}, occurs at a nonzero distance from the nucleus. [The reader is familiar with analogous distinctions. Rhode Island has a higher *population density* than Texas, but the population of Texas (density times area) is greater. Again, matter in the universe has a much higher *mass density* in stars and planets than in intergalactic gas or dust, but the total *mass* of the latter far exceeds that of the former due to the much greater volume of "empty" space.]

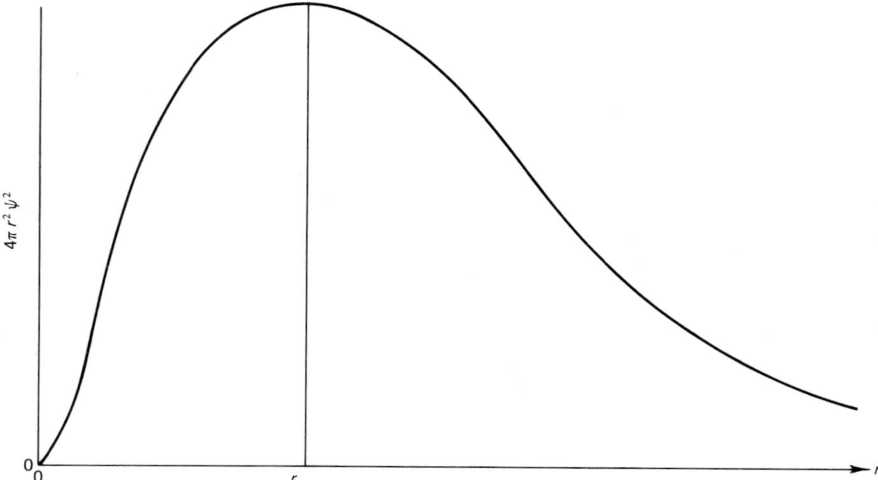

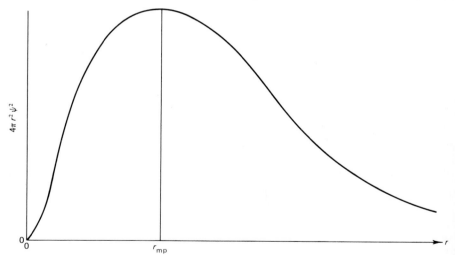

FIG. 4-4 The volume-weighted probability density for the lowest-energy eigenfunction of the hydrogenlike ion. The most probable value of r occurs at r_{mp}.

We can calculate the value of r_{mp} by finding which r value gives the maximum value of $4\pi r^2\psi^2$. Recall that we can do this by finding the value of r that causes the first derivative of $4\pi r^2\psi^2$ to vanish, that is, we require

$$(d/dr)[4\pi r^2 \pi^{-1}(Z/a_0)^3 \exp(-2Zr/a_0)] = 0 \qquad (4\text{-}10)$$

This gives

$$\text{constants} \cdot [2r - (2Zr^2/a_0)] \exp(-2Zr/a_0) = 0 \tag{4-11}$$

The term in brackets vanishes when $r = a_0/Z$, and this is the value of r_{mp}. For $Z = 1$, $r_{\text{mp}} = a_0$; a_0 is the most probable distance of the electron from the nucleus in the hydrogen atom. For the He^+ion ($Z = 2$), the most probable distance is only half as great, consistent with a more contracted charge cloud.

Of more interest, often, is the *average value* of the distance of the electron from the nucleus. If we could sample the instantaneous distance of the electron from the nucleus a large number of times and calculate the average value, what sort of result would we obtain? The probability for finding the electron at any given distance r is given by the volume-weighted probability density of Fig. 4-4. Inspection of that figure suggests that the average value of the position of the electron $\bar{r}$ is greater than r_{mp}, the most probable value. But exactly how much bigger is $\bar{r}$ than r_{mp}? How should we compute the average value? The reader is familiar with the way an average test score is calculated from a collection of scores. For example, suppose the series of scores to be averaged is 0, 2, 6, 6, 7, 7, 7, 10, and that 0 and 10 are the minimum and maximum possible scores. The average is given by

$$\text{average} = \frac{\text{sum of scores}}{\text{number of scores}} = \frac{0 + 2 + 6 + 6 + 7 + 7 + 7 + 10}{8} = \frac{45}{8} \tag{4-12}$$

Another way to write this is

$$\text{average} = \frac{\text{frequency of score} \times \text{score}}{\text{sum of frequencies}}$$

$$= \frac{1\cdot 0 + 0\cdot 1 + 1\cdot 2 + 0\cdot 3 + 0\cdot 4 + 0\cdot 5 + 2\cdot 6 + 3\cdot 7 + 0\cdot 8 + 0\cdot 9 + 1\cdot 10}{1 + 0 + 1 + 0 + 0 + 0 + 2 + 3 + 0 + 0 + 1}$$

or

$$\text{average} = \frac{\sum_{i=0}^{10} (\text{frequency of } i)\cdot i}{\sum_{i=0}^{10} \text{frequency of } i} \tag{4-13}$$

The same idea is used to compute a quantum-mechanical average. For the average value of r we take each possible value of r times its frequency (given by $\psi^2(r)\,dv$)[3] and sum over all these values. (For a continuous variable like r, we must resort to integration to accomplish this.) We divide by the "sum" of frequencies by dividing by $\int \psi^2(r)\,dv$. Thus

$$\bar{r} = \frac{\int^{\text{all space}} r\psi^2\,dv}{\int_{\text{all space}} \psi^2\,dv} = \frac{\int_0^{2\pi} d\phi \int_0^{\pi} \sin\theta\,d\theta \int_0^{\infty} r\psi^2(r) r^2\,dr}{\int_{\text{all space}} \psi^2\,dv} \tag{4-14}$$

[3] The $4\pi r^2$ part of $4\pi r^2\psi^2$ in Fig. 4-4 is included in dv, as will be seen shortly.

The denominator is unity since ψ is normalized. The integrals over θ and ϕ involve parts of the volume element dv, and not ψ^2, because this wavefunction (4-9) does not depend on θ or ϕ. Continuing,

$$\bar{r} = \phi \Big|_0^{2\pi} \cdot -\cos\theta \Big|_0^{\pi} \cdot \pi^{-1}(Z/a_0)^3 \int_0^{\infty} r^3 \exp(-2Zr/a_0)\, dr \qquad (4\text{-}15)$$

Utilizing the information in Appendix 1 for the integral over r, this becomes

$$\bar{r} = 2\pi[-(-1) + 1](1/\pi)(Z/a_0)^3 3!/(2Z/a_0)^4 \qquad (4\text{-}16)$$

$$= 4\pi \cdot (1/\pi)(Z/a_0)^3 \cdot 6a_0^{\,4}/16Z^4 = 3a_0/2Z \qquad (4\text{-}17)$$

(It is useful to remember that integration over the ϕ and θ parts of dv gives 4π as the result *if no other angle-dependent functions occur in the integral.*) Comparing (4-16) with our expression for r_{mp} indicates that $\bar{r}$ is 1.5 times greater than r_{mp}.

Notice that the lowest-energy eigenfunction is finite at $r = 0$ even though V is infinite there. This is allowed by our arguments in Chapter 2 because the infinity in V occurs at only one point, so it can be cancelled by a discontinuity in the derivative of ψ. This is possible only if ψ has a "corner" or "cusp" at $r = 0$ (see Fig. 4-3a).

D. *Quantum Numbers and Nomenclature*

There are three quantum numbers, n, l, and m (all integers), characterizing each solution of the Schrödinger equation (4-6). Of these, only n enters the energy formula (4-8), so all solutions having the same values of n but different values of l and m will be energetically degenerate. As is shown in following sections, these quantum numbers are related in their allowed values. The l quantum number must be nonnegative and smaller than n. The m number may be positive, negative or zero, but its absolute value cannot exceed l. Thus,

$$l = 0, 1, 2, \ldots, n-1 \qquad (4\text{-}18)$$

$$|m| \leq l \qquad (4\text{-}19)$$

For the lowest-energy wavefunction we have already described, $n = 1$, so $l = m = 0$. No other choices are possible, so this level is nondegenerate. The convention (from atomic spectroscopy) is to refer to an $l = 0$ solution as an "s function," or "s orbital." (For $l = 0, 1, 2, 3, 4, 5$, the spectroscopic designation goes s, p, d, f, g, h.) Because n equals unity, the wavefunction is labeled 1s.

When $n = 2$, there are four sets of l and m quantum numbers satisfying rules (4-18) and (4-19). They are listed below with their spectroscopic labels:

$$\begin{array}{llll} l = 0,\ m = 0 & 2\text{s} & l = 1,\ m = 0 & 2\text{p}_0 \\ l = 1,\ m = -1 & 2\text{p}_{-1} & l = 1,\ m = +1 & 2\text{p}_{+1} \end{array} \qquad (4\text{-}20)$$

Extending these rules to the $n = 3$ energy level produces nine functions designated 3s, $3p_{-1}$, $3p_0$, $3p_{+1}$, $3d_{-2}$, $3d_{-1}$, $3d_0$, $3d_{+1}$, $3d_{+2}$. In general, the degeneracy of the energy level characterized by n is n^2.

E. *Nature of the Higher-Energy Solutions*

The second energy level is associated with the 2s, $2p_{-1}$, $2p_0$, and $2p_{+1}$ orbitals. The wavefunction for the 2s state is

$$\psi_{2s} = \frac{1}{4\sqrt{2\pi}}\left(\frac{Z}{a_0}\right)^{3/2}\left(2 - \frac{Zr}{a_0}\right)\exp\left(\frac{-Zr}{2a_0}\right) \tag{4-21}$$

Since this is a function of r only, it is a spherically symmetric function. (In fact, all s orbitals are spherically symmetric.) The 2s orbital is more "spread out" than the 1s orbital because the exponential in ψ_{2s} decays more slowly and because the exponential is multiplied by Zr/a_0 (the 2 becomes negligible compared to Zr/a_0 at large r). As a result, the charge cloud associated with the 2s orbital is more diffuse. (For this reason, when we approximate a polyelectronic atom like beryllium by putting electrons in 1s and 2s orbitals the 2s electrons are referred to as "outer" and the 1s electrons are called "inner.")

At small values of r, $(2 - Zr/a_0)$ is positive, and at large distances it is negative, so ψ_{2s} has a spherical *radial node* (a zero in the r coordinate). In Fig. 4-5 the first four s orbitals are plotted. We see that the nth s orbital has $(n - 1)$ spherical nodal surfaces dividing regions where the wavefunctions have different sign. The appearance of more and more nodes in the radial coordinate as the energy increases is certainly familiar from previous examples. Notice how the wavefunctions oscillate most rapidly and nodes are most closely spaced in the regions near the nucleus where the electron classically would have its greatest kinetic energy.

The 2s orbital is orthogonal to the 1s orbital, and also to all higher s orbitals. This would not be possible if there were no radial nodes. The product $\psi_{1s}\psi_{2s}$ will vanish upon integration only if it either vanishes everywhere or else has positive and negative regions that cancel on integration. Since ψ_{1s} and ψ_{2s} are almost everywhere finite, the former condition does not occur. Since ψ_{1s} has the same sign everywhere, their product can have positive and negative regions only if ψ_{2s} has positive and negative regions, and hence, a node.

Let us now consider the 2p functions. They are

$$\psi_{2p_0} = \frac{1}{4\sqrt{2\pi}}\left(\frac{Z}{a_0}\right)^{3/2}\frac{Zr}{a_0}\exp\left(\frac{-Zr}{2a_0}\right)\cos\theta \tag{4-22}$$

$$\psi_{2p_{\pm 1}} = \frac{1}{8\sqrt{\pi}}\left(\frac{Z}{a_0}\right)^{3/2}\frac{Zr}{a_0}\exp\left(\frac{-Zr}{2a_0}\right)\sin\theta\exp(\pm i\phi) \tag{4-23}$$

All of these functions have the same radial exponential decay as the 2s orbital, so we can say that the 2s and 2p orbitals are about equal in "size." However,

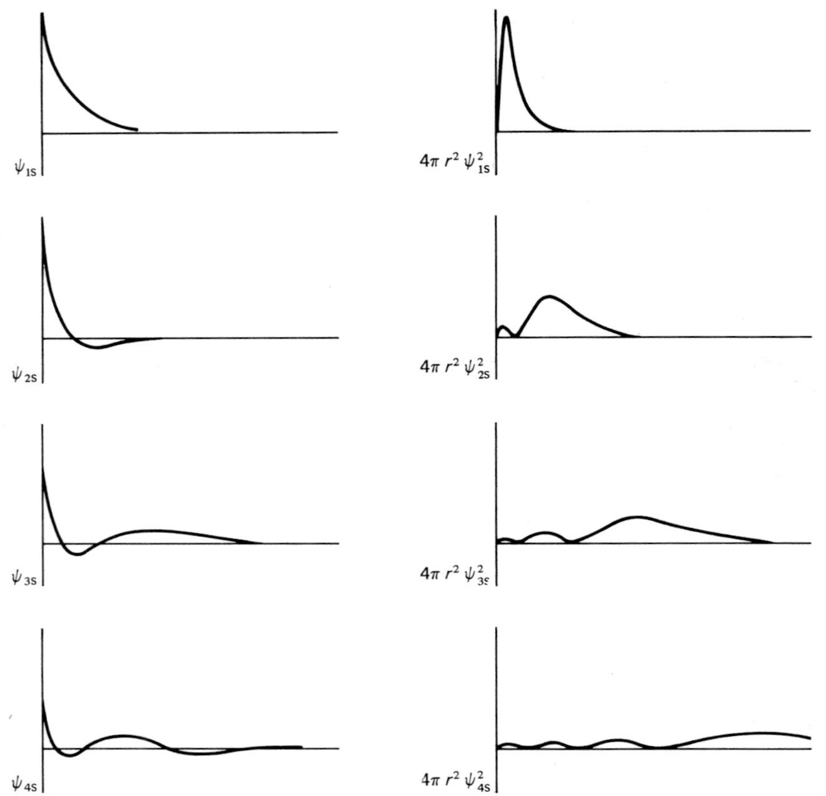

FIG. 4-5 s Wavefunctions versus r and volume-weighted electron densities versus r for the hydrogenlike ion.

since the 2p orbitals contain the factor Zr/a_0 where the 2s contains $(2 - Zr/a_0)$, the 2p orbitals vanish at the nucleus and not at any intermediate r value; they have no radial nodes. The 2p orbitals are endowed with directional properties by their angular dependences. The $2p_0$ orbital is particularly easy to understand because the factors $r \cos\theta$ behave exactly like the z cartesian coordinate. Hence, we can rewrite $2p_0$ (also called $2p_z$) as

$$\psi_{2p_z} = \frac{1}{4\sqrt{2\pi}}\left(\frac{Z}{a_0}\right)^{5/2} z \exp\left(\frac{-Zr}{2a_0}\right) \tag{4-24}$$

(Be careful not to confuse the *atomic number* Z with the *coordinate* z.) The exponential term in Eq. (4-24) is spherically symmetric, resembling a diffuse 1s orbital. The function z vanishes in the xy plane and becomes increasingly positive or negative as we move away from the plane in either direction. As a result, ψ_{2p_z} looks as sketched in Fig. 4-6. It has nearly spherical lobes, one posi-

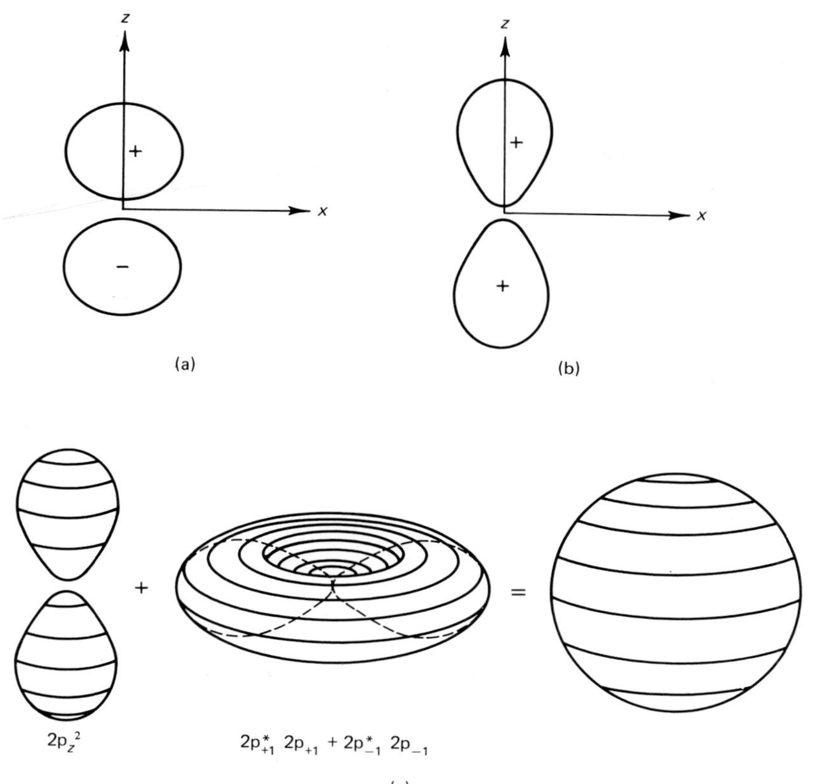

FIG. 4-6 (a) Drawing of the $2p_z$ orbital. (b) Drawing of the square of the $2p_z$ orbital. (c) Drawing of $\psi^2_{2p_z} + \psi^*_{2p-1}\psi_{2p-1} + \psi^*_{2p+1}\psi_{2p+1}$ = spherically symmetric distribution. The curved lines in (c) are a visualization aid and are not mathematically significant.

tive and one negative. When ψ_{2p_z} is squared, the lobes become elongated into the dumbbell shape shown in Fig. 4-6.

The $2p_{\pm 1}$ orbitals are more difficult to visualize since they are complex functions. The charge distributions associated with these orbitals must be real, however. These are given by $\psi^*\psi$, where ψ^* is the complex conjugate of ψ. (Recall that, for complex wavefunctions, $\psi^*\psi$ must be used for probability distributions, rather than ψ^2.) One obtains the complex conjugate of a function by merely reversing the signs of all the i's in the function. It is evident from Eq. (4-23) that $\psi^*_{2p_{+1}} = \psi_{2p_{-1}}$ and $\psi^*_{2p_{-1}} = \psi_{2p_{+1}}$. Hence $\psi^*_{2p_{+1}}\psi_{2p_{+1}} = \psi^*_{2p_{-1}}\psi_{2p_{-1}} = \psi_{2p_{+1}}\psi_{2p_{-1}}$: both the $2p_{+1}$ and the $2p_{-1}$ orbitals give the same charge distribution. This distribution is the same as that for the $2p_z$ orbital except that the angle dependence is $\frac{1}{2}\sin^2\theta$ instead of $\cos^2\theta$. However, since $\sin^2\theta + \cos^2\theta = 1$, it follows that the sum of $2p_{+1}$ and $2p_{-1}$ charge clouds must be such that, when added to the charge cloud for $2p_0$, it produces a spherical charge cloud (since the angular dependence is removed). We already know that the $2p_z$ distribution is dumbbell shaped, so it follows that $2p_{+1}$ and $2p_{-1}$ produce doughnut-shaped distributions. (A sphere minus a dumbbell equals a doughnut. See Fig. 4-6.) The shape can also be inferred from the $\sin^2 \theta$ dependence, which is a maximum in the xy plane.

When solving the particle-in-a-ring problem, we saw that we could arrive at either a set of real trigonometric solutions or a set of complex exponential solutions. Since the ϕ dependence of the $2p_{\pm 1}$ orbitals is identical to that for $m = \pm 1$ solutions of the particle in the ring, the same situation holds here. Because $\psi_{2p_{+1}}$ and $\psi_{2p_{-1}}$ are energetically degenerate eigenfunctions, any linear combination of them is also an eigenfunction of the hamiltonian (Problem 2-10). Therefore, let us find linear combinations which are entirely real. The complex, part of $\psi_{2p_{\pm 1}}$, $\exp(\pm i\phi)$, satisfies the relation

$$\exp(\pm i\phi) = \cos\phi \pm i \sin\phi \tag{4-25}$$

so that

$$\exp(+i\phi) + \exp(-i\phi) = 2\cos\phi \tag{4-26}$$

and

$$i^{-1}[\exp(+i\phi) - \exp(-i\phi)] = 2\sin\phi \tag{4-27}$$

Thus, we have two linear combinations of $\exp(\pm i\phi)$ that are real. It follows immediately that

$$\psi_{2p_x} = \frac{1}{\sqrt{2}}[\psi_{2p_{+1}} + \psi_{2p_{-1}}] = \frac{1}{4\sqrt{2\pi}}\left(\frac{Z}{a_0}\right)^{3/2}\frac{Zr}{a_0}\exp\left(\frac{-Zr}{2a_0}\right)\sin\theta\cos\phi \tag{4-28}$$

$$\psi_{2p_y} = \frac{1}{i\sqrt{2}}[\psi_{2p_{+1}} - \psi_{2p_{-1}}] = \frac{1}{4\sqrt{2\pi}}\left(\frac{Z}{a_0}\right)^{3/2}\frac{Zr}{a_0}\exp\left(\frac{-Zr}{2a_0}\right)\sin\theta\sin\phi \tag{4-29}$$

where the factor $2^{-1/2}$ is used to maintain normality. Since $r \sin\theta\cos\phi$ and $r \sin\theta\sin\phi$ are equivalent to the cartesian coordinates x and y, respectively, Eqs. (4-28) and (4-29) are commonly referred to as the $2p_x$ and $2p_y$ orbitals. They are exactly like the $2p_z$ orbital except that they are oriented along the x and y axes (merely replace the z in Eq. (4-24) with x or y).

The 2s, $2p_x$, $2p_y$, and $2p_z$ orbitals are all orthogonal to one another. This is easily shown from symmetry considerations. Each 2p orbital is antisymmetric to reflection in its nodal plane, whereas 2s is symmetric to all reflections. Hence, the product $\psi_{2s}\psi_{2p}$ is always antisymmetric with respect to some reflection so its integral vanishes. The 2p functions are mutually orthogonal because, if one 2p orbital is antisymmetric for some reflection, the others are always symmetric for that reflection. Hence, the product is antisymmetric for that reflection. Another way to show that the 2p orbitals are mutually orthogonal is to note that they behave like x, y, and z vectors and that these vectors are

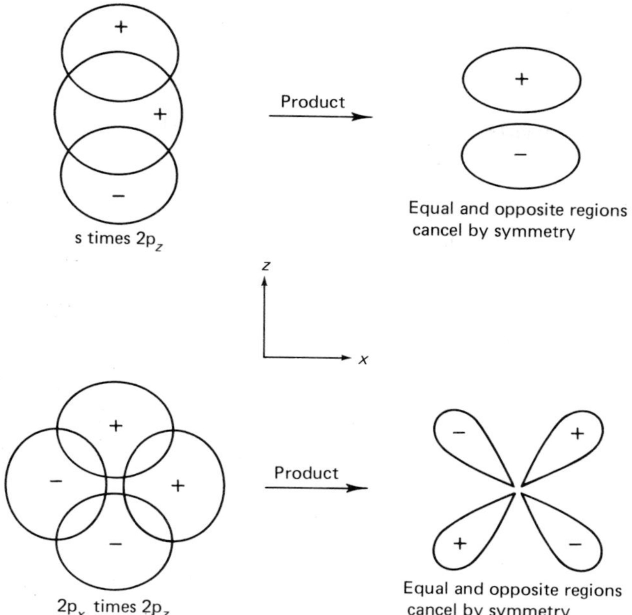

FIG. 4-7 Drawings of orbitals and their products to demonstrate orthogonality.

orthogonal (i.e., perpendicular; orthogonality in functions is equivalent to perpendicularity in vectors). Sometimes the orthogonality of functions is most clearly seen if we sketch out the product and note whether the positive and negative regions cancel by symmetry (Fig. 4-7).

The $n = 3$ level has nine solutions associated with it. The 3s orbital, plotted in Fig. 4-5, has one more node than the 2s orbital and is more diffuse. The 3p orbitals have the same angular terms as did the 2p orbitals so they can be written as real functions having the same directional properties as x, y and z vectors. The 3p orbitals differ from the 2p orbitals in that they possess a radial node and are more diffuse (see Fig. 4-8). The remaining five levels, 3d levels, may also be written in either complex or real form. The real orbitals are given by the formulas

$$\left.\begin{aligned} 3d_{z^2} &= \\ 3d_{x^2-y^2} &= \\ 3d_{xy} &= \\ 3d_{xz} &= \\ 3d_{yz} &= \end{aligned}\right\} \frac{1}{\sqrt{2592\pi}} \left(\frac{Z}{a_0}\right)^{3/2} \left(\frac{2Zr}{3a_0}\right)^2 \exp\left(\frac{-Zr}{3a_0}\right) \begin{cases} (1/\sqrt{3})(3\cos^2\theta - 1) \\ \sin^2\theta \cos 2\phi \\ \sin^2\theta \sin 2\phi \\ \sin 2\theta \cos\phi \\ \sin 2\theta \sin\phi \end{cases} \tag{4-30}$$

These angular factors, times r^2, have directional properties identical to the cartesian subscripts on the left, except that $3d_{z^2}$ is a shorthand for $3d_{3z^2-r^2}$.

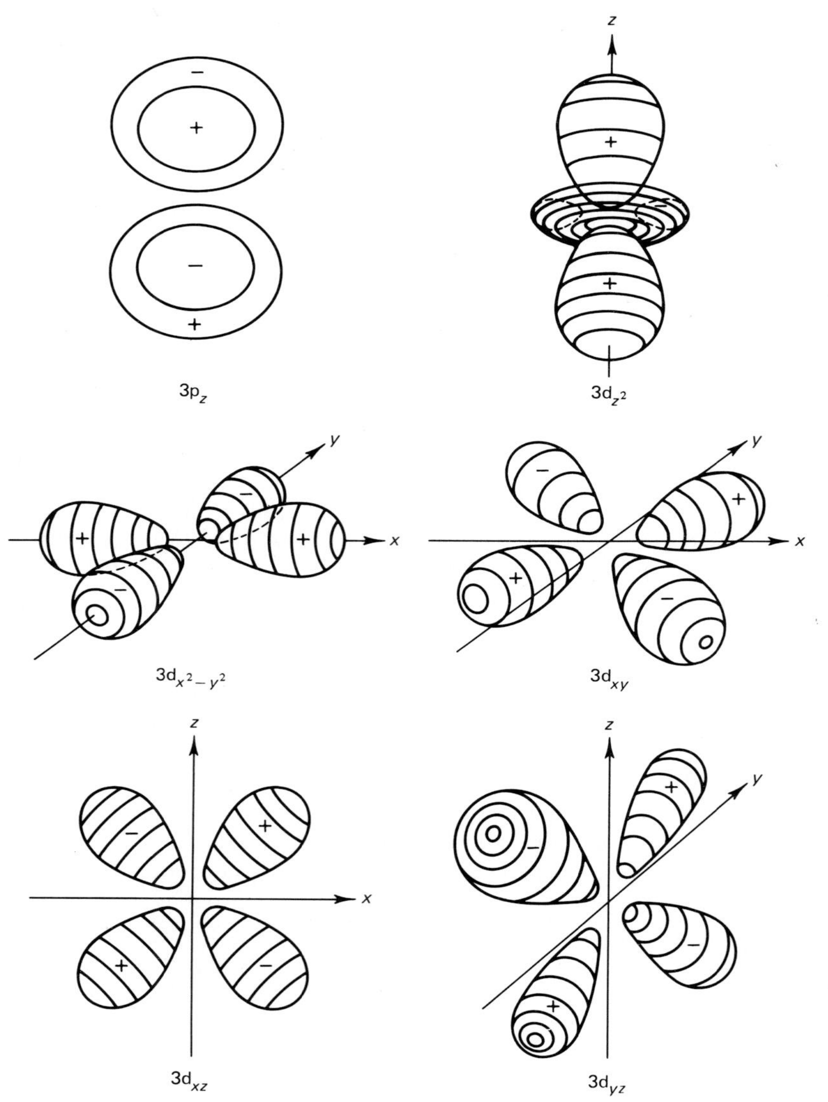

FIG. 4-8 Some hydrogenlike orbitals at the $n = 3$ level.

These orbitals are sketched in Fig. 4-8. It is obvious from these figures that $3d_{x^2-y^2}$ has the same symmetry and orientation as the sum of the two vectors x^2 and $-y^2$, and that the other 3d orbitals have a similar connection with the notation (except for $3d_{z^2}$). The 3d functions are about the same size as the 3p and 3s functions, but have no radial nodes at intermediate r values.

A general pattern emerges when we examine the nodal properties of the orbitals at various energies. At the lowest energy we have no nodes and the level is nondegenerate. At the next level, we find that each function possesses a single node. There is one way to put in a radial node and so we get one 2s orbital. Or we can put in a planar node. But we have three choices for the orientation of this plane leading to three independent p orbitals. At the $n = 3$ level we find orbitals containing two nodes. The possibilities are: two radial nodes (3s), a radial node and a planar node ($3p_x$, $3p_y$, $3p_z$), two planar nodes ($3d_{xy}$, $3d_{xz}$, $3d_{yz}$, $3d_{x^2-y^2}$, $3d_{z^2-x^2}$, $3d_{z^2-y^2}$). (But, since $z^2 - y^2 - (z^2 - x^2) = x^2 - y^2$, the last three 3d orbitals are not linearly independent. Hence the last two are combined to form $3d_{z^2}$: $z^2 - x^2 + z^2 - y^2 = 3z^2 - (x^2 + y^2 + z^2) = 3z^2 - r^2$. This function can be seen to correspond to a positive dumbbell encircled by a small negative doughnut, or "belly band.") It is apparent that the degeneracies between various 2p orbitals, or 3d orbitals, are spatial degeneracies, due only to the physical equivalence of various directions in space. The degeneracy between 2s and 2p, or 3s, 3p, and 3d is not due to spatial symmetry. The fact that an angular node is energetically equivalent to a radial node is a peculiarity of the particular potential ($-Ze^2/r$) for this problem. This degeneracy is removed for noncoulombic central-field potentials, such as $-Ze^2/r^3$.

The eigenfunctions corresponding to states in the energy continuum, like the bound states, can be separated into radial and angular parts. The radial parts of the spherically symmetric eigenfunctions at two nonnegative energies are given in Fig. 4-9. Note that the rate of oscillation of these functions is greatest at the nucleus, where the local kinetic energy is largest, in accord with the ideas presented in Chapters 1 and 2. Unbound-state wavefunctions are not used in most quantum chemical applications, so we will not discuss them further in this book.

4-2 Separation of Variables

We shall indicate in some detail the way in which the Schrödinger equation (4-6) is solved. Recall the strategy of separating variables which we used in Section 2-7:

(1) Express ψ as a product of functions, each depending on only one variable.

(2) Substitute this product into the Schrödinger equation and try to manipulate it so that the equation becomes a sum of terms, each depending on a single variable. These terms must sum to a constant.

(3) Since terms for different variables are independent of each other, the terms for each variable must equal a constant. This enables one to set up an equation in each variable. If this can be done, the initial assumption (1) is justified.

In this case we begin by assuming that

$$\psi(r, \theta, \phi) = R(r)\Theta(\theta)\Phi(\phi) \tag{4-31}$$

Substituting into Eq. (4-6) gives

$$\frac{-h^2}{8\pi^2\mu r^2}\left[\Theta\Phi\frac{d}{dr}\left(r^2\frac{dR}{dr}\right) + R\Phi\frac{1}{\sin\theta}\frac{d}{d\theta}\left(\sin\theta\frac{d\Theta}{d\theta}\right)\right.$$

$$\left. + R\Theta\frac{1}{\sin^2\theta}\frac{d^2\Phi}{d\phi^2}\right] - \frac{Ze^2}{r}R\Theta\Phi = ER\Theta\Phi \qquad (4\text{-}32)$$

Since each derivative operator now acts on a function of a single coordinate, we use total, rather than partial, derivative notation.

Let us first see if we can isolate the ϕ dependence. Multiplying Eq. (4-32) by $(-8\pi\mu r^2 \sin^2\theta/h^2 R\Theta\Phi)$ and rearranging gives

$$\frac{\sin^2\theta}{R}\frac{d}{dr}\left(r^2\frac{dR}{dr}\right) + \frac{8\pi^2\mu r^2\sin^2\theta}{h^2}\left(E + \frac{Ze^2}{r}\right)$$

$$+ \frac{\sin\theta}{\Theta}\frac{d}{d\theta}\left(\sin\theta\frac{d\Theta}{d\theta}\right) + \frac{1}{\Phi}\frac{d^2\Phi}{d\phi^2} = 0 \qquad (4\text{-}33)$$

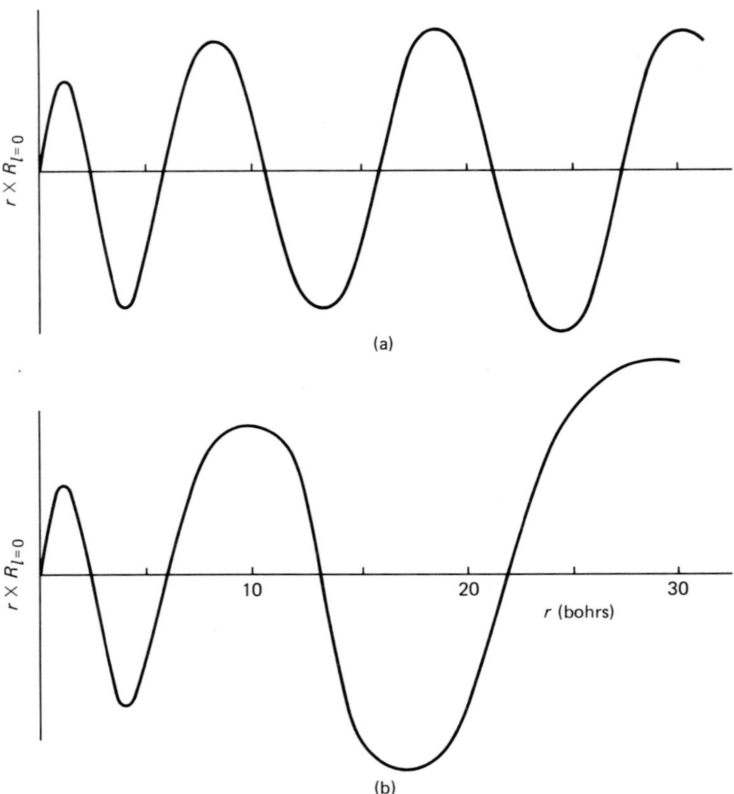

FIG. 4-9 Radial part of unbound H-atom states (times r) versus r at two energies: (a) $E = 13.6$ eV; (b) $E = 0$.

The r and θ dependence is still mixed in the first two terms, but we now have a rather simple term in the coordinate ϕ. Now we can argue, as in Section 2-7, that, as ϕ alone changes, the first three terms in Eq. (4-33) do not change. That is, if only ϕ changes, Eq. (4-33) may be written

$$\text{constant} + \text{constant} + \text{constant} + (1/\Phi)(d^2\Phi/d\phi^2) = 0 \tag{4-34}$$

so that

$$(1/\Phi)(d^2\Phi/d\phi^2) = -m^2 \qquad \text{(a constant)} \tag{4-35}$$

We call the constant $-m^2$ for future mathematical convenience. We can rearrange Eq. (4-35) into the more familiar form for an eigenvalue equation:

$$d^2\Phi/d\phi^2 = -m^2\Phi \tag{4-36}$$

We arrived at Eq. (4-36) by assuming that only ϕ changes while r and θ are constant. However, it should be obvious that the behavior of the term in ϕ is uninfluenced by changes in r and θ since it has no dependence on these coordinates. Thus, by establishing that this term is constant under certain circumstances, we have actually shown that it must be constant under all circumstances.

We can now proceed with further separation of variables. Since we know that the last term in Eq. (4-33) is a constant, we can write

$$\frac{1}{R}\frac{d}{dr}\left(r^2\frac{dR}{dr}\right) + \frac{8\pi^2\mu r^2}{h^2}\left(E + \frac{Ze^2}{r}\right) + \frac{1}{\Theta \sin\theta}\frac{d}{d\theta}\left(\sin\theta\frac{d\Theta}{d\theta}\right) - \frac{m^2}{\sin^2\theta} = 0 \tag{4-37}$$

Note that we have separated the θ and r dependences by dividing through by $\sin^2\theta$. We now have two terms wholly dependent on r and two wholly dependent on θ, their sum being zero. Hence, as before, the sum of the two r-dependent terms must equal a constant, β, and the sum of the θ-dependent terms must equal $-\beta$. Thus

$$\frac{d}{dr}\left(r^2\frac{dR}{dr}\right) + \frac{8\pi^2\mu r^2}{h^2}\left(E + \frac{Ze^2}{r}\right)R = \beta R \tag{4-38}$$

$$\frac{1}{\sin\theta}\frac{d}{d\theta}\left(\sin\theta\frac{d\Theta}{d\theta}\right) - \frac{m^2\Theta}{\sin^2\theta} = -\beta\Theta \tag{4-39}$$

The assumption that $\psi = R\Theta\,\Phi$ has led to separate equations for R, Θ, and Φ. This indicates that the assumption of separability was valid.

4-3 Solution of the R, Θ, and Φ Equations

A. The Φ Equation

The solution of Eq. (4-36) is similar to that of the particle in a ring problem of Section 2-6. The normalized solutions are

$$\Phi = (1/\sqrt{2\pi})\exp(im\phi), \qquad m = 0, \pm 1, \pm 2, \ldots \tag{4-40}$$

As shown is Section 2-6, the constant m must be an integer if Φ is to be a single-valued function which joins smoothly onto itself.

B. *The Θ Equation*

There is great similarity between the mathematical techniques used in solving the R and Θ equations and those used to solve the one-dimensional harmonic oscillator problem of Chapter 3. Hence, we will only summarize the steps involved in these solutions and make a few remarks about the results. More detailed treatments are presented in many texts.[4]

The Θ equation can be solved as follows:

(1) Change the variable to obtain a more convenient form for the differential equation.

(2) Express the solution as a power series and obtain a recursion relation.

(3) Observe that the series diverges for certain values of the variables, producing nonsquare-integrable wavefunctions. Correct this by requiring that the series terminate. This requires that the truncated series be either symmetric or antisymmetric in the variable and also that β of Eq. (4-38) and (4-39) be equal to $l(l + 1)$ with l an integer.

(4) Recognize these truncated series as being the associated Legendre functions.

(5) Return to the original variable to obtain an expression for Θ in terms of the starting coordinate.

Reference to the end of Section 3-4 will illustrate the similarity between this and the harmonic oscillator case.

The final result is

$$\Theta_{l,m}(\theta) = \left[\frac{(2l + 1)}{2}\frac{(l - |m|)!}{(l + |m|)!}\right]^{1/2} P_l^{|m|}(\cos\theta) \tag{4-41}$$

The term in square brackets is a normalizing function, and $P_l^{|m|}(\cos\theta)$ represents some member of the series of associated Legendre functions. When $m = 0$, these become the ordinary Legendre polynomials. The first few Legendre polynomials are

$$P_0(x) = 1, \qquad P_1(x) = x, \qquad P_2(x) = \tfrac{1}{2}(3x^2 - 1),$$
$$P_3(x) = \tfrac{1}{2}(5x^3 - 3x) \tag{4-42}$$

The first few associated Legendre functions are

$$\begin{aligned} P_1^1(x) &= (1 - x^2)^{1/2}, & P_2^1(x) &= 3(1 - x^2)^{1/2}x, \\ P_2^2(x) &= 3(1 - x^2), & P_3^1(x) &= \tfrac{3}{2}(1 - x^2)^{1/2}(5x^2 - 1), \\ P_3^2(x) &= 15(1 - x^2)x, & P_3^3(x) &= 15(1 - x^2)^{3/2} \end{aligned} \tag{4-43}$$

[4] See, e.g., Pauling and Wilson [3, Chapter 5].

It is also true that

$$P_l^{|m|}(x) = 0 \qquad \text{if} \quad |m| > l \tag{4-44}$$

Thus, $\Theta(\theta)$, and hence $\psi(r, \theta, \phi)$, vanishes unless $|m| \leq l$, giving us one of our quantum number rules [Eq. (4-19)].

The associated Legendre functions satisfy an orthogonality relation:

$$\int_{-1}^{+1} P_l^{|m|}(x) P_{l'}^{|m|}(x)\, dx = \frac{2}{(2l+1)} \frac{(l+|m|)!}{(l-|m|)!} \delta_{ll'} \tag{4-45}$$

For a further discussion of these functions, the reader should consult a more advanced text on quantum mechanics.

C. *The R Equation*

The R equation can be solved as follows:

(1) Assume that E is negative (this restricts us to bound states), and note that $\beta = l(l+1)$ from the previous solving of the Θ equation.

(2) Change variables for mathematical convenience.

(3) Find the asymptotic solution pertaining to the large r limit, where the R equation becomes simplified.

(4) Express the wavefunction as a product of the asymptotic solution and an unknown function. Express this unknown function as a power series and (after dealing with some singularities) obtain a recursion relation.

(5) Note that the power series overpowers the asymptotic part of the solution unless the series is truncated. This leads to the requirement that n be integral and hence that E be quantized. It also requires that $n > l$.

(6) Recognize the truncated series to be associated Laguerre polynomials times ρ^l, where ρ is defined below.

The resulting solution is

$$R_{nl}(r) = -\left[\left(\frac{2Z}{na_0}\right)^3 \frac{(n-l-1)!}{2n[(n+l)!]^3}\right]^{1/2} \exp(-\rho/2)\rho^l L_{n+l}^{2l+1}(\rho) \tag{4-46}$$

where $\rho = 2Zr/na_0$ and $a_0 = h^2/4\pi^2\mu e = 5.2917706 \times 10^{-11}$ m (if $\mu = m_e$). The term in brackets is a normalizing function. The exponential term is the asymptotic solution and it guarantees that $R(r)$ will approach zero as r approaches infinity. The third term, ρ^l, is produced in the course of removing singularities (i.e., places where parts of a differential equation become infinite). The last term, $L(\rho)$, symbolizes the various members of the set of associated Laguerre polynomials. Like the Legendre functions, these are mathematically well characterized. A few of the low-index associated Laguerre polynomials are

$$\begin{aligned} L_1^1(\rho) &= 1, & L_2^1(\rho) &= 2\rho - 4, \\ L_3^1(\rho) &= -3\rho^2 + 18\rho - 18, & L_3^3(\rho) &= -6 \end{aligned} \tag{4-47}$$

4-4 Atomic Units

It is convenient to define a system of units that is more natural for working with atoms and molecules. The commonly accepted system of atomic units for some important quantities is summarized in Table 4-1. [Note: the symbol $\hbar$ ("h-cross or h-bar") is often used in place of $h/2\pi$.] Additional data on values of physical quantities, units, and conversion factors can be found in Appendix 12.

TABLE 4-1
Atomic Units

Quantity	Atomic unit in cgs or other units	Values of some atomic properties in atomic units (a.u.)
Mass	$m_e = 9.109534 \times 10^{-28}$ gm	Mass of electron = 1 a.u.
Length	$a_0 = \hbar^2/m_e e^2$ $= 0.52917706 \times 10^{-8}$ cm ($\equiv$ 1 bohr)	Most probable distance of 1s electron from nucleus of H atom = 1 a.u.
Time	$\tau_0 = a_0\hbar/e^2$ $= 2.4189 \times 10^{-17}$ sec	Time for 1s electron in H atom to travel one bohr = 1 a.u.
Charge	$e = 4.803242 \times 10^{-10}$ esu $= 1.6021892 \times 10^{-19}$ coulomb	Charge of electron = -1 a.u.
Energy	$e^2/a_0 = 4.359814 \times 10^{-11}$ erg (= 27.21161 eV $\equiv$ 1 hartree)	Total energy of 1s electron in H atom = $-1/2$ a.u.
Angular momentum	$\hbar = h/2\pi$ $= 1.0545887 \times 10^{-27}$ erg sec	Angular momentum for particle in ring = 0, 1, 2, ... a.u.
Electric field strength	$e/a_0^2 = 5.1423 \times 10^9$ V/cm	Electric field strength at distance of 1 bohr from proton = 1 a.u.

TABLE 4-2
Eigenfunctions for the Hydrogenlike Ion in Atomic Units

Spectroscopic symbol	Formula
1s	$(1/\sqrt{\pi})Z^{3/2} \exp(-Zr)$
2s	$(1/4\sqrt{2\pi})Z^{3/2}(2 - Zr) \exp(-Zr/2)$
$2p_x$	$(1/4\sqrt{2\pi})Z^{5/2}r \exp(-Zr/2) \sin\theta \cos\phi$
$2p_y$	$(1/4\sqrt{2\pi})Z^{5/2}r \exp(-Zr/2) \sin\theta \sin\phi$
$2p_z$	$(1/4\sqrt{2\pi})Z^{5/2}r \exp(-Zr/2) \cos\theta$
3s	$(1/81\sqrt{3\pi})Z^{3/2}(27 - 18Zr + 2Z^2r^2) \exp(-Zr/3)$
$3p_x$	$(\sqrt{2}/81\sqrt{\pi})Z^{5/2}r(6 - Zr) \exp(-Zr/3) \sin\theta \cos\phi$
$3p_y$	$(\sqrt{2}/81\sqrt{\pi})Z^{5/2}r(6 - Zr) \exp(-Zr/3) \sin\theta \sin\phi$
$3p_z$	$(\sqrt{2}/81\sqrt{\pi})Z^{5/2}r(6 - Zr) \exp(-Zr/3) \cos\theta$
$3d_{z^2}(\equiv 3d_{3z^2-r^2})$	$(1/81\sqrt{6\pi})Z^{7/2}r^2 \exp(-Zr/3)(3\cos^2\theta - 1)$
$3d_{x^2-y^2}$	$(1/81\sqrt{2\pi})Z^{7/2}r^2 \exp(-Zr/3) \sin^2\theta \cos 2\phi$
$3d_{xy}$	$(1/81\sqrt{2\pi})Z^{7/2}r^2 \exp(-Zr/3) \sin^2\theta \sin 2\phi$
$3d_{xz}$	$(1/81\sqrt{2\pi})Z^{7/2}r^2 \exp(-Zr/3) \sin 2\theta \cos\phi$
$3d_{yz}$	$(1/81\sqrt{2\pi})Z^{7/2}r^2 \exp(-Zr/3) \sin 2\theta \sin\phi$

In terms of these units, Schrödinger's equation and its resulting eigenfunctions and eigenvalues for the hydrogenlike ion become much simpler to write down. Thus, the Schrödinger equation in atomic units is (assuming infinite nuclear mass, so that $\mu = m_e$)

$$(-\tfrac{1}{2}\nabla^2 - Z/r)\psi = E\psi \tag{4-48}$$

The energies are

$$E_n = -Z^2/2n^2 \tag{4-49}$$

The lowest-energy solution is

$$\psi_{1s} = \sqrt{Z^3/\pi}\,\exp(-Zr) \tag{4-50}$$

The formulas for the hydrogenlike ion solutions (in atomic units) of most interest in quantum chemistry are listed in Table 4-2. The tabulated functions are all in real, rather than complex, form.

4-5 Angular Momentum and Spherical Harmonics

We have now discussed three problems in which a particle is free to move over the entire range of one or more coordinates with no change in potential. The first case was the free particle in one dimension. Here we found the eigenfunctions to be simple trigonometric or exponential functions of x. The trigonometric form is identical to the harmonic amplitude function of a standing wave in an infinitely long string. We might refer to such functions as "linear harmonics." The second case was the particle-in-a-ring problem, which again has solutions which may be expressed either as sine–cosine or exponential functions of the angle ϕ. By analogy with linear motion, we could refer to these as "circular harmonics." Finally, we have described the hydrogenlike ion, where the particle can move over the full ranges of θ and ϕ (i.e., over the surface of a sphere) with no change in potential. The solutions we have just described—the products $\Theta_{l,m}(\theta)\Phi_m(\phi)$—are called *spherical harmonics* and are commonly symbolized $Y_{l,m}(\theta, \phi)$. Thus

$$Y_{l,m}(\theta, \phi) = \left[\frac{(2l+1)}{4\pi}\frac{(l-|m|)!}{(l+|m|)!}\right]^{1/2} P_l^{|m|}(\cos\theta)\exp(im\phi) \tag{4-51}$$

Because so many physical systems have spherical symmetry, spherical harmonics are very important in classical and quantum mechanics.

Closely linked with spherical harmonics is *angular momentum*. Angular momentum is an important physical property because it is conserved in an isolated dynamical system; it is a *constant of motion* for the system. Angular momentum is described by magnitude and direction, so it is a vector quantity.[5]

[5] Strictly speaking, angular momentum is a pseudovector—it is dual to a second order antisymmetric tensor. However, for the remainder of this book, we can and shall ignore this distinction.

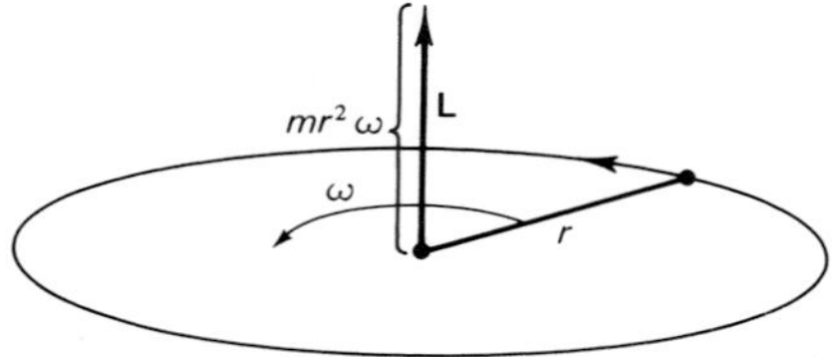

FIG. 4-10 The angular momentum vector **M** for a particle of mass m moving with angular velocity ω about a circular orbit of radius r in the direction indicated.

The classical system, in the absence of external forces, is constrained to move in such a way as to preserve both the direction and the magnitude of this vector. For a mass of m grams moving in a circular orbit of radius r cm with an angular velocity of ω radians per second, the angular momentum has magnitude $mr^2\omega$ g cm^2/sec (or, alternatively, erg seconds). The direction of the vector is given by the right-hand rule: the index finger of the right hand points along the particle trajectory and the extended thumb points along the angular momentum vector (see Fig. 4-10). (Alternatively, in a right-handed coordinate system, motion of a mass in the xy plane from $+x$ toward $+y$ produces angular momentum in the $+z$ direction.) In vector notation, $\mathbf{L} = \mathbf{r} \times \mathbf{p}$, where $\mathbf{L}$ is angular momentum, $\mathbf{r}$ is the position vector, and $\mathbf{p}$ is the linear momentum.

Some of the more interesting properties of angular momentum relate to the situation where circular motion occurs *in the presence of an external field.* A familiar example is a gyroscope mounted on a pivot and experiencing the gravitational field of the earth. The gyroscope flywheel is usually started with the gyroscope in an almost vertical position. As time passes, the tilt of the gyroscope away from the field direction (which we take to be the z direction) increases (see Fig. 4-11). If there were no friction in the bearings, the angle of tilt would not

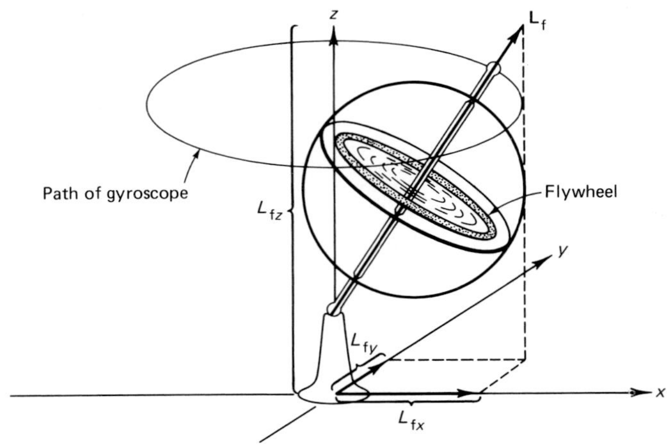

FIG. 4-11 A gyroscope with the angular momentum of the *flywheel*, $\mathbf{L}_f$, together with x, y, and z components of $\mathbf{L}_f$, at a given instant.

change, and the gyroscope would precess about z indefinitely, maintaining whatever angle of tilt it found itself with initially. Notice that, in such a case, the angular momentum due to the flywheel $\mathbf{L}_f$ is conserved *in magnitude only*. Its direction is constantly changing. Thus, $\mathbf{L}_f$ is *not* a constant of motion in the presence of a z-directed field. Neither are the components L_{fx}, and L_{fy}, which change in magnitude as the gyroscope precesses. L_{fz} *is* a constant of motion, however. If we add on to $\mathbf{L}_f$ the angular momentum $\mathbf{L}_g$ due to the precession of the gyroscope as a whole (including the center of mass of the flywheel but ignoring its rotation), we find that the total angular momentum for the gyroscope (including flywheel motion), $\mathbf{L}$ and its components L_x, L_y, and L_z behave similarly to $\mathbf{L}_f$ and its components (see Fig. 4-12). We may summarize these observations from classical physics as follows: a rotating rigid body conserves $\mathbf{L}$ (hence, L_x, L_y, L_z) in the absence of external forces. In the presence of a z-directed, time-independent external force, L_z and $|\mathbf{L}|$, the magnitude of $\mathbf{L}$ (but not its direction) are conserved. Furthermore, in a system comprised of several moving parts, the total angular momentum is the sum of the individual angular momenta, and the z component is the sum of the individual z components:

$$\mathbf{L} = \sum_i \mathbf{L}_i \tag{4-52}$$

$$L_z = \sum_i L_{zi} \tag{4-53}$$

Many characteristics of the classical situation are maintained in quantum mechanics. In particular, it can be shown that a hydrogenlike ion eigenfunction can always be associated with "sharp" values of L_z, but not necessarily for L_x or L_y, and that the *magnitude* of $\mathbf{L}$ is sharp, but not its direction. We have indicated several times in this book that a sharp value (i.e., a constant of motion) exists when a state function is an eigenfunction for an operator associated with the property. For example, all of our hydrogenlike ion wavefunctions are eigenfunctions for the hamiltonian operator, so all are associated with sharp energies. In atomic units, the operator for the z component of angular momentum $\hat{L}_z$ is $(1/i)\ \partial/\partial\phi$. This operator was introduced in section 2-6, where it was given the symbol p_ϕ. (A general discussion on operators will be given in Chapter 6. The

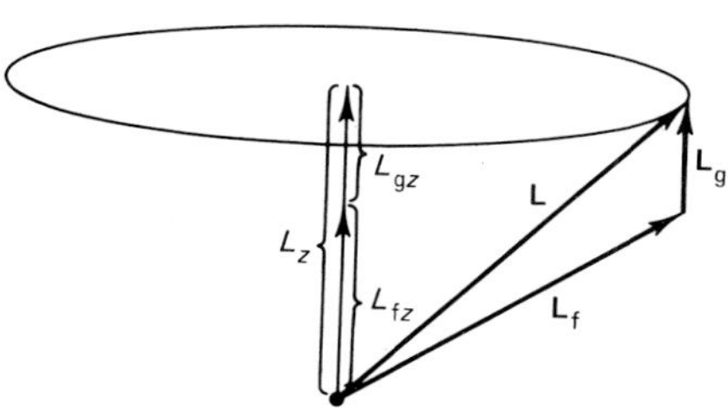

FIG. 4-12 The total angular momentum of the gyroscope $\mathbf{L}$ is shown as the sum of $\mathbf{L}_f$, the angular momentum of the flywheel, and $\mathbf{L}_g$, the angular momentum of the gyroscope. $\mathbf{L}$ precesses, so only L_z and the magnitude of $\mathbf{L}$ are constants of motion.

carat symbol is frequently used to denote an operator.) Our statement tha hydrogenlike eigenfunctions have sharp L_z means that we expect $\hat{L}_z\psi_{n,l,m}(r, \theta, \phi$ $= \text{constant}\cdot\psi_{n,l,m}(r, \theta, \phi)$. Since all these eigenfunctions have $\exp(im\phi)$ as thei only ϕ-dependent term, it follows immediately that

$$\hat{L}_z\psi_{n,l,m} = m\psi_{n,l,m} \tag{4-54}$$

or, equivalently,

$$\hat{L}_z Y_{l,m}(\theta, \phi) = m Y_{l,m}(\theta, \phi) \tag{4-5}$$

Hence, the quantum number m is equal to the z component of angular mome tum in atomic units for the state in question. This means that the angular m mentum associated with an s state ($l = 0$, so $m = 0$) has a zero z componen while a p state ($l = 1$, so $m = -1, 0, +1$) can have a z component of -1, or 1 a.u.

The other quantity that we have stated is conserved in these systems is t magnitude of **L**. In quantum mechanics, it is convenient to deal with the squa of this magnitude L^2. The quantum-mechanical operator associated with th quantity is (in atomic units)

$$\begin{aligned}\hat{L}^2 &= -[(\partial^2/\partial\theta^2) + \cot\theta\,(\partial/\partial\theta) + (1/\sin^2\theta)(\partial^2/\partial\phi^2)] \\ &= -[(1/\sin\theta)(\partial/\partial\theta)\sin\theta\,(\partial/\partial\theta) + (1/\sin^2\theta)(\partial^2/\partial\phi^2)]\end{aligned} \tag{4-5}$$

The result of operating on $Y_{l,m}(\theta, \phi)$ with this operator is

$$\hat{L}^2 Y_{l,m}(\theta, \phi) = l(l+1) Y_{l,m}(\theta, \phi) \tag{4-5}$$

This means that the *square* of the magnitude of the total angular momentum an s state is zero, for a p state it is two, for a d state it is six, etc.

One can construct vector diagrams to parallel these relationships. A few these are sketched in Fig. 4-13.

Operators for $\hat{L}_x$ and $\hat{L}_y$ can also be constructed. They are

$$\hat{L}_x = i[\sin\phi\,(\partial/\partial\theta) + \cot\theta\sin\phi\,(\partial/\partial\phi)] \tag{4-}$$

$$\hat{L}_y = -i[\cos\phi\,(\partial/\partial\theta) - \cot\theta\sin\phi(\partial/\partial\phi)] \tag{4-}$$

The hydrogenlike eigenfunctions are not necessarily eigenfunctions for eit of these operators (Problem 4-15).

It is interesting to consider the physical meaning of these results. I quantity has a sharp value, it means that we will always get that value no mat when we measure that property for systems in the state being considered. Th the z component of angular momentum for hydrogen atoms in the $2p_{+1}$ st will always be measured to be $+1$ a.u. For the x or y component, howe repeated measurements (on an ensemble of $2p_{+1}$ atoms) will yield a spread values. We can measure (or compute) an *average* value of L_x or L_y but nc sharp value. In terms of our mental model (a gyroscope) this seems sens enough except for one thing. Our hydrogenlike eigenfunctions are soluti for a central field potential with *no* external field. Under such conditions,

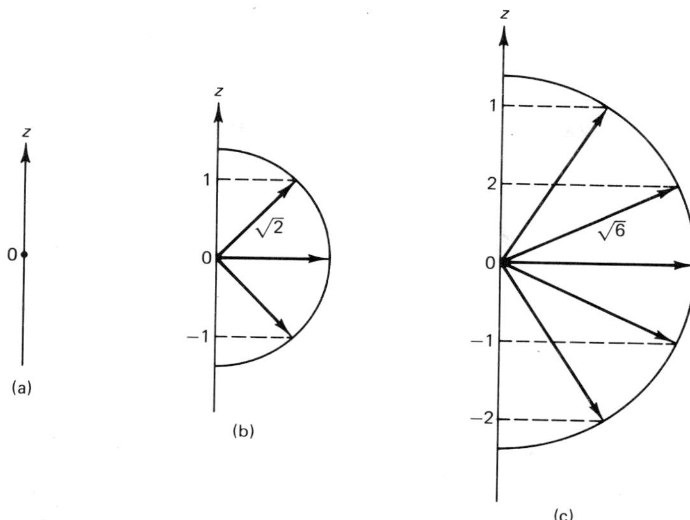

FIG. 4-13 Vector relationships that satisfy the following rules: $L^2 = l(l+1)$, $L_z = m$, $m = -l, -l+1, \ldots, 0, \ldots, l-1, l$. The quantum rules correspond to a classical analog where the gyroscope can have only certain discrete angles of tilt. (a) s; $l = 0$; $l(l+1) = 0$; $m = 0$. (b) p; $l = 1$; $l(l+1) = 2$; $m = -1, 0, +1$. (c) d; $l = 2$; $l(l+1) = 6$; $m = -2, -1, 0, +1, +2$.

L_x, L_y, and L_z are classically all constants of motion. Why, then, are they not all sharp quantum mechanically? The answer is that quantum-mechanical state functions never contain more information than is, in principle, extractable by measurement. To measure a component of angular momentum in a system always means, in practice, subjecting the system to some sort of external force. The hydrogenlike ion wavefunctions cannot simultaneously be eigenfunctions for $\hat{L}_x$, $\hat{L}_y$, and $\hat{L}_z$ because that would give simultaneous sharp values (i.e., *no* uncertainty) for the conjugate variables angular momentum and angular position. This would violate the uncertainty principle, which is in turn a reflection of limitations on our ability to measure one variable without affecting another (see Section 1-8).

It is possible, working only with the quantum-mechanical operators, to generate the eigenvalues of $\hat{L}_z$ and $\hat{L}^2$. More advanced texts should be consulted for a discussion of this approach. We give only the results. They are

$$\hat{L}_z f_{l,m} = m f_{l,m}, \qquad m = -l, -l+1, \ldots, l-1, l \tag{4-60}$$

$$\hat{L}^2 f_{l,m} = l(l+1) f_{l,m} \tag{4-61}$$

These look like the results already given in Eqs. (4-55) and (4-57). There is a difference, however. Here there is no indication that m is an integer, whereas in Eq. (4-55) m must be an integer, as indicated by the presence of zero in its value list. There are *two* ways in which we can have a sequence of the form $-l$, $-l+1, \ldots, l-1, l$. One way is to have an integer series, for example, $-2, -1, 0, +1, +2$, which must contain zero. The other way is to have a half-integer series, for example, $-\frac{3}{2}, -\frac{1}{2}, +\frac{1}{2}, +\frac{3}{2}$, which skips zero. If we work only with the properties of the operators, we find that either possibility is allowed. But if we *assume* that the as yet unspecified eigenfunctions $f_{l,m}$ are separable into θ- and ϕ-dependent parts, we find ourselves restricted to the integer series. For *orbital* angular momentum (due to motion of the electron in the atomic orbital), the z component must be an integer, for we have seen that the state functions ψ contain the spherical harmonics $Y_{l,m}$, which are indeed separable. *Spin* angular momentum (to be discussed in more detail in the next chapter), has half-integer z components, and the eigenfunctions corresponding to spin cannot be expressed with spherical harmonics.

It is true in classical physics that, if a charged particle is accelerated, a magnetic field is produced. Since circular motion of constant velocity requires acceleration (classically) it follows that *a charged particle having angular momentum will also have a magnetic moment.* The magnetic moment is proportional to the angular momentum, colinear with it, and oriented in the same direction if the charge is positive. For an electron, the magnetic moment is given by

$$\boldsymbol{\mu} = -\beta_e \mathbf{L} \tag{4-62}$$

where β_e, the *Bohr magneton*, has a value of 5.788×10^{-9} eV/G (equal to $\frac{1}{2}$ a.u.). If an external magnetic field of strength H is applied along the z axis, the system will interact with this field in a way determined by μ_z, the z component of the magnetic moment. The interaction energy is

$$E = -\mu_z H = \beta_e L_z H = \beta_e m H \tag{4-63}$$

This means that some of the degeneracies among the energy levels of the hydrogenlike ion will be removed by imposing an external magnetic field. For instance, the $2p_{+1}$ and $2p_{-1}$ energy levels will be raised and lowered in energy while 2s and $2p_0$ will be unaffected (see Fig. 4-14). This, in turn, will affect the atomic spectrum for absorption or emission. The splitting of spectral lines due to the imposition of an external magnetic field is known as *Zeeman splitting.* Because the splitting of levels depicted in Fig. 4-14 is proportional to the z component of orbital momentum, given by m, m is often referred to as the *magnetic* quantum number.

In the absence of external fields, eigenfunctions having the same n but different l and m are degenerate. We have seen that this allows us to take linear combinations of eigenfunctions, thereby arriving at completely real eigenfunctions like $2p_x$ and $2p_y$ instead of $2p_{+1}$ and $2p_{-1}$. When a magnetic field is imposed, the degeneracy no longer exists, and we are unable to perform such mixing. Under these conditions, $2p_x$, $2p_y$, $3d_{xy}$, etc. are *not* eigenfunctions, and we are restricted to the pure $m = 0, \pm 1, \pm 2, \ldots$ type solutions.

Thus far we have indicated that the stationary state functions for the

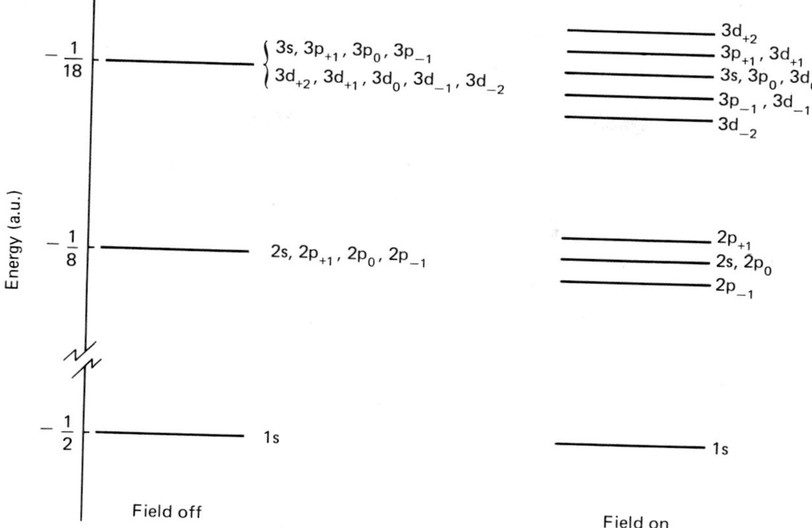

FIG. 4-14 Energy levels of a hydrogenlike ion in absence and presence of a z-directed magnetic field.

hydrogenlike ions are eigenfunctions for $\hat{L}^2$ and $\hat{L}_z$, and we have compared this to the fact that $|\mathbf{L}|$ and L_z are constants of motion for a frictionless gyroscope precessing about an external field axis, but how about other systems? Are their stationary state functions also eigenfunctions for $\hat{L}^2$ and $\hat{L}_z$? A general approach to this kind of question is discussed in Chapter 6. For now we simply note that the spherical harmonics are eigenfunctions of $\hat{L}^2$ and $\hat{L}_z$ [Eqs. (4-55) and (4-57)] and that any state function of the form $\psi(r, \theta, \phi) = R(r)Y_{l,m}(\theta, \phi)$ will necessarily be an eigenfunction of these operators. But the spherical harmonics are solutions associated with spherically symmetric potentials. Therefore, it turns out that eigenfunctions of the time-independent hamiltonian operator are also eigenfunctions for $\hat{L}^2$ and $\hat{L}_z$ *only if the potential is spherically symmetric*. In the more restricted case in which ψ has the form $\psi(r, \theta, \phi) = f(r, \theta)\exp(im\phi)$, ψ will still be an eigenfunction of $\hat{L}_z$ but not of $\hat{L}^2$. This situation applies in systems having *cylindrically* symmetric potentials, dependent on r and θ but not ϕ (e.g., H_2^+). We discuss such cases in more detail in Chapter 7.

4-6 Summary

(1) The Schrödinger equation for an electron moving in the field of a fixed nucleus is almost identical with an equation obtained from separation of variables in reduced-mass coordinates in the moving-nucleus case. The main difference is that m_e in the former equation is replaced by the reduced mass μ in the latter.

(2) The bound-state energies for time-independent states of the hydrogenlike ion depend on the quantum number n (a positive integer) and vary as $-1/n^2$.

This means that the energies get closer together as n increases and that there is an infinite number of such negative energy levels. Each such energy level has degeneracy n^2. A continuum of energies exists for unbound ($E > 0$) states.

(3) Each stationary state wavefunction is characterized by three quantum numbers, n, l, and m, all integers, with l ranging from 0 to $n - 1$ and m ranging from $-l$ to $+l$. If $l = 0$, we have an s state and ψ is spherically symmetric with a cusp at the nucleus. If $l = 1$, we have a p state, etc. In all states there is a finite probability for finding the electron beyond the classical turning point.

(4) Eigenfunctions $R_{n,l}(r)\Theta_{l,m}(\theta)\Phi_m(\phi)$ with $m \neq 0$ are complex but can be mixed to form real eigenfunctions. However, if an external field causes states of different m to be nondegenerate, such mixing is not allowed.

(5) All the stationary state eigenfunctions are orthogonal, and radial and/or planar[6] nodes are instrumental in this. The effect of a radial node on energy is the same as that of a planar node, so that all eigenfunctions with, say three nodes (all radial, all planar, or a combination) are degenerate. This is peculiar to the $-r^{-1}$ potential.

(6) Separation of variables is not "perfectly clean" since the differential equations for R and Θ (Eqs. (4-38) and (4-39)), are linked through β and those for Θ and Φ (Eq. 4-40) are linked through m. This leads to interdependencies in the values of n, l, and m.

(7) Spherical harmonics are the angular parts of solutions to Schrödinger equations for systems having spherically symmetric potentials. These functions are eigenfunctions of $\hat{L}_z$ and $\hat{L}^2$, so such states have sharp values of L_z, L^2, and E. The value of L_z in atomic units is m, and for L^2 it is $l(l + 1)$, where l and m must be integers.

(8) The z component of the magnetic moment due to orbital motion of a charged particle is proportional to m, and so m is called the magnetic quantum number.

(9) Eigenfunctions other than spherical harmonics exist for $\hat{L}^2$ and $\hat{L}_z$ but these are not separable into θ- and ϕ-dependent functions. In these cases l and m can be half-integers. These cases do not arise in orbital motion, but do arise in spin problems.

(10) If V is cylindrically symmetric [i.e., $V = V(r, \theta)$], the eigenfunctions of the hamiltonian are still eigenfunctions for $\hat{L}_z$ but not for $\hat{L}^2$. Hence, m still equals the z component of angular momentum for such a system.

PROBLEMS

4-1 Evaluate the energy *difference* between 1s and 2p states of the hydrogen atom in units of hertz (Hz). (See Appendix 12 for conversion factors.) Use m_e and also the reduced mass μ to see how much error is introduced by assuming a fixed nucleus.

[6] Some "planar" nodes are really curved nodal surfaces. $3d_{z^2}$ is an example of an atomic orbital with such nodes.

4-2 Calculate the distance from the nucleus at which the classical turning point occurs for the 1s electron in the hydrogen atom. Calculate the percentage of electronic charge which quantum mechanics predicts to be beyond this distance.

4-3 Using atomic units, compute for a 1s electron of the hydrogenlike ion($\psi = \sqrt{Z^3/\pi}\exp(-Zr)$):

(a) the most *probable* distance of the electron from the nucleus;
(b) the *average* distance of the electron from the nucleus;
(c) the distance from the nucleus of *maximum probability density*.

Note how these quantities depend upon the nuclear charge, Z.

4-4 Compute the above three quantities for a $2p_0$ electron of the hydrogen *atom*.

4-5 Demonstrate by integration that the 1s and 2s orbitals of the hydrogen atom are orthogonal.

4-6 Calculate the average potential energy for an electron in a 1s orbital of the hydrogen atom and compare this with the total energy. Is this potential energy consistent with the average distance of the electron from the nucleus as calculated in Problem 4-3b? Repeat this problem for the $2p_0$ electron.

4-7 Normalize the function $r\exp(-r)\cos\theta$. (See Appendix 1 for useful integrals.)

4-8 Sketch the $2p_z$ and the $3d_{xy}$ wavefunctions. Demonstrate, without explicitly integrating, that these are orthogonal.

4-9 Show that the sum of the charge distributions of all five 3d orbitals is spherically symmetric.

4-10 Sketch the potential $V = -1/|x|$. Write the Schrödinger equation for an electron in the $x > 0$ half of this potential. (Use atomic units.) (Symmetry enables you to solve the Schrödinger equation in one half of the well and then extend the eigenfunctions symmetrically or antisymmetrically into the other half.) Using procedures described in Chapter 3 for the harmonic oscillator, solve the Schrödinger equation for the energy level formula. Find explicit formulas for the eigenfunctions of the lowest three energy levels.

4-11 Find the atomic unit of velocity consistent with the definitions in Table 3-1 and evaluate it in terms of SI units. What is the speed of light in atomic units?

4-12 Calculate the average value of x for the 1s state of the hydrogen atom. Explain why your result is physically reasonable.

4-13 Calculate the most probable value of θ in the $2p_z$ state of the hydrogen atom.

4-14 Obtain the average value of position, $\bar{x}$, for a particle moving in a one-dimensional harmonic oscillator potential in a state with the normalized wavefunction

$$\psi = (\beta/48^2\pi)^{1/4}[(2\sqrt{\beta}x)^3 - 12\sqrt{\beta}x]\exp(-\beta x^2/2)$$

[There is an easy way to do this problem.]

4-15 Test the $2p_0$ eigenfunction to see if it is an eigenfunction for $\hat{L}_x$ or $\hat{L}_y$ [Eqs. (4-58) and (4-59)]. Show that the 1s function is an eigenfunction of $\hat{L}_x$, $\hat{L}_y$, $\hat{L}_z$, and $\hat{L}^2$. Explain, in terms of the vector model, this seeming violation of the discussion in the text.

4-16 Work out the value of $\hat{L}^2\psi_{2p_0}$ by brute force and show that the result agrees with Eq. (4-57).

4-17 Calculate in hertz the splitting between $2p_0$ and $2p_{+1}$ levels of the hydrogen atom in a magnetic field of 5000 G. Compare this with the 2p → 1s transition energy (in parts per million).

REFERENCES

[1] H. Eyring, J. Walter, and E. D. Kimball, "Quantum Chemistry," Chapter VI. Wiley, New York, 1944.
[2] I. N. Levine, "Quantum Chemistry," 2nd ed. Allyn and Bacon, Boston, Massachusetts.
[3] L. Pauling and E. B. Wilson, Jr., "Introduction to Quantum Mechanics." McGraw-Hill, New York, 1935.

CHAPTER 5

MANY-ELECTRON ATOMS

5-1 The Independent Electron Approximation

In previous chapters we have dealt with the motion of a single particle in various potential fields. When we deal with more than one particle, new problems arise and new techniques are needed. Some of these are discussed in this chapter.

In constructing the hamiltonian operator for a many electron atom, we shall assume a fixed nucleus and ignore the minor error introduced by using electron mass rather than reduced mass. There will be a kinetic energy operator for each electron and potential terms for the various electrostatic attractions and repulsions in the system. Assuming n electrons and an atomic number of Z, the hamiltonian operator is (in atomic units)

$$H(1, 2, 3, \ldots, n) = -\tfrac{1}{2}\sum_{i=1}^{n} \nabla_i^2 - \sum_{i=1}^{n} (Z/r_i) + \sum_{i=1}^{n-1}\sum_{j=i+1}^{n} 1/r_{ij} \qquad (5\text{-}1)$$

The numbers in parentheses on the left-hand side of Eq. (5-1) symbolize the spatial coordinates of each of the n electrons. Thus, 1 stands for x_1, y_1, z_1, or r_1, θ_1, ϕ_1, etc. We shall use this notation frequently throughout this book. Since we are not here concerned with the quantum-mechanical description of the translational motion of the atom, there is no kinetic energy operator for the nucleus in Eq. (5-1). The index i refers to the electrons, so we see that Eq. (5-1) provides us with the desired kinetic energy operator for each electron, a nuclear–electronic attraction term for each electron, and an interelectronic repulsion term for each *distinct* electron pair. (The summation indices guarantee that $1/r_{12}$ and $1/r_{21}$ will not *both* appear in H. This prevents counting the same physical interaction twice. The indices also prevent nonphysical self-repulsion terms, such as $1/r_{22}$, from occurring.) Frequently used alternative notations for the double summation in Eq. (5-1) are $\frac{1}{2}\sum_{i \neq j}^{n} 1/r_{ij}$, which counts each interaction twice and divides by two, and $\sum_{i<j}^{n}$ or $\sum'_{i,j}$, which is merely a shorthand symbol for the expression in Eq. (5-1). In each of these alternative notations, the summation is still over two indices, but the second $\sum$ symbol is "understood."

For the helium atom, Eq. (5-1) becomes (see Fig. 5-1)

$$H(1, 2) = -\tfrac{1}{2}\nabla_1^2 - \tfrac{1}{2}\nabla_2^2 - (2/r_1) - (2/r_2) + (1/r_{12}) \qquad (5\text{-}2)$$

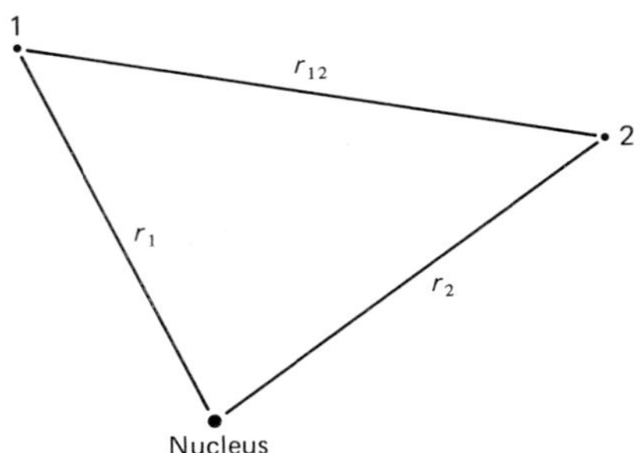

FIG. 5-1 Interparticle coordinates for a three-particle system consisting of two electrons and a nucleus.

The helium hamiltonian (5-2) can be rewritten as

$$H(1, 2) = h(1) + h(2) + 1/r_{12} \tag{5-3}$$

where

$$h(i) = -\tfrac{1}{2}\nabla_i^2 - 2/r_i \tag{5-4}$$

In Eq. (5-3) we have merely grouped H into two one-electron operators and one two-electron operator. There is no way to separate this hamiltonian *completely* into a sum of one-electron operators without loss of rigor. However, if we wish to *approximate* the hamiltonian for helium in such a way that it becomes separable, we might try simply ignoring the interelectronic repulsion term:

$$H_{\text{approx}} = h(1) + h(2) \tag{5-5}$$

If we do this, our approximate hamiltonian H_{approx} treats the kinetic and potential energies of each electron *completely independently* of the motion or position of the other. For this reason, such a treatment falls within the category of "independent electron approximations."

Notice that each individual one-electron hamiltonian (5-4) is just the hamiltonian for a hydrogenlike ion, so it has as eigenfunctions the 1s, 2s, $2p_x$, etc., functions of Chapter 4 with $Z = 2$. Such one-electron functions are referred to as *atomic orbitals*.[1] Representing them with the symbol ϕ_i (e.g., $\phi_1 = 1s$, $\phi_2 = 2s$, $\phi_3 = 2p_x$, $\phi_4 = 2p_y$, etc.) we have, then,

$$h(1)\phi_i(1) = \epsilon_i\phi_i(1) \tag{5-6}$$

where ϵ_i is referred to as the *orbital energy*, or *one-electron energy* for atomic orbital ϕ_i. As we saw in Chapter 4, ϵ_i is given by

$$\epsilon_i = -\tfrac{1}{2}Z^2/n^2 \tag{5-7}$$

where n is the principal quantum number for ϕ_i, and Z is the nuclear charge in atomic units. The "1" in Eq. (5-6) indicates that $\phi_i(1)$ is a function whose variable is the position of electron 1.

[1] The term "atomic orbital" is used for any one-electron function used to describe the electronic distribution about an atom.

We will now show that *products of the atomic orbitals* ϕ *are eigenfunctions of* H_{approx}. Let the general product of atomic orbitals for helium be written $\phi_i(1)\phi_j(2)$. Then

$$H_{\text{approx}}\phi_i(1)\phi_j(2) = (h(1) + h(2))\phi_i(1)\phi_j(2) \tag{5-8}$$

$$= h(1)\phi_i(1)\phi_j(2) + h(2)\phi_i(1)\phi_j(2) \tag{5-9}$$

But $h(1)$ does not contain any of the variables in $\phi_j(2)$, and so they commute. Similarly, $h(2)$ and $\phi_i(1)$ commute, and

$$\begin{aligned} H_{\text{approx}}\phi_i(1)\phi_j(2) &= \phi_j(2)h(1)\phi_i(1) + \phi_i(1)h(2)\phi_j(2) \\ &= \phi_j(2)\epsilon_i\phi_i(1) + \phi_i(1)\epsilon_j\phi_j(2) \qquad \text{[from Eq. (5-6)]} \\ &= (\epsilon_i + \epsilon_j)\phi_i(1)\phi_j(2) = E\phi_i(1)\phi_j(2). \end{aligned} \tag{5-10}$$

Thus, $\phi_i(1)\phi_j(2)$ is an eigenfunction of H_{approx}, and the eigenvalue E is equal to the sum of the orbital energies. These results are yet another example of the general rules stated in Section 2-7 for separable hamiltonians. Indeed, once we recognized that H_{approx} is separable, we could have written these results down at once.

Since the above terminology and results are so important for understanding many quantum-chemical calculations, we will summarize them here:

(1) The hamiltonian for a multielectron system cannot be separated into one-electron parts without making some approximation.

(2) Ignoring interelectron repulsion operators is one way to allow separability.

(3) The one-electron operators in the resulting approximate hamiltonian for an atom are hydrogenlike ion hamiltonians. Their eigenfunctions are called *atomic orbitals*.

(4) Simple products of atomic orbitals are eigenfunctions for the approximate hamiltonian.

(5) *In this approximation* the total energy is equal to the sum of the one-electron energies.

5-2 Simple Products and Electron Exchange Symmetry

In the independent particle model just described, the wavefunction for the lowest-energy state for helium is 1s(1)1s(2) since this has the lowest possible sum of one-electron energies. The *electronic configuration* for this state is symbolized $1s^2$, the superscript telling us how many electrons are in 1s orbitals. What might we expect for the electronic configuration of the lowest excited state? The answer is 1s2s (superscript "ones" are implicit). (At this point there is no reason for preferring this configuration to, say, $1s2p_x$, but we shall show later that, in multielectronic systems, the 2s orbital has a lower energy than does a 2p orbital, even though they have the same principal quantum number.) Thus, we might write

$$\psi(1, 2) = 1s(1)2s(2) \equiv \underbrace{\sqrt{8/\pi}\exp(-2r_1)}_{\text{He}^+\ 1s}\underbrace{\sqrt{1/\pi}(1 - r_2)\exp(-r_2)}_{\text{He}^+\ 2s} \quad (5\text{-}11)$$

If one were to calculate $\bar{r}_1$, the average distance from the nucleus for electron 1, using this wavefunction, he would obtain a value of $\frac{3}{4}$ a.u., consistent with the 1s state of a helium ion. For electron 2 we would find an average value, $\bar{r}_2$, of 3 a.u., characteristic of the 2s state (Problem 5-2). How does this correspond to what we would find experimentally?

Before answering this question, we must recall that there are special problems associated with measuring the properties of an atomic system. The process of "seeing" electrons in atoms well enough to pinpoint their positions perturbs an atom so strongly that it cannot be assumed to be in the same state after the measurement. To get around this problem, we can assume that we have a very large number of identically prepared helium atoms, and that a single measurement of electronic positions will be made on each atom. It is assumed that the average of the instantaneous r values for a billion systems is identical to the average r value for a billion instants in a single undisturbed system.

When we consider the measurement of average values for r_1 and r_2 in helium, we immediately encounter another problem. Say we can effect a simultaneous measurement of the two electronic distances in the first He atom. We call these r_1 and r_2 and tabulate them for future averaging. Then we move on to a new helium atom and measure r_1 and r_2 for it. But we clearly have no way of identifying a particular one of these electrons with a particular one of the earlier pair. There is no connection between r_1 for one atom and r_1 for the next since all electrons are identical. If we want to know r, we can only average them all together and leave it at that.

Thus, the wavefunction (5-11) does not seem to be entirely satisfactory since it enables us to calculate $\bar{r}_1 \neq \bar{r}_2$, something that is *in principle* impossible to measure. We need to modify the wavefunction so that it yields an average value for r_1 and r_2 (or for any quantity) that is independent of our choice of electron labels. This means that the electron density itself, given by $\psi(1, 2)^2$, must be independent of our electron labeling scheme.

In a two-electron system like helium, there are only two ways to arrange the labels "1" and "2" in a single product function. For example, the product 1s2s can be written

$$1s(1)2s(2) \qquad \text{or} \qquad 2s(1)1s(2) \quad (5\text{-}12)$$

Squaring these gives two different functions, namely,

$$\begin{aligned} 1s^2(1)2s^2(2) &= (8/\pi)\exp(-4r_1)(1/\pi)(1 - 2r_2 + r_2^2)\exp(-2r_2) \\ 2s^2(1)1s^2(2) &= (8/\pi)\exp(-4r_2)(1/\pi)(1 - 2r_1 + r_1^2)\exp(-2r_1) \end{aligned} \quad (5\text{-}13)$$

These are different since they predict, for instance, different distributions for electron 1. The functions (5-12) are said to differ by an interchange of electron indices, or coordinates. (Since electron labels denote position coordinates, interchange of labels in the mathematical formula corresponds to interchanging position of electrons in the physical model.) For ψ^2 to be invariant under such an interchange, it is necessary that ψ itself be either symmetric or antisymmetric under the interchange. That is, if P is an interchange operator such that $Pf(1, 2) = f(2, 1)$ then we need a ψ such that

$$P\psi = \pm\psi \tag{5-14}$$

since then

$$P(\psi^2) = (P\psi)^2 = (\pm\psi)^2 = \psi^2$$

One such wavefunction is given by the *sum* of eigenfunctions (5-12),

$$\psi_s = (1/\sqrt{2})[1s(1)2s(2) + 2s(1)1s(2)] \tag{5-15}$$

since

$$P\psi_s = (1/\sqrt{2})[1s(2)2s(1) + 2s(2)1s(1)] = \psi_s$$

(the factor $1/\sqrt{2}$ keeps the wavefunction normalized). Wavefunction (5-15) is thus symmetric under electron interchange. Is Eq. (5-15) still an eigenfunction for H_{approx}? Yes, because the eigenfunctions (5-12) are degenerate (both have $E = \epsilon_{1s} + \epsilon_{2s}$) and can therefore be mixed together in any way we choose and still be eigenfunctions. The antisymmetric combination is

$$\psi_a = (1/\sqrt{2})[1s(1)2s(2) - 2s(1)1s(2)] \tag{5-16}$$

Thus far we have shown that simple products of atomic orbitals give us two degenerate eigenfunctions of H_{approx} for the configuration 1s2s and that these eigenfunctions fail to have the required symmetry properties for interchange of electron coordinates. But we have shown that, by taking the sum and difference of these simple products, we can form new eigenfunctions of H_{approx} that are respectively symmetric and antisymmetric with respect to the interchange of electron coordinates, so that ψ^2 is invariant to electron interchange.

We have indicated in Chapter 2 that a *nondegenerate* eigenfunction must be symmetric or antisymmetric for any operation that leaves the hamiltonian unchanged. Here we are discussing *degenerate* functions and are arguing from physical intuition that the eigenfunctions must be symmetric or antisymmetric for electron interchange. This suggests that we ask whether the hamiltonian is unchanged by electron interchange. First we examine H_{approx}:

$$PH_{\text{approx}} = P[h(1) + h(2)] = h(2) + h(1) = H_{\text{approx}} \tag{5-17}$$

Our approximate hamiltonian *is* invariant to electron exchange, so any *non-degenerate* eigenfunctions must be symmetric or antisymmetric for interchange of electron labels (or positions). Only because the 1s2s configuration leads to *degenerate* eigenfunctions were we able to find unsymmetric eigenfunctions like Eq. (5-12). This situation is reminiscent of the particle-in-a-ring system discussed in Chapter 2. Let us now examine the full hamiltonian H:

$$PH(1, 2) = P[h(1) + h(2) + 1/r_{12}] = h(2) + h(1) + 1/r_{21} = H(1, 2) \tag{5-18}$$

Since r_{12} and r_{21} are the same distance, it is evident that H is invariant to interchange of electron labels. This means that eigenfunctions of $H(1, 2)$ also must be either symmetric or antisymmetric under electron interchange unless there is degeneracy. Now the product functions (5-13), (5-15), and (5-16) are not *eigenfunctions* of H since it is not completely separable into one-electron parts, but we can take such product functions to be *approximate* solutions to H. If we do this, it turns out that they are *not degnerate* in terms of their average energies. (We shall show this later.) Hence, we should choose the symmetric and antisymmetric forms (5-15) and (5-16) as *approximate*, nondegenerate solutions for H since they show the symmetry characteristics that we know must be possessed by nondegenerate eigenfunctions of H. We should not choose the forms (5-12) since they lack the proper symmetry.

We now summarize the points we have tried to convey in this section.

(1) A simple product function of the type 1s(1)2s(2) enables one to calculate different expectation values for electrons 1 and 2. This makes no physical sense since the electrons are *identical particles* and hence are not physically distinguishable.

(2) Wavefunctions that overcome this difficulty must be either symmetric or antisymmetric with respect to exchange of electron labels (coordinates).

(3) The fact that this kind of "exchange symmetry" must be present is also (or alternatively) seen from the fact that H (and also H_{approx}) is invariant under such an exchange operation.

(4) Since these two symmetry eigenfunctions are *degenerate* eigenfunctions for H_{approx}, unsymmetric[2] eigenfunctions are possible for H_{approx}.

(5) Product type wavefunctions cannot be eigenfunctions for H, but, if we use such wavefunctions as approximate solutions, we should use those combinations that at least satisfy the symmetry requirements of the problem.

5-3 Electron Spin and the Exclusion Principle

Chemical and spectral evidence indicates that metals in Groups IA and IB of the periodic table are reasonably well represented by an electron configura-

[2] A function is unsymmetric for any operation that produces neither plus nor minus that function; i.e., if $Pf = y$ and $y \neq \pm f$, f is unsymmetric under the operation P.

tion wherein one loosely held "valence" electron occupies an s orbital and all other electrons occur in pairs in orbitals of lower principal quantum number. Thus, lithium has a ground-state electronic structure approximated by the configuration $1s^2 2s$, sodium by $1s^2 2s^2 2p^6 3s$, copper by $1s^2 2s^2 2p^6 3s^2 3p^6 3d^{10} 4s$, etc. (A configuration indicating that all orbitals of given n and l are doubly occupied, leaving no other electrons, is often called a *closed shell.* Thus, the above cited examples each consist of a closed shell plus one s valence electron.) The observation that each atomic orbital in such configurations is occupied by no more than two electrons was without a theoretical explanation for some time.

When an atom like sodium is placed in an external magnetic field, what should be the magnetic moment of the atom due to orbital motion of the electrons? The s electrons should contribute nothing since, by definition of s, $l = 0$ and hence the magnetic quantum number $m = 0$ for such electrons. An electron in a p orbital may have an orbital magnetic moment, but if all p levels ($l = 1$, $m = +1, 0, -1$) are equally occupied, the *net* magnetic moment should be zero. It is clear, then, that we might expect atoms in Groups IA and IB to possess no magnetic moment due to electron orbital motion. Nevertheless, Stern and Gerlach [1, 2] found that, when a beam of unexcited silver atoms is passed through an inhomogeneous magnetic field, it splits into two components as though each silver atom possesses a small magnetic moment capable of taking on either of two orientations in the applied field. (In a *homogeneous* magnetic field, the north and south poles of a magnetic dipole experience equal but oppositely directed forces, causing the dipole to become *oriented.* An example is a magnetic compass in the magnetic field of the earth. In an *inhomogeneous* magnetic field the poles experience opposite but unequal forces, causing the entire dipole to be *accelerated through space* in addition to being oriented.) Uhlenbeck and Goudsmit [3] and Bichowsky and Urey [4] independently suggested that the electron behaves as though it were a particle of finite radius spinning about its center of mass. Such a spinning particle would classically have angular momentum and, since it is charged, an accompanying magnetic moment.[3]

If we accept this model of electron spin, then we can rationalize our experimental facts if we assume each electron is capable of being in one of but two possible opposite spin states. This is done in the following way. If we attribute *opposite* spins to the two 1s electrons in, say, silver, their spin moments should cancel. Similarly, all other orbital-sharing electrons would contribute nothing if their spins were opposed. Only the outermost (5s) electron would have an

[3] This classical model is pedagogically useful and is responsible for the term "spin," which is still employed to describe the fourth quantum number. However, it is now realized that spin has no classical counterpart. Whereas it appears as a natural consequence of a *relativistic* quantum mechanical treatment of the hydrogen atom, it must be added on as an "extra" effect in nonrelativistic treatments. In this book, we will continue to make use of the classical spin model.

uncancelled spin moment. Its two possible orientations would cause the beam to split into two components as is observed.[4]

The evident need for the introduction of the concept of electron spin means that our wavefunctions of earlier sections are incomplete. We need a wavefunction that tells us not only the probability that an electron will be at given r, θ, ϕ coordinates in three-dimensional space at any instant, but also the probability that it will be in one or the other spin state. Rather than seeking detailed mathematical descriptions of spin state functions, we will simply symbolize them $\alpha(\omega)$ and $\beta(\omega)$ where ω is a "spin coordinate" (for most practical purposes, a labeling index). Then the symbol $\phi(1)\alpha(1)$ will mean that electron number 1 is in a spatial distribution corresponding to space orbital ϕ, and that it has spin α. In the independent electron scheme, then, we could write the "spin orbital" (includes space and spin parts) for the valence electron of silver either as $5s(1)\alpha(1)$ or $5s(1)\beta(1)$. These two possibilities both occur in the atomic beam and interact differently with the inhomogeneous magnetic field.

We now focus on the manner in which spin considerations affect wavefunction symmetry. The electrons are still identical particles, so our particle distribution must be insensitive to our choice of labels. This last statement is equivalent to saying that ψ must be symmetric or antisymmetric for interchange of electron *space and spin coordinates*. Let us examine this situation in the case of ground state helium and lithium atoms.

In the independent electron approximation, the lowest-energy configuration for helium is $1s^2$. Let us write the various conceivable spin combinations for this configuration. They are

$$\left.\begin{matrix} 1s(1)\alpha(1)1s(2)\alpha(2) \\ 1s(1)\alpha(1)1s(2)\beta(2) \\ 1s(1)\beta(1)1s(2)\alpha(2) \\ 1s(1)\beta(1)1s(2)\beta(2) \end{matrix}\right\} = 1s(1)1s(2)\left\{\begin{matrix} \alpha(1)\alpha(2) & \quad (5\text{-}19) \\ \alpha(1)\beta(2) & \quad (5\text{-}20) \\ \beta(1)\alpha(2) & \quad (5\text{-}21) \\ \beta(1)\beta(2) & \quad (5\text{-}22) \end{matrix}\right.$$

It is easy to see that the common space term $1s(1)1s(2)$ is symmetric for electron interchange. Likewise, $\alpha(1)\alpha(2)$ and $\beta(1)\beta(2)$ are each symmetric, so Eqs. (5-19) and (5-22) are totally symmetric wavefunctions. The spin parts of Eqs. (5-20) and (5-21) are unsymmetric (not *anti*symmetric) for interchange, so these wavefunctions are not satisfactory. However, we can take the sum and difference of Eqs. (5-20) and (5-21) to obtain

$$1s(1)1s(2)\left\{\begin{matrix} (1/\sqrt{2})[\alpha(1)\beta(2) + \beta(1)\alpha(2)] & \quad (5\text{-}23) \\ (1/\sqrt{2})[\alpha(1)\beta(2) - \beta(1)\alpha(2)] & \quad (5\text{-}24) \end{matrix}\right.$$

[4] Actually, other experimental evidence, such as splitting of atomic spectral lines due to applied magnetic fields, was also available. Furthermore, experience with the quantum theory of orbital angular momentum played a role in the treatment of electron spin. The reader should not think that the historical development of quantum theory of spin was as naive or simple as we make it appear here.

The $2^{-1/2}$ serves to maintain normality if we assume α and β to be orthonormal:

$$\int \alpha^*(1)\alpha(1)\, d\omega(1) = \int \beta^*(1)\beta(1)\, d\omega(1) = 1 \tag{5-25}$$

$$\int \alpha^*(1)\beta(1)\, d\omega(1) = \int \beta^*(1)\alpha(1)\, d\omega(1) = 0 \tag{5-26}$$

(Here, integration over ω is in effect equivalent to summing over the possible electron indices. If, for a particular electron index, the spins agree, then the integral equals unity. If they disagree, the integral vanishes.) Wavefunction (5-23) consists of symmetric space and spin parts, so it is overall symmetric. Wavefunction (5-24) contains a symmetric space part times an antisymmetric spin part, so it is overall antisymmetric. We have succeeded, then, in writing down four wavefunctions for the configuration $1s^2$ having proper symmetry for electron interchange. Three of these, Eqs. (5-19), (5-22), (5-23), are symmetric and one, Eq. (5-24), is antisymmetric. Experimentally, we know that the ground state of helium is a *singlet*, that is, there is but one such state. *This suggests that the wavefunction must be antisymmetric.*

Now let us try lithium. The lowest-energy configuration should be $1s^3$, and we can write eight unique space–spin orbital products:

$$1s(1)1s(2)1s(3)\begin{cases} \alpha(1)\alpha(2)\alpha(3) & (5\text{-}27)\\ \alpha(1)\alpha(2)\beta(3) & (5\text{-}28)\\ \alpha(1)\beta(2)\alpha(3) & (5\text{-}29)\\ \beta(1)\alpha(2)\alpha(3) & (5\text{-}30)\\ \alpha(1)\beta(2)\beta(3) & (5\text{-}31)\\ \beta(1)\alpha(2)\beta(3) & (5\text{-}32)\\ \beta(1)\beta(2)\alpha(3) & (5\text{-}33)\\ \beta(1)\beta(2)\beta(3) & (5\text{-}34) \end{cases}$$

Of these, the first and last are totally symmetric for all electron interchanges. The remaining six are unsymmetric for two out of three possible interchanges. Can we make appropriate linear combinations of these as we did for helium? Let us try. The problem is simplified by recognizing that, if we start with, say, two α's and one β, we still have that number of α's and β's after interchange of electron labels. Hence, we mix together only functions that agree in total numbers of α's and β's, i.e., (5-28), (5-29), (5-30) with each other, or (5-31), (5-32), (5-33) with each other. Let us try the sum of (5-28), (5-29), and (5-30). Ignoring normalization, this gives the spin function

$$\alpha(1)\alpha(2)\beta(3) + \alpha(1)\beta(2)\alpha(3) + \beta(1)\alpha(2)\alpha(3) \tag{5-35}$$

Interchanging electron spin coordinates 1 and 2 gives

$$\alpha(2)\alpha(1)\beta(3) + \alpha(2)\beta(1)\alpha(3) + \beta(2)\alpha(1)\alpha(3)$$

which, upon reordering each product, is easily seen to be identical to (5-35). The same result arises from interchanging 1 and 3 or 2 and 3, and so (5-35) is symmetric for all interchanges. The sum of (5-31), (5-32), and (5-33) is likewise symmetric. Can we find any combinations that are totally antisymmetric? A few attempts with pencil and paper should convince one that it is impossible to find a combination that is antisymmetric for all interchanges. Experimentally, we know that no state of lithium corresponds to a $1s^3$ configuration.

To summarize, we have found that for the configuration $1s^2$ we can write three wavefunctions that are symmetric and one that is antisymmetric under exchange of electron space and spin coordinates, while for the configuration $1s^3$ we can construct symmetric or unsymmetric ones. The physical observation is that atoms exist having an electronic structure approximately represented by the configuration $1s^2$, but not by $1s^3$. This and other physical evidence has led to the recognition of the *exclusion principle*: Wavefunctions must be *antisymmetric* with respect to simultaneous interchange of space *and* spin coordinates of electrons.[5] In invoking the exclusion principle, we exclude all of the $1s^3$ wavefunctions and three out of the four wavefunctions we were able to construct for the ground state of helium, leaving (5-24) as the only acceptable wavefunction.

We have seen that the ground state configuration of lithium cannot be $1s^3$. Can we satisfy the exclusion principle with the next-lowest energy configuration $1s^22s$? We will try to find a satisfactory solution, but our manipulations will be simplified if we streamline our notation. We will write a function such as $1s(1)1s(2)2s(3)\alpha(1)\beta(2)\alpha(3)$ as $1s1s2s\alpha\beta\alpha$, allowing *position* in the sequence to stand for the electron label. Interchanging electrons 1 and 2 is then represented by switching the order of space functions in positions 1 and 2 *and* spin functions in positions 1 and 2 thusly

$$1s1s2s\alpha\beta\alpha \xrightarrow{1\rightleftharpoons 2} 1s1s2s\beta\alpha\alpha \tag{5-36}$$

This interchange produced a new function rather than merely reversing the sign of our starting function. But if we take the difference between the two products in Eq. (5-36), we will have a function that is antisymmetric to 1, 2 interchange: $1s1s2s(\alpha\beta\alpha - \beta\alpha\alpha)$. Now we subject this to a 1, 3 interchange and the new products produced are subtracted to give a function that is antisymmetric to both 1, 2 and 1, 3 interchange: $1s1s2s(\alpha\beta\alpha - \beta\alpha\alpha) + 2s1s1s(\alpha\alpha\beta - \alpha\beta\alpha)$. This is subjected to a 2, 3 interchange. The second half of our function is already antisymmetric for this interchange, but the first half generates new terms, which

[5] A broader statement is: Wavefunctions must be antisymmetric (symmetric) with respect to simultaneous interchange of space and spin coordinates of fermions (bosons). A fermion is characterized by half-integral spin quantum number; a boson is characterized by integral spin quantum number. Electrons have spin quantum number $\frac{1}{2}$ and are therefore fermions.

are again subtracted. The resulting wavefunction, antisymmetric for all interchanges, is

$$(1/\sqrt{6})[1s1s2s(\alpha\beta\alpha - \beta\alpha\alpha) + 1s2s1s(\beta\alpha\alpha - \alpha\alpha\beta) + 2s1s1s(\alpha\alpha\beta - \alpha\beta\alpha)] \tag{5-37}$$

The factor $6^{-1/2}$ normalizes (5-37) since each of the six space–spin products is normalized and orthogonal to each other product by virtue of either space-orbital or spin-orbital disagreement, or both. Note that, whereas the two-electron wavefunction for helium was separable into a single space function times a spin function, the lithium wavefunction must be written as a linear combination of such products. This is usually true when we deal with more than two electrons.

Since $1s^2 2s$ is the lowest-energy configuration for which we can write an antisymmetrized wavefunction, this *is* the ground state configuration for lithium in this independent-electron approximation.

In summary, phenomenological evidence suggests that an electron can exist in either of two "spin states" in the presence of a magnetic field. Writing wavefunctions including spin functions and comparing these with experimental facts indicates that states exist only for wavefunctions which satisfy the exclusion principle.

5-4 Slater Determinants and the Pauli Principle

It was pointed out by Slater [5] that there is a simple way to write wavefunctions guaranteeing that they will be antisymmetric for interchange of electronic space and spin coordinates: one writes the wavefunction as a determinant. For the $1s^2 2s$ configuration of lithium, one would write

$$\psi = \frac{1}{\sqrt{6}} \begin{vmatrix} 1s(1)\alpha(1) & 1s(2)\alpha(2) & 1s(3)\alpha(3) \\ 1s(1)\beta(1) & 1s(2)\beta(2) & 1s(3)\beta(3) \\ 2s(1)\alpha(1) & 2s(2)\alpha(2) & 2s(3)\alpha(3) \end{vmatrix} \tag{5-38}$$

Expanding this according to the usual rules governing determinants (see Appendix 2) gives

$$\begin{aligned}\psi = (1/\sqrt{6})[&1s(1)\alpha(1)1s(2)\beta(2)2s(3)\alpha(3) + 2s(1)\alpha(1)1s(2)\alpha(2)1s(3)\beta(3) \\ &+ 1s(1)\beta(1)2s(2)\alpha(2)1s(3)\alpha(3) - 2s(1)\alpha(1)1s(2)\beta(2)1s(3)\alpha(3) \\ &- 1s(1)\beta(1)1s(2)\alpha(2)2s(3)\alpha(3) - 1s(1)\alpha(1)2s(2)\alpha(2)1s(3)\beta(3)]\end{aligned} \tag{5-39}$$

This can be factored and shown to be identical to wavefunction (5-37) of the preceding section.

A simplifying notation in common usage is to delete the α, β symbols of the spin-orbitals and to let a bar over the space orbital signify β spin, absence of a bar being understood to signify α spin. In this notation, Eq. (5-38) would be written

$$\psi = \frac{1}{\sqrt{6}} \begin{vmatrix} 1s(1) & 1s(2) & 1s(3) \\ 1\bar{s}(1) & 1\bar{s}(2) & 1\bar{s}(3) \\ 2s(1) & 2s(2) & 2s(3) \end{vmatrix} \tag{5-40}$$

The general prescription to follow in writing a Slater determinantal wavefunction is very simple:

(1) Choose the configuration to be represented. $1s1\bar{s}2s$ was used above. (Here we write $1s1\bar{s}2s$ rather than $1s^2 2s$ to emphasize that the two 1s electrons occupy different spin-orbitals.) For our general example, we will let U_i stand for a general spin-orbital and take a four-electron example of configuration U_1U_2 U_3U_4.

(2) For n electrons, set up an $n \times n$ determinant with $(n!)^{-1/2}$ as normalizing factor. Every position in the first *row* should be occupied by the first spin-orbital of the configuration; every position in the second row by the second spin-orbital, etc. Now put in electron indices so that all positions in *column* 1 are occupied by electron 1, column 2 by electron 2, etc.

In the case of our four-electron configuration, the recipe gives

$$\psi = \frac{1}{\sqrt{4!}} \begin{vmatrix} U_1(1) & U_1(2) & U_1(3) & U_1(4) \\ U_2(1) & U_2(2) & U_2(3) & U_2(4) \\ U_3(1) & U_3(2) & U_3(3) & U_3(4) \\ U_4(1) & U_4(2) & U_4(3) & U_4(4) \end{vmatrix} \tag{5-41}$$

Notice that the principal diagonal (top left to bottom right) contains our original configuration $U_1U_2U_3U_4$. Often, the Slater determinant is represented in a space-saving way by simply writing the principal diagonal between short vertical bars. The normalizing factor is deleted. Thus, Eq. (5-41) would be symbolized as $|U_1(1)U_2(2)U_3(3)U_4(4)|$.

We have indicated the general recipe for writing down a Slater determinant, and we have seen that, for the configuration $1s1\bar{s}2s$, this gives an antisymmetric wavefunction. Now we will give a general proof of the antisymmetry of such wavefunctions. We have already seen that interchanging the space and spin coordinates of electrons 1 and 2 corresponds to going through the wavefunction and changing all the 1's to 2's and vice versa; i.e., electron *labels* denote coordinates. In a Slater determinant, interchanging electron labels 1 and 2 is the same thing as interchanging columns 1 and 2 of the determinant. [See Eq. (5-41) and note that columns 1 and 2 differ only in electron index.] But a determinant reverses sign upon interchange of two rows or columns. (See Appendix 2 for a summary of the properties of determinants.) Hence, any Slater determinant reverses sign (i.e., is antisymmetric) upon the interchange of space and spin coordinates of any two electrons.

Suppose we tried to put two electrons into the same space-orbital with the same spin. This would require that the same spin-orbital be written twice in the configuration, causing two rows of the Slater determinant to be identical. [If both 1s electrons in Eq. (5-40) had α spin, the bars would be absent from row 2.] We just stated that the determinant must reverse sign upon interchange of two rows. If we interchange two *identical* rows, we change nothing yet the sign must reverse: the determinant must be equal to zero. Thus, the determinantal wavefunction vanishes when we try to put more than one electron into the same spin-orbital, indicating that this is not a physically allowed situation. This is a generalization of our earlier discovery that no $1s^3$ configuration is allowed by the exclusion principle, such a configuration requiring at least two electrons to have the same space and spin functions.

This restriction on allowable electronic configurations is more familiar to chemists as the Pauli principle: *In assigning electrons to atomic orbitals in the independent electron scheme, no two electrons are allowed to have all four quantum numbers (n, l, m, spin) the same.* **The Pauli principle is a restatement of the exclusion principle as it applies in the special case of an orbital approximation to the wavefunction.**

5-5 Singlet and Triplet States for the 1s2s Configuration of Helium

We showed in Section 5-2 that two *space* functions having proper space symmetry could be written for the configuration 1s2s. One was symmetric (Eq. 5-15) and one was antisymmetric (Eq. 5-16). Now we find that spin functions must be included in our wavefunctions, and in a way that makes the final result antisymmetric when space and spin coordinates are interchanged. We can accomplish this by multiplying the symmetric space function by an antisymmetric spin function, calling the result $\psi_{s,a}$. Thus,

$$\psi_{s,a}(1,2) = (1/\sqrt{2})[1s(1)2s(2) + 2s(1)1s(2)](1/\sqrt{2})[\alpha(1)\beta(2) - \beta(1)\alpha(2)] \tag{5-42}$$

Alternatively, we can multiply the antisymmetric space term by any one of the three possible symmetric spin terms:

$$\psi_{a,s}(1,2) = (1/\sqrt{2})[1s(1)2s(2) - 2s(1)1s(2)]\begin{cases}\alpha(1)\alpha(2) & \text{(5-43a)}\\ (1/\sqrt{2})[\alpha(1)\beta(2) + \beta(1)\alpha(2)] & \text{(5-43b)}\\ \beta(1)\beta(2) & \text{(5-43c)}\end{cases}$$

All four of these wavefunctions satisfy the exclusion principle and each is linearly independent of the others, indicating that four distinct physical states arise from the configuration 1s2s.

There are a number of important points that can be illustrated using these wavefunctions. The first has to do with Slater determinants. Let us write down a Slater determinantal expression corresponding to wavefunction (5-43a). The configuration is $1s(1)\alpha(1)2s(2)\alpha(2)$, giving the Slater determinant (where absence of a bar indicates α spin)

$$\psi_{a,s}(1, 2) = \frac{1}{\sqrt{2}}\begin{vmatrix} 1s(1) & 1s(2) \\ 2s(1) & 2s(2) \end{vmatrix} \tag{5-44}$$

which, upon expansion, gives us Eq. (5-43a). If we attempt the same process to obtain Eq. (5-43b), we encounter a difficulty. The configuration $1s(1)\alpha(1)$ $2s(2)\beta(2)$ leads to a 2×2 determinant, which, upon expansion, gives *two* product terms, whereas Eq. (5-43b) involves *four* product terms. The Slater determinantal functions corresponding to Eqs. (5-42) and (5-43b) are, in fact,

$$\psi_{\substack{s,a \\ a,s}}(1, 2) = \frac{1}{\sqrt{2}}\left\{\frac{1}{\sqrt{2}}\begin{vmatrix} 1s(1) & 1s(2) \\ 2\bar{s}(1) & 2\bar{s}(2) \end{vmatrix} \pm \frac{1}{\sqrt{2}}\begin{vmatrix} 1\bar{s}(1) & 1\bar{s}(2) \\ 2s(1) & 2s(2) \end{vmatrix}\right\} \tag{5-45}$$

The lesson to be gained from this is that a *single Slater determinant does not always display all of the symmetry possessed by the correct wavefunction.*

Next we will investigate the energies of the states as they are described by these wavefunctions. We have already pointed out that they are degenerate eigenfunctions of H_{approx}, but we will now examine their interactions with the full hamiltonian (5-2). Since our wavefunctions are not eigenfunctions of this hamiltonian, we cannot compare eigenvalues. Instead we must calculate the average values of the energy for each wavefunction, using the formula

$$\bar{E} = \int \psi^* H \psi \, d\tau \bigg/ \int \psi^* \psi \, d\tau \tag{5-46}$$

The symbol "$d\tau$" stands for integration over space and spin coordinates of the electrons: $d\tau = dv\,d\omega$. Since both space and spin parts of our wavefunctions are normalized [cf. Eqs. (5-25) and (5-26)], the denominator of Eq. (5-46) is unity and may be ignored. The energy thus is given by the expression

$$\bar{E} = \int \psi^*[-\tfrac{1}{2}\nabla_1^2 - \tfrac{1}{2}\nabla_2^2 - (2/r_1) - (2/r_2) + (1/r_{12})]\psi \, d\tau \tag{5-47}$$

Notice that the energy operator H contains no terms that would interact with spin functions α and β. (Such terms do arise at higher levels of refinement, but we ignore them for now.) Hence, the spin terms of ψ can be integrated separately, and, since all spin factors in Eqs. (5-42) and (5-43) are normalized, this gives a factor of unity in all four cases. This means that the average energies will be entirely determined by the space parts of the wavefunctions. This, in turn, means that all three states (5-43), which have the same space term, will have the same energy but that the state approximated by the function (5-42) may have a different energy. If our approximate representation of the exact eigenfunctions is physically realistic, we expect helium to display two excited state energies in the energy range consistent with a 1s2s configuration. Furthermore, we expect one of these state energies to be triply degenerate.

Which of these two state energies should be higher? To determine this requires that we expand our energy expression (5-47) for each of the two space functions (5-42) and (5-43).

$$\begin{aligned}\bar{E}_{\substack{1\\3}} = \tfrac{1}{2}\iint &[1s^*(1)2s^*(2) \pm 2s^*(1)1s^*(2)][-\tfrac{1}{2}\nabla_1^2 - \tfrac{1}{2}\nabla_2^2 - (2/r_1) \\ &- (2/r_2) + (1/r_{12})][1s(1)2s(2) \pm 2s(1)1s(2)]\, dv(1)\, dv(2)\end{aligned} \tag{5-48}$$

(The subscript on $\bar{E}$ refers to the degeneracy of whichever energy level we are considering.) This expands into a large number of terms. Integrals over one-electron operators may be written as products of two integrals, each over a different electron.[6] Thus, the expansion over the kinetic energy operators gives

$$\begin{aligned}\tfrac{1}{2}\Big\{&\int 1s^*(1)[-\tfrac{1}{2}\nabla_1^2]1s(1)\, dv(1) \cancelto{1}{\int 2s^*(2)2s(2)\, dv(2)} \\
&+ \int 2s^*(2)[-\tfrac{1}{2}\nabla_2^2]2s(2)\, dv(2) \cancelto{1}{\int 1s^*(1)1s(1)\, dv(1)} \\
&+ \int 2s^*(1)[-\tfrac{1}{2}\nabla_1^2]2s(1)\, dv(1) \cancelto{1}{\int 1s^*(2)1s(2)\, dv(2)} \\
&+ \int 1s^*(2)[-\tfrac{1}{2}\nabla_2^2]1s(2)\, dv(2) \cancelto{1}{\int 2s^*(1)2s(1)\, dv(1)} \\
&\pm \int 1s^*(1)[-\tfrac{1}{2}\nabla_1^2]2s(1)\, dv(1) \cancelto{0}{\int 2s^*(2)1s(2)\, dv(2)} \\
&\pm \int 2s^*(2)[-\tfrac{1}{2}\nabla_2^2]1s(2)\, dv(2) \cancelto{0}{\int 1s^*(1)2s(1)\, dv(1)} \\
&\pm \int 2s^*(1)[-\tfrac{1}{2}\nabla_1^2]1s(1)\, dv(1) \cancelto{0}{\int 1s^*(2)2s(2)\, dv(2)} \\
&\pm \int 1s^*(2)[-\tfrac{1}{2}\nabla_2^2]2s(2)\, dv(2) \cancelto{0}{\int 2s^*(1)1s(1)\, dv(1)}\Big\}\end{aligned} \tag{5-49}$$

The orthogonality of the 1s and 2s orbitals causes the terms preceded by $\pm$ to vanish. Furthermore, integrals that differ only in the variable label [such as those in the second and third terms of (5-49)] are equal, so that this expansion becomes

$$\int 1s^*(1)[-\tfrac{1}{2}\nabla_1^2]1s(1)\, dv(1) + \int 2s^*(1)[-\tfrac{1}{2}\nabla_1^2]2s(1)\, dv(1) \tag{5-50}$$

[6] We have already shown that, if the $1/r_{12}$ term is absent, the energy is equal to $E_{1s} + E_{2s}$ for He^+, which is equal to -2.5 a.u. Therefore, the detailed breakdown leading to Eqs. (5-49)–(5-51) is not necessary. However, we will present it in detail in the belief that some students will benefit from another specific example of integration of two-electron products over one-electron operators.

Expansion of Eq. (5-48) over $(-2/r_1 - 2/r_2)$ proceeds analogously to give

$$\int 1s^*(1)(-2/r_1)1s(1)\,dv(1) + \int 2s^*(1)(-2/r_1)2s(1)\,dv(1) \qquad (5\text{-}51)$$

The final term in the hamiltonian, $1/r_{12}$, occurs in four two-electron integrals:

$$\begin{aligned}\tfrac{1}{2}\Big\{&\iint 1s^*(1)2s^*(2)(1/r_{12})1s(1)2s(2)\,dv(1)\,dv(2)\\ &+\iint 2s^*(1)1s^*(2)(1/r_{12})2s(1)1s(2)\,dv(1)\,dv(2)\\ &\pm\iint 1s^*(1)2s^*(2)(1/r_{12})2s(1)1s(2)\,dv(1)\,dv(2)\\ &\pm\iint 2s^*(1)1s^*(2)(1/r_{12})1s(1)2s(2)\,dv(1)\,dv(2)\Big\}\end{aligned} \qquad (5\text{-}52)$$

The first two integrals of (5-52) differ only by an interchange of labels "1" and "2," and so they are equal to each other. The same is true of the second pair. Thus, the average value of the energy is

$$\begin{aligned}\bar{E}_{\substack{1\\3}} = &\int 1s^*(1)[-\tfrac{1}{2}\nabla_1{}^2]1s(1)\,dv(1) + \int 1s^*(1)[-2/r_1]1s(1)\,dv(1)\\ &+\int 2s^*(1)[-\tfrac{1}{2}\nabla_1{}^2]2s(1)\,dv(1) + \int 2s^*(1)[-2/r_1]2s(1)\,dv(1)\\ &+\iint 1s^*(1)2s^*(2)(1/r_{12})1s(1)2s(2)\,dv(1)\,dv(2)\\ &\pm\iint 1s^*(1)2s^*(2)(1/r_{12})2s(1)1s(2)\,dv(1)\,dv(2)\end{aligned} \qquad (5\text{-}53)$$

Notice that, since $-\frac{1}{2}\nabla^2 - 2/r$ is the hamiltonian for He^+, the first two integrals of Eq. (5-33) combine to give the average energy of He^+ in its 1s state. The second pair gives the energy for He^+ in the 2s state. Thus, Eq. (5-53) can be written

$$E_{\substack{1\\3}} = E_{1s} + E_{2s} + J \pm K \qquad (5\text{-}54)$$

where J and K represent the last two integrals in Eq. (5-53). No bars appear on E_{1s} or E_{2s} because these "average energies" are identical to the eigenvalues for the He^+ hamiltonian (Problem 5-13).

The integral J denotes electrons 1 and 2 as being in "charge clouds" described by 1s*1s and 2s*2s, respectively. The operator $1/r_{12}$ gives the electrostatic repulsion energy between these two charge clouds. Since these charge clouds are everywhere negatively charged, all the interactions are repulsive, and it is necessary that this "coulomb integral" J be positive. Alternatively, we can argue that the functions 1s*1s, 2s*2s, and $1/r_{12}$ are everywhere positive, so the integrand of J is everywhere positive and J must be positive.

The integral K is called an "exchange integral" because the two product functions in the integrand differ by an exchange of electrons. This integral gives the net interaction between an electron "distribution" described by 1s*2s, and another electron in the same distribution. (These distributions are mathematical functions, not physically realizable electron distributions.) The 1s2s function is sketched in Fig. 5-2. Because the 2s orbital has a radial node, the 1s2s function (which is the same as 1s*2s since the 1s function is real) also has a radial node. Now the function 1s(1)2s(1)1s(2)2s(2) will be positive whenever r_1 and r_2 are either both smaller or both larger than the radial node distance (R in Fig. 5-2). But when one r value is smaller than R and the other is greater, corresponding to the electrons being on opposite sides of the nodal surface, the product 1s(1)2s(1)1s(2)2s(2) is negative. These positive and negative contributions to K are weighted by the function $1/r_{12}$, which is always positive and hence unable to affect the sign of the integrand. But $1/r_{12}$ is smallest when the electrons are far apart. This means that $1/r_{12}$ tends to reduce the contributions where the electrons are on opposite sides of the node (i.e., the negative contributions), and so the value of K turns out to be positive (although not as large in magnitude as J, which has no negative contribution at all).

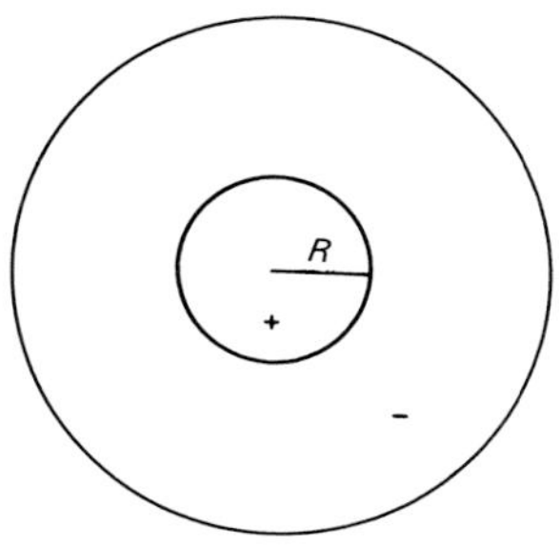

FIG. 5-2 The function produced by multiplying together hydrogenlike 1s and 2s orbitals. R is the radius of the spherical nodal surface.

Since the integral K is positive, we can see from Eq. (5-54) that *the triply degenerate energy level lies below the singly degenerate one, the separation between them being 2K*. (We note in passing that these independent-electron wavefunction energies are *not* simply the sum of one-electron energies as was the case when we used H_{approx}, thereby ignoring interelectronic repulsion.)

The experimental observation agrees qualitatively with these results. There are two state energies associated with the 1s2s configuration. When the atom is placed in an external magnetic field, the lower state-energy-level splits into three levels. The state having the higher energy has a "multiplicity" of one and is called a singlet. The lower-energy with multiplicity three is called a triplet. (The reference to "a triplet state" should not be construed to mean that this is one state. It is a triplet of states.)

It is possible to use vector arguments similar to those presented in Chapter 4 to understand why the triply degenerate level splits into three different levels in the presence of a homogeneous magnetic field. Let us first consider the case of a single electron. We have already indicated that two spin states are possible,

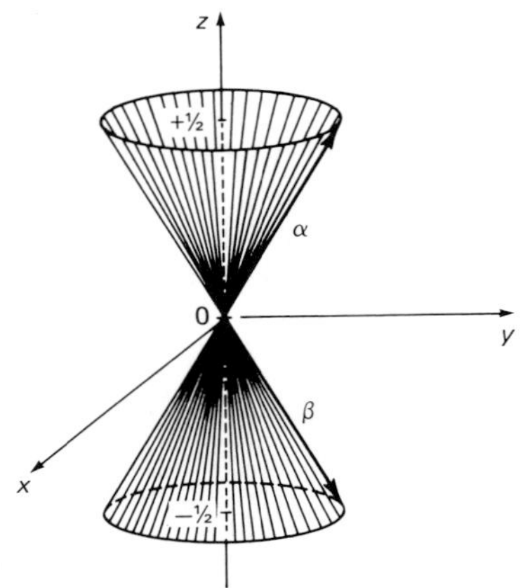

FIG. 5-3 The angular momentum vectors for α and β precess around the magnetic field axis z. The z components of these vectors are constant and have values of $+\frac{1}{2}$ and $-\frac{1}{2}$ a.u. respectively.

which we have labeled α and β. In a magnetic field the angular momentum vectors precess about the field axis z, as depicted in Fig. 5-3. The z components of the angular momentum vectors are constant but the x and y components are not. Because the *allowed* z components must in general differ by one atomic unit (stated but not proved in Chapter 4), and because there are but two allowed values (inferred from observations such as the splitting of a beam of silver atoms into two components), and because the two kinds of state are *oppositely* affected by magnetic fields, it is concluded that the z components of angular momentum (labeled M_s) are equal to $+\frac{1}{2}$ and $-\frac{1}{2}$ a.u. for α and β, respectively. As noted in Chapter 4, such half-integrals correspond to eigenfunctions that cannot be expressed as spherical harmonics. We will not pursue the question of detailed expressions for α and β here. (However, see the problems at the end of Chapter 9.)

Now let us turn to the two-electron system. We will assume that the magnetic moments of the two electrons interact independently with the external field. (This ignores the fact that each electron senses a small contribution to the magnetic field resulting from the magnetic moment of the other electron. Another factor that could affect the magnetic field sensed by the spin moment is the magnetic moment resulting from the *orbital* motions of the electrons, although this is not present if both electrons are taken to be in s atomic orbitals (AOs). Such spin–spin and spin–orbit interactions are neglected in our discussion but are very important in the theories of hyperfine structure in electric and magnetic spectroscopy.) For two electrons, we can imagine four situations: $\alpha\alpha$, $\alpha\beta$, $\beta\alpha$, and $\beta\beta$. Vector diagrams representing the angular momenta for these cases are given in Fig. 5-4. The corresponding z components of spin angular momentum (labeled M_s) are evidently $+1$, 0, 0, and -1 a.u., respectively. The spin combinations $\alpha\beta + \beta\alpha$ [from the triplet (5-43b)] and $\alpha\beta - \beta\alpha$ [from the singlet (5-42)] are linear combinations of $\alpha\beta$ and $\beta\alpha$. However, since these two functions have the

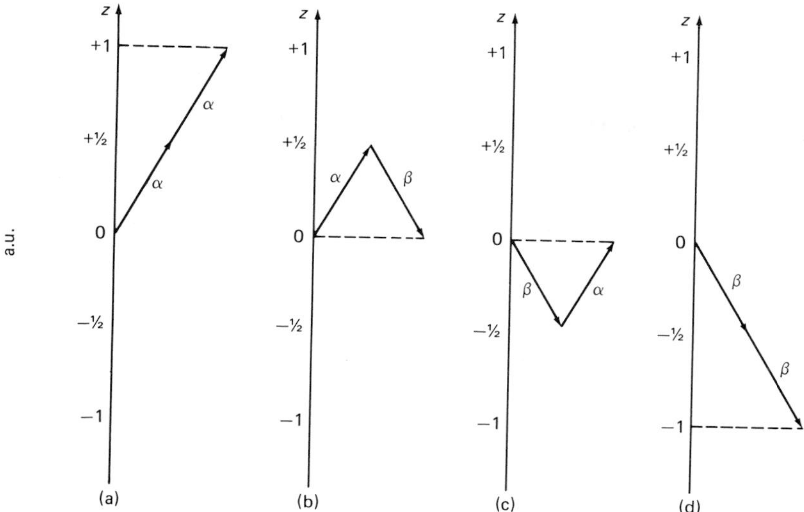

FIG. 5-4 Vector diagrams illustrating that M_s, the z components of spin angular momentum, for (a) $\alpha\alpha$, (b) $\alpha\beta$, (c) $\beta\alpha$, and (d) $\beta\beta$ spin states are respectively $+1$, 0, 0, and -1 a.u.

same value for the z component of angular momentum (zero), their linear combinations will also have that value. It follows that the z components of the spin angular momenta of the triplet of states (5-43) are $+1$, 0, and -1 a.u., and for the singlet (5-42) it is zero. Because the electrons are charged, these spin angular momenta correspond to spin magnetic moments, which interact differently with the applied magnetic field to give splitting of the triplet (see Fig. 5-5). It is customary to refer to all three spin states in (5-43) as having *parallel* spins even though the vector diagram for the (5-43b) state is not particularly in accord with this terminology. For the singlet state, the spins are said to be *opposed*, or *antiparallel*.

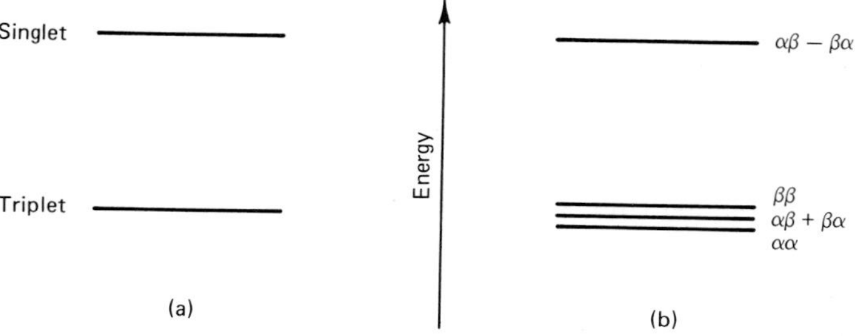

FIG. 5-5 Energy levels for singlet and triplet levels of 1s2s helium in (a) absence, and (b) presence of an external magnetic field.

So far, our independent-electron approximate solutions for the helium atom hamiltonian seem to be successful at reproducing and "explaining" experimental observations, at least qualitatively. In fact, the success of this mathematical model has been sufficient for it (or extensions of it) to be the basis for our qualitative understanding of atomic structure and much of quantum chemistry. Nevertheless, one must be cautious in interpreting approximate solutions and assuming that these interpretations are valid in the real atom. We close this section with an example of the kind of error such approximate solutions can lead to.

An empirical rule due to Hund regarding atomic spectra is that, for a given configuration, the states of highest multiplicity have the lowest energy. We have found that states of configuration 1s2s obey this rule and we might try to find a reason for the empirical rule by examining our wavefunctions.

We begin by noting that the triplet state energy is calculated to be less than the singlet because the former has an average value for $1/r_{12}$ of $J - K$, the latter of $J + K$. Since K is positive and smaller than J, this means that our wavefunctions give a smaller average value for $1/r_{12}$ in the triplet state. This *suggests* that the average value of r_{12} is larger for the triplet. (Note that $(1/r_{12})_{\text{av}} \neq 1/(r_{12})_{\text{av}}$, so it does not *prove* it.) The energy for the triplet thus appears to be lower because the electrons are, on the average, farther apart than they are in the singlet, lowering the interelectronic repulsion energy.

Further support for this explanation comes from an examination of the space parts of the wavefunctions. For the triply degenerate level, the space term is antisymmetric. What happens to this function when electrons 1 and 2 "collide"—that is, when $r_1, \theta_1, \phi_1 = r_2, \theta_2, \phi_2$? When this happens, 1s(1), which stands for $1s(r_1, \theta_1, \phi_1)$, must equal 1s(2). Similarly, 2s(1) = 2s(2), and so the antisymmetric space function

$$(1/\sqrt{2})[1s(1)2s(2) - 2s(1)1s(2)] \tag{5-55}$$

and its square must vanish. Thus, there is a zero probability for electrons 1 and 2 being simultaneously at the same place. Since the wavefunction is continuous and smooth, it follows that the wavefunction *approaches* zero as electrons 1 and 2 *approach* each other. This tendency of the wavefunction to disfavor close proximity between electrons of parallel spin is referred to as the "Fermi hole," and it is built into any wavefunction that is properly antisymmetrized.

Looking at the symmetric space function of the nondegenerate state, we see that there is no tendency for ψ to vanish when $r_1 = r_2$. (Since we know that electrons repel each other regardless of spin, we might expect some sort of "coulomb hole" to exist. Its absence here is due to our independent-electron approximations, as will be shown later.)

Our approximate wavefunctions suggest, then, that the electrons are indeed farther apart, on the average, in the triplet, due to a "correlation" of their motions called the Fermi hole. It is a fact, however, that as one goes to better and better approximations for the wavefunction, this "explanation" becomes invalid [6]. The triplet remains lowest in energy, but the average value of $1/r_{12}$ reverses behavior, becoming *larger* in the triplet!

Average values for various parts of the hamiltonian operator are given in Table 5-1. These averages are over wavefunctions for the singlet and triplet states of the 1s2p configuration for helium. The quality of the wavefunctions improves as we go from I to III in Table 5-1, I being somewhat better than the level of approximation we have been discussing, III being almost exactly correct. Note the behavior of the average value for $1/r_{12}$ in the singlet compared to the triplet as the wavefunction quality improves.

TABLE 5-1
Average Values for 2^1P *and* 2^3P *States of the Helium Atom (Hartrees)*[a]

	Average values of wavefunction[b]					
	I		II		III	
Operator	2^1P	2^3P	2^1P	2^3P	2^1P	2^3P
H	−1.7995	−1.9864	−2.1225	−2.1313	−2.1238	−2.1332
$-\frac{1}{2}\nabla_1^2 - \frac{1}{2}\nabla_2^2$	1.7995	1.9864	2.1225	2.1313	2.1238	2.1332
$-(2/r_1) - (2/r_2)$	−4.2344	−4.4531	−4.4796	−4.5234	−4.4927	−4.5330
$1/r_{12}$	0.6354	0.4804	0.2347	0.2607	0.2450	0.2666

[a] See Messmer and Birss [6].
[b] I, II, and III refer to different wavefunctions of increasing quality.

The warning should be clear. Usable approximations to eigenfunctions are very useful in understanding, predicting, and calculating observable phenomena. But one must always be aware of the possibility of significant differences existing between the real system and the mathematical model for that system.

5-6 The Self-Consistent Field, Slater-Type Orbitals, and the Aufbau Principle

Up to now we have used wavefunctions that, while not being eigenfunctions of the hamiltonian, are eigenfunctions of an "effective hamiltonian" obtained by ignoring the interelectronic repulsion operator $1/r_{ij}$. That is, these wavefunctions would be exactly correct if the electrons in helium were attracted by the nucleus, but somehow did not repel each other. For this reason, we have referred to this as an independent electron approximation. We cannot expect such a wavefunction to give very good numerical predictions of charge density or energy. (The energies for He as calculated by wavefunctions of varying quality are given in Table 5-2.) Since the electrons really do repel each other,

TABLE 5-2
Average Values for Energy Calculated from Helium Atom Ground State Approximate Wavefunctions[a]

Wavefunction description	$\bar{E}$(eV)
1. Product of He^+ orbitals	-74.83
2. Product of hydrogenlike orbitals with ξ fixed by SCF method	-77.48
3. Best product-type wavefunction	-77.870917
4. Nonorbital wavefunction of Pekeris [9]. This wavefunction uses functions of r_1, r_2 and r_{12} as coordinates and has the form of an exponential times a linear combination of 1078 terms	-79.00946912

[a] $\bar{E} = \int \psi^* H\psi \, d\tau / \int \psi^*\psi \, d\tau$, where H is given by Eq. (5-2).

we expect the actual electron density to be more diffuse than that given by the above model. Methods have been devised that partially overcome this problem by retaining the convenient form of orbital products but modifying the formulas for the orbitals themselves to make them more diffuse.

Let the ground state of helium be our example. Suppose that we take the ordinary independent-electron wavefunction as our initial approximation:

$$1s(1)1s(2) \equiv \sqrt{8/\pi}\exp(-2r_1)\sqrt{8/\pi}\exp(-2r_2) \tag{5-56}$$

These atomic orbitals are *correct* only if electrons 1 and 2 do not "see" each other via a repulsive interaction. They really do repel each other, and we can *approximate* this repulsion by saying that electron 2 "sees" electron 1 as a smeared out, time-averaged charge cloud rather than the rapidly moving point charge which is actually present. The initial description for this charge cloud is just the absolute square of the initial atomic orbital occupied by electron 2: $[1s(2)]^2$. Our approximation now has electron 1 moving in the field of a positive nucleus embedded in a spherical cloud of negative charge. Thus, for electron 1, the positive nuclear charge is "shielded" or "screened" by electron 2. Hence, electron 1 should occupy an orbital that is less contracted about the nucleus. Let us write this new orbital in the form

$$1s'(1) = \sqrt{\xi^3/\pi}\exp(-\xi r_1) \tag{5-57}$$

where ξ is related to the screened nuclear charge seen by electron 1. The mathematical methods used to evaluate ξ will be described later in this book.

Next we turn to electron 2, which we now take to be moving in the field of the nucleus shielded by the charge cloud *due to electron 1, now in its expanded orbital.* Just as before, we find a new orbital of form (5-57) for electron 2. Now, however, ξ will be different because the shielding of the nucleus by electron 1 is different from what it was in our previous step. We now have a new distribution for electron 2, but this means that we must recalculate the orbital for electron 1 since this orbital was appropriate for the screening due to electron 2 in its *old*

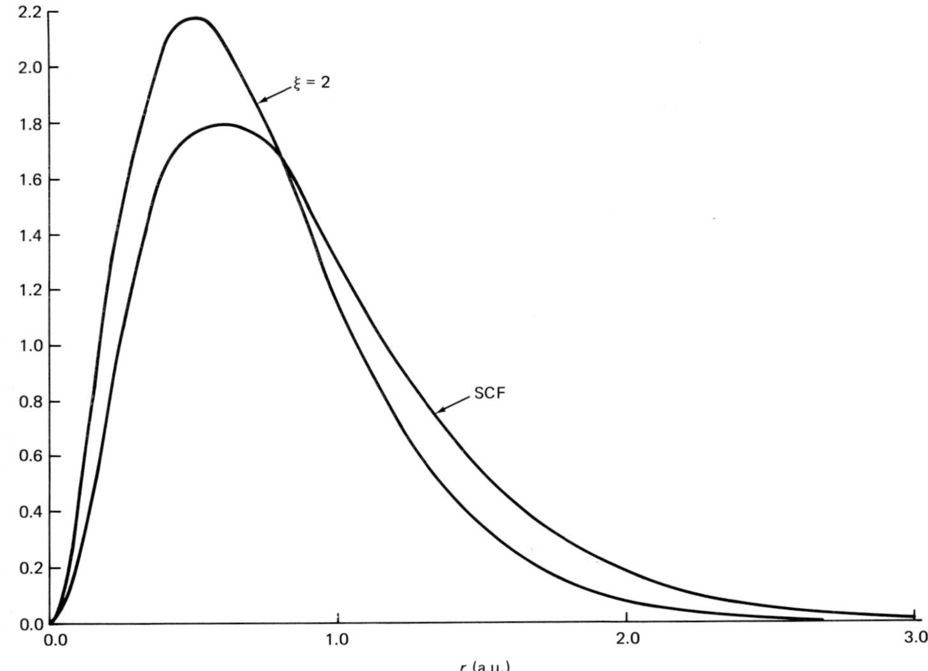

FIG. 5-6 Electron distribution in helium as given by SCF and "unshielded" independent electron approximations.

orbital. After revising the orbital for electron 1, we must revise the orbital for electron 2. This procedure is continued back and forth between electrons 1 and 2 until the value of ξ converges to an unchanging value (under the constraint that electrons 1 and 2 ultimately occupy orbitals having the same value of ξ). Then the orbital for each electron is consistent with the potential due to the nucleus and the charge cloud for the other electron: the electrons move in a "self-consistent field" (SCF).

The result of such a calculation is a wavefunction in much closer accord with the actual charge density distributions of atoms than that given by the complete neglect of interelectron repulsion.[7] A plot of the electron density distribution in helium as given by wavefunction (5-56) and by a similar wavefunction with optimized ξ is given in Fig. 5-6. Because each electron senses only the time-averaged charge cloud of the other in this approximation, it is still an independent-electron treatment. The hallmark of the independent electron treatment is a wavefunction containing only a product of one-electron functions.

[7] SCF wavefunctions also give the lowest average energy for an atom or molecule at a certain level of approximation. A thorough discussion of this approach is given in Chapter 11.

There are no functions of, say, r_{12}, which would make ψ depend on the instantaneous distance between electrons 1 and 2.

Atomic orbitals that are eigenfunctions for the one-electron hydrogenlike ion (for integral or nonintegral Z) are called hydrogenlike orbitals. In Chapter 4 we noted that many hydrogenlike orbitals have radial nodes. In actual practice, this mathematical aspect causes increased complexity in solving integrals in quantum chemical calculations. Much more convenient are a class of modified orbitals called *Slater-type orbitals* (STOs). These differ from their hydrogenlike counterparts in that they have no radial nodes. Angular terms are identical in the two types of orbital. The unnormalized radial term for an STO is

$$R(n, Z, s) = r^{(n-1)} \exp[-(Z - s)r/n] \tag{5-58}$$

where Z is the nuclear charge in atomic units, n is the principal quantum number, and s is a "screening constant" which has the function of reducing the nuclear charge Z "seen" by an electron. Slater [7] constructed rules for determining the values of s that will produce STOs in close agreement with those one would obtain by an SCF calculation. These rules, appropriate for electrons up to the 3d level, are

(1) The electrons in the atom are divided up into the following groups: 1s|2s, 2p|3s, 3p|3d.

(2) The shielding constant s for an orbital associated with any of the above groups is the sum of the following contributions:

(a) nothing from any group to the right (in the above list) of the group under consideration;

(b) 0.35 from each other electron in the group (except 0.30 in the 1s group);

(c) for an s or p orbital, 0.85 for each electron with principal quantum number less by 1, and 1.00 for each electron still "farther in"; For a d electron, 1.00 for all electrons farther in.

For example, nitrogen, with ground state configuration $1s^2 2s^2 2p^3$, would have the same radial part for the 2s and 2p STOs. This would be given by the formula ($n = 2$, $Z = 7$, $s = 4 \times 0.35 + 2 \times 0.85 = 3.1$)

$$R_{2s,2p}(2, 7, 3.1) = r^{(2-1)} \exp[-(7 - 3.1)r/2] = r \exp(-1.95\, r)$$

For the 1s level, $n = 1, Z = 7, s = 0.30$, and

$$R_{1s} = \exp(-6.7r)$$

Comparing orbital exponents, we see that the 1s charge cloud is compressed much more tightly around the nucleus than are the 2s and 2p "valence orbital" charge clouds. Slater-type orbitals are very frequently used in quantum chemistry because they provide us with very good approximations to self-consistent field atomic orbitals (SCF–AOs) with almost no effort.

Clementi and Raimondi [8] have published a refined list of rules for the shielding constant, which extends to the 4p level. Their rules include contributions to shielding due to the presence of electrons in shells "outside" the orbital under consideration. Such contributions are not large, and, up to the 3d level, there is reasonably good agreement between these two sets of rules.

The fact that STOs have no radial nodes results in some loss of orthogonality. Angular terms still give orthogonality between orbitals having different l or m quantum numbers, but STOs differing *only* in their n quantum number are nonorthogonal. Thus, 1s, 2s, 3s, . . . are nonorthogonal. Similarly $2p_z$, $3p_z$, ... or $3d_{xy}$, $4d_{xy}$, . . . are nonorthogonal. In practice, this feature is handled easily. The only real problem arises if one *forgets* about this nonorthogonality when making certain calculations.

When carrying out SCF calculations on multielectronic atoms, one finds that the orbital energies for 2s and 2p functions are not the same. Similarly, 3s 3p, and 3d orbitals are nondegenerate. Yet these orbitals were degenerate in the one-electron hydrogenlike system in which energy was a function of n but not of l or m. Why are these orbital energies nondegenerate in the many-electron calculation? A reasonable explanation can be found by considering the comparative effectiveness with which a pair of 1s electrons screen the nucleus from a 3s or a 3p electron. Comparing the 3s, 3p, and 3d *hydrogenlike* orbital formulas in Table 4-2 shows that the 3s orbital is finite at the nucleus, decreasing proportionally to r for small r. The 3p orbitals vanish at the nucleus but grow as r for small r. The 3d orbitals vanish at the nucleus but grow as r^2 for small r. The result of all this is that an s electron spends a larger amount of its time near the nucleus than a p electron of the same principal quantum number, the p electron spending more time near the nucleus than the d, etc. Hence, the s electron penetrates the "underlying" charge clouds more effectively and is therefore less effectively shielded from the nucleus. Since the s electron "sees" a greater effective nuclear charge, its energy is lower than that of the p electron. (This effect is not obvious in STOs since the 3s and 3p STOs have the same radial function which vanishes at the nucleus. However, the STO for 3d does reflect the nondegeneracy since Slater's rules give it a different screening constant from 3s or 3p.)

The tendency for higher l values to be associated with higher orbital energies leads to the following orbital ordering:

$$1s\ 2s\ 2p\ 3s\ 3p\ 4s\ 3d\ 4p\ 5s\ 4d\ 5p\ 6s\ 5d\ 4f\ 6p\ 7s\ 6d\ 5f \cdots \tag{5-59}$$

When we get to principal quantum numbers of 3 and higher, the energy differences between different l values for the same n become comparable to the differences between different n levels. Thus, in some atoms, the 4s level is almost the same as the 3d level, etc.

The energy-ordering scheme (5-59) coupled with the Pauli or exclusion principle and Hund's rule leads us to a simple prescription for "building up" the electronic configurations of atoms. This "*aufbau*" principle is familiar to chemists and leads naturally to a correlation between electronic structure and the periodic table. The procedure is to place all the electrons of the atom into atomic orbitals, two to an orbital, starting at the low-energy end of the list (5-59) and working up in energy. In addition, when filling a set of degenerate levels like the five 3d levels, one half-fills all the levels with electrons of parallel spin before filling any of them. This prescription enables one to guess the electronic configuration of any atom, once its atomic number is known, unless it happens to put us into a region of ambiguity, where different levels have almost the same energy. (Electronic configurations for such atoms are deduced from experimentally determined chemical, spectral, and physical properties.) The configuration for carbon (atomic number 6) would be $1s^2 2s^2 2p^2$, with the understanding that p electrons occupy *different* p orbitals and have parallel spins. (Recall that we expect the most stable of all the states arising from the configuration $1s^2 2s^2 2p^2$ to be the one of highest multiplicity. The 2p electrons can produce either a singlet or a triplet state just as could the two electrons in the 1s2s configuration of helium. The triplet should be the ground state and this corresponds to parallel spins, which *requires* different p orbitals by the exclusion principle.)

It is important to realize that the orbital ordering (5-59) used in the *aufbau* process is not fixed, but depends on the atomic number Z. The ordering in (5-59) cannot be blindly followed in all cases. For instance, the ordering shows that 5s fills before 4d. It is true that element 38, strontium, has a $\cdots 4p^6 5s^2 4d^0$ configuration. But a later element, paladium, number 46, has $\cdots 4p^6 4d^{10} 5s^0$ as its ground state configuration. The effect of adding more protons and electrons has been to depress the 4d level more than the 5s level.

In closing this chapter, we should emphasize again a point frequently forgotten by chemists. In the orbital approach to many-electron systems we have a convenient *approximation*. This is an imperfect but useful way to describe atomic structure. There are more accurate ways to approximate eigenfunctions of many-electron hamiltonians, but this usually involves more difficulty in interpretation. The orbital representation of ψ appears to be the best compromise between accuracy and convenience for most chemical purposes.

PROBLEMS

5-1 Write down the hamiltonian operator for the lithium atom.

5-2 Calculate the values of $\bar{r}_1$ and $\bar{r}_2$ consistent with the He wavefunction $\psi(1, 2) = 1s(1)2s(2)\cdots$ (Eq. 5-12a).

5-3 Calculate the energy in electron volts of a photon with associated wavelength 0.1 a.u. Compare this result with the ionization potential in electron volts of the hydrogen atom in its ground state.

5-4 Show that the wavefunction (5-15) is normalized if 1s and 2s are orthonormal.

5-5 Show that the wavefunction (5-16) is antisymmetric with respect to exchange of electron coordinates.

5-6 Show that the wavefunction (5-37) would vanish if 2s were replaced throughout by 1s, giving a $1s^3$ configuration.

5-7 Produce a totally antisymmetric wavefunction starting from the configuration $1s(1)\alpha(1)2p(2)\beta(2)1s(3)\beta(3)$. Use the method described for Eq. (5-37) and use a determinantal function as a check.

5-8 Set up the integral of the product between $(1s1s2s\alpha\beta\alpha)^*$ and $2s1s1s\alpha\alpha\beta$. (Use symbols rather than explicit atomic orbital formulas.) Factor the integral into a product of integrals over one-electron space functions and one-electron spin functions. Indicate the value of each of the resulting six integrals and of their product.

5-9 (a) Write down the Slater determinantal wavefunction for the configuration $1s1\bar{s}2p_z$.

(b) Expand this determinant into a linear combination of products.

(c) Recalling that $2p_z(3) = 0$ when $r = 0$ (i.e., electron 3 is on the nucleus), write down the nonzero part of expansion (b) when $r_3 = 0$, $r_1 = 1$ a.u., $r_2 = 2$ a.u. [Do not evaluate the expression; just use symbols like 1s $(r = 1)$.] Also write down the nonzero part of (b) when $r_2 = 0$, $r_1 = 1$, $r_3 = 2$, and when $r_1 = 0$, $r_2 = 2$, $r_3 = 1$. Is there any physical difference between saying "electron 3 is at the nucleus" and saying "an electron is at the nucleus?" Explain.

5-10 Make simple two-dimensional "circle sketches" of the 1s and 2s hydrogen-like AOs. Also sketch their products. Use these sketches to explain why J *must* be positive, K should be positive, and J should be greater than K. [See Eqs. (5-53) and (5-54) for definitions of J and K.]

5-11 Referring to Table 5-1, what simple relationships can you find between $\bar{E}$, $\bar{T}$, and $\bar{V}$ for these calculations?

5-12 Write down the ground state configuration for the fluorine atom. Use Slater's rules to find the orbital exponents $\xi = (Z - s)/n$ for 1s and 2s, 2p orbitals.

5-13 Show that the average value of an operator for a state described by an *eigenfunction* for that operator is identical to the eigenvalue associated with that eigenfunction.

5-14 Explain briefly the observation that the energy difference between the $1s^22s^1(^2S_{1/2})$ state and the $1s^22p^1(^2P_{1/2})$ state for Li is 14,904 cm^{-1}, whereas for Li^{2+} the $2s^1(^2S_{1/2})$ and $2p^1(^2P_{1/2})$ states are essentially degenerate. (They differ by only 2.4 cm^{-1}.)

5-15 In Chapter 4 it was stated that the magnitude of the square of the angular momentum was given by $l(l + 1)$ a.u., and that z components could be any of the values $-l, -l + 1, \ldots, l - 1, l$ a.u. Similar relations hold for spin. From this fact plus the knowledge that the possible z components of spin angular momentum are $\pm\frac{1}{2}$ a.u., can you calculate the length of the spin angular momentum vector?

5-16 It has been shown that, for a single spinning electron, two symmetric spin states are possible having z components of spin angular momentum M_s of $+\frac{1}{2}$ and $-\frac{1}{2}$ a.u. Thus, for one unpaired electron, we have a spin multiplicity of 2. For two electrons we found three symmetric spin states ($M_s = +1, 0, -1$). Thus, two unpaired electrons give a spin multiplicity of 3. Show that, in general, for n "unpaired" electrons (i.e., n electrons with symmetric spin functions) the spin multiplicity is equal to $n + 1$.

REFERENCES

[1] O. Stern, *Z. Physik* **7**, 249 (1921).
[2] W. Gerlach and O. Stern, *Z. Physik* **8**, 110 (1922).
[3] E. G. Uhlenbeck and S. Goudsmit, *Naturwissenschaften* **13**, 953 (1925); *Nature* **117**, 264 (1926).
[4] R. Bichowsky and H. C. Urey, *Proc. Natl. Acad. Sci.* **12**, 80 (1926).
[5] J. C. Slater, *Phys. Rev.* **34**, 1293 (1929).
[6] R. P. Messmer and F. W. Birss, *J. Phys. Chem.* **73**, 2085 (1969).
[7] J. C. Slater, *Phys. Rev.* **36**, 57 (1930).
[8] E. Clementi and D. L. Raimondi, *J. Chem. Phys.* **38**, 2686 (1963).
[9] C. L. Pekeris, *Phys. Rev.* **115**, 1216 (1959).

CHAPTER 6

POSTULATES AND THEOREMS OF QUANTUM MECHANICS

6-1 Introduction

The first part of this book has treated a number of systems from a fairly physical viewpoint, using intuition as much as possible. Now, armed with the concepts already developed, the reader should be in a better position to understand the more formal foundation to be described in this chapter. This foundation is presented as a set of postulates. From these follow proofs of various theorems. The ultimate test of the validity of the postulates comes in comparing the theoretical predictions with experimental data. The extra effort required to master the postulates and theorems is repaid many times over when we seek to solve problems of chemical interest.

6-2 The Wavefunction Postulate

We have already described most of the requirements that a wavefunction must satisfy. ψ must be acceptable (i.e., single valued, nowhere infinite, continuous, with a piecewise continuous first derivative). For bound states (i.e., states in which the particles lack the energy to achieve infinite separation classically) we require that ψ be square integrable. So far we have considered only cases where the state of the system does not vary with time. For much of quantum chemistry, these are the cases of interest, but, in general a state may change with time, and ψ will be a function of t in order to follow the evolution of the system.

Gathering all this together, we arrive at

Postulate I *Any bound state of a dynamical system of n particles is described as completely as possible by an acceptable, square-integrable function* $\Psi(q_1, q_2, \ldots, q_{3n}, \omega_1, \omega_2, \ldots, \omega_n, t)$, *where the q's are spatial coordinates, ω's are spin coordinates, and t is the time coordinate.* $\Psi^*\Psi\, d\tau$ *is the probability that the space–spin coordinates lie in the volume element* $d\tau$ $(\equiv d\tau_1\, d\tau_2 \cdots d\tau_n)$ *at time t, if* Ψ *is normalized.*

For example, suppose we have a two-electron system in a time-dependent state described by the wavefunction $\Psi(x_1, y_1, z_1, \omega_1, x_2, y_2, z_2, \omega_2, t)$. The spin coordinates ω would each be some combination of spin functions α and β. If we integrate $\Psi^*\Psi$ over the spin coordinates of both electrons, we are left with a *spin-free* density function. Call it $\rho(x_1, y_1, z_1, x_2, y_2, z_2, t) \equiv \rho(v_1, v_2, t)$. We interpret $\rho(v_1, v_2, t)\, dv_1\, dv_2$ as the probability that electron 1 is in dv_1 (i.e., between x_1 and $x_1 + dx$, y_1 and $y_1 + dy$, and z_1 and $z_1 + dz$) *and* electron two is in dv_2 at time t. If we now integrate over the coordinates of electron 2, we obtain a new density function, $\rho'(v_1, t)$, which describes the probability of finding electron 1 in various volume elements at various times regardless of the position of electron 2.

6-3 The Postulate for Constructing Operators

Much of the substance of the second postulate is already familiar. We earlier used arguments based on de Broglie waves to construct hamiltonian operators. We then noted that the kinetic energy part of the operators can be identified with a classical term like $p_x^2/2m$ through the relation $p_x \leftrightarrow (\hbar/i)\, \partial/\partial x$. The potential energy terms in the hamiltonian operators are completely classical, however. Thus, we could have constructed the quantum mechanical hamiltonians by writing down the *classical* energy expressions in terms of momenta and position, and then replacing every momentum term by the appropriate partial differential operator. This is an example of the use of part *c* of:

Postulate II *To every observable dynamical variable M there can be assigned a linear hermitian operator $\hat{M}$. One begins by writing the classical expression, as fully as possible in terms of momenta and positions. Then:*

(a) *If M is q or t, $\hat{M}$ is q or t. (q and t are space and time coordinates.)*

(b) *If M is a momentum, p_j, for the jth particle, the operator is* $(\hbar/i)\, \partial/\partial q_j$, *where q_j is conjugate to p_j* (e.g., *x_j is conjugate to p_{xj}*).

(c) *If M is expressible in terms of the q's, p's and t, $\hat{M}$ is found by substituting the above operators in the expression for M in such a way that $\hat{M}$ is hermitian.*

The reason for specifying that $\hat{M}$ must be hermitian is that the eigenvalues of a hermitian operator must be real numbers.[1] We shall discuss this and other aspects of hermiticity (including its definition) later in this chapter.

As an explicit example of this procedure, we reconsider the hydrogen atom. Assuming a fixed nucleus (infinite inertia), the classical expression for the total energy of the system is

$$E_{\text{classical}} = (1/2m_e)(p_x^2 + p_y^2 + p_z^2) - e^2/(x^2 + y^2 + z^2)^{1/2}$$

where the first term is just the kinetic energy of the electron and the second term is the electrostatic potential energy. The coordinate origin is on the nucleus. Application of Postulate II retains the position variables x, y, and z of the

[1] In this text (and in quantum chemistry in general) a caret indicates an operator and *not* a unit vector quantity as in classical physics.

potential term unchanged, but replaces p_x by $(\hbar/i)\,\partial/\partial x$, etc.:

$$\frac{1}{2m_e}(p_x^2 + p_y^2 + p_z^2) \Rightarrow \frac{1}{2m_e}\left\{\left(\frac{h}{2\pi i}\frac{\partial}{\partial x}\right)^2 + \left(\frac{h}{2\pi i}\frac{\partial}{\partial y}\right)^2 + \left(\frac{h}{2\pi i}\frac{\partial}{\partial_z}\right)^2\right\}$$

$$= \frac{-h^2}{8\pi^2 m_e}\nabla^2$$

Thus, we arrive at

$$\hat{H} = (-h^2/8\pi^2 m_e)\,\nabla^2 - [e^2/(x^2 + y^2 + z^2)^{1/2}]$$

and we are now free to transform $\hat{H}$ to other coordinate systems if we wish.

6-4 The Time-Dependent Schrödinger Equation Postulate

We have discussed only cases where neither the hamiltonian H nor ψ is time dependent. In those cases we required that ψ be an eigenfunction of H. In the more general case in which Ψ and $\mathscr{H}$ are time dependent,[2] a different requirement is imposed by

Postulate III The state functions (or wavefunctions) satisfy the equation

$$\mathscr{H}\Psi(q, t) = \frac{-\hbar}{i}\frac{\partial}{\partial t}\Psi(q, t) \tag{6-1}$$

where $\mathscr{H}$ is the hamiltonian operator for the system.

We should check to see if this is consistent with the time-independent Schrödinger equation we have been using. Suppose that the hamiltonian is time independent. Let us see if a solution to Eq. (6-1) exists when $\Psi(q, t)$ is separated into a product of space- and time-dependent functions: $\Psi(q, t) = \psi(q)f(t)$. Inserting this into Eq. (6-1) gives

$$H\psi(q)f(t) = \frac{-\hbar}{i}\frac{\partial}{\partial t}\psi(q)f(t) \tag{6-2}$$

Dividing by $\psi(q)f(t)$ gives

$$\frac{H\psi(q)}{\psi(q)} = \frac{(-\hbar/i)(\partial/\partial t)f(t)}{f(t)} \tag{6-3}$$

Since each side of Eq. (6-3) depends on a different variable, the two sides must equal the same constant, which we call E. This gives

$$H\psi(q) = E\psi(q) \tag{6-4}$$

and

$$\frac{-\hbar}{i}\frac{d}{dt}f(t) = Ef(t) \tag{6-5}$$

[2] $\mathscr{H}$ and Ψ symbolize time dependence; H and ψ symbolize time independence.

The first of these equations is just the time-independent Schrödinger equation we have been using. The second equation has the solution $f(t) = A \exp(-iEt/\hbar)$. Hence, f^*f equals a constant, and so $\Psi^*\Psi = \psi^*\psi f^*f \propto \psi^*\psi$. Since f has no significant effect on energy or particle distribution, we can ignore it in dealing with stationary states. The situation is analogous to the case of standing waves discussed in Chapter 1.

Note that while we have shown that solutions may exist in which Ψ is separable, this does *not* mean that every solution of Eq. (6-1) with $\mathscr{H} = H$ is separable (i.e., stationary). We can imagine a situation where a system in a stationary state is suddenly perturbed to produce a new time-independent hamiltonian. Ψ will change as the system adjusts to this new situation, giving us a case where the hamiltonian is time-independent (after the perturbation, at least) and Ψ is not a stationary state function. The way in which Ψ evolves in time is governed by Eq. (6-1).

6-5 The Postulate Relating Measured Values to Eigenvalues

The second postulate indicated that every observable variable of a system (such as position, momentum, velocity, energy, dipole moment) was associated with an hermitian operator. The connection between the observed value of a variable and the operator is given by

Postulate IV Any result of a measurement of a dynamical variable is one of the eigenvalues of the corresponding operator.

Any measurement always gives a *real* number, and so this postulate requires that eigenvalues of the appropriate operators be real. We will prove later that hermitian operators satisfy this requirement.

If we measured the electronic energy of a hydrogen atom (the negative of its ionization potential), we could get any of the allowed eigenvalues ($-1/2n^2$ a.u.) but no intermediate value. What if, instead, we measured the distance of the electron from the nucleus. By Postulate II, the operator for this property is just the variable r itself. Hence, we need to consider the eigenvalues of r in the equation

$$r\,\delta(r, \theta, \phi) = \lambda\,\delta(r, \theta, \phi) \tag{6-6}$$

where δ is an eigenfunction and λ is a real number. We can rewrite this equation as

$$(r - \lambda)\,\delta(r, \theta, \phi) = 0 \tag{6-7}$$

This form makes it more apparent that δ must vanish at all points in space except those where $r = \lambda$. But λ is an eigenvalue of r and hence is a possible result of a measurement. Thus, we see that Postulate IV implies some connection between a measurement of, say, $r = 2$ a.u. and an eigenfunction of r that is finite only at $r = 2$ a.u. We symbolize this eigenfunction $\delta(r - 2)$, this "δ function" being zero whenever the argument is not zero. If instead we measured the *point* in space of the electron, rather than just the distance from the nucleus, and found it to be r_0, θ_0, ϕ_0, then the corresponding eigenfunction of the position operator would be $\delta(r - r_0)\,\delta(\theta - \theta_0)\,\delta(\phi - \phi_0)$. This function vanishes everywhere except at r_0, θ_0, ϕ_0.

It is evident that any value of λ from zero to infinity in Eq. (6-7) is an eigenvalue since the nonzero portion of a delta function may be placed anywhere. This means that, unlike the energy measurement, the measurement of the distance of the electron from the nucleus can have any value.

The eigenfunctions of the position operator are called *Dirac delta functions.* They are "spike" functions having infinitesimal width. They are normalized through the equation

$$\int \delta(x - x_0)\, dx = 1 \tag{6-8}$$

where the integration range includes x_0.[3] On first acquaintance, these functions seem mathematically peculiar, but they make physical sense in the following way. One can interpret the actual measurement of position as a process which forces the particle to acquire a certain position at some instant. At that instant, ψ^2 for the system (now perturbed by the measuring process) ought to give unit probability for finding the particle at that point (where it definitely is) and zero probability elsewhere, and this is just what the Dirac delta function does.[4]

Postulate IV, then, is in accord with a picture wherein the process of measurement forces the measured system into an eigenstate for the appropriate operator, giving the corresponding eigenvalue as the measurement. This definition of "measurement" is somewhat restrictive and can be deceptive. Often scientists refer to measurements that are really measurements of average values rather than eigenvalues. This point is discussed further below.

6-6 The Postulate for Average Values

Suppose that we had somehow prepared a large number of hydrogen atoms so that they were all in the same, known, stationary state. Then we could measure the distance of the electron from the nucleus once in each atom and

[3] The reader should avoid confusing the Dirac delta function $\delta(x - x_0)$ with the Kronecker delta $\delta_{i,j}$ encountered earlier. They are similar in that both vanish unless $x = x_0$ in the former and $i = j$ in the latter. But they differ in that the *value* of $\delta_{i,i}$ is definite (unity) while the value of $\delta(x_0 - x_0)$ is not defined. The Dirac delta function has definite value only in integrated expressions like Eq. (6-8). The spin functions α and β may be thought of as Dirac delta functions in the spin "coordinate" ω. The Dirac delta function is admittedly unusual, and one tends to be uneasy with it at first. This function is important and useful in quantum mechanics. However, since we will make almost no use of it in this text, we will not develop the topic further.

[4] Notice that Eq. (6-8) does not involve $\delta^*\delta$, but merely δ. Because δ is nonzero only at one point, $\delta^*\delta$ is likewise nonzero only at the same point. The two are therefore not independent functions. It is convenient to view the δ function as both the eigenvalue for the position operator and also as the probability distribution function for the particle.

average these measurements to obtain an average value. We have alread indicated that this average would be given by the sum of all the r values, eac multiplied by its frequency of occurrence, which is given by $\psi^2\, dv$ if ψ is norma ized. Since r is a continuous variable, the sum becomes an integral. This is th content of:

Postulate V *When a large number of identical systems have the same sta function* ψ, *the expected average of measurements on the variable M* (*one measur ment per system*) *is given by*

$$M_{\text{av}} = \int \psi^* \hat{M} \psi \, d\tau \Big/ \int \psi^* \psi \, d\tau \qquad (6\text{-}$$

The denominator is unity if ψ is normalized.

It is important to understand the distinction between average value an eigenvalue as they relate to measurements. A good example is the dipole momen The dipole moment operator for a system of n charged particles is $\hat{\mu} = \sum_{i=1}^{n} z_i$ where z_i is the charge on the ith particle and $\mathbf{r}_i$ is its position vector with respe to an arbitrary origin. (We get this by writing the classical formula and observir that momentum terms do not appear. Hence, the quantum-mechanical operat is the same as the classical expression.) What will the eigenfunctions and eige values of $\hat{\mu}$ be like?

The charge z_i is only a number, while $\mathbf{r}_i$ is a position operator, which h Dirac delta functions as eigenfunctions. For a hydrogen atom, one eigenfunctic of r_i would be a delta function at $r = 1$ a.u., $\theta = 0$, $\phi = 0$. The correspondir eigenvalue for $\hat{\mu}$ would be the dipole moment obtained when a proton and a electron are separated by 1 a.u., clearly a finite number. But "everybody knows that an unperturbed atom in a stationary state has zero dipole moment. Th difficulty is resolved when we recognize that "measurement of a variable" Postulates IV and V means measuring the value of a variable at a given instan Hence, we must distinguish between the *instantaneous dipole moment* of an ator which can have any value from among the eigenvalues of $\hat{\mu}$, and the *avera dipole moment*, which is zero for the atom. When a scientist refers to the dipo moment, he is usually understood to be referring to the average dipole momen Indeed, the usual measurements of dipole moment are measurements th effectively average over many molecules or long times (in atomic terms) or bot

6-7 Hermitian Operators

Let ϕ and ψ be any square-integrable functions and $\hat{A}$ be an operator, having the same domain. $\hat{A}$ is defined to be hermitian if

$$\int \psi^* \hat{A} \phi \, dv = \int \phi \hat{A}^* \psi^* \, dv \qquad (6\text{-}1$$

The integration is over the entire range of each spatial coordinate. Recall th the asterisk signifies reversal of the sign of i in a complex or imaginary term. T hermitian property has important consequences in quantum chemistry.

As an example of a test of an operator by Eq. (6-10), let us take the ψ and ϕ to be square-integrable functions of x and $\hat{A}$ to be $i(d/dx)$. Then the left-hand side of Eq. (6-10) becomes, upon integration by parts,

$$\int_{-\infty}^{+\infty} \psi^*(i\, d\phi/dx)\, dx = i\psi^*\phi\Big|_{-\infty}^{+\infty} - i\int_{-\infty}^{+\infty} (d\psi^*/dx)\phi\, dx = -i\int_{-\infty}^{+\infty} \phi(d\psi^*/dx)\, dx \tag{6-11}$$

Since ψ and ϕ are square integrable, they (and their product) must vanish at infinity, giving the zero term in Eq. (6-11). We now write out the right-hand side of Eq. (6-10):

$$\int_{-\infty}^{+\infty} \phi(i\, d/dx)^*\psi^*\, dx = -i\int_{-\infty}^{+\infty} \phi(d\psi^*/dx)\, dx, \tag{6-12}$$

where the minus sign comes from carrying out the operation indicated by the asterisk. Equation (6-12) is equal to Eq. (6-11), and so the operator $i(d/dx)$ is hermitian. Since the effect of i was to introduce a necessary sign reversal, it is apparent that the equality would not result for $\hat{A} = d/dx$. Clearly, any hermitian operator involving a first derivative in any cartesian coordinate must contain the factor i. The operators for linear momenta (Chapter 2) are examples of this.

It is important to realize that Eq. (6-10) does not imply that $\psi^*\hat{A}\phi = \phi\hat{A}^*\psi^*$. A simple example will make this clearer. Let $\hat{A}$ be the hydrogen atom hamiltonian, $\hat{H} = -\frac{1}{2}\nabla^2 - 1/r$, and let ϕ be the 1s eigenfunction: $\phi = (1/\sqrt{\pi})\exp(-r)$. Also, let $\psi = \sqrt{8/\pi}\exp(-2r)$ which is not an eigenfunction of $\hat{H}$. Then, since $H\phi = -\frac{1}{2}\phi$,

$$\psi^* H\phi = -\tfrac{1}{2}\psi^*\phi \tag{6-13}$$

But

$$\phi H^*\psi^* = \phi[-\tfrac{1}{2}(1/r^2)(d/dr)r^2(d/dr) - 1/r]\sqrt{8/\pi}\exp(-2r) \tag{6-14}$$

$$= \phi[(1/r) - 2]\sqrt{8/\pi}\exp(-2r) = [(1/r) - 2]\psi^*\phi \tag{6-15}$$

(Since ψ has no θ or ϕ dependence, the parts of H^* that include $\partial/\partial\theta$ and $\partial/\partial\phi$ have been omitted in Eq. (6-14).) Here we have two functions, $-\frac{1}{2}\psi^*\phi$ and $[(1/r) - 2]\psi^*\phi$. They are obviously different. However, by Eq. (6-10), their integrals are equal since $\hat{H}$ is hermitian.

6-8 Proof That Eigenvalues of Hermitian Operators Are Real

Let $\hat{A}$ be an hermitian operator with a square-integrable eigenfunction ψ. Then

$$\hat{A}\psi = a\psi \tag{6-16}$$

Each side of Eq. (6-16) must be expressible as a real and an imaginary part. The real parts must be equal to each other and so must the imaginary parts.

Taking the complex conjugate of Eq. (6-16) causes the imaginary parts to reverse sign, but they remain equal. Therefore, we may write

$$\hat{A}^*\psi^* = a^*\psi^* \tag{6-17}$$

We multiply Eq. (6-16) from the left by ψ^* and integrate over all spatial variables:

$$\int \psi^*\hat{A}\psi \, dv = a \int \psi^*\psi \, dv \tag{6-18}$$

Similarly, we multiply Eq. (6-17) from the left by ψ and integrate:

$$\int \psi\hat{A}^*\psi^* \, dv = a^* \int \psi\psi^* \, dv \tag{6-19}$$

Since $\hat{A}$ is hermitian, the left-hand sides of Eqs. (6-18) and (6-19) are equal by definition (Eq. 6-10). Therefore, the right-hand sides are equal, and their difference is zero:

$$(a - a^*) \int \psi^*\psi \, dv = 0 \tag{6-20}$$

Since ψ is square integrable the integral cannot be zero. Therefore, $a - a^*$ is zero, which requires that a be real.

6-9 Proof That Eigenfunctions of an Hermitian Operator Form an Orthonormal Set

Let ψ and ϕ be two square-integrable eigenfunctions of the hermitian operator $\hat{A}$:

$$\hat{A}\psi = a_1\psi \tag{6-21}$$

$$\hat{A}^*\phi^* = a_2\phi^* \tag{6-22}$$

Multiplying Eq. (6-21) from the left by ϕ^* and Eq. (6-22) from the left by ψ, and integrating gives

$$\int \phi^*\hat{A}\psi \, dv = a_1 \int \phi^*\psi \, dv \tag{6-23}$$

$$\int \psi\hat{A}^*\phi^* \, dv = a_2 \int \psi\phi^* \, dv \tag{6-24}$$

The left sides of Eqs. (6-23) and (6-24) are equal by (6-11), and

$$(a_1 - a_2) \int \phi^*\psi \, dv = 0. \tag{6-25}$$

If $a_1 \neq a_2$, the integral vanishes. This proves that nondegenerate eigenfunction are orthogonal.

If $a_1 = a_2$, Eq. (6-25) is satisfied even when the integral is finite. Therefore degenerate eigenfunctions need not be orthogonal. But they must be linear independent or else they are the self-same function, and if they are linearly independent, they can be converted to an orthogonal pair. Hence, it is always possible to express the eigenfunctions of an hermitian operator as an orthogonal set. Furthermore, the functions must be square integrable, hence normalizable, and so we may take the eigenfunctions to be orthonormal.

One way to orthogonalize two nonorthogonal, linearly independent functions (which may or may not be eigenfunctions) will now be demonstrated. Let the functions be ψ and ϕ (assumed normalized) and the integral of their product have the value S:

$$\int \psi^* \phi \, dv = S \tag{6-26}$$

We keep one of the functions unchanged, say ψ, and let $\phi' \equiv \phi - S\psi$ be our new second function. ψ and ϕ' are orthogonal since

$$\int \psi^* \phi' \, dv = \int \psi^*(\phi - S\psi) \, dv = \underbrace{\int \psi^* \phi \, dv}_{S} - S \underbrace{\int \psi^* \psi \, dv}_{1} = 0 \tag{6-27}$$

(The new function ϕ' needs to be renormalized.) This process, known as *Schmidt orthogonalization*, may be generalized and applied sequentially to any number of linearly independent functions.

6-10 Proof That Commuting Operators Have Simultaneous Eigenfunctions

$\hat{A}$ and $\hat{B}$ are commuting operators if, for the general square-integrable function f, $\hat{A}\hat{B}f = \hat{B}\hat{A}f$. This can be written $(\hat{A}\hat{B} - \hat{B}\hat{A})f = 0$, which requires that $\hat{A}\hat{B} - \hat{B}\hat{A} = \hat{0}$. ($\hat{0}$ is called the null operator. It satisfies the equation, $\hat{0}f = 0$.) This difference of operator products is called the *commutator* of $\hat{A}$ and $\hat{B}$ and is usually symbolized[5] by $[\hat{A}, \hat{B}]$. If the commutator $[\hat{A}, \hat{B}]$ vanishes, then $\hat{A}$ and $\hat{B}$ commute.

We will now prove an important property of commuting operators, namely, that they have "simultaneous" eigenfunctions. Let β_i be the eigenfunctions for $\hat{B}$: $\hat{B}\beta_i = b_i\beta_i$. For the moment, assume all the numbers b_i are different (i.e., the eigenfunctions β_i are nondegenerate). Let $[\hat{A}, \hat{B}] = \hat{0}$. Then

$$\hat{B}(\hat{A}\beta_i) = \hat{A}\hat{B}\beta_i = \hat{A}b_i\beta_i = b_i(\hat{A}\beta_i) \tag{6-28}$$

The parentheses emphasize that the function obtained by operating on β_i with $\hat{A}$ is an eigenfunction of $\hat{B}$ with eigenvalue b_i. But that function can only be a constant times β_i itself. Hence, for nondegenerate β_i we have that $\hat{A}\beta_i = c\beta_i$, and so β_i is an eigenfunction of $\hat{A}$. This proves that the nondegenerate eigenfunctions for one operator will also be eigenfunctions for any other operators that commute with it.

[5] Other less common conventions are $[\hat{A}, \hat{B}]_-$ and $(\hat{A}, \hat{B})$.

If β_i is degenerate with other functions $\beta_{i,k}$, then we can only go so far as t say that $\hat{A}\beta_i = \sum_k c_k\beta_{i,k}$, for this general linear combination is an eigenfunctio of $\hat{B}$ having eigenvalue b_i. But if this is so, then β_i is evidently not necessarily a eigenfunction of $\hat{A}$. We shall not prove it here, but it is possible to show that on can always find *some* linear combinations of $\beta_{i,k}$ to produce a set of new func tions, β_i', which *are* eigenfunctions of $\hat{A}$ (and remain eigenfunctions of $\hat{B}$ as well) Therefore we can state that, if $\hat{A}$ and $\hat{B}$ commute, there exists a set of function that are eigenfunctions for $\hat{A}$ and $\hat{B}$ simultaneously.

An example of this property occurred in the particle-in-a-ring systen described in Chapter 2. The hamiltonian and angular momentum operator commute for that system. There we found one set of functions, the trigonometri functions, which are eigenfunctions for $\hat{H}$ but not for $\hat{p}_\phi$. But by mixing th energy-degenerate sines and cosines we produced exponential functions that ar eigenfunctions for both of these operators.

Another example concerns the familiar symmetry operations for reflection rotation, etc. If one of these operations, symbolized $\hat{R}$, commutes with th hamiltonian, then we should expect there to be a set of eigenfunctions for $\hat{I}$ that are simultaneously eigenfunctions for $\hat{R}$. It was proved in Chapter 2 tha this means that nondegenerate eigenfunctions must be symmetric or anti symmetric with respect to $\hat{R}$.

A symmetry operator which leaves $\hat{H}$ unchanged can be shown to commut with $\hat{H}$. That is, if $\hat{R}\hat{H} = \hat{H}$, then $\hat{R}\hat{H}f = \hat{H}\hat{R}f$, where f is any function. T show this, let $\hat{R}$ be, say, a reflection operator. Then $\hat{R}$ operates on functions an operators to its right by reflecting the appropriate coordinates: $\hat{R}f(q) = f(Rq)$ If $\hat{H}$ is invariant under reflection $\hat{R}$, then $H(q) = H(Rq)$, and it follows tha $\hat{R}\hat{H}(q)f(q) = \hat{H}(Rq)f(Rq) = \hat{H}(q)f(Rq) = \hat{H}(q)\hat{R}f(q)$. We shall formall develop the ramifications of symmetry in quantum chemistry in Chapter 13.

6-11 Completeness of Eigenfunctions of an Hermitian Operator

In Chapter 3 we discussed the concept of completeness in connection wit the power series expansion of a function. Briefly, a series of functions[6] $\{\phi$ having certain restrictions (e.g., all derivatives vary smoothly) is said to b *complete* if an arbitrary function f having the same restrictions can be expresse in terms of the series[7]

$$f = \sum_k c_i\phi_i \qquad (6\text{-}29$$

[6] A symbol in braces is frequently employed to represent an entire set of functions.

[7] Equation (6-29) is overly restrictive in that it requires that the function and the serie have identical values at every point, whereas it is possible for them to disagree at points o zero measure. However, at the level of this book, we can ignore this distinction and us Eq. (6-29) without encountering difficulty.

Proofs exist that certain hermitian operators corresponding to observable properties have eigenfunctions forming a complete set in the space of well-behaved (continuous, single-valued, square-integrable) functions. These proofs are difficult and will not be given here.[8] Instead we shall introduce

Postulate VI The eigenfunctions for any quantum mechanical operator corresponding to an observable variable constitute a complete, orthonormal set.

We will now use this property to investigate further the nature of the average value of an operator. Let the system be in some state ψ (normalized), not an eigenfunction of $\hat{M}$. However, $\hat{M}$ possesses eigenfunctions $\{\mu\}$ that must form a complete, orthonormal set. Therefore, we can express ψ in terms of μ's:

$$\psi = \sum_i c_i \mu_i \tag{6-30}$$

Now we calculate the average value of M:

$$\begin{aligned} M_{\text{av}} &= \int \psi^* \hat{M} \psi \, dv = \int \sum_i c_i^* \mu_i^* \hat{M} \sum_j c_j \mu_j \, dv \\ &= \sum_i \sum_j c_i^* c_j \int \mu_i^* \hat{M} \mu_j \, dv \end{aligned} \tag{6-31}$$

But $\hat{M}\mu_i = m_i \mu_i$, and so

$$M_{\text{av}} = \sum_i \sum_j c_i^* c_j \int \mu_i^* m_j \mu_j \, dv = \sum_i \sum_j c_i^* c_j m_j \int \mu_i^* \mu_j \, dv \tag{6-32}$$

But $\{\mu\}$ is an orthonormal set, and so

$$M_{\text{av}} = \sum_i \sum_j c_i^* c_j m_j \, \delta_{ij} = \sum_i c_i^* c_i m_i \tag{6-33}$$

What does this expression mean? Each measurement of the property corresponding to $\hat{M}$ must give one of the eigenvalues m_i (Postulate IV) and the average of many such measurements must be M_{av}. Equation (6-33) states how the individual measurements must be weighted to give the average, so it follows that each $c_i^* c_i$ is a measure of the relative frequency for observing the corresponding m_i. Putting it another way, the absolute squares of the mixing coefficients in Eq. (6-30) give the probabilities that a measurement of the variable M will give the corresponding eigenvalue.

6-12 The Variation Principle

Most of the calculations of quantum chemistry are based on the variation principle which states: *For any normalized, acceptable function* ϕ,

$$H_{\text{av}} \equiv \int \phi^* \hat{H} \phi \, d\tau \geq E_0 \tag{6-34}$$

[8] See, e.g., Kemble [1, Section 25].

where E_0 is the lowest eigenvalue of $\hat{H}$.

This statement is easily proved. We expand ϕ in terms of $\{\psi_i\}$, the complete, orthonormal set of eigenfunctions of $\hat{H}$:

$$\phi = \sum_i c_i \psi_i \tag{6-35}$$

As in the preceding section, this leads to

$$\int \phi^* \hat{H} \phi \, d\tau = \sum_i c_i^* c_i E_i \tag{6-36}$$

Now $c_i^* c_i$ is never negative, and so Eq. (6-36) is merely a weighted average of the eigenvalues E_i. Such an average can never be lower than the lowest contributing member, and the principle is proved.

The variation principle is sometimes stated in an equivalent way by saying that the average value of $\hat{H}$ over ϕ is an *upper bound* for the lowest eigenvalue of $\hat{H}$.

6-13 Measurement, Commutators, and Uncertainty

We indicated earlier that we can equate the process of measuring the value of a variable M to a process of forcing the system to take on for an instant a definite value for that variable. But this means that, for that instant at least, the system has a state function which is an eigenfunction of $\hat{M}$. We now can ask "What other variables can we also know definite values for at that same instant?" The answer is, any variable P for whose operator $\hat{P}$ the state function is simultaneously an eigenfunction. For example, if we measure the exact position of the electron in the hydrogen atom, we force it into a state having as wavefunction a Dirac delta function. Since this function is also an eigenfunction for the diple moment operator, it follows that we also know the (instantaneous) dipole moment for the atom at that instant. But the delta function is not an eigenfunction of $\hat{H}$, and so we do not know the electronic energy of the atom. (Physically, we can argue that the interaction between the system and the position-measuring apparatus perturbs the energy of the system so that we lose any knowledge of it.) However, we can express the Dirac delta function as a linear combination of eigenfunctions of $\hat{H}$. The absolute squares of the coefficients in this expression tell us the probabilities for observing the various values of E if we were to measure it immediately following the position measurement (before the electron has time to move away from its measured position). However, we do not *know* the value of E until we make a measurement for it and, when we do, we force the atom into a state described by an eigenfunction of $\hat{H}$. But this new eigenfunction does not give a definite value for position. Thus, we see that position and instantaneous dipole moment can be measured simultaneously, but that position and energy cannot because no eigenfunction for position can also be an eigenfunction for energy. *Energy and position operators fail to have simultaneous eigenfunctions because they do not commute whereas position and dipole moment operators do commute.*

Another example of a commuting pair of operators is the angular momentum and hamiltonian operators for the particle in a ring of constant potential (see Section 2-6). If we measure the angular momentum and obtain, say, $-2\hbar$, then we know that we have forced the system into a state with wavefunction $(2\pi)^{-1/2}\exp(-2i\phi)$ and that the energy must be $4h^2/8\pi^2 I$.

Among the properties of greatest interest in molecular quantum mechanics are energy, symmetry, and electron orbital angular momentum because, for many molecules, some of these operators commute. Thus, if we know that an oxygen molecule is in a nondegenerate stationary electronic state, we know that it is possible to characterize that state by a definite value of the orbital angular momentum along the internuclear axis. Also, we know that the wavefunction must be symmetric or antisymmetric for inversion through the molecular midpoint.

The reader may suspect that there is some connection between commutators and the uncertainty principle, and this is indeed the case. It can be shown[9] that the product of widths of simultaneous measurements (i.e., the uncertainty in their values) of two variables satisfies the relation

$$\Delta a \cdot \Delta b \geq \tfrac{1}{2}\left|\int \psi^*[\hat{A}, \hat{B}]\psi \, d\tau\right| \tag{6-37}$$

where ψ is normalized, and the absolute value $|X|$ is defined as the positive square root of X^*X. If A and B are conjugate variables, such as position and momentum, Eq. (6-37) becomes $\Delta a \cdot \Delta b \geq \hbar/2$, which is Heisenberg's uncertainty relation. If $\hat{A}$ and $\hat{B}$ commute, the right-hand side of Eq. (6-37) vanishes, and the values of both variables may, in theory, be simultaneously known exactly.

6-14 Summary

In this chapter we have presented a set of postulates and drawn upon some examples from earlier chapters to illustrate them. We have explicitly listed six postulates, but we could have written down seven. *Postulate VII* would be the exclusion principle, discussed in Chapter 5:

Postulate VII ψ *must be antisymmetric* (*symmetric*) *for the exchange of identical fermions* (*bosons*).

Some of the postulates and proofs described in this chapter are most important for what follows in this book, and we list these points here.

(1) ψ describes a state as completely as possible and must meet certain mathematical requirements (single valued, etc.). $\psi^*\psi$ is the density distribution function for the system.

[9] See Merzbacher [2, Section 8-6].

(2) For any observable there is an operator (hermitian) which is constructed from the classical expression according to a simple recipe. (Operators related to "spin" are the exception because the classical analog does not exist.) The eigenvalues for such an operator are the possible values we can measure for that quantity. The act of measuring the quantity forces the system into a state described by an eigenfunction of the operator. Once in that state, we may know exact values for other quantities only if their operators commute with the operator associated with our measurement.

(3) If the hamiltonian operator for a system is time independent, stationary eigenfunctions exist of the form $\psi(q, \omega) \exp(-iEt/\hbar)$. The time-dependent exponential does not affect the measurable properties of a system in this state and is almost always completely ignored in any time-independent problem.

(4) The formula for the quantum-mechanical average value [Eq. (6-9)] is equivalent to the arithmetic average of all the possible measured values of a property times their frequency of occurrence [Eq. (6-33)]. This means that it is impossible to devise a function that satisfies the general conditions on ψ and leads to an average energy lower than the lowest eigenvalue of $\hat{H}$.

(5) The eigenfunctions for an operator corresponding to an observable quantity form a complete set, which may be assumed orthonormal. The eigenvalues are all real.

(6) Any operation that leaves $\hat{H}$ unchanged also commutes with $\hat{H}$.

PROBLEMS

6-1 Prove that d^2/dx^2 is hermitian.

6-2 Integrate the expressions in Eqs. (6-13) and (6-15) to show that their integrals are equal.

6-3 Prove that, if a normalized function is expanded in terms of an orthonormal set of functions, the sum of the absolute squares of the expansion coefficients is unity.

6-4 Show that a particular coefficient c_k in Eq. (6-30) is given by $c_k = \int \mu_k{}^* \psi \, dv$.

6-5 A particle in a ring is in a state with wavefunction $\psi = 1/\sqrt{\pi} \cos(2\phi)$.

(a) Calculate the average value for the angular momentum by evaluating $\int \psi^* \hat{p}_\phi \psi \, d\phi$, where $\hat{p}_\phi = (\hbar/i)\, d/d\phi$. (Use symmetry arguments to evaluate the integral.)

(b) Express ψ as a linear combination of exponentials and evaluate the average value of the angular momentum using the formula $p_{\phi\text{av}} = \sum_i c_i{}^* c_i p_{\phi i}$ where $p_{\phi i}$ is the eigenvalue for the ith exponential function.

6-6 Using Eq. (6-37), show that $\Delta x \cdot \Delta p_x \geq \hbar/2$.

6-7 What condition must the function ϕ satisfy for the *equality* part of $\geq$ to hold in Eq. (6-34)?

6-8 Suppose you had an operator and a set of eigenfunctions for it that were associated with real eigenvalues. Does it necessarily follow that the operator is hermitian as defined by Eq. (6-10)? [*Hint:* Consider d/dr and the set of all functions $\exp(-ar)$, where a is real and positive definite.]

6-9 Show that the nonstationary state having wavefunction

$$\Psi = (1/\sqrt{2})\psi_{1s} \exp(it/2) + (1/\sqrt{2})\psi_{2p_0} \exp(it/8)$$

is a solution to Schrödinger's time dependent equation when H is the time-independent H of the hydrogen atom. Use atomic units (i.e., $\hbar = 1$).

6-10 From the definition that $\phi' = \phi - S\psi$ [see the discussion following Eq. (6-26)], evaluate the normalizing constant for ϕ' assuming that ϕ and ψ are normalized.

6-11 Given the two normalized *nonorthogonal* functions $(1/\sqrt{\pi}) \exp(-r)$ and $\sqrt{1/3\pi}\, r \exp(-r)$, construct a new function ϕ that is orthogonal to the first function and lies within the function space spanned by these two functions, *and is normalized.*

REFERENCES

[1] E. C. Kemble, "The Fundamental Principles of Quantum Mechanics with Elementary Applications." Dover, New York, 1958.

[2] E. Merzbacher, "Quantum Mechanics." Wiley, New York, 1961.

CHAPTER 7

THE VARIATION METHOD

7-1 The Spirit of the Method

The proof of the Rayleigh–Ritz variation principle (Section 6-12) involves essentially two ideas. The first is that any function can be expanded into a linear combination of other functions which span the same function space. Thus, for example, $\exp(ikx)$ can be expressed as $\cos(kx) + i\sin(kx)$. An exponential can also be written as a linear combination of powers of the argument:

$$\exp(x) = 1 + x + x^2/2! + x^3/3! + \cdots + x^n/n! + \cdots \tag{7-1}$$

The second idea is that, if a function is expressed as a linear combination of eigenfunctions for the energy operator, then the average energy associated with the function is a weighted average of the energy eigenvalues. For example, if

$$\phi = (1/\sqrt{2})\psi_1 + (1/\sqrt{2})\psi_2 \tag{7-2}$$

where

$$\hat{H}\psi_1 = E_1\psi_1, \qquad \hat{H}\psi_2 = E_2\psi_2, \qquad E_1 \neq E_2 \tag{7-3}$$

then, measuring the energy of many systems in states described by ϕ would give the result E_1 half of the time and E_2 the other half. The average value, $\frac{1}{2}E_1 + \frac{1}{2}E_2$ must lie between E_1 and E_2. Alternatively, if

$$\phi' = \sqrt{\tfrac{1}{3}}\psi_1 + \sqrt{\tfrac{2}{3}}\psi_2 \tag{7-4}$$

measurements would give E_1 one-third of the time, and E_2 the rest of the time, for an average that still must lie between E_1 and E_2. It should be evident that, even when ϕ is a linear combination of many eigenfunctions ψ_i, the average value of E can never lie below the lowest or above the highest eigenvalue.

The variation *method* is based on the idea that, by varying a function to give the lowest average energy, we tend to maximize the amount of the lowest-energy eigenfunction ψ_0 present in the linear combination already discussed. Thus, if we minimize

$$\bar{E} = \int \phi^* \hat{H} \phi \, dv \Big/ \int \phi^* \phi \, dv \tag{7-5}$$

the resulting ϕ should tend to resemble ψ_0 since we have maximized (in a sense) the amount of ψ_0 in ϕ by this procedure.

7-2 Nonlinear Variation: The Hydrogen Atom

We have already seen (Chapter 4) that the lowest-energy eigenfunction for the hydrogen atom is (in atomic units)

$$\psi_{1s} = (1/\sqrt{\pi}) \exp(-r) \tag{7-6}$$

Suppose we did not know this and used the variation method to optimize the normalized trial function

$$\phi = \sqrt{\xi^3/\pi} \exp(-\xi r) \tag{7-7}$$

In this example, when $\xi = 1$, ϕ becomes identical to ψ_{1s}, but in more complicated systems the trial function never becomes identical to an eigenfunction of the hamiltonian. Nevertheless, this is a good example to start with since there are few mathematical complexities to obscure the philosophy of the approach.

The variation method requires that we minimize

$$\bar{E} = \int \phi^* \hat{H} \phi \, dv \tag{7-8}$$

by varying ξ. [ϕ is normalized, so no denominator is required in Eq. (7-8).] Since the trial function ϕ has no θ- or ϕ-dependent terms for ∇^2 to operate on, only the radial part of ∇^2 is needed in $\hat{H}$. Thus [from Eq. (4-7)]

$$\hat{H} = -\frac{1}{2}\frac{1}{r^2}\frac{d}{dr} r^2 \frac{d}{dr} - \frac{1}{r} \tag{7-9}$$

According to Eq. (7-8), we need first to evaluate the quantity $\hat{H}\phi$:

$$\hat{H}\phi = \left[-\frac{1}{2}\frac{1}{r^2}\frac{d}{dr} r^2 \frac{d}{dr} - \frac{1}{r}\right]\sqrt{\xi^3/\pi} \exp(-\xi r) \tag{7-10}$$

$$\vdots$$

$$= [(\xi - 1)/r - \xi^2/2]\sqrt{\xi^3/\pi} \exp(-\xi r) \tag{7-11}$$

Incorporating this into Eq. (7-8) gives (after integrating θ and ϕ in dv to give 4π)

$$\bar{E} = 4\pi(\xi^3/\pi) \int_0^\infty [(\xi - 1)/r - \xi^2/2] \exp(-2\xi r) r^2 \, dr \tag{7-12}$$

$$= 4\xi^3\{(\xi - 1) \int_0^\infty r \exp(-2\xi r) \, dr - (\xi^2/2) \int_0^\infty r^2 \exp(-2\xi r) \, dr\} \tag{7-13}$$

Using the integral table in Appendix 1, we obtain

$$\bar{E} = (\xi^2/2) - \xi \tag{7-14}$$

Now we have a simple expression for $\bar{E}$ as a function of ξ. To obtain the minimum, we set the derivative of $\bar{E}$ to zero:

$$d\bar{E}/d\xi = 0 = \xi - 1 \tag{7-15}$$

As we expected, $\xi = 1$. Inserting this value for ξ into Eq. (7-14) gives $\bar{E} = -\frac{1}{2}$ a.u., which is identical with the lowest eigenvalue for the hydrogen atom.

This example demonstrates that minimizing $\bar{E}$ for a trial function causes the function to become like the lowest eigenfunction for the system. But it is more realistic to examine a case where the trial function is incapable of becoming exactly identical with the lowest eigenfunction. Suppose we assumed a trial form (normalized) of

$$\phi = \sqrt{\xi^5/3\pi}\, r \exp(-\xi r) \tag{7-16}$$

Proceeding as before, we first evaluate $\hat{H}\phi$:

$$\hat{H}\phi = [(-1/r^2) + (2\xi - 1)/r - \xi^2/2]\phi \tag{7-17}$$

This leads to

$$\bar{E}(\xi) = \tfrac{4}{3}[(\xi^2/8) - 3\xi/8] \tag{7-18}$$

so that

$$d\bar{E}/d\xi = 0 = \tfrac{4}{3}[(\xi/4) - \tfrac{3}{8}] \tag{7-19}$$

and $\bar{E}$ is a minimum when $\xi = \frac{3}{2}$. Thus, our energy-optimized ϕ is

$$\phi = \sqrt{3^5/96\pi}\, r \exp(-3r/2) \tag{7-20}$$

This is obviously not identical to the eigenfunction given by Eq. (7-6), but it must be expressible as a linear combination of hydrogen atom eigenfunctions, and the amount of ψ_{1s} present should be quite large unless the trial form was unwisely chosen. Since ϕ also must contain contributions from higher energy eigenfunctions, it follows that $\bar{E}$ must be higher in energy than $-\frac{1}{2}$ a.u. We test this by inserting $\xi = \frac{3}{2}$ into Eq. (7-18), obtaining an $\bar{E}$ of $-\frac{3}{8}$ a.u., (-0.375 a.u.). This value is above the lowest eigenvalue, but it is well below the second-lowest eigenvalue ($-\frac{1}{8}$ a.u.) associated with 2s, 2p eigenfunctions, and so we know that ϕ does indeed contain much 1s character. We can find out exactly how much 1s eigenfunction is contained in ϕ by calculating the overlap between ϕ and the 1s eigenfunction. That is, since the 1s function is orthogonal to all the other hydrogen atom eigenfunctions;

$$\int \psi_{1s}\psi_j\, dv = \begin{cases} 0, \ldots, j \neq 1s \\ 1, \ldots, j = 1s \end{cases} \tag{7-21}$$

and since

$$\phi = c_{1s}\psi_{1s} + \sum_{j \neq 1s} c_j\psi_j \tag{7-22}$$

it follows that

$$\int \psi_{1s}\phi\, dv = c_{1s}\overbrace{\int \psi_{1s}\psi_{1s}\, dv}^{1} + \sum_{j\neq 1s} c_j \overbrace{\int \psi_{1s}\psi_j\, dv}^{0} = c_{1s} \tag{7-23}$$

Integrating $\int \psi_{1s}\phi\, dv$, where ϕ is given by Eq. (7-20), gives $c_{1s} = 0.9775$, so ϕ does indeed "contain" a large amount of ψ_{1s}. (If $c_{1s} = 1$, then ψ_{1s} and ϕ are identical.)

This suggests another way of trying to get a "best" approximate wavefunction. We could find the value of ξ that maximized the overlap between ϕ and ψ_{1s}. This maximizes c_{1s} in Eq. (7-22). If one does this (Problem 7-2), one obtains $\xi = \frac{5}{3}$, which corresponds to an overlap of 0.9826 and an $\bar{E}$ of -0.370 a.u. At first sight, this seems puzzling. ϕ ($\xi = \frac{5}{3}$) has a larger amount of ψ_{1s} in it, but $\phi(\xi = \frac{3}{2})$ has a lower average energy. But it is really not so unreasonable. Maximizing the value of c_{1s} causes ξ to take on a certain value which may cause the coefficient for some high-energy state (say, 6s) to become relatively larger, producing a tendency to raise the average energy. On the other hand, minimizing $\bar{E}$ is a process that is implicitly concerned with what *all* the coefficients are doing. This allows for a different sort of compromise wherein c_{1s} may be allowed to be a bit smaller if the associated energy loss is more than compensated for by a favorable shifting in values of higher coefficients (e.g., if c_{2s} increases and c_{6s} decreases). The purpose of this discussion is to emphasize that the variation method optimizes the trial function in a certain sense (best energy), but that other kinds of optimization are conceivable. The optimization that gives best overlap is not generally useful because it requires that we know the exact solution to begin with. If we vary ξ to obtain optimal agreement for $\bar{r}$, or $\bar{V}$, or $\overline{r^2}$, we would find a different value of ξ appropriate for each property. In each case, however, we would need to know the correct value of $\bar{r}$, etc., before starting. A great virtue of the energy variation method is that it does not require foreknowledge of the exact eigenvalue or eigenfunction. However, the function that gives the lowest value for $\bar{E}$ might not be especially good in describing other properties. This is demonstrated in Fig. 7-1 and Table 7-1. The figure indicates that the trial function differs from the exact function chiefly near the nucleus, where $r < 1$. This discrepancy shows up when we compare average values for various powers of r. The operators r, r^2, and r^3 become large when r is large. Thus, these operators magnify $\psi^2\, dv$ at large r. Since the two functions are fairly similar at large r, the average values show fair agreement. But r^{-1} and r^{-2} become large when r is small. Thus, the fact that the approximate function is too small at small r shows up as a marked disagreement in the average value of r^{-2}, this average being much larger for the exact function (see Table 7-1). *Any trial function that is known to be especially inaccurate in some region of space (e.g., at small r) will give unreliable average values for operators that are largest in that region of space (e.g., r^{-2}).*

Choosing a trial form such as Eq. (7-16), which must vanish at $r = 0$,

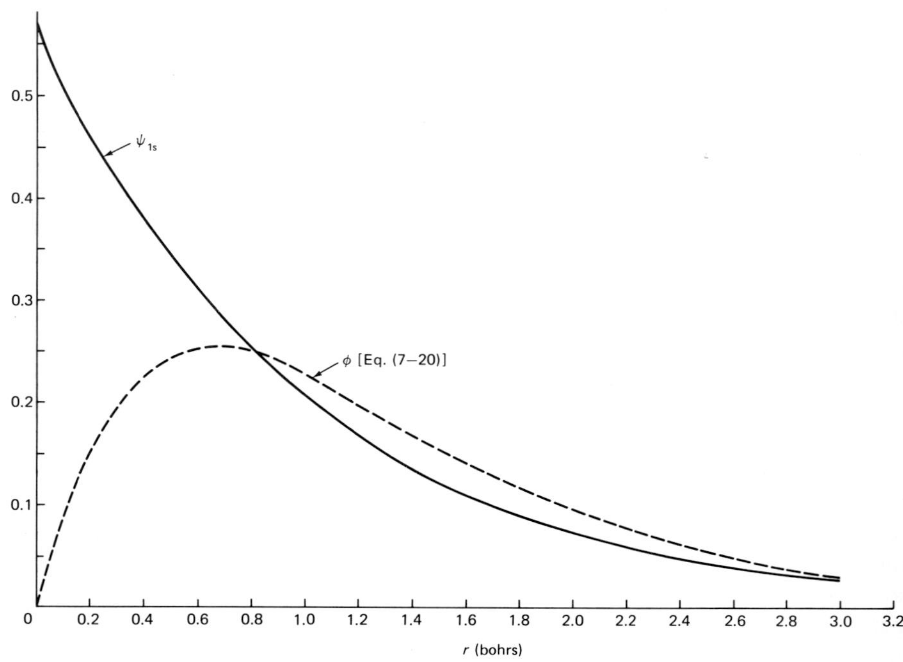

FIG. 7-1 Plots of ψ_{1s} and ϕ [Eq. (7-20)] versus *r*.

might seem foolish since we know that ψ_{1s} does not vanish at $r = 0$. And if we were interested in electron density at the nucleus for, say, calculating the Fermi contact interaction, this would indeed by a self-defeating choice. But if our interest is in energies or other properties having operators that are large in regions where the trial function is not too deficient, this choice would serve. One often settles for a mathematically convenient form even though it is known

TABLE 7-1
Comparison between Exact Values for Some Properties of (1s) *Hydrogen and Values Calculated from the Function Eq.* (7-20)

Quantity	Exact (1s) value (a.u.)	Trial function value (a.u.)
$\bar{E}$	$-\frac{1}{2}$	$-\frac{3}{8}$
Electron density at nucleus	$1/\pi$	0
$\bar{r}$	1.5	1.67
$\overline{r^2}$	3.0	3.33
$\overline{r^3}$	7.5	7.78
$\overline{r^{-1}}$	1.0	0.75
$\overline{r^{-2}}$	2.0	0.75

to be inadequate in some way. Care must then be exercised, however, to avoid using that trial wavefunction in ways which emphasize its inadequacies.

7-3 Nonlinear Variation: The Helium Atom

We mentioned in Chapter 5 that the ground-state wavefunction 1s(1)1s(2) for helium was much too contracted if the 1s functions were taken from the He^+ ion without modification. Physically, this arises because, in He^+, the single electron sees only a doubly positive nucleus, whereas in He each electron sees a doubly positive nucleus *and* another electron, so that in He the repulsion between electrons prevents them from spending as much time near the nucleus as in He^+. Somehow, the 1s functions should be modified to reflect this behavior. We will now show how the variation method may be used to accomplish this.

The form of the hydrogenlike ion 1s solution is

$$1s = \sqrt{Z^3/\pi}\exp(-Zr) \tag{7-24}$$

For He^+, $Z = 2$, but we have just seen that this gives a function that is too contracted. Smaller values of Z would cause the function to die away more slowly with r. Therefore, it is reasonable to replace the atomic number Z with a variable parameter ξ and find the value of ξ that gives the lowest average energy. Hence, we let

$$1s'(1) = \sqrt{\xi^3/\pi}\exp(-\xi r_1) \tag{7-25}$$

and our trial wavefunction is[1]

$$\phi(1, 2) = 1s'(1)1s'(2)(1/\sqrt{2})[\alpha(1)\beta(2) - \beta(1)\alpha(2)] \tag{7-26}$$

The average energy is [since $\phi(1, 2)$ is normalized]

$$\bar{E} = \iint \phi^*(1, 2)\hat{H}(1, 2)\phi(1, 2)\, d\tau(1)\, d\tau(2) \tag{7-27}$$

Since $\hat{H}(1, 2)$ contains no spin operators at our level of approximation, the integral separates into an integral over the space coordinates of both electrons and an integral over the spin coordinates of both electrons. The integration over spins gives a factor of unity. There remains

$$\bar{E} = \iint 1s'(1)1s'(2)\hat{H}(1, 2)1s'(1)1s'(2)\, dv(1)\, dv(2) \tag{7-28}$$

[1] In this trial function, ξ has the same value in each atomic orbital. This is not a necessary restriction. There is no physical reason for not choosing the more general trial function where orbitals with different ξ are used. Symmetry requires that such a function be written $2^{-1/2}[1s'(1)1s''(2) + 1s''(1)1s'(2)]\, 2^{-1/2}[\alpha(1)\beta(2) - \beta(1)\alpha(2)]$. This type of function is called a "split-shell" wavefunction. It gives a lower energy for He than does the function (7-26). However, for most quantum-chemical calculations split shells are not used, the gain in accuracy usually not being commensurate with the increased computational effort.

where

$$\hat{H}(1, 2) = -\tfrac{1}{2}\nabla_1^2 - \tfrac{1}{2}\nabla_2^2 - (2/r_1) - (2/r_2) + (1/r_{12}) \tag{7-29}$$

and where the θ and ϕ parts of ∇^2 can be ignored since $\phi(1, 2)$ is independent of these variables. The calculation is easier if we recognize that

$$\hat{H}(1, 2) = \hat{H}_{He^+}(1) + \hat{H}_{He^+}(2) - 1/r_{12} \tag{7-30}$$

This allows us to express Eq. (7-28) as the sum of three integrals, the first of these being

$$\iint 1s'(1)1s'(2)\hat{H}_{He^+}(1)1s'(1)1s'(2)\, dv(1)\, dv(2) \tag{7-31}$$

Since the operator in the integrand operates only on coordinates of electron 1, we can separate this into a product of two integrals:

$$\int 1s'(2)1s'(2)\, dv(2) \int 1s'(1)\hat{H}_{He^+}(1)1s'(1)\, dv(1) \tag{7-32}$$

The 1s′ functions are normalized, and so the first integral is unity. The second integral is almost identical to the integral in Eq. (7-8) and has the value $(\xi^2/2) - 2\xi$. Therefore, the first of the three integrals mentioned above equals $(\xi^2/2) - 2\xi$. The second of the three integrals is identical with Eq. (7-31) except that the operator acts on electron 2 instead of 1. This integral is evaluated in the same manner and gives the same result. The third integral, in which the operator is $1/r_{12}$, is more difficult to evaluate. This interesting and instructive problem constitutes a detour from the main sequence of ideas in this chapter and is therefore discussed in Appendix 3. We here simply take the result, $5\xi/8$, and proceed with the variation calculation.

We now have an expression for $\bar{E}$ as a function of ξ:

$$\bar{E} = 2[(\xi^2/2) - 2\xi] + \tfrac{5}{8}\xi = \xi^2 - \tfrac{27}{8}\xi \tag{7-33}$$

Minimizing $\bar{E}$ with respect to ξ gives

$$d\bar{E}/d\xi = 0 = 2\xi - \tfrac{27}{8} \tag{7-34}$$

so that

$$\xi = \tfrac{27}{16} \tag{7-35}$$

This value of ξ is smaller than the unmodified He^+ value of 2, as we anticipated. Let us see how much the average energy has been improved. According to Eq. (7-33), when ξ is 2, $\bar{E}$ is equal to -2.75 a.u. When $\xi = \tfrac{27}{16}$, $\bar{E}$ equals -2.848 a.u., so the average energy has been lowered by approximately 0.1 a.u., or 2.7 eV, or 62 kcal/mole. (The exact energy for He is -2.9037 a.u.) Further analysis would show that, by decreasing ξ, we have decreased the average kinetic energy (the less compressed wavefunction changes slope less rapidly), raised the nuclear–electron attraction energy from a large negative to a smaller negative value (the decreased attraction resulting from the electrons being farther from the nucleus, on the average), and decreased the interelectronic repulsion energy from a higher positive value to a lower one. The variational procedure has allowed the wavefunction to adjust to the best compromise it can achieve among these three factors. If ξ becomes less than $\frac{27}{16}$, the loss of nuclear–electron attraction is too great to be offset by the loss of interelectronic repulsion and kinetic energy.

Because the variable parameter in the preceding examples always occurs in an exponent, these are referred to as *nonlinear* variation calculations. Such calculations tend to become mathematically complicated and are not frequently used except for fairly simple systems. The fact that the hamiltonian operator is a *linear* operator [i.e., $\hat{H}(c_1\phi_1 + c_2\phi_2) = c_1\hat{H}\phi_1 + c_2\hat{H}\phi_2$] makes a linear variation procedure more convenient for most purposes.

7-4 Linear Variation: The Polarizability of the Hydrogen Atom

Suppose we wish to express a wavefunction ψ (which may be approximate) as a linear combination of two known functions ϕ_1 and ϕ_2:

$$\psi(c_1, c_2) = c_1\phi_1 + c_2\phi_2 \tag{7-36}$$

The question is, what values of c_1 and c_2 give a ψ that best approximates the exact wavefunction for a particular system? The usual approach is to determine which values of c_1 and c_2 give the ψ associated with the minimum average energy attainable. The technique for achieving this, called the *linear variation method*, is by far the most common type of quantum chemical calculation performed.

An example of a problem that can be treated by this method is the polarizability of the hydrogen atom. The wavefunction for the unperturbed hydrogen atom in its ground state is spherically symmetrical. But, when a uniform z-directed external electric field of strength F is imposed, the positive nucleus and the negative electron are attracted in opposite directions, which leads to an electronic distribution that is skewed with respect to the nucleus. The wavefunction describing this skewed distribution may be *approximated* by mixing with the unperturbed 1s function some $2p_z$ function: $\psi = c_1 1s + c_2 2p_z$. As indicated in Fig. 7-2, this produces a skewed wavefunction because the $2p_z$ function is of the same sign as the 1s function on one side of the nucleus and of the opposite sign on the other. We will work out the details of this example after developing the method for the general case.

Let the *generalized* trial function ψ be a linear combination of known functions $\phi_1, \phi_2, \ldots, \phi_n$. (This set of functions is called the *basis set* for the calculation.)

$$\psi = c_1\phi_1 + c_2\phi_2 + \cdots + c_n\phi_n \tag{7-37}$$

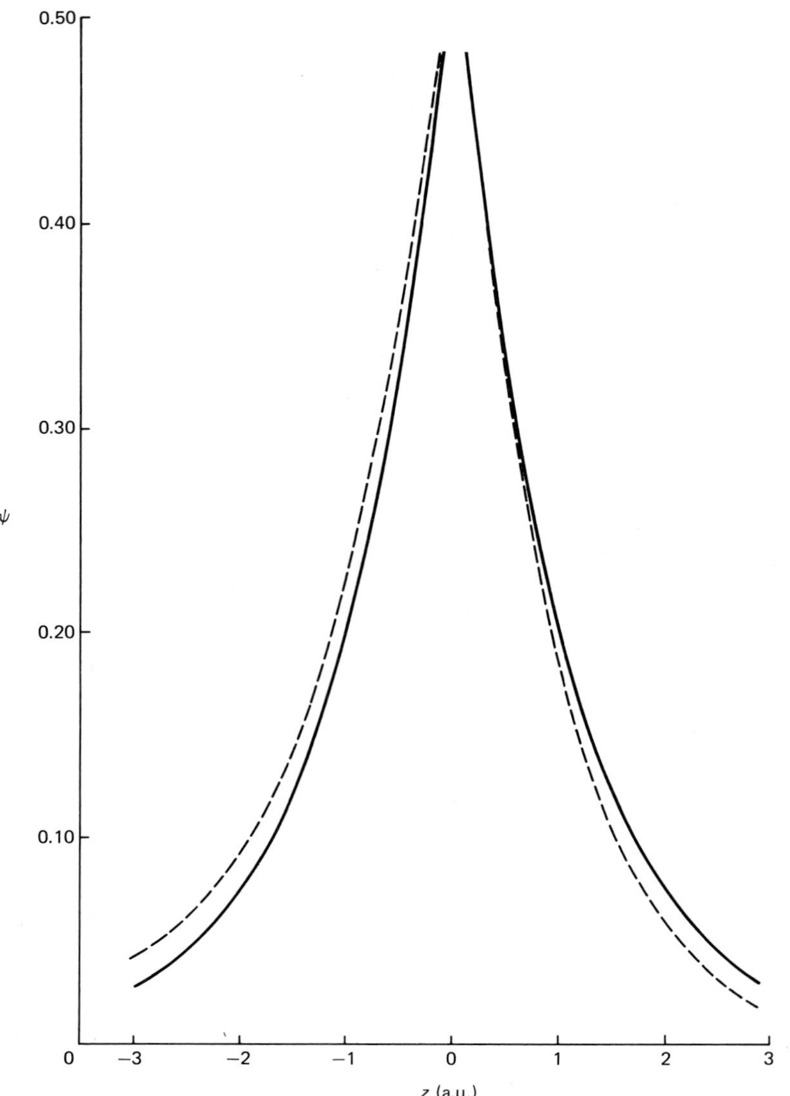

FIG. 7-2 Values of ψ versus z for 1s state of H atom (—) and for approximate wavefunction given by 0.982 1s -0.188 $2p_z$ (---). The nucleus is at $z = 0$ for each case.

where the coefficients c are to be determined so that

$$\int \psi^* \hat{H} \psi \, d\tau \Big/ \int \psi^* \psi \, d\tau = \bar{E} \tag{7-38}$$

is minimized. Substituting Eq. (7-37) into Eq. (7-38) gives

$$\bar{E} = \frac{\int (c_1{}^*\phi_1{}^* + c_2{}^*\phi_2{}^* + \cdots + c_n{}^*\phi_n{}^*)\hat{H}(c_1\phi_1 + c_2\phi_2 + \cdots + c_n\phi_n)\,d\tau}{\int (c_1{}^*\phi_1{}^* + c_2{}^*\phi_2{}^* + \cdots + c_n{}^*\phi_n{}^*)(c_1\phi_1 + c_2\phi_2 + \cdots + c_n\phi_n)\,d\tau} = \frac{\text{num}}{\text{denom}} \tag{7-39}$$

Since we will be dealing with cases in which the c's and ϕ's are real, we will temporarily omit the complex conjugate notation to simplify the derivation. At the minimum value of $\bar{E}$,

$$\partial\bar{E}/\partial c_1 = \partial\bar{E}/\partial c_2 = \cdots = \partial\bar{E}/\partial c_n = 0 \tag{7-40}$$

The partial derivative of Eq. (7-39) with respect to c_1 is

$$\begin{aligned}\frac{\partial\bar{E}}{\partial c_1} &= \frac{\int \phi_1\hat{H}(c_1\phi_1 + \cdots + c_n\phi_n)\,d\tau}{\text{denom}} + \frac{\int (c_1\phi_1 + \cdots + c_n\phi_n)\hat{H}\phi_1\,d\tau}{\text{denom}} \\ &\quad - (\text{num})(\text{denom})^{-2}\left[\int \phi_1(c_1\phi_1 + \cdots + c_n\phi_n)\,d\tau \right. \\ &\quad \left. + \int (c_1\phi_1 + \cdots + c_n\phi_n)\phi_1\,d\tau\right] \\ &= 0\end{aligned} \tag{7-41}$$

Multiplying through by denom, recalling that num/denom equals $\bar{E}$, and rearranging, gives

$$\begin{aligned}c_1\left[\int \phi_1\hat{H}\phi_1\,d\tau - \bar{E}\int \phi_1\phi_1\,d\tau\right] + c_2\left[\int \phi_1\hat{H}\phi_2\,d\tau - \bar{E}\int \phi_1\phi_2\,d\tau\right] + \cdots \\ + c_n\left[\int \phi_1\hat{H}\phi_n\,d\tau - \bar{E}\int \phi_1\phi_n\,d\tau\right] = 0\end{aligned} \tag{7-42}$$

At this point, it is convenient to switch to an abbreviated notation:

$$\int \phi_i\hat{H}\phi_j\,d\tau \equiv H_{ij} \tag{7-43}$$

$$\int \phi_i\phi_j\,d\tau \equiv S_{ij} \tag{7-44}$$

The integral S_{ij} is normally called an *overlap integral* since its value is, in certain cases, an indication of the extent to which the two functions ϕ_i and ϕ_j occupy the same space. Use of this abbreviated notation produces, for Eq. (7-42),

$$c_1(H_{11} - \bar{E}S_{11}) + c_2(H_{12} - \bar{E}S_{12}) + \cdots + c_n(H_{1n} - \bar{E}S_{1n}) = 0 \tag{7-45}$$

A similar treatment for $\partial\bar{E}/\partial c_i$ gives a similar equation:

$$c_1(H_{i1} - \bar{E}S_{i1}) + c_2(H_{i2} - \bar{E}S_{i2}) + \cdots + c_n(H_{in} - ES_{in}) = 0 \tag{7-46}$$

Thus, requiring that $\partial\bar{E}/\partial c_i$ vanish for all coefficients produces n homogeneous linear equations (homogeneous, all equal zero; linear, all c_i's to first power). If one chooses a value for $\bar{E}$, there remain n unknowns—the coefficients c_i. (The integrals H_{ij} and S_{ij} are presumably knowable since $\hat{H}$ and the functions ϕ_i are known.) Of course, one trivial solution for Eqs. (7-46) is always possible, namely, $c_1 = c_2 = \cdots = c_n = 0$. But this corresponds to $\psi = 0$, a case of no physical interest. Are there nontrivial solutions as well? *In quantum chemical calculations, nontrivial solutions usually exist only for certain discrete values of* $\bar{E}$. This provides the approach for solving the problem. First, find those values of $\bar{E}$ for which nontrivial coefficients exist. Second, substitute into Eqs. (7-46) whichever of these values of $\bar{E}$ one is interested in and solve for the coefficients. (Each value of $\bar{E}$ has its own associated set of coefficients.) But how do we find these particular values of $\bar{E}$ that yield nontrivial solutions to Eqs. (7-46)? The answer is given in Appendix 2, where it is shown that *the condition which must be met by the coefficients of a set of linear homogeneous equations in order that nontrivial solutions exist is that their determinant vanish.* Notice that, in the standard treatment given in Appendix 2, the coefficients are *known* and x, y, and z are unknown. Here, however, the coefficients c_i are unknown, and H_{ij} and S_{ij} are known. Therefore, it is the determinant of the H's, S's and $\bar{E}$ in Eqs. (7-46) that must equal zero:

$$\begin{vmatrix} H_{11} - \bar{E}S_{11} & H_{12} - \bar{E}S_{12} & \cdots & H_{1n} - \bar{E}S_{1n} \\ H_{21} - \bar{E}S_{21} & H_{22} - \bar{E}S_{22} & \cdots & H_{2n} - \bar{E}S_{2n} \\ \vdots & \vdots & & \vdots \\ H_{n1} - \bar{E}S_{n1} & H_{n2} - \bar{E}S_{n2} & \cdots & H_{nn} - \bar{E}S_{nn} \end{vmatrix} = 0 \tag{7-47}$$

Expansion of this determinant gives a single equation containing the unknown $\bar{E}$. Any value of $\bar{E}$ satisfying this equation is associated with a nontrivial set of coefficients. The lowest of these values of $\bar{E}$ is the minimum average energy achievable by variation of the coefficients. Substitution of this value of $\bar{E}$ back into Eqs. (7-46) produces n simultaneous equations for the n coefficients. Equations (7-46) are referred to as the *secular equations.* The determinant in Eq. (7-47) is called the *secular determinant.*

This method is best illustrated by example, and we will now proceed with the problem of a hydrogen atom in a z-directed uniform electric field of strength F a.u. As mentioned earlier, a suitable choice of functions to mix together to approximate the accurate wavefunction is the 1s and $2p_z$ hydrogenlike functions. The choice of two basis functions leads to a 2×2 secular determinantal equation:

$$\begin{vmatrix} H_{11} - \bar{E}S_{11} & H_{12} - \bar{E}S_{12} \\ H_{21} - \bar{E}S_{21} & H_{22} - \bar{E}S_{22} \end{vmatrix} = 0 \tag{7-48}$$

If we arbitrarily associate the 1s function with the index 1 and the $2p_z$ function with index 2 (consistent with $\psi = c_1 1s + c_2 2p_z$), then the terms in the determinant are (returning to general complex conjugate notation):

$$H_{11} = \int 1s^* \hat{H} 1s \, d\tau, \qquad H_{12} = \int 1s^* \hat{H} 2p_z \, d\tau$$
$$H_{21} = \int 2p_z^* \hat{H} 1s \, d\tau, \qquad H_{22} = \int 2p_z^* \hat{H} 2p_z \, d\tau \tag{7-49}$$

(The electron label has been omitted since there is only one electron.) The corresponding S integrals are obtained from these if $\hat{H}$ is omitted in each case. The hamiltonian operator is just that for a hydrogen atom with an additional term to account for the z-directed field:

$$\hat{H} = -\tfrac{1}{2}\nabla^2 - (1/r) - Fr\cos\theta \tag{7-50}$$

[The energy of a charge $-e$ in a uniform electric field of strength F and direction z is $-eFz$. In atomic units, one unit of field strength is $e/a_0^2 = 5.142 \times 10^9$ V/cm. The unit of charge in atomic units is e, so this symbol does not appear explicitly in Eq. (7-50). Also, the identity $z = r\cos\theta$ has been used.] This may also be written

$$\hat{H} = \hat{H}_{\text{hyd}} - Fr\cos\theta \tag{7-51}$$

where $\hat{H}_{\text{hyd}}$ is the hamiltonian for the unperturbed hydrogen atom.

The secular determinant contains four H-type and four S-type terms. However, evaluating these eight integrals turns out to be much easier than one might expect. In the first place, $S_{12} = S_{21}$ since these integrals differ only in the order of the two functions in the integrand, and the functions commute. Also, because $\hat{H}$ is hermitian, it follows immediately that $H_{21} = H_{12}^*$. This leaves us with three S terms and three H terms to evaluate. The three S terms are simple. Because the hydrogenlike functions are orthonormal, S_{11} and S_{22} equal unity, and S_{12} vanishes. These points have already reduced the secular determinantal equation to

$$\begin{vmatrix} H_{11} - \bar{E} & H_{12} \\ H_{12}^* & H_{22} - \bar{E} \end{vmatrix} = 0 \tag{7-52}$$

Consider next the term H_{11}. This may be written as

$$H_{11} = \int 1s^* \hat{H}_{\text{hyd}} 1s \, d\tau - \int 1s^* (Fr\cos\theta) 1s \, d\tau \tag{7-53}$$

But the 1s function is an eigenfunction of $\hat{H}_{\text{hyd}}$ with eigenvalue $-\frac{1}{2}$ a.u. Therefore, the first integral on the right-hand side of Eq. (7-53) is

$$\int 1s^* \hat{H}_{\text{hyd}} 1s \, d\tau = -\tfrac{1}{2} \int 1s^* 1s \, d\tau = -\tfrac{1}{2} \quad \text{a.u.} \tag{7-54}$$

The second term on the right-hand side of Eq. (7-53) is zero by symmetry since 1s*1s is symmetric for reflection in the xy plane while $r \cos \theta$ ($= z$) is antisymmetric. Thus, $H_{11} = -\frac{1}{2}$ a.u. Similarly, $H_{22} = -\frac{1}{8}$ a.u. [Recall that the eigenvalues of hydrogen are equal to $-1/(2n^2)$, and here $n = 2$.] All that remains is H_{12}:

$$H_{12} = \int 1s^* \hat{H}_{\text{hyd}} 2p_z \, d\tau - F \int 1s^*(r \cos \theta) 2p_z \, d\tau \tag{7-55}$$

The first term on the right-hand side is easily shown to be zero:

$$\int 1s^* \hat{H}_{\text{hyd}} 2p_z \, d\tau = \int 1s^*(-\tfrac{1}{8}) 2p_z \, d\tau = 0 \tag{7-56}$$

Here we employ the fact that $2p_z$ is an eigenfunction of $\hat{H}_{\text{hyd}}$ and then the fact that 1s and $2p_z$ are orthogonal. The second term on the right-hand side must be written out in full and integrated by "brute force." It is remarkable that, of the eight terms originally considered, only one needs to be done by detailed integration. Proceeding, we substitute formulas for 1s and $2p_z$ in this last integral to obtain

$$-F \iiint (\pi)^{-1/2} \exp(-r)[r \cos \theta](32\pi)^{-1/2} r \exp(-r/2) \cos \theta (r^2 \sin \theta) \, dr \, d\theta \, d\phi \tag{7-57}$$

We consider the integration over spin to have been carried out already, giving a factor of unity. Integrating over ϕ to obtain 2π, and regrouping terms gives

$$-2\pi F/(4\sqrt{2}\pi) \int_0^\infty r^4 \exp(-3r/2) \, dr \int_0^\pi \cos^2 \theta \sin \theta \, d\theta \tag{7-58}$$

$$= -(F/2\sqrt{2})[4!/(\tfrac{3}{2})^5][\tfrac{2}{3}] = -2^{15/2} F/3^5 \quad \text{a.u.} \tag{7-59}$$

This completes the task of evaluating the terms in the secular determinant. The final result is (in atomic units)

$$\begin{vmatrix} -\frac{1}{2} - \bar{E} & -2^{15/2}(F/3^5) \\ -2^{15/2}(F/3^5) & -\frac{1}{8} - \bar{E} \end{vmatrix} = 0 \tag{7-60}$$

which expands to

$$\tfrac{1}{16} + (5\bar{E}/8) + \bar{E}^2 - 2^{15} F^2/3^{10} = 0 \tag{7-61}$$

This is quadratic in $\bar{E}$ having roots

$$\bar{E} = -\tfrac{5}{16} \pm (\tfrac{9}{64} + 2^{17} F^2/3^{10})^{1/2}/2 \tag{7-62}$$

When no external field is present, $F = 0$ and the roots are just $-\frac{1}{2}$ and $-\frac{1}{8}$ a.u., the 1s and $2p_z$ eigenvalues for the unperturbed hydrogen atom. As F increases from zero, the roots change, as indicated in Fig. 7-3. We see that, for a given

[2] Since H_{12} is real, it is clear that $H_{21} = H_{12}$.

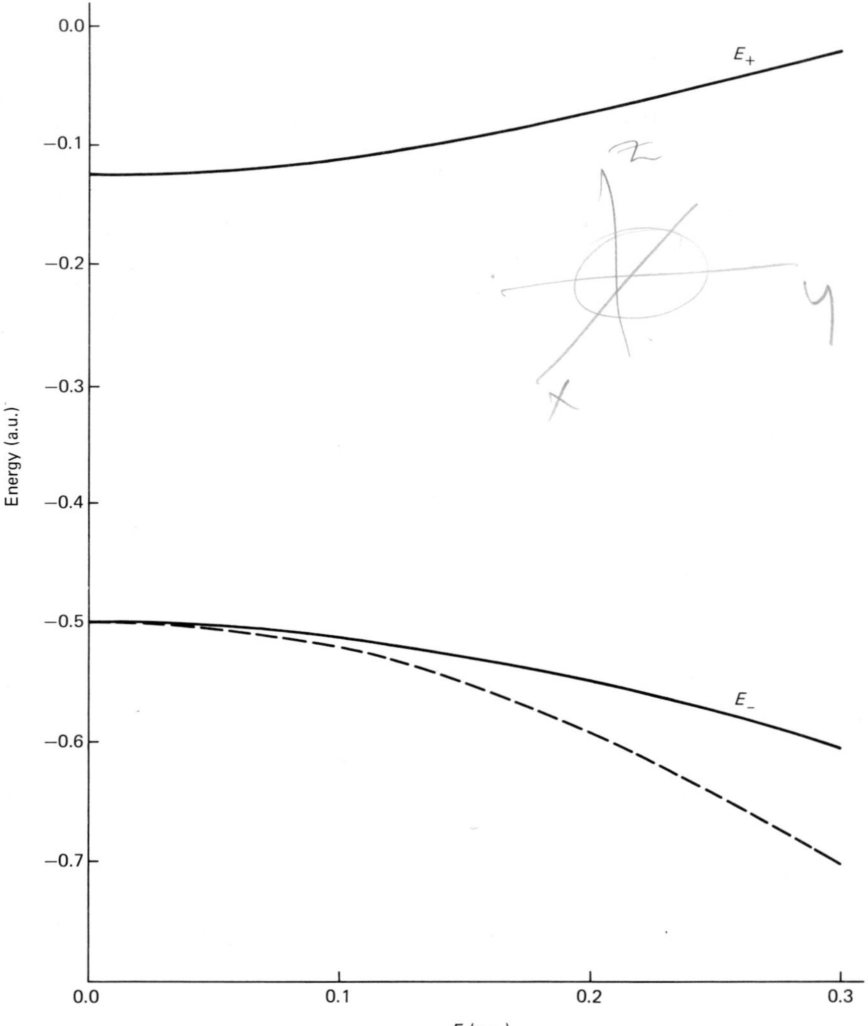

FIG. 7-3 Average energies for hydrogen atom in a uniform electric field of strength F as given by linear variation calculation using 1s, 2p basis. (– – –) Results from accurate calculations.

field strength, there are only two values of $\bar{E}$ that will cause the determinant to vanish. If either of these two values of $\bar{E}$ is substituted into the secular equations related to Eq. (7-52), then nontrivial values for c_1 and c_2 can be found. Thus, at $F = 0.1$ a.u., $\bar{E} = -0.51425$ a.u., and $\bar{E} = -0.1107$ a.u. are values of $\bar{E}$ for which $\partial\bar{E}/\partial c_1$ and $\partial\bar{E}/\partial c_2$ both vanish. The former is the minimum, the latter the maximum in the curve of $\bar{E}$ versus c_1. (The normality requirement results in the two c's being dependent, and so $\bar{E}$ may be plotted against either of them.) Since the variation principle tells us that $\bar{E} \geq E_{\text{lowest exact}}$, we can say immediately that the energy of the hydrogen atom in a uniform electric field of 0.1 a.u. is -0.51425 a.u. or lower. That is, -0.51425 a.u. is an *upper bound* to the true energy.

Now that we have the value of the lowest $\bar{E}$, we can solve for c_1 and c_2 and obtain the approximate ground state wavefunction. The homogeneous equations related to the determinant in Eq. (7-52) are

$$c_1(H_{11} - \bar{E}) + c_2 H_{12} = 0 \tag{7-63}$$

$$c_1 H_{12} + c_2(H_{22} - \bar{E}) = 0 \tag{7-64}$$

Substituting -0.51425 for $\bar{E}$, and inserting the values for H_{11}, H_{22}, and H_{12} found earlier gives (when $F = 0.1$ a.u.)

$$0.01425c_1 - 0.074493c_2 = 0 \tag{7-65}$$

$$-0.074493c_1 + 0.38925c_2 = 0 \tag{7-66}$$

Equation (7-65) gives

$$c_1 = 5.2275c_2 \tag{7-67}$$

If we substitute this expression for c_1 into Eq. (7-66) we get

$$-0.3892c_2 + 0.3892c_2 = 0 \tag{7-68}$$

This is useless for evaluating c_2. It is one of the properties of such a set of homogeneous equations that the last unused equation is useless for determining coefficients. This arises because an equation like (7-63) still equals zero when c_1 and c_2 are both multiplied by the same arbitrary constant. Therefore, these equations are inherently capable of telling us the *ratio* of c_1 and c_2 only, and not their absolute values. We shall determine absolute values by invoking the requirement that ψ be normalized. In this case, this means that (see Problem 7-9)

$$c_1{}^2 + c_2{}^2 = 1 \tag{7-69}$$

or

$$(5.2275c_2)^2 + c_2{}^2 = 1 \tag{7-70}$$

which gives

$$c_2 = \pm 0.18789 \tag{7-71}$$

If we arbitrarily choose the positive root for c_2, it follows from Eq. (7-67) that $c_1 = 0.98219$.

Thus, when $F = 0.1$ a.u., the linear variation method using a 1s, $2p_z$ basis set gives an upper bound to the energy of $\bar{E} = -0.51425$ a.u. and a corresponding approximate wavefunction of

$$\psi = 0.98219\ 1s + 0.18789\ 2p_z \tag{7-72}$$

As mentioned earlier, the admixture of $2p_z$ with 1s produces the skewed charge distribution shown in Fig. 7-2.

It is important to note that the extent of mixing between 1s and $2p_z$ depends partly on the size of the off-diagonal determinantal element H_{12}. When H_{12} is zero (no external field), no mixing occurs. As H_{12} increases, mixing increases. Generally speaking, the larger the size of the off-diagonal element connecting two basis functions in the secular determinant, the greater the degree of mixing of these basis functions in the final solution, other factors being equal. H_{ij} is sometimes referred to as the *interaction element* between basis functions i and j.

If we carried through the same procedure using the *maximum* $\bar{E}$ of -0.1107 a.u., we would obtain the approximate wavefunction

$$\psi' = 0.98219\ 2p_z - 0.18789\ 1s \tag{7-73}$$

This wavefunction is orthogonal to ψ. It may be proved that the *second root*, $\bar{E} = -0.1107$ is an upper bound for the energy of the *second-lowest state* of the hydrogen atom in the field (see Appendix 4). However, ψ' is probably not too good an approximation to the exact wavefunction for that state. This is partly because the wavefunction is one that *maximizes* $\bar{E}$. Hence, there is no particular tendency for the procedure to isolate the second-lowest state from the infinite manifold of states. Also, our basis set was chosen with an eye toward its appropriateness for approximating the lowest state. The true second-lowest state might be expected to contain significant amounts of 2s, which is not included in this basis.

The values of $\bar{E}$ versus c_1 are plotted in Fig. 7-4. The values of $\bar{E}$ that we obtained by the variation procedure correspond to the extrema in this figure. The low-energy extreme corresponds to a wavefunction that shifts negative charge in the direction it is attracted by the field. The high-energy extreme corresponds to a wavefunction that shifts charge in the opposite direction. (When a calculation is performed over a more extensive basis to produce more than two roots, the highest and lowest roots correspond, respectively, to the maximum and minimum, the other roots to saddle points, on the energy hypersurface.)

The detailed treatment just completed is rather involved, and so we now summarize the main points. Step 1 involved selection of a basis set of functions which is capable of approximating the exact solution. Step 2 was the construction of the secular determinant, including evaluation of all the H_{ij}- and S_{ij}-type integrals. Step 3 was the conversion of the determinantal equation into its equivalent equation in powers of $\bar{E}$ and solution for the roots $\bar{E}$. Step 4 was the

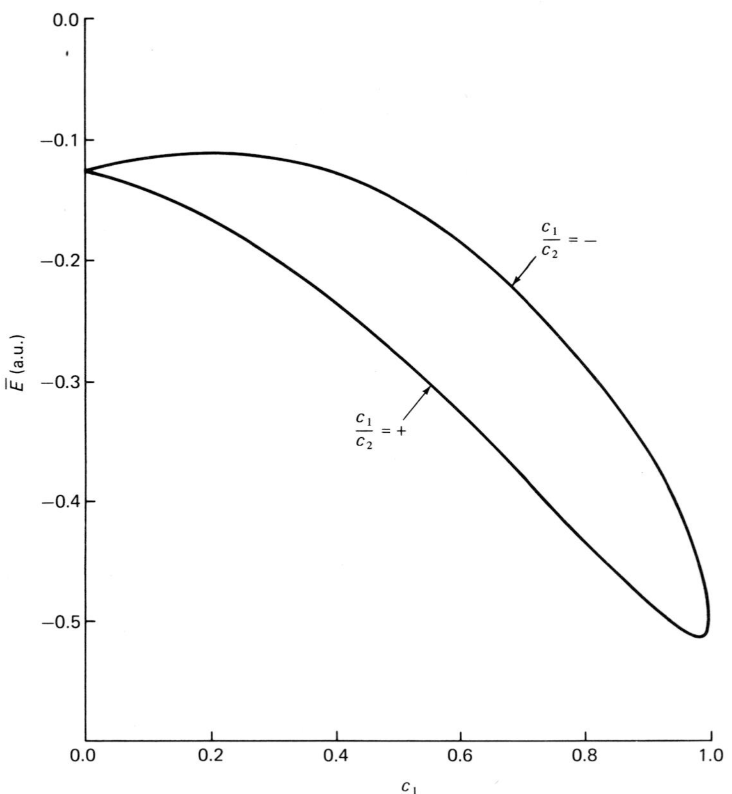

FIG. 7-4 $\bar{E}$ versus c_1 for hydrogen atom in a uniform electric field of strength 0.1 a.u.

substitution of an $\bar{E}$ of interest into the simultaneous equations that are related to the secular determinant and solution for c_1/c_2. Finally, we used the normality requirement to arrive at convenient values for c_1 and c_2.

There are many ways one could increase the flexibility of the trial function in an effort to increase the accuracy of the calculation. By adding additional basis functions, one would stay within the linear variation framework, merely increasing the size of the secular determinant. If these additional basis functions are of appropriate symmetries, they will cause the minimum energy root to be lowered further and will mix into the corresponding wavefunction to make it a better approximation to the eigenfunction for the system. Also, the additional functions will increase the number of roots $\bar{E}$, thereby providing upper bounds for the energies of the third-, fourth-, etc.-lowest states of the system. Another possibility is to allow nonlinear variation of the 1s and $2p_z$ orbital exponents, in combination with linear variation. This would be more involved than the calculation we have shown here, but could easily be accomplished with the aid of a computer.

7-5 Linear Combination of Atomic Orbitals: The H_2^+ Molecule–Ion

We are now ready to consider using the linear variation method on molecular systems. We begin with the simplest case, H_2^+. This molecule–ion has enough symmetry so that we could guess many important features of the solution without calculation. However, to demonstrate the method, we shall first simply plunge ahead mathematically, and discuss symmetry later.

The H_2^+ system consists of two protons separated by a variable distance R, and a single electron (see Fig. 7-5). The hamiltonian for this molecule is, in atomic units

$$\hat{H}(\mathbf{r}_A, \mathbf{r}_B, \mathbf{r}_1) = -\tfrac{1}{2}[\nabla_1^2 + \nabla_A^2/1836 + \nabla_B^2/1836] - (1/r_{A1}) - (1/r_{B1}) + (1/R) \tag{7-74}$$

Since all the particles in the system are capable of motion, the exact eigenfunction of $\hat{H}$ will be a function of the coordinates of the electron and the protons. However, the protons are each 1836 times as heavy as the electron, and in states of chemical interest their velocity is much smaller than that of the electron. This means that, to a very good degree of approximation, the electron can respond instantly to changes in internuclear separation. In other words, whenever the nuclei are separated by a given distance R, no matter how they got there, the motion of the electron will always be described in the same way by ψ. This means that we can separate the electronic and nuclear motions with little loss of accuracy.[3] Given an internuclear separation, we can solve for the electronic wavefunction by ignoring nuclear motion [i.e., omitting ∇_A^2 and ∇_B^2 in Eq. (7-74)]. This gives us a hamiltonian for the electronic energy and nuclear repulsion energy of the system:

$$\hat{H}(\mathbf{r}_A, \mathbf{r}_B, \mathbf{r}_1) = -\tfrac{1}{2}\nabla_1^2 - (1/r_{A1}) - (1/r_{B1}) + (1/R) \tag{7-75}$$

For a given internuclear separation R, the internuclear repulsion $1/R$ is a constant, and we can omit it and merely add it on again after we have found the

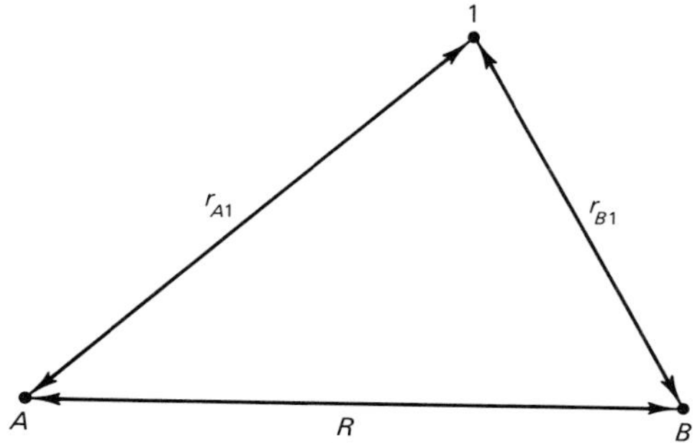

FIG. 7-5 The H_2^+ molecule–ion. A and B are protons. The electron is numbered "1."

[3] However, there are times when coupling of electronic and nuclear motions becomes important.

electronic energy. If we let $\hat{H}_{\text{elec}}$ stand for the first three terms on the right-hand side of Eq. (7-75), we can write

$$\hat{H}_{\text{elec}}\psi_{\text{elec}}(\mathbf{r}_1) = E_{\text{elec}}\psi_{\text{elec}}(\mathbf{r}_1) \tag{7-76}$$

and

$$E_{\text{elec}} + E_{\text{nuc rep}} = E_{\text{elec}} + 1/R \tag{7-77}$$

Solving Eq. (7-76) for E_{elec} for every value of R allows us to plot the electronic and also the total energy of the system as a function of R. But $E_{\text{elec}}(R) + 1/R$ is just the *potential energy for nuclear motion.* Therefore, this quantity can be inserted as the potential in the hamiltonian operator for *nuclear* motion:

$$\hat{H}_{\text{nuc}}(\mathbf{r}_A, \mathbf{r}_B) = [-1/2(1836)](\nabla_A{}^2 + \nabla_B{}^2) + E_{\text{elec}}(R) + 1/R \tag{7-78}$$

$$\hat{H}_{\text{nuc}}(\mathbf{r}_A, \mathbf{r}_B)\psi_{\text{nuc}}(\mathbf{r}_A, \mathbf{r}_B) = E_{\text{nuc}}\psi_{\text{nuc}}(\mathbf{r}_A, \mathbf{r}_B) \tag{7-79}$$

The eigenfunctions of Eq. (7-79) describe the translational, vibrational and rotational states of the molecule. Note that the eigenvalues of the hamiltonian for *nuclear* motion are *total* energies for the system because they contain the electronic energy in their potential parts. Hence,

$$E_{\text{tot}} = E_{\text{nuc}} \tag{7-80}$$

But

$$\psi_{\text{tot}}(\mathbf{r}_A, \mathbf{r}_B, \mathbf{r}_1) = \psi_{\text{elec}}(\mathbf{r}_1)\psi_{\text{nuc}}(\mathbf{r}_A, \mathbf{r}_B) \tag{7-81}$$

This approximation—that the electronic wavefunction depends only on the *positions* of nuclei and not on their momenta—is called the *Born–Oppenheimer* approximation.[4] Only to the extent that this approximation holds true is it valid, for example, to separate electronic and vibrational wavefunctions and treat various vibrational states as a subset existing in conjunction with a given electronic state. We will assume the Born–Oppenheimer approximation to be valid in all cases treated in this book.

Making the Born–Oppenheimer approximation for $H_2{}^+$, we seek to solve for the electronic eigenfunctions and eigenvalues with the nuclei fixed at various separation distances R. We already know these solutions for the two extremes of R. When the two nuclei are widely separated, the lowest-energy state is a 1s hydrogen atom and a distant proton. (Since there is a choice about which nucleus is "the distant proton," there are really two degenerate lowest-energy states.) When $R = 0$, the system becomes $He.^+$ These two extremes are commonly referred to as the *separated-atom* and *united-atom* limits, respectively.

[4] It is analogous to the concept of reversibility in thermodynamics: The piston moves so slowly in the cylinder that the gas can always maintain equilibrium, so pressure depends only on position; the nuclei move so slowly in a molecule that the electrons can always maintain their optimum motion at each R, so electronic energy depends only on nuclear position.

In carrying out a linear variation calculation on H_2^+, our first problem is choice of basis. In the separated-atom limit, the appropriate basis for the ground state would be a 1s atomic orbital (AO) on each proton. Then, regardless of which nucleus the electron resided at, the basis could describe the wavefunction correctly. The appropriate basis at the united-atom limit is a hydrogenlike 1s wavefunction with $Z = 2$. At intermediate values of R, choice of an appropriate basis is less obvious. One possible choice is a large number of hydrogenlike orbitals or, alternatively, Slater-type orbitals (STOs), all centered at the molecular midpoint. Such a basis is capable of approximating the exact wavefunction to a high degree of accuracy, provided a sufficiently large number of basis functions is used.[5] Calculations using such a basis are called *single-center expansions*. A different basis, and one that is much more popular among chemists, is the *separated-atom basis*—a 1s hydrogen AO centered on each nucleus. At finite values of R, this basis can produce only an approximation to the true wavefunction. One way to improve this approximation is to allow additional AOs on each nucleus, 2s, 2p, 3s, etc., thereby increasing the mathematical flexibility of the basis. If we restrict our basis to AOs that are occupied in the separated-atom limit ground state (the 1s AOs in this case), then we are performing what is called a *minimal basis set* calculation. For now, we will use a minimal basis set.

The wavefunction that we produce by linear variation will extend over the whole H_2^+ molecule, and its square will tell us how the electron density is distributed in the molecule. Hence, the one-electron molecular wavefunction is referred to as a *molecular orbital* (MO) just as the one-electron atomic wavefunction is referred to as an *atomic orbital* (AO). With a basis set of the type we have selected, the MOs are expressed as linear combinations of AOs. For this reason, this kind of calculation is referred to as a *minimal basis set linear combination of atomic orbitals–molecular orbital* (LCAO–MO) calculation.

Our second problem, now that we have selected a basis, is construction of the secular determinant. Since we have only two basis functions ($1s_A$, $1s_B$), we expect a 2×2 determinant:

$$\begin{vmatrix} H_{AA} - ES_{AA} & H_{AB} - ES_{AB} \\ H_{BA} - ES_{BA} & H_{BB} - ES_{BB} \end{vmatrix} = 0 \tag{7-82}$$

Here we have used the notation developed earlier, where

$$H_{AB} = \int 1s_A{}^*(1)\hat{H}_{\text{elec}}(1)1s_B(1)\, d\tau(1) \tag{7-83}$$

etc. E of Eq. (7-82) is the *average* value of the energy. Henceforth, the bar is omitted.

[5] The hydrogenlike orbitals are a complete set if the continuum functions are included. Hence, this set can allow one to approach arbitrarily close to the exact eigenfunction and eigenvalue. The Slater-type orbitals do not constitute a complete set.

If we take our basis functions to be normalized, $S_{AA} = S_{BB} = 1$. Since our basis functions and hamiltonian are all real, their integrals will be real. Therefore, $S_{AB} = S_{BA}$ and $H_{AB} = H_{BA}^* = H_{BA}$. Since the hamiltonian is invariant to an interchange of the labels A and B, it follows that $H_{AA} = H_{BB}$. (H_{AA} is the energy of an electron when it is in a 1s AO on one side of the molecule, H_{BB} when it is on the other side.) This leaves us with

$$\begin{vmatrix} H_{AA} - E & H_{AB} - ES_{AB} \\ H_{AB} - ES_{AB} & H_{AA} - E \end{vmatrix} = 0 \tag{7-84}$$

We now have only three terms to evaluate—H_{AA}, H_{AB}, and S_{AB}. Since these terms are dependent on R, it is more convenient to expand the determinant and solve for E in terms of these three unevaluated quantities. Expansion of Eq. (7-84) gives a quadratic equation in E:

$$E^2(1 - S_{AB}^2) + E(2H_{AB}S_{AB} - 2H_{AA}) + H_{AA}^2 - H_{AB}^2 = 0 \tag{7-85}$$

Use of the standard formula for the roots of a quadratic equation gives, after some manipulation,

$$E_{\pm} = \frac{H_{AA} \pm H_{AB}}{1 \pm S_{AB}} \tag{7-86}$$

To arrive at numerical values for E_+ and E_- requires that we choose a value for R and explicitly evaluate H_{AA}, H_{AB}, and S_{AB}. We know in advance that S_{AB} increases monotonically from zero at $R = \infty$ to unity at $R = 0$ because $1s_A$ and $1s_B$ are each normalized and everywhere positive. H_{AA} is the average energy of an electron in a 1s AO on nucleus A, subject also to an attraction by nucleus B. Hence, H_{AA} should be lower than the energy of the isolated H atom ($-\frac{1}{2}$ a.u.) whenever R is finite. H_{AB} is easily expanded to

$$H_{AB} = \int 1s_A(-\tfrac{1}{2}\nabla^2 - 1/r_B)1s_B\, dv + \int 1s_A(-1/r_A)1s_B\, dv \tag{7-87}$$

The operator in the first integrand is simply the hamiltonian operator for a hydrogen atom centered at nucleus B. This operator operates on $1s_B$ to give $-\frac{1}{2}1s_B$. Hence, the first integral becomes simply $-\frac{1}{2}S_{AB}$. The second integral in Eq. (7-87) gives the attraction between a nucleus and the "overlap charge." Thus, H_{AB} is zero at $R = \infty$ and negative for finite R. The formulas for these terms are (after nontrivial mathematical evaluation)

$$S_{AB} = \int 1s_A 1s_B\, dv = \exp(-R)[1 + R + R^2/3] \tag{7-88}$$

$$H_{AA} = \int 1s_A \hat{H}_{\text{elec}} 1s_A\, dv = -\tfrac{1}{2} - (1/R)[1 - e^{-2R}(1 + R)] \tag{7-89}$$

$$H_{AB} = \int 1s_A \hat{H}_{\text{elec}} 1s_B\, dv = -S_{AB}/2 - e^{-R}(1 + R) \tag{7-90}$$

When $R = 2$ a.u., $S_{AB} = 0.586$, $H_{AA} = -0.972$ a.u. and $H_{AB} = -0.699$ a.u. Inserting these values into Eq. (7-86) gives $E_+ = -1.054$ a.u. and $E_- = -0.661$ a.u. These are electronic energies. Internuclear repulsion energy ($+\frac{1}{2}$ a.u.) can be added to these values to give -0.554 a.u. and -0.161 a.u., respectively.

The ways in which H_{AA}, H_{AB}, S_{AB}, and $1/R$ contribute to the energy are illustrated for $R = 2$ a.u. in Fig. 7-6. H_{AA} is lower than the energy of an isolated

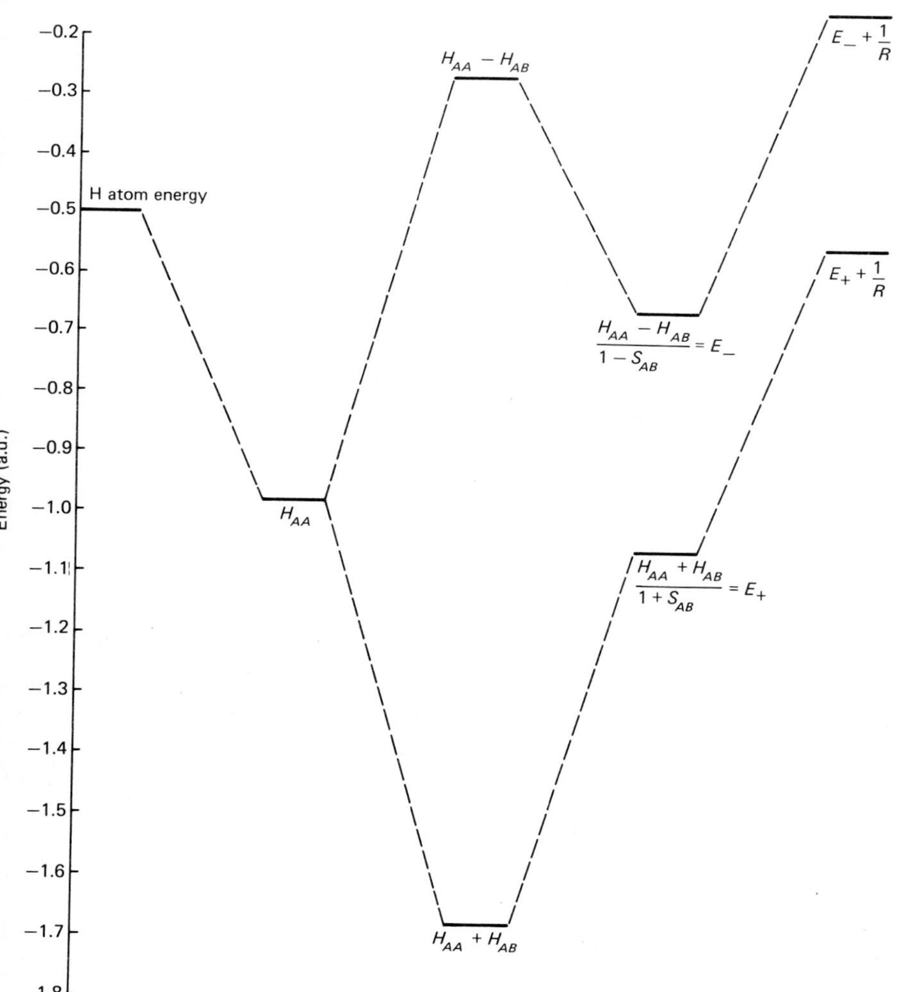

FIG. 7-6 Contributions to energy of H_2^+ at $R = 2$ in minimal basis LCAO–MO calculation.

H atom because the electron experiences additional nuclear attraction at $R = 2$. The effect of the H_{AB} interaction element is to split the energy into two levels equally spaced above and below H_{AA}. The S_{AB} term has the effect of partially negating this splitting. The internuclear repulsion energy $1/R$ merely raises each level by $\frac{1}{2}$ a.u. The lower energy, $E_+ + 1/R$, has a final value that is lower than the separated-atom energy of $-\frac{1}{2}$ a.u. Since the *exact* energy at $R = 2$ must be as low or lower than our value of -0.554 a.u., we can conclude that the H_2^+ molecule–ion has a state that is stable, with respect to dissociation into $H + H^+$, by at least 0.054 a.u., or 1.47 eV, or 33.9 kcal/mole, neglecting vibrational energy effects.

The data depicted in Fig. 7-6 are sometimes presented in the abbreviated form of Fig. 7-7. The energy levels for the pertinent AOs of the separated atoms are indicated on the left and right, and the final energies (either electronic or electronic plus internuclear) are shown in the center.

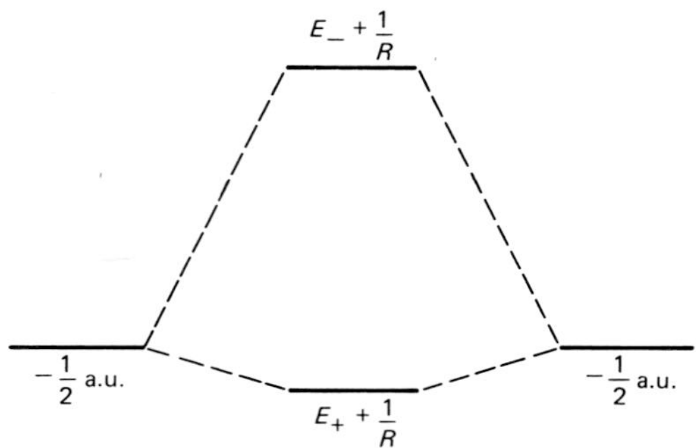

FIG. 7-7 Separated atom energies and energies at an intermediate R for H_2^+.

The behavior of these energies as a function of R is plotted in Fig. 7-8. Included for comparison are the exact energies for the two lowest-energy states of H_2^+. Only the lower of these shows stability with respect to molecular dissociation. Both energy levels approach infinity asymptotically as R approaches zero because of internuclear repulsion. (The zero of energy corresponds to complete separation of the protons and electron.)

Having found the roots $E_\pm$ for the secular determinant, we can now solve for the coefficients which describe the approximate wavefunctions in terms of our basis set. Let us first find the approximate wavefunction corresponding to the lower energy. To do this, we substitute the expression for E_+ [Eq. (7-86)] into the simultaneous equations associated with the secular determinant (7–84):

$$c_A(H_{AA} - E_+) + c_B(H_{AB} - E_+S_{AB}) = 0 \tag{7-91}$$

$$c_A(H_{AB} - E_+S_{AB}) + c_B(H_{AA} - E_+) = 0 \tag{7-92}$$

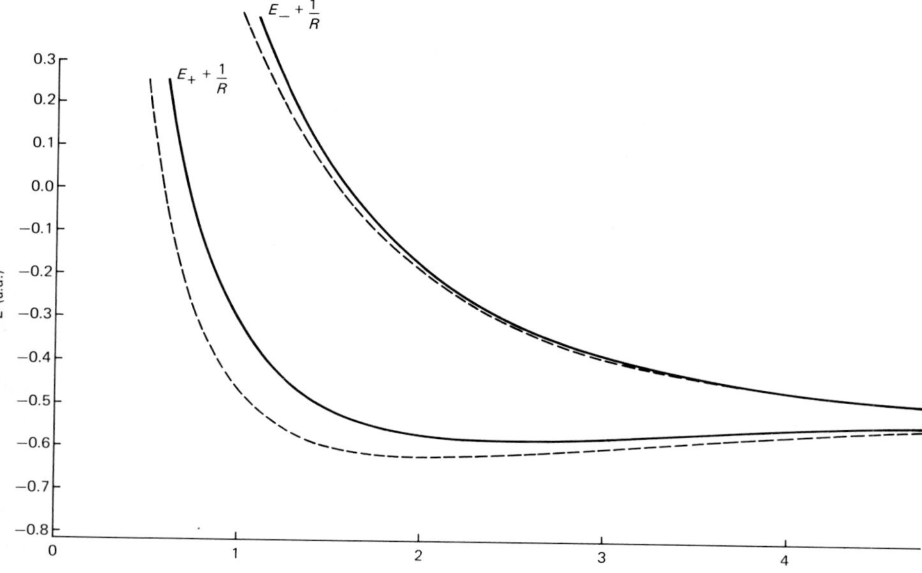

FIG. 7-8 $E_\pm + 1/R$ versus R for H_2^+. (———) Calculation described in text. (- - -) Exact calculation.

Equation (7-91) leads to

$$c_A[H_{AA} - (H_{AA} + H_{AB})/(1 + S_{AB})] = -c_B[H_{AB} - (H_{AA} + H_{AB})S_{AB}/(1 + S_{AB})] \tag{7-93}$$

which ultimately gives

$$c_A = c_B \tag{7-94}$$

The same procedure for E_- produces the result

$$c_A = -c_B \tag{7-95}$$

The normality requirement is

$$\int \psi^*\psi \, dv = 1 = (c_A 1s_A + c_B 1s_B)^2 \, dv$$

$$= c_A{}^2 \int \overset{1}{1s_A{}^2 \, dv} + c_B{}^2 \int \overset{1}{1s_B{}^2 \, dv} + 2c_A c_B \int \overset{S_{AB}}{1s_A 1s_B \, dv} \tag{7-96}$$

so that

$$c_A{}^2 + c_B{}^2 + 2c_A c_B S_{AB} = 1 \tag{7-97}$$

For $c_A = c_B$, this gives

$$c_A = 1/[2(1 + S_{AB})]^{1/2} = c_B \tag{7-98}$$

For $c_A = -c_B$,

$$c_A = 1/[2(1 - S_{AB})]^{1/2} = -c_B \tag{7-99}$$

Therefore, the LCAO–MO wavefunction corresponding to the lower energy E_+ is

$$\psi_+ = \frac{1}{\sqrt{2(1 + S_{AB})}}(1s_A + 1s_B) \tag{7-100}$$

The higher-energy solution is

$$\psi_- = \frac{1}{\sqrt{2(1 - S_{AB})}}(1s_A - 1s_B) \tag{7-101}$$

Just as was true for AOs, there are a number of ways to display these MOs pictorially. One possibility is to plot the value of $\psi_\pm$ or $\psi_\pm{}^2$ along a ray passing through both nuclei. (Other rays could also be chosen if we were especially interested in other regions.) Another approach is to plot contours of ψ or ψ^2 on a plane containing the internuclear axis. Still another way is to sketch a three dimensional view of a surface of constant value of ψ or ψ^2 containing about 90–95% of the wavefunction or the electronic charge. All of these schemes are shown in Fig. 7-9 for ψ_+ and ψ_-.

The wavefunctions ψ_+ and ψ_- may be seen from Fig. 7-9 to be, respectively, symmetric and antisymmetric for inversion through the molecular midpoint [They are commonly called *gerade* (German for *even*) and *ungerade*, respectively. This would be expected for nondegenerate *eigenfunctions* of the hamiltonian since it is invariant to inversion. But ψ_+ and ψ_- are not eigenfunctions. They are only approximations to eigenfunctions. How is it that they show the proper symmetry characteristics of eigenfunctions? The reason is that the symmetry of the $H_2{}^+$ molecule is manifested as a symmetry in our secular determinant of Eq. (7-84). Note that the determinant is symmetric for reflection across either diagonal. The symmetry for reflection through the principal diagonal (which runs from upper left to lower right) is due to the hermiticity of $\hat{H}$, and is always present in the secular determinant for any molecule regardless of symmetry. Symmetry for reflection through the other diagonal is due to the fact that the hamiltonian is invariant to inversion and also to the fact that the basis functions at the two ends of the molecule are identical. When the AOs in a basis set are interchanged (times $\pm$ 1) by a symmetry operation of the molecule, the basis set is said to be *balanced* for that operation. Thus, a $1s_A$ and $1s_B$ basis is balanced for inversion in $H_2{}^+$, but a $1s_A$ and $2s_B$ basis is not. Whenever a symmetry balanced basis is used for a molecule, the symmetry of the molecule is manifested in the secular determinant and ultimately leads to approximate MOs which show the proper symmetry characteristics.

[6] Hermiticity requires that $H_{ij} = H_{ji}^*$. If H_{ij} is imaginary, the determinant will be antisymmetric for reflection through the principal diagonal.

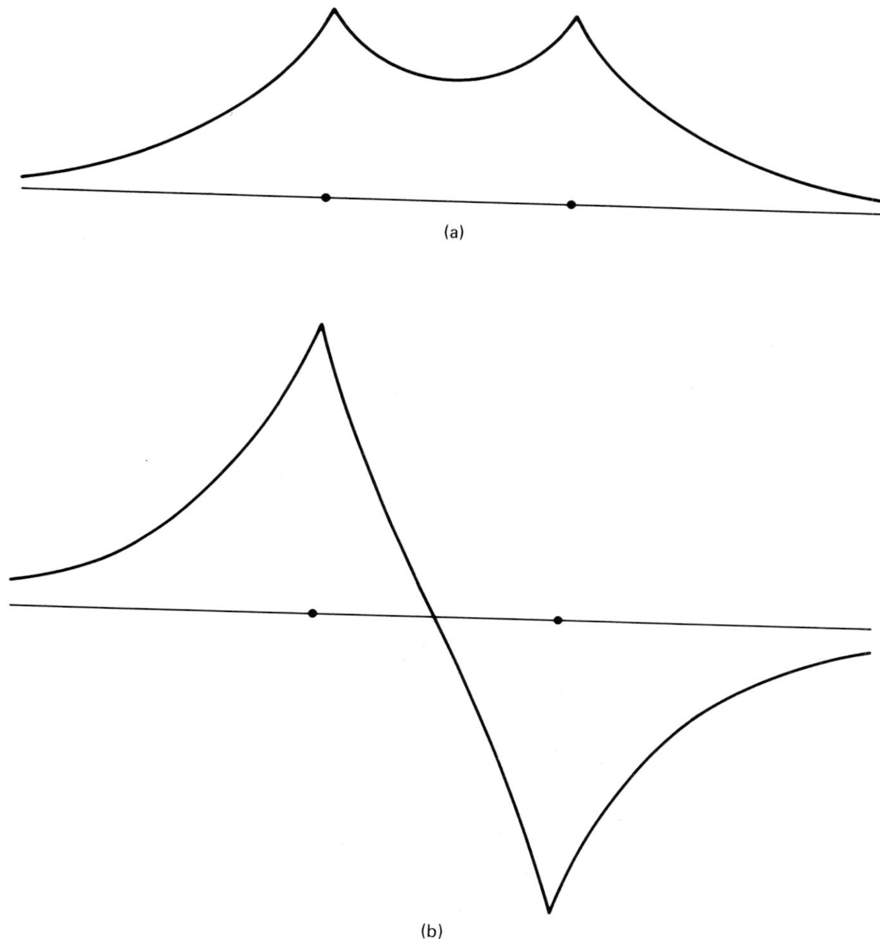

FIG. 7-9 (a) Plot of ψ_+ along the z axis. [Eq. (7-100)]. (b) Plot of ψ_- along the z axis [Eq. (7-101)].

Since the eigenfunctions for $H_2{}^+$ must be gerade or ungerade, and since we started with the simple balanced basis $1s_A$ and $1s_B$, it should be evident that it is unnecessary to go through the linear variation procedure for this case. With such a simple basis set, there is only one possible gerade linear combination of AOs, namely $1s_A + 1s_B$. Similarly, $1s_A - 1s_B$ is the only possible ungerade combination. Therefore, we could have used symmetry to guess our solutions at the outset. Usually, however, we are not so limited in our basis. We shall see that, while symmetry is useful in such circumstances, it does not suffice to produce the variationally best solution.

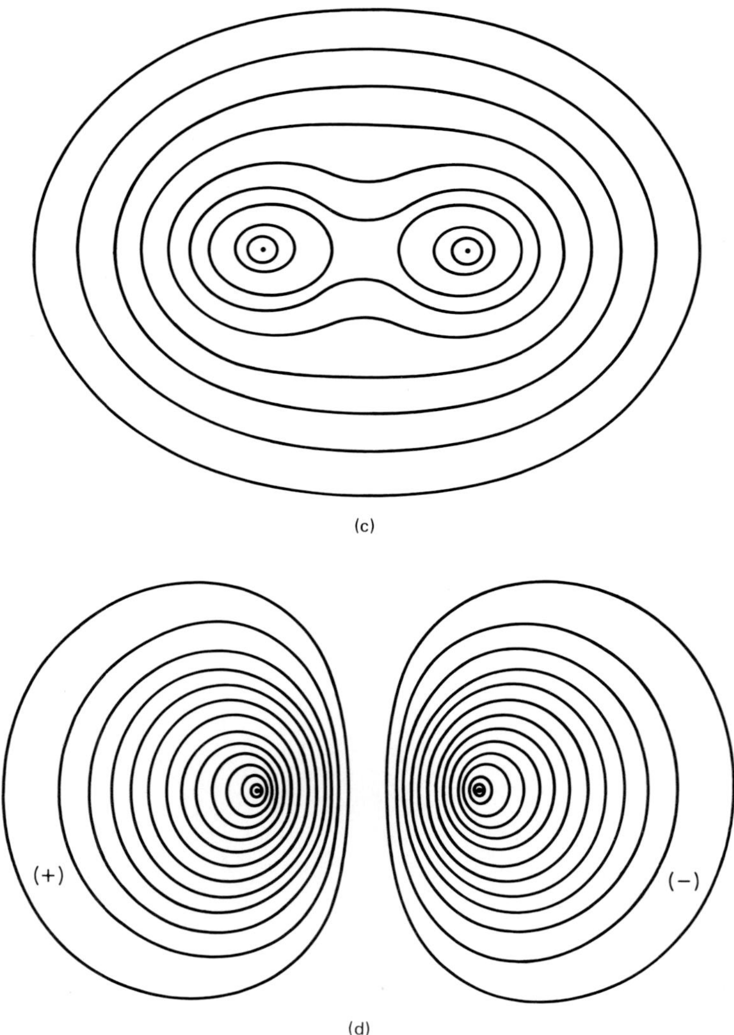

FIG. 7-9 (c) Contour diagram of ψ_+. (d) Contour diagram of ψ_-.

According to the theorem proved in Appendix 4, the *n*th lowest root of a linear variation calculation for a state function must lie above the *n*th lowest exact eigenvalue for the system. However, the two states we are dealing with have different symmetries. In such a case, a more powerful boundedness theorem holds—one that holds even if we are not using a linear variation procedure. To prove this, we first recognize that every H_2^+ *eigenfunction* is either *gerade* (i.e. symmetric for inversion) or *ungerade*. Since the lowest-energy approximate

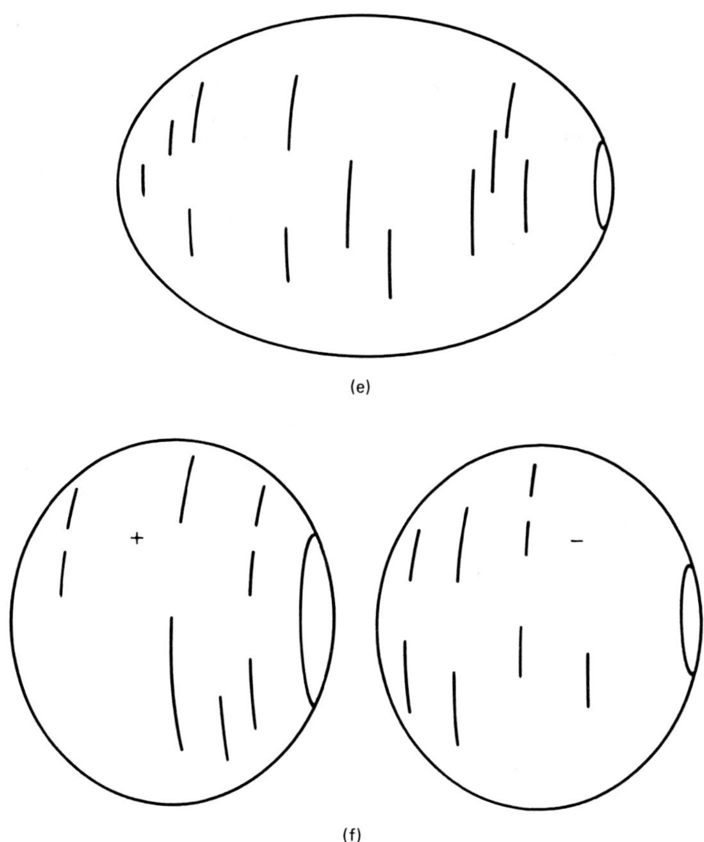

FIG. 7-9 (e) Three-dimensional sketch of contour envelope for ψ_+ and (f) for ψ_-.

wavefunction ψ_+ is *gerade*, it must be expressible as a linear combination of these *gerade* eigenfunctions. Hence, its average energy E_+ cannot be lower than the lowest eigenvalue for the *gerade* eigenfunctions. Similarly, E_- cannot be lower than the lowest eigenvalue for the *ungerade* eigenfunctions, and we have a separate lower bound for the average energy of trial functions of each symmetry type. For this reason, our approximate energies in Fig. 7-8 must lie above the exact energies for both states. If we were to make further efforts to lower the average energy of the ungerade function, even by going outside the linear variation procedure, we could never fall below the exact energy for the lowest-energy *ungerade* state unless we somehow allowed our trial function to change symmetry. This means that a lowest average energy criterion can be used in attempting to find the lowest-energy state *of each symmetry type* for a system, by either linear or nonlinear variation methods.

Inspection of Fig. 7-9 shows that the charge distribution for the state described by ψ_+ is augmented at the molecular midpoint compared to the charge due to unperturbed atoms. This state is also the one that gives $H_2{}^+$ stability at finite R. Because this MO puts charge into the bond region and stabilizes the molecule, it is commonly called a *bonding* MO. In the state described by ψ_-, charge is shifted out of the bond region and the molecule is unstable at finite R, and so ψ_- is called an *antibonding* MO.

Because the potential in $H_2{}^+$ (or in any linear molecule) is independent of ϕ, the angle about the internuclear axis, the ϕ dependence of the wavefunctions is always of the form

$$\Phi(\phi) = (1/\sqrt{2\pi}) \exp(im\phi), \qquad m = 0, \pm 1, \pm 2, \ldots \tag{7-102}$$

This fact may be arrived at in two ways. One way is to write down the Schrödinger equation for $H_2{}^+$ using spherical polar coordinates or elliptical coordinates. (ϕ is a coordinate in each of these coordinate systems.) Then one attempts to separate coordinates and finds that the ϕ coordinate is indeed separable from the others and yields the equation

$$d^2\Phi(\phi)/d\phi^2 = -m^2\Phi(\phi) \tag{7-103}$$

The acceptable solutions of this are the functions (7-102). The other approach is to note that, since the potential in $\hat{H}$ has no ϕ dependence, $\hat{H}$ commutes with $\hat{p}_\phi$, the angular momentum operator, so that the eigenfunctions of $\hat{H}$ are simultaneously eigenfunctions of $\hat{p}_\phi$. We know the eigenfunctions of $\hat{p}_\phi$ are the functions (7-102), and thus, we know that these functions must also give the ϕ dependence of the eigenfunctions of $\hat{H}$.

Two important conclusions emerge. First, each nondegenerate $H_2{}^+$ wavefunction must have a ϕ dependence given by one of the functions (7-102). This tells us something about the shapes of the wavefunctions. Second, the nondegenerate $H_2{}^+$ wavefunctions are eigenfunctions of $\hat{p}_\phi$, which means that an electron in any one of these states has a definite, unvarying (i.e., sharp) component of angular momentum of value $m\hbar$ cgs units (m a.u.) along the internuclear axis. It is thus useful to know the m value associated with a given one-electron wavefunction. A standard notation is used, which is analogous to the atomic orbital notation wherein s, p, d, f, correspond to l values of 0, 1, 2, 3, respectively. The corresponding Greek lower-case letters σ, π, δ, ϕ indicate values of $|m|$ of 0, 1, 2, 3, respectively, in one-electron orbitals of linear molecules. Thus, for the case at hand, ψ_+ and ψ_- are both σ MOs because they are cylindrically symmetrical (i.e., no ϕ dependence), which requres that m be zero. Because ψ_+ is a *gerade* function, it is symbolized σ_g. ψ_-, then, is a σ_u MO.

Let us now examine the dependence of our LCAO–MO results on our original choice of basis. The 1s AOs we have used are capable of giving the exact energy when $R = \infty$, but become increasingly inadequate as R decreases. As a result, Fig. 7-8 shows that, for both states, the approximate energy deviates more and more from the exact energy as R decreases. At $R = 0$, our σ_g function becomes a single 1s H atom ($Z = 1$) AO centered on a doubly positive nucleus. Yet we know that the lowest-energy *eigenfunction* for that situation is a single 1s He^+ ($Z = 2$) AO. An obvious way to improve our wavefunction, then, is to allow the 1s basis functions to change their orbital exponents as R changes. This adds a nonlinear variation, and the calculation is more complicated. It is very easily performed with the aid of a computer, however, and we summarize the results in Figs. 7-10 and 7-11. The internuclear repulsion has been omitted from the energies in Fig. 7-10. The lowest approximate energy curve is now in perfect agreement with the exact electronic energy both at $R = 0$ and $R = \infty$, and shows improved, though still not perfect, agreement at intermediate R. The R dependence of the orbital exponent for this wavefunction (Fig. 7-11) varies smoothly from 1 at $R = \infty$ to 2 at $R = 0$, as expected. In contrast, the σ_u function fails to reach a well-defined energy at $R = 0$ because the function becomes indeterminate at that point. [At $R = 0$, $1s_A - 1s_B$ becomes $(1s_A - 1s_A) = 0$.] However, Figs. 7-10 and 7-11 indicate that the exact energy is $-\frac{1}{2}$ a.u. at $R = 0$, corresponding to the $n = 2$ level of He^+, and that the orbital exponent in our 1s basis functions approaches 0.4 in the effort to approximate this state function at small R. To understand this behavior, we must once again consider the symmetries of these functions.

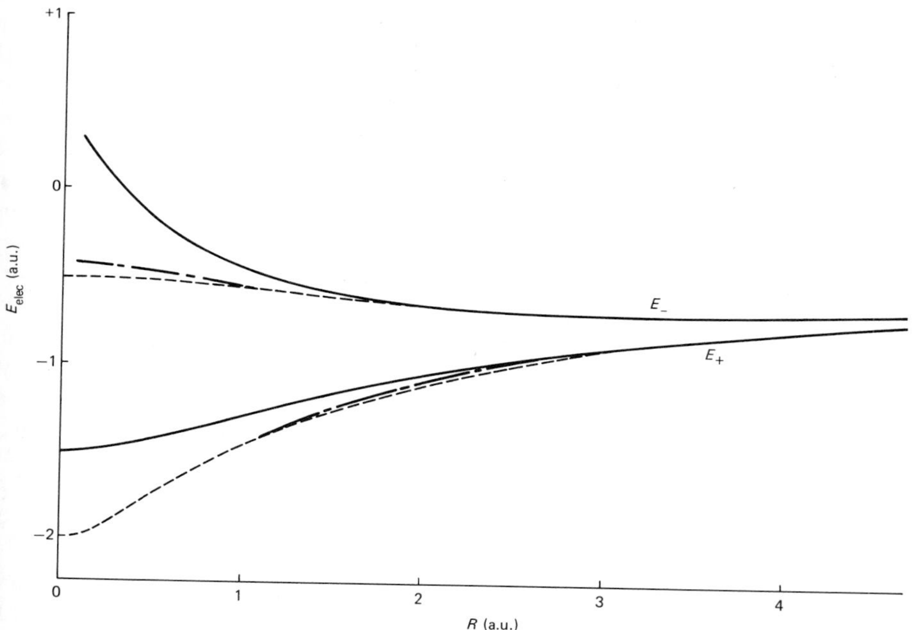

FIG. 7-10 E_+ and E_- for H_2^+ from (– – –) exact, (- - -) variable ξ, and (——) fixed ξ ($\xi = 1$) treatments.

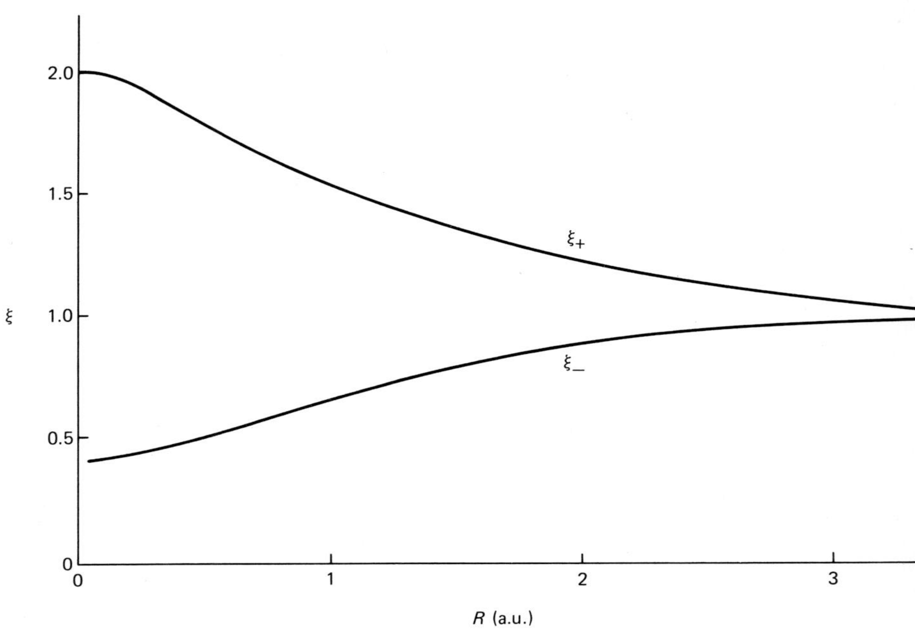

FIG. 7-11 Values of ξ minimizing E_+ and E_- as a function of R.

We have already seen that the nondegenerate eigenfunctions of H_2^+ must be either gerade or ungerade, and we note in Fig. 7-10 that the energy curve for the gerade state is continuous as is the one for the ungerade state. In other words, as we move along a given curve, we are always referring to a wavefunction of the *same* symmetry. This continuity of symmetry along an energy curve is central to many applications of quantum chemistry. The reason for continuity of symmetry can be seen by considering a molecule having some element of symmetry, and having a nondegenerate wavefunction or molecular orbital (which must be symmetric or antisymmetric with respect to the symmetry operations of the molecule). If we change the molecule infinitesimally (without destroying its symmetry), we expect the wavefunction to change infinitesimally also. In particular it should not change symmetry because this is generally not an infinitesimal change. (To change symmetry requires adding or removing nodes changing signs in parts of the function. Such changes have more than infinitesimal efforts on ψ and on kinetic and potential parts of the energy.) The entire curve can be traversed by an infinite number of such infinitesimal but symmetry conserving steps.

The continuity of symmetry enables the σ_g state of H_2^+ to correlate with an s-type AO of He^+ as R goes to zero. This correlation is *symmetry allowed* because the s-type AOs of He^+ have the proper symmetry characteristics—they are *gerade* and have no dependence on angle about the axis that is the internuclear axis when $R > 0$ (see Fig. 7-12). In contrast, the σ_u MO cannot correlate with an s-type AO. It must correlate with an AO which is cylindrically symmetrical about the old internuclear axis but is antisymmetric for inversion. A p-type AO pointing along the old internuclear axis (called a p_σ AO) satisfies these requirements.

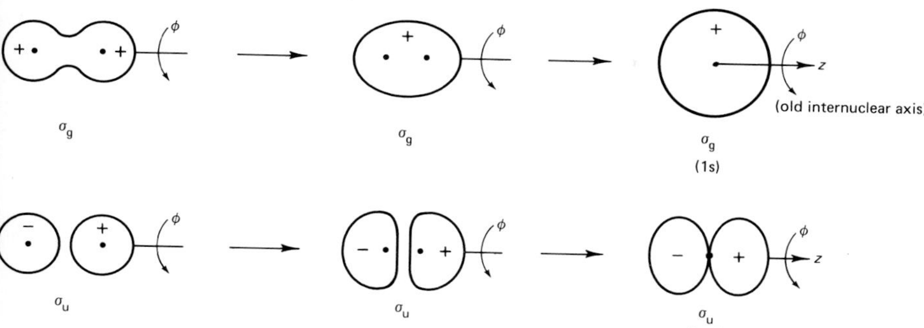

FIG. 7-12 Sketches demonstrating how separated atom functions can be related to united-atom functions through symmetry invariance. These functions are not drawn to a common scale.

These symmetry requirements help us understand the σ_u curves of Figs. 7-10 and 7-11. The exact energy goes to $-\frac{1}{2}$ a.u. at $R = 0$ because the σ_u state of H_2^+ correlates with a 2p AO of He^+. Our basis set is incapable of reproducing a 2p AO at $R = 0$, and so the calculated energy curve fails to rejoin the exact curve at $R = 0$. At small R, our basis set is attempting to approximate the two lobes of an evolving 2p AO. Apparently the orbital exponent that best enables the basis to accomplish this is around 0.4.

7-6 Molecular Orbitals of Homonuclear Diatomic Molecules

We have already seen how one produces the ground configurations for many-electron *atoms* by placing pairs of electrons of opposite spin into AOs, starting with the lowest-energy AO and working up. Subsequent manipulation of this product function to produce proper space and spin symmetry yields the approximate wavefunction. Precisely the same procedure is used for molecules. Thus, the electronic configurations for H_2^+, H_2, and H_2^- are $1\sigma_g$, $(1\sigma_g)^2$, and $(1\sigma_g)^2 1\sigma_u$, respectively, and the approximate wavefunction for H_2 is provided by the Slater determinant $|1\sigma_g(1)1\bar{\sigma}_g(2)|$. When we come to consider heavier homonuclear diatomic molecules, such as O_2, we must place electrons in higher energy MOs. Such MOs are still provided by the minimal basis set, which now includes 1s, 2s, and three 2p AOs on each atom since these AOs are occupied in the separated atoms. We now consider the natures of the additional MOs produced by this larger basis.

We begin by making a change to a basis set that is mathematically equivalent to the starting set but is more convenient for discussing and analyzing the problem. This new set is the set of *symmetry orbitals* (SOs) $(1s_A \pm 1s_B)$, $(2s_A \pm 2s_B)$, etc. From our original ten AOs, we thus produce ten SOs. These may be normalized, if desired. Each of these SOs has definite symmetry. The SOs built from 2s AOs must be of σ_g and σ_u symmetry since the 2s AOs act like 1s AOs for all the symmetry operations of the molecule. The 2p AOs pointing along the internuclear axis have cylindrical symmetry and hence also give rise to a σ_g and a σ_u SO. (We will take the internuclear axis to be coincident with the z axis, and so these SOs are constructed from $2p_0$ (or $2p_z$) AOs.) The functions $(2p_{+1_A} \pm 2p_{+1_B})$ are π SOs because $|m| = 1$. Since it is difficult to visualize complex functions, however, the usual practice is to take linear combinations of

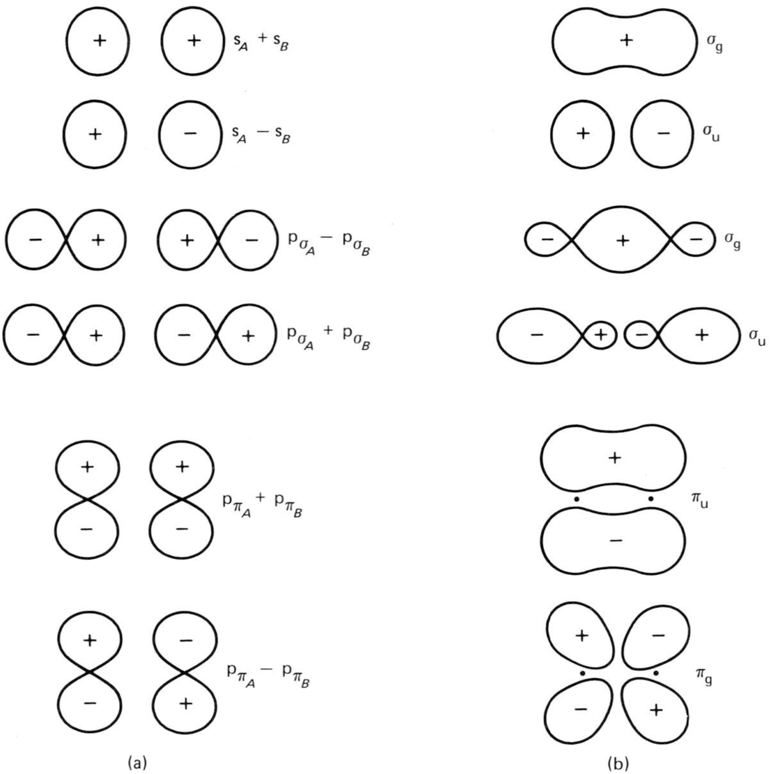

FIG. 7-13 Symmetry orbitals constructed from s- and p-type AOs. (a) Sketches according to an idealized convention that ignores overlap between AOs on A and B. (b) Effects of overlap. Note that the $p_{\sigma A} - p_{\sigma B}$ combination is bonding. This depends on our having chosen a common z axis for both atoms. Sometimes the z axes are chosen to point from each atom toward the other. In that case, $p_{\sigma A} - p_{\sigma B}$ becomes antibonding.

the complex π functions to produce a corresponding set of real functions. (This is completely analogous to forming real p_x and p_y AOs from complex p_{+1} and p_{-1} AOs.) Thus, we obtain $(2p_{x_A} \pm 2p_{x_B})$ and $(2p_{y_A} \pm 2p_{y_B})$, which are not eigenfunctions for the angular momentum operator anymore, but are still given the symbol π. From Fig. 7-13, we see that the *positive* combinations give *ungerade* π SOs. This is just the opposite of the case for σ- type SOs. We conclude from Fig. 7-13 that σ_g and π_u SOs will tend to place charge *into* the bond and hence contribute to bonding, whereas σ_u and π_g SOs will contribute antibonding character.

Even though these SOs are only a basis set, the reader may nevertheless recognize that conversion to this symmetrized basis goes a long way toward producing our ultimate MOs. Indeed, our $(1s_A \pm 1s_B)$ SOs, if normalized, are the same as the MOs we obtained for H_2^+. The essential advantage of a symmetrized basis set is that it simplifies the secular determinant and makes it easier to understand and describe the mixing of the basis functions by the hamiltonian. For instance, since our MOs must have pure σ, π, δ, . . . and also g or u symmetry, and since our SOs are already of pure symmetry, we expect no further mixing to occur between SOs of *different* symmetry in forming MOs. This suggests that the interaction element H_{ij} between SOs ϕ_i and ϕ_j of different symmetry should vanish. This is easily proved by noting that $\hat{H}$ is symmetric for all symmetry operations of the molecule, and, if ϕ_i and ϕ_j differ in symmetry for some operation, their product is antisymmetric for that operation, and therefore $\phi_i^* \hat{H} \phi_j$ is antisymmetric and its integral vanishes. Similarly, S_{ij} vanishes, and $H_{ij} - ES_{ij}$ vanishes except in positions connecting basis functions of identical symmetry. As a result, our secular determinant over SOs has the form (7-104), where the notation $\sigma_g[1s]$ indicates a σ_g SO made from $1s_A$, $1s_B$ AOs etc.

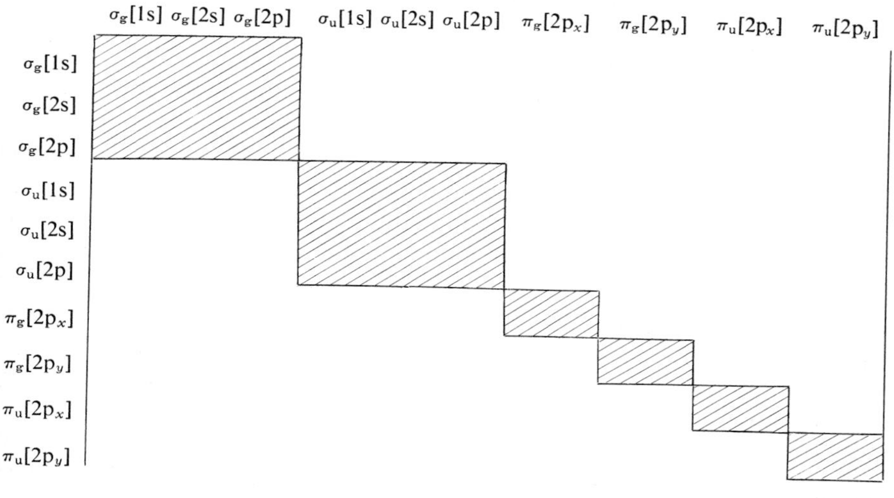

(7-104)

By placing basis functions of like symmetry together, we have emphasized the block–diagonal form of our determinant, all elements in the nonshaded areas being zero by symmetry. (The $\pi_g[2p_x]$ and $\pi_g[2p_y]$ do not interact because of symmetry disagreements for reflection in the xz and yz planes.) Each of the nonzero blocks of (7-104) is a separate determinant (which is just a number), and the value of determinant (7-104) is simply the product of these six smaller determinants. Hence, if any *one* of these small determinants is zero, the large determinant is zero, thereby satisfying our determinantal equation. Therefore, each of these small determinants may be employed in a separate determinantal equation, and the problem is said to be *partitioned* into six smaller problems. It follows immediately that we can get mixing among the three σ_g SOs to produce three σ_g MOs and likewise for the σ_u set, and that the π SOs are already MOs and undergo no further mixing.

What will be the nature of the lowest-energy σ_g MO? It will not be pure $\sigma_g[1s]$ because admixture of $\sigma_g[2s]$ and $\sigma_g[2p]$ SOs can produce charge shifts that will lower the energy. But the $\sigma_g[2s]$ and $\sigma_g[2p]$ SO energies are much higher than the $\sigma_g[1s]$ (mainly because the 2s and 2p AOs are higher in energy *in the atoms*, and the atomic contributions still dominate in the molecule). Any energy *decrease* to be gained by charge shifting must be weighed against the energy *increase* due to the mixing in of such high energy components. The former very quickly become overbalanced by the latter, so the lowest energy σ_g MO is almost pure $\sigma_g[1s]$ SO, the $\sigma_g[2s]$ and $\sigma_g[2p]$ SOs coming in only very slightly. This exemplifies an important general feature of quantum chemical calculations: mixing between basis orbitals tends to be small if they have widely different energies in the system. *Thus, we now have two factors governing the extent of mixing of functions ϕ_i and ϕ_j—the size of the interaction element H_{ij}, and the difference in energy between them in the system ($H_{ii} - H_{jj}$).*

A label we can use for this lowest-energy MO that avoids implying that it is identical to the $\sigma_g[1s]$ SO is $1\sigma_g$. This stands for "the lowest-energy σ_g MO." Because of the low energy of the 1s AOs, the next-lowest MO is almost pure $\sigma_u[1s]$, and we label it $1\sigma_u$.

When considering the remaining two σ_g MOs, we can expect substantial mixing between $\sigma_g[2s]$ and $\sigma_g[2p]$ SOs because these functions are not very different in energy. In the hydrogen atom, the 2s and 2p AOs are degenerate, and, as we move along the periodic table, they become split farther and farther apart in energy. Therefore, we might expect to find the greatest mixing for B_2 and C_2, and to find less mixing for O_2 and F_2. Figure 7-14 is a schematic diagram of the MO energy levels we should expect for F_2. Here the $2\sigma_g$ MO is primarily the $\sigma_g[2s]$ SO and the $3\sigma_g$ MO is mainly the $\sigma_g[2p]$ SO. Similarly $2\sigma_u$ and $3\sigma_u$ are mainly $\sigma_u[2s]$ and $\sigma_u[2p]$, respectively. The 1π and 3σ MOs are degenerate at the separated atom limit, where they are all 2p AOs. As the atoms come together and interact, the π levels split apart less than the σ levels because the $2p_x$ and $2p_y$ AOs approach each other side to side, whereas the $2p_\sigma$ AOs

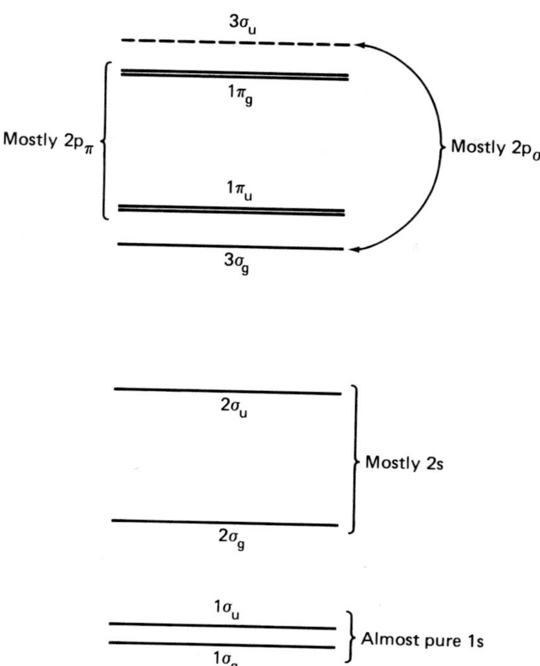

FIG. 7-14 Schematic of MO energy level order for F_2. The vertical axis is *not* an accurate energy scale. For instance, the 1σ levels are very much lower in energy relative to the other levels than is suggested by the drawing. (---) indicates that the orbital is unoccupied in the ground state.

approach end to end. The latter mode produces larger overlap and leads to larger interaction elements and greater splitting. (Because of the symmetry of the molecule, the $1\pi_u$ MOs are always degenerate, and they may be mixed together in any way. In particular, we can regard them as being $1\pi_{ux}$ and $1\pi_{uy}$ or $1\pi_{u+1}$ and $1\pi_{u-1}$ with equal validity. The same situation holds for the $1\pi_g$ pair.) From the ordering of energy levels in Fig. 7-14 we obtain for F_2 the configuration

$$F_2: \quad (1\sigma_g)^2(1\sigma_u)^2(2\sigma_g)^2(2\sigma_u)^2(3\sigma_g)^2(1\pi_u)^4(1\pi_g)^4 \tag{7-105}$$

Now we will consider what happens for lighter molecules. Recall that here the 2s and 2p AOs are closer together in energy. This allows greater mixing between the SOs containing these AOs and produces increased energy level splitting. Thus, the $\sigma_g[2s]$ and $\sigma_g[2p]$ SOs mix together more, and the resulting splitting causes an additional lowering in energy of the $2\sigma_g$ level and an increase for the $3\sigma_g$ level, compared to the F_2 case. In a similar way the $2\sigma_u$ and $3\sigma_u$ levels are lowered and raised, respectively, by increased mixing between $\sigma_u[2s]$

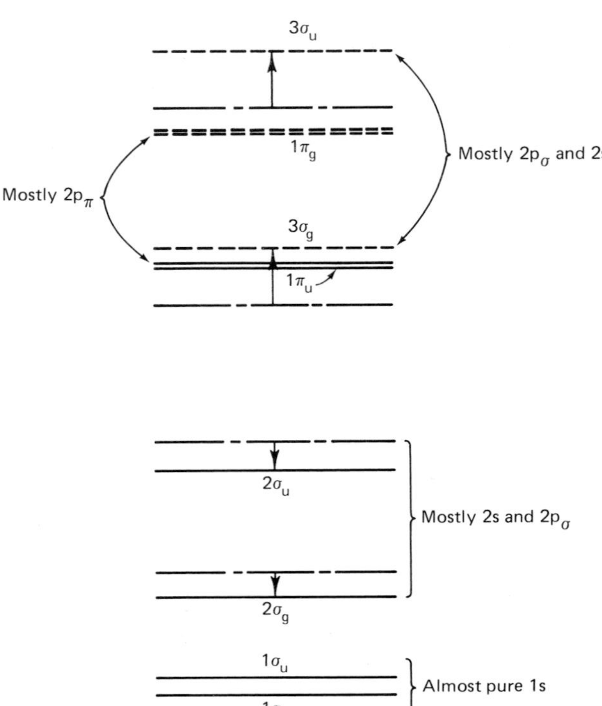

FIG. 7-15 A schematic diagram of the MO energy level order for C_2. The 2s and $2p_\sigma$ symmetry functions mix more strongly in producing 2σ and 3σ MOs than is the case in F_2. The level shifts discussed in the text are indicated by dashed lines and arrows. (- - -) represent F_2 levels. Note the inversion of the order of the $1\pi_u$ and $3\sigma_g$ levels. The orbital ordering is deduced from spectra. (See Mulliken [1].) (———) represent energies of orbitals not occupied by electrons. Note that there is no well-defined energy ordinate for this figure, and no accurate relationship between absolute values of orbital energies within a molecule or between molecules is implied.

and $\sigma_u[2p]$ SOs. The resulting energy level pattern for C_2 is shown in Fig. 7-15. Note that the splitting has pushed the $3\sigma_g$ level *above* the $1\pi_u$ level. As a result, C_2 has the configuration

$$C_2: \quad (1\sigma_g)^2(1\sigma_u)^2(2\sigma_g)^2(2\sigma_u)^2(1\pi_u)^4 \tag{7-106}$$

The above discussion is an effort to *rationalize* orbital energies obtained from calculations or deduced from molecular spectra. We have not yet described the details of how one goes about carrying out MO calculations on these molecules, nor will we in this chapter. However, even in the absence of precise numerical results, it is possible for such qualitative arguments to be very useful in understanding and predicting features of a wide range of chemical reactions.

The molecular configurations obtained from the patterns of Figs. 7-14 and

7-15 yield predicted molecular properties that are in strikingly good qualitative agreement with experimental observations. The data in Table 7-2 show that, when we go from H_2^+ to H_2, adding a second electron to a bonding MO, the bond length decreases and the dissociation energy increases. Adding a third electron (He_2^+) causes partial occupation of the antibonding $1\sigma_u$ MO and causes the bond length to increase and the dissociation energy to decrease. The four electron molecule He_2 is not observed, as is consistent with its configuration. The relative inertness of N_2 as a chemical reactant becomes understandable from the fact that it has six more "bonding electrons" than antibonding electrons, giving a net of three bonds—one σ and two π bonds. For N_2 to react, it is necessary to supply enough energy to at least partially break these bonds prior to forming new bonds. The configurations of Table 7-2 indicate that some molecules will have closed shells, whereas others will have one or more unpaired electrons. For example, O_2 has a configuration in which the degenerate $1\pi_g$ level "contains" two electrons. Several states can be produced from such a configuration, just as several states could be produced from the 1s2s configuration for He. Hund's rule states that the state of highest multiplicity is lowest in energy. For n unpaired electrons, the highest multiplicity achievable is $n + 1$. For O_2, this is three, and we expect the ground state of the O_2 molecule to be a triplet. This is observed to be the case.

Close perusal of Table 7-2 indicates that some of the data are not in accord with the simple qualitative ideas just presented. For example, Li_2^+ is more strongly bonded than is Li_2, even though the former has fewer bonding electrons. However, the Li_2^+ ion–molecule is longer than Li_2. H_2^- is less strongly bound than isoelectronic He_2^+, yet it has a shorter equilibrium internuclear separation. Irregularities such as these require more detailed treatment. However, one of the useful characteristics of a *qualitative* approach is that it enables us to recognize cases that deviate from our expectations and therefore warrant further study.

In Figs. 7-14 and 7-15, we saw how MOs are related to SOs for the separated atoms. Let us now consider how the separated atom SOs correlate with the united atom AOs. Recall that these orbitals are correlated by requiring them to be of identical symmetry. In Fig. 7-16 some of the possible SOs and united-atom AOs, together with their symmetry labels, are shown. Note that the σ_g SOs can correlate with s or dσ AOs, σ_u SOs with pσ AOs, π_u SOs with pπ AOs and π_g SOs with dπ AOs. This gives us all the information we need except for resolving the ambiguities *within* a given symmetry type. For instance, which of the 1s, 2s, 3s, 3dσ, . . . in the AOs correlates with which of the σ_g[1s], σ_g[2s], σ_g[2p], σ_g[3s], . . . in the SOs? This question is resolved by use of the noncrossing rule, which states that, *in correlation diagrams, energy levels associated with orbitals or states of the same symmetry will not cross.* This requires that we match up the lowest-energy united-atom AO of a given symmetry with the lowest-energy SO of that symmetry, and so on up the ladder. This leads to the diagram in Fig. 7-17. The line

TABLE 7-2
Some Properties of Homonuclear Diatomic Molecules and Ions in Their Ground Electronic States

Molecule	MO configuration	Net number of bonding electrons	Binding energy, D_e (eV)	Equilibrium internuclear separation, R_e(Å)	Multiplicity
H_2^+	$1\sigma_g$	1	2.7928	1.06	2
H_2	$1\sigma_g^2$	2	4.747745	0.7414	1
H_2^-	$1\sigma_g^2 1\sigma_u$	1	1.7[a]	0.8	2
He_2^+	$1\sigma_g^2 1\sigma_u$	1	2.5	1.08	2
He_2	$1\sigma_g^2 1\sigma_u^2$	0	0.001[b]	2.88	1
He_2^-	$[He_2]2\sigma_g$	1	No data		
Li_2^+	$[He_2]2\sigma_g$	1	1.29	3.14	2
Li_2	$[He_2]2\sigma_g^2$	2	1.05	2.673	1
Li_2^-	$[He_2]2\sigma_g^2 2\sigma_u$	1	~1.3(?)	3.2	2
Be_2^+	$[He_2]2\sigma_g^2 2\sigma_u$	1	No definitive data		
Be_2	$[He_2]2\sigma_g^2 2\sigma_u^2$	0	0, 0.7	—	1
Be_2^-	$[Be_2]1\pi_u$	1	~0.3	2.4	2
B_2^+	$[Be_2]1\pi_u$	1	1.8	—	2
B_2	$[Be_2)1\pi_u^2$ (?)	2	~3	1.589	3 or 5[c]
B_2^-	$[Be_2]1\pi_u^3$	3	No data		
C_2^+	$[Be_2]1\pi_u^3$	3	5.3	1.301	2
C_2	$[Be_2]1\pi_u^4$	4	6.36	1.2425	1
C_2^-	$[Be_2]1\pi_u^4 3\sigma_g$	5	8.6	—	2
N_2^+	$[Be_2]1\pi_u^4 3\sigma_g$	5	8.86	1.116	2
N_2	$[Be_2]1\pi_u^4 3\sigma_g^2$	6	9.90	1.098	1
N_2^-	$[Be_2]1\pi_u^4 3\sigma_g^2 1\pi_g$	5	~8.3	—	—
O_2^+	$[Be_2]1\pi_u^4 3\sigma_g^2 1\pi_g$	5	6.7796	1.1171	2
O_2	$[Be_2]3\sigma_g^2 1\pi_u^4 1\pi_g^2$	4	5.2132	1.2075	3
O_2^-	$[Be_2]3\sigma_g^2 1\pi_u^4 1\pi_g^3$	3	4.14	1.32	2
F_2^+	$[Be_2]3\sigma_g^2 1\pi_u^4 1\pi_g^3$	3	3.39	1.32	2
F_2	$[Be_2]3\sigma_g^2 1\pi_u^4 1\pi_g^4$	2	1.65	1.42	1
F_2^-	$[Be_2]3\sigma_g^2 1\pi_u^4 1\pi_g^4 3\sigma_u$	1	~1.3	1.9	2
Ne_2^+	$[Be_2]3\sigma_g^2 1\pi_u^4 1\pi_g^4 3\sigma_u$	1	~1.1	1.7	2
Ne_2	$[Be_2]3\sigma_g^2 1\pi_u^4 1\pi_g^4 3\sigma_u^2$	0	0.003[b]	3.09	1

[a] This state is unstable with respect to loss of an electron, but is stable with respect to dissociation into an atom and a negative ion.

[b] From Hirschfelder *et al.* [2]. It may be shown that any two neutral atoms will have some range of R where the attractive part of the van der Waals' interaction dominates. For He_2, this minimum is so shallow and the nuclei so light that a stable state (including vibrations) probably cannot exist. For Ne_2, a stable state should exist. The data for He_2 and Ne_2 are *calculated* from considerations of intermolecular forces.

[c] The multiplicity of the lowest state is not certain. The triplet and quintet are both very low lying.

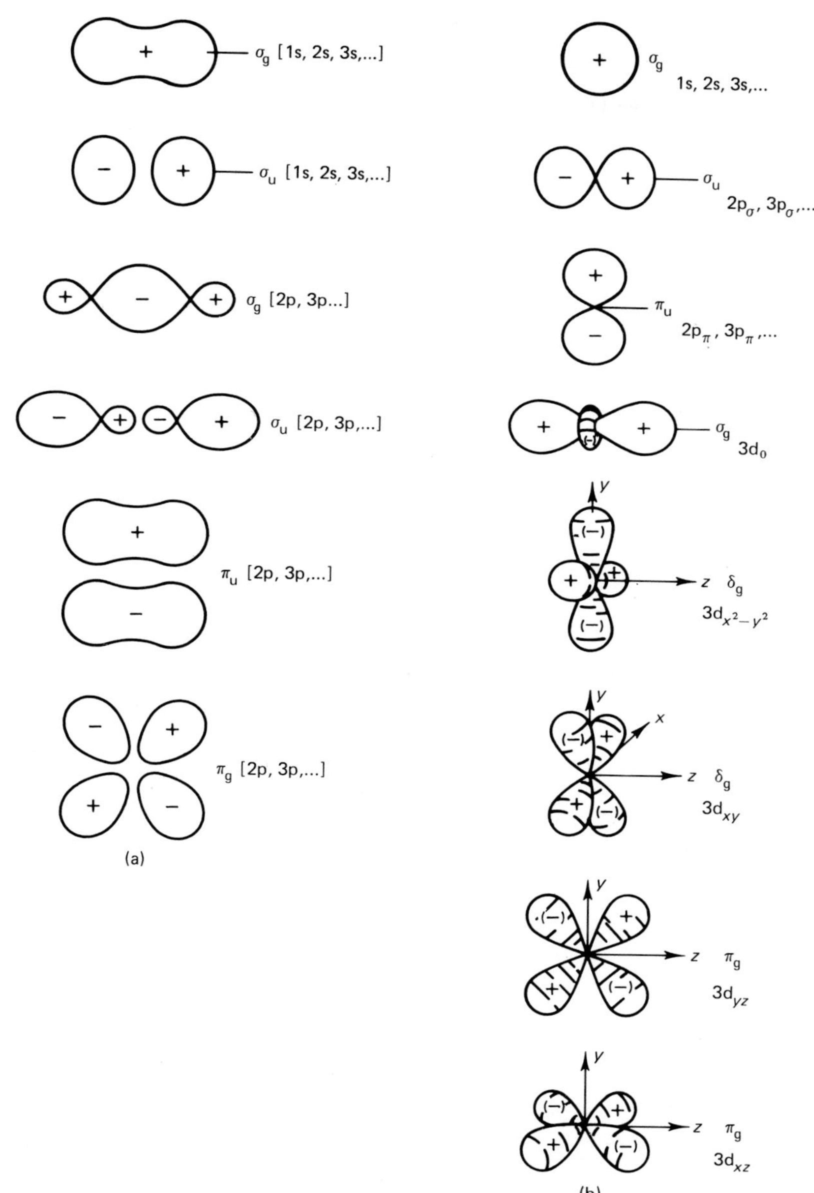

FIG. 7-16 (a) Symmetry orbitals for molecular range. (b) United-atom AOs characterized by symmetry with respect to z axis.

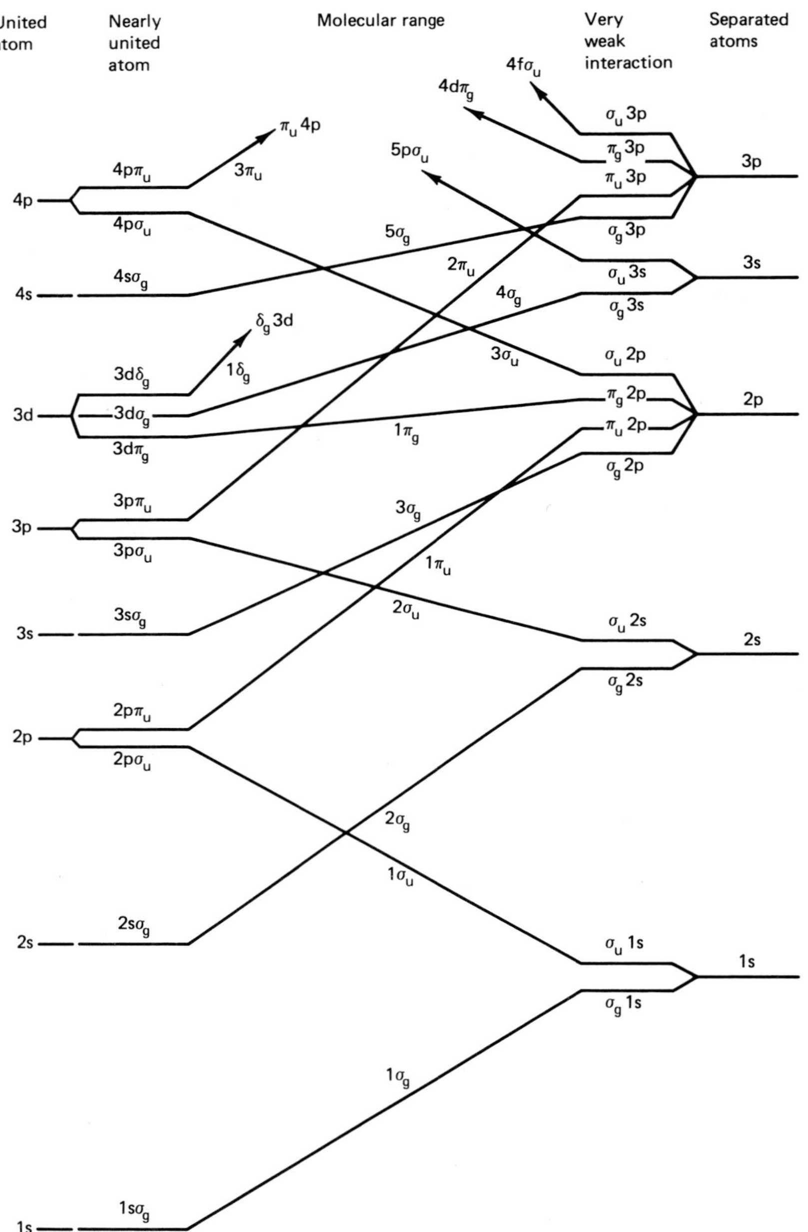

FIG. 7-17 Correlation diagram between separated-atom orbitals and united-atom orbitals for homonuclear diatomic molecules. Energy ordinate and internuclear separation abscissa are only suggestive. No absolute values are implied by the sketch. [Note: For $H_2{}^+$ $\sigma_g 2p$ correlates with $3d\sigma_g$, $\sigma_g 3s$ with $3s\sigma_g$. This arises because the separability of the $H_2{}^+$ hamiltonian (in the Born–Oppenheimer approximation) leads to an additional quantum

interconnecting the 1s AO of the united atom with the 1s AOs of the separated atoms refers, at intermediate R, to the $1\sigma_g$ MO. We have already seen that this MO may contain contributions from $\sigma_g[2s]$ and $\sigma_g[2p]$ SOs. Thus, the correlation diagram tells us what orbitals the $1\sigma_g$ MO "turns into" at the limits of R, but does *not* imply that, at other R values, this MO is comprised totally of 1s AOs.

Study of this correlation diagram reveals that the antibonding MOs (σ_u and π_g) are the MOs which correlate with higher energy united-atom AOs and hence favor the separated atoms in terms of energy. This illustrates the fact that there are often several ways to explain the effects of an orbital. We may focus on energies, and note that bonding and antibonding MOs correlate with low-energy and high-energy united-atom orbitals, respectively. Or, as we saw earlier, we can focus on charge distributions and their attractions for nuclei, and note that bonding MOs concentrate charge in the bond region, attracting the nuclei together, whereas antibonding MOs shift charge *outside* the bond, attracting the nuclei apart.

Three common labeling conventions are used in Fig. 7-17. A level may be labeled with reference to the separated atom AOs to which it correlates. The separated atom AO symbol is placed *to the right* of the MO symmetry symbol (e.g., $\sigma_g 2s$). Note the absence of square brackets, which we used to symbolize the SO ($2s_A + 2s_B$). The symbol $\sigma_g 2s$ means "the MO of σ_g symmetry that correlates with 2s AOs at $R = \infty$." An alternative label indicates the united-atom orbital with which the MO correlates. Here the AO label is placed *to the left* of the symmetry symbol (e.g., $3p\sigma_u$). The u and g subscripts in the united-atom notation are redundant and are often omitted. However, they are helpful in drawing correlation diagrams. Finally, the MOs may be simply numbered in their energy order within each symmetry type, as mentioned earlier (e.g., $2\sigma_g$).

The noncrossing rule mentioned above is an important aid in constructing correlation diagrams for many processes. It is called a *rule* rather than a *law* because it can only be shown to be highly improbable, not impossible, for two levels of the same symmetry to cross. Thus, imagine that we have a molecule with some variable parameter λ and also with a symmetry operation R which is not lost as λ varies. For example, λ might be the H–O–H angle in water, and R could be reflection through the plane bisecting the H–O–H angle. Suppose that we have a complete set of basis functions and that, at each value of λ, we manage

---

number for this molecule. In essence, the H_2^+ wavefunction in elliptical coordinates may be written $\psi = L(\lambda)M(\mu)e^{im\phi}$. The function L may have nodal surfaces of elliptical shape. M may have nodes of hyperbolic shape. In the correlation diagram for H_2^+, it is necessary that ellipsoidal nodes correlate with spherical nodes in the united atom, while hyperboloid nodes correlate with hyperboloid nodes (which may be planar). Sketching $2p\sigma_g$ and $3s\sigma_g$ and comparing them with $3s\sigma_g$ and $3d\sigma_g$ (i.e., $3d_{3z^2-r^2}$) makes clear how this "nodal control" results in what, at first sight, appears to be a violation of the noncrossing rule. For H_2^+, modifications for higher-energy states will also be required. For example, $4s\sigma_g$ will correlate with $\sigma_g 4s$, not $\sigma_g 3p$.]

to express exactly all but two of the eigenfunctions for the molecule. This uses up all but two dimensions of our function space, leaving us, at each value of λ, with two eigenfunctions to determine and two functions in terms of which to express them. (These functions change with λ, but the above argument has nevertheless served to reduce our problem to two dimensions.) Now let the two functions remaining from our original basis be mixed to become orthonormal and also individually either symmetric or antisymmetric for R. We label these symmetrized basis functions χ_1 and χ_2. Because we began with a complete basis, it must be possible to express the as yet undetermined wavefunctions ψ_1 and ψ_2 *exactly* as linear combinations of χ_1 and χ_2 at each value of λ. Furthermore, if ψ_1 and ψ_2 are, say, both antisymmetric for R, it is necessary that χ_1 and χ_2 also both be antisymmetric. If ψ_1 and ψ_2 have opposite symmetries, however, χ_1 and χ_2 also have opposite symmetries. (In the latter case, χ_1 and χ_2 can only mix to produce unsymmetric functions, and so we know that χ_1 and χ_2 are already identical with ψ_1 and ψ_2.) To determine the mixing coefficients and state energies for ψ_1 and ψ_2, we solve the 2×2 secular equation over the basis χ_1, χ_2:

$$\begin{vmatrix} H_{11} - E & H_{12} \\ H_{12} & H_{22} - E \end{vmatrix} = 0 \tag{7-107}$$

The roots are

$$E\pm = \tfrac{1}{2}\{H_{11} + H_{22} \pm [4H_{12}^2 + (H_{11} - H_{22})^2]^{1/2}\} \tag{7-108}$$

The crossing of energy levels for ψ_1 and ψ_2 requires that, at some value of λ, E_+ equals E_-. From Eq. (7-108), we see that this requires that the term in brackets vanish, which requires that H_{12} *and* $H_{11} - H_{22}$ vanish. Now, if χ_1 and χ_2 (and hence ψ_1 and ψ_2) have opposite symmetries for R, H_{12} vanishes for all values of λ, and the curves will cross whenever H_{11} equals H_{22}. But if χ_1 and χ_2 (and hence ψ_1 and ψ_2) have the *same* symmetry for R, H_{12} is not generally zero. In this situation, the curve crossing requires that *both* H_{12} and $H_{11} - H_{22}$ *happen to pass through zero* at the same vaue of λ. This simultaneous occurrence of two functions passing through zero is so unlikely that it is safe to assume it will not happen.

If the molecule possesses several elements of symmetry, H_{12} will vanish at all λ if ψ_1 and ψ_2 disagree in symmetry for *any one* of them, so the noncrossing rule applies only to states having wavefunctions of identical symmetry for *all* symmetry operations of the molecule.

A similar treatment for orbitals and orbital energy levels is possible, and the noncrossing rule applies for orbital energies as well as for state energies.

7-7 Basis Set Choice and the Variational Wavefunction

One of the places where human decision can effect the outcome of a variational calculation is in the choice of basis. Some insight into the ways this choice effects the ultimate results is necessary if one is to make a wise choice of basis, or recognize which calculated results are "physically real" and which are artifacts of basis choice.

One question we can ask is this: Is a minimal basis set equally appropriate for calculating an MO wavefunction for, say, B_2 as F_2? In each case we use 10 AOs and 2 spin functions producing a total of 20 spin MOs. With B_2, however, we have 10 electrons to go into these spin MOs, and in F_2 we have 18 electrons. In all but the crudest MO calculations, the total energy is minimized in a manner that depends on the natures of only the occupied MOs. In effect, then, the calculation for B_2 produces the 10 "best" spin MOs from a basis set of 20 spin-AOs, whereas that for F_2 produces the 18 best MOs from a different basis set of 20 spin-AOs. In a sense, then, the basis for F_2 is less flexible than that for B_2. Of course, the use of separated atom orbitals is a conscious effort to choose that basis that best spans the same function space as the best MOs. To the extent that this strategy is successful, the above problem is obviated (i.e., if both sets are perfect, additional flexibility is useless). The strategy is not completely successful, however, and comparison of results of minimal basis set calculations down a series of molecules such as B_2, C_2, N_2, O_2, and F_2 may be partially hampered by this ill-defined inequivalence in basis set adequacy. In contrast, comparison of calculated results in a series of molecules such as C_nH_{2n+2} is much less likely to suffer from this particular problem because the minimal basis set grows with increasing n in a way to keep pace with the number of electrons.

Let us now briefly consider how basis sets might vary in adequacy for different states of a given molecule. We will compare the wavefunction for the ground state of a molecule with the wavefunction for a Rydberg state. Rydberg states are so named because their spectral lines progress toward the ionization limit in a manner similar to the spectral pattern for hydrogenlike ions (called a Rydberg series).[7] Hence, the Rydberg states of molecules are in some way like excited states of the hydrogen atom. This can be understood by visualizing an excited state for, say, N_2 wherein one electron is, on the average, very far away from the rest of the molecule, which is now an N_2^+ "core." As the excited electron moves to orbitals farther and farther out, the N_2^+ core becomes effectively almost like a point positive charge. As a result, the coupling between the angular momentum of this orbital and the internuclear axis grows progressively weaker, so that the motion of the Rydberg electron becomes more and more independent of orientation of the core. It is not surprising that a hydrogenlike AO centered in the bond becomes more and more appropriate as a basis for describing this orbital. In contrast, such a "single-center" basis normally requires many terms to accurately describe MOs in ground or non-Rydberg excited states. Thus, for a Rydberg state of N_2, one would do well to choose a basis set of AOs located on the nuclei to describe the MOs of the N_2^+ core, and

[7] See A. B. F. Duncan [3].

to use an AO (or several AOs) centered between the nuclei to describe the orbital for the Rydberg electron.

Thus far we have kept the discussion within the framework of homonuclear diatomic molecules. When we come to heteronuclear diatomics, for example, CO, we lose inversion symmetry and we can no longer symmetry balance our basis. This means that a given basis may be more inadequate for representing the wavefunction on one end of the molecule than on the other. As a result, the electronic charge will be shifted toward the end where the basis set is best able to minimize the energy. This charge shift is an artifact of basis set imbalance, but, since we have no way to evaluate this imbalance, it is difficult to tell how much it affects our results. Mulliken has published some calculations on the HF molecule which illustrate this problem in a striking way. Table 7-3 is a list of total energies and dipole moments calculated for HF using a variety of basis sets. The first column of data arises from a minimal basis set of STOs ($1s_H$, $1s_F$, $2s_F$, $2p_{\sigma F}$, $2p_{\pi x F}$, $2p_{\pi y F}$) with orbital exponents evaluated from Slater's rules for atoms. The second column results if the orbital exponents are allowed to vary independently to minimize the molecular energy. The basis set for the third column is obtained by augmenting the previous basis with additional STOs centered on the H nucleus ($2s_H$, $2p_{\sigma H}$, $2p_{\pi x H}$, $2p_{\pi y H}$). Finally, the fourth column results from use of a basis set which has been augmented (over the minimal basis) at *both* nuclei in a way thought to be appropriately balanced. As the basis set grows increasingly flexible, the average energy becomes lower, but the expectation value for the dipole moment does not converge uniformly toward the observed value. In particular, by augmenting the basis on hydrogen only, we create a very unbalanced basis, which causes charge to shift too much toward the hydrogen end of the molecule.

TABLE 7-3
Energies and Dipole Moments for Hydrogen Fluoride Calculated by the Variation Method Using Different Basis Sets[a]

	Min STO Slater ξ	Min STO best ξ	Min STO F; Aug STO H (very unbalanced)	Aug. STO F and H (balanced)	Exp
E (a.u.)	−99.4785	−99.5361	−99.6576	−100.0580	−100.527
μ (H^+F^-)	0.85*D*	1.44*D*	0.92*D*	1.98*D*	1.82*D*[b]

[a] See Mulliken [4].
[b] Data from Weiss [5].

These problems with basis set adequacy are difficult to overcome completely. Fortunately, with a certain amount of experience, insight, and caution, it is nevertheless possible to carry out variational calculations and interpret their results to obtain reliable and useful information.

7-8 Beyond the Orbital Approximation

Most of our discussion of the variation method has been restricted to calculations within the orbital approximation. To avoid leaving an inaccurate impression of the capabilities of the variation method, we shall briefly describe some calculations on some small (two-electron) systems where the method can be employed to its fullest capabilities. These calculations are listed in Table 7-4.

TABLE 7-4
Results of Some Very Accurate Variational Calculations on Two-Electron Systems

System	Minimized energy[a] (a.u.)	Estimated maximum energy error $\bar{E} - E_{\text{exact}}$ (a.u.)
He (ground singlet)[b]	−2.9037225	0.0000012
He (ground singlet)[c]	−2.903724375	0.000000001
He (lowest triplet)[c]	−2.17522937822	0.00000000001
H_2 (ground singlet)[d]	−1.17447498301776[e]	*f*

[a] Uncorrected for nuclear motion and relativistic effects.
[b] From Kinoshita [6].
[c] From Pekeris [7].
[d] From Kolos and Wolniewicz [8].
[e] At $R = 1.401078$ a.u.
[f] Appears to have converged to within a few hundredths of a reciprocal centimeter.

The calculation on He by Kinoshita expresses the spatial part of the wavefunction as

$$\psi(ks, kt, ku) = e^{-ks/2} \sum_{\substack{l,m,n=0 \\ n,\text{ even}}}^{\infty} c_{l,m,n}(ks)^{l-m}(ku)^{m-n}(kt)^n \tag{7-109}$$

where

$$s = r_1 + r_2, \quad u = r_{12}, \quad t = -r_1 + r_2 \tag{7-110}$$

and k and $c_{l,m,n}$ are variable parameters. The exponential term causes the wavefunction to vanish as either electron goes to infinite r, and the terms in the sum build up a polynomial in one- and two-electron coordinates, reminiscent of the form of eigenfunctions for the harmonic oscillator and the hydrogenlike ion. Kinoshita carried out his calculation to as many as 39 terms, obtaining an energy that he estimated to differ from the exact result by no more than 1.2×10^{-6} a.u. A subsequent calculation by Pekeris, using a related approach, required solving a secular determinant of order 1078 and yielded an energy estimated to be accurate to 1.0×10^{-11} a.u. Applying corrections for coupling between electronic and nuclear motions, and also for relativistic effects, Pekeris arrived at a theoretical value for the ionization potential of He of 198310.687 cm^{-1} compared to the experimental value of $198310.8_2 \pm 0.15\ cm^{-1}$.

Extremely accurate variational calculations have been carried out on H_2 by Kolos and Wolniewicz. They used elliptic coordinates and an r_{12} coordinate and expressed their wavefunction as an expansion in powers of these coordinates, analogous in spirit to the Kinoshita wavefunction described above. Their most accurate wavefunctions contain 100 terms and are calculated for a range of R values. After including corrections for relativistic effects and nuclear motion, Kolos and Wolniewicz arrived at a theoretical value for the *dissociation energy* in H_2 of 36117.4 cm^{-1} compared to what was then the best experimental value $36113.6 \pm 0.5\ cm^{-1}$. Subsequent redetermination of the experimental value gave $36117.3 \pm 1.0\ cm^{-1}$.[8]

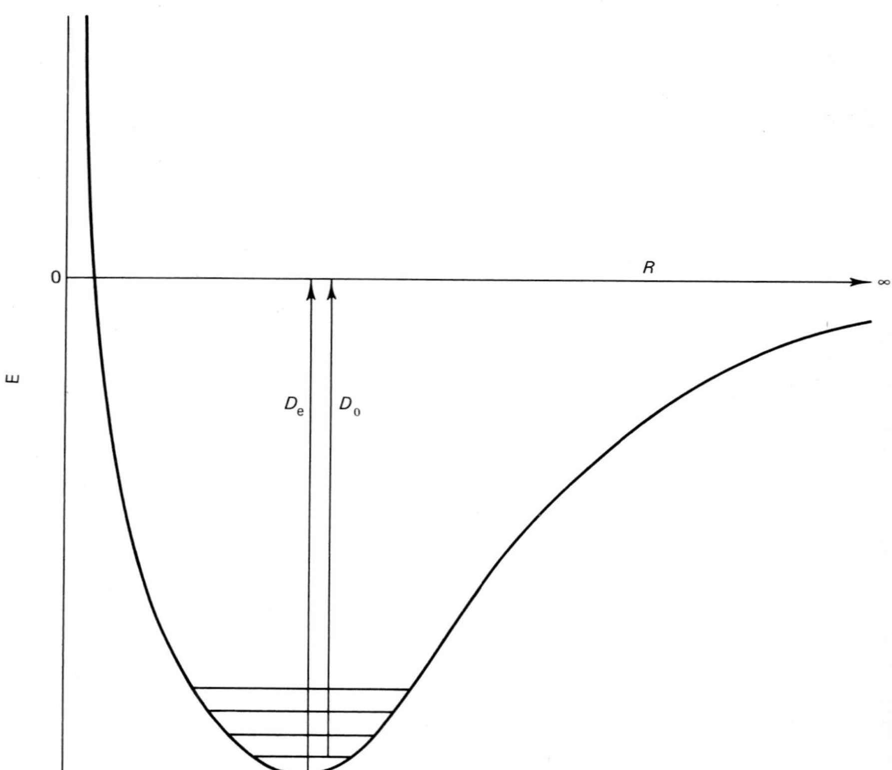

FIG. 7-18 Schematic showing the distinction between D_0, the dissociation energy from the lowest vibrational level, and D_e, the binding energy, which does not take vibrational energy into account. The zero of energy is the energy of the separated atoms.

[8] See Herzberg [9].

The *dissociation energy* is the energy required to separate a molecule into its constituent atoms, starting with a molecule in its lowest vibrational state. The *binding energy* is the energy for the corresponding process if we omit the vibrational energy of the molecule (see Fig. 7-18). These quantities are often much more sensitive measures of the accuracies of calculations than are total energies. The reason for this is easily understood when we recognize that the binding energy is a fairly small difference between two large numbers—the total energy of the molecule and the total energy of the separated atoms. Unless our errors in these two large energies are equal, the residual error is magnified (in terms of percentage) when we take the difference. Thus, the best total energy for H_2 in a certain orbital approximation is -1.133629 a.u., which is 96.7% of the total energy. However, the corresponding binding energy is -0.133629 a.u., which is 76.6% of the correct value. The need to calculate accurate binding energies is sometimes referred to as the need to achieve "chemical accuracy."

The variational calculations cited above are among the most accurate performed, and they give an indication of the capabilities of the method. Properties other than energy predicted from such wavefunctions are also very accurate. For example, Pekeris' best wavefunction for the first triplet state of helium gives an electron density at the nucleus of 33.18416 electrons per cubic bohr compared with the experimental value 33.18388 ± 0.00023 deduced from hyperfine splitting. For most systems of chemical interest, calculations of this sort become much too impractical to be considered. For this reason the orbital approximation, with all its limitations, is used in most quantum-chemical calculations on systems having more than two electrons.

PROBLEMS

7-1 Let $\phi = \exp(-\alpha r^2)$ be a trial function (not normalized) for the ground state of the hydrogen atom. Use the variation method to determine the minimum energy attainable from this form by variation of α. Find the average value of r and the most probable value of r for this wavefunction. Compare these r values and the average energy with the exact values.

7-2 Let $\phi(\alpha) = (\alpha^5/3\pi)^{1/2} r \exp(-\alpha r)$ be a trial function for the ground state of the hydrogen atom:

(a) Verify that the variation method gives $\alpha = \frac{3}{2}$, $\bar{E} = -\frac{3}{8}$ a.u.

(b) Verify that $\phi(\frac{3}{2})$ has an overlap of 0.9775 with the 1s function.

(c) Find the value of α that maximizes the overlap of ϕ with the 1s function and determine the average energy of this new ϕ.

7-3 ϕ_a and ϕ_b are chosen as the normalized basis functions for an LCAO wavefunction for a one-electron, heteronuclear, diatomic molecule. It is found that the values for some integrals involving these functions are

$$\int \phi_a \hat{H} \phi_a \, dv = -2 \quad \text{a.u.}, \qquad \int \phi_a \hat{H} \phi_b \, dv = -\tfrac{1}{2} \quad \text{a.u.},$$

$$\int \phi_b \hat{H} \phi_b \, dv = -1 \quad \text{a.u.}, \qquad \int \phi_a \phi_b \, dv = \tfrac{1}{3},$$

where $\hat{H}$ is the molecular hamiltonian. Set up the secular determinantal equation and find the lowest electronic energy that can be computed from an LCAO wavefunction $c_a\phi_a + c_b\phi_b$. Find c_a and c_b such that $\bar{E}$ is minimized and the wavefunction is normalized.

7-4 Show that, at $R = \infty$, the ψ_+ and ψ_- wavefunctions for H_2^+ are capable of describing a state wherein the electron is in a 1s orbital on atom A.

7-5 The reduced symmetry of heteronuclear (compared to homonuclear) diatomic molecules results in their having a different correlation diagram. Set up a correlation diagram for heteronuclear diatomics. Be sure to indicate that the energy levels of each type of AO are not identical for the separated atoms. Comparing correlation diagrams for homonuclear and heteronuclear molecules, does it seem reasonable that He_2 is unstable, whereas the isoelectronic LiH and $LiHe^+$ are stable molecules?

7-6 Following are some Slater orbital coefficients for some MO's of F_2 calculated by Ransil [10] (the $2p_\sigma$ STOs are defined according to z axes pointing from each atom toward the other):

$$1\sigma_g \quad c_{1s,A} = c_{1s,B} = 0.70483 \qquad 2\sigma_g \quad c_{1s,A} = c_{1s,B} = 0.17327$$
$$c_{2s,A} = c_{2s,B} = 0.00912 \qquad c_{2s,A} = c_{2s,B} = -0.67160$$
$$c_{2p_\sigma,A} = c_{2p_\sigma,B} = -0.00022 \qquad c_{2p_\sigma,A} = c_{2p_\sigma,B} = -0.08540$$

We see that the $1\sigma_g$ MO is almost entirely made from 1s AOs on A and B. However, the $2\sigma_g$ MO contains what appears to be an anomalously large amount of 1s AO. This turns out to be an artifact of the fact that Slater-type 2s orbitals are not orthogonal to 1s AOs on the same center. For F_2, the STO 1s, 2s overlap is 0.2377. Use this fact to construct a new orbital, 2s′, which is orthogonal to 1s. Express the $2\sigma_g$ MO of Ransil in terms of the basis functions 1s, 2s′, and $2p_\sigma$ on centers A and B. You should find the 1s coefficients much reduced.

7-7 A different trial function for calculating the polarizability of the hydrogen atom in a uniform electric field of strength F is

$$\psi_{\text{trial}} = \psi_{1s}(c_1 + c_2 z)$$

This is somewhat similar to the example in the text, since $z\psi_{1s}$ gives a p-like function, but not exactly the $2p_z$ eigenfunction.

(a) Use this form to find an expression for the minimum $\bar{E}$ as a function of F. What value of $\bar{E}$ does this give for $F = 0.1$ a.u.? Can you suggest why this trial function is superior to the one used in the text?

(b) The polarizability is defined to be α in the expression

$$E = -\tfrac{1}{2} - \tfrac{1}{2}\alpha F^2$$

What value of α do you obtain? [Exact $\alpha = 4.5$ a.u.] 1 a.u. of field strength is equal to e/a_0^2. Deduce the value of 1 a.u. of polarizability.

7-8 Which hydrogen atom state should be more polarizable, the 1s or 2s? [Consider the factors that determine the extent of mixing between basis functions.] Explain your reasoning.

7-9 Show that $\psi = c_1 1s_A + c_2 2p_{zA}$ is normalized if $c_1^2 + c_2^2 = 1$.

7-10 A possible basis function for representing the $1\sigma_g$ wavefunction of H_2^+ is a 1s-like AO $(\xi^3/\pi)^{1/2}\exp(-\xi r)$ located at the bond center. Assuming an internuclear separation of 2 a.u., find the ξ value that minimizes $\bar{E}$. Is this basis function adequate to predict a bound H_2^+ molecule? [Use Appendix 3 to help you develop your formulas.]

7-11 Examining Eq. (7-86), and letting $H_{AB} = kH_{AA}$, what relationship between k and S_{AB} is necessary if the σ_g MO is to be lower in energy than the σ_u MO? [Assume that H_{AA} is negative, and that k and S_{AB} are positive.]

7-12 Evaluate Eqs. (7-89) and (7-90) at $R = 0$ to show that $H_{AA} = H_{AB}$ at this point.

7-13 ϕ_a and ϕ_b are chosen to be a normalized set of basis functions for an LCAO wavefunction for a one-electron homonuclear diatomic system. It is found that the values for the integrals involving these functions are

$$\int \phi_a{}^*\hat{H}\phi_a \, dv = -2 \quad \text{a.u.}, \qquad \int \phi_b{}^*\hat{H}\phi_b \, dv = -2 \quad \text{a.u.},$$

$$\int \phi_a{}^*\hat{H}\phi_b \, dv = -1 \quad \text{a.u.}, \qquad \int \phi_a{}^*\phi_b \, dv = \tfrac{1}{4}.$$

Find an upper bound for the exact lowest electronic energy for this system. Find the corresponding LCAO *normalized* approximate wavefunction.

7-14 The normalized function $\phi = (2/\sqrt{45\pi})r^2 \exp(-r)$ can be expanded in terms of hydrogen atom eigenfunctions:

$$\phi = c_1\psi_{1s} + c_2\psi_{2s} + c_3\psi_{2p_0} + \cdots$$

where $\psi_{1s} = (1/\sqrt{\pi}) \exp(-r)$ and $\psi_{2p_0} = (1/\sqrt{32\pi})\, r \exp(-r/2) \cos\theta$. Evaluate c_1 and c_3.

7-15 Consider the one-electron molecule–ion HeH^{2+}:

(a) Write down the hamiltonian (nonrelativistic, Born–Oppenheimer approximation) for the electronic energy in atomic units for this system.

(b) Calculate the electronic energies for the lowest energy state of this system in the separated atom and united atom limits.

7-16 A homonuclear diatomic system has the ground-state MO configuration $1\sigma_g{}^2 1\sigma_u{}^2 2\sigma_g{}^2 2\sigma_u{}^2\, 1\pi_u{}^4 3\sigma_g{}^2\, 1\pi_g{}^2$:

(a) What is the *net* number of bonding electrons?

(b) What spin multiplicity would you expect for the ground state?

(c) What would you expect the effect to be on the dissociation energy of this molecule of ionization (1) from the $1\pi_g$ MO? (2) from the $3\sigma_g$ MO?

(d) Upon ionization (one-electron) from the $1\pi_g$ level, what would be the spin multiplicity of the resulting ion?

7-17 Characterize each of the following *atomic* orbitals with the symbols σ, π, δ, and also g or u. Let the z axis be the reference axis for angular momentum.

$$\begin{array}{cccc} 1s & 2p_z & 3p_y & 3d_{xy} \\ 2s & 2p_x & 3d_{z^2} & 3d_{xz} \end{array}$$

7-18 Indicate whether you expect each of the following homonuclear diatomic MOs to be bonding or antibonding. Sketch the MO in each case:

(a) σ_u (b) π_u (c) δ_g

7-19 Use sketches and symmetry arguments to decide which of the following integrals vanish for diatomic molecules (the x, y, and z axes are shown in Fig. P7-19):

(a) $\int 2p_{za}1s_b \, dv$, (b) $\int 2p_{ya}1s_b \, dv$, (c) $\int 2p_{za}2p_{yb} \, dv$, (d) $\int 2p_{ya}3d_{yzb} \, dv$

(e) $\int 2p_{za}3d_{yzb} \, dv$, (f) $\int 1s_a\hat{H}2p_{xa} \, dv$, (g) $\int 1s_a\hat{H}2p_{za} \, dv$

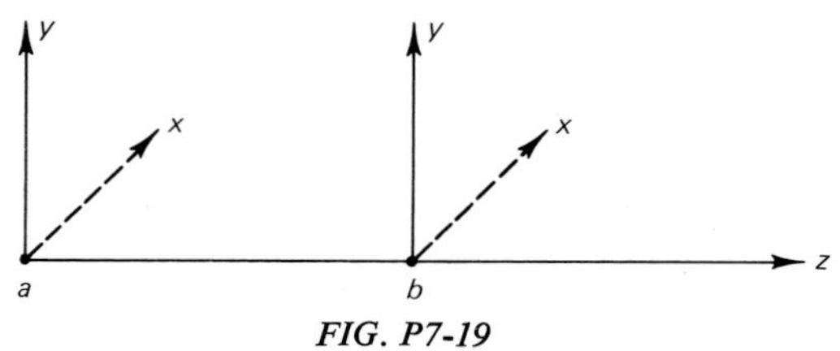

FIG. P7-19

7-20 Prove that optimized trial function (7-20) *must* contain contributions from continuum wavefunctions.

7-21 Compare the orbital exponent for a 1s AO in He as found by the variation method [Eq. (7-35)] with that given by Slater's rules (Chapter 5).

7-22 Given the approximate wavefunction for the lowest state of a particle in a one-dimensional box (Fig. P7-22):

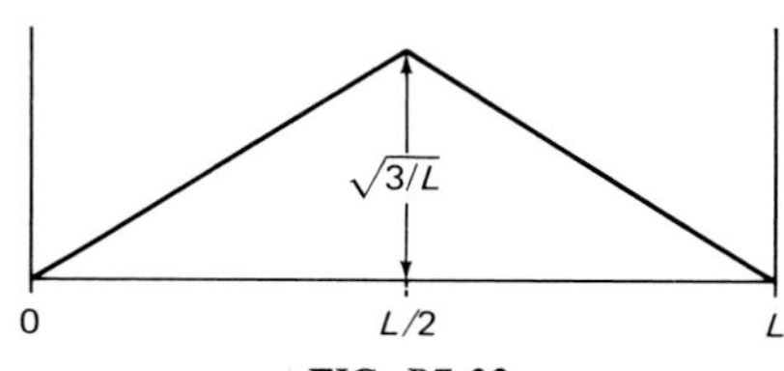

FIG. P7-22

$$\begin{aligned} \phi &= \sqrt{3/L}\,(2x/L), && 0 \le x \le L/2 \\ \phi &= \sqrt{3/L}\,[2(L-x)/L], && L/2 \le x \le L \\ \phi &= 0, && 0 > x > L \end{aligned}$$

(a) Resolve ϕ into the box eigenfunctions. That is evaluate c_n in the expression

$$\phi = \sum_{n=1}^{\infty} c_n \psi_n,$$

where

$$\psi_n = \sqrt{2/L}\,\sin(n\pi x/L), \quad 0 \le x \le L, \qquad \psi_n = 0, \quad 0 > x > L$$

(b) Using the coefficients from part (a) compare the value of ϕ at $x = L/2$ with the values one obtains from the

$$\phi_{\text{approx}} = \sum_{n=1}^{m} c_n \psi_n, \qquad \text{with} \quad m = 1, 3, 5, 7, \text{ and } 9$$

(c) Use the coefficients from part (a) to obtain an expression for $\bar{E}$ appropriate for ϕ. Estimate the value of the infinite series and thereby estimate $\bar{E}$. Compare this value to E_{exact}.

REFERENCES

[1] R. S. Mulliken, *Rev. Mod. Phys.* **2**, 60, 506 (1930); **3**, 90 (1931); **4**, 1 (1932).
[2] J. O. Hirschfelder, C. F. Curtiss, and R. B. Bird, "Intermolecular Forces." Wiley, New York, 1964.
[3] A. B. F. Duncan, "Rydberg Series in Atoms and Molecules." Academic Press, New York, 1971.

[4] R. S. Mulliken, *J. Chem. Phys.* **36**, 3428 (1962).
[5] R. Weiss, *Phys. Rev.* **131**, 659 (1963).
[6] T. Kinoshita, *Phys. Rev.* **150**, 1490 (1957).
[7] C. L. Pekeris, *Phys. Rev.* **115**, 1216 (1959).
[8] W. Kolos and L. Wolniewicz, *J. Chem. Phys.* **49**, 404 (1968).
[9] G. Herzberg, *J. Mol. Spectry.* **33**, 147 (1970).

CHAPTER 8

THE SIMPLE HÜCKEL METHOD AND APPLICATIONS

8-1 The Importance of Symmetry

Our discussions of the particle in a box, the harmonic oscillator, the hydrogen atom, and homonuclear diatomic molecules have all included emphasis on the role which symmetry plays in determining the qualitative nature of the eigenfunctions. When we encounter larger systems, detailed and accurate solutions become much more difficult to perform and interpret, but symmetry continues to exert strong control over the solutions.

In this chapter, we will describe a rather simple quantum chemical method which was formulated in the early 1930s by E. Hückel. One of the strengths of this method is that, by virtue of its crudeness and simplicity, the effects of symmetry and topology on molecular characteristics are easily seen. Also, the simplicity of the model makes it an excellent pedagogical tool for illustrating many quantum chemical concepts, such as bond order, electron densities, and orbital energies. Finally, the method and some of its variants continue to be useful for certain research applications. Indeed, it is difficult to argue against the proposition that every graduate student of organic chemistry should be acquainted with the Hückel molecular orbital (HMO) method.

8-2 The Assumption of σ–π Separability

The simple Hückel method was devised to treat electrons in unsaturated molecules like ethylene and benzene. By 1930 it was recognized that unsaturated hydrocarbons are chemically more reactive than are alkanes, and that their spectroscopic and thermodynamic properties are different too. The available evidence suggested the existence of loosely held electrons in unsaturated molecules.

We have already seen that, when atoms combine to form a *linear* molecule, we can distinguish between MOs of type σ, π, δ, . . . depending on whether the MOs are associated with an m quantum number of 0, 1, 2, ... Thus, in acetylene (C_2H_2), the minimal basis set of AOs on carbon and hydrogen lead to σ and π MOs. Let us imagine that our acetylene molecule is aligned along the z

cartesian axis. Then the p_x π-type AOs on the carbons are antisymmetric for reflection through a plane containing the molecular axis and the y axis. The p_y π-type AOs are antisymmetric for reflection through a plane containing the molecular axis and the x axis. The p_z AOs, which are σ-type functions, are symmetric for reflection through any plane containing the molecular axis. It has become standard practice to carry over the σ–π terminology to planar (but nonlinear) molecules, where m is no longer a "good" quantum number. In this expanded usage, *a π orbital is one that is antisymmetric for reflection through the plane of the molecule*, a σ orbital being symmetric for that reflection.

Hückel found that, by treating only the π electrons explicitly, it is possible to reproduce theoretically many of the observed properties of unsaturated molecules such as the uniform C–C bond lengths of benzene, the high-energy barrier to internal rotation about double bonds, and the unusual chemical stability of benzene. Subsequent work by a large number of investigators has revealed many other useful correlations between experiment and this simple HMO method for π electrons.

Treating only the π electrons explicitly and ignoring the σ electrons is clearly an approximation, yet it appears to work surprisingly well. Physically, Hückel's approximation may be viewed as one which has the π electrons moving in a potential field due to the nuclei and a "σ core," which is assumed to be frozen as the π electrons move about. Mathematically, the *σ–π separability* approximation is

$$E_{\text{tot}} = E_\sigma + E_\pi \tag{8-1}$$

where E_{tot} is taken to be the electronic energy E_{el} plus the internuclear replusion energy V_{nn}.

Let us consider the implications of Eq. (8-1). We have already seen (Chapter 5), that a *sum* of energies is consistent with a sum of hamiltonians and a product-type wavefunction. This means that, if Eq. (8-1) is true, the wavefunction of our planar molecule should be of the form (see Problem 8-1)

$$\psi(1, \ldots, n) = \psi_\pi(1, \ldots, k)\psi_\sigma(k+1, \ldots, n) \tag{8-2}$$

and our hamiltonian should be separable into π and σ parts:

$$\mathscr{H}(1, 2, \ldots, n) = \mathscr{H}_\pi(1, 2, \ldots, k) + \mathscr{H}_\sigma(k+1, \ldots, n) \tag{8-3}$$

Equations (8-2) and (8-3) lead immediately to Eq. (8-1):

$$\begin{aligned}\bar{E} &= \frac{\int \psi_\pi^* \psi_\sigma^* (\mathscr{H}_\pi + \mathscr{H}_\sigma)\psi_\pi\psi_\sigma \, d\tau(1, \ldots, n)}{\int \psi_\pi^*\psi_\sigma^*\psi_\pi\psi_\sigma \, d\tau(1, \ldots, n)} \\ &= \frac{\int \psi_\pi^* \mathscr{H}_\pi \psi_\pi \, d\tau(1, \ldots, k)}{\int \psi_\pi^*\psi_\pi \, d\tau(1, \ldots, k)} + \frac{\int \psi_\sigma^* \mathscr{H}_\sigma \psi_\sigma \, d\tau(k+1, \ldots, n)}{\int \psi_\sigma^*\psi_\sigma \, d\tau(k+1, \ldots, n)} \\ &= E_\pi + E_\sigma\end{aligned} \tag{8-4}$$

If these equations were valid, one could ignore ψ_σ and legitimately minimize E_π by varying ψ_π, but the equations are *not* valid because it is impossible to rigorously satisfy Eq. (8-3). We cannot define $\hat{\mathscr{H}}_\pi$ and $\hat{\mathscr{H}}_\sigma$ so that they individually depend completely on separate groups of electrons and still sum to the correct total hamiltonian. For example, we might define $\hat{\mathscr{H}}_\pi$ and $\hat{\mathscr{H}}_\sigma$ as

$$\hat{\mathscr{H}}_\pi(1, \ldots, k) = -\tfrac{1}{2}\sum_{i=1}^{k} \nabla_i^2 + \sum_{i=1}^{k} V_{\mathrm{ne}}(i) + \tfrac{1}{2}\sum_{i=1}^{k}\sum_{\substack{j=1,\\ j\neq i}}^{k} 1/r_{ij} \tag{8-5}$$

$$\hat{\mathscr{H}}_\sigma(k+1, \ldots, n) = -\tfrac{1}{2}\sum_{i=k+1}^{n} \nabla_i^2 + \sum_{i=k+1}^{n} V_{\mathrm{ne}}(i) + \tfrac{1}{2}\sum_{i=k+1}^{n}\sum_{\substack{j=k+1,\\ j\neq i}}^{n} (1/r_{ij}) + V_{\mathrm{nn}} \tag{8-6}$$

where $V_{\mathrm{ne}}(i)$ represents the attraction between electron i and all the nuclei. These hamiltonians do indeed depend on the separate groups of electrons, but they leave out the operators for repulsion between σ and π electrons:

$$\hat{\mathscr{H}} - \hat{\mathscr{H}}_\pi - \hat{\mathscr{H}}_\sigma = \sum_{i=1}^{k}\sum_{j=k+1}^{n} 1/r_{ij} \tag{8-7}$$

In short, the σ and π electrons really do interact with each other, and the fact that the HMO method does not *explicitly* include such interactions must be kept in mind when we consider the applicability of the method to certain problems. Some account of σ–π interactions is included *implicitly* in the method, as we shall see shortly.

8-3 The Independent π-Electron Assumption

The HMO method assumes further that the wavefunction ψ_π is a product of one-electron functions and that the hamiltonian $\hat{\mathscr{H}}_\pi$ is a sum of one-electron operators. Thus, for n π electrons,

$$\psi_\pi(1, 2, \ldots, n) = \phi_i(1)\phi_j(2)\cdots\phi_l(n) \tag{8-8}$$

$$\hat{\mathscr{H}}_\pi(1, 2, \ldots, n) = \hat{H}_\pi(1) + \hat{H}_\pi(2) + \cdots + \hat{H}_\pi(n) \tag{8-9}$$

and

$$\int \phi_i^*(1)\hat{H}_\pi(1)\phi_i(1)\, d\tau(1) \Big/ \int \phi_i^*(1)\phi_i(1)\, d\tau(1) \equiv E_i \tag{8-10}$$

It follows that the total π energy E_π is a sum of one-electron energies:

$$E_\pi = E_i + E_j + \cdots + E_l \tag{8-11}$$

This means that the π electrons are being treated as though they are independent of each other, since E_i depends only on ϕ_i and is not influenced by the presence or absence of an electron in ϕ_j. However, this cannot be correct because π electrons in fact interact strongly with each other. Once again, such interactions will be roughly accounted for in an *implicit* way by the HMO method.

The implicit inclusion of interelectronic interactions is possible because we never actually write down a detailed expression for the π one-electron hamiltonian operator $\hat{H}_\pi(i)$. (We *cannot* write it down because it results from a π–σ separability assumption and an independent π-electron assumption, and both assumptions are incorrect.) $\hat{H}_\pi(i)$ is considered to be an "effective" one-electron operator—an operator that somehow includes the important physical interactions of the problem so that it can lead to a reasonably correct energy value E_i. Now, the HMO method ultimately evaluates E_i *via* parameters that are evaluated by appeal to experiment. Hence, it is a *semiempirical* method. Since the experimental numbers must include effects resulting from all the interelectronic interactions, it follows that these effects are implicitly included to some extent in the HMO method through its parameters.

It was pointed out in Chapter 5 that, when the independent electron approximation [Eqs. (8-8)–(8–11)] is taken, all states belonging to the same configuration become degenerate. In other words, considerations of space–spin symmetry do not affect the energy in that approximation. Therefore, the HMO method can make no explicit use of spin orbitals or Slater determinants, and so ψ_π is normally taken to be a single product function as in Eq. (8-8). The Pauli principle is provided for by assigning no more than two electrons to a single MO.

8-4 Setting up the Hückel Determinant

A. Identifying the Basis Atomic Orbitals and Constructing a Determinant

The allyl radical, C_3H_5, is a planar molecule[1] with three unsaturated carbon centers (see Fig. 8-1). The minimal basis set of AOs for this molecule consists of a 1s AO on each hydrogen and 1s, 2s, $2p_x$, $2p_y$, and $2p_z$ AOs on each carbon. Of all these AOs only the $2p_z$ AOs at the three carbons are antisymmetric for reflection through the molecular plane.

Following Hückel, we ignore all the σ-type AOs and take the three $2p_z$ AOs as our set of basis functions. Notice that this restricts us to the carbon atoms. The hydrogens are not treated explicitly in the simple HMO method. We label our three basis functions $\chi_1\ \chi_2\ \chi_3$ as indicated in Fig. 8-2. We will assume these AOs to be normalized.

Suppose that we now perform a linear variation calculation using this basis set. We know this will lead to a 3×3 determinant whose roots will be

[1] The minimum energy conformation of the allyl system is planar. We will ignore the deviations from planarity resulting from vibrational bending of the system.

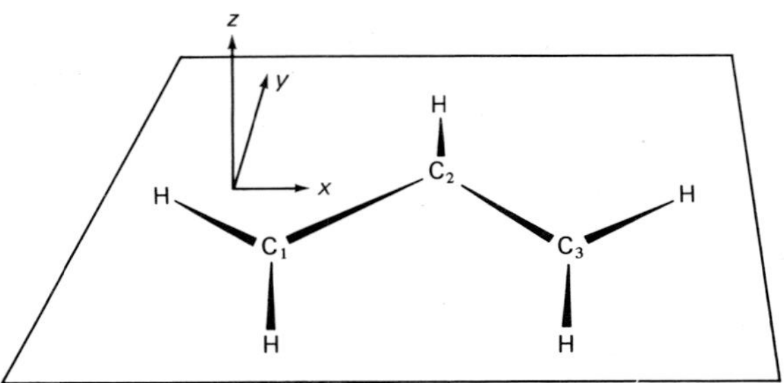

FIG. 8-1 Sketch of the nuclear framework for the allyl radical. All the nuclei are coplanar. The z axis is taken to be perpendicular to the plane containing the nuclei.

MO energies that can be used to obtain MO coefficients. The determinantal equation is

$$\begin{vmatrix} H_{11} - ES_{11} & H_{12} - ES_{12} & H_{13} - ES_{13} \\ H_{21} - ES_{21} & H_{22} - ES_{22} & H_{23} - ES_{23} \\ H_{31} - ES_{31} & H_{32} - ES_{32} & H_{33} - ES_{33} \end{vmatrix} = 0 \tag{8-12}$$

where

$$H_{ij} = \int \chi_i \hat{H}_\pi \chi_j \, dv \tag{8-13}$$

$$S_{ij} = \int \chi_i \chi_j \, dv \tag{8-14}$$

Since H_{ij} and S_{ij} are integrals over the space coordinates of a single electron, the electron index is suppressed in Eqs. (8-13) and (8-14).

B. *The Quantity* α

We have already indicated that there is no way to write an explicit expression for $\hat{H}_\pi$ that is both consistent with our separability assumptions and physically correct. But, without an expression for $\hat{H}_\pi$, how can we evaluate the integrals H_{ij}? The HMO method sidesteps this problem by carrying certain of

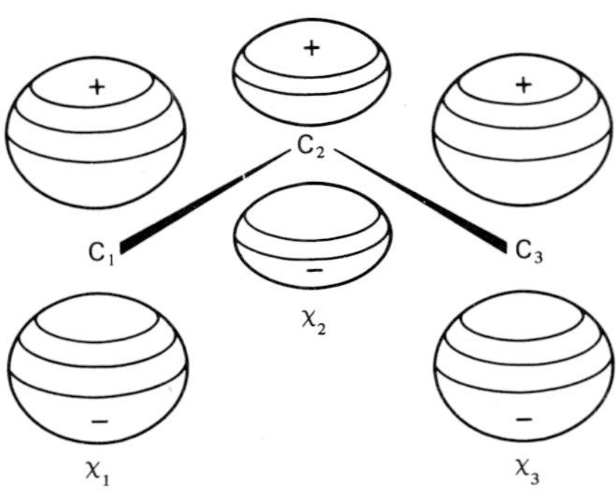

FIG. 8-2 The three π-type AOs in the minimal basis set of the allyl radical.

the H_{ij} integrals along as symbols until they can be evaluated empirically by matching theory with experiment.

Let us first consider the integrals H_{11}, H_{22}, and H_{33}. The interpretation consistent with these integrals is that H_{11}, for instance, is the average energy of an electron in AO χ_1 experiencing a potential field due to the entire molecule. Symmetry requires that $H_{11} = H_{33}$. H_{22} should be different since an electron in AO χ_2 experiences a different environment than it does when in χ_1 or χ_3. It seems likely, however, that H_{22} is not *very* different from H_{11}. In each case, we expect the dominant part of the potential to arise from interactions with the local carbon atom, with more distant atoms playing a secondary role. Hence, one of the approximations made in the HMO method is that all H_{ii} are identical if χ_i is on a carbon atom. The symbol α is used for such integrals. Thus, for the example at hand, $H_{11} = H_{22} = H_{33} = \alpha$. The quantity α is often called the *coulomb integral*.[2]

C. *The Quantity β*

Next, we consider the *resonance integrals* or *bond integrals* H_{12}, H_{23}, and H_{13}. (The requirement that $\hat{H}_\pi$ be hermitian plus the fact that the χ's and H_π are real suffices to make these equal to H_{21}, H_{32}, and H_{31}, respectively.) The interpretation consistent with these integrals is that H_{12}, for instance, is the energy of the overlap charge between χ_1 and χ_2. Symmetry requires that $H_{12} = H_{23}$ in the allyl system. However, even when symmetry does not require it, the assumption is made that all H_{ij} are equal to the same quantity (called β) when i and j refer to "neighbors" (i.e., atoms connected by a σ bond). It is further assumed that $H_{ij} = 0$ when i and j are not neighbors. Therefore, in the allyl case, $H_{12} = H_{23} \equiv \beta$, $H_{13} = 0$.

D. *Overlap Integrals*

Since the χ's are normalized, $S_{ii} = 1$. The overlaps between neighbors are typically around 0.3. Nevertheless, in the HMO method, all S_{ij} $(i \neq j)$ are taken to be zero. Although this seems a fairly drastic approximation, it has been shown to have little effect on the qualitative nature of the solutions.

E. *Further Manipulation of the Determinant*

Our determinantal equation for the allyl system is now much simplified. It is

$$\begin{vmatrix} \alpha - E & \beta & 0 \\ \beta & \alpha - E & \beta \\ 0 & \beta & \alpha - E \end{vmatrix} = 0 \tag{8-15}$$

[2] The term "coulomb integral" for α is unfortunate since the same name is used for repulsion integrals of the form $\int \chi_1(1)\chi_2(2)(1/r_{12})\chi_1(1)\chi_2(2)dv$. The quantity α also contains kinetic energy and nuclear–electronic attraction energy.

Dividing each row of the determinant by β corresponds to dividing the whole determinant by β^3. This will not affect the equality. Letting $(\alpha - E)/\beta \equiv x$, we obtain the result

$$\begin{vmatrix} x & 1 & 0 \\ 1 & x & 1 \\ 0 & 1 & x \end{vmatrix} = 0 \tag{8-16}$$

which is the form we will refer to as the *HMO determinantal equation.* Notice that x occurs on the principal diagonal, 1 appears in positions where the indices correspond to a bond, 0 appears in positions (e.g., 1, 3) corresponding to no bond. This gives us a simple prescription for writing the HMO determinant for any unsaturated hydrocarbon system directly from a sketch of the molecular structure. The rules are (1) sketch the framework defined by the n *unsaturated* carbons; (2) number the atoms $1, \ldots, n$ (the ordering of numbers is arbitrary); (3) fill in the $n \times n$ determinant with x's on the diagonal, 1's in positions where row–column indices correspond to bonds, 0's elsewhere. See Fig. (8-3) for examples. As a check, it is useful to be sure the determinant is symmetric for reflection through the diagonal of x's. This is necessary since, if atoms i and j are neighbors, 1's must appear in positions i, j *and* j, i of the determinant.

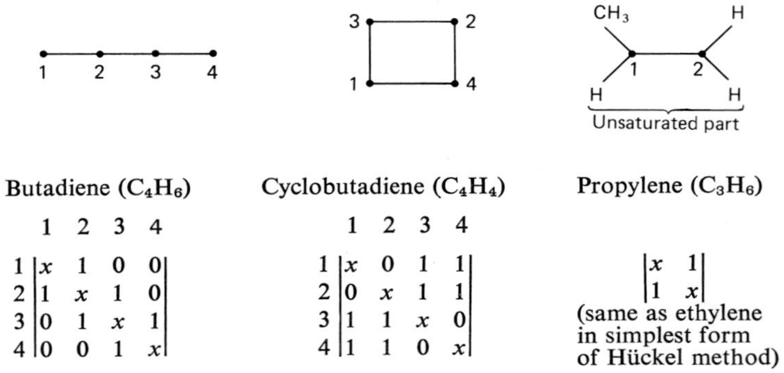

FIG. 8-3 HMO determinants for some small systems.

Since the Hückel determinant contains only information about the number of unsaturated carbons and how they are connected together, it is sometimes referred to as a *topological determinant.* (Topology refers to properties that are due to the *connectedness* of a figure, but are unaffected by twisting, bending, etc.)

8-5 Solving the HMO Determinantal Equation for Orbital Energies

The HMO determinantal equation for the allyl system (8-16) can be expanded to give

$$x^3 - 2x = 0 \tag{8-17}$$

or

$$x(x^2 - 2) = 0 \tag{8-18}$$

Thus, the roots are $x = 0$, $x = \sqrt{2}$, and $x = -\sqrt{2}$. Recalling the definition of x, these roots correspond respectively to the energies $E = \alpha$, $E = \alpha - \sqrt{2}\beta$, $E = \alpha + \sqrt{2}\beta$.

How should we interpret these results? Since α is supposed to be the energy of a pi electron in a carbon 2p AO in the molecule, we expect this quantity to be negative (corresponding to a bound electron). Since β refers to an electron in a bond region, it too should be negative. Therefore, the lowest-energy root should be $E_1 = \alpha + \sqrt{2}\beta$, followed by $E_2 = \alpha$, with $E_3 = \alpha - \sqrt{2}\beta$ being the highest-energy root. (It is convenient to number the orbital energies sequentially, starting with the lowest, as we have done here.)

We have just seen that bringing three $2p_\pi$ AOs together in a linear arrangement causes a splitting into three MO energy levels. This is similar to the splitting into two energy levels produced when two 1s AOs interact, discussed in connection with H_2^+. In general, n linearly independent separated AOs will lead to n linearly independent MOs.

The ground-state π-electron configuration of the allyl system is built up by putting electrons in pairs into the MOs, starting with those of lowest energy. Thus far, we have been describing our system as the allyl radical. However, since we have as yet made no use of the number of π electrons in the system, our results so far apply equally well for the allyl cation, radical, or anion. Configurations and total π energies for these systems in their ground states are depicted in Fig. 8-4. The total π-electron energies are obtained by summing the one-electron energies, as indicated earlier.

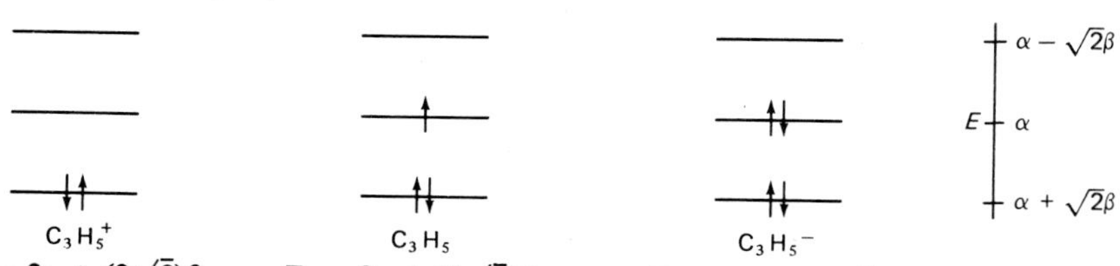

$E_\pi = 2\alpha + (2\sqrt{2})\beta$, $E_\pi = 3\alpha + (2\sqrt{2})\beta$, $E_\pi = 4\alpha + (2\sqrt{2})\beta$

FIG. 8-4 π-Electron configurations and total energies for the ground states of the allyl cation, radical, and anion.

8-6 Solving for the Molecular Orbitals

We still have to find the coefficients which describe the MOs as linear combinations of AOs. Recall from Chapter 7 that this is done by substituting energy roots of the secular determinant back into the simultaneous equations. For the allyl system, the simultaneous equations corresponding to the secular determinant (8-16) are

$$c_1x + c_2 = 0 \tag{8-19}$$

$$c_1 + c_2x + c_3 = 0 \tag{8-20}$$

$$c_2 + c_3x = 0 \tag{8-21}$$

(Compare these equations with the secular determinant in Eq. (8-16) and note the obvious relation.) As we noted in Chapter 7, homogeneous equations like these can give us only ratios between c_1, c_2, and c_3, not their absolute values. So we anticipate using only two of these equations and obtaining absolute values by satisfying the normality condition. Because we are neglecting overlap between AOs, this corresponds to requiring

$$c_1^2 + c_2^2 + c_3^2 = 1 \tag{8-22}$$

The roots x are, in order of increasing energy, $-\sqrt{2}$, 0, $+\sqrt{2}$. Let us take $x = -\sqrt{2}$ first. Then

$$-\sqrt{2}c_1 + c_2 = 0 \tag{8-23a}$$

$$c_1 - \sqrt{2}c_2 + c_3 = 0 \tag{8-23b}$$

$$c_2 - \sqrt{2}c_3 = 0 \tag{8-23c}$$

Comparing Eqs. (8-23a) and (8-23c) gives $c_1 = c_3$. Equation (8-23a) gives $c_2 = \sqrt{2}c_1$. Inserting these relations into the normality equation (8-22) gives

$$c_1^2 + (\sqrt{2}c_1)^2 + c_1^2 = 1 \tag{8-24}$$

$$4c_1^2 = 1, \qquad c_1 = \pm\tfrac{1}{2} \tag{8-25}$$

It makes no difference which sign we choose for c_1 since any wavefunction is equivalent to its negative. (Both give the same ψ^2.) Choosing $c_1 = +\frac{1}{2}$ gives

$$c_1 = \tfrac{1}{2}, \qquad c_2 = 1/\sqrt{2}, \qquad c_3 = \tfrac{1}{2} \tag{8-26}$$

These coefficients define our lowest-energy MO, ϕ_1:

$$\phi_1 = \tfrac{1}{2}\chi_1 + (1/\sqrt{2})\chi_2 + \tfrac{1}{2}\chi_3 \tag{8-27}$$

A similar approach may be taken for $x = 0$ and $x = +\sqrt{2}$. The results are

$$(x = 0): \quad \phi_2 = (1/\sqrt{2})\chi_1 - (1/\sqrt{2})\chi_3 \tag{8-28}$$

$$(x = +\sqrt{2}): \quad \phi_3 = \tfrac{1}{2}\chi_1 - (1/\sqrt{2})\chi_2 + \tfrac{1}{2}\chi_3 \tag{8-29}$$

The allyl system MOs are sketched in Fig. 8-5.

The lowest-energy MO, ϕ_1, has no nodes (other than the molecular-plane node common to all π MOs) and is said to be bonding in the C_1–C_2 and C_2–C_3 regions. It is reasonable that such a bonding MO should have an energy wherein

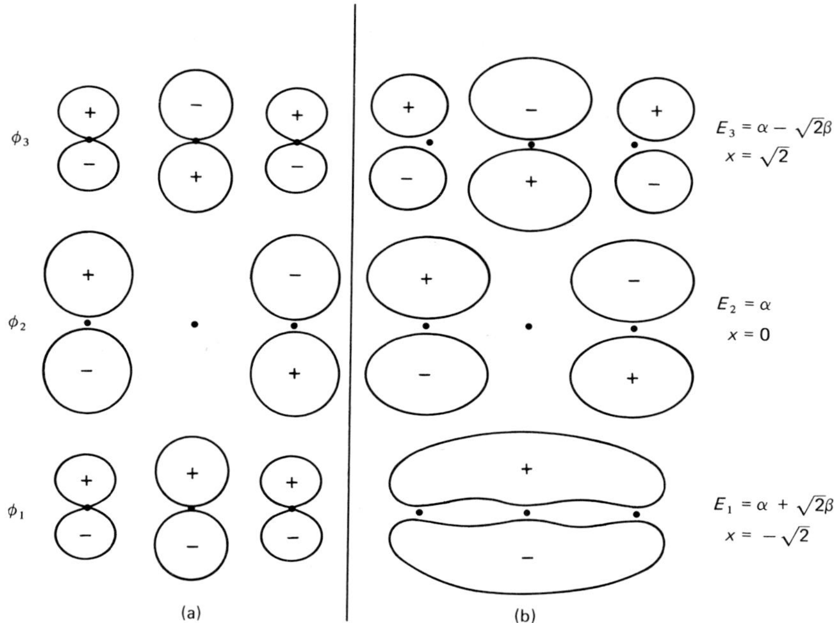

FIG. 8-5 Sketches of the allyl system MOs. (a) emphasizes AO signs and magnitudes. (b) resembles more closely the actual contours of the MOs.

the bond-related term β acts to lower the energy, as is true here. The second-lowest energy MO, ϕ_2, has a nodal plane at the central carbon. Because there are no π AOs on *neighboring* carbons in this MO, there are no interactions at all, and β is absent from the energy expression. This MO is said to be *nonbonding*. The high-energy MO, ϕ_3, has nodal planes intersecting both bonds. Because the π AOs show sign disagreement across both bonds, this MO is everywhere antibonding and β terms act to raise the orbital energy above α.

8-7 The Cyclopropenyl System: Handling Degeneracies

The allyl system results when three π AOs interact in a linear arrangement wherein $H_{12} = H_{23} = \beta$, but $H_{13} = 0$. We can also treat the situation where the three π AOs approach each other on vertices of an ever-shrinking equilateral triangle. In this case, each AO interacts equally with the other two. This triangular system is the cyclopropenyl system C_3H_3 given in Fig. 8-6.

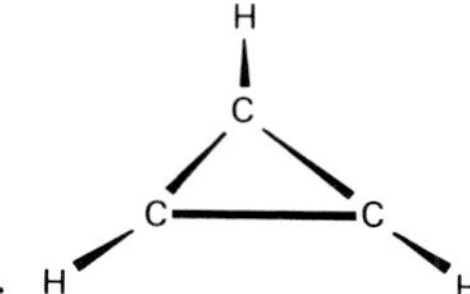

FIG. 8-6 The cyclopropenyl system (all nuclei are coplanar).

The HMO determinantal equation for this system is

$$\begin{vmatrix} x & 1 & 1 \\ 1 & x & 1 \\ 1 & 1 & x \end{vmatrix} = 0, \qquad x^3 + 2 - 3x = 0 \tag{8-30}$$

This equation can be factored as

$$(x + 2)(x - 1)(x - 1) = 0 \tag{8-31}$$

Therefore, the roots are $x = -2, +1, +1$.

Since the root $x = 1$ occurs twice, we can expect there to be *two* independent HMOs having the same energy—a double degeneracy. The energy scheme and ground state electron configuration for the cyclopropenyl radical (three π electrons) (**I**) gives a total E_π of $3\alpha + 3\beta$. We can surmise from these orbital

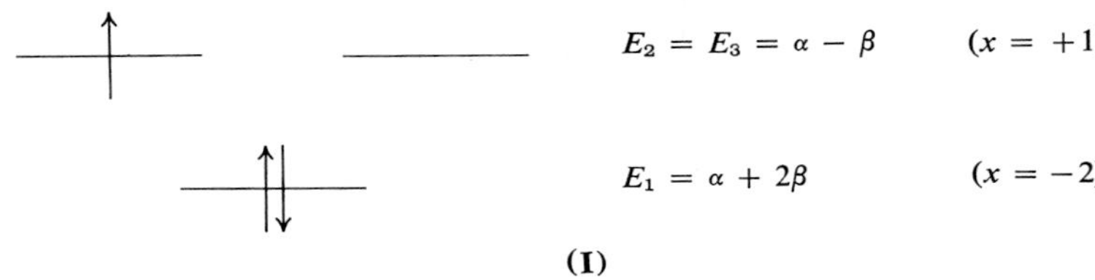

(**I**)

energies that ϕ_1 is a bonding MO, whereas ϕ_2 and ϕ_3 are predominantly antibonding. To see if this is reflected in the nodal properties of the MOs, let us solve for the coefficients. The equations consistent with the HMO determinant and with orbital normality are

$$\begin{aligned} c_1x + c_2 + c_3 &= 0 \\ c_1 + c_2x + c_3 &= 0 \\ c_1 + c_2 + c_3x &= 0 \\ c_1^2 + c_2^2 + c_3^2 &= 1 \end{aligned} \tag{8-32}$$

Setting $x = -2$ and solving gives

$$\phi_1 = (1/\sqrt{3})\chi_1 + (1/\sqrt{3})\chi_2 + (1/\sqrt{3})\chi_3 \tag{8-33}$$

For this MO, the coefficients are all of the same sign, so that the AOs show sign agreement across all bonds and all interactions are bonding.

To find ϕ_2 and ϕ_3 is trickier. We begin by inserting $x = +1$ into our simultaneous equations. This gives

$$c_1 + c_2 + c_3 = 0 \qquad \text{(three times)} \tag{8-34}$$

$$c_1^2 + c_2^2 + c_3^2 = 1 \tag{8-35}$$

With three unknowns and two equations, an infinite number of solutions is possible. Let us pick a convenient one: $c_1 = -c_2$, $c_3 = 0$. The normalization equirement then gives $c_1 = 1/\sqrt{2}$, $c_2 = -1/\sqrt{2}$, $c_3 = 0$. Let us call this olution ϕ_2:

$$\phi_2 = (1/\sqrt{2})\chi_1 - (1/\sqrt{2})\chi_2 \tag{8-36}$$

We still need to find ϕ_3. There remain an infinite number of possibilities, so et us pick one: $c_1 = 1/\sqrt{2}$, $c_2 = 0$, $c_3 = -1/\sqrt{2}$. We have used our experience vith ϕ_2 to choose c's that guarantee a normalized ϕ_3. Also, it is clear that ϕ_3 s linearly independent of ϕ_2 since they contain different AOs. But it is desirable o have ϕ_3 *orthogonal* to ϕ_2. Let us test ϕ_2 and ϕ_3 to see if they are orthogonal:

$$S = \int \phi_2\phi_3\, dv = \tfrac{1}{2}\int (\chi_1 - \chi_2)(\chi_1 - \chi_3)\, dv$$

$$= \tfrac{1}{2}\left\{\int \overset{1}{\chi_1^2\, dv} - \int \overset{0}{\chi_1\chi_3\, dv} - \int \overset{0}{\chi_1\chi_2\, dv} + \int \overset{0}{\chi_2\chi_3\, dv}\right\} = \tfrac{1}{2} \tag{8-37}$$

ince $S \neq 0$, ϕ_2 and ϕ_3 are nonorthogonal. We can project out that part of ϕ_3 vhich is orthogonal to ϕ_2 by using the Schmidt orthogonalization procedure lescribed in Section 6-9. We seek a new function ϕ_3', given by

$$\phi_3' = \phi_3 - S\phi_2 \tag{8-38}$$

vhere

$$S = \int \phi_2\phi_3\, dv = \tfrac{1}{2} \tag{8-39}$$

Therefore,

$$\phi_3' = \phi_3 - \tfrac{1}{2}\phi_2 = 1/(2\sqrt{2})(\chi_1 + \chi_2 - 2\chi_3) \tag{8-40}$$

This function is orthogonal to ϕ_2 but is not normalized. Renormalizing gives

$$\phi_3'' = (1/\sqrt{6})(\chi_1 + \chi_2 - 2\chi_3) \tag{8-41}$$

n summary, to produce HMO coefficients for degenerate MOs, pick any two ndependent solutions from the infinite choice available, and orthogonalize them ising the Schmidt (or any other) orthogonalization procedure.

The MOs for the cyclopropenyl system *as seen from above the molecular lane* are sketched in Fig. 8-7. The MO ϕ_2 can be seen to have both antibonding C_1–C_2) and nonbonding (C_1–C_3, C_2–C_3) interactions. ϕ_3'' has antibonding C_1–C_3, C_2–C_3) and bondng (C_1–C_2) interactions. The interactions are of such ize and number as to give an equal net energy value ($\alpha - \beta$) in each case. Since odal planes produce antibonding or nonbonding situations, it is not surprising hat higher and higher-energy HMOs in a system display more and more nodal lanes. Notice that the MOs ϕ_2 and ϕ_3'' have the same *number* of nodal planes one, not counting the one in the molecular plane) but that these planes are erpendicular to each other. This is a common feature of some degenerate rthogonal MOs in cyclic molecules.

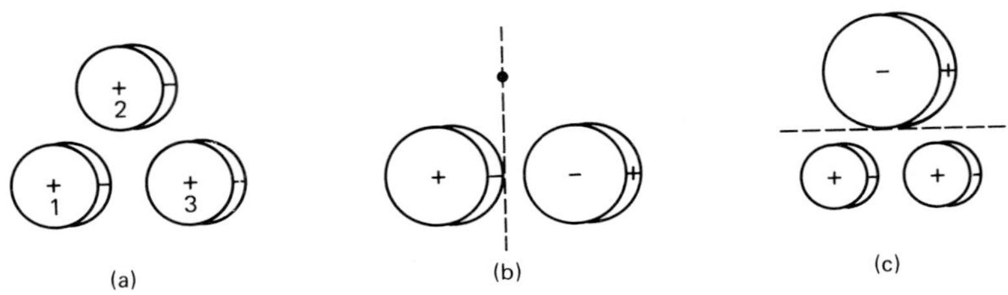

FIG. 8-7 The HMOs for the cyclopropenyl system: (a) $\phi_1 = (1/\sqrt{3})(\chi_1 + \chi_2 + \chi_3)$; (b) $\phi_2 = (1/\sqrt{2})(\chi_1 - \chi_2)$; (c) $\phi_3'' = (1/\sqrt{6})(\chi_1 + \chi_2 - 2\chi_3)$. The nodal planes intersect the molecular plane at the dotted lines.

It is important to notice the symmetry characteristics of these MOs. ϕ_1 is either symmetric or antisymmetric for every symmetry operation of the molecule. (It is antisymmetric for reflection through the molecular plane, symmetric for rotation about the threefold axis, etc.) This must be so for any nondegenerate MO. But the degenerate MOs ϕ_2 and ϕ_3'' are neither symmetric nor antisymmetric for certain operations. (ϕ_2 is antisymmetric for reflection through the plane indicated by the dotted line in Fig. 8-7, but is neither symmetric nor antisymmetric for rotation about the threefold axis by 120°.) In fact, one can easily show that, given a cycle with an odd number of centers, each with one AO of a common type, there is but *one* way to combine the AOs (to form a *real* MO) so that the result is symmetric or antisymmetric for all rotations and reflections of the cycle. Hence, an HMO calculation for a three-, five-, seven-, . . . membered ring can give only *one* nondegenerate MO. However, for a cycle containing an *even* number of centers, the analogous argument shows that *two* nondegenerate MOs exist.

8-8 Charge Distributions from HMOs

Now that we have a method that provides us with orbitals and orbital energies, it should be possible to get information about the way the π-electron charge is distributed in the system by squaring the total wavefunction ψ_π. In the case of the neutral allyl radical, we have (taking ψ_π to be a simple product of MOs)

$$\psi_\pi = \phi_1(1)\phi_1(2)\phi_2(3) \tag{8-42}$$

Hence, the probability for simultaneously finding electron 1 in $dv(1)$, electron 2 in $dv(2)$ and electron 3 in $dv(3)$ is

$$\psi_\pi^2(1, 2, 3)\, dv(1)\, dv(2)\, dv(3) = \phi_1^2(1)\phi_1^2(2)\phi_2(3)^2\, dv(1)\, dv(2)\, dv(3) \tag{8-43}$$

For most physical properties of interest, we need to know the probability for finding *an* electron in a three-dimensional volume element dv. Since the probability for finding an electron in dv is the *sum* of the probabilities for finding each electron there, the *one-electron density function* ρ for the allyl radical is (Problem 8-21)

$$\rho = 2\phi_1^2 + \phi_2^2 \tag{8-44}$$

where we have suppressed the index for *the* electron. If we integrate ρ over all space, we obtain a value of three. This means we are certain of finding a total π charge corresponding to three π electrons in the system.

To find out how the π charge is distributed in the molecule, let us express ρ in terms of AOs. First, we write ϕ_1^2 and ϕ_2^2 separately:

$$\begin{aligned}\phi_1^2 &= \tfrac{1}{4}\chi_1^2 + \tfrac{1}{2}\chi_2^2 + \tfrac{1}{4}\chi_3^2 + (1/\sqrt{2})\chi_1\chi_2 + (1/\sqrt{2})\chi_2\chi_3 + \tfrac{1}{2}\chi_1\chi_3 \\ \phi_2^2 &= \tfrac{1}{2}\chi_1^2 + \tfrac{1}{2}\chi_3^2 - \chi_1\chi_3\end{aligned} \tag{8-45}$$

If we were to integrate ϕ_1^2, we would obtain

$$\begin{aligned}\int \phi_1^2\,dv &= \tfrac{1}{4}\int \overset{1}{\chi_1^2\,dv} + \tfrac{1}{2}\int \overset{1}{\chi_2^2\,dv} + \tfrac{1}{4}\int \overset{1}{\chi_3^2\,dv} + (1/\sqrt{2})\int \overset{0}{\chi_1\chi_2\,dv} \\ &\quad + (1/\sqrt{2})\int \overset{0}{\chi_2\chi_3\,dv} + \tfrac{1}{2}\int \overset{0}{\chi_1\chi_3\,dv} \\ &= \tfrac{1}{4} + \tfrac{1}{2} + \tfrac{1}{4} = 1\end{aligned} \tag{8-46}$$

Thus, one electron in ϕ_1 shows up, upon integration, as being "distributed" $\frac{1}{4}$ at carbon 1, $\frac{1}{2}$ at carbon 2, and $\frac{1}{4}$ at carbon 3. We say that the *atomic π-electron densities* due to an electron in ϕ_1 are $\frac{1}{4}$, $\frac{1}{2}$, $\frac{1}{4}$ at C_1, C_2, and C_3, respectively. If we accumulate these figures for all the electrons, we arrive at a total π-electron density for each carbon. For the allyl radical, Table 8-1 shows that each atom has a π-electron density of unity.

TABLE 8-1
HMO π Electron Densities in the Allyl Radical

	Carbon atom		
Electron	1	2	3
1 in ϕ_1	$\frac{1}{4}$	$\frac{1}{2}$	$\frac{1}{4}$
2 in ϕ_1	$\frac{1}{4}$	$\frac{1}{2}$	$\frac{1}{4}$
3 in ϕ_2	$\frac{1}{2}$	0	$\frac{1}{2}$
Sum	1	1	1

Generalizing this approach gives for the total π-electron density q_i on atom i

$$q_i = \sum_{k}^{\text{all MOs}} n_k c_{ik}^2 \tag{8-47}$$

Here k is the MO index, c_{ik} is the coefficient for an AO on atom i in MO k, and n_k, the "occupation number," is the number of electrons (0, 1, or 2) in MO k. (In those rare cases in which c_{ik} is complex, c_{ik}^2 in Eq. (8-47) must be replaced by $c_{ik}^* c_{ik}$.)

If we apply Eq. (8-47) to the cyclopropenyl radical, we encounter an ambiguity. If the odd electron is assumed to be in MO ϕ_2 of Fig. 8-7, we obtain $q_1 = q_2 = \frac{7}{6}$, $q_3 = \frac{4}{6}$. On the other hand, if the odd electron is taken to be in ϕ_3'', $q_1 = q_2 = \frac{5}{6}$, $q_3 = \frac{8}{6}$. The HMO method resolves this ambiguity by assuming that each of the degenerate MOs is occupied by half an electron. This has the effect of forcing the charge distribution to show the overall symmetry of the molecule. In this example, it follows that $q_1 = q_2 = q_3 = 1$. The general rule is that, for purposes of calculating electron distributions, the electron occupation is averaged in any set of partially occupied, degenerate MOs.

In actuality, the equilateral triangular structure for the cyclopropenyl radical is unstable, and therefore the above-described averaging process is only a theoretical idealization. It is fairly easy to see that a distortion from equilateral to isosceles form will effect the MO energies E_1, E_2, and E_3'' differently. In particular, a distortion of the sort depicted in Fig. 8-8 would have little effect on E_1 but would raise E_2 (increased antibonding) and lower E_3'' (decreased antibonding and increased bonding). Thus, there is good reason for the cyclopropenyl radical to be more stable in an isosceles rather than equilateral triangular form. This is an example of the Jahn–Teller theorem, which states, in effect,

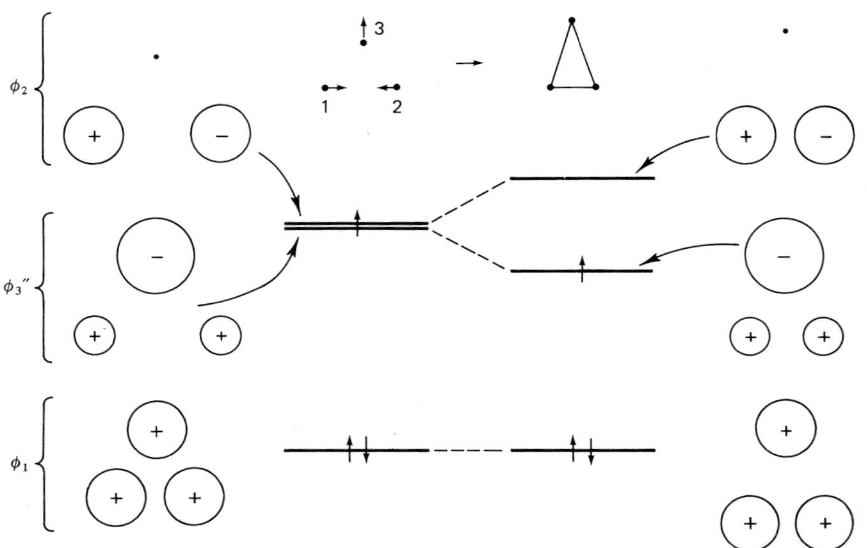

FIG. 8-8 When the equilateral structure is distorted by decreasing R_{12} and increasing R_{13}, R_{23}, the energies associated with ϕ_1, ϕ_2, ϕ_3'' shift as shown.

that a system having an odd number of electrons in degenerate MOs will change its nuclear configuration in a way to remove the degeneracy.[3] The preference of the cyclopropenyl radical for a shape less symmetrical than what we might have anticipated is frequently called "Jahn–Teller distortion."[4]

Many times we are interested in comparing the π-electron distribution *in the bonds* instead of on the atoms. In the integrated expression (8-46) are cross terms that vanish under the HMO assumption of zero overlap, but the overlaps are not actually zero, especially between AOs on nearest neighbors. Hence, we might view the factors $1/\sqrt{2}$ as indicating how much overlap charge is being placed in the C_1–C_2 and C_2–C_3 bonds by an electron in ϕ_1. The C_1–C_3 bond is usually ignored because these atoms are not nearest neighbors and therefore have much smaller AO overlap. Since $S_{12} = S_{23} = S_{ij}$ for neighbors i and j in any π system, (assuming equal bond distances), we need not include S_{ij} explicitly in our bond index. If we proceed in this manner, two electrons in ϕ_1 would then give us a "bond order" of $2/\sqrt{2} = 1.414$. It is more convenient in practice to divide this number in half, because then the calculated π-bond order for ethylene turns out to be unity rather than two. Since ethylene has one π-bond, this can be seen to be a more sensible index.

As a result of these considerations, the π-bond order (sometimes called "mobile bond order") of the allyl radical is $\sqrt{2}/2$ $(=0.707)$ in each bond. (Electrons in ϕ_2 make no contribution to bond order since c_2 vanishes. This is consistent with the "nonbonding" label for ϕ_2.)

Generalizing the argument gives, for p_{ij}, the *π-bond order* between *nearest-neighbor* atoms i and j:

$$p_{ij} = \sum_{k}^{\text{all MOs}} n_k c_{ik} c_{jk} \tag{8-48}$$

where the symbols have the same meanings as in Eq. (8-46). In cases in which partially filled degenerate MOs are encountered, the averaging procedure described in connection with electron densities must be employed for bond orders as well.

8-9 Some Simplifying Generalizations

Thus far we have presented the bare bones of the HMO method using fairly small systems as examples. If we try to apply this method directly to larger molecules, it is very cumbersome. A ten-carbon-atom system leads to a 10×10 HMO determinant. Expanding and solving this for roots and coefficients is tedious. However, there are some short cuts available for certain cases. In the event that the system is too complicated to yield to these, one can use computer programs which are readily available.

[3] Linear systems are exceptions to this rule. Problems are also encountered if there is an odd number of electrons and spin–orbit coupling is substantial.

[4] See Salem [1, Chapter 8].

For straight chain and monocyclic planar, conjugated hydrocarbon systems, simple formulas exist for HMO energy roots and coefficients. These are derivable from the very simple forms of the HMO determinants for such systems.[5] We state the results without proof.

For a straight chain of n unsaturated carbons numbered sequentially,

$$x = -2\cos[k\pi/(n+1)], \qquad k = 1, 2, \ldots, n \tag{8-49}$$

$$c_{lk} = [2/(n+1)]^{1/2}\sin[kl\pi/(n+1)] \tag{8-50}$$

where l is the atom index and k the MO index.

For a cyclic polyene of n carbons,

$$x = -2\cos(2\pi k/n), \qquad k = 0, 1, \ldots, n-1 \tag{8-51}$$

$$c_{lk} = n^{-1/2}\exp(2\pi ikl/n), \qquad i = \sqrt{-1} \tag{8-52}$$

The coefficients derived from Eq. (8-52) for monocyclic polyenes will be complex when the MO is one of a degenerate pair. In such cases one may take linear combinations of these degenerate MOs to produce MOs with real coefficients, if one desires.

There is also a diagrammatic way to find the energy levels for linear and monocyclic systems. Let us consider monocycles first. One begins by drawing a circle of radius $2|\beta|$. Into this circle inscribe the cycle, point down, as shown in Fig. 8-9 for benzene. Project sideways the points where the polygon intersects the circle. The positions of these projections correspond to the HMO energy levels if the circle center is assumed to be at $E = \alpha$ (see Fig. 8-9). The number of intersections at a given energy is identical to the degeneracy. The numerical values for E are often obtainable from such a sketch by inspection or simple trigonometry.

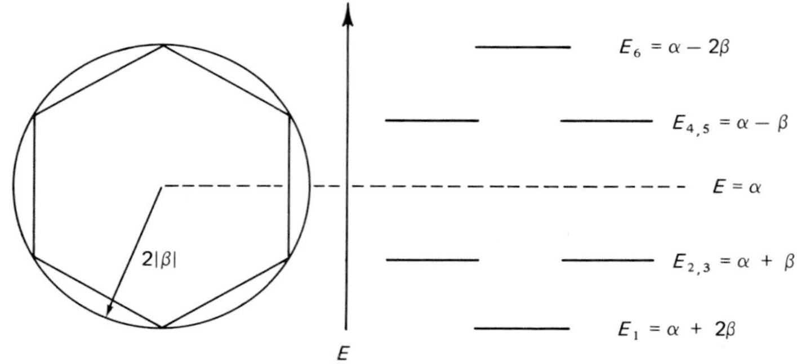

FIG. 8-9 HMO energy levels for benzene produced by projecting intersections of hexagon with a circle of radius $2|\beta|$.

[5] See Coulson [2].

For straight chains, a modified version of the above method may be used. For an n-carbon chain, inscribe a cycle with $2n + 2$ carbons into the circle as before. Projecting out all intersections *except the highest and lowest*, and *ignoring degeneracies* gives the proper roots. This is exemplified for the allyl system in Fig. 8-10.

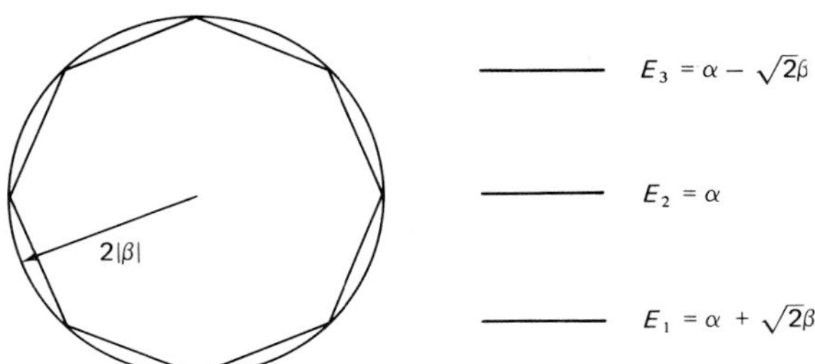

FIG. 8-10 HMO energy levels for allyl system ($n = 3$) produced by projecting the intersections of octagon ($n = 2 \times 3 + 2$) with a circle of radius $2|\beta|$.

Examination of the energy levels in Figs. 8-9 and 8-10 reveals that the orbital energies are symmetrically disposed about $E = \alpha$. Why is this so? Consider the allyl system. The lowest-energy MO has two bonding interactions. The highest-energy MO differs *only* in that these interactions are now antibonding. [See Fig. 8-5 and note that the coefficients in ϕ_1 and ϕ_3 are identical except for sign in Eqs. (8-27) and (8-29).] The role of the β terms is thus reversed and so they act to raise the orbital energy for ϕ_3 just as much as they lower it for ϕ_1. A similar situation holds for benzene. As we will see shortly, the lowest energy corresponds to an MO without nodes between atoms, so this is a totally bonding MO. The highest-energy MO has nodal planes between all neighbor carbons, and so every interaction is antibonding. An analogous argument holds for the degenerate pairs of benzene MOs. These observations suggest that the energy of an MO should be expressible as a function of the net bond order associated with it, and this is indeed the case. The energy of the ith MO is given by the expression

$$E_i = \int \phi_i \hat{H}_\pi \phi_i \, dv = \int \sum_k c_{ki} \chi_k \hat{H}_\pi \sum_l c_{li} \chi_l \, dv \tag{8-53}$$

$$= \sum_k \sum_l c_{ki} c_{li} \int \chi_k \hat{H}_\pi \chi_l \, dv \tag{8-54}$$

When the atom indices k and l are identical, the integral is equal to α; when k and l are neighbors, it equals β. Otherwise it vanishes. Hence, we may write

$$E_i = \sum_k c_{ki}^2 \alpha + \sum_{k,l}^{\text{neighbors}} c_{ki} c_{li} \beta \tag{8-55}$$

However, c_{ki}^2 is $q_{k,i}$, the electron density at atom k due to one electron in MO ϕ_i, and $c_{ki}c_{li}$ is $p_{kl,i}$, the bond order between atoms k and l due to an electron in ϕ_i. Therefore,

$$E_i = \sum_k q_{k,i}\alpha + 2 \sum_{k<l}^{\text{neighbors}} p_{kl,i}\beta \tag{8-56}$$

We have seen that the sum of electron densities must equal the total number of electrons present. For one electron in ϕ_i, this gives additional simplification.

$$E_i = \alpha + 2\beta \sum_{k<l}^{\text{bonds}} p_{kl,i} \tag{8-57}$$

The *total* π-electron energy is the sum of one-electron energies. For n π electrons

$$E_\pi = n\alpha + 2\beta \sum_{k<l}^{\text{bonds}} p_{kl} \tag{8-58}$$

where p_{kl} is the *total* π-bond order between neighbors k and l. Hence, the individual orbital energies directly reflect the amount of bonding or antibonding described by the MOs, and the total energy reflects the net bonding or antibonding due to all the π electrons together.

Does this "pairing" of energy levels observed for allyl and benzene always occur? It is easy to show that it cannot in rings with an odd number of carbon centers. Consider the cyclopropenyl system. The lowest-energy MO is nodeless, totally bonding and has an energy of $\alpha + 2\beta$. [Note from Eq. (8-51) and also from the diagram method that every monocyclic system has a totally bonding MO at this energy.] To transform these three bonding interactions into antibonding interactions of equal magnitude requires that we cause a sign reversal across every bond. This is impossible, for, if c_1 disagrees in sign with c_2 and c_3, then c_2 and c_3 must agree in sign and cannot yield an antibonding interaction.

Not surprisingly, this has all been considered in a rigorous mathematical fashion. Systems containing a ring with an odd number of atoms are "nonalternant" systems. All other homonuclear unsaturated systems are "alternant" systems. An alternant system can always have asterisks placed on some of the centers so that no two neighbors are both asterisked or unasterisked. For nonalternants, this is not possible (see Fig. 8-11). It is convenient to subdivide

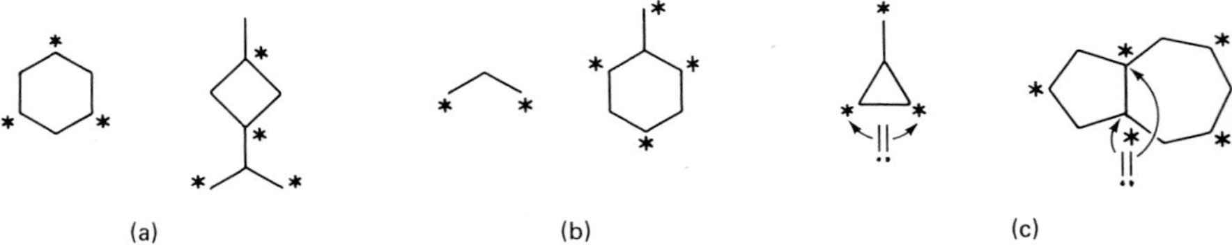

FIG. 8-11 (a) Even and (b) odd alternants have no two neighbors identical in terms of an asterisk label. (c) Nonalternants have neighbors that are identical.

alternant systems into even alternants or odd alternants according to whether the number of centers is even or odd. With this terminology defined, we can now state the *pairing theorem* and some of its immediate consequences.

The theorem states that, for alternant systems, (1) energy levels are paired such that, for each level at $\epsilon = \alpha + k\beta$ there is a level at $\epsilon = \alpha - k\beta$; (2) MOs that are paired in energy differ only in the signs of the coefficients for one of the sets (asterisked or unasterisked) of AOs.

It is easy to see that an immediate result of this theorem is that an odd-alternant system, which must have an odd number of MOs, must have a non-bonding ($E = \alpha$) MO that is not paired with another MO. It is also possible to show that the electron density is unity at every carbon for the neutral ground state of an alternant system. The proofs of the pairing theorem and some of its consequences are given in Appendix 5.

Another useful short cut exists that enables one to sketch qualitatively the MOs for any linear polyene. The HMOs for the allyl and butadiene systems are given in Fig. 8-12. Notice that the envelopes of positive (or negative) sign in these MOs are similar in appearance to the particle in a one-dimensional "box" solutions described in Chapter 2. This similarity makes it fairly easy to guess

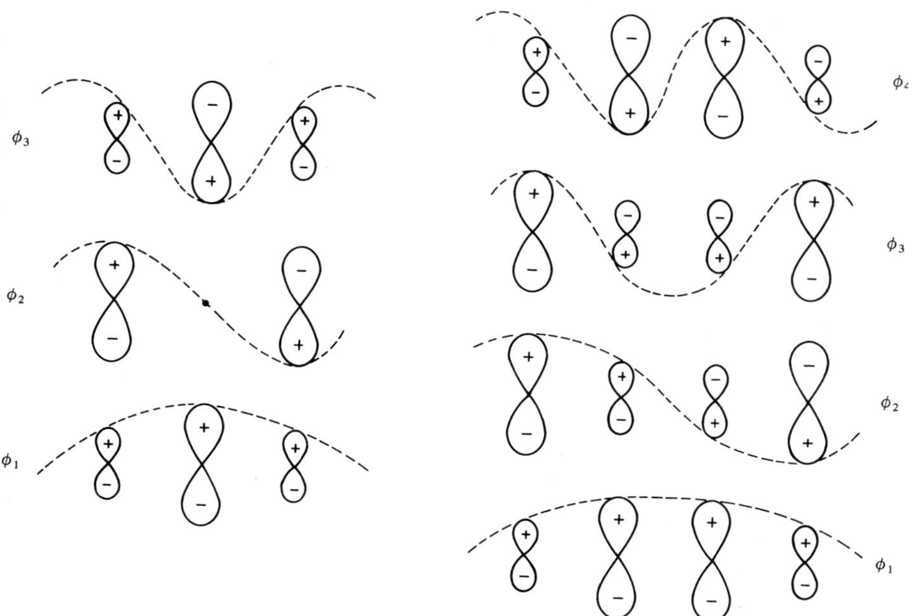

FIG. 8-12 MOs for the allyl and butadiene systems. The dotted lines emphasize the similarity between an envelope, or contour, of positive ψ_π for these systems and the particle in a one-dimensional box solutions.

the first few MOs for pentadienyl, hexatriene, etc. Also, if one knows the lowest-energy half of the MOs for such molecules, one can generate the remaining MOs by appeal to the second part of the pairing theorem. (The edges of the one-dimensional box should extend about one C–C bond length beyond the terminal atoms.)

For larger, more complicated systems, like naphthalene, it is possible to use symmetry properties of the molecule to help choose a basis of symmetry orbitals. As was mentioned in our discussion of homonuclear diatomic molecules, this has the effect of partitioning the secular determinant into a set of smaller determinants, thereby making the problem computationally less tedious. This procedure is described by Streitwieser [3] and Levine [4] and will not be described here since, in recent times, it has become common practice to do only the simplest HMO calculations by hand. Complicated systems are subjected to solution by computer[6] or else by appeal to HMO tabulations in print.[7]

8-10 HMO Calculations on Some Simple Molecules

Thus far, we have used the allyl and cyclopropenyl systems as examples. We will now describe the results of HMO calculations on some other simple but important systems.

A. Ethylene (Even Alternant)

The Hückel determinantal equation is

$$\begin{vmatrix} x & 1 \\ 1 & x \end{vmatrix} = 0$$

and so $x^2 - 1 = 0$; $x = +1, -1$. The resulting orbital energies and coefficients are

$$\begin{aligned} E_1 &= \alpha + \beta, \qquad \phi_1 = (1/\sqrt{2})\chi_1 + (1/\sqrt{2})\chi_2 \\ E_2 &= \alpha - \beta, \qquad \phi_2 = (1/\sqrt{2})\chi_1 - (1/\sqrt{2})\chi_2 \end{aligned} \tag{8-59}$$

These, with the ground state electronic configuration indicated, are shown in (**II**). π-Electron densities and π-bond order are indicated in the diagram beneath the MO sketches. Ethylene is an even alternant, so it has paired energies, unit electron densities, and coefficients related by a sign change.

[6] Many types of quantum-chemical computer programs are available from: Quantum Chemistry Program Exchange, Chemistry Department, Indiana University, Bloomington, Indiana 47401. See also Appendix 8 of this text.

[7] See Coulson and Streitwieser [5], Streitwieser and Brauman [6], and Heilbronner and Straub [7]. See also Appendix 6 of this text.

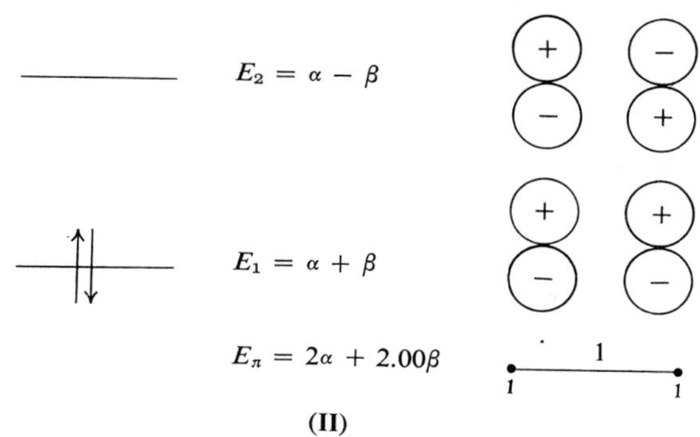

(II)

B. Butadiene (Even Alternant)

1 2 3 4

$$\begin{vmatrix} x & 1 & 0 & 0 \\ 1 & x & 1 & 0 \\ 0 & 1 & x & 1 \\ 0 & 0 & 1 & x \end{vmatrix} = 0$$

This problem can be solved by expansion to a polynomial in x and factoring, but it is simpler to use Eq. (8-49) or the decagon in a circle of radius $2|\beta|$. The coefficients are obtainable from Eq. (8-50). The results are

$$E_4 = \alpha - 1.618\beta, \quad E_3 = \alpha - 0.618\beta, \quad E_2 = \alpha + 0.618\beta,$$
$$E_1 = \alpha + 1.618\beta, \quad E_\pi = 4\alpha + 4.472\beta$$

$$\begin{aligned} \underset{(4)}{\phi_1} &= 0.372\chi_1 \underset{(-)}{+} 0.602\chi_2 + 0.602\chi_3 \underset{(-)}{+} 0.372\chi_4 \\ \underset{(3)}{\phi_2} &= 0.602\chi_1 \underset{(-)}{+} 0.372\chi_2 - 0.372\chi_3 \underset{(+)}{-} 0.602\chi_4 \end{aligned} \qquad (8\text{-}60)$$

0.894 0.447 0.894
1 1 1 1

The MOs are given in Fig. 8-12. ϕ_1 is bonding in all bonds, ϕ_2 is bonding in the outer bonds, antibonding in the central bond. As a result, butadiene has a lower π-bond order in the central bond than in the outer bonds. This is in pleasing accord with the experimental observation that the central bond in butadiene is significantly longer than the outer bonds.

The formal structural formula for butadiene (**III**), indicating two pure

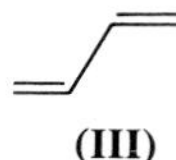

(III)

double bonds and one pure single bond, is clearly not an adequate description since we have just found the central bond to have some π-bonding order (0.447) and the outer bonds to be less π bonding than ethylene (0.894). The MO parlance is that the π electrons in butadiene are *delocalized* over the entire carbon system rather than being restricted to the formal double bonds only.

Because the HMO method allows for no interaction between terminal carbons (i.e., $H_{1,4} = 0$), there is no distinction between *cis*- and *trans*-butadiene in this calculation. However, if a weak interaction were postulated, it is not difficult to see that ϕ_1 would give a bonding end-to-end contribution, ϕ_2 a substantially larger antibonding interaction, leading to a prediction (in agreement with experiment) that *trans*-butadiene is the more stable form.

C. *Cyclobutadiene* (*Even Alternant*)

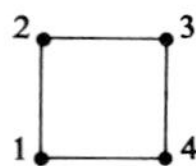

Inscribing this molecule in a circle gives us the orbital energies immediately (**IV**).

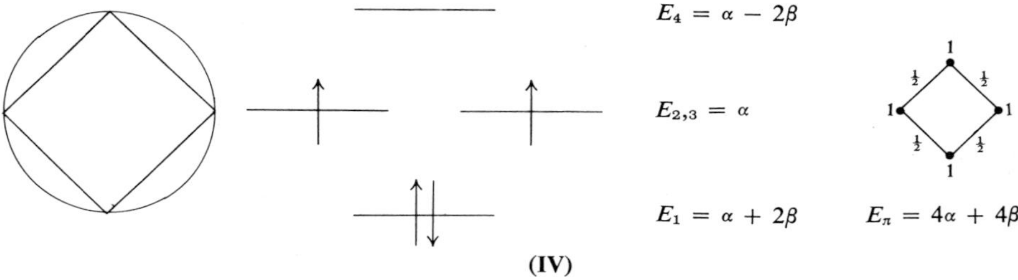

(**IV**)

Since ϕ_1 and ϕ_4 are nondegenerate, they must be symmetric or antisymmetric for the various rotations and reflections of the molecule. Also, ϕ_1 and ϕ_4 must have the same coefficients excepting for sign changes.

It follows at once that

$$\phi_1 = \tfrac{1}{2}\chi_1 + \tfrac{1}{2}\chi_2 + \tfrac{1}{2}\chi_3 + \tfrac{1}{2}\chi_4, \qquad \phi_4 = \tfrac{1}{2}\chi_1 - \tfrac{1}{2}\chi_2 + \tfrac{1}{2}\chi_3 - \tfrac{1}{2}\chi_4$$

ϕ_2 and ϕ_3 are degenerate, so there is some arbitrariness here. However, we expect each of these MOs to have a nodal plane, and these planes should be perpendicular to each other if ϕ_2 and ϕ_3 are to be orthogonal. Therefore, we choose the pair having nodal planes indicated by dashed lines (**V**). The four MOs for

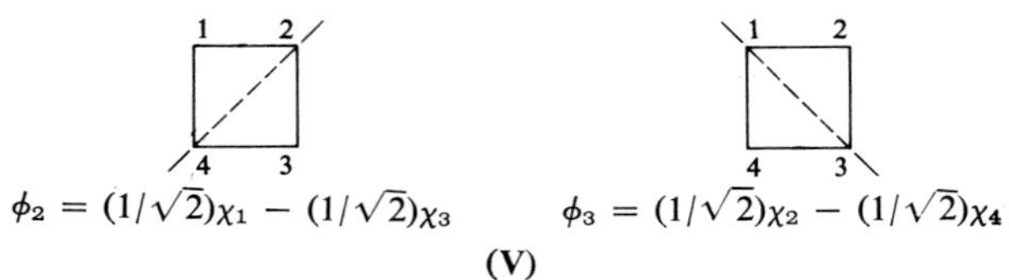

$$\phi_2 = (1/\sqrt{2})\chi_1 - (1/\sqrt{2})\chi_3 \qquad \phi_3 = (1/\sqrt{2})\chi_2 - (1/\sqrt{2})\chi_4$$

(**V**)

cyclobutadiene *as seen from above* are shown in (**VI**). It is clear that ϕ_2 and ϕ_3 are nonbonding because the nodal planes prevent interactions between neigh-

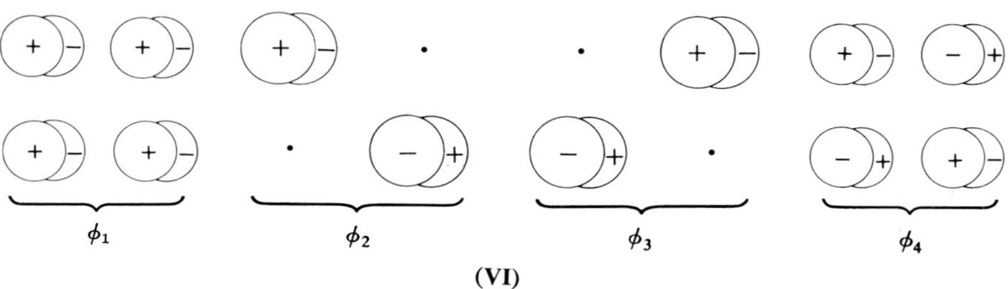

(VI)

bors, but it looks like ϕ_2 and ϕ_3 violate the pairing theorem since they cannot be interchanged by changing signs of coefficients. This is only an apparent violation, because it is easy to find an equivalent pair of MOs that follow the rule. We need only choose nodal planes that are rotated 45° (**VII**) from those we

$$\phi_2' = \tfrac{1}{2}\chi_1 - \tfrac{1}{2}\chi_2 - \tfrac{1}{2}\chi_3 + \tfrac{1}{2}\chi_4 \qquad \phi_3' = \tfrac{1}{2}\chi_1 + \tfrac{1}{2}\chi_2 - \tfrac{1}{2}\chi_3 - \tfrac{1}{2}\chi_4$$

(VII)

selected previously. These MOs are linear combinations of ϕ_2 and ϕ_3 and are equivalent to them for purposes of calculating electron densities and bond orders. They are still nonbonding MOs (E still equals α), but now it is not because of a nodal plane preventing nearest-neighbor interactions, but because bonding and antibonding interactions occur in equal number and magnitude.

Notice that this is an example of an even alternant system with nonbonding MOs. Thus, whereas an odd alternant system *must* have *an* unpaired nonbonding MO, even alternants *may* have nonbonding MOs in pairs.

Since this system is alternant, it must have π-electron densities of unity in its ground neutral state. This would be necessary however, even if the molecule were not alternant, due to the fact that all carbons are equivalent by symmetry. Hence, they must all have the same electron density. Since it must sum to four electrons, the density of each atom must be unity. The same argument applies to the cyclopropenyl radical, a nonalternant that, nevertheless, has all electron densities equal to unity (if the unpaired electron is divided between degenerate MOs).

Symmetry also requires all four bonds to be identical. Since the total energy, $4\alpha + 4\beta$, is related to bond order through Eq. (8-58), it follows at once that the total bond order is 2, and so each bond has order $\frac{1}{2}$.

D. Benzene (Even Alternant)

Benzene is another molecule whose high symmetry enables one to use shortcuts. The orbital energies have already been found from the hexagon-in-a-circle diagram (see Fig. 8-9). The lowest- and highest-energy MOs must show all the symmetry of the molecule, as they are nondegenerate. Therefore,

$$\underset{(6)}{\phi_1} = (1/\sqrt{6})(\chi_1 \underset{(-)}{+} \chi_2 + \chi_3 \underset{(-)}{+} \chi_4 + \chi_5 \underset{(-)}{+} \chi_6)$$

where the carbon atoms are numbered sequentially around the ring.

The degenerate MOs ϕ_2 and ϕ_3 should have one nodal plane each, and these should be perpendicular to each other.[8] If we take one plane as shown in **(VIII)**

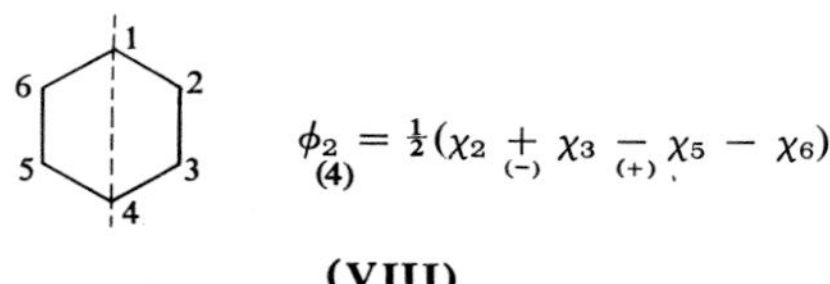

$$\underset{(4)}{\phi_2} = \tfrac{1}{2}(\chi_2 \underset{(-)}{+} \chi_3 \underset{(+)}{-} \chi_5 - \chi_6)$$

(VIII)

we can immediately write down ϕ_2. The node for ϕ_3 is given in **(IX)**. It is obvious

1 2 3 4 5 6

(IX)

that χ_6, χ_1, χ_2 have coefficients of the same sign, and that $c_2 = c_6 = -c_5 = -c_3$ and also $c_1 = -c_4$. However, c_1 need not equal c_2 as these atoms are differently placed with respect to the nodal plane. To determine these coefficients, we will use the fact that the neutral ground-state π densities are all unity in this system. We consider first atom number 1. Its electron density due to two electrons in ϕ_1 and two electrons in ϕ_2 is $\frac{1}{6} + \frac{1}{6} + 0 + 0 = \frac{1}{3}$. Therefore, two electrons in ϕ_3 must produce a contribution of $\frac{2}{3}$. Hence the coefficient for this atom in ϕ_3 must be $1/\sqrt{3}$. A similar argument for atom 2 gives a coefficient of $1/\sqrt{12}$ (or, one can use the normality condition for ϕ_3). As a result,

$$\underset{(5)}{\phi_3} = (1/\sqrt{3})(\chi_1 \underset{(-)}{+} \tfrac{1}{2}\chi_2 - \tfrac{1}{2}\chi_3 \underset{(+)}{-} \chi_4 - \tfrac{1}{2}\chi_5 \underset{(-)}{+} \tfrac{1}{2}\chi_6)$$

Appeal to the pairing theorem generates ϕ_4 and ϕ_5 as indicated.

By symmetry, all bond orders must be identical, and their sum must be 4, since $E = 6\alpha + 8\beta$. Therefore, $p_{12} = p_{23} = \cdots = p_{61} = \frac{4}{6} = 0.667$.

The hexagon in a circle applies to ethylene ($n = 2, 2n + 2 = 6$) as well as to benzene. As a result, the orbital energies for ϕ_2, ϕ_3 of benzene are identical to E_1 for ethylene. Examination of these MOs (Fig. 8-13) makes the reason for their energy agreement clear. Molecular orbital ϕ_2 of benzene is more revealing than is ϕ_3 in this context. The nodal plane produces an MO corresponding to two

[8] This statement applies to the real forms of ϕ_2 and ϕ_3. The complex forms [derivable from Eq. (8-52)] do not have a planar node. The situation is analogous to the $2p_{+1}$, $2p_{-1}$ versus $2p_x$, $2p_y$ orbitals for the H atom.

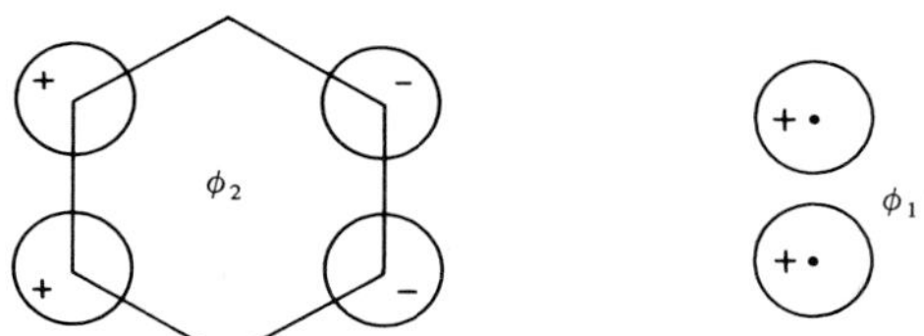

FIG. 8-13 ϕ_2 for benzene and ϕ_1 for ethylene have the same HMO energy. The MOs are sketched as seen from above.

noninteracting ethylene MOs. Hence, an electron in this MO is always in a situation that is indistinguishable (under HMO approximations) from that in ϕ_1 of ethylene.

In this section, we have tried to illustrate some of the properties of HMO solutions for simple systems and to indicate how symmetry and other relations are useful in producing and understanding HMO results. It is often convenient to have HMO results for various simple systems readily available in a condensed form. Therefore, a summary of results for a number of molecules is provided in Appendix 6.

8-11 Summary: The Simple HMO Method for Hydrocarbons

(1) The assumption is made that the π-electron energy can be minimized independently of σ electrons. This is an approximation.

(2) The assumption is made that each π electron sees the same field (the repulsion due to the other π electrons is presumably included "in effect," in a time averaged way) so that the π electrons are treated as independent particles. This approximation leads to a total wavefunction that is a simple product of one-electron MOs and a total π energy that is a sum of one-electron energies. Except for use of the Pauli principle to build up configurations, no explicit treatment is made of electron spin.

(3) The basis set is chosen to be a $2p_\pi$ AO from each carbon atom in the unsaturated system. Choosing a basis set of AOs means our MOs will be linear combinations of AOs, and so this is an LCAO–MO method.

(4) The Hückel determinant summarizes the connectedness of the unsaturated system, and is independent of *cis–trans* isomerism or bond length variation.

(5) The energy of each MO is expressed in terms of atomic terms, α, and bond terms, β. The amount of α in each MO energy is always unity because the sum of π-electron densities for one electron in the MO is always unity. The amount of β present is related to the net bonding or antibonding character of the MO.

(6) Alternant systems display paired energy levels and corresponding MOs having coefficients related by simple sign reversals. For ground-state neutral alternants, the electron densities are all unity.

(7) A caveat: One can perform HMO calculations on very large systems such as pentahelicene (**X**) thereby making the implicit assumption that this is a

(X)

planar molecule. But repulsion between protons on the terminal rings is sufficient to cause this molecule to deviate from planarity. Hence, one must recognize that, in certain cases, an HMO calculation refers to a planar "ideal" not actually achieved by the molecule.

8-12 Relation between Bond Order and Bond Length

In this and following sections we will describe some of the relations between HMO theoretical quantities and experimental observations.[9]

It is natural to look for a correlation between calculated π-bond orders and experimentally determined bond lengths. A high bond order should correspond to a large π charge in the bond region, which should yield a shorter, stronger bond. The bond-order–bond-length results for certain simple systems,

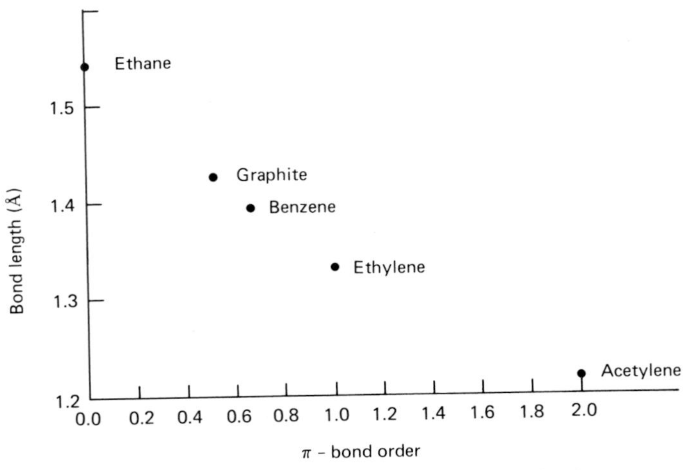

FIG. 8-14 π-Bond order versus bond length for some simple unsaturated hydrocarbons.

[9] For a more complete discussion of these phenomena as well as many others, see Streitwieser [3].

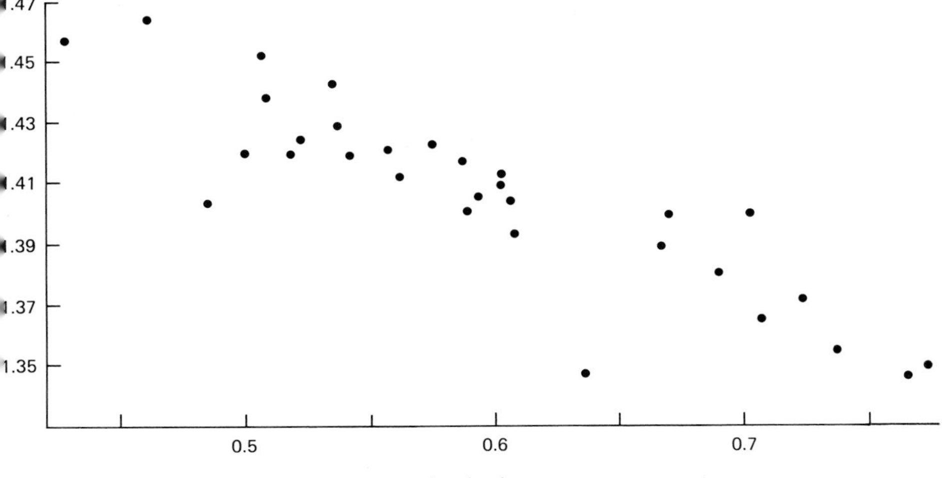

FIG. 8-15 Bond lengths versus π-bond orders for benzene, graphite, naphthalene, anthracene, phenanthrene, triphenylene, and pyrene.

given as a graph in Fig. 8-14, do indeed show the anticipated behavior. However, as more and more data are added (Fig. 8-15) it becomes clear that an exact linear relation between these quantities does not exist at this level of refinement. Efforts to improve the situation by refining the theory have been made, but the relatively large uncertainty in experimentally determined bond lengths has been a severe handicap. Nevertheless, the correlation between bond order and bond length is good enough to make it useful for rough predictions of bond length *variations.* An example of this is given in Fig. 8-16, where calculated and observed bond lengths for phenanthrene are plotted. Even though the predicted *absolute* values of bond lengths are imperfect, the theoretical values show a rough parallelism with observed values as we go from bond to bond. The relation used here to calculate the theoretical bond lengths from HMO bond orders is due to Coulson [8] and has the form

$$R = s - \frac{s - d}{1 + k(1 - p)/p} \tag{8-61}$$

Here, s is the single bond length, d the double bond length, p the π-bond order, k an adjustable parameter, and R the predicted length. The double bond length d is taken to be 1.337 Å, the bond length of ethylene. The single bond length may be taken to be the length of the C–C bond in ethane, 1.54 Å, or it may be set by fitting to data points (such as those in Fig. 8-15) on the assumption that the single bond between two CH_2 groups (i.e., ethylene with its π bind "turned off") is not necessarily the same length as the single bond between two CH_3 groups. Both of these alternatives have been used in Fig. 8-16. Other

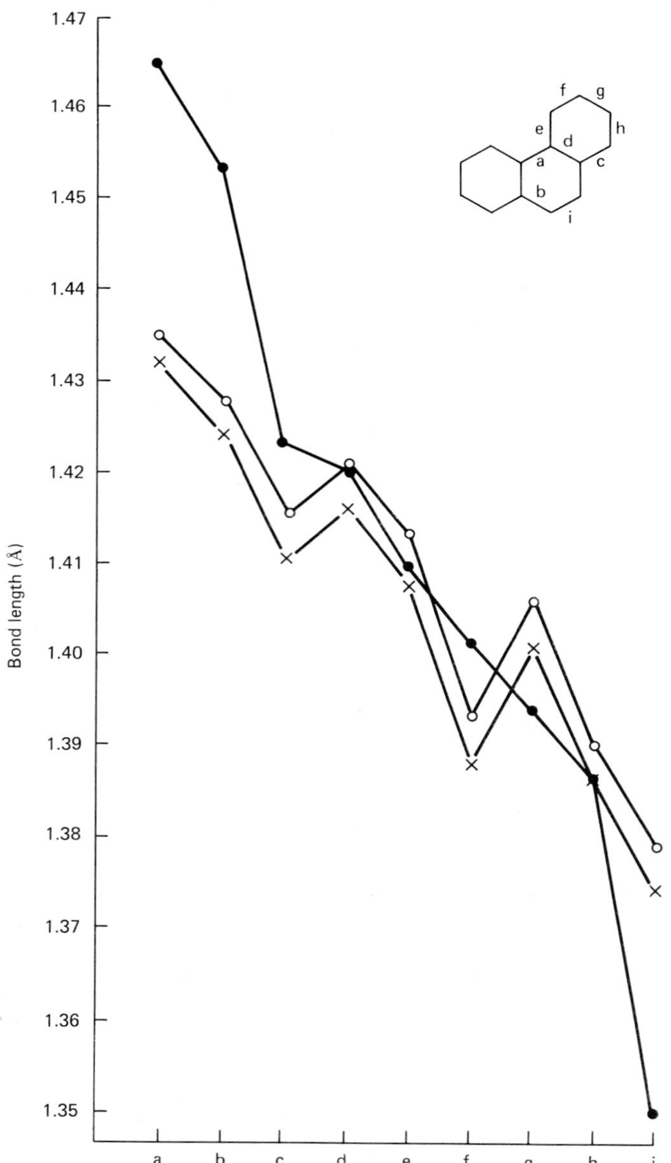

FIG. 8-16 Theoretical versus experimental bond lengths for phenanthrene in order of decreasing observed length: (●) experimental; (×) theoretical with $s = 1.54$ Å, $k = 0.765$; (○) theoretical with $s = 1.515$ Å, $k = 1.05$.

mathematical forms have also been suggested. Because of the scatter in the data, there is little basis for preferring one formula over another. It seems generally true that all the proposed relationships work best for bonds in condensed ring systems, and most poorly for bonds in acyclic polyenes (e.g., butadiene) or between rings (e.g., biphenyl).

8-13 π-Electron Densities and Electron Spin Resonance Hyperfine Splitting Constants[10]

The hyperfine structure of electron spin resonance (ESR) spectra results from the interaction between the magnetic moment due to an unpaired electron spin and the magnetic moments of certain nuclei (usually protons) in the molecule. The interaction between an *unpaired π electron* and a proton falls off rapidly with increasing separation. Therefore, the hyperfine structure is generally ascribed to interactions involving protons directly bonded to carbons in the π system (α protons) or else separated from the π system by two σ bonds (β protons). The equilibrium position of an α proton is in the nodal plane of the π system, and it is clear that any net spin density at the proton must be only *indirectly* due to the presence of an unpaired π electron. This indirect effect arises because the unpaired π electron interacts slightly differently with α- and β-spin σ electrons, and so the spatial distributions of these become slightly different, producing net spin density at the proton; the σ electrons are said to be *spin polarized* by the π electron (see Fig. 8-17).

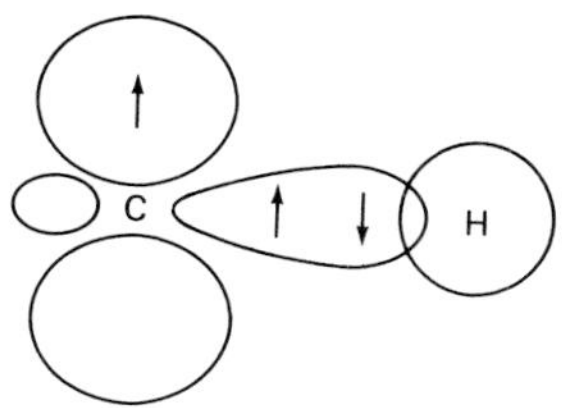

FIG. 8-17 The unpaired π-spin density at carbon repels both σ electrons in the C–H bond region, but does not repel them equally. As a result, slight spin imbalance due to σ electrons occurs at the proton.

The extent of spin polarization at a given hydrogen should depend on the percentage of time the unpaired π electron spends on the carbon to which that hydrogen is bonded. It is therefore reasonable to look for relationships between the distribution of *π-spin* density in a radical and the hyperfine coupling constants characterizing its ESR spectrum. The simplest assumption one can make in this regard, called the McConnell relation, is that the hyperfine splitting constant, $a_{H\mu}$, for a proton directly bonded to the μth carbon, is proportional to the net spin density ρ_μ on that carbon:

$$a_{H\mu} = Q\rho_\mu \tag{8-62}$$

[10] A number of reviews on this subject have been published. See, for example, Gerson and Hammons [9].

The HMO method predicts that the spin density at the μth carbon due to an unpaired electron in the mth MO is simply $|c_{\mu m}|^2$. This is only a first approximation to ρ_μ, but a graph of observed splitting constants plotted against ρ_μ calculated in this way shows a respectable correlation (Fig. 8-18). The proportionality factor Q, given by the slope of the line of best fit, varies somewhat depending on the type of system and the charge of the radical. Thus, in Fig. 8-18, where all the data are from aromatic fused ring hydrocarbon radical anions, the correlation is quite good. As data for nonalternants and radical cations are added (Fig. 8-19) the scatter increases.

Some ESR spectra are interpreted to be consistent with the presence of some *negative* spin density. That is, if the extra π electron is taken to have α spin, some of the carbons appear to have an excess of β-spin π density. Now the

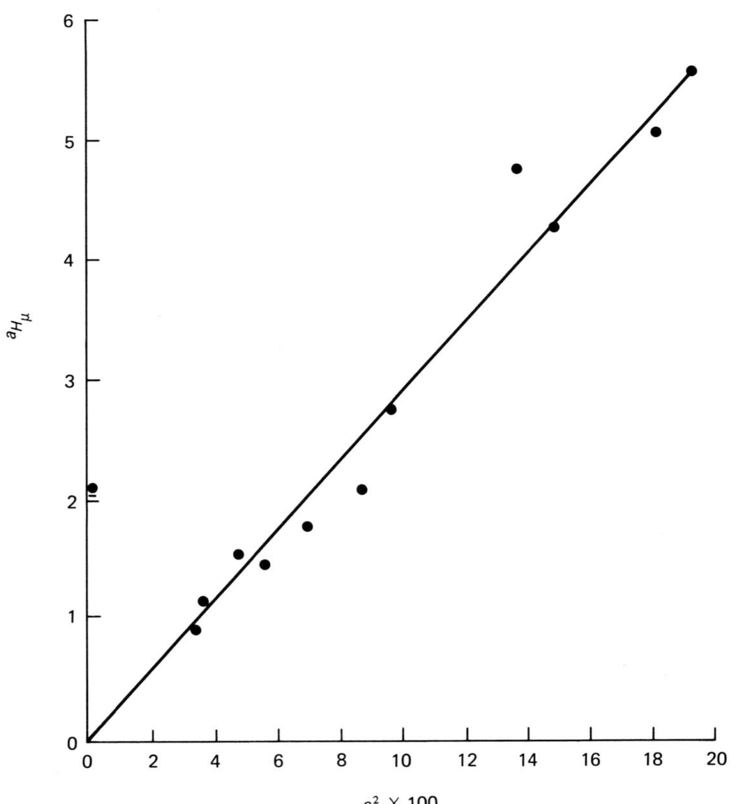

FIG. 8-18 ESR splitting constants a_{H_μ} versus HMO unpaired spin densities. The systems are fused ring alternant hydrocarbon radical anions (naphthalene, anthracene, tetracene, pyrene). The underlined point is thought to result from negative spin density. (Data from Streitwieser [3].)

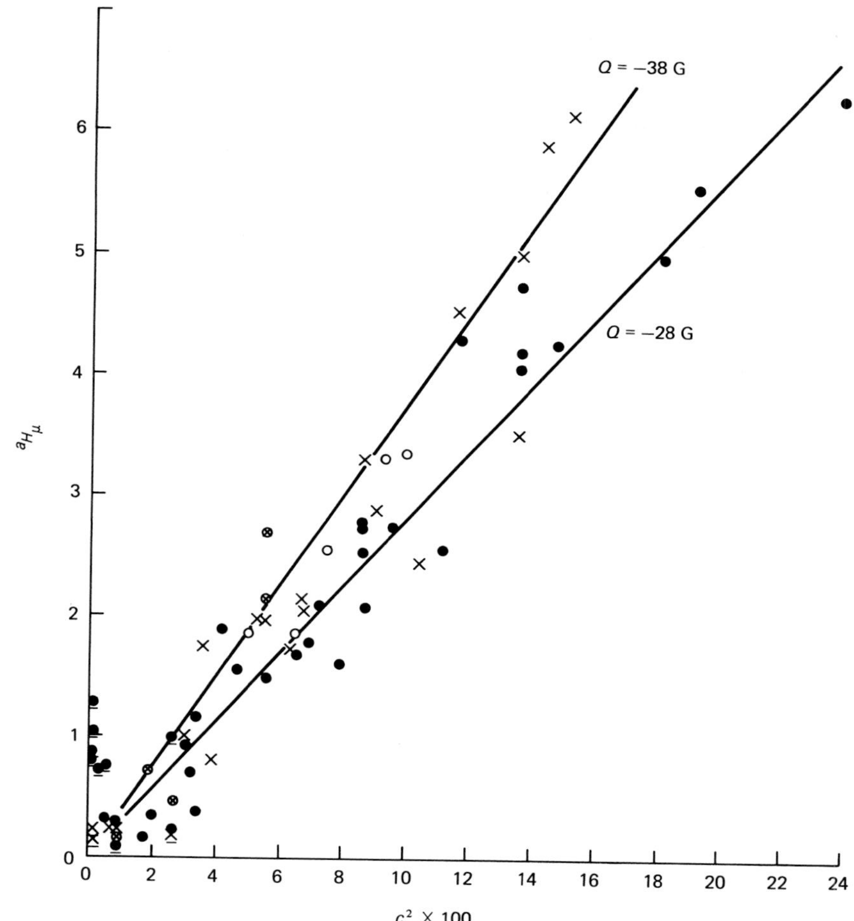

FIG. 8-19 ESR hyperfine splitting constants versus c^2 for the highest occupied MO of the radical. All data are from hydrocarbon radical anions or cations of alternant or nonalternant type. (●) Anion radical; (×) cation radical. Uncertain assignments: (○) anion; (⊗) cation. The two correlation lines are merely sight fitted to the anion and cation points separately and suggest that Q for cations should be larger than for anions. Points thought to result from negative spin density are underlined. [See Tables I, III, VIII, XII, XIII, XIV, XV, XVI, XVII, XVIII of Gerson and Hammons [9], and Table 6.2 of Streitwieser [3] for data plotted here.]

amount of splitting seen in ESR spectra depends only on the *magnitudes* of spin densities at the protons, not on whether these spin densities are α or β, and the presence of negative spin density does not produce a *qualitative* change in an ESR spectrum (such as a "negative splitting," whatever that might be). Rather it leads to an increase in the total *amount* of spin density in the system, and this, in turn, leads to an increase in the sum of splitting constants (over what would be predicted in the absence of negative spin density). For example, the HMO prediction for allyl radical would give a net spin density of $\frac{1}{2}$ at each terminal carbon and zero at the central carbon. [The odd electron is in the nonbonding MO $(1/\sqrt{2})\chi_1 - (1/\sqrt{2})\chi_3$.] However, we might imagine the situation wherein there is a net spin of $\frac{2}{3}\alpha$ at each terminal carbon and $\frac{1}{3}\beta$ at the central atom. This retains a net spin value of 1α yet results in a larger splitting constant $a_{H\mu}$ for every proton in the molecule. It is possible to think of a physical explanation for this kind of spin distribution. The π electrons in lower-energy, filled MOs are being spin polarized similarly to the σ electrons mentioned earlier. If an α-spin electron in effect repels electrons of β spin more strongly than those of α spin, a buildup of β spin on the central carbon of allyl radical could be expected. Because this secondary effect is expected to be fairly small, a *net* negative spin density is likely only on carbons where the primary effect ($c_{\mu m}^2$) is zero or quite small. Methods for calculating this spin polarization (which will not be described here) indicate that certain of the splitting constants plotted in Figs. 8-18 and 8-19 do in fact result from negative spin densities. These data points are indicated in the figures, and it can be seen that they do indeed occur where $c_{\mu m}^2$ and $a_{H\mu}$ are small. This secondary effect is masked at higher values of $c_{\mu m}^2$ and $a_{H\mu}$, but presumably accounts for some of the scatter in the data. (Some scatter also results from solvent dependence of $a_{H\mu}$. Several solvents were used in experiments yielding the data in Fig. 8-19.)

Because of the pairing-theorem relation between coefficients of MOs, the ESR spectra of the radical cation and anion of an alternant system should appear very similar. Hückel molecular orbital theory would predict them to be identical except for a slight change of scale due to a change in the factor Q. In practice, this similarity has been observed to hold fairly well.

8-14 Orbital Energies and Oxidation–Reduction Potentials

Many conjugated hydrocarbons can be oxidized or reduced in solution using standard electrochemical techniques. Since oxidation involves removing an electron from the highest occupied (π) MO (HOMO), it is reasonable to expect molecules with lower-lying HOMOs to have larger oxidation potentials. Similarly, we might expect reduction to be easier for compounds wherein the lowest unoccupied MO (LUMO) is lower in energy [see (**XI**)]. Thus, compound A should have a lower oxidation potential than compound B since $E_m{}^A > E_m{}^B$, but compound B should have the lower reduction potential. A plot of oxidation potential versus E_m in units of β for a series of aromatic hydrocarbons (Fig. 8-20) yields a correlation which is remarkably free of scatter. Figure 8-21 indicates a similar correlation for reduction potential versus E_{m+1}.

Since oxidation–reduction potentials correlate with HOMO–LUMO energies, and since these energies are paired in even alternant systems, we

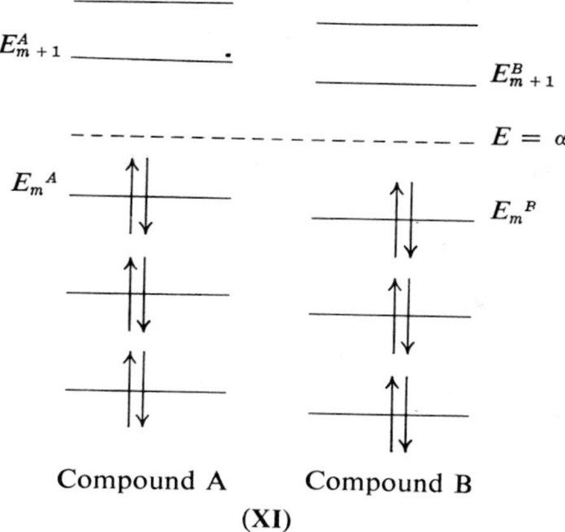

(XI)

should expect a plot of oxidation vs reduction potential for such compounds to be linear also.

The data in Figs. 8-20 and 8-21 provide a connection between theoretical energy differences in units of β, and experimental energies. From the slope in Fig. 8-20 we obtain that $\beta \cong -2.03$ eV, or -46.8 kcal/mole. Similarly, the reduction potential data of Fig. 8-21 gives $\beta = -2.44$ eV $= -56.3$ kcal/mole.

One must be cautious in interpreting the above values of β. The problem is that the experimental numbers include effects of physical processes not included in the theory. For example, when a neutral molecule in solvent becomes oxidized or reduced, solvation energy changes occur. One might argue that the fit of the data to straight lines in Figs. 8-20 and 8-21 implies this sort of contribution to be small, but the sensitivity of redox potentials to solvent nature indicates that this is not the case. However, in larger molecules, solvation energy change upon ionization tends to be smaller, and larger molecules also tend to have E_m and E_{m+1} closer to the $E = \alpha$ level. In other words, we expect both solvation energy change *and* redox potential to be proportional to E_m or E_{m+1}. Therefore, they can be combined in a single linear relation. There is, in general, no guarantee that "extra" contributing effects will be of a nature to be correctly assimilated into the theoretical formula, but, for this effect, it happens that this is at least partially the case.

Another extra effect to consider is the π-electron repulsion energy. Because the energies of the HOMO and LUMO are both associated with the neutral molecule, their energies fail to reflect the decrease or increase of π-electron repulsion energy resulting from loss or gain of a π electron. Here again, however, we expect the magnitude of the effect to be larger for smaller molecules, where the change in π densities is greatest, and also where E_m and E_{m+1} deviate most from α. Thus, as before, this extra effect will not necessarily upset the linear relation expected from simpler considerations.

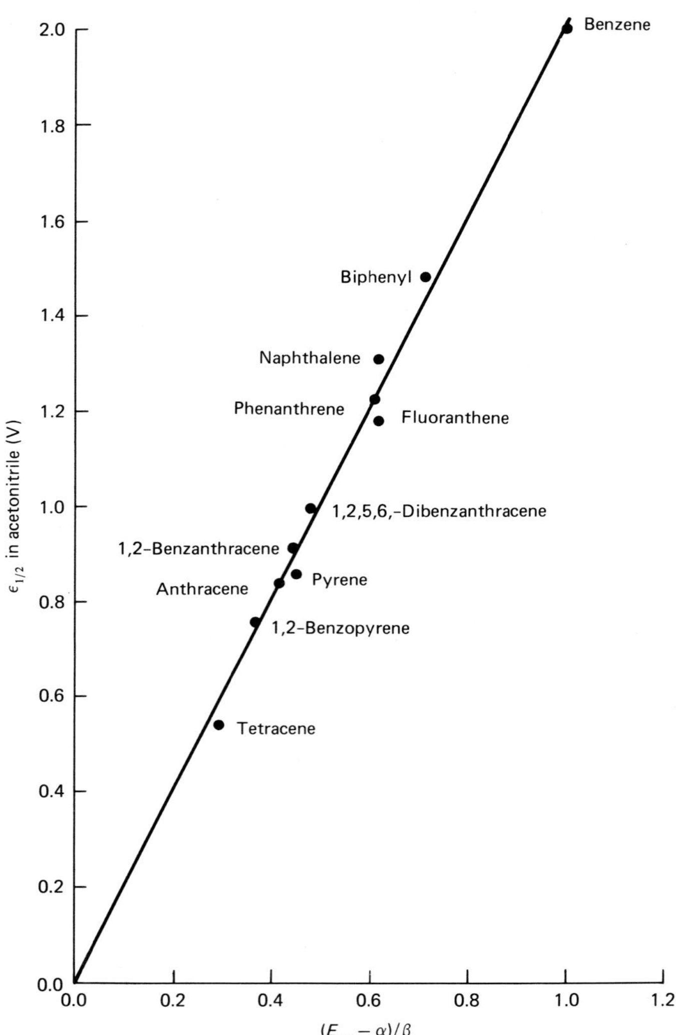

FIG. 8-20 Oxidation potentials in acetonitrile solution versus energy of HOMO (in units of β). ($\epsilon_{1/2}$ from Lund [10].)

In view of the crudity of the HMO method together with the fact that the empirical value of β includes the effects of several extra processes, the β values cited above for oxidation and reduction are considered to be in fairly good agreement.

8-15 Orbital Energies and Ionization Potentials

Suppose that monochromatic light is beamed into a gaseous sample of a compound. If the light is of sufficient energy, electrons will be "knocked out"

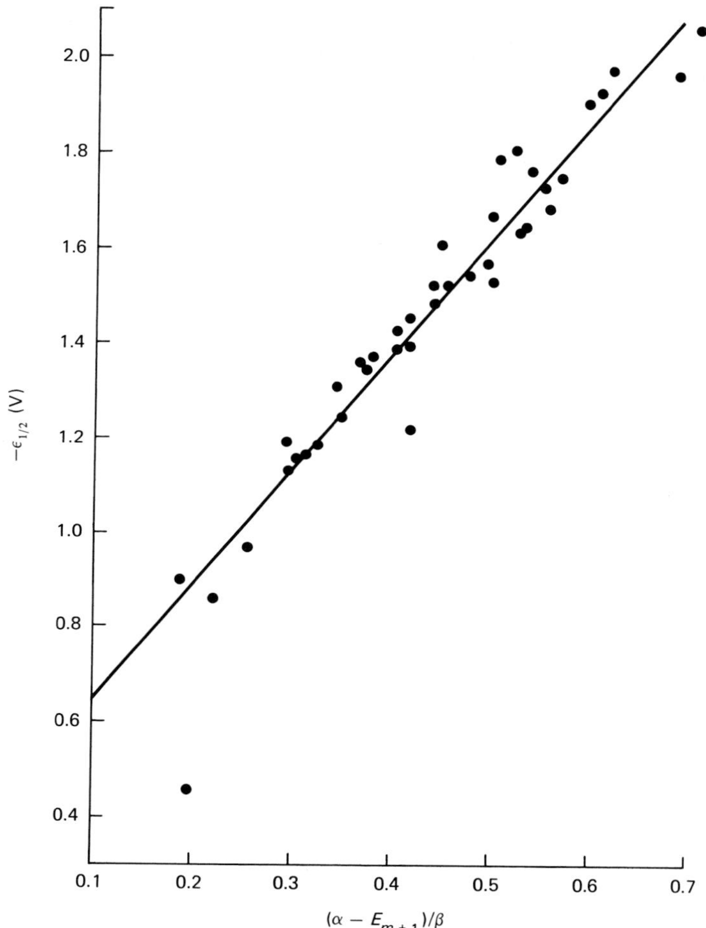

FIG. 8-21 First reduction potential in 2-methoxyethanol versus energy of LUMO (in units of β). ($\epsilon_{1/2}$ from Bergman [11].)

of the molecules. The kinetic energy of such a photoelectron will be equal to the kinetic energy of the incident photon ($h\nu$) minus the energy needed to remove the electron from the molecule, that is, the ionization potential. Measurement of the kinetic energies of photoelectrons emitted in this manner is known as "photoelectron spectroscopy" [12].

In measuring the kinetic energies of photoelectrons from, say, benzene, it is found that a large number are near a particular energy value, another large number of electrons are near a different value, and so on for several kinetic energy values. Because the electrons tend to clump near several kinetic energy values, it follows that we are, in effect, measuring several ionization potentials. It is reasonable to associate these with removal of electrons from different MOs

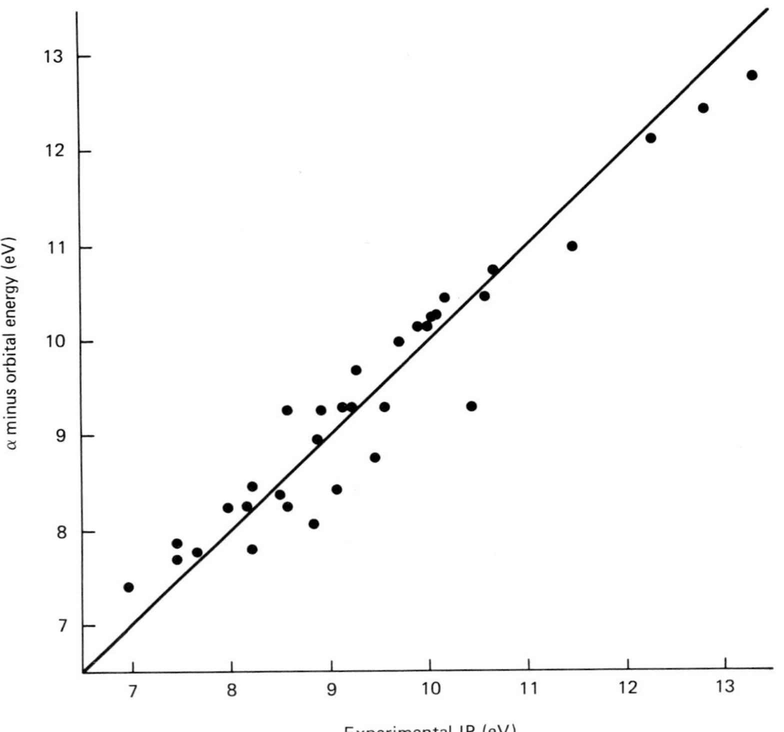

FIG. 8-22 Experimental ionization potentials for alternant and nonalternant hydrocarbons versus HMO orbital energies using $\alpha = -6.553$ eV, $\beta = -2.734$ eV.

of the molecule.[11] A correlation plot (Fig. 8-22) between HMO orbital energies and experimentally measured ionization potentials for a number of alternant and nonalternant hydrocarbons has been produced by Brogli and Heilbronner [13]. Their best fit was achieved using $\alpha = -6.553 \pm 0.340$ eV, $\beta = -2.734 \pm 0.333$ eV, where the limits define a range for the predicted ionization potential (IP) that will include the experimental value nine times out of ten (a 90% confidence level). There is a fair degree of scatter in the correlation plot. By making some additional refinements in the theory, Brogli and Heilbronner succeeded in substantially improving the correlation. We will describe this refinement in Section 8-18.

In this section, we have dealt only with ionization potentials assigned to removal of a π electron. Removal of electrons from σ orbitals is also observed. If the impinging photons are of X-radiation frequencies, the inner shell electron

[11] Note that each ionization potential is associated with removal of an electron from a different MO of the *neutral* molecule. This differs from the first, second, etc. ionization potentials produced by *successive* ionization.

ionization potentials are seen. Quantum-chemical treatments of these ionization potentials are possible using theoretical methods described later.

8-16 π-Electron Energy and Aromaticity

When propene is hydrogenated to form propane, the increase in heat content ΔH°_{298} (called the *heat of hydrogenation*) is -30.1 kcal/mole. The heat of hydrogenation for 1-butene is -30.3 kcal/mole. In general, the heat of hydrogenation of an isolated double bond is about -30 kcal/mole. A similar constancy holds for the contribution of a double bond to the heat of formation of a molecule. Therefore, isolated double bonds fit easily into the usual chemical device of estimating the energy of a molecule by adding together contributions from the substituent parts. This additivity appears to be violated when double bonds are conjugated. Thus, the heat of hydrogenation for *trans*-1,3-butadiene is -57.1 kcal/mole compared with the value of -60.6 kcal/mole for a pair of butene double bonds. Since the hydrogenation product in each case is butane, the energy difference of 3.5 kcal/mole must be due to the greater stability of conjugated double bonds.

There is a theoretical parallel to this. The HMO energy for butadiene is $4\alpha + 4.472\beta$. For a pair of *isolated* double bonds, we double the energy of ethylene to obtain $4\alpha + 4\beta$. Therefore, the HMO method indicates that the conjugated double bonds are stabilized by 0.472β.

Because the π electrons in butadiene are delocalized over all three C–C bonds, this 0.472β has often been referred to as *delocalization energy*. It has been common practice for many years to equate this theoretical delocalization energy for a molecule to its experimentally measured "extra" stability (e.g., for butadiene, $0.472|\beta| = 3.5$ kcal/mole).

More recently, Dewar and co-workers [14, Chapter 5; 15; 16] have demonstrated that conjugated double bonds may be successfully included in an additivity scheme. Hess and Schaad [17, 18] have considered this idea in the context of the HMO method. They distinguish between several kinds of C–C single and double bond energy as indicated in Table 8-2. Using these values of bond energy, the π energy of butadiene is calculated to be $2 \times 2.000\beta + 0.4660\beta + 4\alpha = 4\alpha + 4.4660\beta$ compared with the HMO result of $4\alpha + 4.472\beta$. The error is 0.006β, less than 0.002β per π electron. Hess and Schaad show that this level of agreement holds for acyclic polyenes in general, even when there is much branching. Thus, it seems that conjugated double bonds in acyclic molecules fit into an additivity scheme after all.

There is an important difference between the energy additivity scheme for conjugated systems described above and the familiar additivity scheme used for C—H, C—C, and isolated C=C bonds. In the latter cases the energy "contributed" by the bond is generally thought of as being the same as the energy of that bond in the molecule (at least in an averaged way—some care must be

TABLE 8–2
π- Bond Types and Effective Binding Energies for Carbon–Carbon Double and Single Bonds[a]

Bond type		Effective binding energy in units of β
C H C=C H H		2.0000
C C C=C H H	(*cis* or *trans*)	2.0699
C H C=C C H		2.0000
C C C=C C H		2.1083
C C C=C C C		2.1716
H H C—C C(=) (=)C	(*cis* or *trans*)	0.4660
C(=) H C—C C (=)C	(*cis* or *trans*)	0.4362
C(=) (=)C C—C C C	(*cis* or *trans*)	0.4358

[a] The numbers associated with these bonds are not unique. They satisfy six simultaneous equations. Hence, any two of them may be given arbitrary values and the remaining six found by solving the simultaneous equations. Different arbitrary assignments lead to different sets of numbers, all equally valid and all giving identical pi-electron energies. These numbers can only be applied when a bond has an unambiguous formal identity, which means we must deal with acyclic polyenes (even number of centers and electrons).

exercised with definitions), and, furthermore, the bond is thought to be fairly independent of the identity of the molecule. For instance, a C—H bond in butane is very similar to one in heptane. But this is not the case for conjugated molecules. Inspection of Fig. 8-23 shows that a single bond between (formal) double bonds varies significantly in bond order from molecule to molecule. Since the total π-electron energy depends on bond order [Eq. (8-58)], we can tell at once that the *actual* theoretical energy contribution due to such a single

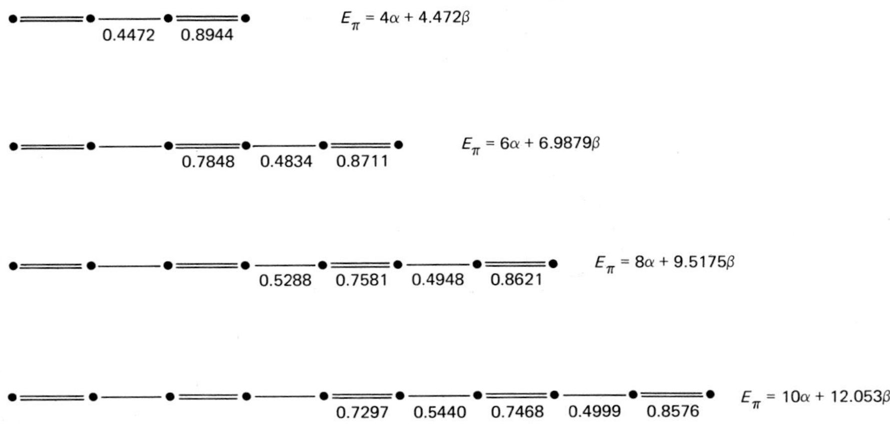

FIG. 8-23 HMO bound orders for butadiene, hexatriene, octatetraene, and decapentaene.

bond varies from 0.8944β in butadiene to 1.088β in decapentaene. However, examination of Fig. 8-23 reveals that, in going from molecule to molecule, as the "single" bonds increase in π-bond order, the "double" bonds decrease in order. Thus, adding an additional C=C—C group to a chain adds a constant amount of bond energy (about 2.54β) to the total π energy, but this energy increment contains contributions from bond order changes over the whole molecule. We have, then, an *additive* scheme for a *delocalized* effect. For this reason, the bond energy contributions of Table 8-2 are called *effective* bond energies.

We are now in a position to consider the concept of aromaticity. The term "aromatic" originally referred to organic molecules having pleasant odors. Later it referred to a class of molecules having a high degree of unsaturation. Benzene was recognized as the parent compound for many such molecules, and the term "aromatic" has come to mean "having chemical properties peculiar to benzene and some of its relatives." The chemical stability of these molecules, their relatively low heats of combustion or of hydrogenation, and their tendency to prefer substitution rather than addition (thereby preserving their π systems intact) distinguish these molecules from ordinary polyenes and have come to be called "aromatic properties," or manifestations of "aromaticity."[12] These properties suggest that the π electrons in aromatic systems are unusually low in energy, contributing to both the thermodynamic and the kinetic stability of the systems. We can test whether this is the case by calculating an "expected" π energy for benzene using the bond energies of Table 8-2 and an alternating single-double bond, or Kekulé, structure. The result, $6\alpha + 7.61\beta$, is significantly

[12] The definition of the term "aromatic" is not generally agreed upon. This is partly due to the fact that some molecules are "like benzene" in some properties, "unlike benzene" in others. For discussion of this problem see Bergmann and Pullman [19].

less stable (by 0.39β) than the HMO energy of $6\alpha + 8\beta$. We shall refer to this difference as the "resonance energy" (RE) of the system.

$$\mathrm{RE} = E_\pi(\mathrm{HMO}) - E_\pi \ (\text{from Table 8-1}) \tag{8-63}$$

By this definition, a positive RE (in units of β) corresponds to extra molecular stabilization. If we divide the RE by the number of π electrons, we obtain the RE per electron (REPE). Hence, the REPE for benzene is 0.065β. Following Dewar we shall refer to a system having significantly positive REPE as "aromatic", significantly negative REPE as "antiaromatic," and negligible REPE as nonaromatic, or polyolefinic. (Recall that β is a negative quantity. When REPE is tabulated in eV, it is conventional to use the absolute value of β in eV so as to retain positive REPE for "aromatic" molecules.)

Cyclic polyenes differ from acyclic polyenes in that many of them show significant values for REPE. Some results of Schaad and Hess [18] are reproduced in Fig. 8-24. It is evident that a strong correlation exists between REPE and the presence or absence of aromatic properties.

The change from very aromatic to very antiaromatic nature as we go from a six-membered to a four-membered system is striking. If we examine the HMO energy levels, it is not difficult to see why these monocycles are so different. The six π electrons in benzene all occupy bonding MOs, whereas cyclobutadiene has two nonbonding electrons (**XII**). The situation is optimal for benzene not

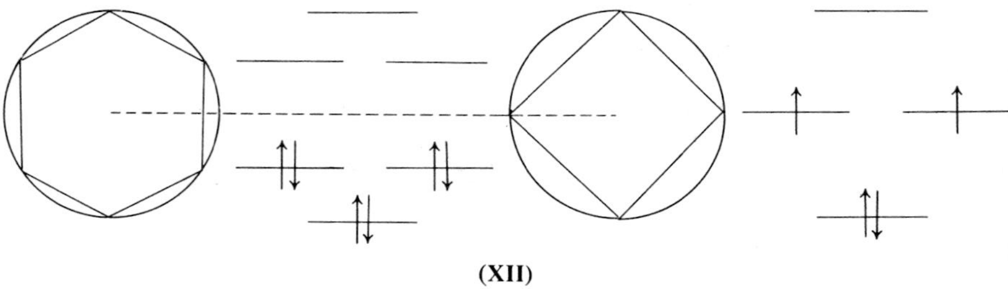

(XII)

only because all its π electrons are bonding, but also because all the bonding levels are fully occupied. Because all monocycles have a nondegenerate lowest level followed by higher-energy pairs of degenerate levels, it is not hard to

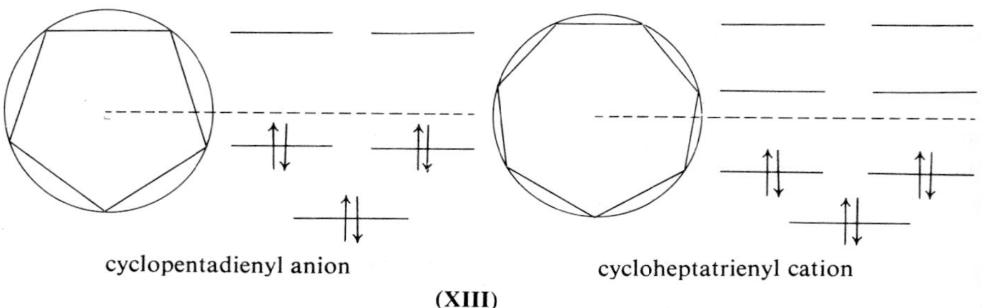

(XIII)

Molecule	REPE (eV) ($\|\beta\| = 1.4199$ eV)	*Chemical properties*
	0.092	Very stable; Undergoes substitution only under forcing conditions
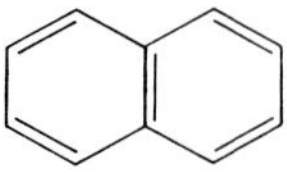	0.078	
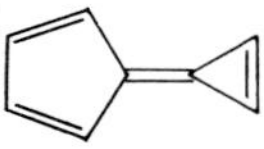	0.061	Simple derivatives isolated; undergo electrophilic substitution
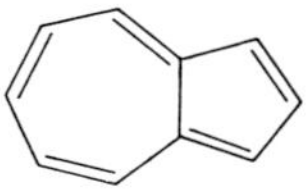	0.032	Known, stable compound
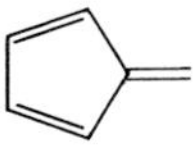	-0.003	Isolated, but reactive
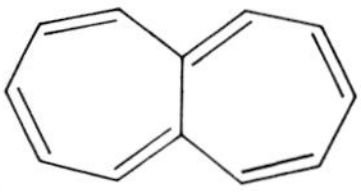	-0.006	Isolated, but reactive
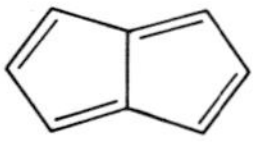	-0.026	Me derivative observed spectroscopically at $-196°C$
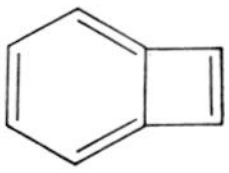	-0.038	Never prepared
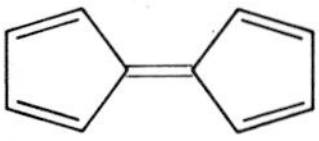	-0.047	Prepared in very dilute solution; extremely reactive
	-0.381	Prepared at 8°K, vanished at 35°K

FIG. 8–24 Resonance energy per electron for a number of molecules. (From Schaad and Hess [18].)

describe the conditions that should produce maximum stability. There should be $4n + 2$ electrons (2 for the lowest level and 4 for each of the n higher bonding levels), and there should be more than $4n$ centers (either $4n + 1$, $4n + 2$, or $4n + 3$) to force the n doubly degenerate levels to all be bonding. The stability of cyclopentadienyl anion (6 electrons, 5 centers) and cycloheptatrienyl cation (6 electrons, 7 centers) was correctly predicted from these simple considerations (**XIII**). Extensive research has gone on in efforts to find examples where $n \neq 1$, but results are often complicated by angle strain and deviation from planarity in the molecule.[13]

[13] See Breslow [20, p. 90].

In a molecule containing both cyclic and acyclic parts, does the RE arise only from the cyclic part? For certain cases, the answer is yes. Dewar has recognized that side or connecting chains contribute nothing to the RE of a system when the chain in question is the same in all formal structures for the molecule. For example, stilbene can be written in four equivalent formal ways, as shown below. The linking chain is identical in all cases, and it should not

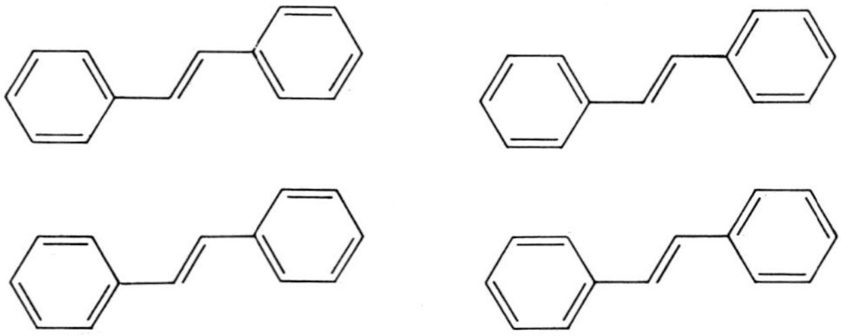

(XIV)

contribute to the RE. Calculations confirm that the RE for stilbene is just double that for benzene.

The intimate relation between aromaticity and the possibility for more than one equivalent formal structure for a molecule has long been recognized. These "mobile" bonds tend to favor equal bond lengths in contrast to the strong alternation characteristic of acyclic polyenes. In benzene, the extra stabilization may be viewed as resulting from the fact that all six bonds are identical and have a higher bond order (0.667) than the average for double and single acyclic bonds. In antiaromatic cyclobutadiene, the four identical bonds have a bond order of 0.5, which is significantly below the average for acyclics. The very different bond orders in these two molecules is fully consistent with the energy argument based on the $4n + 2$ rule described earlier.[14]

To summarize, the π bonds in acyclic polyenes exhibit *delocalization* in the sense that bond orders are not transferable from one molecule to another, *additivity* in *effective* bond energies, *immobility* in formal bonds. Cyclic molecules do *not* exhibit additivity of effective energies or immobility of formal bonds. Their energy deviations from energy calculated assuming additivity and immobility are good indicators of kinetic and thermodynamic stability. Aromatic molecules

[14] It has been noted that bond length equalization associated with bond mobility results in π energy lowering when the C–C–C angles are near 120°. When the angle is very different from this, π energies are higher than expected. This has led to suggestions that "strain energy" may be an important factor in aromaticity. Because of the present lack of a quantum mechanical quantity equivalent to strain energy, and because the HMO method may include effects of σ electrons in an implicit but poorly understood way, it is very hard to know whether such suggestions are at variance with other statements or are simply equivalent to them but stated from a different viewpoint.

possess extra stability because their π electrons[15] are more bonding than those in acyclic polyenes. Antiaromatics are unstable because their π electrons are less bonding.

From a consideration of experimental heats of atomization, Schaad and Hess have evaluated β to be -1.4199 eV. The physical processes involved in dissociating a gas-phase molecule into constituent atoms are quite different from those involved in adding or removing a π electron from a molecule in a solvent. Therefore, it is not surprising that the β value obtained from heats of atomization differs substantially from values obtained from redox experiments. Indeed, it is this variability of β as we compare HMO theory with different types of experiment that compensates for many of the oversights and simplifications of the approach. It is remarkable that, with but one such parameter, HMO theory does as well as it does.

8-17 Extension to Heteroatomic Molecules

The range of application of the HMO method could be greatly extended if atoms other than carbon could be treated. Consider pyridine as an example (**XV**). A π electron at a carbon atom contributes an energy α to E_π. The contribution

(XV)

due to a π electron at nitrogen is presumably something different. Let us take it to be $\alpha' = \alpha + h\beta$, where h is a parameter that will be fixed by fitting theoretical results to experiment. If the π electron is attracted more strongly to nitrogen than to carbon, h will be a positive number. In a similar spirit, we will take the energy of a π electron in a C–N bond to be $\beta' = k\beta$ and evaluate k empirically. Not surprisingly, the values of h and k appropriate for various heteroatoms depend somewhat on which molecules and properties are used in the evaluation procedure. A set of values compiled and critically discussed by Streitwieser [4] is given in Table 8-3. Other sets have been published.[16]

The dots over each symbol indicate the number of π electrons contributed by the atom. In pyridine, the formal bond diagram indicates a six π-electron system, implying that the nitrogen atom contributes one π electron. We also

[15] It is not necessarily true that all the "extra" stability of aromatic molecules is attributable to π-electron effects; σ-Electron energies also depend on bond lengths and bond angles. Hence, we may be seeing, once again, a situation where the π-electron treatment includes other effects implicitly. Hess and Schaad [18] indicate that σ energies and π energies are indeed simply related over the bond-length range of interest.

[16] See McGlynn *et al.* [21, p. 87].

TABLE 8-3
Parameters for Heteroatoms in the Hückel Method[a]

Heteroatom	h	Heteroatomic bond	k
$\dot{\text{N}}$	0.5	$\text{C}\overset{..}{=}\dot{\text{N}}$	1.0
$\ddot{\text{N}}$	1.5	$\text{C—}\ddot{\text{N}}$	0.8
$\overset{+}{\text{N}}$	2.0		
$\dot{\text{O}}$	1.0	$\text{C=}\dot{\text{O}}$	1.0
$\ddot{\text{O}}$	2.0	$\text{C—}\ddot{\text{O}}$	0.8
$\overset{+}{\text{O}}$	2.5	$\text{N—}\ddot{\text{O}}$	0.7
$\ddot{\text{F}}$	3.0	$\text{C—}\ddot{\text{F}}$	0.7
$\ddot{\text{Cl}}$	2.0	$\text{C—}\ddot{\text{Cl}}$	0.4
$\ddot{\text{Br}}$	1.5	$\text{C—}\ddot{\text{Br}}$	0.3
S′[b]	0.0	C—S′	0.8
S″	0.0	C—S″	0.8
		S′—S″	1.0
Methyl (inductive $\dot{\text{C}}_\alpha$—Me)	$-0.5 = h_{c_\alpha}$	C—Me	0.0
Methyl (heteroatom $\dot{\text{C}}_\alpha$—$\ddot{\text{M}}$e)	$0.2 = h_{\text{Me}}$	C_α—Me	0.7
Methyl (conjugative $\dot{\text{C}}_\alpha$—C$\overset{..}{\equiv}$H$_3$)	$-0.1 = h_{c_\alpha}$	C_α—C	0.8
	$-0.1 = h_c$	C—H$_3$	3.0
	$-0.5 = h_{\text{H}3}$		

[a] Consistent with the philosophy of this approach is a distinction between single, double, and intermediate C—C bonds. Streitwieser recommends $k_{\text{C—C}} = 0.9$, $k_{\text{C}\overset{..}{=}\text{C}} = 1.0$, $k_{\text{C=C}} = 1.1$.

[b] Sulfur is treated as a pair of AOs with a total of two π electrons, i.e., a sulfur in an aromatic ring is *formally* treated as *two* adjacent atoms S′ and S″ with the indicated parameters.

can argue that, of the five valence electrons of nitrogen, two are involved in σ covalent bonds with neighboring carbons, two more are in a σ lone pair, leaving one for the π system. Therefore, the atom parameter to use for this molecule is $h = 0.5$. The pyridine ring, like benzene, admits two equivalent structural formulas, and so the C—N bonds should be intermediate between double and single, symbolized $\text{C}\overset{..}{=}\dot{\text{N}}$ in Table 8-3. Since $k = 1.0$ in this case, $\beta' = \beta$, and pyridine will have an HMO determinant differing from the benzene determinant only in the diagonal position corresponding to the nitrogen atom—the 1,1 position according to our (arbitrary) numbering scheme. For this position, instead of x, we will have

$$x' = (\alpha' - E)/\beta = (\alpha + 0.5\beta - E)/\beta = (\alpha - E)/\beta + 0.5\beta/\beta = x + 0.5 \tag{8-64}$$

The pyrrole molecule has a nitrogen atom of the type $\ddot{\text{N}}$ (XVI). Since three valence electrons of nitrogen are in covalent σ bonds, two remain for inclusion in the π system. Therefore, pyrrole has a total of six π electrons. The unique

(XVI)

structural formula indicates that the C—$\ddot{N}$ bond is formally single, and $k = 0.8$, $h = 1.5$ are the appropriate parameters here. Also, the carbon–carbon bonds are now formally single or double. If we choose to distinguish among these bonds using the parameters in Table 8-3, the resulting HMO determinant is

$$\begin{vmatrix} x+1.5 & 0.8 & 0 & 0 & 0.8 \\ 0.8 & x & 1.1 & 0 & 0 \\ 0 & 1.1 & x & 0.9 & 0 \\ 0 & 0 & 0.9 & x & 1.1 \\ 0.8 & 0 & 0 & 1.1 & x \end{vmatrix}$$

The methyl group can also be incorporated into the HMO method. Several approaches have been suggested. One is simply to modify the coulomb integral α for the carbon to which the methyl group is attached. A methyl group is thought to release sigma electrons to the rest of the molecule as compared to a substituent hydrogen. This suggests that an atom having a methyl group attached to it will be a bit electron rich and hence will be less attractive to π electrons. Use of a negative h parameter for this carbon is appropriate. This method is called the *inductive* model. Use of the inductive model does not add any new centers or any more π electrons to the conjugated system to which the methyl group is attached. The carbon to which the methyl is bonded is merely treated as a heteroatom. A second approach is to treat the methyl group itself as a heteroatom. As we shall see shortly, the methyl group has two electrons that can participate (to a slight extent) in the π system, and so use of this *heteroatom* model adds one more center and two more π electrons for each methyl group included in this way. A third approach is the *conjugative* model. Because the methyl group has *local* threefold symmetry, the σ MOs for the methyl group resemble the π MOs of cyclopropenyl in symmetry characteristics. The three types of symmetry solutions are given in Fig. 8-25 for a methyl group on a benzene ring (compare with Fig. 8-7). Notice that the MO at the right of the figure is of the same symmetry as a π AO on the benzene ring. This means that the two electrons in this "methyl group MO" can participate in the π system of the molecule. To emulate this picture in our HMO determinant, we must add two π electrons and two more centers to our system (one for C and one for H_3) and find h and k values for the two new centers and bonds. The inductive effect of the methyl

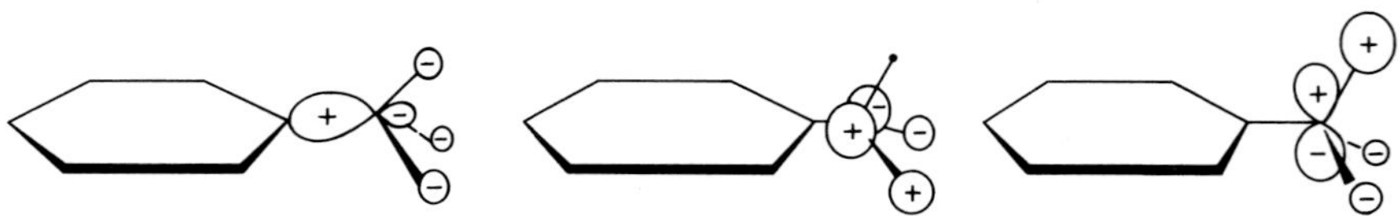

FIG. 8-25 Three MO symmetry solutions for a methyl group attached to a benzene ring.

group on the neighboring ring carbon is often included in this model. In most cases, it is probably safe to say that the conjugative model is superior to the heteroatom model, which is, in turn, better than the inductive model, but no extensive critical comparison of these three models has been made. Parameters for all three approaches are included in Table 8-3. (C_α is the ring carbon.)

8-18 Self-Consistent Variations of α and β

Efforts have been made to improve the HMO method by taking account of molecular π charge distribution. Suppose that we carry out an HMO calculation on a nonalternant molecule and find an electron density of 1.2 at one carbon and 0.8 at another. It is reasonable to argue that a π electron at the latter carbon is more strongly bound because it experiences less repulsion from other π electrons there. We can try to account for this by making α at that atom more negative. Thus, we could take

$$\alpha_i' = \alpha_i + \omega(1 - q_i)\beta \tag{8-65}$$

where q_i is the π-electron density at atom i and ω is a parameter (assumed positive) to be fixed empirically. If $q < 1$, then α' is more negative than α. If $q > 1$, α' is less negative. Having now modified α (using a trial value for ω), we must set up our new HMO determinant and solve it again. This yields new MOs, new values of q_i, and therefore new values of α'. We repeat this process over and over until electron densities remain essentially unchanged for two successive iterations. At this point, the electron densities *leading to* the HMO determinant are the same as those *produced by* the determinant, and the solution is said to be self-consistent with respect to electron densities. This procedure, often referred to as the "ω technique," discourages extreme deviations of electronic densities from the "norm" of unity at each carbon and thereby helps to compensate for the lack of explicit inclusion of pi electron repulsion in the HMO method. Streitwieser's calculations have led him to favor a value of ω of 1.4.

A similar idea has been applied to variations of the bond integral β. Suppose that we carry out an HMO calculation and find a π-bond order of 0.5 in one bond and 0.9 in another. We expect that the latter bond is in fact shorter than the former. We could roughly predict how much shorter it is by using the bond-order–bond-length relation described earlier. It is reasonable to modify β in these bonds on the basis of predicted length differences, set up a new HMO determinant, solve again, find new bond orders, and iterate until self-consistency is achieved with respect to bond orders.

These modifications to the simple HMO method improve predictions of some properties but not others. For example, Brogli and Heilbronner [13] have found that orbital energy correlation with ionization potential is significantly improved through inclusion of the effects of bond length variations in the *neutral molecule and the cation.* This improved correlation, shown in Fig. 8-26, showed no additional improvement upon subsequent variation of α as a function of electron density. On the other hand, π-electron contributions to dipole moments, calculated from electronic excess or deficiency at each center, are very sensitive to variation of α, and quite insensitive to variation of β. However, for most applications of HMO theory, it is probably fair to say that improvements resulting from these methods are modest.

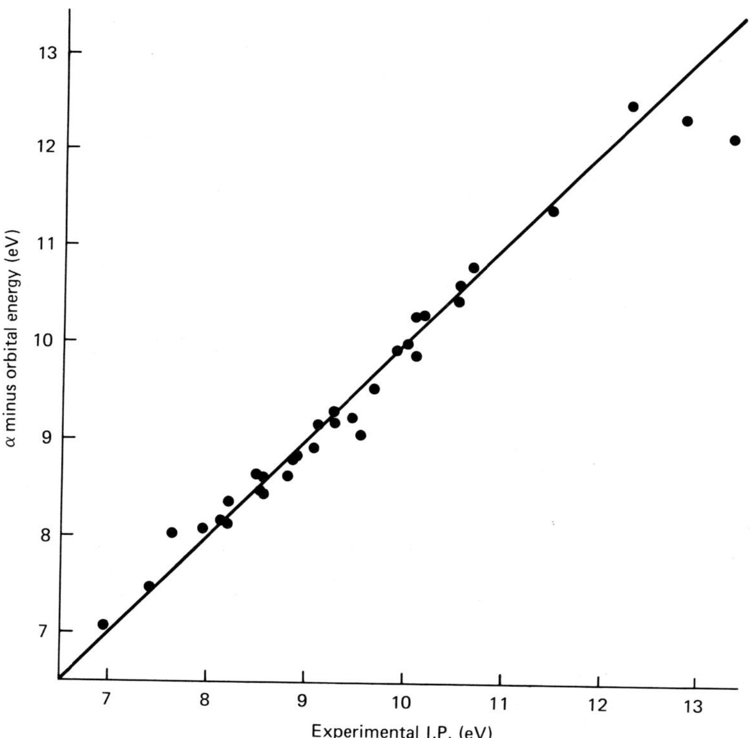

FIG. 8-26 Experimental ionization potential for alternant and nonalternant hydrocarbons versus orbital energy using a modified HMO technique which includes provisions for bond length variation in molecule and cation. (Compare with Fig. 8-22.)

8-19 HMO Reaction Indices

In this section, we discuss some applications of the HMO method to *reactivities* of conjugated molecules. The reactions of conjugated molecules that have received most of this theoretical treatment are:

(1) electrophilic aromatic substitution (**XVII**),

1 2 + Cl_2, $FeCl_3$ $\xrightarrow{k_1}$ Cl + H^+ ; $\xrightarrow{k_2}$ Cl + H^+

(XVII)

(2) nucleophilic aromatic substitution (**XVIII**);

1 2 + CH_3Li $\xrightarrow{k_1}$ CH_3 + LiH ; $\xrightarrow{k_2}$ CH_3 + LiH

(XVIII)

(3) radical addition (**XIX**).

1 2 + $CCl_3^{\bullet}$ $\xrightarrow{k_1}$ CCl_3 H ; $\xrightarrow{k_2}$ CCl_3 H

(XIX)

For any of these reactions, we imagine there to be a path of least energy connecting reactants with products. For the two distinct reaction positions, 1 and 2 on naphthalene, the activation energies ϵ may differ, as indicated in Fig. 8-27.

The problem is somehow to relate the differences in ϵ (inferred from relative rate data) to a number based on quantum chemical calculations. To do this in a sensible way requires that we have some idea of the detailed way in which the reaction proceeds—we have to know what the reaction coordinate is. In some

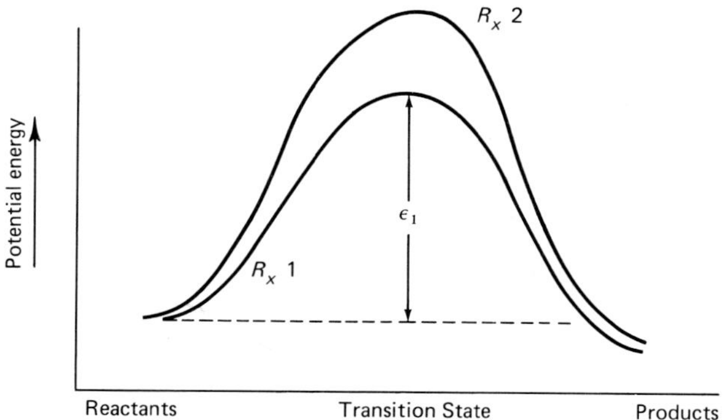

FIG. 8-27 Generalized energy versus reaction coordinate for reaction at two positions in naphthalene.

cases, this is fairly well known. For electrophilic aromatic substitution reactions, evidence suggests that a positive electrophile (e.g., Cl^+) approaches the substrate (say, naphthalene). As it draws closer, it causes a significant polarization of the π-electron charge distribution, drawing it toward the site of attack. Ultimately, it forms a partial bond with the carbon. At this stage, the carbon has already begun to loosen its bond to hydrogen, but it is at least partially bonded to four atoms (**XX**). This means that the ability of the carbon to participate in the

(XX)

aromatic system is temporarily hampered. At this point, the system is at or near the transition state. Thereafter, as H^+ leaves, the potential energy decreases and Cl moves into the molecular plane. A similar detailed mechanism is thought to apply for nucleophilic reactions except that the attacking group is negative.

For attack by a neutral radical, electrostatic attraction and charge polarization should not be significant factors. The radical bonds to the site of attack to produce a more-or-less tetrahedrally bonded carbon. This again leads to an interruption of the π system, but now it is not temporary as it was in the substitution reactions.

Based on these simple pictures, a number of MO quantities, often referred to as *reaction indices*, have been proposed as indicators of preferred sites for reaction. It is useful to divide these into two categories—those purporting to relate to early stages of the reaction, and those specifically related to the intermediate stage.

Perhaps the most obvious reaction index to use for the earliest stages of electrophilic or nucleophilic reactions is the *π-electron density*. If Cl^+ is attracted to π charge, it should be attracted most to those sites where π density is greatest. (Such an ion should be attracted to sites having excessive σ charge density also, but our basic HMO assumptions ignore any variations in σ density.) For an alternant hydrocarbon like naphthalene, all π densities are unity, so this index is of no use. For nonalternant molecules, however, it can be quite helpful. Azulene has varying HMO π densities (**XXI**). (More sophisticated calculations

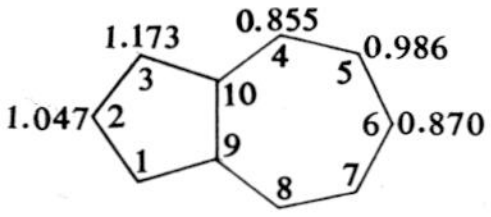

1.173 0.855 0.986 1.047 0.870

(XXI)

described in future chapters are in qualitative agreement with these π-electron density variations.) Experimentally, it is found that electrophilic substitution by Cl occurs almost entirely at position 1 (or 3). Nucleophilic substitution by CH_3 (from CH_3Li) occurs at the position of least π-electron density, namely 4 (or 8).

The charge density index refers to the nature of the molecule before allowance is made for perturbing effects due to the approaching reactant. Such a method is often called a "first-order" method, a terminology that is discussed more fully in Chapter 12. For alternant molecules, it is necessary to proceed to a higher-order method, one that reflects the ease with which molecular charge is drawn toward some atom, or pushed away from it, as approach by a charged chemical reactant makes that atom more or less attractive for electrons. An index which measures this is called *atom self-polarizability*, symbolized $\pi_{r,r}$. The formulas for this and related polarizabilities are derived in Chapter 12. For now, we simply note that the formula is

$$\pi_{r,r} \equiv \partial q_r/\partial \alpha_r = 4 \sum_{j}^{\text{occ}} \sum_{k}^{\text{unocc}} c_{rj}^2 c_{rk}^2/(E_j - E_k) \tag{8-66}$$

A larger absolute value of $\pi_{r,r}$ means that a larger change in π density q_r occurs as a result of making atom r more or less attractive for electrons. ($\pi_{r,r}$ is negative since $E_j - E_k$ is negative. This makes physical sense because it means that if $\delta\alpha_r$ is negative, making atom r more attractive, δq_r is positive, indicating that charge accumulates there.) Since the most polarizable site should most easily accommodate either a positive- or a negative-approaching reactant, this index should apply for both electrophilic and nucleophilic reactions. For naphthalene, the values are $\pi_{11} = -0.433/|\beta|$, $\pi_{22} = -0.405/|\beta|$. This agrees with the experimentally observed fact that the 1 position of naphthalene is more reactive for both types of reaction.

Examination of Eq. (8-66) indicates that the MOs near the energy gap between filled and empty MOs will tend to contribute most heavily to $\pi_{r,r}$ because, for these, $E_j - E_k$ is smallest. For this reason, the highest occupied and lowest unfilled MO (HOMO and LUMO) are often the determining factor in relative values of π_{rr}. Fukui[17] named these the *frontier orbitals* and suggested that electrophilic substitution would occur preferentially at the site where the HOMO had the largest squared coefficient. In nucleophilic substitution, the approaching reagent seeks to *donate* electronic charge to the substrate, so here the largest squared coefficient for the LUMO should determine the preferred site. For even alternants like naphthalene, the pairing theorem forces these two MOs to have their absolute maxima at the same atom. The HOMO–LUMO coefficients for naphthalene are 0.425 and 0.263 for atoms 1 and 2, respectively, in accord with our expectations. For the nonalternant molecule azulene, discussed above, the largest HOMO coefficient occurs at atoms 1 and 3, which have already been mentioned to be the preferred sites for electrophilic attack. The largest LUMO coefficient occurs at atom 6, with atoms 4 and 8 having the second-largest value (see Appendix 6). Atoms 4 and 8 are the preferred sites for nucleophilic attack. Here, then, is a case where the charge density and frontier MO indices are not in agreement. The results suggest that, when significant π-density variations occur, this factor should be favored over higher-order indices. However, the whole approach is so crude that no ironclad rule can be formulated.

For radical attack, some other index should be used, for we do not expect electrostatic or polarization effects to be important in such reactions. An index called the *free valence*[18] has been proposed for free radical reactions. One assumes that the free radical begins bonding to a carbon atom in early stages of the reaction and that the ease with which this occurs depends on how much residual bonding capacity the carbon has after accounting for its regular π bonds. Thus, free valence is taken to be the difference between the maximum π bonding a carbon atom is capable of and the amount of π bonding it actually exhibits in the unreacted substrate molecule. The extent of π bonding is taken as the sum of all the orders of π bonds involving the atom in question. A common choice for a maximally bonded carbon is the central atom in trimethylenemethane (**XXII**). Each bond in this neutral system has a π-bond order of $1/\sqrt{3}$, and

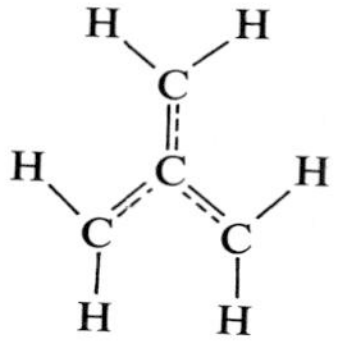

H H
C
C
H H
C C
H H

(**XXII**)

[17] See Fujimoto and Fukui [22].
[18] See Coulson [23].

so the total π-bond order associated with the central carbon is $\sqrt{3}$.[19] Thus, the free valence for some atom r is defined as

$$F_r = \sqrt{3} - \sum_{s}^{\text{neighbors of } r} p_{rs} \tag{8-67}$$

A common way of representing the situation schematically is indicated in (**XXIII**) for butadiene. Bond orders are indicated on the bonds and free valences

$$\begin{array}{cccc} \mathrm{C} \xrightarrow{} \!\!\overset{0.894}{\text{———}}\!\! & \mathrm{C} \overset{0.447}{\text{———}} & \mathrm{C} \text{———} & \mathrm{C} \\ \downarrow & \downarrow & & \\ 0.838 & 0.391 & & \end{array}$$

(XXIII)

by arrows. It is clear that butadiene has a good deal more "residual bonding capacity" on its terminal atoms, and this is consistent with the fact that free radical attack on butadiene occurs predominantly on the end atoms. Other examples of correlation between free valence and rate of free radical addition have been reported.[20] A plot of rate data for methyl radical addition to conjugated molecules versus the largest free valence of the molecule is shown in Fig. 8-28. (We assume that the kinetics is dominated by the atom(s) having the maximum free valence.)

The indices described above are most appropriate for indicating the relative ease of reaction *in the early stages*. By the time the reactants have reached the transition state, the substrate is quite far from its starting condition, so charge densities, polarizabilities, free valences calculated from the wavefunction of the unperturbed molecule may no longer be very appropriate. If the energy curves being compared through our indices behave in the simple manner described in Fig. 8.27, so that the higher-energy curve in early stages is also the higher-energy curve in the region of the transition state, such indices can be useful. Also, such simple behavior is very likely to occur when we compare a single type of reaction down a series of molecules of similar type, as in Fig. 8-28 (see also Problem 8-25). Experience, however, has indicated that indices more closely linked to the nature of the transition state are more generally reliable. We now describe one such reactivity index.

We mentioned earlier that addition and substitution reactions are expected to interrupt the π system at the site of attack. For substitution reactions, this interruption is only temporary and is presumably most severe in the transition state. For addition reactions, it is permanent. The *localization energy* is defined as the π energy lost in this process of interrupting the π system.

As an example, let us return to the naphthalene molecule. The situations resulting from interruption of the π system by *neutral radical* attack at positions

[19] Sometimes the three sigma bonds are included in this calculation, giving $3 + \sqrt{3}$. This has no effect on the question of *relative* values of F_r.

[20] See Streitwieser [3] and Salem [1].

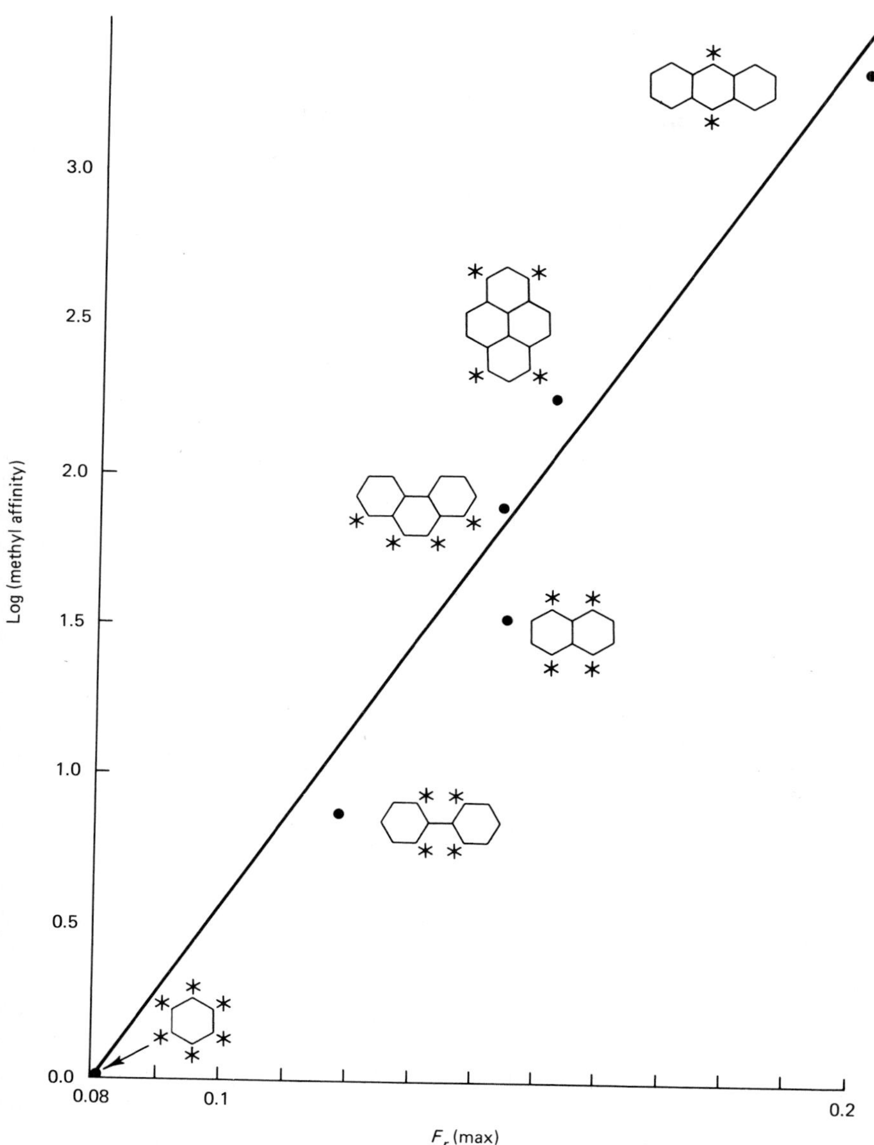

FIG. 8-28 Rate data for methyl radical addition are plotted against the maximum free valence found in each molecule. The original "methyl affinity" (Levy and Szwarc [24]) has been multiplied by $6/m$, where m is the number of sites having maximum free valence. (The asterisks in the figure identify these sites.)

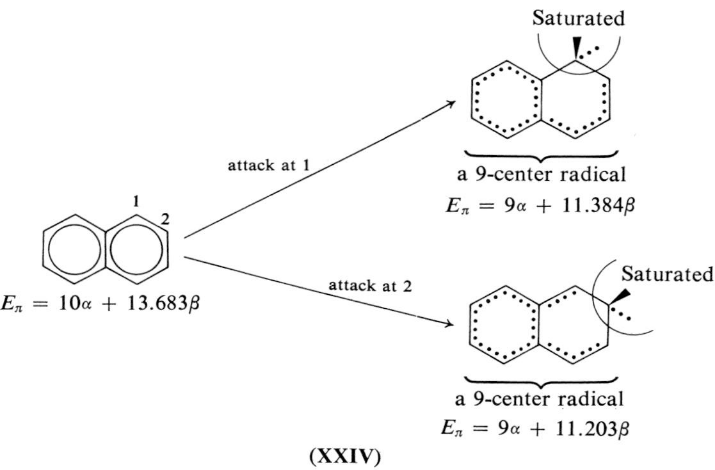

(XXIV)

1 and 2 are illustrated in **(XXIV)**. The remaining unsaturated fragment is, in each case, a neutral radical. [If attack were by a negative ion (nucleophilic), the fragment would be topologically the same but would be negatively charged. Likewise, attack by a positive electrophilic reagent leads to a positively charged fragment.] No matter where attack occurs, our π energy must go from $10\alpha + \cdots \beta$ to $9\alpha + \cdots \beta$. This decrease by α is thus not expected to differ from case to case and hence is ignored in our localization energy calculation. The decrease in π energy is thus $2.299|\beta|$ for attack at position 1 and $2.480|\beta|$ for position two. These localization energies (labeled $L_1^{\bullet}$ and $L_2^{\bullet}$ for the case of radical attack) indicate that attack at position 1 should be favored since the energy cost is smaller there, and this is in accord with observation. (The 1 position is more reactive for all three types of reaction—radical addition, nucleophilic substitution, and electrophilic substitution. See Problem 8-22.)

It is interesting to compare the various indices we have discussed for a single molecule to see how well they agree. Data for azulene are collected in Table 8-4. Experimentally, azulene is known to preferentially undergo electrophilic substitution at positions 1 and 3, nucleophilic substitution at positions 4 and 8, and radical addition in positions 1 and 3. Consider first electrophilic reaction. Examining the table indicates that position 1 is heavily favored by q_r, HOMO distribution, and L_r^+. The only other index relevant for this process, π_{rr}, favors position 4. For nucleophilic reaction, q_r, π_{rr}, L_r^- all favor position 4. The LUMO index favors position 6, but not decisively over position 4. For radical addition, LUMO favors position 6, F_r and $L_r^{\bullet}$ favor position 4. The latter two indices, however, favor 4 over 1 by only a slight margin. Thus, for a nonalternant molecule like azulene, these numbers are not completely trustworthy and must be interpreted with caution. One difference between a molecule like anthracene and one like azulene is that all the C–C–C angles in the former

TABLE 8-4
Reactivity Indices for Azulene

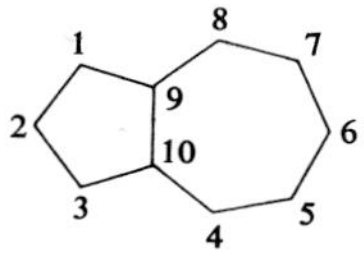

r (atom no)	q_r	$-\lvert\beta\rvert\pi_{r,r}$	HOMO c_r^2	LUMO c_r^2	F_r	$L_r^+(\lvert\beta\rvert)$	$L_r^\cdot(\lvert\beta\rvert)$	$L_r^-(\lvert\beta\rvert)$
1	*1.173*	0.425	*0.2946*	0.0040	0.480	*1.924*	2.262	2.600
2	1.047	0.419	0.0000	0.0997	0.420	2.362	2.362	2.362
4	*0.855*	*0.438*	0.0256	0.2208	*0.482*	2.551	*2.240*	*1.929*
5	0.986	0.429	0.1126	0.0104	0.429	2.341	2.341	2.341
6	0.870	0.424	0.0000	*0.2610*	0.454	2.730	2.359	1.988

molecule are similar (~120°) whereas in azulene they differ. One might anticipate that the smaller angles in the five-membered subunit, being already closer to the tetrahedral angle characteristic of saturated carbons, would allow easier substitution or addition than would be the case in the seven-membered subunit. This factor is ignored in our calculations of L_r and might easily tip the balance to favor position 1 over position 4 for radical attack since $L_1^\cdot$ and $L_4^\cdot$ are so close in value. In short, these HMO reactivity index approaches are once again techniques that ignore many aspects of the physical processes being followed. It seems likely that many of these will cancel out of comparisons among similar molecules, but disimilarities between or within molecules (most often encountered in nonalternant systems) will cause such cancellations to be less complete. For more discussion of these and other HMO reaction indices, the reader is referred to more specialized discussions.[21]

8-20 Conclusions

In this chapter, we have seen how certain basic features of molecular structure manifest themselves in molecular properties. The *connectedness*, or σ bond network, defines the bond positions where π electrons can congregate to lower the energy of the system. The extent of congregation is a useful measure of bond length and also is directly contributory to the total energy of the system. The symmetry restrictions for MOs have been emphasized. The fairly successful correlation of HMO results with certain experimental measurements suggests that the method effectively accounts for the controlling factors in some molecular properties.

But we have omitted discussion of other properties that correlate only poorly with HMO theory. Notable in this regard are spectral energies. The

[21] See Streitwieser [3], Salem [1], Dewar [14], and Klopman [25].

natural idea of relating a spectral transition energy to a difference between orbital energies has not been very successful in HMO theory, except when one restricts attention to a particular band in a series of related molecules. This is at least partly due to improper handling of electron exchange symmetry in the HMO method leading to an inability to distinguish between different states of a given configuration.

The HMO method can be an extremely instructive way to approach a problem since it can describe the manner in which certain important factors are operating. Also, for some situations, its predictive power is rather good. Certainly the successes of this method encourage further theoretical effort. However, the limitation to conjugated systems, the reliance on an increasing number of parameters as extensions are made, the inability to conform to some kinds of experimental measurement, and the conceptual slipperyness of the quantities used in the method have all contributed to a decline of interest in further tinkering with HMO theory. More powerful computers have made it possible for more complicated but better defined methods to be used.

PROBLEMS

8-1 Show that, if $\hat{H} = \hat{H}_1 + \hat{H}_2 + \hat{H}_3$, and $\hat{H}_i\phi_j(i) = E_j\phi_j(i)$, then $\psi_{\text{prod}} = \phi_1(1)\phi_2(2)\phi_3(3)$ and $\psi_{\text{det}} = |\phi_1(1)\phi_2(2)\phi_3(3)|$ are both eigenfunctions of $\hat{H}$ and have the same eigenvalue. Show also that $\psi = (1/\sqrt{2})[\phi_1(1)\phi_2(2)\phi_3(3) + \phi_1(1)\phi_2(2)\phi_4(3)]$ is an eigenfunction of $\hat{H}$ if and only if $E_3 = E_4$.

8-2 Set up the HMO determinant for each of the following molecules:

(a) [structure: cyclobutene ring with two exocyclic =CH₂ groups; atoms labelled H, C—C, C—C, C—H]

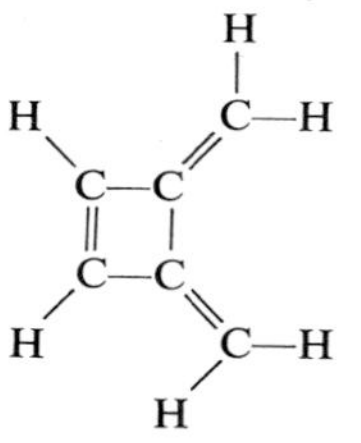

(b) [structure: two cyclopropene rings joined by C=C; atoms labelled H, C, C=C, H]

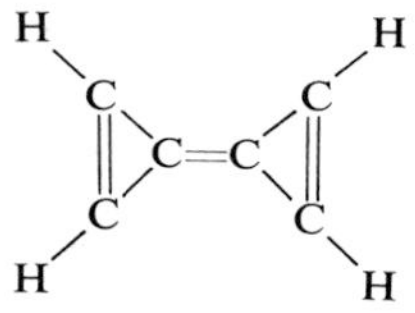

(c) $H_3C—CH_2—CH_2—CH{=}CH_2$ (d) $H_2C{=}CH—CH_2—CH_2—CH{=}CH_2$

(e) $H—C{\equiv}C—H$

8-3 Set up and solve the Hückel determinantal equation for 2-allylmethyl (also called trimethylenemethane) (**XXV**). Display the orbital energy levels and indicate

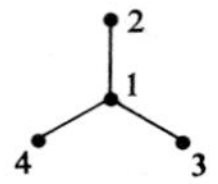

[diagram: central atom 1 bonded to atoms 2, 3, 4]

(**XXV**)

the electron configuration for the neutral ground state. Calculate E_π. Find the coefficients for all MO's. [Be sure that degenerate MOs are orthogonal.] *Calculate* the charge densities and bond orders.

8-4 Suppose that two MOs of a molecule are given by the formulas

$$\phi_1 = (1/\sqrt{3})\chi_1 + (1/\sqrt{3})\chi_2 + (1/\sqrt{3})\chi_3,$$
$$\phi_2 = (1/\sqrt{3})\chi_3 + (1/\sqrt{3})\chi_4 + (1/\sqrt{3})\chi_5,$$

where the χ's are AOs which are assumed to be orthonormal. By inspection, what is the overlap between these MOs?

8-5 Verify for yourself (by trial and error) the last statement of Section 8-7.

8-6 Demonstrate in detail how to obtain Eq. (8-44) from (8-43). Show that the same result occurs if $\psi_\pi = |\phi_1(1)\bar{\phi}_1(2)\phi_2(3)|$.

8-7 What is the Hückel *orbital* energy for the following MO? (Assume that all centers are carbons.) [*Hint:* Use Eq. (8-56).]

c_1	c_2	c_3	c_4	c_5
$\frac{1}{3}$	$\sqrt{\frac{2}{3}}$	0	$-\frac{1}{3}$	$-\frac{1}{3}$

8-8 Without performing an HMO calculation, sketch the MOs for the pentadienyl radical. Use the particle-in-a-box solutions and the pairing theorem as a guide.

8-9 Can you suggest a reason why the HMO method, with the assumption that $H_{ii} = \alpha$ for all i, tends to be more successful with alternant hydrocarbons than with nonalternant ones?

8-10 The bond lengths given in Table P8-10 have been reported for ovalene (**XXVI**). Using a library source or a computer program, obtain HMO bond orders for ovalene and calculate theoretical bond lengths using a relation from Section 8-12. Make a comparison plot for ovalene of the type shown in Fig. 8-16.

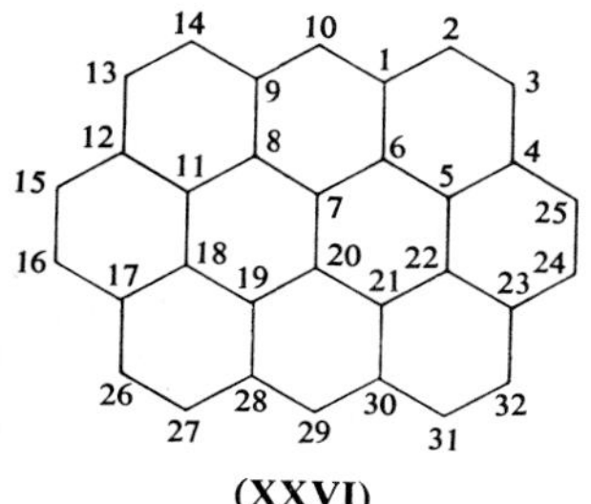

(**XXVI**)

TABLE P8–10

Bond	Length (Å)	Bond	Length (Å)
1–2	1.445	1–10	1.401
2–3	1.354	6–7	1.419
3–4	1.432	4–25	1.411
4–5	1.429	24–25	1.366
5–6	1.429	5–22	1.424
6–1	1.425	7–20	1.435

8-11 Horrocks *et al.* [26] report experimental bond lengths for quinoline complexed to nickel. They display a comparison plot that uses theoretical data from an MO method more refined than the simple HMO method. Using the appropriate hetero-nuclear parameters, perform on the computer an HMO calculation for quinoline. Calculate theoretical C–C bond distances and compare them with the experimental and theoretical data of Horrocks *et al.*

8-12 When the molecule $CH_2{=}CH{-}CH{=}O$ absorbs light of a certain frequency, a lone-pair electron on oxygen (called "n" for "nonbonding") is promoted to the lowest empty π MO of the molecule (called π^*; hence, an $n \rightarrow \pi^*$ transition). Assuming that the π MOs of this molecule are identical to those in butadiene, which C–C bond would you expect to become longer and which shorter as a result of this transition? Calculate the expected bond length changes using butadiene data. (*Observed:* $\Delta CH_2{-}CH \cong +0.06$ Å, $\Delta CH{-}CH \cong -0.04$ Å).

8-13 ESR coupling constants are shown in Table P8-13 for six hydrocarbon anion radicals. Use HMO tabulations in the literature (or a computer) to obtain π-electron MO coefficients for these systems. Construct a plot of coupling constant a_{H_μ} versus $c_{\mu i}^2$, where i is the MO containing the unpaired electron (a_{H_μ} values are in gauss).

TABLE P8-13

Structure	Coupling constants
	3.75
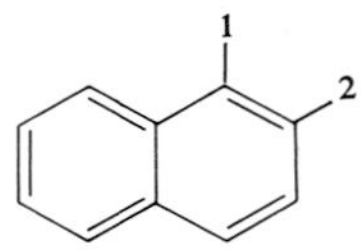	5.01 1.79
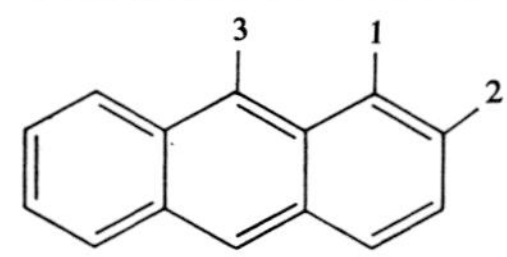	2.74 1.57 5.56
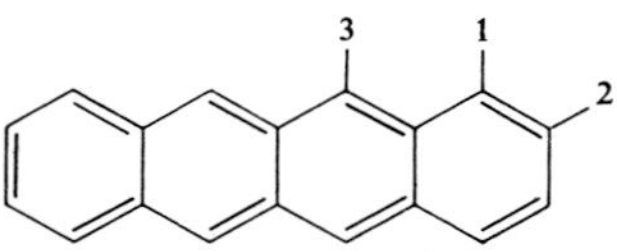	1.49 1.17 4.25
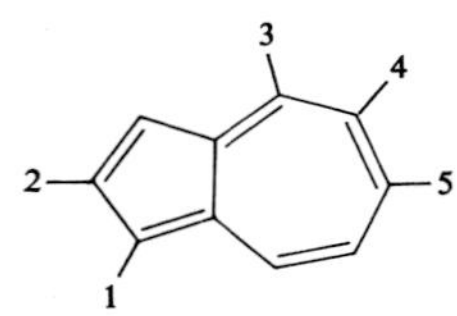	0.27 3.95 6.22 1.34 8.83
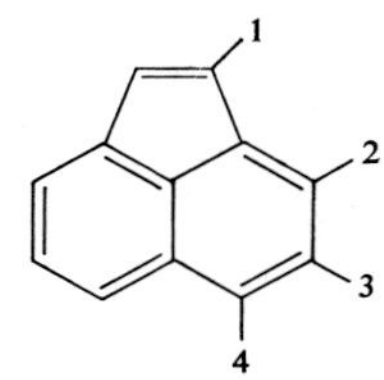	3.[illegible] 4.[illegible] 0.[illegible] 5.[illegible]

8-14 Polarographic half-wave potentials for oxidation and reduction of aromatic hydrocarbons are given in Table P8-14.

(a) Make separate plots of these data against energy (in units of β) of the highest occupied and lowest empty MO respectively. (Use tabulations or a computer program.)

(b) Now plot reduction versus oxidation half-wave potential for this series. Explain adherence to or deviation from linearity.

TABLE P 8–14

Compound	Structure	Reduction half-wave potential in 2-methoxyethanol (V)	Oxidation half-wa potential in acetonitrile (V)
Tetracene	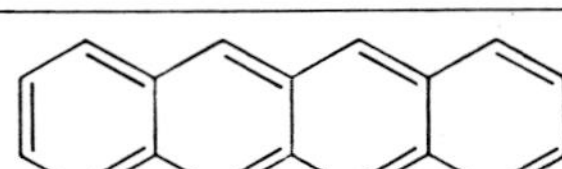	1.135	0.54
1,2-Benzpyrene	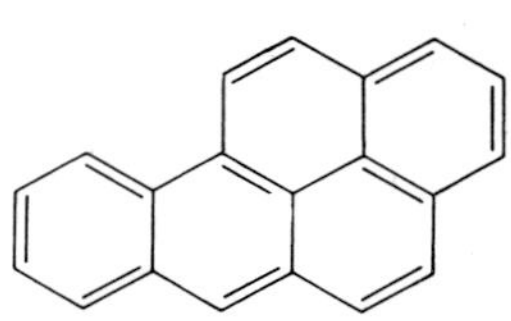	1.36	0.76
Anthracene	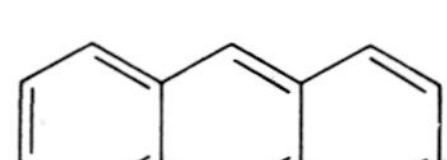	1.46	0.84

BLE P 8–14 (*Continued*)

Compound	Structure	Reduction half-wave potential in 2-methoxyethanol (V)	Oxidation half-wave potential in acetonitrile (V)
yrene	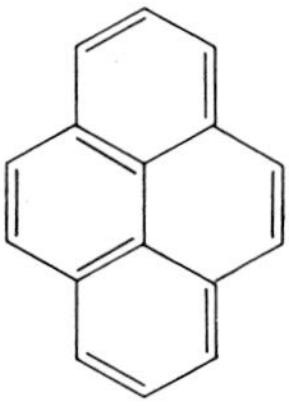	1.61	0.86
2-Benzanthracene	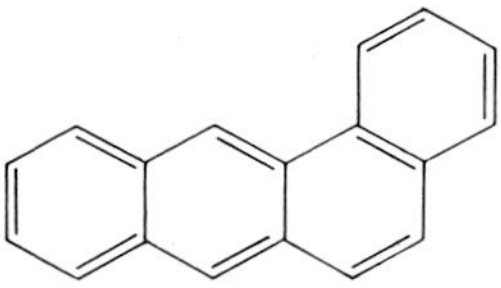	1.53	0.92
2,5,6-Dibenzanthracene	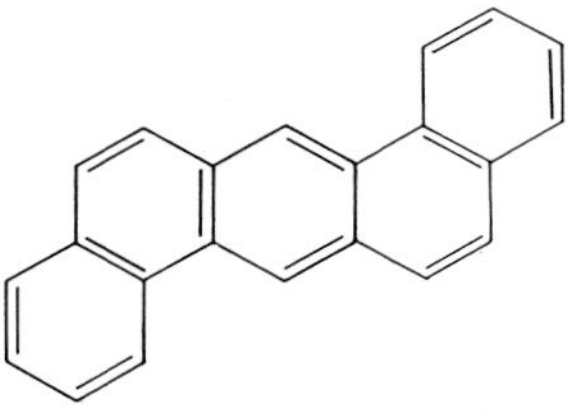	1.545	1.00
henanthrene	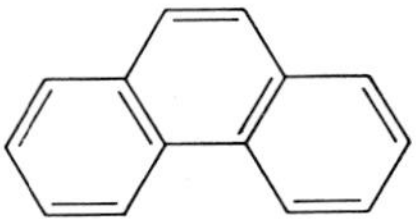	1.935	1.23
luoranthene	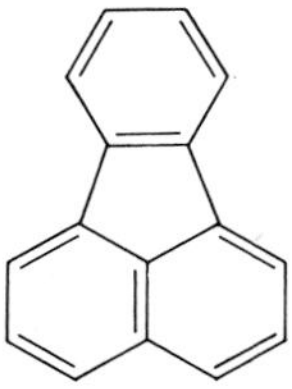	1.345	1.18
aphthalene	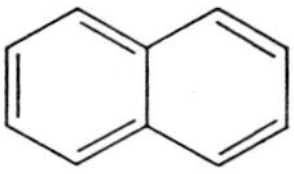	1.98	1.31
iphenyl	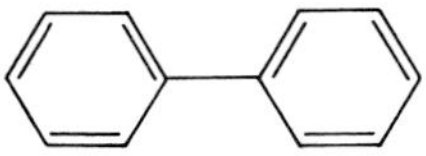	2.075	1.48

8-15 Use tabulated or computer generated HMO data for *neutral* azulene (**XXVII**) to answer the following questions (Tabulated data may be found in Appendix 6.):

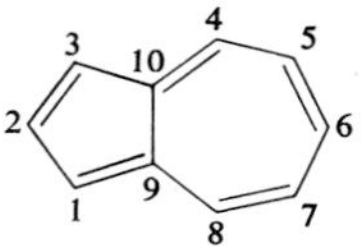

(XXVII)

(a) What values would you expect for oxidation and reduction half-wave potentials for this molecule under conditions described in Problem 8-14?

(b) If an electron were removed from the highest occupied MO to produce an ion, which bonds would you expect to lengthen, which to shorten?

8-16 Use the effective bond energies of Table 8-2 to calculate the expected π energy for (**XXVIII**). Compare this with the HMO energy of $18\alpha + 21.906\beta$.

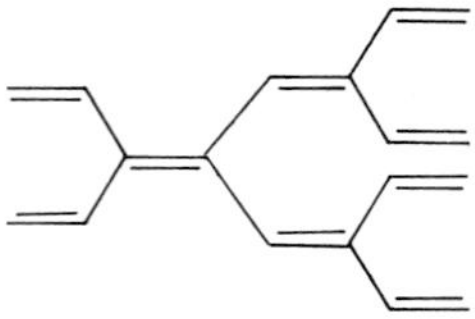

(XXVIII)

8-17 Obtain the HMO data for naphthalene (**XXIX**) and perylene (**XXX**):

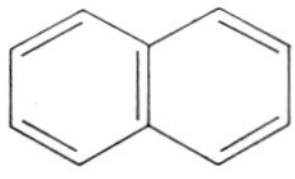

(XXIX)

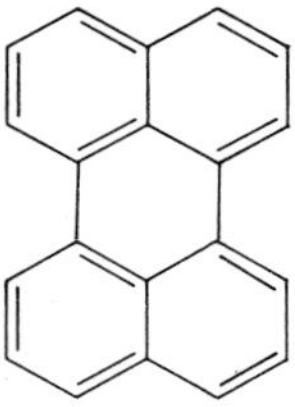

(XXX)

(a) For each molecule, compare E to the energy predicted by use of Table 8-2. Categorize each molecule as aromatic, nonaromatic or antiaromatic.

(b) Compare the RE for these two molecules. Does the central ring in perylene appear to be contributing?

(c) Draw formal bond structures for perylene. What can you conclude about the two bonds connecting naphthalene units in perylene?

(d) Use HMO bond orders to calculate a predicted length for these two bonds. How do they compare with the observed 1.471 Å value? Is this observed length consistent with your conclusion of Part (c)?

8-18 The third, fourth, and fifth molecules in Fig. 8-24 have dipole moments. Assuming that the individual rings attract or repel charge in accordance with our expectations from the $4n + 2$ rule, predict the direction of the π-electronic contribution to the dipoles. (Dipoles are defined by chemists as being directed from positive toward negative ends of electric dipoles. Physicists use the opposite convention.) How would you expect the π-electron densities to vary in these molecules? Compare your expectations with tabulated densities.

8-19 How many π electrons are there in each of the following neutral molecules?

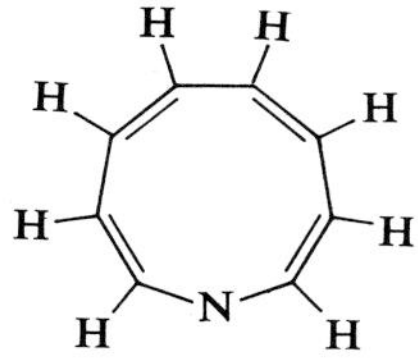

(a) 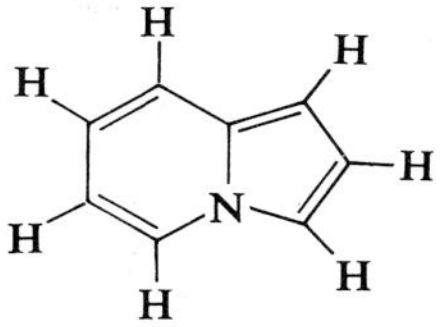 (b) 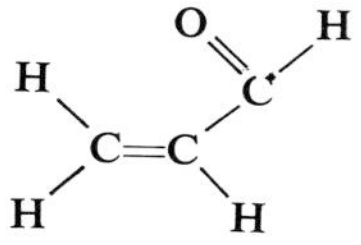 (c)

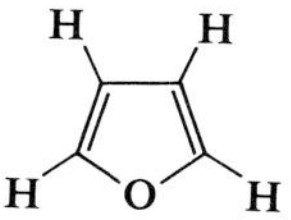

(d) 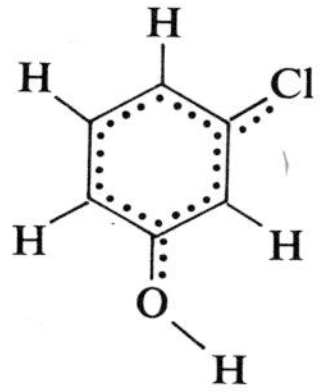 (e)

8-20 Use the parameters in Table 8-3 to construct the HMO determinant for molecule (**XXXI**). Use the conjugative model for the methyl group.

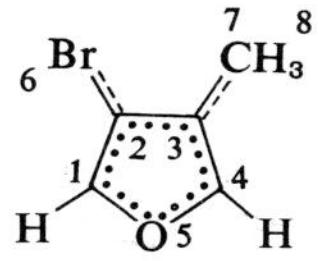

(**XXXI**)

8-21 Substitution of a nitrogen for a carbon in benzene changes the HMO energy levels, but not drastically. Hence the stability of the six π-electron molecule pyridine can still be rationalized by the $4n + 2$ role. Which member of each of the following pairs of molecules would you expect to be stable on the basis of such arguments?

(a)  or 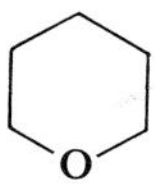 (b) 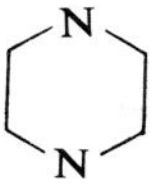 or 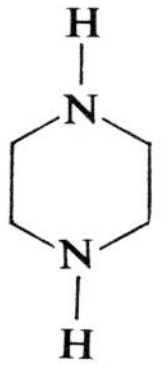 (c)  or

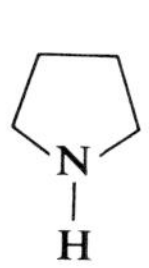

8-22 It is observed that many even alternant hydrocarbons tend to undergo nucleophilic substitution, electrophilic substitution, and radical addition at the same site(s). Rationalize this behavior in terms of the following indices (where appropriate): q_r, HOMO, LUMO, L_r.

8-23 Can π_{rr} be a successful index for nucleophilic *and* electrophilic substitution if these are observed to occur at different sites?

8-24 For the methylene cyclopropene system C_4H_4 (see Appendix 6 for HMO data and atomic numbering scheme):

(a) calculate the free valences for the neutral molecule;

(b) decide, using three appropriate reactivity indices, which site is most susceptible to electrophilic attack.

(c) Decide which protons would lead to hyperfine splitting of the ESR spectrum of the radical anion, according to the simple Hückel approach.

(d) Decide whether the second-lowest MO is net bonding or net antibonding. Why?

8-25 Published data for free radical ($CCl_3\cdot$) addition to hydrocarbons are shown in Table P8-25; see Kooyman and Farenhorst [27]. Using standard tabulations or computer programs, obtain F_r values for each molecule. Choose the largest value for each molecule and plot this against the log of the *modified* rate constant. In each case, modify the rate constant by dividing k by the *number* of sites on the molecule having the maximum F_r value. [If a molecule has F_r values differing by 0.002 or less, treat them as equal.] If any data points deviate greatly from the general trend, try to give an explanation.

TABLE P8-25

Molecule	Structure	Rate constant
Benzene	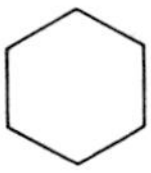	$<10^{-3}$ (use this limit)
Biphenyl	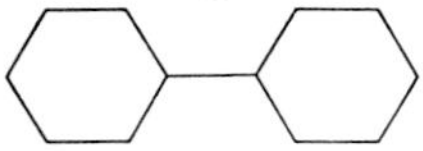	2.7×10^{-3}
Triphenylene	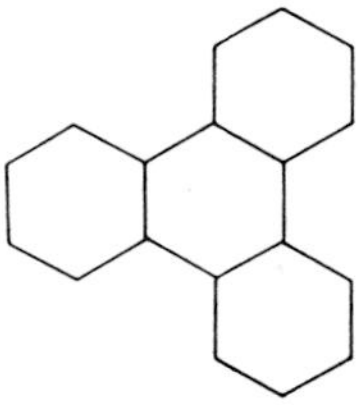	$<4 \times 10^{-2}$ (use this limit)
Phenanthrene	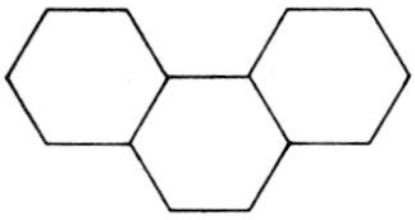	1.6×10^{-2}
Naphthalene	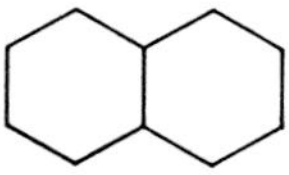	4×10^{-2}
Chrysene	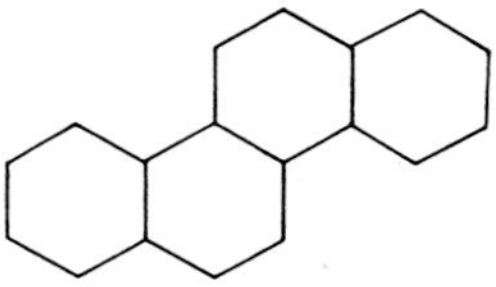	6.7×10^{-2}

TABLE P8-25 (*Continued*)

Molecule	Structure	Rate constant
Pyrene	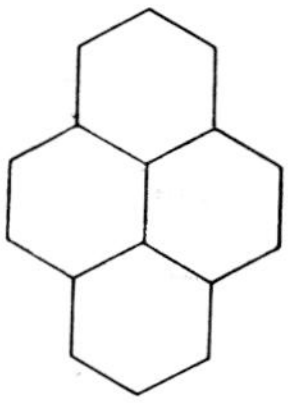	1.3
Stilbene	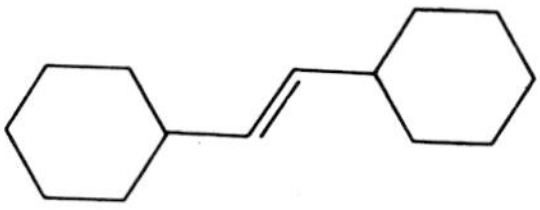	1.0
1,2,5,6-Dibenzanthracene	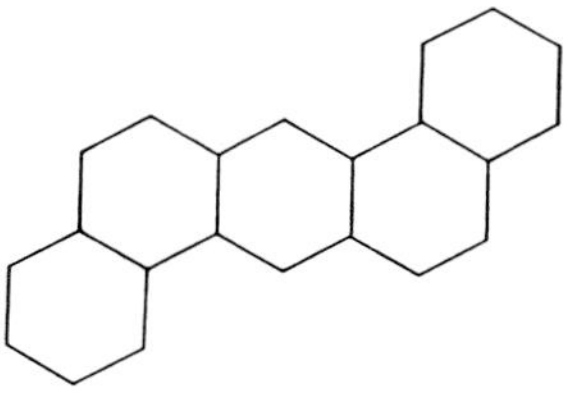	3.7
Styrene	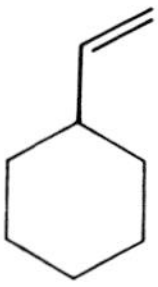	12.5
Anthracene	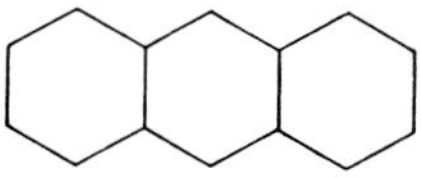	22
Benzanthracene	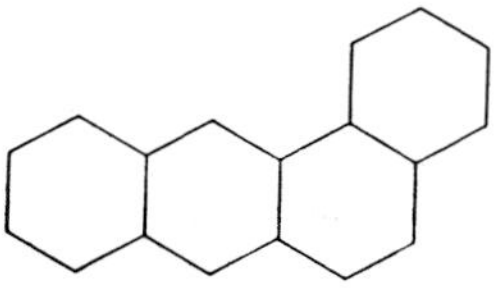	30
3,4-Benzopyrene	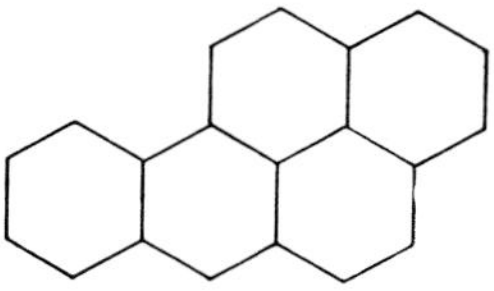	70
Naphthacene	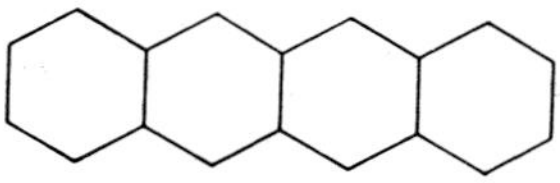	102

REFERENCES

[1] L. Salem, "The Molecular Orbital Theory of Conjugated Systems." Benjamin, New York, 1966.
[2] C. A. Coulson, *Proc. Roy. Soc.* (*London*) **A164**, 383 (1938).
[3] A. Streitwieser, Jr., "Molecular Orbital Theory for Organic Chemists." Wiley, New York, 1961.
[4] I. N. Levine, "Quantum Chemistry," Vol. I. Allyn & Bacon, Boston, 1970.
[5] C. A. Coulson and A. Streitwieser, Jr., "Dictionary of π-Electron Calculations." Freeman, San Francisco, 1965.
[6] A. Streitwieser, Jr., and J. I. Brauman, "Supplemental Tables of Molecular Orbital Calculations." Pergamon, Oxford, 1965.
[7] E. Heilbronner and P. A. Straub, "HMO's." Springer-Verlag, Berlin and New York, 1966.
[8] C. A. Coulson, *Proc. Roy. Soc.* (*London*) **A169**, 413 (1939).
[9] F. Gerson and J. H. Hammons, *in* "Nonbenzenoid Aromatics" (P. J. Snyder, ed.), Vol. II. Academic Press, New York, 1971.
[10] H. Lund, *Acta Chem. Scand.* **11**, 1323 (1957).
[11] I. Bergman, *Trans. Faraday Soc.* **50**, 829 (1954).
[12] D. W. Turner, "Molecular Photoelectron Spectroscopy." Wiley (Interscience), New York, 1970.
[13] F. Brogli and E. Heilbronner, *Theoret. Chim. Acta* **26**, 289 (1972).
[14] M. J. S. Dewar, "The Molecular Orbital Theory of Organic Chemistry." McGraw-Hill, New York, 1969.
[15] M. J. S. Dewar and C. de Llano, *J. Am. Chem. Soc.* **91**, 789 (1969).
[16] M. J. S. Dewar, A. J. Harget, and N. Trinajstic, *J. Am. Chem. Soc.* **91**, 6321 (1969).
[17] B. A. Hess, Jr., and L. J. Schaad, *J. Am. Chem. Soc.* **93**, 305, 2413 (1971).
[18] L. J. Schaad and B. A. Hess, Jr., *J. Am. Chem. Soc.* **94**, 3068 (1972).
[19] E. D. Bergmann and B. Pullman, eds., *Jerusalem Symp. Quantum Chem. Biochem.* **3** (1971).
[20] R. Breslow, *Chem. Eng. News* (June 28, 1965).
[21] S. P. McGlynn, L. G. Vanquickenborne, M. Kinoshita, and D. G. Carroll, "Introduction To Applied Quantum Chemistry." Holt, New York, 1972.
[22] H. Fujimoto and K. Fukui, *in* "Chemical Reactivity and Reaction Paths" (G. Klopman, ed.). Wiley (Interscience), New York, 1974.
[23] C. A. Coulson, *Trans. Faraday Soc.* **42**, 265 (1946).
[24] M. Levy and M. Szwarc, *J. Chem. Phys.* **22**, 1621 (1954).
[25] G. Klopman, ed., "Chemical Reactivity and Reaction Paths." Wiley (Interscience), New York, 1974.
[26] W. de W. Horrocks, D. H. Templeton, and A. Zalkin, *Inorg. Chem.* **7**, 2303 (1968).
[27] E. C. Kooyman and E. Farenhorst, *Trans. Faraday Soc.* **49**, 58 (1953).

CHAPTER 9

MATRIX FORMULATION OF THE LINEAR VARIATION METHOD

9-1 Introduction

In Chapter 7 we developed a method for performing linear variational calculations. The method requires solving a determinantal equation for its roots, and then solving a set of simultaneous homogeneous equations for coefficients. This procedure is not the most efficient for programmed solution by computer. In this chapter we describe the *matrix* formulation for the linear variation procedure. Not only is this the basis for many quantum-chemical computer programs, but it also provides a convenient framework for formulating the various quantum-chemical methods we shall encounter in future chapters.

Vectors and matrices may be defined in a formal, algebraic way, but they also may be given geometric interpretations. The formal definitions and rules suffice for quantum-chemical purposes. However, the terminology of matrix algebra is closely connected with the geometric ideas that influenced early development. Furthermore, most chemists are more comfortable if they have a physical or geometric model to carry along with mathematical discussion. Therefore, we append some discussion of geometrical interpretation to the algebraic treatment.[1]

9-2 Matrices and Vectors

A. Definitions

A matrix is an ordered array of elements satisfying certain algebraic rules. We write our matrices with parentheses on the left and right of the array.[2] Unless otherwise stated, we restrict the elements to be numbers (which need not be real). In general, however, as long as the rules of matrix algebra can be

[1] More thorough discussions of matrix algebra at a level suitable for the nonspecialist are given by Aitken [1] and Birkhoff and MacLane [2].

[2] Some authors use brackets.

observed, there is no restriction on what the elements may be. In expression (9-1), we have written a matrix in three ways:

$$\begin{pmatrix} 1.2 & 3.8 & -4.0 \\ 5.0 & 1.0 & 0.0 \\ 9.1 & 0.0 & -3+4i \\ 6.0 & -1.0 & -1.0 \end{pmatrix} \equiv \begin{pmatrix} c_{11} & c_{12} & c_{13} \\ c_{21} & c_{22} & c_{23} \\ c_{31} & c_{32} & c_{33} \\ c_{41} & c_{42} & c_{43} \end{pmatrix} \equiv \mathsf{C} \tag{9-1}$$

On the left, the numerical elements are written explicitly. In the center they are symbolized by a subscripted letter. On the right the entire matrix is indicated by a single symbol. We will use sans serif, upper-case symbols to represent matrices. Individual matrix elements will be symbolized either by a subscripted lower-case symbol (e.g., c_{12}) or by a subscripted symbol for the matrix in parentheses (e.g., $(\mathsf{C})_{12}$).

It is useful to recognize rows and columns in a matrix. The sample matrix given above has four rows and three columns, so it is said to have *dimensions* 4×3. When subscripts are used to denote position in a matrix, the convention is that the first subscript indicates the row, the second indicates the column. (The order "row–column" is important to remember. The mnemonic "RC," or "Roman Catholic" is helpful.) Rows are numbered from top to bottom, columns from left to right. There is no limit on the dimensions for matrices, but we usually will be concerned in a practical way with finite-dimensional matrices in this book.

If a matrix has only one column or row, it is called a *column vector* or *row vector*, respectively. We will use sans serif, lower-case symbols to denote *column* vectors. Additional symbols, described shortly, will be used to denote row vectors. These two kinds of vector behave differently under the rules of matrix algebra, so it is important to avoid confusing them.

If a matrix has only one row and one column, its behavior under the rules of matrix algebra becomes identical to the familiar behavior of ordinary *scalars* (i.e., numbers), and so a 1×1 matrix is simply a number.

The similarity in appearance between a matrix and a determinant may be deceptive. A determinant is denoted by bounding with vertical straight lines, and is equal to a *number* that can be found by reducing the determinant according to a prescribed procedure (see Appendix 2). For this to be possible, the determinant must be square (i.e., have the same number of rows as columns). A matrix is not equal to a number and need not be square. (However, one can take the determinant of a square matrix A. This *number* is symbolized $|\mathsf{A}|$ and is *not* the same as A without the vertical bars.)

Two matrices are *equal* if all elements in corresponding positions are equal. Thus, $\mathsf{A} = \mathsf{B}$ means $a_{ij} = b_{ij}$ for all i and j.

B. *Complex Conjugate, Transpose, and Hermitian Adjoint of a Matrix*

We define the *complex conjugate* of a matrix A to be the matrix A^*, formed by replacing every element of A by its complex conjugate. If $\mathsf{A} = \mathsf{A}^*$, A is a *real* matrix. (Every element is real.)

We define the *transpose* of a matrix A to be the matrix $\tilde{\mathsf{A}}$, formed by interchanging row 1 and column 1, row 2 and column 2, etc. The transpose of the 4×3 matrix in expression (9-1) is the 3×4 matrix given in

$$\tilde{\mathsf{C}} = \begin{pmatrix} 1.2 & 5.0 & 9.1 & 6.0 \\ 3.8 & 1.0 & 0.0 & -1.0 \\ -4.0 & 0.0 & -3 + 4i & -1.0 \end{pmatrix} \tag{9-2}$$

If we denote some column vector as p, we can symbolize the corresponding row vector as $\tilde{\mathsf{p}}$. Thus, the tilde symbol is one device we can use to indicate a row vector.

Transposing a square matrix corresponds to "reflecting" it through its *principal diagonal* (which runs from upper left to lower right) as indicated in

$$\mathsf{A} = \begin{pmatrix} 1 & 2 & 3 \\ 4 & 5 & 6 \\ 7 & 8 & 9 \end{pmatrix}, \qquad \tilde{\mathsf{A}} = \begin{pmatrix} 1 & 4 & 7 \\ 2 & 5 & 8 \\ 3 & 6 & 9 \end{pmatrix} \tag{9-3}$$

If $\mathsf{A} = \tilde{\mathsf{A}}$, A is a *symmetric* matrix.

We define the *hermitian adjoint* of A to be the matrix $\mathsf{A}^\dagger$, formed by taking the transpose of the complex conjugate of A (or the complex conjugate of the transpose. The order of these operations is immaterial.) Hence, $\mathsf{A}^\dagger = (\tilde{\mathsf{A}})^* = (\widetilde{\mathsf{A}^*})$. If $\mathsf{A} = \mathsf{A}^\dagger$, A is a *hermitian* matrix.

C. *Addition and Multiplication of Matrices and Vectors*

Multiplication of a matrix by a scalar is equivalent to multiplying every element in the matrix by the scalar. Addition of two matrices is accomplished by adding elements in corresponding positions in the matrices. Thus, for example,

$$\begin{pmatrix} 1 & 2 \\ 3 & 4 \end{pmatrix} + 2\begin{pmatrix} 5 & 6 \\ 7 & 8 \end{pmatrix} = \begin{pmatrix} 1 + 10 & 2 + 12 \\ 3 + 14 & 4 + 16 \end{pmatrix} = \begin{pmatrix} 11 & 14 \\ 17 & 20 \end{pmatrix}$$

and it is evident that the operation of matrix addition is possible only within sets of matrices of identical dimensions.

Matrix multiplication is a bit more involved. We start by considering multiplication of vectors. Two types of vector multiplication are possible. If we multiply a row vector on the left times a column vector on the right, we take the *product* of the leading element of each *plus* the product of the second element of each, plus..., etc., thereby obtaining a *scalar* as a result. Hence, this is called *scalar* multiplication of vectors. For example,

$$(1 \quad 2 \quad 3)\begin{pmatrix}4\\5\\6\end{pmatrix} = 1 \times 4 + 2 \times 5 + 3 \times 6 = 32$$

This kind of multiplication requires an equal number of elements in the two vectors. It is important to retain in mind the basic operation described here: summation of products taken by sweeping *across a row on the left* and *down a column on the right*. Since there exists but *one* row on the left and *one* column on the right, we obtain *one* number as the result.

The other possibility is to multiply a column vector on the left times a row vector on the right. Employing the same basic operation as above, we sweep across row 1 on the left and down column 1 on the right, obtaining a product that we will store in position (1, 1) of a matrix to keep track of its origin. The product of row 1 times column 2 gives us element (1, 2) and so on. In this way, we generate a whole matrix of numbers. For example,

$$\begin{pmatrix}1\\2\end{pmatrix}(3 \quad 4 \quad 5) = \begin{pmatrix}1 \times 3 & 1 \times 4 & 1 \times 5\\2 \times 3 & 2 \times 4 & 2 \times 5\end{pmatrix} = \begin{pmatrix}3 & 4 & 5\\6 & 8 & 10\end{pmatrix}$$

This is an example of *matrix* multiplication of vectors. Just as before, the number of columns on the left (one) equals the number of rows on the right. Now, however, the number of elements in the vectors may differ, and the dimensions of the matrix reflect the dimensions of the original vectors.

The two types of vector multiplication may be symbolized as follows, using our notation for scalars, row vectors, column vectors, and matrices:

$$\tilde{\mathsf{a}}\mathsf{b} = c \tag{9-4}$$

$$\mathsf{a}\tilde{\mathsf{b}} = \mathsf{C} \tag{9-5}$$

Multiplying two matrices together is most simply viewed as scalar multiplying all the rows in the left matrix by all the columns of the right matrix. Thus, in $\mathsf{AB} = \mathsf{C}$, the element c_{ij} is the (scalar) product of row i in A times column j in B. This process is possible only when the number of columns in A equals the number of rows in B. Thus, AB may exist as a matrix C, while BA may not exist due to a disagreement in number of rows and columns. If A and B are both square matrices and have equal dimension, then AB and BA both exist, but they still need not be equal. That is, *matrix multiplication is not commutative.*

In a triple product of matrices, ABC, one can multiply AB first (call the result D) and then multiply DC to get the final result (call it F). Or, if one takes $\mathsf{BC} = \mathsf{E}$, then one always finds $\mathsf{AE} = \mathsf{F}$. Thus, the result is invariant to the choice between $(\mathsf{AB})\mathsf{C}$ or $\mathsf{A}(\mathsf{BC})$, and so matrix multiplication is *associative*.

D. Diagonal Matrices, Unit Matrices, and Inverse Matrices

A *diagonal matrix* is a square matrix having zeros everywhere except on the principal diagonal. Diagonal matrices of equal dimension commute with each other, but a diagonal matrix does not, in general, commute with a nondiagonal matrix.

A *unit* matrix $\mathsf{1}$ is a special diagonal matrix. Every diagonal element has a value of unity. A unit matrix times any matrix (of appropriate dimension) gives that same matrix as product. That is, $\mathsf{1A} = \mathsf{A1} = \mathsf{A}$. It follows immediately that the unit matrix commutes with any *square* matrix of the same dimension.

We define the *left inverse* of a matrix A to be A^{-1}, satisfying the matrix equation $\mathsf{A}^{-1}\mathsf{A} = \mathsf{1}$. The right inverse is defined to satisfy $\mathsf{AA}^{-1} = \mathsf{1}$.

In most of our quantum-chemical applications of matrix algebra, we will be concerned only with vectors and *square* matrices. For square matrices, the left and right inverses are identical, and so we refer simply to the inverse of the matrix.

E. Complex Conjugate, Inverse, and Transpose of a Product of Matrices

If $\mathsf{AB} = \mathsf{C}$, then $\mathsf{C}^* = (\mathsf{AB})^* = \mathsf{A}^*\mathsf{B}^*$. In words, the complex conjugate of a product of matrices is equal to the product of the complex conjugate matrices. This is demonstrable from the observation that $(\mathsf{C})_{ij} = (\mathsf{A})_{i1}(\mathsf{B})_{1j} + (\mathsf{A})_{i2}(\mathsf{B})_{2j} + \cdots$ and $(\mathsf{C})_{ij}^* = (\mathsf{A})_{i1}^*(\mathsf{B})_{1j}^* + (\mathsf{A})_{i2}^*(\mathsf{B})_{2j}^* + \cdots$, and so the complex conjugate is produced by taking the complex conjugate of every element in A and B but not changing their order of combination.

If $\mathsf{AB} = \mathsf{C}$, then $\mathsf{C}^{-1} = (\mathsf{AB})^{-1} = \mathsf{B}^{-1}\mathsf{A}^{-1}$. In words, the inverse of a product of matrices is equal to the product of inverses, *but with the order reversed.* We can easily show that this satisfies the rules of matrix algebra. $\mathsf{C}^{-1}\mathsf{C} = (\mathsf{AB})^{-1}\mathsf{AB} = \mathsf{B}^{-1}\mathsf{A}^{-1}\mathsf{AB} = \mathsf{B}^{-1}\mathsf{1B} = \mathsf{B}^{-1}\mathsf{B} = \mathsf{1}$. If we failed to reverse the order, we would instead have $\mathsf{A}^{-1}\mathsf{B}^{-1}\mathsf{AB}$ and, because the matrices do not commute, we would be prevented from carrying through the reduction to $\mathsf{1}$.

If $\mathsf{AB} = \mathsf{C}$, then $\tilde{\mathsf{C}} = (\widetilde{\mathsf{AB}}) = \tilde{\mathsf{B}}\tilde{\mathsf{A}}$. The transpose of a product is the product of transposes, again in reverse order. Since $\tilde{\mathsf{C}}$ has c_{ij} and c_{ji} interchanged, it follows that, where we had row i of A times column j of B, we must now have row j of A times column i of B. But this is the same as column j of $\tilde{\mathsf{A}}$ times row i of $\tilde{\mathsf{B}}$. To obtain row on left and column on right for proper multiplication, we must have $\tilde{\mathsf{B}}\tilde{\mathsf{A}}$.

F. A Geometric Model

Consider a vector in two-dimensional space emanating from the origin of a cartesian system as indicated in Fig. 9-1a. We can summarize the information contained in this vector (magnitude and direction) by writing down the x and y

components of the vector terminus, (3, 2) in this case. It must be understood that the first number corresponds to the x component and not the y, and so the vector (3, 2) carries its information through number *position* as well as number *value*.

If we multiply both numbers in the vector by 2, the result, (6, 4), corresponds to a vector collinear to the original but twice as long. Therefore

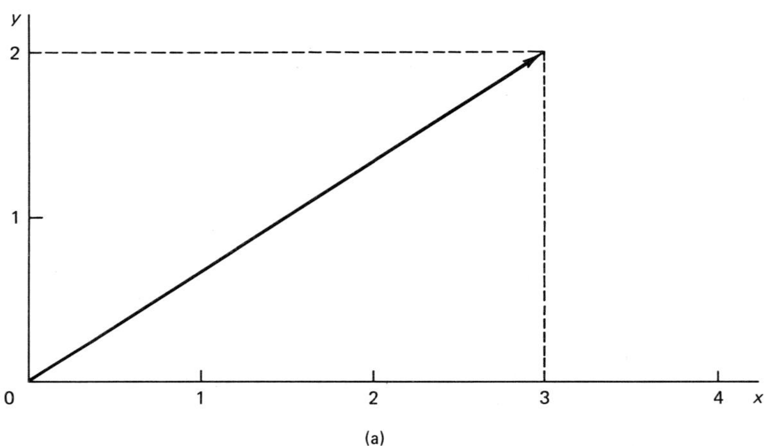

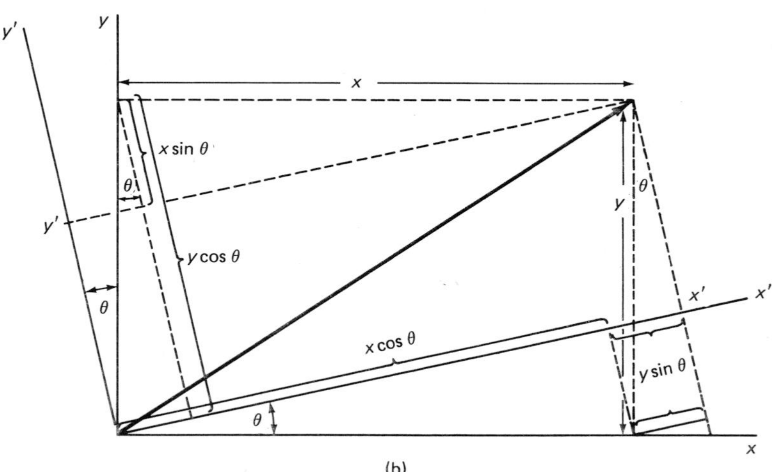

FIG. 9-1 (a) The vector (3 2). (b) The same vector and its relationship to two cartesian axis systems.

ultiplying a vector by a *number* results in a change of *scale* but no change in rection. Hence, the term "scalar" is often used in place of "number" in vector rminology.

Suppose that we rotated the cartesian axes counterclockwise through an igle θ, maintaining them orthogonal to each other and not varying the distance ales. We imagine our original vector to remain unrotated during this *coordinate ansformation*. (Equivalently, we can imagine rotating the vector *clockwise* by θ, eeping the axes fixed.) We wish to know how to express our vector in the new ordinate system. The situation is depicted in Fig. 9-1b. Inspection reveals at the new coordinates (x', y') are related to the old (x, y) as follows:

$$x' = x\cos\theta + y\sin\theta, \qquad y' = -x\sin\theta + y\cos\theta \tag{9-6}$$

we make use of matrix algebra, we can express Eqs. (9-6) as a matrix equation:

$$\begin{pmatrix} x' \\ y' \end{pmatrix} = \begin{pmatrix} \cos\theta & \sin\theta \\ -\sin\theta & \cos\theta \end{pmatrix} \begin{pmatrix} x \\ y \end{pmatrix} \tag{9-7}$$

ultiplying the two-dimensional vector (call it v) by the 2×2 matrix (call it R) enerates a new vector v', which gives the coordinates of our vector in the new ordinate system:

$$\mathsf{v}' = \mathsf{R}\mathsf{v} \tag{9-8}$$

/e have, then, a parallel between the vectors v' and v and matrix R on the one and, and the two-dimensional "geometrical" vector and rotating coordinate stem on the other. R *represents* the rotation and is often referred to as a *otation* matrix.

If we were to perform the rotation in the opposite direction, the rotation atrix would be the same except for the $\sin\theta$ terms, which would reverse sign:

$$\left.\begin{matrix}\text{rotation of coordinates} \\ \text{clockwise by } \theta\end{matrix}\right\} \rightarrow \begin{pmatrix} \cos\theta & -\sin\theta \\ \sin\theta & \cos\theta \end{pmatrix} \tag{9-9}$$

ote that this is just $\tilde{\mathsf{R}}$, the transpose of R.

If we were to rotate counterclockwise by θ and then clockwise by θ, we ould end up with our original coordinates for the vector. Thus, we should xpect

$$\tilde{\mathsf{R}}\mathsf{R}\mathsf{v} = \mathsf{v} \tag{9-10}$$

r

$$\tilde{\mathsf{R}}\mathsf{R} = 1 \tag{9-11}$$

Note that the *order* of operations is consistent with reading from right to left, st as with differential operators. Thus, $\tilde{\mathsf{R}}\mathsf{R}$ means that first R is performed, en $\tilde{\mathsf{R}}$.) Relation (9-11) is easily verified by explicit multiplication. Thus we see that, if we think of a matrix as representing some coordinate transformation in geometrical space, the inverse of the matrix represents the reverse transformation. In this *particular* example, the *transpose* of the transformation matrix turns out to be the inverse transformation matrix. When this is so, the matrix is said to be *orthogonal.* (Orthogonal transformations do not change the angles between coordinate axes; orthogonal axes remain orthogonal—hence the name "orthogonal.") The analogous transformation for matrices having complex or imaginary coefficients is called a *unitary* transformation. A unitary matrix has its hermitian adjoint as inverse: $\mathsf{A}^\dagger\mathsf{A} = 1$.

While it is easy to visualize a coordinate transformation in two or three dimensions, it is more difficult in higher-dimensional situations. Nevertheless, the mathematics and terminology carry forward to any desired dimension and are very useful. One may, if one wishes, talk of vectors and coordinate transformations in hyperspace, or one can eschew such mental constructs and simply follow the mathematical rules without a mental model.

One must be a bit cautious about inverses of matrices. In the rotation described above, we have a unique way of relating each x, y point in one coordinate system to a coordinate set x', y' in the other. The transformation does not entail any loss of information and can therefore be "undone." Such transforma-

TABLE 9-1
Some Matrix Rules and Definitions for a Square Matrix A *of Dimension n*

$\mathsf{A} = \mathsf{B}$	Matrix equality; means $a_{ij} = b_{ij}, \quad i, j = 1, n$
$\mathsf{A} + \mathsf{B} = \mathsf{C}$	Matrix addition; $c_{ij} = a_{ij} + b_{ij}, \quad i, j = 1, n$
$c\mathsf{A} = \mathsf{B}$	Multiplication of A by scalar; $b_{ij} = c \cdot a_{ij}, \quad i, j = 1, n$
$\mathsf{AB} = \mathsf{C}$	Matrix multiplication; $c_{ij} = \sum_{k=1}^{n} a_{ik}b_{kj}, \quad i, j = 1, n$
$\lvert\mathsf{A}\rvert$	The determinant of the matrix A (see Appendix 2)
A^{-1}	The inverse of A; $\mathsf{A}^{-1}\mathsf{A} = \mathsf{A}\mathsf{A}^{-1} = 1$ If A^{-1} exists, A is *nonsingular* and $\lvert\mathsf{A}\rvert \neq 0$.
A^*	The complex conjugate of A; $a_{ij} \rightarrow a_{ij}^*, \quad i, j = 1, n$ If $\mathsf{A}^* = \mathsf{A}$, A is *real.*
$\tilde{\mathsf{A}}$	The transpose of A; $(\tilde{\mathsf{A}})_{ij} = a_{ji}$ (rows and columns interchanged) If $\tilde{\mathsf{A}} = \mathsf{A}$, symmetric; if $\tilde{\mathsf{A}} = -\mathsf{A}$, antisymmetric; if $\tilde{\mathsf{A}} = \mathsf{A}^{-1}$, orthogonal.
$\mathsf{A}^\dagger$	The hermitian adjoint of A; $(\mathsf{A}^\dagger)_{ij} = a_{ji}^*$ $(\mathsf{A}^\dagger = \tilde{\mathsf{A}}^*)$ If $\mathsf{A}^\dagger = \mathsf{A}$, hermitian. If $\mathsf{A}^\dagger = \mathsf{A}^{-1}$, unitary.
$(\mathsf{ABC})^* = \mathsf{A}^*\mathsf{B}^*\mathsf{C}^*$	Complex conjugate of product
$\widetilde{(\mathsf{ABC})} = \tilde{\mathsf{C}}\tilde{\mathsf{B}}\tilde{\mathsf{A}}$	Transpose of product
$(\mathsf{ABC})^\dagger = \mathsf{C}^\dagger\mathsf{B}^\dagger\mathsf{A}^\dagger$	Hermitian adjoint of product
$(\mathsf{ABC})^{-1} = \mathsf{C}^{-1}\mathsf{B}^{-1}\mathsf{A}^{-1}$	Inverse of product
$\lvert\mathsf{ABC}\rvert = \lvert\mathsf{A}\rvert \cdot \lvert\mathsf{B}\rvert \cdot \lvert\mathsf{C}\rvert$	Determinant of product (any order)
$\mathsf{T}^{-1}\mathsf{AT}$	A similarity transformation If $\mathsf{T}^{-1} = \mathsf{T}^\dagger$, this is a *unitary* transformation. If $\mathsf{T}^{-1} = \tilde{\mathsf{T}}$, this is an *orthogonal* transformation.

tions (and their matrices) are called *nonsingular*. A nonsingular matrix is recognizable through the fact that its determinant must be nonzero. If we had a transformation which, for example, caused all or some points in one coordinate system to coalesce into a single point in the transformed system, we would lose our ability to back-transform in a unique way. Such a *singular* transformation has no inverse, and the determinant of a singular matrix is zero.

G. *Similarity Transformations*

A matrix product of the form $\mathsf{A}^{-1}\mathsf{HA}$ is called a *similarity transformation* on H. If A is orthogonal, then $\tilde{\mathsf{A}}\mathsf{HA}$ is a special kind of similarity transformation, called an *orthogonal transformation*. If A is unitary, then $\mathsf{A}^\dagger\mathsf{HA}$ is a *unitary transformation* on H. There is a physical interpretation for a similarity transformation, which will be discussed in a later chapter. For the present, we are concerned only with the mathematical definition of such a transformation. The important feature is that the eigenvalues, or "latent roots," of H are preserved in such a transformation (see Problem 9-5).

In this section we have quickly presented the salient rules of matrix algebra and hinted at their connection with geometric operations. The results are summarized in Table 9-1 for ease of reference.

9-3 Matrix Formulation of the Linear Variation Method

We have seen that the independent-electron approximation leads to a series of MOs for a molecular system. If the MOs are expressed as a linear combination of n basis functions (which are often approximations to AOs, although this is not necessary), the variation method leads to a set of secular equations:

$$\begin{aligned} (H_{11} - ES_{11})c_1 + (H_{12} - ES_{12})c_2 + \cdots + (H_{1n} - ES_{1n})c_n &= 0 \\ &\vdots \\ (H_{n1} - ES_{n1})c_1 \qquad\qquad\qquad + \cdots + (H_{nn} - ES_{nn})c_n &= 0 \end{aligned} \tag{9-12}$$

All terms have been defined in Chapter 7. Given a value for E that satisfies the associated *determinantal* equations, we can solve this set of secular equations for ratios between the c_i's. Requiring MO normality establishes convenient numerical values for the c_i's.

A matrix equation equivalent to Eq. (9-12) is[3]

$$\begin{pmatrix} H_{11} - ES_{11} & H_{12} - ES_{12} & \cdots & H_{1n} - ES_{1n} \\ \vdots & & & \\ H_{n1} - ES_{n1} & & \cdots & H_{nn} - ES_{nn} \end{pmatrix} \begin{pmatrix} c_1 \\ c_2 \\ \vdots \\ c_n \end{pmatrix} = \begin{pmatrix} 0 \\ 0 \\ \vdots \\ 0 \end{pmatrix} \tag{9-13}$$

[3] Quantum-chemical convention is to use upper case letters for individual elements of the matrices H, S, and E. This differs from the usual convention.

The matrix in Eq. (9-13) is clearly the difference between two matrices. Thi enables us to rewrite the equation in the form

$$\begin{pmatrix} H_{11} & H_{12} & \cdots & H_{1n} \\ \vdots & & & \vdots \\ H_{n1} & & \cdots & H_{nn} \end{pmatrix} \begin{pmatrix} c_1 \\ c_2 \\ \vdots \\ c_n \end{pmatrix} = E \begin{pmatrix} S_{11} & S_{12} & \cdots & S_{1n} \\ \vdots & & & \vdots \\ S_{n1} & & \cdots & S_{nn} \end{pmatrix} \begin{pmatrix} c_1 \\ c_2 \\ \vdots \\ c_n \end{pmatrix} \qquad \text{(9-14}$$

or

$$\mathsf{H}\mathsf{c}_i = E_i \mathsf{S}\mathsf{c}_i, \qquad i = 1, 2, \ldots, n \qquad \text{(9-15}$$

where we have introduced the subscript i to account for the fact that there ar many possible values for E and that each one has its own characteristic set c coefficients. Note that the "*eigenvector*" c_i is a *column* vector and that eac element in c_i is (effectively) multiplied by the scalar E_i according to Eq. (9-15)

In general, there are as many MOs as there are basis functions, and so Eq (9-15) represents n separate matrix equations. We can continue to use matri notation to reduce these to a single matrix equation. We do this by stackin the n c vectors together, side by side, to produce an $n \times n$ matrix C. Th numbers E must also be combined into an approxiate matrix form. We must b careful to do this in such a way that the scalar E_1 still multiplies only c_1 (nov column 1 of C) E_2 multiplies only c_2, and so forth. This is accomplished in th following equation:

$$\begin{pmatrix} H_{11} & \cdots & H_{1n} \\ \vdots & & \vdots \\ H_{n1} & \cdots & H_{nn} \end{pmatrix} \begin{pmatrix} c_{11} & \cdots & c_{1n} \\ \vdots & & \vdots \\ c_{n1} & \cdots & c_{nn} \end{pmatrix}$$
$$= \begin{pmatrix} S_{11} & \cdots & S_{1n} \\ \vdots & & \vdots \\ S_{n1} & \cdots & S_{nn} \end{pmatrix} \begin{pmatrix} c_{11} & \cdots & c_{1n} \\ \vdots & & \vdots \\ c_{n1} & \cdots & c_{nn} \end{pmatrix} \begin{pmatrix} E_1 & 0 & 0 & \cdots & 0 \\ 0 & E_2 & 0 & \cdots & 0 \\ \vdots & \vdots & \vdots & & \vdots \\ 0 & 0 & 0 & \cdots & E_n \end{pmatrix} \qquad \text{(9-16}$$

or

$$\mathsf{HC} = \mathsf{SCE} \qquad \text{(9-17}$$

The matrix E is a diagonal matrix of orbital energies (often referred to a the *matrix of eigenvalues*). C is the matrix of coefficients (or *matrix of eigen vectors*), and each *column* refers to a different MO. The first column of C refer to the MO having energy E_1. In multiplying E by C from the left, each coefficien in column 1 becomes multiplied by E_1. This would not occur if we multiplie E by C_1 from the right. Therefore, HC = SCE is correct, whereas HC = ESC i incorrect.

9-4 Solving the Matrix Equation

Since we know the basis functions and the effective hamiltonian (in principle, at least), we are in a position to evaluate the elements in H and S. How do we then find C and E?

Let us first treat the simplified situation where our basis set of functions is orthonormal, either by assumption or design. Then all the off-diagonal elements of S (which correspond to overlap between *different* basis functions) are zero, and all the diagonal elements are unity because of normality. In short, $\mathsf{S} = \mathsf{1}$. Therefore, Eq. (9-17) becomes

$$\mathsf{HC} = \mathsf{CE} \tag{9-18}$$

and our problem is, given H, find C and E.

Now, we want a set of coefficients that correspond to normalized MOs. We have seen earlier that, for an orthonormal basis set, this requires each MO to have coefficients satisfying the equation (assuming real coefficients)

$$c_{1i}^2 + c_{2i}^2 + \cdots + c_{ni}^2 = 1 \tag{9-19}$$

We can write this as a vector equation

$$\tilde{\mathsf{c}}_i \mathsf{c}_i \equiv (c_{i1} \quad c_{i2} \quad \cdots \quad c_{in}) \begin{pmatrix} c_{1i} \\ c_{2i} \\ \vdots \\ c_{ni} \end{pmatrix} = 1 \tag{9-20}$$

Furthermore, we know that any two different MOs must be orthogonal to each other. That is $\tilde{\mathsf{c}}_i \mathsf{c}_j = 0$, $i \neq j$. All this may be summarized in the matrix equation

$$\tilde{\mathsf{C}}\mathsf{C} = \mathsf{1} \tag{9-21}$$

Hence, the coefficient matrix is *orthogonal.* In the more general case in which coefficients may be complex, C is *unitary*; i.e., $\mathsf{C}^\dagger\mathsf{C} = \mathsf{1}$. Our problem, then, is, given H, find a unitary matrix C such that $\mathsf{HC} = \mathsf{CE}$ with E diagonal.

We can multiply both sides of a matrix equation by the same matrix and preserve the equality. However, because matrices do not necessarily commute, we must be careful to carry out the multiplication from the left on both sides, or from the right on both sides. Thus, multiplying Eq. (9-18) from the left by $\mathsf{C}^\dagger$, we obtain

$$\mathsf{C}^\dagger\mathsf{HC} = \mathsf{C}^\dagger\mathsf{CE} = \mathsf{1E} = \mathsf{E} \tag{9-22}$$

where we have used the fact that C is unitary. Now our problem may be stated as, given H, find a unitary matrix C such that $\mathsf{C}^\dagger\mathsf{HC}$ is diagonal.[4] Several

[4] Not every matrix (not even every square matrix) can be diagonalized by a unitary transformation, but every *hermitian* matrix can be so diagonalized.

techniques exist for finding such a matrix C. These are generally much more suitable for machine computation than are determinantal manipulations. Some of these methods are discussed in detail in Appendix 9.

We can illustrate that the allyl radical energies and coefficients already found by the HMO method do in fact satisfy the relations $\mathsf{C}^\dagger\mathsf{C} = \mathsf{1}$ and $\mathsf{C}^\dagger\mathsf{H}\mathsf{C} = \mathsf{E}$. The matrix C can be constructed from the HMO coefficients and is

$$\mathsf{C} = \begin{pmatrix} 1/2 & 1/\sqrt{2} & 1/2 \\ 1/\sqrt{2} & 0 & -1/\sqrt{2} \\ 1/2 & -1/\sqrt{2} & 1/2 \end{pmatrix} \tag{9-23}$$

Therefore

$$\mathsf{C}^\dagger\mathsf{C} = \begin{pmatrix} 1/2 & 1/\sqrt{2} & 1/2 \\ 1/\sqrt{2} & 0 & -1/\sqrt{2} \\ 1/2 & -1/\sqrt{2} & 1/2 \end{pmatrix}\begin{pmatrix} 1/2 & 1/\sqrt{2} & 1/2 \\ 1/\sqrt{2} & 0 & -1/\sqrt{2} \\ 1/2 & -1/\sqrt{2} & 1/2 \end{pmatrix}$$

$$= \begin{pmatrix} 1 & 0 & 0 \\ 0 & 1 & 0 \\ 0 & 0 & 1 \end{pmatrix} = \mathsf{1} \tag{9-24}$$

The matrix H for the allyl radical is, in HMO theory,

$$\mathsf{H} = \begin{pmatrix} \alpha & \beta & 0 \\ \beta & \alpha & \beta \\ 0 & \beta & \alpha \end{pmatrix} \tag{9-25}$$

The reader should verify that

$$\mathsf{C}^\dagger\mathsf{H}\mathsf{C} = \begin{pmatrix} \alpha + \sqrt{2}\beta & 0 & 0 \\ 0 & \alpha & 0 \\ 0 & 0 & \alpha - \sqrt{2}\beta \end{pmatrix} = \mathsf{E} \tag{9-26}$$

The diagonal elements can be seen to correspond to the HMO energies. Note that the energy in the (1, 1) position of E corresponds to the MO with coefficients appearing in *column* 1 of C, illustrating the positional correlation of eigenvalues and eigenvectors referred to earlier.

If the basis functions are not orthogonal, $\mathsf{S} \neq \mathsf{1}$ and the procedure is slightly more complicated. Basically, one first transforms to an *orthogonal* basis to obtain an equation of the form $\mathsf{H}'\mathsf{C}' = \mathsf{C}'\mathsf{E}$. One diagonalizes H' as indicated above to find E and C', where C' is the matrix of coefficients in the *orthogonalized* basis. Then one back transforms C' into the original basis set to obtain C. There are many choices available for the orthogonalizing transformation. The Schmidt transformation, based on the Schmidt orthogonalization procedure described in Chapter 6, is popular because it is very rapidly performed by a computer. The details of this procedure are discussed in Appendix 9. Here we will simply indicate the matrix algebra involved. Let the matrix that transforms a nonorthonormal basis to an orthonormal one be symbolized A. As shown in Appendix 9, this matrix satisfies the relation

$$\mathsf{A}^\dagger\mathsf{S}\mathsf{A} = \mathsf{1} \tag{9-27}$$

Furthermore, $|\mathsf{A}| \neq 0$ and so A^{-1} exists. We can insert the unit matrix (in the form $\mathsf{A}\mathsf{A}^{-1}$) wherever we please in the matrix equation $\mathsf{HC} = \mathsf{SCE}$ without affecting the equality. Thus,

$$\mathsf{HAA}^{-1}\mathsf{C} = \mathsf{SAA}^{-1}\mathsf{CE} \tag{9-28}$$

Multiplying from the left by $\mathsf{A}^\dagger$ gives

$$\mathsf{A}^\dagger\mathsf{HAA}^{-1}\mathsf{C} = \mathsf{A}^\dagger\mathsf{SAA}^{-1}\mathsf{CE} \tag{9-29}$$

By Eq. (9-27), this reduces to

$$(\mathsf{A}^\dagger\mathsf{HA})(\mathsf{A}^{-1}\mathsf{C}) = (\mathsf{A}^{-1}\mathsf{C})\mathsf{E} \tag{9-30}$$

where the parentheses serve only to make the following discussion clearer. If we *define* $\mathsf{A}^\dagger\mathsf{HA}$ to be H', and $\mathsf{A}^{-1}\mathsf{C}$ to be C', Eq. (9-30) becomes

$$\mathsf{H}'\mathsf{C}' = \mathsf{C}'\mathsf{E} \tag{9-31}$$

Since we know the matrix H and can compute A from knowledge of S, it is possible to write down an *explicit* H' matrix for a given problem. Then, knowing H' (which is just the *hamiltonian matrix* for the problem in the orthonormal basis), we can seek the unitary matrix C' such that $\mathsf{C}'^\dagger\mathsf{H}'\mathsf{C}'$ is diagonal. These diagonal elements are our orbital energies. (Note that E in Eq. (9-31) is the same as E in $\mathsf{HC} = \mathsf{SCE}$.) To find the coefficients for the MOs in terms of the *original* basis (i.e., to find C), we use the relation

$$\mathsf{AC}' = \mathsf{A}(\mathsf{A}^{-1}\mathsf{C}) = \mathsf{1C} = \mathsf{C} \tag{9-32}$$

One nice feature of this procedure is that, even though we use the inverse matrix A^{-1} in our *formal* development, we never need to actually compute it. (A and $\mathsf{A}^\dagger$ are used to find H', and A is used to find C.) This is fortunate because calculating inverse matrices is a relatively slow process.

A few more words should be said about the process of diagonalizing a hermitian matrix H with a unitary transformation. Two methods are currently in wide use. The older, slower method, known as the *Jacobi* method, requires a series of steps on the starting matrix. In the first step, a matrix O_1 is constructed that causes the largest off-diagonal pair of elements of H to vanish in the transformation $\mathsf{H}_1 = \tilde{\mathsf{O}}_1\mathsf{HO}_1$. Now a second transformation matrix O_2 is constructed to force the largest off-diagonal pair of elements in H_1 to vanish in the transformation $\tilde{\mathsf{O}}_2\mathsf{H}_1\mathsf{O}_2 = \tilde{\mathsf{O}}_2\tilde{\mathsf{O}}_1\mathsf{HO}_1\mathsf{O}_2$. This procedure is continued. However, since each transformation affects more elements in the matrix than just the biggest pair, we eventually "unzero" the pair that was zeroed in forming H_1 or H_2, etc. This means that many more transformations are required than there are off-diagonal pairs. Eventually, however, the off-diagonal elements will have been nibbled away (while the diagonal elements have been building up) until they are all smaller in magnitude than some preselected value, and so we stop the process. The transformation matrix C corresponds to the accumulated product $\mathsf{O}_1\mathsf{O}_2\mathsf{O}_3\ldots$.

A more recently discovered, faster procedure is the Givens–Householder–Wilkinson method. Here, H is first *tridiagonalized*, which means that all elements are made to vanish except those on the main diagonal *as well as on the codiagonals above and below the main diagonal.* This similarity transformation can be done in a few steps, each step zeroing all the necessary elements in an entire row and column. The eigenvalues for the tridiagonal matrix (and hence for the original matrix) may be found one at a time as desired. If only the third lowest eigenvalue is of interest, that one alone can be computed. This is a useful degree of freedom which results in substantial savings of time. Once an eigenvalue is found, its corresponding eigenvector may be computed.

Details of both diagonalization procedures are described in Appendix 9.

9-5 Summary

The steps to be performed in a matrix solution for a linear variation calculation are:

(1) From the basis set, calculate the overlap matrix S.

(2) From the basis set and hamiltonian operator, calculate the hamiltonian matrix H.

(3) If $\mathsf{S} \neq \mathsf{1}$, find an orthogonalization procedure. In the Schmidt method, A is such that $\mathsf{A}^\dagger\mathsf{S}\mathsf{A} = \mathsf{1}$. The matrix equation may now be written in the form $\mathsf{H}'\mathsf{C}' = \mathsf{C}'\mathsf{E}$.

(4) Find C' such that $\mathsf{C}'^\dagger\mathsf{H}'\mathsf{C}'$ is a diagonal matrix. The diagonal elements are the roots E.

(5) If necessary, back transform: $\mathsf{A}\mathsf{C}' = \mathsf{C}$. The columns of C contain the MO coefficients appropriate for the original basis set.

PROBLEMS

9-1 Evaluate the following according to the rules of matrix algebra:

(a) $\begin{pmatrix} 6 & 7 & 8 \end{pmatrix}\begin{pmatrix} 9 \\ 10 \\ 11 \end{pmatrix}$ (b) $\begin{pmatrix} 6 \\ 7 \end{pmatrix}\begin{pmatrix} a & b & c \end{pmatrix}$

(c) $\begin{pmatrix} 4 & 6 \\ i & -3 \end{pmatrix} + 7\begin{pmatrix} 3 & 1 \\ -1 & 3 \end{pmatrix}$ (d) $\begin{pmatrix} \cos\theta & -\sin\theta \\ \sin\theta & \cos\theta \end{pmatrix}\begin{pmatrix} \cos\theta & \sin\theta \\ -\sin\theta & \cos\theta \end{pmatrix}$

(e) $\begin{pmatrix} i & 4 \\ 1 & 7 \\ 0 & -3 \end{pmatrix}\begin{pmatrix} 3 & 2 \\ 4 & 7 \end{pmatrix}$ (f) $\begin{pmatrix} 3 & 2 \\ 4 & 7 \end{pmatrix}\begin{pmatrix} i & 4 \\ 1 & 7 \\ 0 & -3 \end{pmatrix}$

(g) $\begin{vmatrix} \cos\theta & -\sin\theta \\ \sin\theta & \cos\theta \end{vmatrix}$

9-2 If $H_{ij} = \int \chi_i^* \hat{H} \chi_j \, d\tau$ and $\hat{H}$ is hermitian, show that H is a hermitian matrix.

9-3 Let

$$\mathsf{A} = \begin{pmatrix} a_{11} & a_{12} \\ a_{21} & a_{22} \end{pmatrix}, \quad \mathsf{B} = \begin{pmatrix} b_{11} & b_{12} \\ b_{21} & b_{22} \end{pmatrix}$$

Show that, in general, $\mathsf{AB} \neq \mathsf{BA}$.

9-4 Let

$$\mathsf{A} = \begin{pmatrix} 1 & 0 & 0 \\ 0 & 2 & 0 \\ 0 & 0 & 3 \end{pmatrix}, \quad \mathsf{B} = \begin{pmatrix} 4 & 0 & 0 \\ 0 & 5 & 0 \\ 0 & 0 & 6 \end{pmatrix}, \quad \text{and} \quad \mathsf{C} = \begin{pmatrix} 1 & 0 & 1 \\ 0 & 1 & 0 \\ 1 & 0 & 1 \end{pmatrix}$$

Show that $\mathsf{AB} = \mathsf{BA}$, but $\mathsf{AC} \neq \mathsf{CA}$. Compare the matrix AC with CA. Do these matrices show any simple relationship? Can you relate this to properties of A and C mathematically?

9-5 The "latent roots" λ_i of A are solutions to the equation $|\mathsf{A} - \lambda_i \mathsf{1}| = 0$, $i = 1, 2, \ldots, n$, where n is the dimension of A.

(a) Show that, under a similarity transformation $\mathsf{B} = \mathsf{T}^{-1}\mathsf{AT}$, the latent roots are preserved.

(b) Demonstrate that diagonalization of A via a similarity transformation produces the latent roots as the diagonal elements.

9-6 Show that, if a matrix has any latent roots equal to zero, it has no inverse.

9-7 The *trace* (or *spur*) of a matrix is the sum of the elements on the principal diagonal. Thus, $\operatorname{tr} \mathsf{A} = \sum_{i=1}^{n} a_{ii}$.

(a) Show that the trace of a triple product of matrices is invariant under cyclic permutation. That is, $\operatorname{tr}(\mathsf{ABC}) = \operatorname{tr}(\mathsf{CAB}) = \operatorname{tr}(\mathsf{BCA})$ but not $\operatorname{tr}(\mathsf{CBA})$.

(b) Show that the trace of a matrix is invariant under a similarity transformation.

9-8 The *norm* of a matrix is the positive square root of the sum of the absolute squares of all the elements.

For a real matrix A,

$$\text{norm } \mathsf{A} = \left[\sum_{i,j=1}^{n} a_{ij}^2\right]^{1/2} = \left[\sum_i \sum_j (\tilde{\mathsf{A}})_{i,j}(\mathsf{A})_{j,i}\right]^{1/2}$$

Prove that the norm of a real matrix is preserved in an orthogonal transformation (or, you may prefer to prove that the norm of any matrix is preserved in a unitary transformation).

9-9 Use the facts that the trace, the determinant, and the norm of a matrix are invariant under an orthogonal transformation to find the eigenvalues of the following matrices:

(a) $\begin{pmatrix} 0 & 1 & 1 \\ 1 & 0 & 1 \\ 1 & 1 & 0 \end{pmatrix}$, (b) $\begin{pmatrix} 1/2 & 1/\sqrt{2} & 1/2 \\ 1/\sqrt{2} & 0 & -1/\sqrt{2} \\ 1/2 & -1/\sqrt{2} & 1/2 \end{pmatrix}$, (c) $\begin{pmatrix} 0 & 1 & 0 \\ 1 & 2 & 1 \\ 0 & 1 & 0 \end{pmatrix}$

9-10 Consider the matrix

$$\begin{pmatrix} \cos\theta & 0 \\ -\sin\theta & 0 \end{pmatrix}$$

What is the effect of this transformation on $\binom{3}{2}$? On $\binom{3}{3}$?

Can the transformation be uniquely reversed? (That is, for, say, $\theta = 0$, and given a transformed vector $\binom{3}{0}$, can one uniquely determine the vector this was transformed from?)

Does the matrix have an inverse? Evaluate its determinant.

9-11 What are the eigenvectors for the matrix.

$$\mathsf{H} = \begin{pmatrix} 1 & 0 & 0 \\ 0 & -3 & 0 \\ 0 & 0 & -2 \end{pmatrix}?$$

9-12 Show that, if A and B have "simultaneous eigenvectors" (i.e., both diagonalized by the same similarity transformation), then A and B commute.

9-13 If $\mathsf{HC} = \mathsf{CE}$, and $\mathsf{C}^\dagger\mathsf{C} = \mathsf{1}$, then $\mathsf{C}^\dagger\mathsf{HC} = \mathsf{E}$, and we seek a unitary transformation that diagonalizes H. If $\mathsf{HC} = \mathsf{SCE}$, and $\mathsf{C}^\dagger\mathsf{SC} = \mathsf{1}$, then $\mathsf{C}^\dagger\mathsf{HC} = \mathsf{C}^\dagger\mathsf{SCE} = \mathsf{1E}$, and $\mathsf{C}^\dagger\mathsf{HC} = \mathsf{E}$. Since this is the same working equation as the one we found above, why do we not proceed in the same way? Why do we bother orthogonalizing our basis first?

9-14 We have mentioned that a matrix may be used to represent the rotation of coordinates by some angle θ. Such a rotation is a geometric *operation*, so we have, in effect, represented an *operator* with a matrix. It is possible to represent other operators in a similar way. Indeed, an alternative approach to quantum mechanics exists in which the whole formalism is based on matrices and their properties (matrix mechanics, as opposed to wave mechanics). A particularly interesting example is provided by the matrices constructed by Pauli to represent spin operators and functions. It was mentioned in Chapter 5 that spin functions α and β satisfy rules similar to those for orbital angular momentum. Two of these are

$$\hat{S}_z\alpha = \tfrac{1}{2}\alpha, \qquad \hat{S}_z\beta = -\tfrac{1}{2}\beta$$

But it was pointed out that α and β could not be expressed in terms of spherical harmonics. Pauli represented this operator and functions by

$$\alpha = \begin{pmatrix} 1 \\ 0 \end{pmatrix}, \qquad \beta = \begin{pmatrix} 0 \\ 1 \end{pmatrix}, \qquad \hat{S}_z = \frac{1}{2}\begin{pmatrix} 1 & 0 \\ 0 & -1 \end{pmatrix}$$

Using these definitions, show that

$$\int \alpha^\dagger\beta\, d\omega = \int \beta^\dagger\alpha\, d\omega = 0, \qquad \int \alpha^\dagger\alpha\, d\omega = \int \beta^\dagger\beta\, d\omega = 1,$$

$$\hat{S}_z\alpha = \tfrac{1}{2}\alpha, \qquad \hat{S}_z\beta = -\tfrac{1}{2}\beta.$$

[*Note:* since α and β are essentially the Dirac delta functions in the spin coordinate ω, the process of integration reduces here to scalar multiplication of vectors.]

REFERENCES

[1] A. C. Aitken, "Determinants and Matrices," 4th ed. Wiley (Interscience), New York, 1946.

[2] G. Birkhoff and S. MacLane, "A Survey of Modern Algebra." Macmillan, New York, 1953.

CHAPTER 10

THE EXTENDED HÜCKEL METHOD

10-1 The Extended Hückel Method

The extended Hückel (EH) method is much like the simple Hückel method in many of its assumptions and limitations. However, it is of more general applicability since it takes account of all valence electrons, σ *and* π, and it is of more recent vintage because it can only be carried out on a practical basis with the aid of a computer. The basic methods of extended Hückel calculations have been proposed at several times by various people. We will describe the method of Hoffmann [1], which, because of its systematic development and application, is the EHMO method in common use.

The method is described most easily by reference to an example. We will use methane (CH_4) for this purpose.

A. *Selecting Nuclear Coordinates*

The first choice we must make is the molecular geometry to be used. For methane, we will take the H–C–H angles to be tetrahedral and C–H bond distances of 1.1 Å. We can try altering these dimensions later.

Cartesian coordinates for the five atoms are listed in Table 10-1, and the orientation of the nuclei in cartesian space is indicated in Fig. 10-1. (Even though the eigenvalues and MOs one finally obtains are independent of how CH_4 is oriented in cartesian space,[1] it is generally a good idea to choose an orientation that causes some cartesian and symmetry axes to coincide. The resulting

TABLE 10-1
Cartesian Coordinates (in Angstroms) for Atoms of Methane Oriented as Shown in Fig. 10-1

Atom	x	y	z
C	0.0	0.0	0.0
H_a	0.0	0.0	1.1
H_b	1.03709	0.0	−0.366667
H_c	−0.518545	0.898146	−0.366667
H_d	−0.518545	−0.898146	−0.366667

[1] It sometimes happens that an approximation is made which causes the solution to depend on orientation. This is called "loss of rotational invariance."

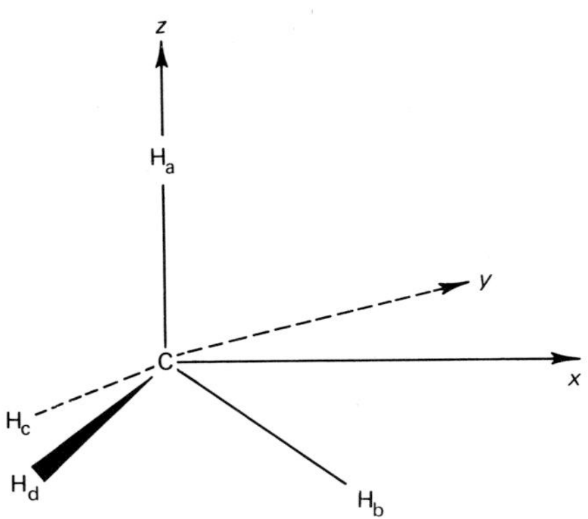

FIG. 10-1 Orientation of methane in cartesian axis system.

expressions for MOs in terms of AOs are generally much simpler to sketch an interpret.)

B. The Basis Set

Next we must select the basis set of functions with which to express th MOs. The extended Hückel method uses the normalized valence AOs for thi purpose. For CH_4, this means a 1s AO on each hydrogen and a 2s, $2p_x$, $2p_y$ and $2p_z$ AO on carbon. The inner-shell 1s AO on carbon is not included. Th AOs are represented by Slater-type orbitals (STOs). Except for the 1s AOs o hydrogen, the exponential parameters of the STOs are determined from Slater' rules (Chapter 5). Various values for the hydrogen 1s AO exponent have bee suggested. These have ranged from the 1.0 given by Slater's rules to a value o $\sqrt{2}$. We will use a value of 1.2, which is near the optimal value for H_2 (see Chapter 7). The STOs for methane are listed in Table 10-2.

TABLE 10-2
Basis AOs for Methane

AO no.	Atom	Type	n^a	l^a	m^a	exp
1	C	2s	2	0	0	1.625
2	C	$2p_z$	2	1	0	1.625
3	C	$2p_x$	2	1	(1)[b]	1.625
4	C	$2p_y$	2	1	(1)[b]	1.625
5	H_a	1s	1	0	0	1.200
6	H_b	1s	1	0	0	1.200
7	H_c	1s	1	0	0	1.200
8	H_d	1s	1	0	0	1.200

[a] n, l, m are the quantum numbers described in Chapter 4.
[b] $2p_x$ and $2p_y$ are formed from linear combinations of $m = +1$ and $m = -1$ STOs, and neither of these AOs can be associated with a particular value of m.

C. *The Overlap Matrix*

Knowing the AO functions and their relative positions enables us to cal-
ulate all their overlaps. This would be a tedious process with pencil and paper. Iowever, the formulas have been programmed for automatic computation, so is step is included in any EH computer program.[2] The computed overlap atrix for the methane molecule is shown in Table 10-3. This matrix is sym-

ABLE 10-3
)verlap Matrix for STOs of Table 10-2

	1	2	3	4	5	6	7	8
	1.0000	0.0	0.0	0.0	0.5133	0.5133	0.5133	0.5133
	0.0	1.0000	0.0	0.0	0.4855	−0.1618	−0.1618	−0.1618
	0.0	0.0	1.0000	0.0	0.0	0.4577	−0.2289	−0.2289
	0.0	0.0	0.0	1.0000	0.0	0.0	0.3964	−0.3964
	0.5133	0.4855	0.0	0.0	1.0000	0.1805	0.1805	0.1805
	0.5133	−0.1618	0.4577	0.0	0.1805	1.0000	0.1805	0.1805
	0.5133	−0.1618	−0.2289	0.3964	0.1805	0.1805	1.0000	0.1805
	0.5133	−0.1618	−0.2289	−0.3964	0.1805	0.1805	0.1805	1.0000

netric (since the overlap between two AOs is independent of their numbering rder) and has diagonal elements of unity since the AOs are normalized. The ero values in the first four rows and columns reflect the orthogonality between ll the s and p AOs on carbon. Other zero values result when hydrogen 1s AOs re centered in nodal planes of carbon p AOs. The geometry of the system is learly reflected in the overlap matrix. For instance, the overlap of the $2p_z$ AO f carbon with the hydrogen 1s AO at H_a is large and positive, while its verlaps with AOs on H_b, H_c, and H_d are negative, equal, and of smaller magni-ude. The 2s AO of carbon, on the other hand, overlaps all 1s AOs equally. Also, the overlap between every pair of hydrogen 1s AOs is the same. Features uch as these provide a useful check on the correctness of our initial cartesian oordinates.

D. *The Hamiltonian Matrix*

We have the overlap matrix S. Next we must find the hamiltonian matrix H. Then we will be in a position to solve the equation HC = SCE for C and E. The matrix H is calculated from a very approximate but simple recipe. The basic deas are similar in spirit to those described in connection with the interpretations f α and β in the simple Hückel method. The energy integral H_{ii} in the EH method s taken to be equal to the energy of an electron in the ith AO of the isolated atom in the appropriate state. The various ionization potentials of atoms are

[2] Several such programs are available from Quantum Chemistry Program Exchange, Chemistry Dept., Room 204, Indiana University, Bloomington, Indiana 47401.

known,[3] so this presents no great difficulty. However, one special problem must be dealt with, namely, finding the appropriate state. In the isolated carbon atom, the lowest-energy states are associated with the configuration $1s^22s^22p^2$. In a saturated molecule such as methane, however, carbon shares electrons with four hydrogens, and calculations indicate that the 2s and all three 2p AOs are about equally involved in forming occupied MOs. That is, in the molecule, carbon behaves as though it were in the $2s2p^3$ configuration. This configuration (shortened to sp^3) is referred to as the *valence state* of carbon in this molecule. Since this is an "open-shell" configuration (i.e., not all the electrons are spin-paired in filled orbitals), there are several actual physical states (corresponding to different spin and orbital angular momenta) that are associated with this configuration. Thus, there are several real physical states, with different ionization potentials, associated with our mentally constructed sp^3 valence state for the atom in a molecule. The question is, what real ionization potentials should we use to evaluate our valence state ionization potential (VSIP)? The approach which is used is simply to *average* the real IPs for loss of a 2p or a 2s electron, the average being taken over all states associated with the sp^3 configuration. Various authors recommend slightly different sets of VSIPs.[4] We use here the values tabulated by Pople and Segal [7]. Because of the rather crude nature of the EH method, the slight variations in VSIP resulting from different choices are of little consequence.[5] For methane, we have

$$(C_{2s}):\quad H_{11} = -19.44 \quad \text{eV} = -0.7144 \quad \text{a.u.} \tag{10-1}$$

$$(C_{2p}):\quad H_{22} = H_{33} = H_{44} = -10.67 \quad \text{eV} = -0.3921 \quad \text{a.u.} \tag{10-2}$$

$$(H_{1s}):\quad H_{55} = H_{66} = H_{77} = H_{88} = -13.60 \quad \text{eV} = -0.50000 \quad \text{a.u.} \tag{10-3}$$

The off-diagonal elements of H are evaluated according to[6]

$$H_{ij} = KS_{ij}(H_{ii} + H_{jj})/2 \tag{10-4}$$

where K is an adjustable parameter. The rationalization for such an expression is that the energy of interaction should be greater when the overlap between AOs is greater, and that an overlap interaction energy between low-energy AOs should be lower than that produced by an equal amount of overlap between higher-energy AOs. We will discuss the energy versus overlap relation in more detail in a later section. The value of K suggested by Hoffmann [1] is

[3] See Moore [2].

[4] See Skinner and Pritchard [3], Hinze and Jaffé [4], Basch *et al.* [5], Anno [6], and Pople and Segal [7].

[5] The proper valence state for carbon in methane differs from that in ethylene, which in turn differs from that in acetylene. Generally, this is ignored in EHMO calculations and a compromise set of VSIPs is selected for use over the whole range of molecules.

[6] This formula is often called the Wolfsberg–Helmholtz relation.

1.75. The reasons for choosing this value will be discussed shortly. For now, we accept this value and arrive at the hamiltonian matrix given in Table 10-4.

By examining H we can guess in advance some of the qualitative features of the MOs that will be produced. For instance, the value of $H_{25}(-0.3790 \text{ a.u.})$

TABLE 10-4
The Extended Hückel Hamiltonian Matrix for CH_4[a]

	1	2	3	4	5	6	7	8
1	−0.7144	0.0	0.0	0.0	−0.5454	−0.5454	−0.5454	−0.5454
2	0.0	−0.3921	0.0	0.0	−0.3790	0.1263	0.1263	0.1263
3	0.0	0.0	−0.3921	0.0	0.0	−0.3573	0.1787	0.1787
4	0.0	0.0	0.0	−0.3921	0.0	0.0	−0.3094	0.3094
5	−0.5454	−0.3790	0.0	0.0	−0.5000	−0.1579	−0.1579	−0.1579
6	−0.5454	0.1263	−0.3573	0.0	−0.1579	−0.5000	−0.1579	−0.1579
7	−0.5454	0.1263	0.1787	−0.3094	−0.1579	−0.1579	−0.5000	−0.1579
8	−0.5454	0.1263	0.1787	0.3094	−0.1579	−0.1579	−0.1579	−0.5000

[a] All energies in a.u.

indicates a strong energy-lowering interaction between the $2p_z$ AO and the 1s AO on H_a. This interaction refers to AOs with positive and negative lobes *as they are assigned in the basis set*. Therefore, we expect a low-energy (bonding) MO to occur where these AOs are mixed with coefficients of the same sign so as not to affect this AO sign relation. A high-energy MO should also exist where the mixing occurs through coefficients of opposite sign, producing an antibonding interaction. The values of H_{26}, H_{27}, and H_{28} are positive, due to negative overlap in corresponding positions of S. In this case, energy lowering will be associated with mixing $2p_z$ with 1s AOs on hydrogens b, c, and d, *but now the mixing coefficients will have signs that reverse the AO sign relations from those pertaining in the original basis*. The AOs that are orthogonal have zero interaction, and so mixing between such AOs will not affect MO energies. (When such AOs are mixed in the same MO, it is often the result of arbitrary mixing between degenerate MOs. In such cases, one can find an orthogonal pair of MOs such that two noninteracting AOs do not appear in the same MO. Methane will be seen to provide an example of this.)

E. The Eigenvalues and Eigenvectors

Having H and S, we now can use the appropriate matrix-handling programs to solve HC = SCE for the matrix eigenvalues on the diagonal of E and the coefficients for the MOs, which are given by the columns of C. The eigenvalues for methane, together with their occupation numbers, are given in Table 10-5. The corresponding coefficients are given in Table 10-6.

TABLE 10-5
MO Energies for Methane by Extended Hückel Method

MO no.	Energy (a.u.)	Occ. no.
8	1.1904	0
7	0.2068	0
6	0.2068	0
5	0.2068	0
4	−0.5487	2
3	−0.5487	2
2	−0.5487	2
1	−0.8519	2

Only two of the eight MOs are nondegenerate. These two MOs must be symmetric or antisymmetric for every symmetry operation of the molecule. This is easily checked by sketching the MOs, referring to the coefficients in the appropriate columns of Table 10-6. The lowest nondegenerate energy occurs in position 1 of our eigenvalue list (Table 10-5), and so the coefficients for this MO are to be found in column 1 of Table 10-6. This column indicates that the MO

TABLE 10-6
Coefficients Defining MOs for Methane

	MO number							
	1	2	3	4	5	6	7	8
1(2s)	0.5842	0.0	0.0	0.0	0.0	0.0	0.0	1.6795
2(2p_z)	0.0	0.5313	−0.0021	−0.0007	−0.0112	−0.0137	1.1573	0.0
3(2p_x)	0.0	0.0021	0.5313	−0.0021	1.1573	−0.0178	0.0110	0.0
4(2p_y)	0.0	0.0007	0.0021	0.5313	0.0176	1.1572	0.0139	0.0
5(1s_a)	0.1858	0.5547	−0.0022	−0.0007	0.0105	0.0128	−1.0846	−0.6916
6(1s_b)	0.1858	−0.1828	0.5237	−0.0019	−1.0260	0.0114	0.3518	−0.6916
7(1s_c)	0.1858	−0.1853	−0.2589	0.4542	0.4943	−0.8977	0.3558	−0.6916
8(1s_d)	0.1858	−0.1865	−0.2626	−0.4516	0.5213	0.8734	0.3770	−0.6916

ϕ_1 is equal to 0.5842 2s + 0.1858 $1s_a$ + 0.1858 $1s_b$ + 0.1858 $1s_c$ + 0.1858 $1s_d$, where the symbols 2s, $1s_a$, etc., stand for AOs on carbon, H_a, etc. A sketch of this MO appears in Fig. 10-2. It is obviously symmetric for all rotations and reflections of a tetrahedron. Notice that this MO is bonding in all four C–H bond regions since the 2s STO on carbon is in phase agreement with all the hydrogen 1s AOs. The higher-energy, nondegenerate MO ϕ_8 is qualitatively similar to ϕ_1 except that the signs are reversed on the 1s AOs (see Table 10-6). Hence, this MO has the same symmetry properties as ϕ_1, but is antibonding in the C–H regions.

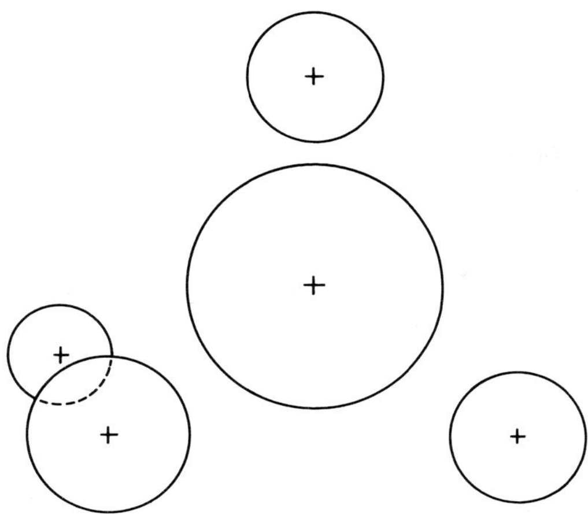

FIG. 10-2 A drawing of the lowest-energy nondegenerate EHMO for methane. The AOs are drawn as though they do not overlap. This is done only to make the drawing simpler. Actually, the AOs overlap strongly.

Since these two MOs resemble the 2s STO in being symmetric for all the symmetry operations of a tetrahedron, we will refer to them as s-type MOs.

The remaining six MOs are grouped into two energy levels, each level being triply degenerate. (It is possible to predict from symmetry considerations alone that the energy levels resulting from this calculation will be nondegenerate and triply degenerate. This is discussed in a later chapter.) Because they are degenerate, the MOs cannot be expected to show *all* the symmetry of the molecule, but it should be possible for them to show *some* symmetry. Consider ϕ_2, as given by column 2 of Table 10-6. This is mainly constructed from the $2p_z$ AO on carbon and 1s AOs on the four hydrogens. Small contributions from $2p_x$ and $2p_y$ are also present, however. It would be nice to remove these small contributions and "clean up" the MO. We can do this, as mentioned earlier, by mixing ϕ_2 with appropriate amounts of ϕ_3 and ϕ_4 since these are all degenerate. The equations that our cleaned-up MO, ϕ_2', must satisfy are

$$\phi_2' = d_2\phi_2 + d_3\phi_3 + d_4\phi_4 \tag{10-5}$$

where (in order to cause all $2p_x$ and $2p_y$ contributions to vanish)

$$\begin{aligned} 0.0021d_2 + 0.5313d_3 + -0.0021d_4 &= 0.0, \\ 0.0007d_2 + 0.0021d_3 + 0.5313d_4 &= 0.0 \\ d_2^2 + d_3^2 + d_4^2 &= 1 \end{aligned} \tag{10-6}$$

As a result,

$$\phi_2' = 0.9999\phi_2 - 0.0040\phi_3 - 0.0013\phi_4 \tag{10-7}$$

A similar procedure to produce an orbital with no p_z or p_y contribution (ϕ_3'), and one with no p_z or p_x contribution (ϕ_4') gives

$$\phi_3' = 0.9999\phi_3 + 0.0040\phi_2 - 0.0040\phi_4 \tag{10-8}$$

$$\phi_4' = 0.9999\phi_4 + 0.0013\phi_2 + 0.0039\phi_3 \tag{10-9}$$

The coefficients for these MOs appear in Table 10-7.

TABLE 10-7
Coefficients for MOs ϕ_2', ϕ_3', ϕ_4'

	ϕ_2'	ϕ_3'	ϕ_4'
2s	0.0	0.0	0.0
$2p_z$	0.5313	0.0	0.0
$2p_x$	0.0	0.5313	0.0
$2p_y$	0.0	0.0	0.5313
$1s_a$	0.5547	0.0	0.0
$1s_b$	−0.1849	0.5228	0.0
$1s_c$	−0.1849	−0.2614	0.4529
$1s_d$	−0.1849	−0.2614	−0.4529

There is no fundamental change produced by intermixing degenerate MOs in this way. The total electronic density and the orbital energies are uninfluenced. The only advantage is that the cleaned-up MOs are easier to sketch and visualize. The MOs ϕ_2', ϕ_3', and ϕ_4' are given in Fig. 10-3.

Each of the MOs in Fig. 10-3 is symmetric or antisymmetric for some of the operations that apply to a tetrahedron. ϕ_2' is symmetric for rotations about the z axis by $2\pi/3$, and also for reflection through the xz plane. This same reflection plane is a symmetry plane for ϕ_3' and ϕ_4', but neither of these MOs shows

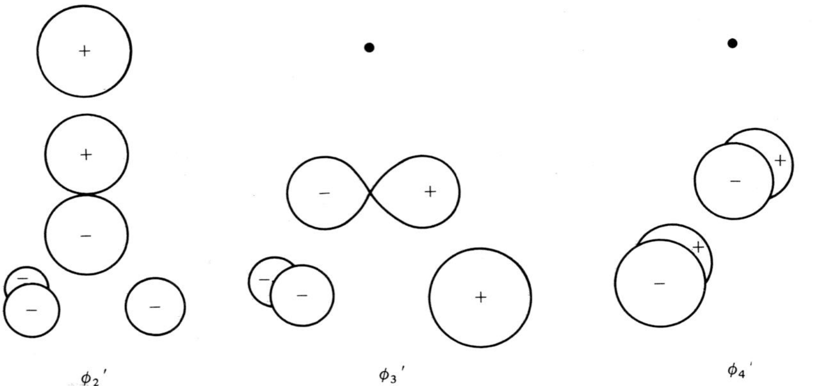

FIG. 10-3 The three lowest-energy degenerate MOs of methane.

symmetry or antisymmetry for rotation about the z axis. Each MO contains one p AO and, perforce, has the symmetry of that AO. We shall refer to these as p-type MOs. Note that hydrogen 1s AOs lying in the nodal plane of a p AO do not mix with that p AO in formation of MOs. This results from zero interaction elements in H, which, in turn, results from zero overlap elements in S. Note also that the MO ϕ_2' is the MO that we anticipated earlier on the basis of inspection of the matrix H. Because of phase agreements between the 1s AOs and the adjacent lobes of the p AOs, these are C–H bonding MOs.

A similar "cleaning up" procedure can be performed on ϕ_5, ϕ_6, and ϕ_7. These turn out to be the C–H antibonding mates to the MOs in Fig. 10-3.

The broad results of this calculation are that there are four occupied C–H bonding MOs, one of s type and three of p type. At higher energies are four unoccupied C–H antibonding MOs, again one of s type and three of p type.

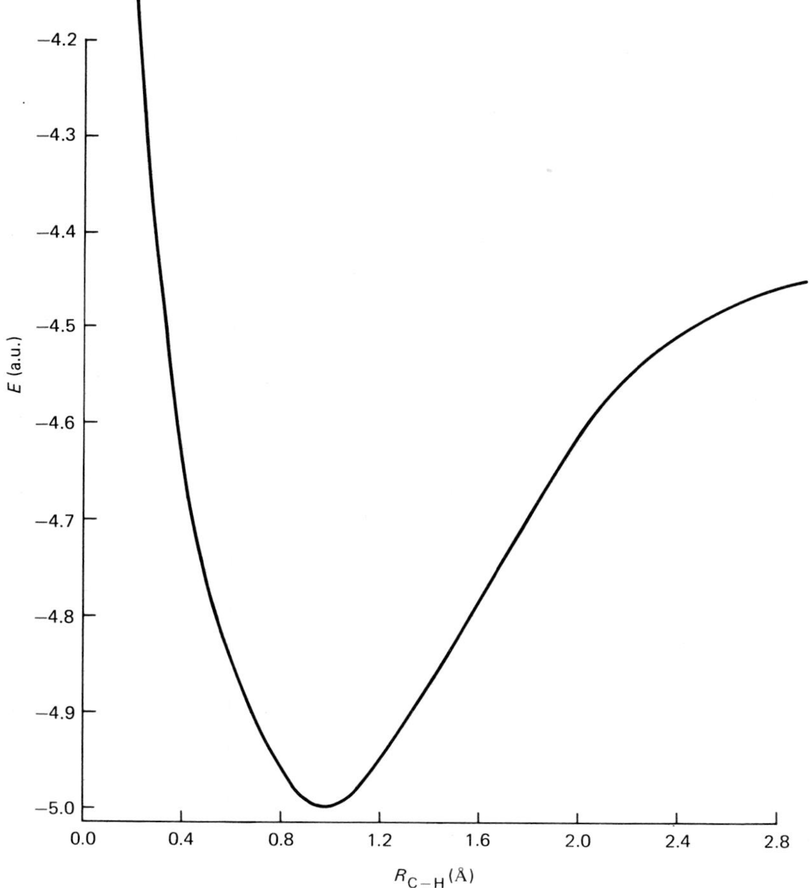

FIG. 10-4 Total extended Hückel energy for CH_4 as a function of C–H bond length.

Note that the s- and the three p-type MOs fall into the same energy pattern as the s and p *AOs* of isolated carbon. Because of their highly symmetric tetrahedral geometry, the hydrogen atoms do not lift the degeneracy of the p AOs. There are many molecules and complexes in which a cluster of atoms or molecules surrounds a central atom in such a highly symmetric way that the degeneracies among certain AOs on the central atom are retained.

F. The Total Energy

The total EH energy is taken as the sum of the one-electron energies. For methane, this is $2 \times (-0.8519) + 6 \times (-0.5487)$, or -4.9963 a.u. There is some ambiguity as to how this energy is to be interpreted. For instance, does it include any of the internuclear repulsion energy? Also, what problems will arise from our neglect of inner-shell electrons? By comparing EH total energy changes with experimental energy changes, it has been decided[7] that the *change*

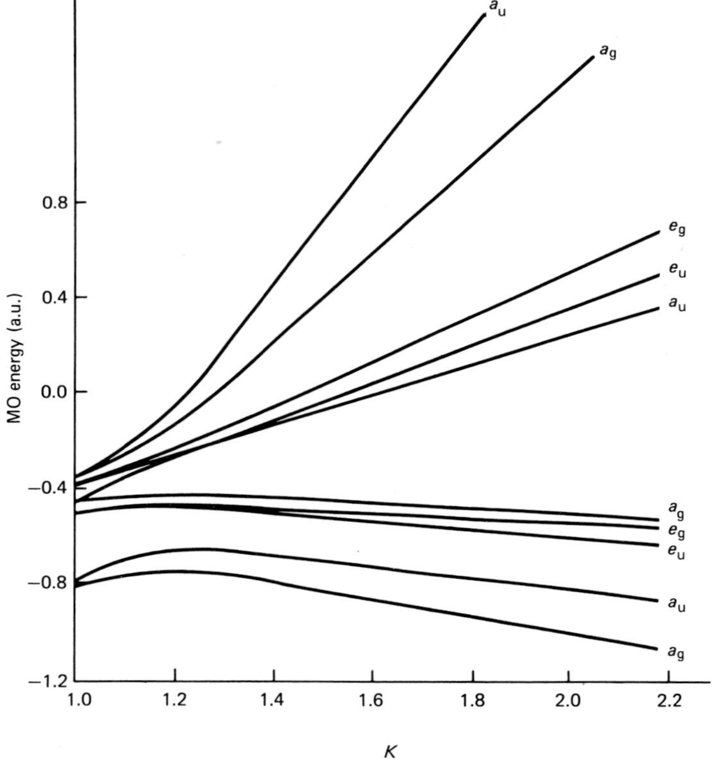

FIG. 10-5 Staggered ethane MO energies versus *K*. C–H distances are 1.1 Å; C–C distance is 1.54 Å; all angles are tetrahedral.

[7] See Hoffmann [1].

in EH total energy upon change of geometry is approximately the same as the actual change in total electronic plus nuclear repulsion energy for the system. Thus, our value of -4.9963 a.u. is not a realistic value for the total (nonrelativistic) energy of methane (the actual value is -40.52 a.u.), but it is meaningful when compared to EH energies for methane at other geometries. For example, if we uniformly lengthen or shorten all the C–H bonds in methane and repeat our EH calculation several times, we can generate an energy curve versus $R_{\text{C-H}}$ for the symmetrical stretch vibrational mode of methane. The resultant plot is given in Fig. 10-4. The EH total energy is minimized at about $R_{\text{C-H}} = 1$ Å, reasonably close to the experimentally observed 1.1-Å distance for the minimum *total* energy of methane.

The appearance of the curve in Fig. 10-4 does encourage us to equate EH total energy changes to changes in actual electronic-plus-nuclear-repulsion

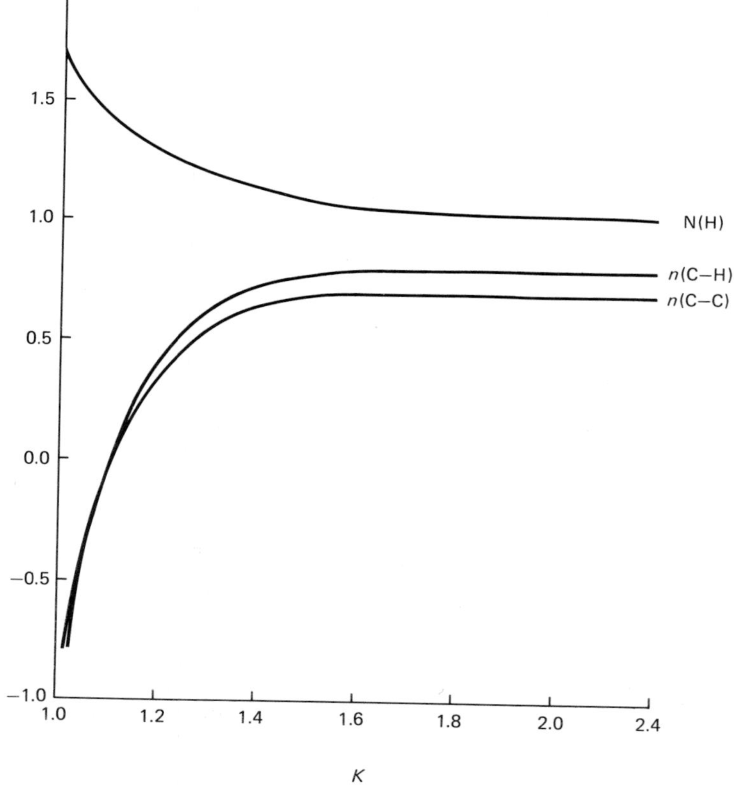

FIG. 10-6 Mulliken gross population on H [N(H)] and Mulliken overlap populations in C–C and C–H bonds [n(C–C) and n(C–H)] of ethane as calculated by the EH method with various values of K.

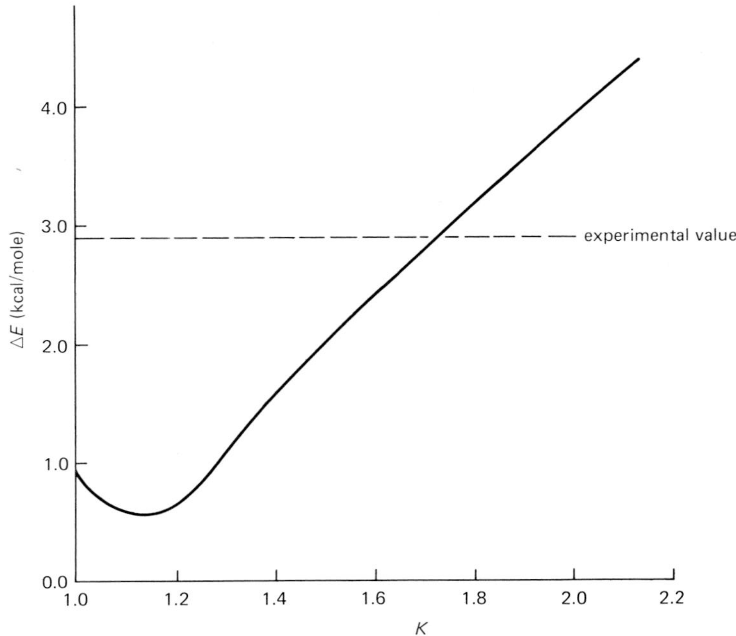

FIG. 10-7 Extended Hückel energy difference between staggered and eclipsed ethanes as a function of *K*.

energies. As we shall see later, this procedure fails for some molecules (notably H_2) and for methane may be regarded as fortuitous.

G. *Fixing the Parameter K*

We mentioned earlier that Hoffmann suggested a value of 1.75 for *K*. We will now indicate the considerations behind this suggestion.

Hoffmann used the ethane molecule C_2H_6 to evaluate *K*. A plot of the orbital energies of staggered ethane as a function of *K* is shown in Fig. 10-5. The energies are linearly dependent on *K* at values of *K* greater than about 1.5. At lower values, the lines curve and some crossing occurs. Hence, in order that the MO energy order not be highly sensitive to *K*, its value should exceed 1.5. A plot of the amount of electronic charge in a bond or at an atom in ethane, as calculated by the EHMO method, versus *K* is shown in Fig. 10-6. We will describe the details of such calculations shortly, but for now, we merely note that the disposition of charge in ethane becomes rather insensitive to *K* at values of *K* greater than about 1.5. In Fig. 10-7 a plot of the EH total energy difference between staggered and eclipsed ethanes versus K is given. This energy difference has an experimentally determined value of 2.875 ± 0.025 kcal/mole, the staggered form being more stable. To give reasonable agreement with this experimental value, K should be about 1.75. Thus, the value $K = 1.75$ is selected because the MO energy order and charge distribution are not sensitive to K in this region and because this value of K gives the correct total energy change for a known physical process. We have also seen earlier that this same value of K leads to a reasonable prediction for the equilibrium bond length in CH_4. Notice that the evaluation of K comes by matching the EH total energy *change* to the total (nuclear repulsion plus electronic) observed energy *change* for internal rotation in ethane. This is consistent with our earlier interpretation of EH total energy.

10-2 Mulliken Populations

We found that the electron densities and bond orders calculated in the simple Hückel method were extremely useful for relating theory to observable molecular properties such as electron spin-resonance splittings or bond lengths. Hence, it is desirable that we find analogous quantities to describe the distribution of electrons in an all-valence-electron method like the EH method. A number of suggestions have been made. The one we use is due to Mulliken [8]. It is the most widely used, and, as we shall see, it has an especially direct and useful connection with the EH method.

Consider a real, normalized MO, ϕ_i, made up from two normalized AOs, χ_j and χ_k:

$$\phi_i = c_{ji}\chi_j + c_{ki}\chi_k \tag{10-10}$$

We square this MO to obtain information about electronic distribution:

$$\phi_i^2 = c_{ji}^2\chi_j^2 + c_{ki}^2\chi_k^2 + 2c_{ji}c_{ki}\chi_j\chi_k \tag{10-11}$$

If we integrate Eq. (10-11) over the electronic coordinates, we obtain (since ϕ_i, χ_j, and χ_k are normalized)

$$1 = c_{ji}^2 + c_{ki}^2 + 2c_{ji}c_{ki}S_{jk} \tag{10-12}$$

where S_{jk} is the overlap integral between χ_j and χ_k. Mulliken suggested that one electron in ϕ_i should be considered to contribute c_{ji}^2 to the electron *net AO population* of χ_j, c_{ki}^2 to the population of χ_k, and $2c_{ji}c_{ki}S_{jk}$ to the *overlap population* between χ_j and χ_k. If there are two electrons in ϕ_i, then these populations should be doubled.

Let q_j^i symbolize the net AO population of χ_j due to one electron in MO ϕ_i, and p_{jk}^i symbolize the overlap population between χ_j and χ_k due to this same electron. The above example leads to the following general definitions:

$$q_j^i = c_{ji}^2 \tag{10-13}$$

$$p_{jk}^i = 2c_{ji}c_{ki}S_{jk} \tag{10-14}$$

We can now sum the contributions due to all the electrons present in the model system, obtaining a *Mulliken net AO population* q_j for each AO χ_j, and a *Mulliken overlap population* p_{jk} for each distinct AO pair χ_j and χ_k:

$$q_j = \sum_i^{\text{MOs}} n_i c_{ji}^2 \equiv \sum_i^{\text{MOs}} n_i q_j^i \tag{10-15}$$

$$p_{jk} = 2 \sum_i^{\text{MOs}} n_i c_{ji} c_{ki} S_{jk} \equiv \sum_i^{\text{MOs}} n_i p_{jk}^i \tag{10-16}$$

Notice that the sum of all the net AO *and* overlap populations must be equal to the total number of electrons in the model system. (In the EH method, this is the total number of *valence* electrons.) This contrasts with the situation in the simple Hückel method where the sum of electron densities *alone*, exclusive of bond orders, equals the total number of pi electrons.

The Mulliken populations are useful indices of the location of electronic charge in the molecule and its bonding or antibonding nature. The contributions to such populations from *one* electron in MO $\phi_{4'}$ of methane are given below (data taken from Tables 10-7 and 10-3):

$$q_{2p_y}^{4'} = (0.5313)^2 = 0.2823 \tag{10-17}$$

$$q_{1s_c}^{4'} = q_{1s_d}^{4'} = (0.4529)^2 = 0.2051 \tag{10-18}$$

$$p_{2p_y-1s_c}^{4'} = p_{2p_y-1s_d}^{4'} = 2(0.5313)(0.4529)(0.3964) = 0.1908 \tag{10-19}$$

$$p_{1s_c-1s_d}^{4'} = 2(0.4529)(-0.4529)(0.1805) = -0.0740 \tag{10-20}$$

All the other populations for $\phi_{4'}$ are zero. These numbers show that an electron in this MO contributes about 28% of an electron to the carbon $2p_y$ net AO population, 20–21% to each of two hydrogen AOs, 19% to each of two C–H bonds, and a negative 7% to the region between H_c and H_d. The last corresponds to an antibonding interaction, as is obvious from an examination of the sketch of $\phi_{4'}$ in Fig. 10-3. (A negative overlap population is interpreted to mean that the amount of charge in the overlap region is less than what would exist if one squared the two AOs and then combined them.)

By summing over the contributions due to all eight valence electrons, we obtain the Mulliken populations shown in Table 10-8. These data are part of the normal output of an EH computer program. The matrix is symmetric, and only the unique elements are tabulated. Such a matrix is named a *Mulliken overlap population matrix*.

The data in Table 10-8 indicate that the hydrogens have positive overlap populations with the 2s and 2p AOs of carbon but have small negative overlap populations with each other. This corresponds to saying that the hydrogens interact with the carbon AOs in a bonding way and in a weakly antibonding way

TABLE 10-8
Mulliken Net AO and Overlap Populations for Methane as Computed by the Extended Hückel Method

	2s	$2p_z$	$2p_x$	$2p_y$	$1s_a$	$1s_b$	$1s_c$	$1s_d$
2s	0.6827	0.0	0.0	0.0	0.2229	0.2229	0.2229	0.2229
$2p_z$		0.5645	0.0	0.0	0.5723	0.0636	0.0636	0.0636
$2p_x$			0.5645	0.0	0.0	0.5087	0.1272	0.1272
$2p_y$				0.5645	0.0	0.0	0.3815	0.3815
$1s_a$					0.6844	−0.0491	−0.0491	−0.0491
$1s_b$						0.6844	−0.0491	−0.0491
$1s_c$							0.6844	−0.0491
$1s_d$								0.6844

with each other. The symmetry equivalence of the four hydrogen atoms results in their having identical net AO populations.

Often we are interested in knowing how the hydrogen atoms interact with the carbon *in toto*, rather than with the 2s and 2p AOs separately. This can be obtained simply by summing all the carbon atom AO contributions together to give a reduced overlap population matrix, shown in Table 10-9. The reduced population matrix makes evident the equivalence of the four C–H bonds, all of which have a total overlap population of 0.7952 electrons.

TABLE 10-9
Reduced Net AO and Overlap Population Matrix for Methane

	C	H_a	H_b	H_c	H_d
C	2.3762	0.7952	0.7952	0.7952	0.7952
H_a		0.6844	−0.0491	−0.0491	−0.0491
H_b			0.6844	−0.0491	−0.0491
H_c				0.6844	−0.0491
H_d					0.6844

The Mulliken population scheme described above assigns some electronic charge to AOs, the rest to overlap regions. An alternative scheme, which assigns all the charge to AOs, was also proposed by Mulliken. One simply divides each overlap population in half, assigning half of the charge to each of the two participating AOs. When all the overlap populations have been reassigned in this way, the electronic charge is all in the AOs, and the sum of these AO charges still equals the total number of electrons. Mulliken called the AO populations resulting from this procedure *gross AO populations*. We will use the symbol

$N(X)$ for the gross population in X, where X can be an AO or an atom (i.e., the sum of all gross AO populations on one atom). Clearly

$$N(X) = q_x + \tfrac{1}{2} \sum_{j \neq x} p_{xj} \tag{10-21}$$

The gross AO populations, gross atomic populations, and the resultant atomic charges (obtained by combining electronic and nuclear charges) for methane are listed in Table 10-10. These data suggest that the carbon has lost

TABLE 10-10
Gross AO Populations, Gross Atomic Populations, and Net Atomic Charges for Methane

	Gross AO population	Gross atom population	Net atomic charge
C_{2s}	1.128	3.966	+0.0334
C_{2p}[a]	0.946		
H[a]	1.008	1.008	−0.0083

[a] All 2p AOs and all H AOs have identical values because they are equivalent through symmetry.

a very small amount of charge to hydrogen upon formation of the molecule. It would be very risky, however, to place much faith in such an interpretation. It turns out that populations are rather sensitive to choice of VSIPs. For example, Hoffmann's original choice of VSIPs differs from that used here, and he obtained gross populations for hydrogen atoms of around 0.9, giving net positive charges of 0.1. Thus, absolute values are not very useful, but *changes* in gross population as we go from one hydrogen to another in the same hydrocarbon molecule or in closely related molecules do appear to be rather insensitive to VSIP choice and are often in accord with results of more accurate calculations.

10-3 Extended Hückel Energies and Mulliken Populations

In Chapter 8 it was shown that a simple quantitative relation exists between the energy of a simple Hückel MO and the contributions of the MO to bond orders [Eq. (8-56)]. The more bonding such an MO is, the lower is its energy. A similar relationship will now be shown to hold for extended Hückel energies and Mulliken populations.

The orbital energy for the real MO ϕ_i is (ignoring the spin variable)

$$E_i = \int \phi_i \hat{H} \phi_i \, dv \Big/ \int \phi_i^2 \, dv \tag{10-22}$$

$$= \sum_{j,k}^{\text{AOs}} c_{ji} c_{ki} H_{jk} \Big/ \sum_{j,k}^{\text{AOs}} c_{ji} c_{ki} S_{jk} \tag{10-23}$$

Assume that ϕ_i is normalized, and so the denominator is unity. The numerator of Eq. (10-23) contains diagonal and off-diagonal terms. If we separate these, and substitute the relation (10-4) for the off-diagonal terms, we obtain

$$E_i = \sum_{j}^{\text{AOs}} c_{ji}^2 H_{jj} + 2 \sum_{j<k}^{\text{AOs}} c_{ji} c_{ki} K S_{jk} (H_{jj} + H_{kk})/2 \tag{10-24}$$

Comparison with Eqs. (10-13) and (10-14) shows that the first sum contains contributions to net AO populations and the second sum contains overlap population contributions. That is,

$$E_i = \sum_{j}^{\text{AOs}} q_j{}^i H_{jj} + \sum_{j>k}^{\text{AOs}} p_{jk}^i K (H_{jj} + H_{kk})/2 \tag{10-25}$$

This equation indicates that the energy of an extended Hückel MO is equal to its net contributions to AO populations times AO energy weighting factors plus its contributions to overlap populations times overlap energy weighting factors.

By summing over all MOs times occupation numbers, we arrive at a relation between *total* EH energy and net AO and overlap populations:

$$E = \sum_{j}^{\text{AOs}} q_j H_{jj} + \sum_{j<k}^{\text{AOs}} p_{jk} K (H_{jj} + H_{kk})/2 \tag{10-26}$$

Equations (10-25) and (10-26) are useful because they permit us to understand computed energies in terms of electron distributions. This is helpful when we seek to understand energy changes which occur as molecules are stretched, bent, or twisted.

There is an important difference between the extended Hückel formulas (10-25) and (10-26) and their simple Hückel counterparts. In a simple Hückel MO, the charge density contributions q^i always add up to unity, contributing α to the MO energy (omitting hereroatom cases). The deviation of the MO energy from α is thus due only to the bond-order contributions p^i. As a result, for hydrocarbons, the simple Hückel MO that is the more bonding of a pair is *always* lower in energy. This is not so, however, in extended Hückel MOs. Since the sum of AO and overlap populations must equal the number of electrons present, we can increase the total amount of overlap population *only* at the expense of net AO populations. Therefore, energy lowering due to the second sum of Eq. (10-25) is purchased at the expense of that due to the first sum. This complicates the situation and requires that we take a more detailed look before issuing any blanket statements.

The following simple example provides a convenient reference point for discussion. Consider two identical 1s AOs, χ_a and χ_b, on identical nuclei separated by a distance R. These AOs combine to form MOs of σ_g and σ_u symmetry. The σ_g MO has an associated positive overlap population and equal positive net AO populations for χ_a and χ_b. If R now is decreased slightly, the overlap population increases slightly (say by 2δ), so the net AO populations must each decrease by δ. The energy change for the MO, then, is

$$\Delta E_{\sigma_g} = -\delta(H_{aa} + H_{bb}) + 2\,\delta K(H_{aa} + H_{bb})/2 \qquad (10\text{-}27)$$

Since the molecule is homonuclear, $H_{aa} = H_{bb}$, and

$$\Delta E_{\sigma_g} = 2\,\delta H_{aa}(K - 1) \qquad (10\text{-}28)$$

If $K > 1$, ΔE_{σ_g} is negative (since H_{aa} is negative). This analysis shows that the choice of 1.75 as the value for K has the effect of making the increase in overlap population dominate the energy change. If K were less than unity, the net AO population changes would dominate.

The above example suggests that the EHMO method lowers the energy by maximizing weighted overlap populations at the expense of net AO populations. It also suggests that the EH energy should be lowered whenever a molecule is distorted in a way that enables overlap population to increase. These are useful rules of thumb, but some caution must be exercised since the existence of several different kinds of atom in a molecule leads to a more complicated relation than that in the above example.

Our methane example illustrates the above ideas. We have already seen that the total EH energy for methane goes through a minimum around $R_{\text{C–H}} = 1$ Å. Let us see how the individual MO energies change as a function of $R_{\text{C–H}}$ and try to rationalize their behaviors in terms of the overlap population changes. A plot of the MO energies is given in Fig. 10-8. The lowest-energy MO is s type and C–H bonding. The overlap between H 1s AOs and the C 2s STO increases as $R_{\text{C–H}}$ decreases. As a result, the energy of this MO decreases as $R_{\text{C–H}}$ decreases, favoring formation of the united atom. The second-lowest energy level is triply degenerate and belongs to p-type C–H bonding MOs. A glance at Fig. 10-3 indicates that overlap between AOs will first increase in magnitude as $R_{\text{C–H}}$ decreases. But ultimately, at small $R_{\text{C–H}}$ this behavior must be reversed because the 1s and 2p AOs are orthogonal when they are isocentric. Therefore, as $R_{\text{C–H}}$ decreases, the overlap population first increases, then decreases toward zero. Consequently, the EH energy of this level first decreases, then increases. Since there are six electrons in this level and only two in the lowest-energy MO, this one dominates the total energy and is responsible for the minimum in Fig. 10-4. The two remaining (unoccupied) levels belong to antibonding MOs, and the overlap population becomes more negative as $R_{\text{C–H}}$ decreases. The p-type level rises less rapidly and eventually passes through a maximum (not shown) because the overlap population must ultimately approach zero as $R_{\text{C–H}}$ approaches zero.

It is important to remember that all these remarks apply to the EH method only. The relationships between the EH method and other methods or with experimental energies is yet to be discussed.

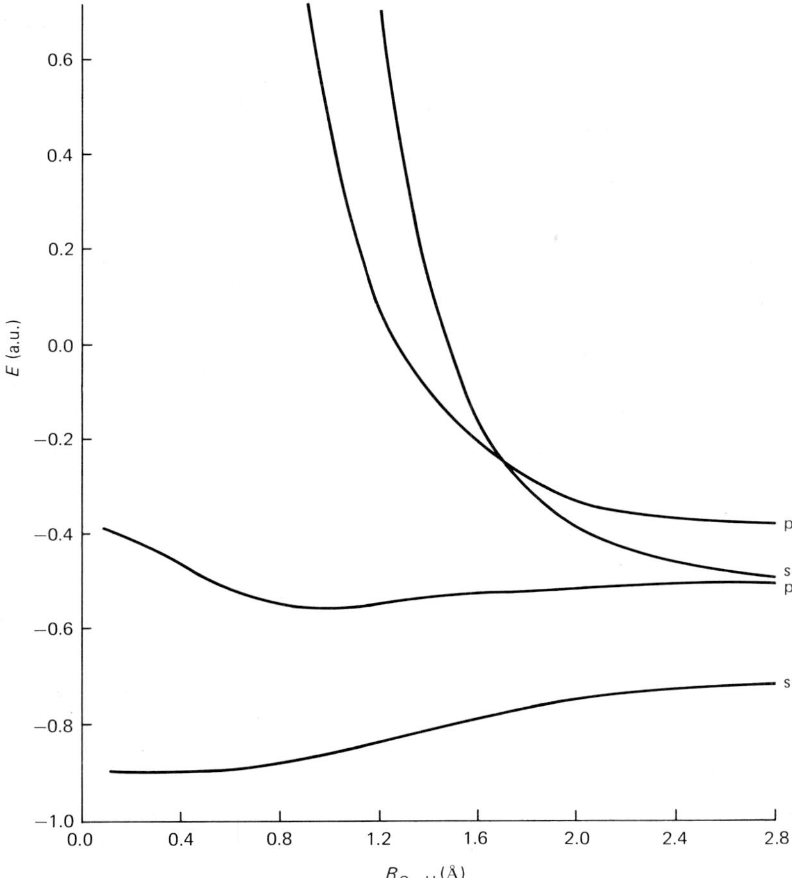

FIG. 10-8 Extended Hückel MO energies for methane as a function of R_{C-H}.

10-4 Extended Hückel Energies and Experimental Energies

We have seen that a change in EH energy reflects certain changes in calculated Mulliken populations. We now consider the circumstances that should exist in order that such EH energy changes agree roughly with actual total energy changes for various systems.

In essence, there are two requirements. First, the population changes calculated by the EH method ought to be in qualitative agreement with the charge shifts which actually occur in the real system. This condition is not always met. Some systems, especially those having unpaired electrons, are not accurately representable by a single-configuration wavefunction (that is, by a single product or a single Slater determinant). An example of this was seen for some 1s2s states of helium (see Chapter 5). Since the EHMO method is based on a single configuration, it is much less reliable for treating such systems. Special methods exist for handling such systems, but they normally are not applied at the Hückel level of approximation.

The second requirement is that, as the charge shifts in the real system, the total energy should change in the way postulated by the EH method. For instance, if the charge increases in bond regions, this should tend to lower the total energy. In actuality, this does not always happen. We can see this by returning to our example of two identical 1s AOs separated by R. The associated σ_g MO increases its overlap population monotonically as R decreases. Therefore, the EH postulate predicts that the total energy should decrease monotonically. It is clear, however, that this does not happen in any real system. If our system is H_2, we know that the experimental energy decreases with decreasing R until $R = R_e$, and increases thereafter (Fig. 7-18). If our system is He_2^{2+}, the experimental total energy *increases* as R decreases, due to the dominance of internuclear repulsion.[8] Consideration of many examples such as these indicates that the postulate is usually qualitatively correct when we are dealing with interactions between neutral, fairly nonpolar systems that are separated by a distance greater than a bond length typical for the atoms involved. These, then, are circumstances under which the EHMO method might be expected to be qualitatively correct.

In brief, we find two kinds of condition limiting the applicability of the EH method. The first is that the system must be reasonably well represented by a single configuration. Hence, closed-shell systems are safest. The second condition is that we apply the method to uncharged nonpolar systems where the nuclei that are undergoing relative motion are not too close to each other.

These conditions are often satisfied by molecules undergoing internal rotation about single bonds. Thus, it is indeed appropriate that the internal rotation barrier in ethane was used to help calibrate the method. A comparison of other EH calculated barriers with experimental values (Table 10-11) gives us some idea of the capabilities and limitations of the method. For all the molecules listed, the most stable conformation predicted by the EH method agrees with experiment. This suggests that one can place a fair amount of reliance on the conformational predictions of the method, at least for threefold symmetric rotors. Also, certain gross quantitative trends, such as the significant reduction as we proceed down the series ethane, methylamine, methanol, are displayed in the EH results, but it is evident that the quantitative predictions of barrier height

[8] Actually, He_2^{2+} has a minimum at short R in its energy curve due to an avoidance of curve crossing (discussed in Chapter 14), but this minimum is unstable with respect to the separated ions. See Pauling [9].

TABLE 10-11
Energy Barriers for Internal Rotation about Single Bonds[a]

Molecule	Barrier (kcal/mole)[b]	
	Calculated	Experiment
CH_3–CH_3	3.04	2.88
CH_3–NH_2	1.66	1.98
CH_3–OH	0.45	1.07
CH_3–CH_2F	2.76	3.33
CH_3–CHF_2	2.39	3.18
CH_3–CF_3	2.17	3.25
CH_3–CH_2Cl	4.58	3.68
CH_3–$CHCH_2$	1.20	1.99
cis-CH_3–CHCHCl	0.11	0.62
CH_3–CHO	0.32	1.16
CH_3–NCH_2	0.44	1.97

[a] Calculated barriers are for rigid rotation, where no bond length or angle changes occur except for the torsional angle change about the internal axis.

[b] The stable form for the first seven molecules has the methyl C–H bonds staggered with respect to bonds across the rotor axis. For the last four molecules, the stable form has a C–H methyl bond eclipsing the double bond.

are not very good. This is not too surprising since the method was calibrated on hydrocarbons. Introduction of halogens, nitrogen, or oxygen produces greater polarity and might be expected to require a different parametrization.

For reasons outlined earlier, we expect even less accuracy in EH calculations of molecular deformations involving bond-angle or bond-length changes. This expectation is generally reinforced by calculation. Molecular shape predictions become poorer for more polar molecules (water is calculated to be most stable when it is linear), and bond-length predictions are quite poor too.

Results such as these have tended to restrict use of the EH method to qualitative predictions of conformation in molecules too large to be conveniently treated by more accurate methods. However, just as the simple Hückel method underwent various refinements (such as the ω technique) to patch up certain inadequacies, so has the EH method been refined. Such refinements[9] have been shown to give marked improvement in numerical predictions of various properties. Activity in this area will undoubtedly continue, and the reader with special interest in using such techniques should consult the literature.

[9] See Kalman [10], Boyd [11], and the references cited in these papers. Also, see Anderson and Hoffmann [12] and Anderson [13].

PROBLEMS

The following output is produced by an EH calculation on the formaldehyde molecule, and is referred to in Problems 10-1 to 10-10.

Formaldehyde (Ground State) Orbital Numbering

Orbital	Atom	n	l	m	x	y	z	exp	H_{ii}
1	H-1	1	0	0	−0.550000	0.952600	0.0	1.200	−13.60
2	H-2	1	0	0	−0.550000	−0.952600	0.0	1.200	−13.60
3	C-3	2	0	0	0.0	0.0	0.0	1.625	−19.44
4	C-3	2	1	0	0.0	0.0	0.0	1.625	−10.67
5	C-3	2	1	1	0.0	0.0	0.0	1.625	−10.67
6	C-3	2	1	1	0.0	0.0	0.0	1.625	−10.67
7	O-4	2	0	0	1.220000	0.0	0.0	2.275	−32.38
8	O-4	2	1	0	1.220000	0.0	0.0	2.275	−15.85
9	O-4	2	1	1	1.220000	0.0	0.0	2.275	−15.85
10	O-4	2	1	1	1.220000	0.0	0.0	2.275	−15.85

$H_{ij} = KS_{ij}(H_{ii} + H_{jj})/2$, with $K = 1.75$.

Distance Matrix (a.u.)

	1	2	3	4
1	0.0	3.6004	2.0787	3.7985
2	3.6004	0.0	2.0787	3.7985
3	2.0787	2.0787	0.0	2.3055
4	3.7985	3.7985	2.3055	0.0

Total effective nuclear repulsion = 17.69537317 a.u.

Formaldehyde Eigenvalues

Eigenvalues (a.u.)	Occ. no.	Eigenvalues (a.u.)	Occ. no.
$E(1) = 1.039011$	0	$E(6) = -0.587488$	2
$E(2) = 0.472053$	0	$E(7) = -0.597185$	2
$E(3) = 0.314551$	0	$E(8) = -0.611577$	2
$E(4) = -0.342162$	0	$E(9) = -0.755816$	2
$E(5) = -0.517925$	2	$E(10) = -1.242836$	2

Sum = −8.625654 a.u.

Total Overlap Matrix

	1	2	3	4	5	6	7	8	9	10
1	1.0000	0.1534	0.5133	0.0	−0.2428	0.4204	0.0813	0.0	−0.0729	0.0392
2	0.1534	1.0000	0.5133	0.0	−0.2428	−0.4204	0.0813	0.0	−0.0729	−0.0392
3	0.5133	0.5133	1.0000	0.0	0.0	0.0	0.3734	0.0	−0.3070	0.0
4	0.0	0.0	0.0	1.0000	0.0	0.0	0.0	0.2146	0.0	0.0
5	−0.2428	−0.2428	0.0	0.0	1.0000	0.0	0.4580	0.0	−0.3056	0.0
6	0.4204	−0.4204	0.0	0.0	0.0	1.0000	0.0	0.0	0.0	0.2146
7	0.0813	0.0813	0.3734	0.0	0.4580	0.0	1.0000	0.0	0.0	0.0
8	0.0	0.0	0.0	0.2146	0.0	0.0	0.0	1.0000	0.0	0.0
9	−0.0729	−0.0729	−0.3070	0.0	−0.3056	0.0	0.0	0.0	1.0000	0.0
10	0.0392	−0.0392	0.0	0.0	0.0	0.2146	0.0	0.0	0.0	1.0000

Eigenvectors

	1	2	3	4	5	6	7	8	9	10
1	0.5279	0.7683	0.8924	0.0	−0.4281	−0.2016	0.0	−0.2141	−0.2721	0.0011
2	0.5279	0.7683	−0.8924	0.0	0.4281	−0.2016	0.0	0.2141	−0.2721	0.0011
3	−1.3964	−0.5553	0.0000	0.0	−0.0000	−0.0460	0.0	−0.0000	−0.4875	0.2550
4	0.0	0.0	0.0	0.9940	0.0	0.0	0.2456	0.0	0.0	0.0
5	−0.6043	1.1727	−0.0000	0.0	0.0000	0.2768	0.0	0.0000	0.2245	0.0685
6	0.0000	−0.0000	−1.2519	0.0	−0.3813	0.0000	0.0	−0.3179	0.0000	0.0000
7	0.8367	−0.4799	0.0000	0.0	0.0000	−0.0884	0.0	−0.0000	0.3066	0.8481
8	0.0	0.0	0.0	−0.4532	0.0	0.0	0.9181	0.0	0.0	0.0
9	−0.6960	0.3412	−0.0000	0.0	0.0000	−0.8317	0.0	−0.0000	0.3327	0.0252
10	−0.0000	0.0000	0.2511	0.0	0.6475	0.0000	0.0	−0.7600	−0.0000	−0.0000

Mulliken Overlap Populations for 12 Electrons

	1	2	3	4	5	6	7	8	9	10
1	0.6876	−0.0702	0.2920	0.0	0.1134	0.3890	−0.0210	0.0	−0.0225	−0.0180
2	−0.0702	0.6876	0.2920	0.0	0.1134	0.3890	−0.0210	0.0	−0.0225	−0.0180
3	0.2920	0.2920	0.6097	0.0	0.0	0.0	0.1058	0.0	0.1443	0.0
4	0.0	0.0	0.0	0.1207	0.0	0.0	0.0	0.1936	0.0	0.0
5	0.1134	0.1134	0.0	0.0	0.2634	0.0	0.1876	0.0	0.1880	0.0
6	0.3890	0.3890	0.0	0.0	0.0	0.4929	0.0	0.0	0.0	−0.0046
7	−0.0210	−0.0210	0.1058	0.0	0.1876	0.0	1.6420	0.0	0.0	0.0
8	0.0	0.0	0.0	0.1936	0.0	0.0	0.0	1.6857	0.0	0.0
9	−0.0225	−0.0225	0.1443	0.0	0.1880	0.0	0.0	0.0	1.6061	0.0
10	−0.0180	−0.0180	0.0	0.0	0.0	−0.0046	0.0	0.0	0.0	1.9939

Charge Matrix for MOs with Two Electrons in Each

	1	2	3	4	5	6	7	8	9	10
1	0.1664	0.3881	0.4266	0.0	0.4258	0.1088	0.0	0.1476	0.3363	0.0004
2	0.1664	0.3881	0.4266	0.0	0.4258	0.1088	0.0	0.1476	0.3363	0.0004
3	0.9171	0.0561	0.0000	0.0	0.0000	0.0028	0.0	0.0000	0.7358	0.2882
4	0.0	0.0	0.0	1.7825	0.0	0.0	0.2175	0.0	0.0	0.0
5	0.3198	1.1155	0.0000	0.0	0.0000	0.3257	0.0	0.0000	0.1775	0.0614
6	0.0000	0.0000	1.1204	0.0	0.4593	0.0000	0.0	0.4203	0.0000	0.0000
7	0.2082	0.0241	0.0000	0.0	0.0000	0.0021	0.0	0.0000	0.1123	1.6534
8	0.0	0.0	0.0	0.2175	0.0	0.0	1.7825	0.0	0.0	0.0
9	0.2220	0.0282	0.0000	0.0	0.0000	1.4518	0.0	0.0000,	0.3017	−0.0037
10	0.0000	0.0000	0.0264	0.0	0.6891	0.0000	0.0	1.2845	0.0000	0.0000

Reduced Overlap Population Matrix Atom by Atom

	1	2	3	4
1	0.6876	−0.0702	0.7945	−0.0615
2	−0.0702	0.6876	0.7945	−0.0615
3	0.7945	0.7945	1.4866	0.8148
4	−0.0615	−0.0615	0.8148	6.9277

Orbital Charges

1	1.018973	6	0.879574
2	1.018973	7	1.767672
3	1.026764	8	1.782529
4	0.217471	9	1.749778
5	0.564637	10	1.973630

Net Charges

1	−0.018973	3	1.311555
2	−0.018973	4	−1.273609

Total charge = 0.000000.

10-1 Use the output to determine the orientation of the molecule with respect to cartesian coordinates. Sketch the molecule in relation to these axes and number the *atoms* in accord with their numbering in the output.

10-2 Use the orbital numbering data together with the overlap matrix to figure out which of the labels 1s, 2s, $2p_x$, $2p_y$, $2p_z$ goes with each of the ten AOs (i.e., it is obvious that AO 1 is a 1s AO, but it is not so obvious what AO 5 is).

10-3 Use your conclusions from above, together with coefficients in the eigenvector matrix to sketch the MOs having energies of −0.756, −0.611, and −0.597 a.u. Which of these are π MOs? Which are σ MOs?

10-4 Label each of the ten MOs "π" or "σ" by inspecting the coefficient matrix.

10-5 What is the Mulliken overlap population between C and O $2p_\pi$ AOs in this molecule? Should removal of an electron from MO 7 cause the C=O bond to shorten or to lengthen?

10-6 Demonstrate that MO 7 satisfies Eq. (10-24). (Note that H_{ii} values in the first table are in units of electron volts, while orbital energies are in atomic units.)

10-7 Use the reduced overlap population matrix to verify that the sum of AO and overlap populations is equal to the number of valence electrons.

10-8 Using MO 7 as your example, verify that the charge matrix table is a tabulation of the contributions of each MO to *gross* atom populations.

10-9 In the list of "orbital charges," are the "orbitals" MOs or AOs? Demonstrate how these numbers are derived from those in the charge matrix.

10-10 What is the physical meaning of the "net charges" in the data? Would you characterize these results as indicative of low polarity? Which end of the molecule should correspond to the negative end of the dipole moment?

10-11 How many MOs will be produced by an EHMO calculation on butadiene?

REFERENCES

[1] R. Hoffmann, *J. Chem. Phys.* **39**, 1397 (1963).

[2] C. E. Moore, Atomic energy levels, *Natl. Bur. Std.* (*U.S.*) *Circ. 467*. Natl. Bur. Std., Washington D.C., 1949.

[3] H. A. Skinner and H. O. Pritchard, *Trans. Faraday Soc.* **49**, 1254 (1953).

[4] J. Hinze and H. H. Jaffé, *J. Am., Chem. Soc.* **84**, 540 (1962).

[5] H. Basch, A. Viste, and H. B. Gray, *Theoret. Chim. Acta* **3**, 458 (1965).

[6] T. Anno, *Theoret. Chim. Acta* **18**, 223 (1970).

[7] J. A. Pople and G. A. Segal, *J. Chem. Phys.* **43**, S136 (1965).

[8] R. S. Mulliken, *J. Chem. Phys.* **23**, 1833, 1841, 2338, 2343 (1955).

[9] L. Pauling, *J. Chem. Phys.* **1**, 56 (1933).

[10] B. L. Kalman, *J. Chem. Phys.* **60**, 974 (1974).

[11] D. B. Boyd, *Theoret. Chim. Acta* **30**, 137 (1973).

[12] A. B. Anderson and R. Hoffmann, *J. Chem. Phys.* **60**, 4271 (1974).

[13] A. B. Anderson, *J. Chem. Phys.* **62**, 1187 (1975).

CHAPTER 11

THE SCF–LCAO–MO METHOD AND EXTENSIONS

11-1 *Ab Initio* Calculations

A rigorous variational calculation on a system involves the following steps.

(1) Write down the hamiltonian operator $\hat{H}$ for the system.

(2) Select some mathematical functional form ψ as the trial wavefunction. This form should have variable parameters.

(3) Minimize

$$\bar{E} = \int \psi^* \hat{H} \psi \, d\tau \Big/ \int \psi^* \psi \, d\tau \qquad (11\text{-}1)$$

with respect to variations in the parameters.

The simple and extended Hückel methods are not rigorous variational calculations. Although they both make use of the secular determinant technique from linear variation theory, no hamiltonian operators are ever written out explicitly and the integrations in H_{ij} are not performed. These are *semiempirical* methods because they combine the theoretical form with parameters fitted from experimental data.

The term *ab initio* ("from the beginning") is used to describe calculations in which the three steps listed above are all explicitly performed. In this chapter we describe a certain kind of *ab initio* calculation called the self-consistent field (SCF) method. This is by far the most commonly encountered type of *ab initio* calculation for atoms or molecules. We also describe a popular method for proceeding beyond the SCF level of approximation.

The SCF method and extensions to it are mathematically and physically considerably more complicated than the one-electron methods already discussed. Thus, one normally does not perform such calculations with pencil and paper, but rather with complicated computer programs. Therefore, in this chapter we are not concerned with *how* one does such calculations because, in most cases, they are done by acquiring a program written by a group of specialists. Rather we are concerned with a description of the mathematical and physical underpinnings of the method. Because the method is simultaneously complicated and rigorously defined, a special jargon has developed. Terms like "Hartree–Fock," or "correlation energy" have specific meanings and are pervasive in the literature. Hence, a good deal of emphasis in this chapter is put on defining some of these important terms.

11-2 The Molecular Hamiltonian

In practice, one usually does not use the complete hamiltonian for an isolated molecular system. The complete hamiltonian includes nuclear and electronic kinetic energy operators, electrostatic interactions between all charged particles, and interactions between all magnetic moments due to spin and orbital motions of nuclei and electrons. Also an accounting for the fact that a moving particle experiences a change in mass due to relativistic effects is included in the complete hamiltonian. The resulting hamiltonian is much too complicated to work with. Usually, relativistic mass effects are ignored, the Born–Oppenheimer approximation is made (to remove nuclear kinetic energy operators), and all magnetic interactions are ignored (except in special cases where we are interested in spin coupling). The resulting hamiltonian for the electronic energy is, in atomic units,

$$\hat{H} = -\tfrac{1}{2}\sum_{i=1}^{n} \nabla_i^2 - \sum_{\mu=1}^{N}\sum_{i=1}^{n} (Z_\mu/r_{\mu i}) + \sum_{i=1}^{n-1}\sum_{j=i+1}^{n} 1/r_{ij} \tag{11-2}$$

where i and j are indices for the n electrons and μ is an index for the N nuclei. The nuclear repulsion energy V_{nn} is

$$V_{\mathrm{nn}} = \sum_{\mu=1}^{N-1}\sum_{\nu=\mu+1}^{N} Z_\mu Z_\nu/r_{\mu\nu} \tag{11-3}$$

In choosing this hamiltonian, we are in effect electing to seek an upper bound for the energy of an idealized nonexistent system—a nonrelativistic system with clamped nuclei and no magnetic moments. If we wish to make a very accurate comparison of our computed results with experimentally measured energies, it is necessary to modify either the experimental or the theoretical numbers to compensate for the omissions in $\hat{H}$.

11-3 The Form of the Wavefunction

The wavefunction for an SCF calculation is one or more antisymmetrized products of one-electron spin–orbitals. We have already seen (Chapter 5) that a convenient way to produce an antisymmetrized product is to use a Slater determinant. Therefore, we take the trial function ψ to be made up of Slater determinants containing spin-orbitals ϕ. If we are dealing with an atom, then the ϕ's are atomic spin-orbitals. For a molecule, they are molecular spin-orbitals.

In our discussion of many-electron atoms (Chapter 5), we noted that certain atoms in their ground states are fairly well described by assigning two electrons, one of each spin, to each AO, starting with the lowest-energy AO and working up until all the electrons are assigned. If the last electron completes the filling of all the AOs at a given energy level, we have a *closed subshell* atomic system. Examples are He($1s^2$), Be($1s^2 2s^2$), and Ne($1s^2 2s^2 2p^6$). Such systems tend to be well approximated by a single determinantal wavefunction if the highest filled level is not too close in energy to the lowest empty level. (Beryllium is the least successfully treated of these three at this level of approximation because the 2s level is fairly close in energy to the 2p level.) A similar situation holds for molecules; that is, the wavefunctions of many molecules in their ground states are well represented by single determinantal wavefunctions with electrons of paired spins occupying identical MOs. Such molecules are said to be *closed-shell* systems. We can represent a trial wavefunction for a $2n$-electron closed-shell system as

$$\psi_{\text{closed shell}} = |\phi_1(1)\bar{\phi}_1(2)\phi_2(3)\bar{\phi}_2(4)\cdots\phi_n(2n-1)\bar{\phi}_n(2n)| \tag{11-4}$$

where we have used the shorthand form for a Slater determinant described in Chapter 5. *For the present, we restrict our discussion to closed-shell single-determinantal wavefunctions.*

11-4 The Nature of the Basis Set

Some functional form must be chosen for the MOs ϕ. The usual choice is to approximate ϕ as a linear combination of "atomic orbitals" (LCAO), these AOs being located on the nuclei. The detailed nature of these AOs, as well as the number to be placed on each nucleus, is still open to choice. We consider these choices later. For now, we simply recognize that we are working within the familiar LCAO–MO level of approximation. If we represent the basis AOs by χ, we have

$$\phi_i = \sum_i c_{ji}\chi_j \tag{11-5}$$

where the constants c_{ji} are as yet undetermined.

11-5 The LCAO–MO–SCF Equation

Having a hamiltonian and a trial wavefunction, we are now in a position to use the linear variation method. The detailed derivation of the resulting equations is complicated and notationally clumsy, and it has been relegated to Appendix 7. Here we discuss the results of the derivation.

For our restricted case of a closed-shell single-determinantal wavefunction, the variation method leads to

$$\hat{F}\phi_i = \epsilon_i\phi_i \tag{11-6}$$

These equations are sometimes called the Hartree–Fock equations, and $\hat{F}$ is often called the Fock operator. The detailed formula for $\hat{F}$ is (from Appendix 7)

$$\hat{F}(1) = -\tfrac{1}{2}\nabla_1{}^2 - \sum_{\mu}(Z_\mu/r_{\mu 1}) + \sum_{j=i}^{n}(2\hat{J}_j - \hat{K}_j) \tag{11-7}$$

The symbols $\hat{J}_j$ and $\hat{K}_j$ stand for operators related to the $1/r_{ij}$ operators in $\hat{H}$. $\hat{J}_j$ is called a *coulomb operator* because it leads to energy terms corresponding to charge cloud repulsions. It is possible to write $\hat{J}_j$ explicitly:

$$\hat{J}_j = \int \phi_j{}^*(2)(1/r_{12})\phi_j(2)\, d\tau(2) \tag{11-8}$$

$\hat{K}_j$ leads ultimately to the production of exchange integrals, and so it is called an *exchange operator*. It is written explicitly in conjunction with a function on which it is operating, viz.

$$\hat{K}_j\phi_i(1) = \int \phi_j{}^*(2)(1/r_{12})\phi_i(2)\, d\tau(2)\phi_j(1) \tag{11-9}$$

Notice that an index exchange has been performed. It is not difficult to see that the expression (see Appendix 11 for bra–ket notation)

$$\langle\phi_i|\hat{F}|\phi_i\rangle = \epsilon_i \tag{11-10}$$

will lead to integrals such as

$$\langle\phi_i|\hat{J}_j|\phi_i\rangle = \langle\phi_i(1)\phi_j(2)|1/r_{12}|\phi_i(1)\phi_j(2)\rangle = J_{ij} \tag{11-11}$$

$$\langle\phi_i|\hat{K}_j|\phi_i\rangle = \langle\phi_i(1)\phi_j(2)|1/r_{12}|\phi_i(2)\phi_j(1)\rangle = K_{ij} \tag{11-12}$$

which are formally the same as the coulomb and exchange terms encountered in Chapter 5 in connection with the helium atom. Notice that, if the spins associated with spin-orbitals ϕ_i and ϕ_j differ, K_{ij} must vanish. This arises because integrations over space and spin coordinates of electron 1 (or 2) in Eq. (11–12) lead to integration over two different (and orthogonal) spin functions. On the other hand, J_{ij} is not affected by such spin agreement or disagreement.

It would appear from Eq. (11-6) that the MOs ϕ are eigenfunctions of the Fock operator and that the Fock operator is, in effect, the hamiltonian operator. There is an important qualitative difference between $\hat{F}$ and $\hat{H}$, however. *The Fock operator is itself a function of the MOs* ϕ. Since the summation index j in Eq. (11-7) includes i, the operators $\hat{J}_i$ and $\hat{K}_i$ must be known in order to write down $\hat{F}$, but $\hat{J}_i$ and $\hat{K}_i$ involve ϕ_i, and ϕ_i is an eigenfunction of $\hat{F}$. Hence, we need $\hat{F}$ to find ϕ_i, and we need ϕ_i to know $\hat{F}$. To circumvent this problem, an iterative approach is used. One makes an initial guess at the MOs ϕ. (One could use a semiempirical method to produce this starting set.) Then these MOs are used to construct an operator $\hat{F}$, which is used to solve for the new MOs ϕ'. These are then used to construct a new Fock operator, which is in turn used to find new MOs, which are used for a new $\hat{F}$, etc., until at last no significant change is detected in two successive steps of this procedure. At this point, the ϕ's *produced by* $\hat{F}$ are the same as the ϕ's that produce the coulomb-and-exchange fields *in* $\hat{F}$. The solutions are said to be self-consistent, and the method is referred to as the self-consistent-field (SCF) method.

11-6 Interpretation of the LCAO–MO–SCF Eigenvalues

The physical meaning of an eigenvalue ϵ_i is best understood by expanding the integral

$$\epsilon_i = \langle \phi_i | \hat{F} | \phi_i \rangle \tag{11-13}$$

with $\hat{F}$ given by Eq. (11-7). We obtain

$$\epsilon_i = \langle \phi_i | -\tfrac{1}{2}\nabla_1{}^2 | \phi_i \rangle - \sum_{\mu} \langle \phi_i | Z_\mu / r_{\mu 1} | \phi_i \rangle + \sum_{j=1}^{n} (2J_{ij} - K_{ij}) \tag{11-14}$$

It is common practice to combine the first two terms of Eq. (11-14), which depend only on the nature of ϕ_i, into a single expectation value of the one-electron part of the hamiltonian, symbolized H_{ii}. Thus,

$$\epsilon_i = H_{ii} + \sum_{j=1}^{n} (2J_{ij} - K_{ij}) \tag{11-15}$$

The quantity H_{ii} is the average kinetic plus nuclear–electronic attraction energy for the electron in ϕ_i.

The sum of coulomb and exchange integrals in Eq. (11-15) contains all the electronic interaction energy. Observe that the index j runs over all the occupied MOs. For a particular value of j, say $j = k \neq i$, this gives $2J_{ik} - K_{ik}$ as an interaction energy. This means that an electron in ϕ_i experiences an interaction energy with the *two* electrons in ϕ_k of

$$2\langle \phi_i(1)\phi_k(2) | 1/r_{12} | \phi_i(1)\phi_k(2) \rangle - \langle \phi_i(1)\phi_k(2) | 1/r_{12} | \phi_k(1)\phi_i(2) \rangle \tag{11-16}$$

The first part is the classical repulsion between the electron having an orbital charge cloud given by $|\phi_i|^2$ and the two electrons having charge cloud $|\phi_k|^2$. The second part is the exchange term which, as we saw in Chapter 5, arises from the antisymmetric nature of the wavefunction. It enters (11-16) only once because the electron in ϕ_i agrees in spin with only one of the two electrons in

ϕ_k. [Equation (11-15) applies because we have restricted our discussion to closed-shell systems.]

The summation over $2J_{ij} - K_{ij}$ includes the case $j = i$. Here we get $2J_{ii} - K_{ii}$. However, examination of Eqs. (11-11) and (11-12) shows that $J_{ii} = K_{ii}$, and we are left with J_{ii}. This corresponds to the repulsion between the electron in ϕ_i (the energy of which we are calculating) and the other electron in ϕ_i. Because these electrons must occur with opposite spin, there is no exchange energy for this interaction.

In brief, then, the quantity ϵ_i, often referred to as an *orbital energy* or a *one-electron energy*, is to be interpreted as the energy of an electron in ϕ_i, resulting from its kinetic energy, its energy of attraction for the nuclei, and its repulsion and exchange energies due to all the other electrons in their charge clouds $|\phi_j|^2$.

11-7 The SCF Total Electronic Energy

It is natural to suppose that the total electronic energy is merely the sum of the one-electron energies, but this is not the case in SCF theory. Consider a two-electron system. The energy of electron 1 includes its kinetic and nuclear attraction energies and its repulsion and exchange energies for electron 2. The energy of electron 2 includes its kinetic and nuclear attraction energies and its repulsion and exchange energies for electron 1. If we sum these, we have accounted properly for kinetic and nuclear attraction energies, but we have included the interelectronic interactions *twice* as much as they actually occur. (The energy of repulsion, say, between two charged particles, 1 and 2, is given by the repulsion of 1 for 2 *or* of 2 for 1, but not by the sum of these.) Therefore, if we sum one-electron energies, we get the total electronic energy plus an extra measure of electron repulsion and exchange energy. We can correct this by subtracting this extra measure away. Thus, for our closed-shell system

$$E_{\text{elec}} = \sum_{i=1}^{n} \left[2\epsilon_i - \sum_{j=1}^{n} (2J_{ij} - K_{ij})\right] \tag{11-17}$$

Comparing Eq. (11-17) with (11-15) makes it evident that we can also write

$$E_{\text{elec}} = \sum_{i=1}^{n} \left[2H_{ii} + \sum_{j=1}^{n} (2J_{ij} - K_{ij})\right] \tag{11-18}$$

or

$$E_{\text{elec}} = \sum_{i=1}^{n} (\epsilon_i + H_{ii}) \tag{11-19}$$

To obtain the *total* (electronic plus nuclear) energy, we add the internuclear repulsion energy for the N nuclei:

$$E_{\text{tot}} = E_{\text{elec}} + V_{\text{nn}} \tag{11-20}$$

$$V_{\text{nn}} = \sum_{\mu=1}^{N-1} \sum_{\nu=\mu+1}^{N} \frac{Z_\mu Z_\nu}{r_{\mu\nu}} \tag{11-21}$$

11-8 Basis Sets

A great deal of research effort has gone into devising and comparing basis sets for *ab initio* calculations. There are essentially two important criteria:

(1) We want a basis set that is capable of describing the actual wavefunction well enough to give chemically useful results.

(2) We want a basis set that leads to integrals F_{ij} and S_{ij}, which we can evaluate reasonably accurately and cheaply on a computer.

Many types of basis set have been examined and two of these have come to dominate the area of *ab initio* molecular calculations. These two, which we refer to as the gaussian and the Slater-type-orbital (STO) basis sets, are actually very similar in many important respects.

Let us consider the STO basis set first. The essence of this basis choice is to place on each nucleus one or more STOs. The number of STOs on a nucleus and the orbital exponent of each STO remain to be chosen. Generally, the larger the number of STOs and/or the greater the care taken in selecting orbital exponents, the more accurate the final wavefunction and energy will be.

At the least sophisticated end of the spectrum of choices is the *minimal basis set of STOs*, which we encountered in Chapter 7. This includes only those STOs that correspond to occupied AOs in the separated atom limit. If we choose a minimal basis set, then we must still decide how to evaluate the orbital exponents in the STOs. One way is to use Slater's rules, which are actually most appropriate for isolated atoms. Another way is to vary the orbital exponents until the energy of the molecular system is minimized. This amounts to performing a nonlinear variational calculation along with the linear variational calculation. For molecules of more than a few atoms, this procedure is prohibitively expensive, for reasons we will describe shortly, but for small molecules (two or three first-row atoms plus a few hydrogens) it is possible to accomplish this task. From this, one discovers what orbital exponent best suits an STO in a molecular environment. This leads us to the third way of choosing orbital exponents—choose the values that were found best for each type of atom in nonlinear variation in smaller molecules.

One may improve the basis by adding additional STOs to various nuclei. Suppose, for example, each carbon 2p AO were represented as a linear combination of two p-type STOs, each having a different orbital exponent. An example of the basic principle involved is indicated in Fig. 11-1. If we treat these functions independently and do a linear variational calculation, they will both be mixed into the final wavefunction to some degree. If the *linear* coefficient for the "inner" STO is much larger, it means that the p-type charge cloud around this atom in the molecule is calculated to be fairly contracted around the nucleus. To describe a more diffuse charge cloud, the wavefunction would contain quite a lot of the "outer" STO, and not so much of the "inner" STO. Thus, we have a linear variation procedure that, in effect, allows for AO expansion and contraction. It is akin to optimizing an orbital exponent, but it does not require nonlinear variation. Of course, one still has to choose the values of the "larger ζ" and "smaller ζ" of Fig. 11-1. This is normally done by optimizing the fit to very accurate atomic wavefunctions or by a nonlinear variation on atoms. A basis set in which every minimal basis AO is represented by an "inner-outer" pair of STOs is often referred to as a "double-ζ" basis set.

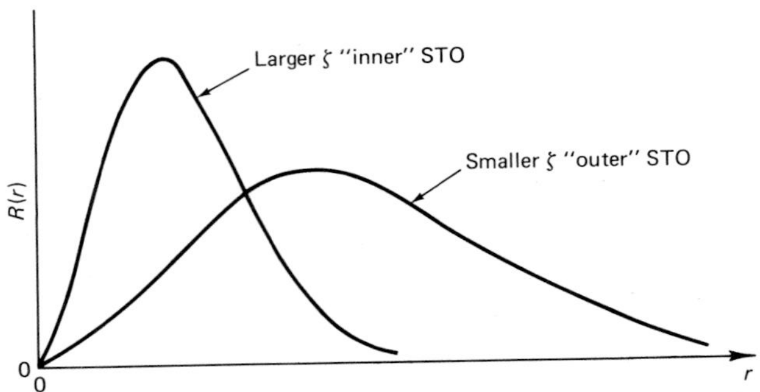

FIG. 11-1 Radial functions $R(r) = r\exp(-\zeta r)$ for 2p-type STOs. The larger ζ value gives an STO more contracted around the nucleus. Hence, it is sometimes called the "inner" STO.

A further kind of extension is frequently made. In addition to the above types of STO, one includes STOs with symmetries different from those present in the minimal basis. This has the effect of allowing charge to be shifted in or out of bond regions in new ways. For example, one could add p-type STOs on hydrogen nuclei. By mixing this with the s-type STOs there, one can describe a skewed charge distribution in the regions of the protons. We have already seen (Chapter 7) that a hydrogen atom in a uniform electric field is polarized in a way which is reasonably well described by an s–p linear combination. Since the hydrogen atom in a molecule experiences an electric field due to the remainder of the molecule, it is not surprising that such p functions are indeed mixed into the wavefunction by the variational procedure if we provide them in the basis set. Similarly, d-type STOs may be added to atoms which, in the minimal basis set, carried only s- and p-type STOs. Functions of this nature are often called *polarization functions* because they allow charge polarization to occur within the molecule as a result of the internally generated electric field.

It should be evident that one could go on indefinitely, adding more and more STOs to the basis, even placing some of them in bonds, rather than on nuclei. This is not normally done because the computing task goes up enormously as we add more basis functions. In fact, the number of integrals to be calculated eventually increases as N^4, where N is the number of basis functions. The evaluation of integrals is the logistic bottleneck in *ab initio* calculations, and for this reason nonlinear variations (of orbital exponents) are impractical for any but smaller molecules. Each new orbital exponent value requires re-evaluation of all the integrals involving that orbital. In essence, a change of orbital exponent is a change of basis set. In linear variations, the basis functions are mixed together but they do not change. Once all the integrals between various basis functions have been evaluated, they are usable for the remainder of the calculation.

The STO basis would probably be the standard choice if it were not for the fact that the many integrals encountered in calculating F_{ij} elements are extremely time consuming to evaluate, even on a computer. This problem has led to the development of an alternative basis set class which is based on gaussian-type functions.

Gaussian functions include an exponential term of the form $\exp(-\alpha r^2)$. The radial dependence of such a function is compared to that for a hydrogenlike 1s function (which is identical to a 1s STO) in Fig. 11-2. There are two obvious problems connected with using gaussian functions as basis functions:

(1) They do not have cusps at $r = 0$ as s-type hydrogenlike AOs do.
(2) They decay faster at large r than do hydrogenlike AOs.

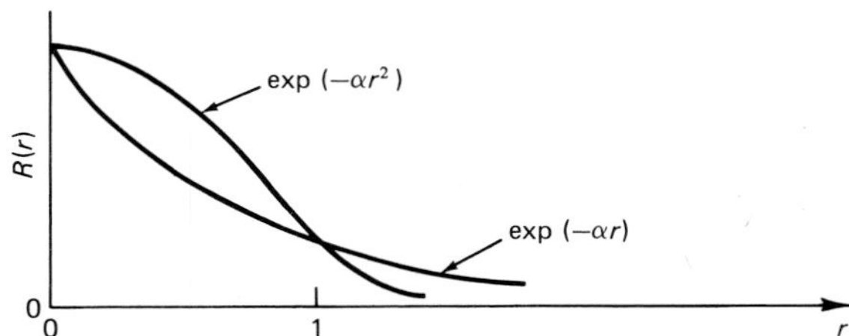

FIG. 11-2 Radial dependence of hydrogenlike and gaussian functions.

Both of these deficiencies are relevant in molecules because, at $r = 0$ (on a nucleus) and at $r = \infty$, the molecular potential is like that in an atom, so similar cusp and asymptotic behavior are expected for molecular and atomic wavefunctions. Balanced against these deficiences is an advantage: gaussian functions have mathematical properties that make it extremely easy to compute the integrals they lead to in F_{ij}. This has led to a practice of replacing each STO in a basis set by a number of gaussian functions. By choosing several values of α in $\exp(-\alpha r^2)$, one can create a set of "primitive" gaussian functions ranging from very compact to very diffuse, and then take a linear combination of these to build up an approximation to the radial part of an STO function. Multiplication by the standard θ and ϕ dependences (spherical harmonics) generates p, d, etc. functions. Once this approximation is optimized, the linear combination of gaussian functions is "frozen," being treated thereafter as a single function insofar as the subsequent molecular variational calculation is concerned. This linear combination of primitive gaussian functions is called a *contracted gaussian function*.

Once we have a contracted gaussian function corresponding to each STO, we can go through the same hierarchy of approximations as before—minimal basis set, double-ζ basis set, double-ζ plus polarization functions—only now using contracted gaussian functions in place of STOs. Typically, *ab initio* calculations involve anywhere from 1 to 7 primitive gaussian functions for each contracted gaussian function.

We have already described a certain amount of quantum-chemical jargon. Some of the basis set descriptions that one could encounter in the literature are as follows:

minimal basis STO (Slater's rules), or [Slater single ζ]
minimal basis STO (best-atom ζ), or [best-atom single ζ]
minimal basis STO (best molecule), or [best-molecule single ζ]
double ζ (best atom)
double ζ (best molecule)
double-ζ gaussian basis
STO-3G [each STO approximated as linear combination of three gaussian primitives]
STO-4-31G [each inner shell STO represented by sum of four gaussians and each valence shell STO split into inner and outer parts (i.e., double ζ) described by three and one gaussian primitives, respectively]

11-9 The Hartree–Fock Limit

It should be apparent that different choices of basis set will produce different SCF wavefunctions and energies. Suppose that we do an SCF calculation on some molecule, using a minimal basis set and obtain a total electronic energy E_1. If we now choose a double-ζ basis and do a new SCF calculation, we will obtain an energy E_2 that normally will be lower than E_1. (If one happens to choose the first basis wisely and the second unwisely, it is possible to find E_2 higher than E_1. We assume here that each improvement to the basis extends the mathematical flexibility while including the capabilities of all preceding bases.) If we now add polarization functions and repeat the SCF procedure, we will find

E_3 to be lower than E_2. We can continue in this way, adding new functions in bonds and elsewhere, always increasing the capabilities of our basis set, but always requiring that the basis describe MOs in a single determinantal wavefunction. The electronic energy will decrease with each basis set improvement, but eventually this decrease will become very slight for any improvement; that is, the energy will approach a limiting value as the basis set approaches mathematical completeness. This limiting energy value is the lowest that can be achieved for a single determinantal wavefunction. It is called the *Hartree–Fock energy*. The MOs that correspond to this limit are called Hartree–Fock orbitals (HF orbitals), and the determinant is called the HF wavefunction. (Sometimes the term "*restricted*" Hartree–Fock is used to emphasize that the wavefunction is restricted to be a single determinantal function for a configuration wherein electrons of α spin occupy the same space orbitals as do the electrons of β spin.)

11-10 Correlation Energy

The Hartree–Fock energy is not as low as the true energy of the system. The mathematical reason for this is that our requirement that ψ be a single determinant is restrictive and we can introduce additional mathematical flexibility by allowing ψ to contain many determinants. Such additional flexibility leads to further energy lowering.

There is a corresponding physical reason for the HF energy being too high. It is connected with the independence of the electrons in a single determinantal wavefunction. To understand this, consider the four-electron wavefunction

$$\psi = |\phi_1(1)\bar{\phi}_1(2)\phi_2(3)\bar{\phi}_2(4)| \qquad (11\text{-}22)$$

Recall from Chapter 5 that the numbers in parentheses stand for the spatial coordinates of an electron; that is, $\phi_1(1)$ really means $\phi_1(x_1, y_1, z_1)\alpha(1)$ or $\phi_1(r_1, \theta_1, \phi_1)\alpha(1)$.[1] In other words, if we pick values of r, θ, and ϕ for each of the four electrons and insert them into Eq. (11-22) we will be able to evaluate each function and we will obtain a determinant of numbers which can be evaluated to give a numerical value for ψ and ψ^2. The latter number (times dv) can be taken as the probability for finding one electron in the volume element around r_1, θ_1, ϕ_1, another electron simultaneously in dv_2 at r_2, θ_2, ϕ_2, etc. The important point to notice is that the effect on ψ^2 of a particular choice of r_1, θ_1, ϕ_1, is not dependent on choices of r, θ, ϕ for other electrons because the form of the wavefunction is *products of functions of independent coordinates*. Physically, this corresponds to saying that the probability for finding an electron in dv_1 at some instant is not influenced by the presence or absence of another electron in some nearby element dv_2 at the same instant. This is consistent with the fact that the Fock operator

[1] Note that ϕ_1 in parentheses represents a coordinate of electron 1, whereas ϕ_1 outside the parentheses represents an MO.

$\hat{F}$ [Eq. (11-7)] treats each electron as though it were moving in the *time-averaged* potential field due to the other electrons.

Because electrons repel each other, there is a tendency for them to keep out of each other's way. That is, in reality, their motions are *correlated.* The HF energy is higher than the true energy because the HF wavefunction is formally incapable of describing correlated motion. The energy difference between the HF and the "exact" (for a simplified nonrelativistic hamiltonian) energy for a system is referred to as the *correlation energy.*

11-11 Koopmans' Theorem

Despite the fact that the total electronic energy is not given by the sum of SCF one-electron energies, it is still possible to relate the ϵ_i's to physical measurements. If certain assumptions are made, it is possible to equate orbital energies with molecular ionization potentials or electron affinities. This identification is related to a theorem due to Koopmans.

Koopmans [1] proved[2] that the wavefunction obtained by removing one electron from ϕ_k or adding one electron to the virtual MO ϕ_j in a Hartree–Fock wavefunction is stable with respect to any subsequent variation in ϕ_k or ϕ_j. Notice that this ignores the question of subsequent variation of all of the MOs ϕ with unchanged occupations. It is not necessarily true that they remain optimized, since the potential they experience is changed by addition or removal of an electron. Nevertheless, Koopmans' theorem suggests a model. It suggests that we approximate the wavefunction for a positive ion by removing an electron from one of the occupied HF MOs for a neutral molecule. Let us do this and compare the electronic energies for the two wavefunctions.

For the neutral molecule, which we assume is a closed-shell system,

$$E = \sum_i \left[2H_{ii} + \sum_j (2J_{ij} - K_{ij})\right] \tag{11-23}$$

For the cation, produced by removing an electron from ϕ_k,

$$E_k{}^+ = \sum_{i \neq k} \left[2H_{ii} + \sum_{j \neq k} (2J_{ij} - K_{ij})\right] + H_{kk} + \sum_{i \neq k} (2J_{ik} - K_{ik}) \tag{11-24}$$

The first sum in Eq. (11-24) gives the total electronic energy due to all but the unpaired electron in ϕ_k. H_{kk} gives the kinetic and nuclear attraction energies for the unpaired electron and the final sum gives the repulsion and exchange energy between this electron and all the others. Now we note that the last sum is exactly equal to the void produced in the first sum due to the restriction $j \neq k$. Therefore, we can combine these by removing the index restriction and deleting the last sum. This gives

$$E_k{}^+ = \sum_{i \neq k} \left[2H_{ii} + \sum_j (2J_{ij} - K_{ij})\right] + H_{kk} \tag{11-25}$$

[2] See also Smith and Day [2].

To compare this with E of Eq. (11-23) we should remove the remaining index restriction. We do this by allowing i to equal k in the sum and simultaneously subtracting the new terms thus produced:

$$E_k^+ = \sum_i [2H_{ii} + \sum_j (2J_{ij} - K_{ij})] - H_{kk} - \sum_j (2J_{kj} - K_{kj}) \quad (11\text{-}26)$$

But, by virtue of Eqs. (11-15) and (11-23), this is

$$E_k^+ = E - \epsilon_k \quad (11\text{-}27)$$

Hence, the ionization potential I_k^0, for ionization from the MO ϕ_k is

$$I_k^0 = E_k^+ - E = -\epsilon_k \quad (11\text{-}28)$$

This illustrates that, within the context of this simplified *model*, the negative of the orbital energies for occupied HF MOs are to be interpreted as ionization potentials. A similar result holds for orbital energies of unoccupied HF MOs and electron affinities. (However, this is less successful in practice; see Problem 11-3.)

In practice, the relation (11-28) is only approximately obeyed. One reason for this has to do with our assumption that doubly occupied SCF MOs produced by a variational procedure on the neutral molecule will be suitable for the doubly occupied MOs of the cation as well. These MO's minimize the energy of the neutral molecule but give an energy for the cation that is higher than what would be produced by an independent variational calculation. For this mathematical reason, we expect the Koopmans' theorem prediction for the ionization potential to be higher than the value predicted by taking the difference between separate SCF calculations on the molecule and cation (which we will symbolize ΔSCF). The corresponding physical argument is that use of Eq. (11-28) views ionization as removal of an electron without any reorganization of the remaining electronic charge. This neglects a process which stabilizes the cation and lowers the ionization potential. Whichever argument we choose, we have here a reason for expecting $-\epsilon$ to be an *overestimate* of the value obtained by independent calculations, ΔSCF.

Another error results from the neglect of change in correlation energy. We have seen that the total SCF energy for the molecule is too high because the single determinantal form of the wavefunction cannot allow for correlated electronic motion. The SCF energy for the cation is too high for the same reason, but the error is different for the two cases because there are fewer electrons in the cation. We expect the neutral molecule to have the greater correlation energy (since it has more electrons)[3] so that proper inclusion of this feature would lower

[3] This reasoning is rather naive. Significant correlation energy contributions can result from a small energy-level separation between filled and empty MOs (rather than from merely the number of electrons), but production of a cation should normally increase this gap and lead to reduced correlation.

the energy of the neutral molecule more than the cation, making the true I_k^0 bigger than that obtained by neglect of correlation. Hence, this leads us to expect ΔSCF to *underestimate* I_k^0. Since $-\epsilon$ overestimates ΔSCF, and ΔSCF underestimates the ionization potential, we can expect some cancellation of errors in using Eq. (11-28).

An illustration of these relations is provided in Table 11-1, where observed *vertical* ionization potentials (i.e., no nuclear relaxation), the appropriate values of $-\epsilon$, and the values of ΔSCF are compared.

TABLE 11-1
Ionization Potentials (in electron volts) of Water as Measured Experimentally and as Calculated from SCF Calculations

		SCF (near HF limit)[b]	
Cation state	Observed[a]	Koopmans	ΔSCF
$^2B_2$	12.62	13.79	11.08
$^2A_1$	14.74	15.86	13.34
$^2B_2$	18.51	19.47	17.61

[a] From Potts and Price [3].
[b] From Dunning *et al.* [4].

11-12 Configuration Interaction

There are several techniques for going beyond the SCF method and thereby including some effects of electron correlation. Some extremely accurate calculations on small atoms and molecules, making explicit use of interparticle coordinates, were described in Section 7-8. There is one general technique, however, that has emerged as being most popular for including effects of correlation in many-electron systems. This technique is called *configuration interaction* (CI).

The mathematical idea of CI is quite obvious. Recall that we restricted our SCF wavefunction to be a single determinant for a closed-shell system. To go beyond the optimum (restricted Hartree–Fock) level, then, we allow the wavefunction to be a linear combination of determinants. Suppose we choose two determinants, D_1 and D_2, each corresponding to a different orbital occupation scheme (i.e., different configurations). Then we can let

$$\psi = c_1 D_1 + c_2 D_2 \tag{11-29}$$

and minimize $\bar{E}$ as a function of the linear mixing coefficients c_1 and c_2.

If we go through the mathematical formalism and express $\bar{E}$ as $\langle\psi|\hat{H}|\psi\rangle/\langle\psi|\psi\rangle$, expand this as integrals over D_1 and D_2, and require $\partial\bar{E}/\partial c_i = 0$, we obtain the same sort of 2 × 2 determinantal equation that we find when minimizing an MO energy as a function of mixing of two AOs, that is, we obtain

$$\begin{vmatrix} H_{11} - \bar{E}S_{11} & H_{12} - \bar{E}S_{12} \\ H_{21} - \bar{E}S_{21} & H_{22} - \bar{E}S_{22} \end{vmatrix} = 0 \tag{11-30}$$

where now

$$H_{ij} = \langle D_i|\hat{H}|D_j\rangle \tag{11-31}$$

$$S_{ij} = \langle D_i|D_j\rangle \tag{11-32}$$

We see that, whereas before we might have had two AOs interacting to form two MOs, here we have two configurations (i.e., two determinantal functions) interacting to form two approximate wavefunctions. Our example involves only two configurations, but there is no limit to the number of configurations that can be mixed in this way.

Since each configuration D contains products of MOs, each of which is typically a sum of AOs, the integrals H_{ij} and S_{ij} can result in very large numbers of integrals over basis functions when they are expanded. This is the sort of situation where a large computer is most helpful, and CI on atoms and molecules, while still expensive, has become almost routine on large computers.

Our purpose in this chapter is not to describe how to carry out a CI calculation, but rather to convey what a CI calculation is and what its predictive capabilities are. Therefore, we will not concern ourselves with the mathematical complexities of evaluating H_{ij} and S_{ij}.[4] But we will consider one practical aspect of CI calculations, namely, how one goes about choosing which configurations should be mixed together, and which ones may be safely ignored.

We begin by considering the H_2 molecule. The LCAO–MO–SCF method expresses the ground state wavefunction for H_2 as

$$\psi(1, 2) = \begin{vmatrix} 1\sigma_g(1)\alpha(1) & 1\sigma_g(2)\alpha(2) \\ 1\sigma_g(1)\beta(1) & 1\sigma_g(2)\beta(2) \end{vmatrix} \tag{11-33}$$

that is, as the configuration $1\sigma_g{}^2$. The SCF procedure mixes the AO basis functions together in the optimum way to produce the $1\sigma_g$ MO.

We have noted at several points in this book that, if one begins with a basis set of n linearly independent functions, one ultimately arrives at n independent MOs. Hence, the $1\sigma_g$ MO of Eq. (11-33) is but one of several MOs produced by the SCF procedure. It is called an *occupied* MO because it is occupied with electrons in this configuration. All the other MOs in this case are *unoccupied* or *virtual* MOs. The virtual MOs of H_2 will have symmetry properties related to the molecular hamiltonian, just as does the occupied MO. Thus, we can refer to $1\sigma_u$, $2\sigma_g$, $2\sigma_u$, $1\pi_u$, $1\pi_g$, etc., virtual MOs of H_2. Which of these virtual MOs are

[4] In most actual calculations, the D's are orthonormal, and $S_{ij} = \delta_{ij}$.

produced by an SCF calculation depends on the number and nature of the AO basis set provided at the outset. If no π-type AOs are provided, no π-type MOs will be produced. If only a minimal basis ($1s_A$ and $1s_B$) is provided, $1\sigma_u$ will be the only virtual MO produced.

It is important to distinguish between the physical content of occupied versus virtual SCF MOs. The SCF procedure finds the set of *occupied* MOs for a system leading to the lowest SCF electronic energy. The virtual orbitals are the residue of this process. The virtual MOs span that part of the basis set function space that the SCF procedure found *least* suitable for describing ψ. The subspace is sometimes referred to as the *orthogonal complement* of the occupied orbital subspace. (Note that this situation differs from that pertaining to Hückel-type calculations, where MOs and energy levels are calculated without regard for electron occupancy. Only after the variational procedure are electrons added.)

Our concern with virtual MOs is due to the fact that they provide a ready means for constructing new configurations to mix with our $1\sigma_g^2$ configuration for H_2. Thus, using some of the above mentioned virtual MOs, we could write determinantal functions corresponding to the excited configurations $1\sigma_g 1\sigma_u$, $1\sigma_g 2\sigma_g$, $1\sigma_g 2\sigma_u$, $1\sigma_g 1\pi_u$, etc.[5] These are commonly referred to as *singly excited* configurations because one electron has been promoted from a ground-state-occupied MO to a virtual MO. (This is *not* meant to imply that the orbital energy difference is equal to the expected spectroscopic energy of the transition.) It is also possible to construct *doubly excited* configurations, such as $1\sigma_u^2$, $1\sigma_u 2\sigma_g$, $2\sigma_g^2$, $1\sigma_u 2\sigma_u$, $1\sigma_u 1\pi_u$, etc. For systems having more electrons, one can write determinants corresponding to triple, quadruple, etc., excitations. If one has a reasonably large number, say 20, of virtual orbitals and, say, 10 electrons to distribute among them, then there is an enormous number of possible configurations. A major step in doing a CI calculation is deciding which configurations might be important in affecting the results and ought therefore to be included.

We can gain insight into this problem by considering our minimal basis set H_2 problem in more detail. We have

$$1\sigma_g = N_g(1s_A + 1s_B) \tag{11-34}$$

$$1\sigma_u = N_u(1s_A - 1s_B) \tag{11-35}$$

where N_g and N_u are normalization constants. The spatial part of the ground configuration is

$$\psi_{\text{space}} = 1\sigma_g(1)1\sigma_g(2) \tag{11-36}$$

which expands to

$$\psi_{\text{space}} = N_g^2[1s_A(1)1s_A(2) + 1s_B(1)1s_B(2) + 1s_A(1)1s_B(2) + 1s_B(1)1s_A(2)]$$

[5] As was shown in Chapter 5, the symmetry requirements of the wavefunction require that each of these open shell configurations be expressed as a linear combination of two 2×2 determinants; for example, $1\sigma_g 2\sigma_u$ stands for the combination

$$(1/\sqrt{2})\{|1\sigma_g(1)2\bar{\sigma}_u(2)| \pm |1\bar{\sigma}_g(1)2\sigma_u(2)|\}$$

If both electrons are near nucleus A, the first term is quite large. This may be rephrased to say that ψ^2 gives a sizable probability for finding both electrons near nucleus A. The second term gives a similar likelihood for finding both electrons near B. These two terms are referred to as *ionic* terms because they become large whenever the instantaneous electronic dispositions correspond to $H_A{}^- H_B{}^+$ and $H_A{}^+ H_B{}^-$, respectively. The last two terms cause ψ^2 to be sizable whenever an electron is near each nucleus. Hence, these are called *covalent* terms, and their presence means that ψ contains significant "covalent character." In fact, because all four terms have the same coefficient, the configuration $1\sigma_g{}^2$ is said to have 50% covalent and 50% ionic character.

Is this bad? It turns out to be no problem at all when the nuclei are close together. Indeed, in the united-atom (helium) limit, the ionic–covalent distinction vanishes. But at large internuclear separations it is very inaccurate to describe H_2 as 50% ionic. In reality, H_2 dissociates to two neutral ground state H atoms—that is, 100% "covalent," with an electron near each nucleus. In short, the SCF–MO description does not dissociate properly. This means that the calculation of $\bar{E}$ versus R_{AB} for H_2 will deviate from experiment more and more as R_{AB} increases This defect in the SCF treatment of H_2 occurs for many other molecular species also.

Can we correct this defect through use of CI? We ask the question this way: "What configuration could we mix with $1\sigma_g{}^2$ in order to make the mixture of covalent and ionic character variable?" Since $1\sigma_g{}^2$ expands to give us covalent and ionic terms of the *same* sign, we need an additional configuration that will give them with *opposite* sign. Then admixture of the two configurations will affect the two kinds of term differently. The configuration that will accomplish this is $1\sigma_u{}^2$:

$$1\sigma_u(1)1\sigma_u(2) = N_u{}^2[1s_A(1)1s_A(2) + 1s_B(1)1s_B(2) - 1s_A(1)1s_B(2) - 1s_B(1)1s_A(2)] \tag{11-37}$$

Mixing these two configurations together gives

$$\begin{aligned}\psi(c_1/c_2) &= c_1 1\sigma_g(1)1\sigma_g(2) + c_2 1\sigma_u(1)1\sigma_u(2)\\ &= (c_1N_g{}^2 + c_2N_u{}^2)[1s_A(1)1s_A(2) + 1s_B(1)1s_B(2)]\\ &\quad + (c_1N_g{}^2 - c_2N_u{}^2)[1s_A(1)1s_B(2) + 1s_B(1)1s_A(2)]\end{aligned} \tag{11-38}$$

If c_1/c_2 is readjusted at each value of R_{AB} to minimize $\bar{E}$, it is evident that the relative weights of covalent and ionic character in Eq. (11-38) will change to suit the circumstances. Actual calculations on this system show that, as R_{AB} gets large, c_1/c_2 approaches a value such that $c_1N_g{}^2 + c_2N_u{}^2$ approaches zero, so that the ionic component of ψ vanishes.

This example illustrates that CI of this sort has an associated physical picture. It suggests that, in any CI calculation involving the dissociation (or extensive stretching) of a covalent bond, important configurations are likely to include double excitations into the antibonding virtual "mates" of occupied bonding MOs.

What about other configurations for H_2? What will $1\sigma_g 2\sigma_g$ do for the calculation, assuming now an extended basis set has produced a $2\sigma_g$ MO? Suppose we take as our trial function

$$\psi = c_1 1\sigma_g{}^2 + c_2 1\sigma_g 2\sigma_g \tag{11-39}$$

where the configurations are understood to stand for determinants. If the $1\sigma_g$ MO has been produced by an SCF calculation on the ground state, and $2\sigma_g$ is a virtual MO from that SCF calculation, then it is possible to show that the CI energy minimum occurs when c_2 in Eq. (11-39) is zero. In other words, these determinants will not mix when they are combined in this way. An equivalent statement is that the mixing element $H_{12} \equiv \langle 1\sigma_g{}^2|H|1\sigma_g 2\sigma_g\rangle$ vanishes. Hence, the CI determinant (11-33) is already in diagonal form, and no variational mixing will occur.

This is an example of *Brillouin's theorem*, which may be stated as follows:

If D_1 is an optimized single determinantal function and D_j is a determinant corresponding to any single excitation out of an orbital ϕ_j occupied in D_1 and into the virtual subspace (orthogonal complement) of D_1, then no improvement in energy is possible by taking $\psi = c_1 D_1 + c_2 D_j$.

The proof of Brillouin's theorem is very simple. We start with a basis set that spans a function space. An SCF calculation is performed, which produces the best single-determinantal wavefunction we can possibly get within this function space. This is D_1. D_j differs from D_1 in only one orbital, which means they differ in only one row. A general property of determinants is that, if two of them differ in only one row or column, any linear combination of the two can be written as a single determinant (see Problem 11-4). This means that any combination $c_1 D_1 + c_2 D_j$ is still expressible as a single determinant. Since D_j makes no use of functions outside our original basis set, $c_1 D_1 + c_2 D_j$ is a single determinant within our original function space. However, D_1 is already known to be the single determinant within this function space that gives the lowest energy, and $c_1 D_1 + c_2 D_j$ cannot do better. QED.

A doubly excited configuration differs from D_1 in two rows, and mixing such a configuration with D_1 produces a result that cannot be expressed as a single determinant.

Because of Brillouin's theorem, it is often decided to omit all single excitations from CI calculations. But it is important to recognize that singly excited configurations *can* affect the results of CI calculations *in the presence of doubly excited configurations*. This comes about because nonzero mixing elements can occur between singly and doubly excited configurations in the CI determinant. To illustrate, let ψ_0 be an SCF single determinant, ψ_1 be a singly excited configuration, and ψ_2 be a "double." Then the CI determinant could be, assuming orthogonal determinants,

$$\begin{vmatrix} H_{00} - E & 0 & H_{02} \\ 0 & H_{11} - E & H_{12} \\ H_{02} & H_{12} & H_{22} - E \end{vmatrix} = 0 \qquad (11\text{-}40)$$

The zeros result from Brillouin's theorem. However, H_{12} does not necessarily vanish, and solution of this 3×3 determinantal equation leads to a wavefunction of the form

$$\psi = c_0\psi_0 + c_1\psi_1 + c_2\psi_2 \qquad (11\text{-}41)$$

with c_1 not zero. ψ_1 comes in on the coattails of ψ_2 and is referred to as a second-order correction. This is not a guarantee that it will be unimportant, however.

Another rule that is useful for recognizing configurations that may be omitted is the rather obvious one that each configuration must share the same set of eigenvalues for operators commuting with the hamiltonian. That is, if ψ is to be associated with a particular symmetry, angular momentum, spin angular momentum, etc., then each configuration in ψ must have that same symmetry, angular momentum, etc. This means that, for the ground state of H_2, $1\sigma_g{}^2$ will not mix with $1\sigma_g 1\sigma_u$ because the latter has overall u symmetry. $1\sigma_u 2\sigma_u$ could contribute, but the symmetrized combination corresponding to the *singlet* state $(|1\sigma_u 2\bar{\sigma}_u| - |1\bar{\sigma}_u 2\sigma_u|)$ must be used rather than the (positive) triplet state combination. The configuration $1\sigma_u 1\pi_u$ will not contribute because it has the wrong total angular momentum.

Even with the aid of all these rules, a calculation on a molecule such as N_2 or O_2 using a reasonably extended basis set gives rise to an enormous number of possible configurations. Additional rules of thumb have been found to help choose the major configurations. It has been found, for example, that triply or higher excited configurations are usually of minor importance. [Since the hamiltonian contains only one- and two-electron operators, interaction elements must vanish between the ground-state configuration and all triply or higher-excited configurations. But, like singly excited configurations, these can, in principle, come in on the coattails of doubly (or other) excited configurations.] A study of the energy change in some process involving primarily the valence electrons (e.g., stretching N_2) really does not require calculation of the correlation energy of the 1s electrons since they are fairly unaffected by the change. Any correlation energy for these electrons tends to cancel itself when initial and final state energies are subtracted. Therefore, in a CI calculation of such a process, it is reasonable to omit configurations corresponding to excitation of a 1s electron. An excellent discussion of these and other refinements practical in CI calculations is available for the reader interested in pursuing such questions further.[6]

[6] See Schaefer [5].

11-13 Examples of *Ab Initio* Calculations

Self-consistent-field and SCF–CI calculations have been made for a large number of systems. The best way to judge the capabilities of these methods is to survey the results.[7]

Table 11-2 provides information on energies for a number of atoms in their ground states. Self-consistent-field energies are presented for three levels of basis set complexity. In the STO single-ζ level, a minimal basis set of one STO

TABLE 11-2
Ground-State Energies (in atomic units) for Atoms, as Computed by the SCF Method and from Experiment

	STO				
Atom	Single ζ^a	Double ζ^a	Hartree–Fock[a]	Exact[b]	Correlation[c] energy
He	−2.8476563	−2.8616726	−2.8616799	−2.9037	−0.0420
Li	−7.4184820	−7.4327213	−7.4327256	−7.4774	−0.0447
Be	−14.556740	−14.572369	−14.573021	−14.6663	−0.0933
B	−24.498369	−24.527920	−24.529057	−24.6519	−0.1228
C	−37.622389	−37.686749	−37.688612	−37.8420	−0.1534
N	−54.268900	−54.397951	−54.400924	−54.5849	−0.1840
O	−74.540363	−74.804323	−74.809370	−75.0607	−0.2513
F	−98.942113	−99.401309	−99.409300	−99.7224	−0.3131
Ne	−127.81218	−128.53511	−128.54705	−128.925	−0.378
Ar	−525.76525	−526.81511	−526.81739	−527.542	−0.725

[a] From Roetti and Clementi [6].
[b] "Exact" equals experimental with relativistic correction but without correction for Lamb shift. See Veillard and Clementi [7].
[c] Correlation energy is "exact" minus HF energy.

per occupied AO is used, and the energy is minimized with respect to independent variation of every orbital exponent ζ. The STO double-ζ basis set is similar except that there are two STOs for each AO, the only restriction being that the STOs have the same spherical harmonics as the AOs to which they correspond. The Hartree–Fock energies are estimated by extrapolating from more extensive basis sets, and represent the limit achievable for the SCF approach using a complete basis set. We can make the following observations:

(1) The improvement in energy obtained when one goes from a single-ζ to a double-ζ STO basis set is substantial, especially for atoms of higher Z.

(2) The agreement between the optimized double-ζ data and the HF energies is quite good. Even for neon, the error is only about 10^{-2} a.u. (0.27 eV). Thus, for atoms, the double-ζ basis is capable of almost exhausting the *energy* capabilities of a single-configuration wavefunction.

[7] For an extensive recent survey, see Schaefer [5].

(3) The disagreement between HF and "exact" energies (i.e., the correlation energy) grows progressively larger down the list. For neon it is almost 0.4 a.u. (10 eV), which is an unacceptable error in chemical measurements.

One might think that the magnitude of the correlation energy in these examples would make SCF calculations on heavy atoms useless for quantitative purposes, but this is not the case. Most frequently we are not concerned with the value of the *total* energy of a system so much as with energy *changes* (e.g., in spectroscopy or in reactions) or else with other properties such as transition moments (for spectroscopic intensities) or, in molecular systems, dipole moments.

Let us, therefore, see how well SCF calculations can predict atomic ionization potentials. We have already indicated (Section 11-11) that there are two ways we can get ionization potentials from SCF calculations. The first, and simplest, is to take the various $-\epsilon_i$, as suggested by Koopmans' theorem. Table 11-3 shows that this gives only rough agreement with experimental values for neon. Another way is to do separate SCF calculations for each excited state produced by removal of an electron from an orbital (i.e., for each "hole state") and equate the ionization potentials to the energy differences between these and the neutral ground state (ΔSCF). This second method requires much more effort. As Table 11-3 indicates, however, the extra effort leads to great improvement in agreement between theoretical and experimental values. We conclude that SCF calculations on atoms and ions give quantitatively useful data on ionization potentials, even for ionization out of deep-lying levels. The Koopmans' theorem approach is less accurate, although still qualitatively useful.

TABLE 11-3
Ionization Potentials of Neon[a]

Ion configuration	Ionization potential (a.u.)		
	Koopmans	ΔSCF	Experiment
$1s2s^22p^6$	32.7723	31.9214	31.98
$1s^22s2p^6$	1.9303	1.8123	1.7815
$1s^22s^22p^5$	0.8503	0.7293	0.7937

[a] From Bagus [8]. The basis set includes 5 s-type and 12 p-type STOs (4 of each m quantum number). ζ's were varied as well as linear coefficients. The neutral ground state gives $E = -128.547$ a.u. (compare Table 11-2).

A related problem is the calculation of energies of excited states of atoms. Weiss [9] has reported calculations on some of the excited states of carbon, and his results are summarized in Fig. 11-3. Inspection of this figure reveals that near-HF calculations only roughly reproduce the energy spectrum, but CI (with

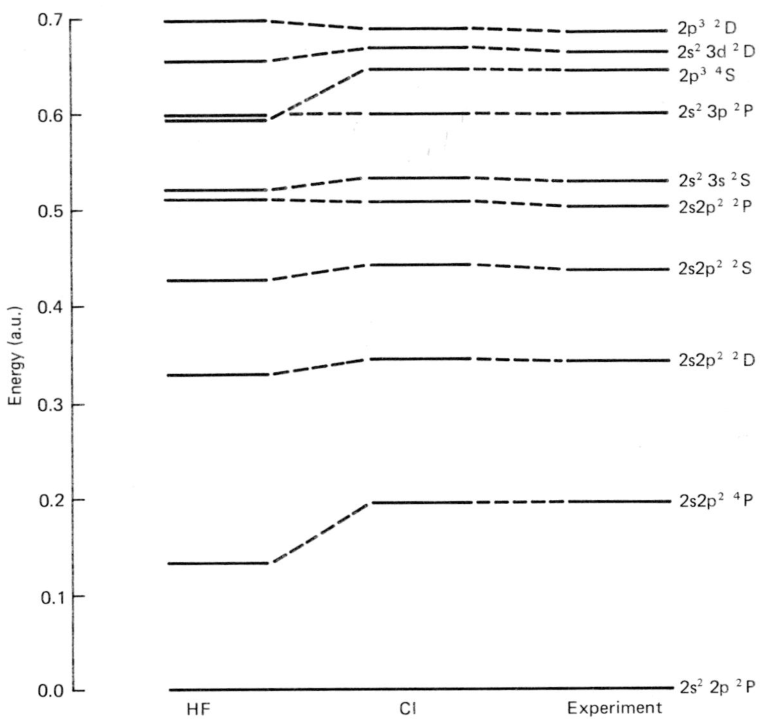

FIG. 11-3 Transition energies in the C^+ ion as calculated by HF, CI, and as measured. (From Weiss [9].) Ionization from the ground state of C^+ occurs at 0.8958 a.u.

four or five configurations) brings about marked improvement. Weiss has omitted configurations involving excitations of 1s electrons, and so these results ignore correlation energy for the inner-shell electrons. The agreement suggests that these electrons experience almost no change in correlation for transitions among these states. Weiss has also calculated oscillator strengths[8] associated with atomic transitions and he finds that CI is necessary before reasonable agreement with experiment is achieved.

In brief, then, the evidence indicates that reasonably accurate atomic ionization potentials can be obtained by high-quality SCF calculations on the neutral and ionized species (ΔSCF, not $-\epsilon$). But it appears that transition energies

[8] The oscillator strength is a measure of the probability (i.e., intensity) of a transition. For a transition between states a and b in a $2n$-electron system it is commonly given by the formula

$$\tfrac{2}{3}(E_b - E_a)\left| \int \psi_a^* \left\{ \sum_{i=1}^{2n} r_i \right\} \psi_b \, d\tau \right|^2$$

and intensities require CI sufficient to account for much of the valence electron correlation.[9]

Before we leave the subject of atoms, it should be pointed out that, for any atom, the expectation value $\bar{T}$ of the kinetic energy operator is equal to $-\bar{E}$ if the wavefunction has been optimized with respect to a scale factor in the coordinates r_1, r_2, etc. This relation, called the virial relation, is proved in Appendix 8. It is necessarily satisfied for any level of calculation that cannot be improved by replacing every r_i in ψ by ηr_i and allowing η to vary. Since the single- and double-ζ STO solutions have already been optimized with respect to such scale parameters, they satisfy the virial relation. Thus, for the beryllium atom, the single-ζ STO value for $\bar{E}$ is (Table 11-2) -14.556740 a.u., and so we know that $\bar{T} = +14.556740$ a.u. and $\bar{V} = -29.113480$ a.u. for this wavefunction (since $\bar{E} = \bar{T} + \bar{V}$). For the double-$\zeta$ wavefunction $\bar{T} = +14.572369$ a.u., etc. The Hartree–Fock wavefunction is, by definition, the lowest-energy solution achievable within a restricted (single determinantal[10]) wavefunction form. Use of a scale factor does not affect the wavefunction form. Hence, no further lowering of $\bar{E}$ below the HF level is possible in this way, and the HF energies $\bar{E}$, $\bar{T}$, and $\bar{V}$ must satisfy the virial relation also. Finally, the exact energies are the lowest achievable for any wavefunction. Again, scaling cannot lower the energy further, so these energies also satisfy the virial relation.

We turn next to *ab initio* calculations on molecules. First, let us compare HF and exact energies for molecules as we did for atoms and see how large the errors due to correlation are. The results are not too different from those for atoms having the same number of electrons, as shown in Table 11-4; that is, the correlation energies for molecules having ten electrons (CH_4, NH_3, H_2O, HF) are about the same as that for neon, whereas that for the 18-electron molecule H_2O_2 is more like the correlation energy for argon. But this is only a very rough rule of thumb. We have already indicated that the correlation energy in a molecule varies with bond length, a factor not present in atomic problems. In order to get a more meaningful idea of the capabilities of *ab initio* calculations on molecules, we must look more closely at specific examples.

A calculation on the OH radical, reported by Cade and Huo [11], provides a good example of the capabilities of the extended basis set LCAO–MO–SCF technique on a small molecule. Their final wavefunction for the ground state at

[9] The differing levels of computation needed to get "good" ionization potentials and "good" transition energies is really a reflection of differences in experimental capabilities. After all, ionization is a transition to an excited state with an unbound electron. But the photoelectron and ESCA techniques typically used to measure ionization potentials are (so far) not capable of the kind of precision one has in traditional spectroscopy. Hence, an error of a few tenths of an electron volt in calculated ionization potential for an "inner" electron does not look nearly as bad as the same error would look in a number to be compared with a standard spectroscopic measurement.

[10] For open-shell systems, more than one determinant may be needed to satisfy symmetry requirements. This is still considered a HF wavefunction.

TABLE 11-4
Estimated Hartree–Fock and Correlation Energies for Selected Molecules[a] and Atoms[b]

Molecule or atom	E (HF) (a.u.)	*E* (correlation) (a.u.)	Molecule or atom	E (HF) (a.u.)	*E* (correlation) (a.u.)
H_2	−1.132	−0.043	Ne	−128.547	−0.378
He	−2.862	−0.042	CO	−112.796	−0.520
BH_3	−26.403	−0.195	N_2	−108.994	−0.540
O (^{1}D)	−74.729	−0.262	Si (^{1}D)	−288.815	−0.505
CH_4	−40.219	−0.291	B_2H_6	−52.835	−0.429
NH_3	−56.225	−0.334	S (^{1}D)	−397.452	−0.606
H_2O	−76.067	−0.364	H_2O_2	−150.861	−0.688
HF	−100.074	−0.373	Ar	−526.817	−0.725

[a] From Ermler and Kern [10].
[b] See Table 11-3.

an internuclear separation $R = 1.8342$ a.u. is presented in Table 11-5. A minimal basis set of STOs for OH would include 1s, 2s, $2p_x$, $2p_y$, and $2p_z$ STOs on oxygen and a single 1s AO on hydrogen. Cade and Huo chose a much more extensive basis. Oxygen is the site for two 1s, two 2s, one 3s, four $2p_\sigma$, one $4f_\sigma$, eight $2p_\pi$, two $3d_\pi$, and four $4f_\pi$ STOs. On hydrogen, there are two 1s, one 2s, one $2p_\sigma$, two $2p_\pi$, and two $3d_\pi$ STOs. (The π-type basis functions are indicated in Table 11-5 for only one of the two directions perpendicular to the O–H axis.) The orbital exponents for all of these STOs have been optimized, and the resulting wavefunction is of "near-Hartree–Fock" quality. The optimized ζ values appear in Table 11-5. The STO labeled $\sigma 2p_O'$ is located on oxygen and has the formula

$$\sigma 2p_O' = (2.13528)^{5/2}\pi^{-1/2} r \exp(-2.13528r)\cos\theta \tag{11-42}$$

There are three σ-type MOs and two π-type MOs to accommodate the nine electrons of this radical. One π-type MO is

$$\begin{aligned}\phi 1\pi_y = {} & 0.37429\pi 2p_{Oy} + 0.46339\pi 2p'_{Oy} + 0.23526\pi 2p''_{Oy} \\ & + 0.01023\pi 2p'''_{Oy} + 0.02871\pi 3d_{Oy} + 0.00506\pi 4f_{Oy} \\ & + 0.02442\pi 2p_{Hy} + 0.00282\pi 3d_{Hy}\end{aligned} \tag{11-43}$$

and the other occupied π-type MO would be the same except with x instead of y. (The z axis is coincident with the internuclear axis.) It is evident that writing out the complete wavefunction given in Table 11-5 would result in a very cumbersome expression. It is a nontrivial problem to relate an accurate but bulky wavefunction such as this to the kinds of simple conceptual schemes chemists like to use. One solution is to have a computer produce contour diagrams of the MOs. Such plots for the valence MOs 2σ, 3σ, and 1π of Table 11-5 are presented in Fig. 11-4.

TABLE 11-5
Near Hartree–Fock Wavefunction for the OH *Molecule in Its Ground-State Configuration* ($1\sigma^2 2\sigma^2 3\sigma^2 1\pi^3$) *at* $R = 1.8342$ a.u.[a]

χ_σ	$C_{1\sigma}$	$C_{2\sigma}$	$C_{3\sigma}$	χ_π	$C_{1\pi}$
$\sigma 1s_O$ ($\zeta = 7.01681$)	0.94291	−0.25489	0.07625	$\pi 2p_O$ ($\zeta = 1.26589$)	0.37429
$\sigma 1s_O'$ (12.38502)	0.09313	0.00358	−0.00153	$\pi 2p_O'$ (2.11537)	0.46339
$\sigma 2s_O$ (1.71794)	−0.00162	0.46526	−0.20040	$\pi 2p_O''$ (3.75295)	0.23526
$\sigma 2s_O'$ (2.86331)	0.00418	0.55854	−0.18328	$\pi 2p_O'''$ (8.41140)	0.01023
$\sigma 3s_O$ (8.64649)	−0.03826	−0.02643	0.00550	$\pi 3d_O$ (1.91317)	0.02871
$\sigma 2p_O$ (1.28508)	−0.00055	0.05179	0.30153	$\pi 4f_O$ (2.19941)	0.00506
$\sigma 2p_O'$ (2.13528)	−0.00056	0.07538	0.37791	$\pi 2p_H$ (1.76991)	0.02442
$\sigma 2p_O''$ (3.75959)	0.00115	0.01874	0.18390	$\pi 3d_H$ (3.32513)	0.00282
$\sigma 2p_O'''$ (8.22819)	0.00059	0.00229	0.00952		
$\sigma 3d_O$ (1.63646)	−0.00047	0.02437	0.04676		
$\sigma 3d_O'$ (2.82405)	0.00016	0.00845	0.01595		
$\sigma 4f_O$ (2.26641)	−0.00013	0.00882	0.01232		
$\sigma 1s_H$ (1.31368)	0.00150	−0.04651	0.21061		
$\sigma 1s_H'$ (2.43850)	−0.00034	0.09413	0.05113		
$\sigma 2s_H$ (2.30030)	0.00000	0.07654	0.04539		
$\sigma 2p_H$ (2.8052)	0.00018	0.01182	0.00999		

[a] From Cade and Huo [11].

Cade and Huo [11] carried out similar calculations for OH at thirteen other internuclear distances and also for the united atom (fluorine) and the separated atoms in the states with which the Hartree–Fock wavefunction correlates. Some of their data are reproduced in Table 11-6. A plot of the electronic plus nuclear repulsion energies is given in Fig. 11-5 along with the experimentally derived curve. It is evident that the near HF curve climbs too steeply on the right, leading to too "tight" a potential well for nuclear motion and too small an equilibrium internuclear separation. This comes about because, as mentioned earlier, the HF solution dissociates to an incorrect mixture of states, some of which are ionic. It is possible to use the HF curve of Fig. 11-5 to derive theoretical values for molecular constants which can be compared to spectroscopic data. The results are displayed in Table 11-6, and they reflect the inaccuracy in the HF energy curve. Included there are the SCF and experimental values for the molecular dipole moment.

We turn now to the behavior of $\overline{V}/\overline{T}$ for the HF wavefunctions of Cade and Huo at various internuclear separations. The data appear in Table 11-7. Observe that the value of -2.00000 for $\overline{V}/\overline{T}$ occurs at three values of R: 0, ∞, and the point where E is a minimum. At $R = 0$ and ∞, we are dealing with one or two atoms, for which we have already seen the HF solution should give $\overline{V}/\overline{T} = -2$. At intermediate R we have a diatomic molecule, for which the virial relation is (see Appendix 8)

$$2\overline{T} + \overline{V} + R\,\partial\overline{E}/\partial R = 0 \tag{11-44}$$

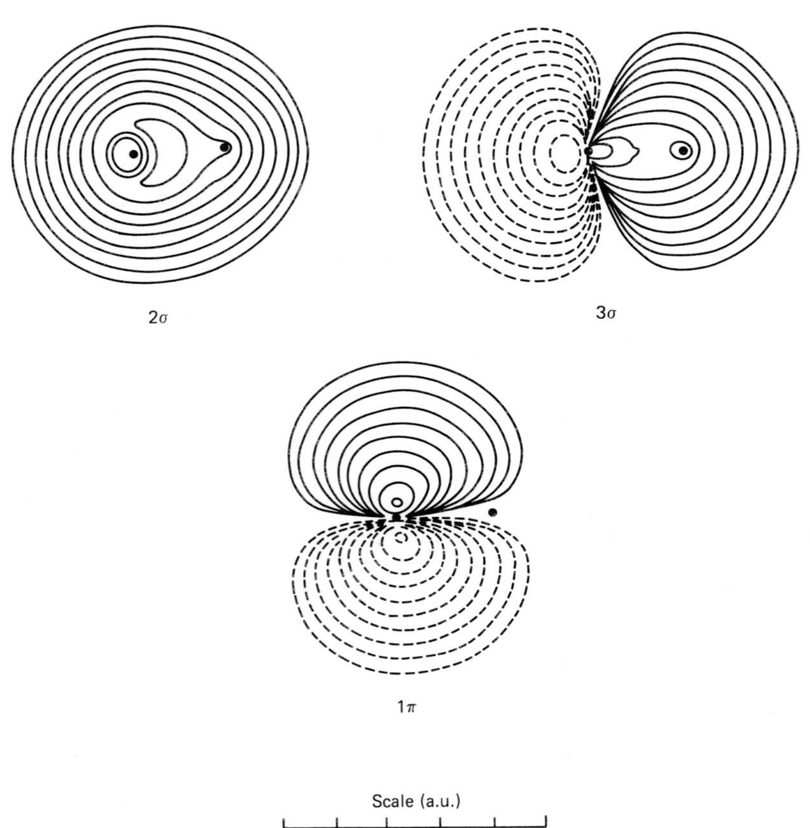

FIG. 11-4 Contour plots of HF valence orbitals for OH as given in Table 11-5. (From Stevens *et al.* [12].)

TABLE 11-6
Spectroscopic Parameters and Dipole Moment for OH *from Theoretical Curves and from Experiment*[a]

Wavefunction	Dipole moment (debyes)	R_e (a.u.)	D_e (eV)	ω_e (cm^{-1})	$\omega_e x_e$ (cm^{-1})	α_e (cm^{-1})
SCF	1.780	1.795	8.831	4062.6	165.09	0.661
CI	1.655	1.838	4.702	3723.6	83.15	0.628
Experimental	1.66 ± .01	1.834	4.63	3735.2	82.81	0.714

[a] From Stevens *et al.* [12].

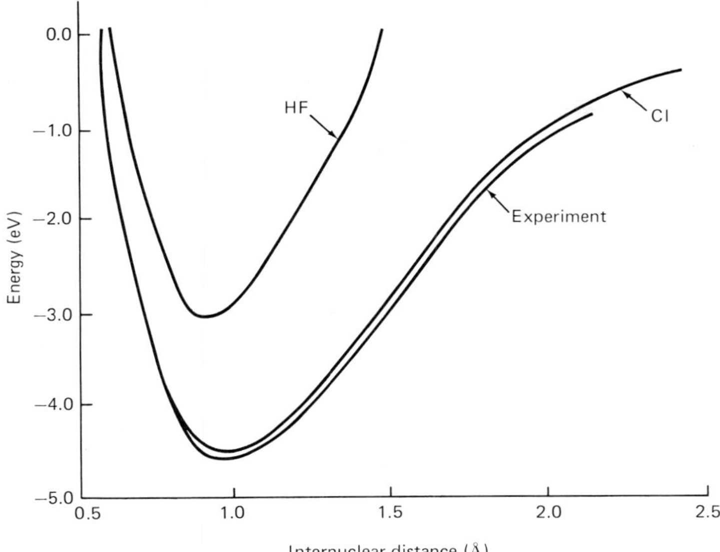

FIG. 11-5 Theoretical and experimental energy curves for OH. (From Stevens *et al.* [12].)

There are three cases to consider. If $\partial\bar{E}/\partial R = 0$, then $\bar{V}/\bar{T} = -2$. This will occur at the minimum of the potential energy curve (and also at any subsidiary maxima or minima). If $\partial\bar{E}/\partial R$ is negative, then, since $\bar{V}/\bar{T} = -2 - (R/\bar{T})(\partial\bar{E}/\partial R)$ and $\bar{T}$ is positive, $\bar{V}/\bar{T}$ will be algebraically higher than -2 (e.g., -1.98). If $\partial\bar{E}/_b R$ is positive, $\bar{V}/\bar{T}$ will be lower than -2. Thus, the values of $\bar{V}/\bar{T}$ in Table 11-7 reflect the slope of a line tangent to the potential energy curve at each R value.

TABLE 11-7
HF *Total Energies and* $\bar{V}/\bar{T}$ *for* OH *as a Function of Internuclear Distance*[a]

R (a.u.)	E (a.u.)	$\bar{V}/\bar{T}$	R (a.u.)	E (a.u.)	$\bar{V}/\bar{T}$
0	−99.40933	−2.00000	1.90	−75.41837	−2.00129
1.40	−75.34382	−1.99076	2.00	−75.41140	−2.00225
1.50	−75.38378	−1.99398	2.10	−75.40163	−2.00300
1.60	−75.40696	−1.99651	2.25	−75.38372	−2.00380
1.70	−75.41829	−1.99850	2.40	−75.36367	−2.00433
1.75	−75.42065	−1.99933	2.60	−75.33582	−2.00474
1.795	−75.42127	−2.00000	2.80	−75.30822	−2.00492
1.8342	−75.42083	−2.00052	∞	−75.30939	−2.00000

[a] From Cade and Huo [11].

As mentioned earlier, it is possible to at least partly include the effects of electron correlation by allowing determinants corresponding to other configurations to mix into the wavefunction. Such calculations have been performed for the OH radical by several groups, and the results of Stevens *et al.* [12] are included in Table 11-6 and Fig. 11-5. These data come from intermixing 14 configurations. It is evident that the inclusion of correlation through CI has markedly improved the agreement with experiment.

Many diatomic molecules have been treated at a comparable level, and it is clear that *ab initio* calculations including CI are capable of giving quite accurate molecular data. In cases in which the diatomic system is experimentally elusive, such calculations may be the best source of data available. A further example of this is provided in Table 11-8, in which are listed dipole moments for ground and

TABLE 11-8
Calculated and Experimental Dipole Moments of Diatomic Molecules (in Debyes)

Molecule and polarity	State	HF at R_e[a]	CI at R_e[a]	Experiment	Reference
Li^+H^-	$X\,^1\Sigma^+$	6.002	5.86	5.83	[13]
C^+N^-	$X\,^2\Sigma^+$	2.301	1.465	1.45 ± 0.08	[14]
C^-N^+	$B\,^2\Sigma^+$	—	0.958	1.15 ± 0.08	[14]
C^-O^+	$X\,^1\Sigma^+$	−0.274	0.12	0.112 ± 0.005	[13]
C^+O^-	$A\,^3\Pi$	2.34	1.43	1.37	[15]
C^-S^+	$X\,^1\Sigma^+$	1.56	2.03	1.97	[13]
C^-S^+	$A\,^1\Pi$	−0.09	0.63	0.63 ± 0.04	[16]
C^-H^+	$X\,^2\Pi$	1.570	1.53	1.46 ± 0.06	[17]
O^-H^+	$X\,^2\Pi$	1.780	1.655	1.66 ± 0.01	[17]
F^-H^+	$X\,^1\Sigma$	1.942	1.805	1.797	[17]
N^-H^+	$X\,^3\Sigma^-$	1.627	1.537	Unknown	[17]

[a] Experimental R_e Value used.

some excited states of diatomic molecules. The dipole moments computed from near HF wavefunctions contain substantial errors. It can be seen that CI greatly improves dipole moments. It has been observed that inclusion of singly excited configurations is very important in obtaining an accurate dipole moment.

Another example of the use of *ab initio* methods on fairly small molecules is provided by the work of Ditchfield, Del Bene, and Pople on predicting molecular structures in ground and excited states. These workers used an extended basis set of contracted Gaussian functions. For excited states, a limited amount of CI was included. The results (Table 11-9) are in good agreement with available experimental data.

We have seen that inclusion of CI often improves the $\bar{E}$ versus R curve because it allows for variable ionic–covalent character in the wavefunction. However, there are some diatomic molecules that maintain a high degree of

TABLE 11-9
Calculated and Experimental Data on Ground and Excited States of Small Molecules[a]

Molecule	State symmetry		Bond distances (Å)			Bond angles (degrees)	
			Ab initio	Experiment		*Ab initio*	Experiment
HCCH	$X\,^1\Sigma_g^+$	CC	1.190	1.203		Linear	Linear
		CH	1.051	1.061			
	^1A_u	CC	1.367	1.388	HCC	125.1	120
		CH	1.079	—			
HCN	$X\,^1\Sigma^+$	CN	1.140	1.154		Linear	Linear
		CH	1.051	1.063			
	$^1A''$	CN	1.300	1.297		127.8	125
		CH	1.086	1.14			
FCN	$X\,^1\Sigma^+$	CN	1.138	1.159		—	—
		CF	1.289	1.262			
	$^3A''$	CN	1.310	—		119.6	—
		CF	1.343	—			
H_2CO	$X\,^1A_1$	CO	1.206	1.203	HCH	116.4	116.5
		CH	1.081	1.101	OCH_2	180	180 (planar)
	$^1A''$	CO	1.273	1.312	HCH	118.9	119
		CH	1.080	1.093	OCH_2	165	149
HNO	$X\,^1A'$	NO	1.231	1.212	HNO	107.4	108.6
		NH	1.080	1.063			
	$^1A''$	NO	1.256	1.241	HNO	114.7	116.3
		NH	1.049	1.036			

[a] From Ditchfield *et al.* [18].

ionic character even when the nuclei are quite widely separated. NaCl is an example. For such systems, the Hartree–Fock energy curve is quite nearly parallel to the exact energy curve throughout the minimum energy region (i.e., the correlation energy is almost constant) and the theoretical values of spectroscopic constants agree quite well with experimental values. (*In vacuo*, an electron ultimately transfers from Cl^- to Na^+, and the experimental curve leads to neutral dissociation products, whereas the HF curve does not. This theoretical error affects the curve only at large R, however, and so has little effect on spectroscopic constants.) Schaefer [5] has reviewed this situation.

Ab initio calculations have been performed on molecular systems much larger than the diatomic molecules referred to above. However, as one moves to molecules having four or more nuclei, one encounters a new difficulty. Integrals now appear which have the form

$$\langle ab|cd\rangle \equiv \langle \chi_a(1)\chi_b(2)|1/r_{12}|\chi_c(1)\chi_d(2)\rangle \qquad (11\text{-}45)$$

where χ_a is a basis function located on nucleus a, etc. Such integrals have basis functions on four different nuclei and are referred to as four-center integrals. If the basis functions χ are STOs, such integrals are relatively slow to evaluate on a computer. If they are gaussian functions, the computation is much faster and this is the main reason for using gaussian basis functions. But the number of such integrals becomes enormous for a reasonable basis set and a medium sized molecule. In fact, the number of such integrals grows as the fourth power of the number of basis functions. Thus, replacing each STO by, say, three gaussian functions, will lead to 3^4 times as many integrals to evaluate. Even though such integrals can be evaluated very rapidly, we eventually come to molecules of such a size that the sheer number of integrals makes for a substantial computing effort. However, Clementi has shown (Table 11-10) that the rate of increase of *significant* three– and four-center integrals falls off when we get to large enough systems. The spatial extension of such molecules means that many three- and four-center integrals are so small that they can be neglected. In addition, symmetry causes many integrals to vanish. Thus, while the number of integrals differs by a factor of 45 for the last two entries of Table 11-10, the computing time for the nonnegligible integrals goes up by a factor of only 5.5.

TABLE 11-10
Typical Computational Time for Integrals in Large Molecular Systems[a]

System	No. electrons	Basis size (primitive gaussians)	No. integrals	Computer time[b] hr	min	sec
H_2O	10	22	32.13×10^3	—	—	01
Na^+–H_2O	20	38	24.67×10^4	—	—	13
Na^+–$(H_2O)_3$	40	82	57.92×10^5	—	1	51
Na^+–$(H_2O)_6$	70	148	60.79×10^6	—	10	45
Carbazole ($C_{12}NH_9$)	88	235	20.17×10^7	1	11	50
Carbazole-2,4,7-trinitro-fluorenone complex $C_{25}N_4O_7H_{14}$	232	618	92.74×10^8	6	30	—

[a] From Clementi and Mehl [19].
[b] IBM 360/195 computer.

Two aspects of the data in Table 11-10 are impressive. First, it is truly remarkable that one can compute integral values at the rate of 32,000 per second, even though no four-center integrals are involved with H_2O. Second, 6.5 hr of IBM 360/195 time is more than most people can afford, and therefore very large systems are at present practically out of reach for all but a few. Nonetheless, it appears that near HF wavefunctions can be calculated for some very large molecules at considerable expense, and that reasonably useful SCF data (but not HF) can be obtained for large molecules at reasonable cost. We shall now review some examples of *ab initio* calculations on larger systems.

Numerous SCF calculations have been reported for barriers to internal rotation in various molecules. The theoretical barriers agree best with experiment for molecules having threefold symmetry in the rotor. Self-consistent-field values are compared with experimental barrier values in Table 11-11. In every

TABLE 11-11
Internal Rotation Barriers from Experiment and as Calculated by the LCAO–MO–SCF Method

	Barrier (kcal/mole)		
Molecule	SCF	Experiment	Reference
CH_3—CH_3	2.58	2.88	[20]
	2.88	—	[21]
CH_3—NH_2	1.12	1.98	[22]
	2.02	—	[21]
CH_3—OH	1.59	1.07	[21]
CH_3—CH_2F	2.59	3.33	[20]
CH_3—N=O	1.05	1.10	[23]
CH_3—CH=CH_2	1.25	1.99	[24]
cis-CH_3—CH=CFH	1.07	1.06	[24]
trans-CH_3—CH=CFH	1.34	2.20	[24]
CH_3—CH=O	1.09	1.16	[25]

case, the theoretical energy curve predicts the correct stable conformation and even does reasonably well at predicting barrier height. The disagreement between different computed values of the barrier for the same molecule reflects differences in basis sets and, sometimes, differences in choices for bond length and angle made by different workers. The evidence to date suggests that *ab initio* calculations approaching the HF limit will ordinarily be within 20% of the experimental barrier. Even this level of accuracy is useful because experimental measurements of barriers in transient molecules or for excited molecules are often very rough, ambiguous or nonexistent.

A large number of *ab initio* calculations have been made on clusters of molecules. Many of these have sought to delineate the distance and angle dependence of hydrogen bond strength between molecules like water or hydrogen fluoride. Del Bene [26], for example, has reported minimal basis set (contracted gaussian function) SCF calculations on pairs of mixed dimers such as NH_2OH–H_2O, HOF–H_2O, $(NH_2OH)_2$, and $(HOF)_2$. In essence, calculations are performed for a given pair of molecules at various relative orientations and distances of separation. Del Bene's calculations suggest that $(NH_2OH)_2$ has an energy preference for a cyclic structure, whereas all the other above mentioned combinations have equilibrium open-chain structures. Clementi and co-workers [27] have calculated the energy of interaction between two water molecules at the Hartree–Fock level (56 gaussian functions on each water molecule) for 216 different nuclear configurations. This has enabled them to map out the HF energy surface for the water–water interaction, and they have derived an analytical fit for this surface. (Because the interaction is so weak and the water molecules are closed-shell systems, one expects little variation in correlation energy as the water molecules move with respect to each other. Hence, the HF surface should parallel the true surface, and comparison with experimental data supports this.) Then, assuming only pairwise interactions, this surface was used to calculate the energies of various configurations for as many as eight water molecules (see Kistenmacher *et al.* [28]). This group [29, 30] has also done HF level calculations for ions surrounded by water molecules, thereby obtaining information on ion–solvent binding energies and ion–solvent distances. Information of this sort is useful in the theories of liquids and aqueous ionic solutions, and is not easily obtained experimentally.

A great deal of attention is being given to the calculation by *ab initio* methods of energy surfaces for chemical reactions. For many years, such efforts were limited to reactions, such as $D + H_2 \rightarrow HD + H$, which involve only a small number of electrons and nuclei. Much more complicated systems are now being explored.

In setting out to perform such a calculation, one likes to have some idea whether the correlation energy of the system will change significantly with nuclear configuration. If it does not, then a Hartree–Fock calculation will parallel the true energy surface. This was the case in the above mentioned hydrogen bonding and ion–water studies. If the correlation energy does change, it is necessary to include CI in the calculation.

As a rough rule of thumb, one expects the correlation energy to change least when the reactants, the intermediate or transition state complex, and the products are all closed-shell systems, hence all approximately equally well described by a single determinantal wavefunction. Some calculations on S_N2 and radical reactions are summarized in Table 11-12. It can be seen that the S_N2 reactions, which do involve closed-shell systems in the three stages mentioned above, are fairly insensitive to the inclusion of CI, whereas the radical reactions undergo extensive change of correlation energy.

The determination of the potential energy surface for the unimolecular rearrangement HNC $\rightleftharpoons$ HCN by Pearson *et al.* [33] provides an example of a very accurate and exhaustive calculation on a fairly small molecule. Because there are only three nuclei, there are only three structural variables to explore, so the number of calculations needed to map out the surface is not too large. (Note that, with three geometric variables, the energy "surface" is really a four-dimensional hypersurface.) The basis set for the initial SCF exploration was made up of contracted Gaussian functions, two for each minimal basis AO

TABLE 11-12
Reaction Barrier Energies for Reactions as Calculated by ab Initio *Methods*

Reactant	Transition	Product	Reaction type	Reaction barrier (kcal/mole) SCF	CI (no. config.)	Reference
$H^- + CH_4$	$(CH_5)^-$	$CH_4 + H^-$	S_N2	59.3	55.2 (6271)	[31]
$F^- + CH_3F$	$(FCH_3F)^-$	$CH_3F + F^-$	S_N2	5.9	5.9 (26910)	[31]
$H^{\cdot} + CH_4$	$CH_5^{:}$	$CH_3 + H_2$	Radical abstraction (axial)	35.2	18 (692)	[32]
$H^{\cdot} + CH_4$	$CH_5^{:}$	$CH_4 + H^{\cdot}$	Radical exchange (inversion)	63.7	41.7 (692)	[32]

(i.e., a double-ζ basis set), plus polarization functions on all three atoms, for a total of 35 basis functions. Each SCF calculation (one for each geometry considered) took 35–40 min on a Univac 1108 computer (equivalent to 1–2 min on a CDC 7600 or an IBM 360/195). The total number of points calculated in characterizing the surface was 97. The minimum energy path over the surface generated by these SCF (near HF) calculations predicts that HCN is 9.5 kcal/mole more stable than HNC, and that the barrier for HNC $\rightarrow$ HCN is 40.2 kcal/mole.

To examine the effects of correlation, these authors next included all single and double excitations within the SCF manifold of orbitals to generate configurations for CI calculations. For linear geometries, this involved 6343 configurations (18 points at 24 min apiece on an IBM 360/195). Nonlinear geometries involved 11,735 configurations (25 points near the saddle point at about 40 min apiece). The energy surface changes somewhat, HCN becoming 14.6 kcal/mole more stable than HNC, and the barrier for HNC $\rightarrow$ HCN becoming 34.9 kcal/mole. HNC has not been unambiguously identified and characterized, and so there are no experimental data for comparison.

An example of a less complete study on a more complicated system is provided by the SCF–CI calculations of Hsu *et al.* [34] on the electrocyclic transformation between two isomers of C_4H_6, cyclobutene and butadiene. This system involves many bond distances and angles (24 parameters), so many of these were fixed at what were thought to be reasonable values, and only 6 parameters were allowed to vary. The basis set for this 10-atom system consisted of 30 contracted gaussian functions. Limited CI was carried out using 260 configurations selected from single, double, triple, and quadruple excitations. The resulting energy surface predicts the proper sterochemistry for the reaction and gives an activation energy in reasonable agreement with experiment.

Furthermore, it enabled the authors to make statements about degree of C–C bond formation, CH_2 rotation, nonplanarity of carbon system, etc. in the transition state as well as at other points along the reaction coordinate. Such statements are much more detailed than can yet be inferred from experiments. However, some of them are also tentative because of the limitations in basis set size, amount of CI, and geometric restrictions. More accurate and exhaustive calculations on systems of this complexity will be forthcoming.

In summary, *ab initio* calculations provide useful data on bond lengths and angles, molecular conformation and internal rotation barriers, for ground and excited states of molecules. They are also useful for calculating ionization potentials, oscillator strengths, dipole moments (as well as other one-electron properties) and excitation energies. If one has access to large blocks of computer time, *ab initio* calculations can reveal the nature of energy surfaces pertaining to chemical reactions or molecular associations, as in fluids. The accuracy of the calculation and the magnitude of the system are limited ultimately by computer speed and capacity.

11-14 Approximate SCF–MO Methods

At the beginning of this chapter it was stated that *ab initio* calculations require exact calculation of all integrals contributing to the elements of the Fock matrix, but we have seen that, as we encounter systems with more and more electrons and nuclei, the number of three- and four-center two-electron integrals becomes enormous, driving the cost of the calculation out of the reach of most researchers. This has led to efforts to find sensible and systematic simplifications to the LCAO–MO–SCF method—simplifications that remain within the general theoretical SCF framework but shorten computation of the Fock matrix.

Since many of the multicenter two-electron integrals in a typical molecule have very small values, the obvious solution to the difficulty is to ignore such integrals. But we wish to ignore them without having to calculate them to see which ones are small since, after all, the reason for ignoring them is to avoid having to calculate them. Furthermore, we want the selection process to be linked in a simple way to considerations of basis set. That is, when we neglect certain integrals, we are in effect omitting certain interactions between basis set functions, which is equivalent to omitting some of our basis functions part of the time. It is essential that we know exactly what is involved here, or we may obtain strange results such as, for example, different energies for the same molecule when oriented in different ways with respect to cartesian coordinates.

A number of variants of a systematic approach meeting the above criteria have been developed by Pople and co-workers, and these are now widely used. The approximations are based on the idea of *neglect of differential overlap* between atomic orbitals in molecules.

Differential overlap dS between two AOs, χ_a and χ_b, is the product of these functions in the differential volume element dv:

$$dS = \chi_a(1)\chi_b(1)\, dv \tag{11-46}$$

The only way for the differential overlap to be zero in dv is for χ_a or χ_b, or both, to be identically zero in dv. Zero differential overlap (ZDO) between χ_a and χ_b in *all* volume elements requires that χ_a and χ_b can never be finite in the same region, that is, the functions do not "touch." It is easy to see that, if there is ZDO between χ_a and χ_b (understood to apply in all dv), then the familiar overlap integral S must vanish too. The converse is not true, however. S is zero for any two *orthogonal* functions even if they touch. An example is provided by an s and a p function on the same center.

It is a much stronger statement to say that χ_a and χ_b have ZDO than it is to say they are orthogonal. Indeed, it is easy to think of examples of orthogonal AOs but impossible to think of any pair of AOs separated by a finite or zero distance and having ZDO. Because AOs decay exponentially, there is always some interpenetration.

The attractive feature of the ZDO approximation is that it causes all three- and four-center integrals to vanish. Thus, in a basis set of AOs χ having ZDO, the integral $\langle\chi_a(1)\chi_b(2)|1/r_{12}|\chi_c(1)\chi_d(2)\rangle$ will vanish unless $a \equiv c$ and $b \equiv d$. This arises from the fact that, if $a \neq c$, $\chi_a{}^*(1)\chi_c(1)$ is identically zero, and this forces the integrand to vanish everywhere, regardless of the value of $(1/r_{12})\chi_b{}^*(2)\chi_d(2)$.

It is not within the scope of this book to give a detailed description or critique of the numerous computational methods based on ZDO assumptions. An excellent monograph [43] on this subject including program listings is available. Some of the acronyms for these methods are listed in Table 11-13. In general, these methods have been popular because they are relatively cheap to use and because they predict certain properties (bond length, bond angle, energy surfaces, electron spin resonance hyperfine splittings, molecular charge distributions, dipole moments, heats of formation) reasonably well. However, they generally do make use of some parameters evaluated from experimental data, and some methods are biased toward good predictions of some properties, while other methods are better for other properties. For a given type of problem, one must exercise judgment in a choice of method.

As an example of the sort of chemical system which becomes accessible to study using such methods, we cite the valence-electron CNDO/2 calculations of Maggiora [44] on free base, magnesium, and aquomagnesium porphines. Such calculations enable us to examine the geometry of the complex (i.e., is the metal ion in or out of the molecular plane, and how is the water molecule oriented?), the effects of the metal ion on ionization potentials, spectra, and orbital energy level spacings, and the detailed nature of charge distribution in the system.

TABLE 11-13
Acronyms for Common Approximate SCF Methods

Acronym	Description
CNDO/1	Complete neglect of differential overlap. Parametrization Scheme no. 1 (Pople and Segal [35]).
CNDO/2	Parametrization scheme no. 2. Considered superior to CNDO/1 (Pople and Segal [36]).
CNDO/BW	Similar to above with parameters selected to give improved molecular structures and force constants. (See Pulfer and Whitehead and references therein.)
INDO	Intermediate neglect of differential overlap. Differs from CNDO in that ZDO is not assumed between AOs on the same center in evaluating one-center integrals. This method is superior to CNDO methods for properties, such as hyperfine splitting, or singlet-triplet splittings, which are sensitive to electron exchange (Pople *et al.* [38]).
MINDO/3	Modified INDO, parameter scheme no. 3. Designed to give accurate heats of formation (Bingham *et al.* [39] and also Dewar [40]).
NDDO	Neglect of diatomic differential overlap. Assumes ZDO only between AOs on different atoms (Pople *et al.* [41]).
MNDO	Modified neglect of diatomic overlap. A semiempirically parametrized version of NDDO. Yields accurate heats of formation and many other molecular properties (Dewar and Thiel [42]).

PROBLEMS

11-1 Use the data in Table 11.3 to calculate the theoretical transition energies for Ne^+ when 1s and 2s electrons are excited into the 2p level. The experimental values are 2s → 2p, 0.989 a.u.; 1s → 2p, 31.19 a.u.

11-2 Use the data in Table 11.1 to estimate separately the errors in ionization potentials for the three states due to

(a) omission of electron correlation,
(b) failure to allow electronic relaxation.

11-3 In Section 11-11, it is argued that neglect of electron correlation and electronic relaxation in setting $I_k^0 = -\epsilon_k$ causes errors of opposite sign, which partly cancel. Would this also occur when Koopmans' theorem is used to predict electron affinities? Why?

11-4 Demonstrate that, if

$$D_1 = \begin{vmatrix} a & c \\ b & d \end{vmatrix} \quad \text{and} \quad D_2 = \begin{vmatrix} a & e \\ b & f \end{vmatrix}, \quad \text{then} \quad D_1 + \lambda D_2 = \begin{vmatrix} a & c + \lambda e \\ b & d + \lambda f \end{vmatrix}$$

11-5 A singly excited configuration ψ_1 differs by one orbital from the ground state ψ_0 and also by one orbital from certain doubly excited configurations ψ_2. Brillouin's theorem gives $\langle\psi_0|H|\psi_1\rangle = 0$, but not $\langle\psi_1|H|\psi_2\rangle = 0$. Where does the attempted proof to show that $\langle\psi_1|H|\psi_2\rangle = 0$ break down?

11-6 Show that, if $\psi = c_0\psi_0 + c_1\psi_1 + c_2\psi_2 + \cdots + c_n\psi_n$, and if ψ is to be an eigenfunction of $\hat{A}$ with eigenvalue a_1, then it is necessary that all the ψ_i $(i = 0, \ldots, n)$ also be eigenfunctions of $\hat{A}$ with eigenvalues a_1.

11-7 How many distinct four-center coulomb and exchange integrals result when one has four nuclei, each being the site of five basis functions? Make no assumptions about symmetry or basis function equivalence or electron spin.

11-8 For a homonuclear diatomic molecule, which of the following singly excited configurations would be prevented for reasons of symmetry from contributing to a CI wavefunction for which the main "starting configuration" is $1\sigma_g{}^2 1\sigma_u{}^2 2\sigma_g{}^2 1\pi_u{}^4$?

(a) $1\sigma_g{}^2 1\sigma_u{}^2 2\sigma_g{}^2 1\pi_u{}^3 1\pi_g$ (i.e., $1\pi_u \rightarrow 1\pi_g$)

(b) $2\sigma_g \rightarrow 3\sigma_g$ (c) $2\sigma_g \rightarrow 1\pi_g$ (d) $1\sigma_g \rightarrow 3\sigma_g$

11-9 Write down the hamiltonian for electrons in the water molecule. Use summation signs with explicit index ranges. Include internuclear repulsion. Use atomic units.

REFERENCES

[1] T. Koopmans, *Physica* **1**, 104 (1933).
[2] D. W. Smith and O. W. Day, *J. Chem. Phys.* **62**, 113 (1975).
[3] A. W. Potts and W. C. Price, *Proc. Roy. Soc. (London)* **A326**, 181 (1972).
[4] T. H. Dunning, Jr., R. M. Pitzer, and S. Aung, *J. Chem. Phys.* **57**, 5044 (1972).
[5] H. F. Schaefer, III, "The Electronic Structure of Atoms and Molecules: A Survey of Rigorous Quantum-Mechanical Results." Addison-Wesley, Reading, Massachusetts, 1972.
[6] C. Roetti and E. Clementi, *J. Chem. Phys.* **60**, 4725 (1974).
[7] A Veillard and E. Clementi, *J. Chem. Phys.* **49**, 2415 (1968).
[8] P. S. Bagus, *Phys. Rev.* **139**, A619 (1965).
[9] A. W. Weiss, *Phys. Rev.* **162**, 71 (1967).
[10] W. C. Ermler and C. W. Kern, *J. Chem. Phys.* **61**, 3860 (1974).
[11] P. E. Cade and W. M. Huo, *J. Chem. Phys.* **47**, 614 (1967).
[12] W. J. Stevens, G. Das, and A. C. Wahl, *J. Chem. Phys.* **61**, 3686 (1974).
[13] S. Green, *J. Chem. Phys.* **54**, 827 (1971).
[14] S. Green, *J. Chem. Phys.* **57**, 4694 (1972).
[15] S. Green, *J. Chem. Phys.* **57**, 2830 (1972).
[16] S. Green, *J. Chem. Phys.* **56**, 739 (1972).
[17] W. J. Stevens, G. Das, A. C. Wahl, M. Krauss, and D. Neumann, *J. Chem. Phys.* **61**, 3686 (1974).
[18] R. Ditchfield, J. Del Bene, and J. A. Pople, *J. Am. Chem. Soc.* **94**, 4806 (1972).
[19] E. Clementi and J. Mehl, *Jerusalem Symp. Quantum Chem. Biochem.* **6**, 137 (1974).
[20] L. C. Allen and H. Basch, *J. Am. Chem. Soc.* **93**, 6373 (1971).
[21] L. Pedersen and K. Morokuma, *J. Chem. Phys.* **46**, 3741 (1967).
[22] W. H. Fink and L. C. Allen, *J. Chem. Phys.* **46**, 2261 (1967).
[23] P. A. Kollman and L. C. Allen, *Chem. Phys. Lett.* **5**, 75 (1970).
[24] E. Scarzafava and L. C. Allen, *J. Am. Chem. Soc.* **93**, 311 (1971).
[25] R. B. Davidson and L. C. Allen, *J. Chem. Phys.* **54**, 2828 (1971).
[26] J. E. Del Bene, *J. Chem. Phys.* **57**, 1899 (1972).
[27] H. Popkie, H. Kistenmacher, and E. Clementi, *J. Chem. Phys.* **59**, 1325 (1973).
[28] H. Kistenmacher, G. C. Lie, H. Popkie, and E. Clementi, *J. Chem. Phys.* **61**, 546 (1974).
[29] H. Kistenmacher, H. Popkie, and E. Clementi, *J. Chem. Phys.* **58**, 1689 (1973); **61**, 799 (1974).
[30] R. O. Watts, E. Clementi, and J. Fromm, *J. Chem. Phys.* **61**, 2550 (1974).
[31] A. Dedieu, A. Veillard, and B. Roos, *Jerusalem Symp. Quantum Chem. Biochem.* **6**, 371 (1974).

[32] K. Morokuma and R. E. Davis, *J. Am. Chem. Soc.* **94**, 1060 (1972).
[33] P. K. Pearson, H. F. Schaefer, III, and U. Wahlgrun, *J. Chem. Phys.* **62**, 350 (1975).
[34] K. Hsu, R. J. Buenker, and S. D. Peyerimhoff, *J. Am. Chem. Soc.* **94**, 5639 (1972); **93**, 2117 (1971).
[35] J. A. Pople and G. A. Segal, *J. Chem. Phys.* **43**, S136 (1965).
[36] J. A. Pople and G. A. Segal, *J. Chem. Phys.* **44**, 3289 (1966).
[37] J. D. Pulfer and M. A. Whitehead, *Can. J. Chem.* **51**, 2220 (1973).
[38] J. A. Pople, D. L. Beveridge, and P. A. Dobosh, *J. Chem. Phys.* **47**, 2026 (1967).
[39] R. C. Bingham, M. J. S. Dewar, and D. H. Lo, *J. Am. Chem. Soc.* **97**, 1285 (1975).
[40] M. J. S. Dewar, *Science* **187**, 1037 (1975).
[41] J. A. Pople, D. P. Santry, and G. A. Segal, *J. Chem. Phys.* **43**, S129 (1965).
[42] M. J. S. Dewar and W. Thiel, *J. Am. Chem. Soc.* **99**, 4899, 4907 (1977).
[43] J. A. Pople and D. L. Beveridge, "Approximate Molecular Orbital Theory." McGraw-Hill, New York, 1970.
[44] G. M. Maggiora, *J. Am. Chem. Soc.* **95**, 6555 (1973).

CHAPTER 12

TIME-INDEPENDENT RAYLEIGH–SCHRÖDINGER PERTURBATION THEORY

12-1 An Introductory Example

Imagine a city having *one million* resident wage earners. The city government plans to raise additional revenue by assessing each such resident a wage tax. This tax will not apply to wage earners residing in suburbs. The government estimates that a \$10 assessment will bring in new revenues of \$10 *million*. This estimate assumes that the city population before imposition of the tax will hold after the tax is imposed as well. But the tax will produce a slight change, or *perturbation*, in the economic climate of the city. It is true that the tax is small, and so few people are likely to move to the suburbs as a result of it. Therefore, it is probably fairly accurate to use the population of the city before the perturbation to calculate the change in revenue brought about by the perturbation. But, if the perturbation were large, say \$1000 a head, we would expect a substantial migration of wage earners to the suburbs, and so the estimate produced by using the original unperturbed population would contain substantial error. Corrections should be made, therefore, to account for population changes produced by the perturbation.

This use of the *unperturbed* population to calculate the change in revenue is a crude example of a certain level of estimation (called "first order") in Rayleigh–Schrödinger perturbation theory.[1] We will now proceed to develop the theory more formally in the context of wavefunctions and energies. The above example has been presented to encourage the reader to anticipate that there is a lot of simple good sense in the results of perturbation theory even though the mathematical development is rather cumbersome and unintuitive.

12-2 Formal Development of the Theory for Nondegenerate States

Perturbation theory involves starting with a system with known hamiltonian, eigenvalues, and eigenfunctions, and calculating the changes in these

[1] Other perturbation methods exist, but the Rayleigh–Schrödinger (R–S) theory is the oldest and the most widely used in quantum chemistry.

eigenvalues and eigenfunctions that result from a small change, or *perturbation*, in the hamiltonian for the system. We restrict the discussion to stationary states of systems having hamiltonians that are not time dependent. Let the known, unperturbed system have H_0 as hamiltonian, and let the eigenfunctions ψ_i be orthonormal. Then

$$H_0\psi_i = E_i\psi_i \tag{12-1}$$

$$\int \psi_i^*\psi_j \, d\tau = \delta_{ij} \tag{12-2}$$

and the functions ψ form a complete set as discussed in Chapter 6. We are interested in the system with hamiltonian

$$H = H_0 + \lambda H' \tag{12-3}$$

where $\lambda H'$ is the perturbation.[2] (The parameter λ is a scalar quantity that will be convenient in the mathematical development of the theory. When the derivation is complete, we will set λ equal to unity so that it no longer appears explicitly in any formula, and then H' must account entirely for the perturbation.) The eigenvalues and eigenfunctions of the perturbed hamiltonian H are unknown. Let us symbolize them as W and ϕ, respectively. Then

$$H\phi_i = W_i\phi_i \tag{12-4}$$

It is clear that, when $\lambda = 0$, then $H = H_0$, $\phi_i = \psi_i$ and $W_i = E_i$. As λ is increased from zero, W_i and ϕ_i change in (we expect) a continuous way. In other words, W_i and ϕ_i are continuous functions of the variable parameter λ, and they are known at the particular value $\lambda = 0$. Therefore, we can expand them[3] as series in powers of λ about the point $\lambda = 0$. Thus, for a given state i,[4]

$$W_i = \lambda^0 W_i^{(0)} + \lambda^1 W_i^{(1)} + \lambda^2 W_i^{(2)} + \lambda^3 W_i^{(3)} + \cdots \tag{12-5}$$

Here we must remember that λ is a variable and $W_i^{(0)}$, $W_i^{(1)}$, etc. are constants. The superscript in parentheses is simply a label to tell us for which power of λ this constant is the coefficient. Since we know that $W_i = E_i$ when $\lambda = 0$, we see at once that $W_i^{(0)}$ in Eq. (12-5) is equal to E_i. Our problem is to evaluate $W_i^{(1)}$, $W_i^{(2)}$, etc. It is traditional to call $W_i^{(0)}$ (or E_i) the *unperturbed energy* or, sometimes, the *energy to zeroth order*. $\lambda W_i^{(1)}$ (which is just $W_i^{(1)}$ after λ is set equal to unity) is the *first-order correction to the energy*, and $W_i^{(0)} + \lambda W_i^{(1)}$ is the *energy to first order*. $\lambda^2 W_i^{(2)}$, $\lambda^3 W_i^{(3)}$, . . ., etc. are the *second-*, *third-*, etc., *order corrections* to the energy. Normally, for expansion in a series to be useful, it is necessary for the

[2] Some treatments expand H as $H_0 + \lambda H' + \lambda^2 H'' + \cdots$ and ultimately achieve working formulas that appear different from those we will achieve. In fact, they are equivalent. For an example of this alternative formulation, see Pauling and Wilson [1, Chapter 6].

[3] In effect, we assume ϕ_i and W_i to be analytic functions of λ in the range $0 \leq \lambda \leq 1$.

[4] It is important to recognize that henceforth the subscript i will refer to the state that we are studying as a function of λ.

series to converge at a reasonable rate. In most simple applications of perturbation theory, only a few orders of correction are made. Thus, one very commonly reads of energies calculated "to first order," or "to second order." Calculations to much higher orders are also made, but these are not as common.

In precisely the same manner, we can expand the unknown eigenfunction ϕ_i as a power series in λ:

$$\phi_i = \phi_i^{(0)} + \lambda\phi_i^{(1)} + \lambda^2\phi_i^{(2)} + \lambda^3\phi_i^{(3)} + \cdots \tag{12-6}$$

Since ϕ_i is a *function* of particle coordinates, $\phi_i^{(0)}$, $\phi_i^{(1)}$, etc. are also functions, but they are invariant to changes in λ. Again, it is clear that $\phi_i^{(0)} = \psi_i$. $\phi_i^{(0)}$ (or ψ_i) is the unperturbed or *zeroth-order wavefunction*, $\lambda\phi_i^{(1)}$ is the *first-order correction* to the wavefunction, etc.

Now we substitute Eqs. (12-3), (12-5), and (12-6) into (12-4) and obtain

$$\begin{aligned}(H_0 + \lambda H')(\phi_i^{(0)} + \lambda\phi_i^{(1)} + \lambda^2\phi_i^{(2)} + \cdots)\\ = (W_i^{(0)} + \lambda W_i^{(1)} + \lambda^2 W_i^{(2)} + \cdots)(\phi_i^{(0)} + \lambda\phi_i^{(1)} + \lambda^2\phi_i^{(2)} + \cdots)\end{aligned} \tag{12-7}$$

The variable in Eq. (12-7) is λ, and each power of λ is linearly independent of all other powers of λ. As indicated in Section 3-4D, this means that Eq. (12-7) can be satisfied for all values of λ only if it is satisfied for *each power* of λ separately. Collecting terms having the zeroth power of λ gives

$$H_0\phi_i^{(0)} = W_i^{(0)}\phi_i^{(0)} \tag{12-8}$$

However, we have already recognized that

$$\phi_i^{(0)} = \psi_i, \qquad W_i^{(0)} = E_i \tag{12-9}$$

and Eq. (12-8) is simply a restatement of Eq. (12-1). Collecting terms from Eq. (12-7) containing λ to the first power we obtain

$$\lambda(H'\phi_i^{(0)} + H_0\phi_i^{(1)} - W_i^{(0)}\phi_i^{(1)} - W_i^{(1)}\phi_i^{(0)}) = 0 \tag{12-10}$$

This equality must hold for any value of λ, so the term in parentheses is zero. Hence, rearranging and making use of Eqs. (12-9), we have the first-order equation

$$(H' - W_i^{(1)})\psi_i + (H_0 - E_i)\phi_i^{(1)} = 0 \tag{12-11}$$

Let us multiply this from the left by ψ_i^* and integrate:

$$\int \psi_i^* H'\psi_i \, d\tau - W_i^{(1)} \int \psi_i^*\psi_i \, d\tau + \int \psi_i^* H_0\phi_i^{(1)} \, d\tau - E_i \int \psi_i^*\phi_i^{(1)} \, d\tau = 0 \tag{12-12}$$

Using the hermitian property of H_0, it is easy to show that the third and fourth terms cancel, leaving

$$\boxed{W_i^{(1)} = \int \psi_i^* H'\psi_i \, d\tau} \tag{12-13a}$$

Thus we have arrived at an expression for the first-order correction to the energy in terms of known quantities. *It is the expectation value for the perturbation operator calculated using the wavefunction of the unperturbed system.* The analogy between this formula and the use of the population of the unperturbed city to calculate additional revenues from a new tax should be apparent. H' corresponds to the tax per wage earner, and $\int \psi_i^* \psi_i \, d\tau$ corresponds to the sum of wage earners in the city before the tax was imposed.

Equation (12-13a) can be written in bra–ket notation (see Appendix 11):

$$\boxed{W_i^{(1)} = \langle \psi_i | H' | \psi_i \rangle} \tag{12-13b}$$

or in the notation wherein an integral is indicated by affixing subscripts to the operator (i.e., as a matrix element)

$$\boxed{W_i^{(1)} = H'_{ii}} \tag{12-13c}$$

In most discussions of perturbation theory one of these alternative notations is used. We will continue our formal development from this point using bra–ket notation for integrals.

To find an expression for $\phi_i^{(1)}$, the first-order correction to the wavefunction for the ith state, we first recognize that we can expand $\phi_i^{(1)}$ in terms of the complete set of eigenfunctions ψ:

$$\phi_i^{(1)} = \sum_j c_{ji}^{(1)} \psi_j \tag{12-14}$$

The summation symbol suggests that ψ is a discrete set of functions. This need not be true. Contributions from functions whose eigenvalues are in a continuum would require integration rather than summation. However, we will use the sum symbol since most actual applications of perturbation theory in quantum chemistry invoke only discrete functions.

We now insert Eq. (12-14) into (12-11) to obtain

$$(H' - W_i^{(1)})\psi_i + (H_0 - E_i) \sum_j c_{ji}^{(1)} \psi_j = 0 \tag{12-15}$$

Multiplying from the left by ψ_k^* and integrating yields

$$\langle \psi_k | H' | \psi_i \rangle - W_i^{(1)} \langle \psi_k | \psi_i \rangle + \sum_j c_{ji}^{(1)} (\langle \psi_k | H_0 | \psi_j \rangle - E_i \langle \psi_k | \psi_j \rangle) = 0 \tag{12-16}$$

If $k = i$, this reduces to Eq. (12-13), as was shown above. If $k \neq i$, the terms in the sum all vanish except when $j = k$. Thus,

$$\langle \psi_k | H' | \psi_i \rangle + c_{ki}^{(1)} (\langle \psi_k | H_0 | \psi_k \rangle - E_i \langle \psi_k | \psi_k \rangle) = 0, \qquad (k \neq i) \tag{12-17}$$

or

$$\boxed{c_{ki}^{(1)} = \frac{\langle \psi_k | H' | \psi_i \rangle}{E_i - E_k}, \qquad k \neq i} \tag{12-18}$$

Inserting this into Eq. (12-14) gives an expression for $\phi_i^{(1)}$:

$$\boxed{\phi_i^{(1)} = \sum_{j \neq i} \frac{\langle \psi_j | H' | \psi_i \rangle}{E_i - E_j} \psi_j} \tag{12-19}$$

This formula prescribes the way the first-order correction to the wavefunction is to be built up from eigenfunctions of the unperturbed system. We discuss this formula in detail later when considering an example.

Note that, if the perturbed state of interest (the ith) is degenerate with another state (the lth), Eqs. (12-18) and (12-19) blow up for k or j equal to l unless $\langle \psi_l | H' | \psi_i \rangle$ vanishes. Therefore, we restrict the theoretical discussion of this section to states of interest that are nondegenerate and discrete. (States of the system other than the ith may be degenerate or continuum states, however.)

If we extract the terms containing λ^2 from Eq. (12-7) and proceed, in the same way as above, to expand $\phi_i^{(2)}$ as a linear combination of unperturbed eigenfunctions,

$$\phi_i^{(2)} = \sum_j c_{ji}^{(2)} \psi_j \tag{12-20}$$

we arrive, after some manipulation, at the following formula for $W_i^{(2)}$:

$$\boxed{W_i^{(2)} = \sum_{j(\neq i)} \frac{\langle \psi_i | H' | \psi_j \rangle \langle \psi_j | H' | \psi_i \rangle}{E_i - E_j}} \tag{12-21}$$

Comparing this with Eq. (12-18) allows us to write

$$W_i^{(2)} = \sum_{j(\neq i)} |c_{ji}^{(1)}|^2 (E_i - E_j) \tag{12-22}$$

or comparing Eqs. (12-19) and (12-21) gives

$$W_i^{(2)} = \langle \psi_i | H' | \phi_i^{(1)} \rangle \tag{12-23}$$

The formula that emerges for $c_{ji}^{(2)}$ of Eq. (12-20) is

$$\boxed{c_{ji}^{(2)} = \sum_{k(\neq i)} \frac{\langle \psi_j | H' | \psi_k \rangle \langle \psi_k | H' | \psi_i \rangle}{(E_i - E_k)(E_i - E_j)} - \frac{\langle \psi_i | H' | \psi_i \rangle \langle \psi_j | H' | \psi_i \rangle}{(E_i - E_j)^2}, \qquad i \neq j} \tag{12-24}$$

The boxed equations are "working equations" since they enable us to calculate the correction terms from the known eigenvalues and eigenfunctions of the unperturbed system. Equation (12-23) is interesting because it indicates that the second-order correction to the energy is calculable if we know the zeroth and first-order functions.[5] Comparing Eqs. (12-13) and (12-23) shows that, whereas the first-order correction for the energy is the average value for the perturbation operator with the unperturbed wavefunction, the second-order correction is an interaction element between two functions, and not an average value in the usual sense.

Higher-order correction terms may be found by proceeding in a similar way with λ^3, λ^4, etc. terms from Eq. (12-7). The equations become progressively more cumbersome and will be of no interest to us for applications to be considered in this book.

Having made use of the parameter λ to keep terms properly sorted, we can now dispense with it by setting it equal to unity. Then

$$H = H_0 + H' \tag{12-25}$$

$$W_i = E_i + W_i^{(1)} + W_i^{(2)} + \cdots \tag{12-26}$$

$$\phi_i = \psi_i + \phi_i^{(1)} + \phi_i^{(2)} + \cdots \tag{12-27}$$

Notice that ϕ_i is not normalized. The normalization coefficient needed will depend on the order to which ϕ_i has been calculated.[6]

12-3 A Uniform Electrostatic Perturbation of an Electron in a "Wire"

A. *Description of the System*

Suppose that a small uniform electric field is applied to an electron somehow constrained to move on a line segment of length L. In the absence of this field, we assume the electron states to be described by the one-dimensional "box" wavefunctions discussed in Chapter 2. The electric field will be treated as a perturbation. The potential energy of the electron is sketched in Fig. 12-1. A uniform field produces a constant gradient (in potential energy) along the line segment. For purposes of discussion, we let the perturbation rise from zero at $x = 0$ to u at $x = L$, but we shall see later that there is a degree of arbitrariness here. The perturbation, then, is given by

$$H' = ux/L, \qquad 0 \le x \le L \tag{12-28}$$

where u, x, and L are measured in atomic units.

B. *The Energy to First Order*

We now ask, what is the effect, to first order, of H' on the energy of the lowest-energy state of the electron? As described in the preceding section, this is

[5] Löwdin [2] has shown that, if we know all the ϕ_i's up to $\phi_i^{(n)}$, we can calculate all the W_i's up to and including $W_i^{(2n+1)}$.

[6] One can guarantee normality up to second order in ϕ_i^2 by setting $c_{ii}^{(1)} = 0$, $c_{ii}^{(2)} = -\frac{1}{2}\sum_k |c_{ki}^{(1)}|^2$ (see Schiff [3]).

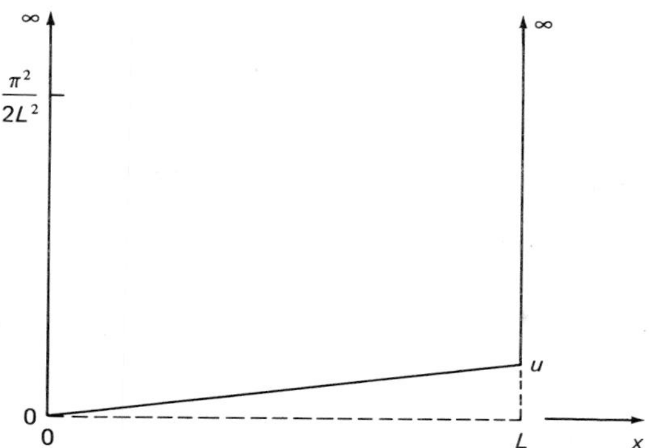

FIG. 12-1 Potential of an electron in line segment of length L in presence of a uniform electric field. The perturbation is "small" if the potential change u across L is small compared to $\pi^2/2L^2$, the energy in atomic units of the lowest unperturbed state.

obtained by calculating the average value of H' using the unperturbed wavefunction:

$$W_1^{(1)} = \int_0^L [\sqrt{2/L}\,\sin(\pi x/L)](ux/L)[\sqrt{2/L}\,\sin(\pi x/L)]\,dx \tag{12-29}$$

We now describe three ways to evaluate this integral. One way is to integrate explicitly, the other two ways involve simple inspection.

1. *Explicit Integration.* Factoring constants from Eq. (12-29) gives

$$W_1^{(1)} = 2u/L^2 \int_0^L \sin^2(\pi x/L)x\,dx \tag{12-30}$$

To achieve a common variable, we multiply x and dx each by π/L and outside by L^2/π^2, thereby keeping the value unchanged:

$$W_1^{(1)} = 2u/\pi^2 \int_0^L \sin^2(\pi x/L)(\pi x/L)\,d(\pi x/L) \tag{12-31}$$

Letting $\pi x/L = y$ and noting that $y = 0, \pi$ when $x = 0, L$, we have

$$W_1^{(1)} = 2u/\pi^2 \int_0^\pi y \sin^2 y\,dy \tag{12-32}$$

Standard tables lead to a value of $\pi^2/4$ for the integral, and

$$W_1^{(1)} = (2u/\pi^2)(\pi^2/4) = u/2 \tag{12-33}$$

To first order, then, the energy of the lowest-energy perturbed state is

$$W = (\pi^2/2L^2) + u/2 \tag{12-34}$$

2. *Evaluation by Inspection: First Method.* Equation (12-34) is certainly a reasonable result since, as the potential is increased everywhere in the box (except at $x = 0$), we expect that the energy of the electron should also increase. The fact that the increase is such a simple quantity ($u/2$) suggests that there might be a simple way to understand this result, and this is indeed the case. Consider the distribution of the electron in the lowest unperturbed state, shown in Fig. 12-2. This distribution is symmetric about the midpoint of the line segment. Consequently, for each instant of time the unperturbed electron spends in element dx_1 of Fig. 12-2, it spends an equal instant in the symmetrically related

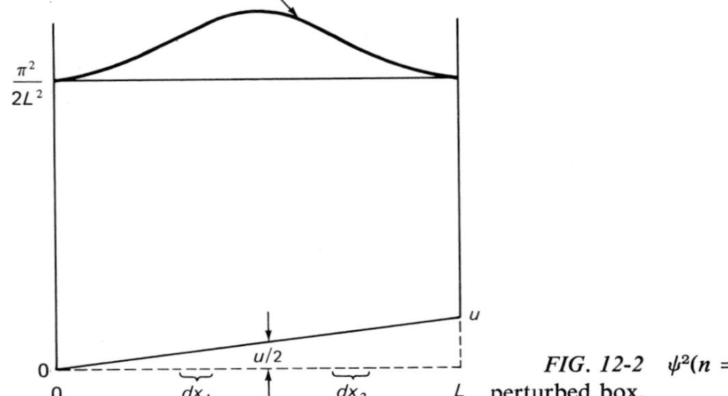

FIG. 12-2 $\psi^2(n = 1)$ for particle in unperturbed box.

element dx_2. In other words, for each instant the electron experiences a perturbation potential *less* than $u/2$, it experiences an instant of potential *greater* (by an equal amount) than $u/2$. Hence, the *average* potential must be precisely $u/2$. Since we know that ψ^2 is symmetric for *every state* in the unperturbed box, we can immediately extend our result and say that the first-order correction to the energy of every state is $u/2$.

The ability to evaluate first-order energies by inspection is very useful. Even in cases where exact evaluation by this technique is not possible, it may still be useful in making an estimate or in checking the reasonableness of a computed result.

3. *Evaluation by Inspection: Second Method.* A variation of the above approach is sometimes useful. We begin by recognizing that, whereas H' is neither symmetric nor antisymmetric about the midpoint of the wire, we can make it antisymmetric by subtracting the constant $u/2$, as indicated in Fig. 12-3. By writing

$$H' = ux/L - u/2 + u/2 \equiv H'_{\text{anti}} + u/2 \tag{12-35}$$

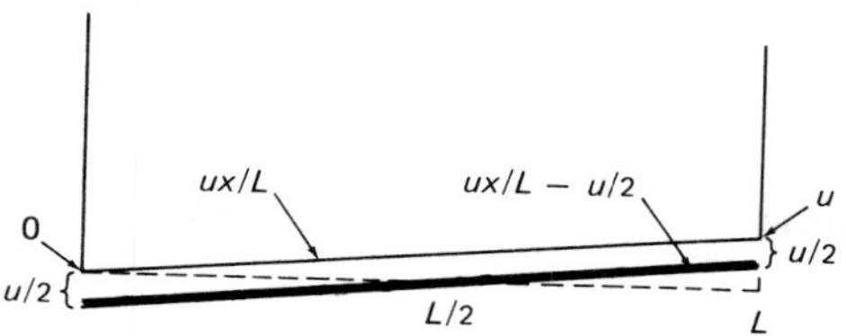

FIG. 12-3 The function ux/L is unsymmetric about $L/2$, but $ux/L - u/2$ is antisymmetric about $L/2$.

we express H' as an antisymmetric function plus a constant. Our integral for $E^{(1)}$ becomes

$$W_1^{(1)} = \int_0^L \psi_{n=1} H'_{\text{anti}} \psi_{n=1}\, dx + \int_0^L \psi_{n=1}(u/2)\psi_{n=1}\, dx \qquad (12\text{-}36)$$

The first integral vanishes because ψ^2 is symmetric. The second integral is just $u/2$ times unity since ψ is normalized. Hence, $W_1^{(1)} = u/2$.

C. *The First-Order Correction to ψ_1*

How should we expect the lowest-energy wavefunction to change in response to the perturbation? Since we are dealing with the lowest-energy state, we might expect the electron to spend more time in the low-potential end of the box (the nonclassical result), and so the wavefunction should tend to become skewed, as shown in Fig. 12-4. In this figure it is demonstrated how the perturbed

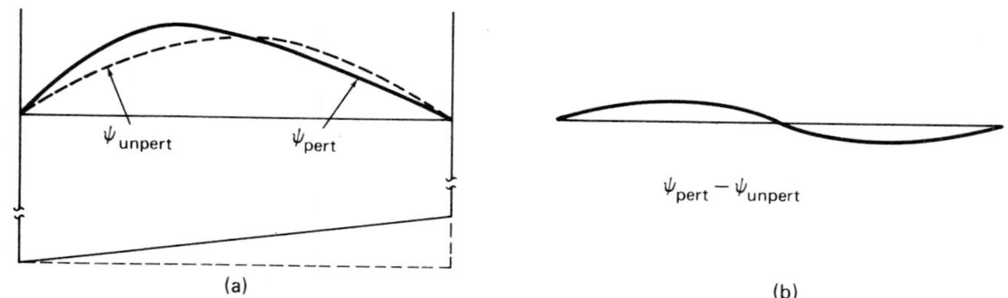

FIG. 12-4 Sketches of lowest-energy wavefunction (a) before and after perturbation and (b) the difference between them.

wavefunction can be resolved into an unperturbed wavefunction and a correction, or difference, function. Since this correction function must increase ψ on the low potential side and decrease ψ on the high potential side, it is clear that it must be close to antisymmetric in nature. According to Eq. (12-19), the first-order approximation $\phi_1^{(1)}$ to this correction function is formed by adding together small amounts of higher-energy wavefunctions. Comparing the correction function in Fig. 12-4 and these higher-energy wavefunctions (Fig. 12-5) leads us

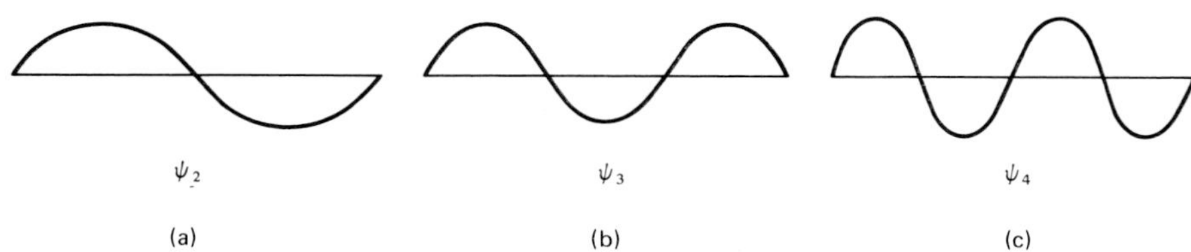

FIG. 12-5 Sketches of the (a) second, (b) third, and (c) fourth ($n = 2, 3, 4$, respectively) wavefunctions ψ for the particle in the unperturbed box.

to expect that ψ_2 will be a heavy contributor, whereas ψ_3, being symmetric, will not contribute strongly. The mixing coefficient for ψ_2 is, according to Eq. (12-18),

$$c_{21}^{(1)} = \frac{\int_0^L (\sqrt{2/L}\,\sin 2\pi x/L)(ux/L)(\sqrt{2/L}\,\sin \pi x/L)\,dx}{-3\pi^2/2L^2} = \frac{32L^2u}{27\pi^4} \qquad \text{(12-37)}$$

Thus, $c_{21}^{(1)}$ is positive, and ψ_2 contributes to $\phi_1^{(1)}$ in the manner expected. The mixing coefficient for ψ_3 is given by

$$c_{31}^{(1)} = \frac{\langle\psi_1|H'_{\text{anti}}|\psi_3\rangle}{E_1 - E_3} + \frac{\langle\psi_1|u/2|\psi_3\rangle}{E_1 - E_3} = 0 + 0 \qquad \text{(12-38)}$$

where we have used expression (12-35) for H'. The first integral vanishes because ψ_1 and ψ_3 are symmetric. The second integral vanishes because they are orthogonal. Clearly, *no* symmetric state will contribute to $\phi_1^{(1)}$.

Since ψ_4 is antisymmetric, it can contribute to $\phi_1^{(1)}$. Upon evaluation, we find that $c_{41}^{(1)}$ is about 2% of $c_{21}^{(1)}$ (Problem 12-8). $c_{41}^{(1)}$ is so much smaller than $c_{21}^{(1)}$ for two reasons. First, the integral $\langle\psi_1|H'|\psi_4\rangle$ in the numerator of $c_{41}^{(1)}$ is much smaller than $\langle\psi_1|H'|\psi_2\rangle$ in $c_{21}^{(1)}$. This means that the shifting of charge produced by adding ψ_4 to ψ_1 is much less helpful for lowering the energy than is that produced by adding ψ_2 to ψ_1. Examination of ψ_2 and ψ_4 (Fig. 12-5) reveals why this is so. ψ_2 causes removal of charge from the right-hand half of the box and accumulation of charge in the left-hand half. ψ_4 causes removal of charge from the second and fourth quarters (numbering from the left) and buildup of charge in the first and third quarters. On balance ψ_4 helps, but charge buildup in the third quarter is not desirable nor is removal of charge from the second quarter, and so ψ_4 is much less helpful than ψ_2. The second reason for $c_{41}^{(1)}$ being so small is that $E_1 - E_4$ in the denominator of $c_{41}^{(1)}$ is five times as big as $E_1 - E_2$ in $c_{21}^{(1)}$. In general, mixing between states of widely different energies is discouraged by the formula for $\phi_i^{(1)}$.

The fact that a large contribution by ψ_j to $\phi_i^{(1)}$ is favored by large $\langle\psi_i|H'|\psi_j\rangle$ and small $|E_i - E_j|$ is strikingly similar to the situation found for variational calculations (Chapter 7). There, the mixing between two basis functions x_i and x_j is favored if $\langle x_i|H|x_j\rangle \equiv H_{ij}$ is large and if $|H_{ii} - H_{jj}|$ is small.

D. *The Role of an Additive Constant in H′*

Review of the results of Sections 12-3B and C will show that addition of a constant to H' will change $W_i^{(1)}$ by the same constant for all states and have no effect on $\phi_i^{(1)}$. The change in energy of all states by a constant is equivalent to a relocation of the zero of energy and is normally of no interest. Our initial statement that the perturbation is produced by a uniform electric field left the additive constant in H' unspecified. We chose to set $H' = 0$ at $x = 0$, but we could have made any of an infinite number of choices for H' at $x = 0$. A more sensible choice would have been the antisymmetric function $H' = ux/L - u/2$ because this leads to changes in wavefunctions due to the perturbation, but introduces no energy change due to a constant potential change ($W_i^{(1)} = 0$ for all states using this H'). In other words, the antisymmetric function includes the relevant physics of the problem and excludes the trivial effects of a constant potential change. Our choice of $H' = ux/L$ was made for pedagogical reasons.

E. *The Calculation of $W_1^{(2)}$*

Since the constant first-order contribution to the energies of all the states is not physically interesting, let us examine the second-order contribution to the ground-state energy $W_1^{(2)}$. Equation (12-23) shows that this is related to the first-order correction to the wavefunction, $\phi_1^{(1)}$, which, as we have already seen, causes the wavefunction to become skewed toward the low-potential end of the box. It is clear from Eq. (12-22) that, in calculating the coefficients for $\phi_1^{(1)}$, we have already done most of the work needed to find $W_1^{(2)}$. We saw earlier that $\phi_1^{(1)}$ is made primarily from ψ_2. For simplicity, we will neglect all higher-energy contributions, and so

$$\phi_1^{(1)} \cong c_2^{(1)}\psi_2 = (32L^2u/27\pi^4)\psi_2 \tag{12-39}$$

and, using Eq. (12-22),

$$W_1^{(2)} \cong (32L^2u/27\pi^4)^2(-3\pi^2/2L^2) \tag{12-40}$$

Thus, the effect of $W_1^{(2)}$ is to *lower* the energy.

We pause at this point to summarize our results. The perturbation raises the potential everywhere in the box. (This depends on our choice of an arbitrary constant.) The energy to first order is increased by a constant amount for every state. This is easily seen by inspection, utilizing simple symmetry features of H' and the unperturbed wavefunctions. The *wavefunction* for the lowest-energy state is skewed, to first order, in a way which is energetically favorable as far as interaction with H' is concerned. The second-order contribution to the *energy* for this state is negative, reflecting this energetically favorable shift of charge. Thus far, everything behaves sensibly. We next examine the behavior of the second-lowest energy state, where some important new features occur.

F. The Effects of the Perturbation on ψ_2

We begin by examining $\phi_2^{(1)}$, the first-order correction to ψ_2. Inspection of Eq. (12-18) leads at once to the observation that $c_{21}^{(1)} = -c_{12}^{(1)}$. This means that, since ψ_2 contributes to $\phi_1^{(1)}$ with a positive coefficient, ψ_1 contributes to $\phi_2^{(1)}$ with a negative coefficient. A sketch of ψ_2 minus a small amount of ψ_1 will show that this has the effect of shifting charge from the left half to the right half of the box. This is just the reverse of what we found for the lowest-energy state.

The antisymmetry of Eq. (12-18) for interchange of i and k allows us to make the following general statement. Let a perturbation occur that raises or lowers the potential more in one region of space than in another. The first-order correction to a given wavefunction will contain higher-energy wavefunctions in a manner to cause charge to shift into regions of lowered (or less raised) potential and it will contain lower-energy wavefunctions in a manner to cause charge to shift into regions of raised (or less lowered) potential.

We have not yet completed our construction of $\phi_2^{(1)}$. We must calculate coefficients for contributions from the higher-energy functions ψ_3, ψ_4, etc. The state ψ_3 should contribute fairly strongly since it has the proper symmetry and is not too distant in energy from E_2:

$$c_{32}^{(1)} = \frac{\langle\psi_2|H'|\psi_3\rangle}{E_2 - E_3} = \frac{3}{5}\frac{32L^2u}{25\pi^4} \tag{12-41}$$

Therefore, ψ_3 contributes to $\phi_2^{(1)}$ with a coefficient about $\frac{3}{5}$ the magnitude of that for ψ_1. The sign of $c_{32}^{(1)}$ is positive and a sketch of ψ_2 plus a small amount of ψ_3 will demonstrate that this causes charge shifting to the left in accord with our general statement above.

Since ψ_4 contributes nothing (by symmetry) and ψ_5 is fairly distant in energy, we will neglect all contributions to $\phi_2^{(2)}$ above ψ_3.

We have, then, two sizable contributions to $\phi_2^{(1)}$, each favoring charge shifts in opposite directions. Let us see how $W_2^{(2)}$ reflects this:

$$W_2^{(2)} \cong c_{12}^{(1)2}(E_2 - E_1) + c_{32}^{(1)2}(E_2 - E_3) \tag{12-42a}$$

$$\cong [c_{12}^{(1)2}(3) + (\tfrac{3}{5}c_{12}^{(1)})^2(-5)]\pi^2/2L^2 \tag{12-42b}$$

$$\cong 1.2c_{12}^{(1)2}\pi^2/2L^2 \tag{12-42c}$$

$W_2^{(2)}$ is the difference between energy contributions of opposite sign. The net result (energy increases) comes about in this case because ψ_1 contributes more heavily than ψ_3.

The fact that contributing wavefunctions from lower and higher energies affect $W_i^{(2)}$ oppositely is made evident by Eq. (12-22). Hence, we can extend our general statement above by adding that the second-order contribution to the energy from states below ψ_i in energy cause the energy of the ith state to go up, contributions from above cause it to go down.

Because the unperturbed energies of the particle in the box increase as n^2, any state (except the lowest) is closer in energy to states below than to states above. Hence, for at least some kinds of perturbation, we might expect these states to "feel" the effects of states at lower energies more strongly and to rise in energy (as far as $W^{(2)}$ is concerned). This is what happens in this example. There are no states below the lowest, and so $W_1^{(2)}$ cannot be positive, but $W_2^{(2)}$ is positive and it turns out that $W_i^{(2)}$ is positive for all higher i as well.

It is interesting to compare these results with those from classical physics. Classically, the particle moves most slowly at the top of the potential gradient and therefore spends most of its time there. The lowest-energy state has responded in the opposite manner, in a way we might call anticlassical. The second and all higher states have responded classically.

12-4 The Ground-State Energy to First Order of Heliumlike Systems

The hamiltonian for a two-electron atom or ion with nuclear charge Z a.u. is (neglecting relativistic effects and assuming infinite nuclear mass)

$$H(1, 2) = -\tfrac{1}{2}(\nabla_1^2 + \nabla_2^2) - Z/r_1 - Z/r_2 + 1/r_{12} \qquad (12\text{-}43)$$

This may be written as a sum of one-electron operators and a two-electron operator:

$$H(1, 2) = H(1) + H(2) + 1/r_{12} \qquad (12\text{-}44)$$

where $H(i)$ is simply the hamiltonian for the hydrogenlike system with nuclear charge Z:

$$H(i) = -\tfrac{1}{2}\nabla_i^2 - Z/r_i \qquad (12\text{-}45)$$

Since we know the eigenvalues and eigenfunctions for $H(i)$, we can let $H(1) + H(2)$ be the unperturbed hamiltonian with $1/r_{12}$ the perturbation. Such a perturbation is not very small, but it is of interest to see how well the method works in such a case. We have, therefore, for the lowest-energy state of the system (for which $i = 1$)

$$H_0 = H(1) + H(2) \qquad (12\text{-}46)$$

$$H' = 1/r_{12} \qquad (12\text{-}47)$$

$$\psi_1 = (Z^3/\pi)\exp[-Z(r_1 + r_2)] \qquad (12\text{-}48)$$

$$E_1 = -Z^2/2 - Z^2/2 = -Z^2 \qquad (12\text{-}49)$$

$$W_1^{(1)} = \langle\psi_1|1/r_{12}|\psi_1\rangle \qquad (12\text{-}50)$$

All quantities are in atomic units. The unperturbed wavefunction is simply the product of two one-electron 1s AOs. Because this is an eigenfunction of the

TABLE 12-1
Comparison of Exact Energy (in atomic units) with Energy to First Order when $H' = r_{12}^{-1}$

Z	System	E_1	$W_1^{(1)}$	$E_1 + W_1^{(1)}$	E_{exact}^a	$E_{\text{exact}} - E_1 - W_1^{(1)}$	%Error
1	H^-	−1.0000	5/8 = 0.6250	−0.3750	−0.52759	−0.15259	28.92
2	He	−4.0000	5/4 = 1.2500	−2.7500	−2.90372	−0.15372	5.29
3	Li^+	−9.0000	15/8 = 1.8750	−7.1250	−7.27991	−0.15491	2.13
4	Be^{2+}	−16.0000	5/2 = 2.50000	−13.5000	−13.65556	−0.15556	1.14
5	B^{3+}	−25.0000	25/8 = 3.1250	−21.8750	−22.03097	−0.15597	0.71
6	C^{4+}	−36.0000	15/4 = 3.7500	−32.2500	−32.40624	−0.15624	0.48
7	N^{5+}	−49.0000	35/8 = 4.3750	−44.6250	−44.78144	−0.15644	0.35
8	O^{6+}	−64.0000	5.0000	−59.0000	−59.15659	−0.15659	0.26
9	F^{7+}	−81.0000	45/8 = 5.6250	−75.3750	−75.53171	−0.15671	0.21
10	Ne^{8+}	−100.0000	25/4 = 6.2500	−93.7500	−93.90680	−0.15680	0.17

[a] E_{exact} is the nonrelativistic energy to thirteenth order in Z^{-1}, truncated at the fifth decimal place. See Scherr and Knight [4].

system in the absence of interelectronic repulsion, it is too contracted about the nucleus.

The first-order correction to the energy is the repulsion between the two electrons in this overly contracted eigenfunction [Eq. (12-48)]. We have encountered this same repulsion integral in our earlier variational calculation on helium-like systems. The evaluation of this integral is described in Appendix 3. Its value is $5Z/8$. Hence, to first order,

$$W_1 = E_1 + W_1^{(1)} = -Z^2 + 5Z/8 \tag{12-51}$$

In Table 12-1, this result is compared with exact energies for the first ten members of this series. Several points should be noted:

(1) The effect of the perturbation to first order is to increase the ground-state energy. This is expected since $1/r_{12}$ is always positive (i.e., repulsive).

(2) The energy to first order is never below the exact ground-state energy. This is a general property of perturbation calculations as is easily proved (Problem 12-2).

(3) The energy to first order is in error by a fairly constant amount through out the series. For H^-, this gives a substantial *percentage* of error and fails to show H^- stable compared with an H atom and an unbound electron. For higher Z, this error becomes *relatively* smaller since $1/r_{12}$ becomes relatively less important compared with Z/r_i. The assumption that H' is a *small* perturbation is thus better fulfilled at large Z and results in $W_1^{(1)}$ being a much smaller correction relative to the total energy W_1. Because "large" and "small" are relative terms, they can be misleading. Since energies of chemical interest are often small differences between large numbers (see the discussion at the end of Chapter 7), errors that were originally relatively small can become relatively large after the subtraction. Therefore, even though perturbation terminology would suggest that the results at $Z = 10$ are better than those at $Z = 1$, this may not be the case for some practical applications.

12-5 Perturbation at an Atom in the Simple Hückel MO Method

Perturbation theory can be used to estimate the effect of a change in the value of the coulomb integral H_{kk} at carbon atom k. This is normally given the value of α, but it might be desirable to consider a different value due, for example, to replacement of an attached hydrogen by some other atom or group. We take the unperturbed Hückel MOs and orbital energies as our starting point and let the perturbed value of H_{kk} be $\alpha + \delta\alpha$. Therefore,

$$H' = \delta\alpha \qquad \text{(at center } k \text{ only)} \tag{12-52}$$

The first-order correction for the energy of ϕ_i, the ith MO, is

$$W_i^{(1)} = \langle\phi_i|H'|\phi_i\rangle \tag{12-53}$$

Now ϕ_i is a linear combination of the AOs χ:

$$\phi_i = \sum_j c_{ji}\chi_j \tag{12-54}$$

and so

$$W_1^{(1)} = \sum_j \sum_l c_{ji}^* c_{li} \langle \chi_j | H' | \chi_l \rangle \tag{12-55}$$

but H' is zero except for $j = l = k$, where it is $\delta\alpha$. Therefore,

$$W_i^{(1)} = c_{ki}^* c_{ki}\, \delta\alpha \tag{12-56}$$

Summing over all the MOs times the number of electrons in each MO gives the first-order correction to the total energy:

$$W^{(1)} = \delta\alpha \sum_i n_i c_{ki}^* c_{ki} = \delta\alpha q_k \tag{12-57}$$

where q_k is the π-electron density at atom k. That the energy change to first order is equal to the change in H_{kk} times the unperturbed electron density at that atom is also easily seen to be an immediate consequence of the alternative energy expression

$$E = \sum_l q_l \alpha_l + 2 \sum_{l<m} p_{lm}\beta_{lm} \tag{12-58}$$

which was derived in Chapter 8.

Calculation of first-order corrections to the MOs proceeds in a straightforward manner using Eq. (12-19) (see Problem 12-7). One of the results of interest from such a calculation is the change in π-electron density at atom l due to a change in the coulomb integral at atom k. The differential expression is

$$\delta q_l = (\partial q_l / \partial \alpha_k)\, \delta\alpha_k = \pi_{l,k}\, \delta\alpha_k \tag{12-59}$$

The quantity of interest $\pi_{l,k}$ is called the *atom–atom polarizability*. We will now derive an expression for $\pi_{l,k}$ in terms of MO coefficients and energies.

We assume that our MOs fall into a completely occupied set $\phi_1, \cdots, \phi_m$ and a completely empty set $\phi_{m+1}, \cdots, \phi_n$. We take $\delta\alpha$ to be positive, which means that center k is made less attractive for electrons.

According to Eq. (12-19) the jth MO is, to first order,

$$\phi_j + \phi_j^{(1)} = \phi_j + \sum_{i=1, i\neq j}^{n} \frac{\langle \phi_j | H' | \phi_i \rangle}{E_j - E_i} \phi_i \tag{12-60}$$

where E_j is the orbital energy of ϕ_j. As indicated above, the integral vanishes except over AO k. Therefore,

$$\phi_j^{(1)} = \sum_{i=1, i\neq j}^{n} \frac{c_{kj}^* c_{ki}\, \delta\alpha_k}{E_j - E_i} \phi_i \tag{12-61}$$

Expanding ϕ_i in terms of AOs, we have

$$\phi_j^{(1)} = \delta\alpha_k \sum_{i=1, i\neq j}^{n} \frac{c_{kj}c_{ki}}{E_j - E_i} \sum_{l=1}^{n} c_{li}\chi_l \tag{12-62}$$

$$= \sum_{l=1}^{n} c_{lj}^{(1)}\chi_l \tag{12-63}$$

where

$$c_{lj}^{(1)} = \delta\alpha_k \sum_{i=1, i\neq j}^{n} \frac{c_{kj}c_{ki}c_{li}}{E_j - E_i} \tag{12-64}$$

The change in density at atom l involves only the doubly occupied MOs $1 - m$:

$$\delta q_l = 2 \sum_{j=1}^{m} [(c_{lj} + c_{lj}^{(1)})^2 - c_{lj}^2] \tag{12-65}$$

$$= 4 \sum_{j=1}^{m} c_{lj}c_{lj}^{(1)} \tag{12-66}$$

where we have neglected $(c_{lj}^{(1)})^2$ because the perturbation is assumed small. Substituting Eq. (12-64) into (12-66) gives

$$\delta q_l = 4\ \delta\alpha_k \sum_{j=1}^{m} \sum_{i=1, i\neq j}^{n} \frac{c_{lj}c_{kj}c_{ki}c_{li}}{E_j - E_i} \tag{12-67}$$

This equation can be simplified further by recognizing that, for j *and* $i < m + 1$, each term with denominator $E_j - E_i$ has a mate with denominator $E_i - E_j$. Hence, the terms differ only in sign and cancel. Therefore,

$$\sum_{j=1, i\neq j}^{m} \frac{c_{lj}c_{kj}c_{ki}c_{li}}{E_j - E_i} = 0 \tag{12-68}$$

and so

$$\delta q_l = 4\ \delta\alpha_k \sum_{j=1}^{m} \sum_{i=m+1}^{n} \frac{c_{lj}c_{kj}c_{ki}c_{li}}{E_j - E_i} \tag{12-69}$$

Comparing Eqs. (12-69) and (12-59) gives

$$\boxed{\pi_{lk} = 4 \sum_{j=1}^{m} \sum_{i=m+1}^{n} \frac{c_{lj}c_{kj}c_{ki}c_{li}}{E_j - E_i}} \tag{12-70}$$

Related quantities, deriveable in a similar manner, are the *bond–atom polarizability*, $\pi_{st,r}$, and the *bond–bond polarizability*, $\pi_{tu,rs}$:

$$\pi_{st,r} = 2 \sum_{j=1}^{m} \sum_{k=m+1}^{n} \frac{c_{rj}c_{rk}(c_{sj}c_{tk} + c_{tj}c_{sk})}{E_j - E_k} \tag{12-71}$$

$$\pi_{tu,rs} = 2 \sum_{j=1}^{m} \sum_{k=m+1}^{n} \frac{(c_{rj}c_{sk} + c_{sj}c_{rk})(c_{tj}c_{uk} + c_{uj}c_{tk})}{E_j - E_k} \tag{12-72}$$

These refer, respectively, to the change in bond order p_{st} induced by a perturbation $\delta\alpha_r$, and to the change in bond order p_{tu} induced by a change in β_{rs}.

The example we have described in this section illustrates that, even though perturbation theory was derived in a framework of eigenfunctions and eigenvalues of an unperturbed hamiltonian, we are not limited to cases where these are known. The Hückel MOs and orbital energies are certainly not eigenfunctions and eigenvalues on the strictest sense since they result from variational calculations using a very limited basis and a hamiltonian that cannot be defined so as to enable one to evaluate $H\phi_i$. However, the HMOs and their orbital energies are eigenvectors and eigenvalues of a matrix equation, and this suffices to make them amenable to treatment by perturbation theory.

12-6 Perturbation Theory for a Degenerate State

Equations (12-19), (12-21), and (12-24) have denominators containing $E_i - E_j$. If ψ_i and ψ_j are degenerate, this leads to difficulty, alerting us to the fact that our earlier derivations do not take proper account of states of interest that are degenerate. The problem results from our initial expansion of ϕ_i as a power series in λ. The leading term in the expansion, $\phi_i^{(0)}$, is the wavefunction that ϕ_i becomes in the limit when $\lambda = 0$. In nondegenerate systems there is no ambiguity; $\phi_i^{(0)}$ has to be ψ_i. But if ψ_i is degenerate with ψ_j, any linear combination of them is also an eigenfunction. We need a method to determine how ψ_i and ψ_j should be mixed together to form the correct zeroth-order functions $\phi_i^{(0)}$ and $\phi_j^{(0)}$.

To find the conditions that $\phi_i^{(0)}$ and $\phi_j^{(0)}$ must satisfy, we return to the first-order perturbation equation (12-11) but with $\phi_i^{(0)}$ in place of ψ_i:

$$(H' - W_i^{(1)})\phi_i^{(0)} + (H_0 - E_i)\phi_i^{(1)} = 0 \tag{12-73}$$

Multiplying from the left by $\phi_j^{(0)*}$ and integrating gives (taking $\phi_i^{(0)}$ and $\phi_j^{(0)}$ to be orthogonal and H_0 hermitian)

$$\langle\phi_j^{(0)}|H'|\phi_i^{(0)}\rangle + (E_j - E_i)\langle\phi_j^{(0)}|\phi_i^{(1)}\rangle = 0 \tag{12-74}$$

If $E_i = E_j$, this gives

$$\langle \phi_j^{(0)} | H' | \phi_i^{(0)} \rangle = 0 \tag{12-75}$$

This means that the first-order perturbation equation is satisfied for degenerate states only when the wavefunctions "diagonalize" the perturbation operator H'. Therefore, our problem reduces to finding those linear combinations of ψ_i and ψ_j that will diagonalize H'. We have already seen two ways to accomplish this in earlier chapters. One way is to construct the matrix H', where $(\mathsf{H}')_{ij} = \langle \psi_i | H' | \psi_j \rangle$, and then find the unitary matrix C which diagonalizes H' in the similarity transformation $\mathsf{C}^\dagger \mathsf{H}' \mathsf{C}$. The elements in C are then the coefficients for the linear combinations of ψ_i and ψ_j, and the diagonal elements of the diagonalized matrix are equal to $\langle \phi_i^{(0)} | H' | \phi_i^{(0)} \rangle$ and $\langle \phi_j^{(0)} | H' | \phi_j^{(0)} \rangle$; they are the first-order corrections to the energy of $\phi_i^{(0)}$ and $\phi_j^{(0)}$. The other method, equivalent to the above, is to set up the determinantal equation

$$\begin{vmatrix} H_{11} - E & H_{12} \\ H_{21} & H_{22} - E \end{vmatrix} = 0 \tag{12-76}$$

and solve for the roots E. Substituting these back into the simultaneous equations corresponding to the determinant gives the coefficients with which ψ_i and ψ_j should be combined. The roots E are the first-order corrections to the energy and are identical to the diagonal matrix elements mentioned above.

In the event that the roots are equal, the perturbation has failed to split the degeneracy to first order and it is then necessary to proceed to higher order. We will not pursue this problem to higher orders, however.

If there are n degenerate states, the above procedure is simply carried out with an $n \times n$ matrix or determinant.

We will now give an example of perturbation theory for a degenerate state.

12-7 Polarizability of the Hydrogen Atom in the $n = 2$ States

In Chapter 7, the polarizability of the hydrogen atom in the 1s state was calculated by the variation method (see Section 7-4 and Problem 7-7). We now use perturbation theory for degenerate states to calculate to first order the polarizabilities of the $n = 2$ states.

The perturbation due to a z-directed uniform electric field is, in atomic units,

$$H' = -Fr\cos\theta \tag{12-77}$$

There are four degenerate states at the $n = 2$ level, giving us a 4×4 secular determinant. If we choose the real AOs as our basis set and let s, x, y, z represent these functions, the determinantal equation is

$$\begin{vmatrix} H'_{ss} - E & H'_{sz} & H'_{sy} & H'_{sx} \\ H'_{zs} & H'_{zz} - E & H'_{zy} & H'_{zx} \\ H'_{ys} & H'_{yz} & H'_{yy} - E & H'_{yx} \\ H'_{xs} & H'_{xz} & H'_{xy} & H'_{xx} - E \end{vmatrix} = 0 \qquad (12\text{-}78)$$

where

$$H'_{yz} = \langle y|H'|z\rangle, \qquad \text{etc.} \qquad (12\text{-}79)$$

The operator H' is antisymmetric for reflection in the xy plane, but symmetric for reflection in the xz or yz planes. It follows from this that all integrals in Eq. (12-78) vanish except for H'_{sz} and H'_{zs}, which are equal. Assigning a value of x (not to be confused with the x coordinate) to these integrals, our equation becomes

$$\begin{vmatrix} -E & x & 0 & 0 \\ x & -E & 0 & 0 \\ 0 & 0 & -E & 0 \\ 0 & 0 & 0 & -E \end{vmatrix} = 0 \qquad (12\text{-}80)$$

The block diagonal form indicates that this is a product of one 2×2 determinant and two 1×1's. Evidently, the proper zeroth-order wavefunctions must be a mixture of 2s and $2p_z$ AOs, with $2p_x$ and $2p_y$ being acceptable as they stand. The roots of the 1×1 determinants are zero, the roots of the 2×2 are $E_+ = +x$, $E_- = -x$. These lead to coefficients that produce the zeroth-order wavefunctions

$$\phi_+^{(0)} = (1/\sqrt{2})(2s + 2p_z) \qquad (12\text{-}81)$$

$$\phi_-^{(0)} = (1/\sqrt{2})(2s - 2p_z) \qquad (12\text{-}82)$$

The roots $+x$ and $-x$ are the first-order corrections to the energy. We now proceed to calculate these quantities:

$$x = \langle 2s|H'|2p_z\rangle = \cdots = 3F \qquad (12\text{-}83)$$

Our perturbation calculation indicates that the $n = 2$ level splits into three levels under the influence of an electric field. Since this splitting occurs to first order, it is sometimes called a *first-order Stark effect*. Since x is proportional to F, the splitting is linear in F, as indicated in Fig. 12-6.

It is instructive to compare these results with the behavior of the 1s state. In the first place, the effect of a uniform electric field on the 1s level is zero, to first order, because $\langle 1s|H'|1s\rangle$ vanishes for reasons of symmetry. Only when first-order corrections are made to the 1s wavefunction are energy effects seen,

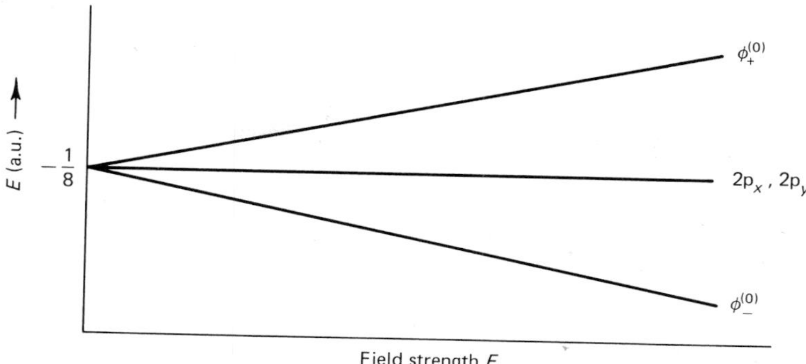

FIG. 12-6 Energy to first order of $n = 2$ level of hydrogen as a function of uniform electric field strength (z-directed field).

and these occur in the second-order energy terms. Therefore, the 1s state gives a *second-order Stark effect*, but no first-order effect. The 1s state gives no first-order effect because the spherically symmetric zeroth-order wavefunction has no electric dipole to interact with the field. But the proper zeroth-order wavefunctions for some of the $n = 2$ states, given by Eqs. (12-81) and (12-82), *do* provide electric dipoles in opposite directions that interact with the field to produce first-order energies of opposite signs.

Notice that the energy change for the second-order effect goes as F^2 [(Eq. (6-62)], whereas that for the first-order effect goes as F. These dependences are indicative of an *induced dipole* and a *permanent dipole*, respectively. The induced dipole for the 1s state depends on the field strength F, since, as F increases, the dipole moment increases (due to mixing in higher states). This induced dipole, which depends on F, then interacts with the field of strength F. Since both the size of the induced dipole and the energy of interaction with the field depend on F to the first power, the energy goes as F^2. For the $n = 2$ wavefunctions $\phi_+^{(0)}$ and $\phi_-^{(0)}$, however, the dipole is permanent.[7] (The mixing to produce these states occurs even in the limit as F goes to zero.) This permanent dipole interacts with the field to give an energy depending on F instead of F^2.

The $2p_x$ and $2p_y$ AOs are not affected to first-order in the perturbation. At higher orders, these AOs (as well as $\phi_+^{(0)}$ and $\phi_-^{(0)}$) mix in higher-energy AOs of symmetries appropriate to produce induced dipoles. However, due to the equivalence of $2p_x$ and $2p_y$ with respect to H', the induced dipole is the same in both cases so that the degeneracy is still not lifted.

The *qualitatively* different behaviors of the $n = 1$ and $n = 2$ levels of hydrogen result from the fact that degenerate eigenfunctions can be mixed together at no energy expense, whereas the $n = 1$ state can produce a dipole only by mixing in higher-energy states. This suggests that the polarizability of

[7] In the language of hybridization (Chapter 13), $\phi_+^{(0)}$ and $\phi_-^{(0)}$ are sp hybrids.

an atom or molecule should be strongly dependent on the availability of fairly low-energy unoccupied orbitals or wavefunctions, and this is indeed the case. As we proceed down the series H^-, He, Li^+, Be^{+2}, . . ., etc., we find that the distance in energy between the occupied state and the higher-energy states increases. Also, we find that the systems become less and less polarizable. Again, if we compare helium and beryllium, both of which are ordinarily considered to have s^2 valence-state configurations, we find beryllium to be much more polarizable. This is due to the presence of empty 2p orbitals lying fairly close in energy to the 2s AO in beryllium. In fact, these two atoms are strongly reminiscent of the $n = 1$, $n = 2$ polarizabilities in hydrogen, the chief difference being that the 2s and 2p levels of beryllium are only close in energy—not actually degenerate.

12-8 Interaction between Two Orbitals: An Important Chemical Model

Qualitative quantum-chemical discussion often relies on a simplified model wherein all interactions are neglected except for the primary one. For example, in considering how a Lewis base and a Lewis acid interact, one might consider only the highest occupied MO (HOMO) of the base (electron donor) and the lowest unfilled MO (LUMO) of the acid (electron acceptor). Consideration of the ways two levels interact will provide some useful rules of thumb and also consolidate some of our earlier findings.[8]

We label the unperturbed orbitals and energies ψ_a, ψ_b, and E_a, E_b. We will work within the Hückel type of framework so that state energy differences may be written as orbital energy differences. The orbitals are allowed to interact with each other by virtue of close approach. We will assume that the perturbation felt by the orbitals is proportional to the overlap between them. (If the systems involved are ions, strong electrostatic interactions will exist as well. Therefore, we assume all systems to be neutral.)

Since the overlap of ψ_a on ψ_b is the same as that of ψ_b on ψ_a, the energy change to first order is the same for both levels and hence we ignore it (unless the levels are degenerate—an eventuality we discuss shortly).

The second-order contributions to the energies are:

$$W_a^{(2)} = \frac{|\langle\psi_a|H'|\psi_b\rangle|^2}{E_a - E_b} \tag{12-84}$$

$$W_b^{(2)} = \frac{|\langle\psi_a|H'|\psi_b\rangle|^2}{E_b - E_a} \tag{12-85}$$

[8] The discussion in this section follows closely that of Hoffmann [5]. That article reviews a variety of illustrative applications of the two-orbital model.

Thus, the second-order energy $W_a^{(2)}$ is positive if $E_a > E_b$, negative if $E_a < E_b$. In other words, the higher-energy level is pushed up, or destabilized, through interaction with the level below, and the lower-energy level is stabilized by interaction with the level above. This behavior, which we noted also in connection with the perturbed particle in a wire, may be summarized by the statement: *interacting levels repel each other.* Equations (12-84) and (12-85) also make clear that *the levels repel each other more strongly the greater their interaction (numerator) and the smaller their energy separation (denominator).*

If $E_a = E_b$, we must set up a 2×2 first-order perturbation determinant using ψ_a and ψ_b as basis, and find the two roots. Just as was true in the polarizability calculation of the preceding section, we will find that one root lies above E_a, and the other lies an equal distance below. Thus, for *degenerate levels*, the repulsion between levels becomes a *first-order effect*.

The first-order mixing of ψ_a and ψ_b parallels the energy results in the expected way. If the second-order energy stabilizes the level, the orbitals are mixed in a bonding fashion. Since we have seen that it is the lower-energy orbital that is stabilized, we can state that, "if two orbitals interact, the lower-energy one of the two mixes into itself the higher-energy one in a bonding way, while the higher-energy orbital mixes into itself the lower one in an antibonding way" [5]. In short, "the upper combination takes the node" [5].

As an example of the utility of this model, consider the norbornadiene molecule (see Fig. 12-7a). According to our understanding of unsaturated systems, the double bonds in this molecule should behave like isolated ethylene double bonds and not like the conjugated bonds of butadiene. But these bonds are at an orientation and proximity allowing significant overlap between $2p_\pi$ AO lobes beneath the molecule. If we treat this system with our two-level mode, the unperturbed MOs are the bonding and antibonding π MOs of two ethylene molecules (Fig. 12-7b). We expect the MO overlap across the molecule to split each of these levels as indicated in Fig. 12-7c, the bonding interaction producing stabilization in each case. (Combinations involving a bonding MO on one side and an antibonding MO on the other are ruled out because symmetry forces the interaction term to vanish. Even if this were not the case, the energy gap between these unperturbed MOs would make such contributions negligible compared to those from the degenerate MOs.)

A careful look at Fig. 12-7c reveals certain implications about norbornadiene. For instance, the ionization potential for norbornadiene should be smaller than that for norbornene, which has but one double bond. Experimental measurements support this contention. Also, since the highest occupied MO of norbornadiene is antibonding between carbons 3 and 5 and also 6 and 2, whereas the lowest empty MO is bonding between these carbons, excitation of an electron from the former MO to the latter should promote formation of quadricyclene (Fig. 12-7d). This compound is a common product in the photochemistry of norbornadienes.

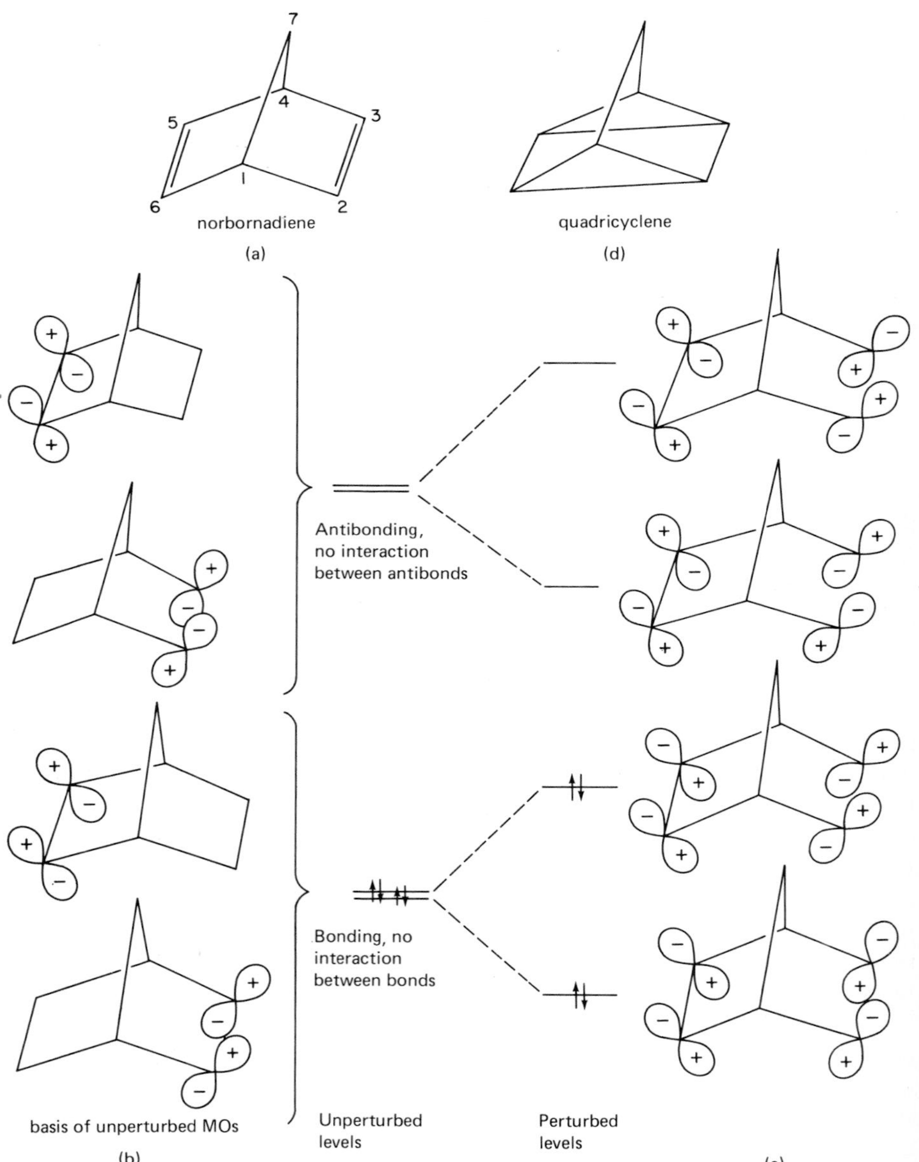

FIG. 12-7 π MOs in norbornadiene: (a) norbornadiene; (b) basis of unperturbed MOs; (c) basis of perturbed MOs; (d) quadricyclene. (After R. Hoffmann [5].)

12-9 Connection between Time-Independent Perturbation Theory and Spectroscopic Selection Rules

Molecules may change to higher- or lower-energy states under the influence of incident light. Such processes are called, respectively, absorption and induced emission. Perturbation theory can be used to study such transitions induced by an external oscillating electromagnetic field. Here we briefly describe a rather simple connection between selection rules and the perturbation theory we have discussed in this chapter.

Let a molecule initially be in a state with wavefunction ψ_i. We are interested in the probability of a transition occurring to some final state with wavefunction ψ_f. A time-dependent perturbation treatment (not given here) indicates that such a transition is probable only when the external field frequency ν satisfies the conservation of energy relation

$$\nu = |E_f - E_i|/h \tag{12-86}$$

Even when this condition is satisfied, however, we may find experimentally that the transition is so improbable as to be undetectable. Evidently some factor other than satisfaction of Eq. (12-86) is also involved.

Since the molecule is being subjected to light, it experiences fluctuating electric and magnetic fields. For ordinary (as opposed to magnetic) spectroscopy, the effects of the magnetic field are negligible compared to those of the electric field. Therefore, we ignore the former and imagine the molecule *at a particular instantaneous value* of an external electric field. As we have seen from earlier sections, this field causes the admixture of unperturbed wavefunctions ψ_1, ψ_2, etc., with ψ_i to form a perturbed wavefunction ϕ_i. For a normalized ϕ_i, we have, therefore,

$$\phi_i = c_i\psi_i + c_1\psi_1 + c_2\psi_2 + \cdots + c_f\psi_f + \cdots \tag{12-87}$$

At a later time, when the perturbation is over, the system returns to an unperturbed state. The probability of returning to the initial state is given by $c_i^*c_i$. The probability of going instead to the final state described by ψ_f is given by $c_f^*c_f$. If c_f is zero, there is no tendency for a transition to that final state to occur and the transition is said to be *forbidden*. If c_f is nonzero, the transition is allowed.

Since the coefficient c_f is given to first order by [see Eq. (12-18)],

$$c_f = \frac{\langle\psi_f|H'|\psi_i\rangle}{E_i - E_f} \tag{12-88}$$

where H' is the perturbation operator for the electric field component of the light, we can say at once that a transition between two states is forbidden (to first order) if $\langle\psi_f|H'|\psi_i\rangle$ vanishes.

One example of a forbidden transition is that between a singlet state and a triplet state of a system. We can see this at once since H' is an *electric* field and does not interact with spin *magnetic* moment. Therefore the orthogonality between ψ_i and ψ_f due to spin functions is uninfluenced by H' and the integral $\langle\psi_f|H'|\psi_i\rangle$ must vanish. In effect, the perturbation H' causes the initial singlet state to become polarized by mixing in other singlet state functions, but gives no impetus for mixing in states of different multiplicity. Transitions between states of different multiplicity are said to be *spin forbidden*.

Another example of a forbidden transition is that between two different s-type states of a hydrogen atom. Such states have spherically symmetric wavefunctions, but H' (the electric field) is antisymmetric for reflection through a plane (to within an additive constant), and so $\langle\psi_f|H'|\psi_i\rangle$ must vanish for reasons of symmetry. It is easy to generalize this argument to other states of the hydrogen atom (p to p, d to d, etc.) and also to certain other atoms (e.g., the alkali metals) electronically similar to hydrogen.

Molecular electronic transitions can be understood from the same standpoint. The intense $\pi \rightarrow \pi^*$ transition in ethylene is a simple example.[9] Let us imagine that the molecule is oriented as shown in Fig. 12-8. Suppose we could

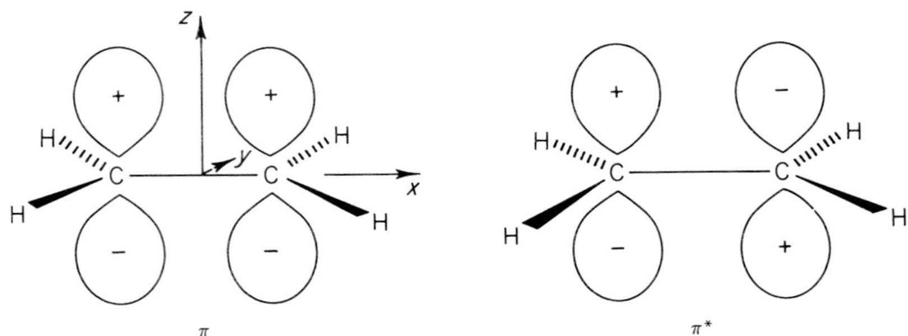

FIG. 12-8 π and π^* MOs for ethylene. The C–C bond is coincident with the x axis and all nuclei lie in the x,y plane.

somehow orient all our molecules this way (in a host matrix or in a crystal) and that we then subjected the sample to plane-polarized light. We will consider what should happen for light polarized in each of the directions x, y, z. First, let us consider the integral $\langle\pi|z|\pi^*\rangle$. The ethylene molecule has three reflection planes of symmetry, so we can examine the symmetry of the integrand with respect to all three reflections. Remember that, if the integrand is antisymmetric for any one of these reflections, the integral vanishes. The function π can be seen, from inspection of Fig. 12-8, to be symmetric for reflection in the xz and yz planes, antisymmetric for reflection in the xy plane. These observations are shown in Table 12-2, along with similar conclusions regarding the symmetries

[9] Here, π^* refers to the antibonding π_g MO, not to complex conjugation.

of the functions π^*, x, y, and z. The symbols "s" and "a" stand for "symmetric" and "antisymmetric." Our integral $\langle\pi|z|\pi^*\rangle$ can now be seen to have an integrand that is symmetric for reflection in the xz plane but antisymmetric for reflection in the xy and yz planes. Hence, this integral vanishes, and this transition is forbidden insofar as light polarized perpendicular to the molecular plane is concerned. According to Table 12-2 $\langle\pi|y|\pi^*\rangle$ also vanishes, but $\langle\pi|x|\pi^*\rangle$

TABLE 12-2
Symmetries of Functions under Reflection through Cartesian Coordinate Planes

	Symmetry operation		
Function	xy reflection	xz reflection	yz reflection
π	a	s	s
π^*	a	s	a
z	a	s	s
x	s	s	a
y	s	a	s
$\pi\ z\ \pi^*$	aaa = a	sss = s	ssa = a
$\pi\ x\ \pi^*$	asa = s	sss = s	saa = s
$\pi\ y\ \pi^*$	asa = s	sas = a	ssa = a

does not vanish for reasons of symmetry. Therefore, the $\pi \rightarrow \pi^*$ transition is allowed and is polarized along the C–C axis. Indeed, because of the significant spatial extension of the π and π^* MOs (compared to AOs), the integral $\langle\pi|x|\pi^*\rangle$ is relatively large, which means that the transition is not only allowed, but it is *intense*.

It is physically reasonable that the $\pi \rightarrow \pi^*$ transition should be polarized along the C–C axis. If some π^* character is mixed with π, it is easy to see that this results in a shift of π charge from one carbon to the other—a shift along the x axis. Conversely, an electric field in the x direction will cause polarization along the x axis, hence mix π^* character into the π MO. When the perturbation is removed, a finite probability exists that the molecule will go to the state wherein π^* is occupied.

In the above example, we imagined all ethylene molecules to be identically oriented. Under those conditions, we would observe a maximum in $\pi \rightarrow \pi^*$ absorption when our incident light was polarized parallel to the molecular axis and zero absorption (ideally) when the polarization axis was perpendicular to the molecular axis. If the light is unpolarized, or if the ethylene is randomly oriented, as in liquid or gaseous states, the absorption is isotropic and allowed because there is always a certain degree of "overlap" between the molecular axes of most of the molecules and the direction of the electric field due to the light.

PROBLEMS

12-1 (a) Show that, if $H = H_0 + H'$ with H and H_0 hermitian, then H' must be hermitian.

(b) Show that, if H' is hermitian, then Eq. (12-21) may be written

$$W_i^{(2)} = \sum_{j \neq i} \frac{|\langle\psi_i|H'|\psi_j\rangle|^2}{E_i - E_j}$$

(c) Show that $\langle\psi_i|\phi_i^{(1)}\rangle = 0$ and $\langle\phi_i^{(1)}|H_0|\psi_i\rangle = 0$.

(d) Find the expression for the normalizing constant for the wavefunction to first order.

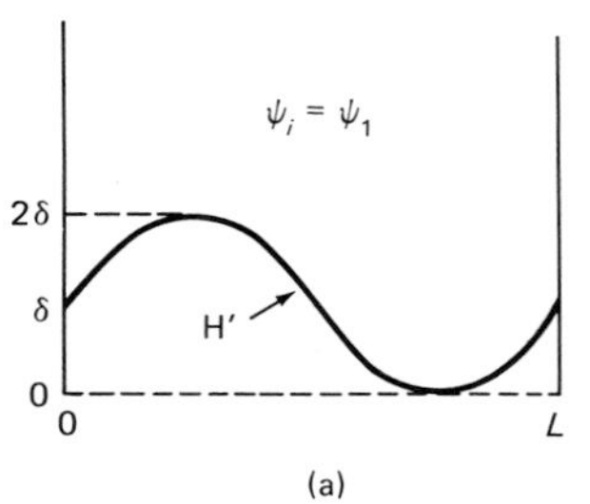

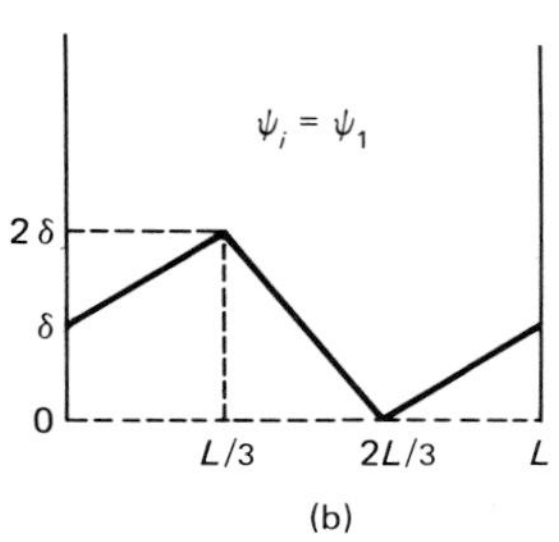

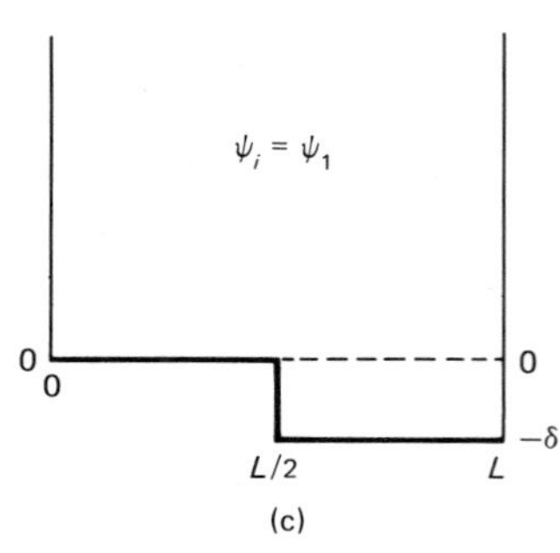

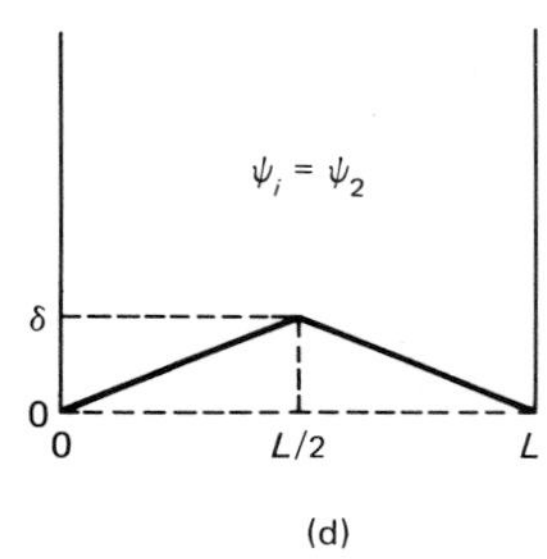

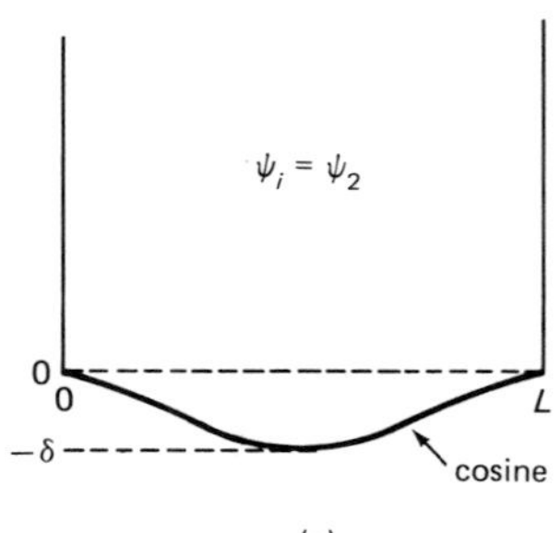

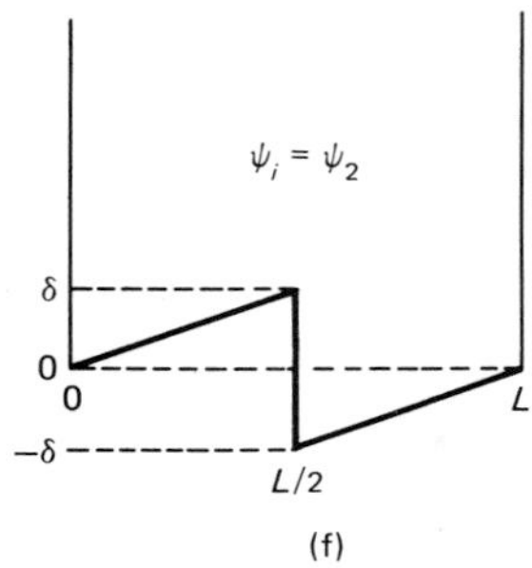

FIG. P12-3 (a) H' = sine function as shown; $\psi_i = \psi_1$. (b) H' as shown; $\psi_i = \psi_1$. (c) H' as shown; $\psi_i = \psi_1$. (d) H' as shown; $\psi_i = \psi_2$. (e) H' = cosine as shown; $\psi_i = \psi_2$. (f) H' as shown; $\psi_i = \psi_2$.

12-2 Prove that the energy to first order for the lowest-energy state of a perturbed system is an upper bound for the exact energy of the lowest-energy state of the perturbed system, that is, that $E_0 + W_0^{(1)} \geqslant W_0$.

12-3 Evaluate by inspection the first-order contributions to the energies for the states shown in Fig. P12-3. In every case the unperturbed state is a particle in the *indicated* state in the one-dimensional, infinitely deep, square well.

12-4 What is the Hückel MO π-electron energy to first order of the molecule **(I)**

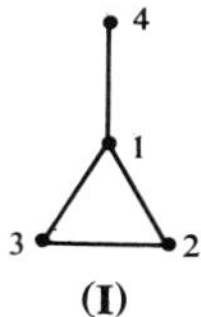

(I)

if C_4 is perturbed by $H' = 0.1\beta$? (See Appendix 6 for Hückel data.)

12-5 Consider the fulvene molecule **(II)** in the HMO approximation (see Appendix

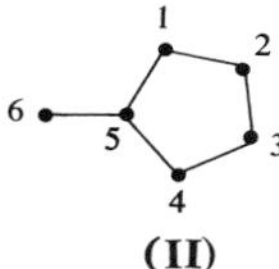

(II)

6). At which carbon will a perturbation involving α affect the total π-electron energy the least?

12-6 A one-dimensional-box potential is perturbed as sketched in Fig. P12-6. From a consideration of the first three wavefunctions of the unperturbed system, ψ_1, ψ_2, ψ_3, which will have its energy increased *most*, to first order, and which least? No explicit calculation is necessary to answer this question.

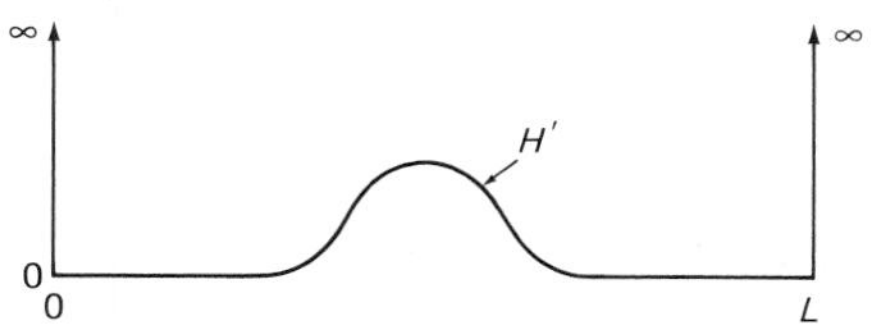

FIG. P12-6

12-7 The unperturbed Hückel MO energy levels of the allyl system are sketched in Fig. P12-7. The system is perturbed so that $H_{22} = \alpha + c\beta$ where c is positive.

(a) Sketch the effects of this perturbation, to first order, on the energy levels.

(b) Calculate to first order the perturbed MOs $\phi_1^{(1)}$, $\phi_2^{(1)}$, $\phi_3^{(1)}$ in terms of the

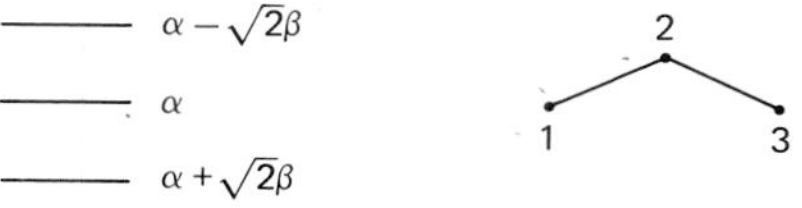

FIG. P12-7

unperturbed MOs ψ_1, ψ_2, ψ_3. Sketch the results in a manner that makes clear the nature of the change in each MO.

12-8 Calculate $c_{41}^{(1)}$ for the perturbed particle in a wire example discussed in Section 12-3. Show that $c_{41}^{(1)}$ is only about 2% as large as $c_{21}^{(1)}$. [Use

$$\int_0^{\pi} y \sin my \sin ny \, dy = [(-1)^{m+n} - 1]2mn/(m^2 - n^2)^2, \qquad m,n, = 1, 2, \ldots, m \neq n]$$

12-9 The cyclopropenyl system is perturbed so that the Hückel matrix element $H_{22} = \alpha + c\beta$, where c is positive.

(a) Ascertain, by calculation or inspection, the appropriate zeroth-order degenerate wavefunctions for this situation.

(b) Sketch the effects of the perturbation on the orbital energies to first order.

12-10 Show that a transition from 3d to 2s in the hydrogen atom is forbidden, regardless of the direction of the electric field or the identity of the d substate. Argue from symmetry.

12-11 A hydrogen atom in the 2s state is metastable, but, when passed through an electric field, its tendency to relax to the 1s state is greatly enhanced. Explain.

12-12 Calculate the atom–atom polarizabilities $\pi_{1,2}$ and $\pi_{1,3}$ for the allyl cation. What do your results indicate will happen to the π-electron densities at atoms 2 and 3 if atom 1 becomes more attractive?

12-13 An electron moves in a harmonic potential, $V = \frac{1}{2}kx^2$. What is the effect, to first order, on the energies of superimposing an electric field, $V' = Ex$? Explain your reasoning.

12-14 Using data from Appendix 6, calculate to first order the energy of fulvene with $\alpha_6 = \alpha + 0.5\beta$. If a computer and Hückel program are available to you, calculate the energy for this perturbed molecule directly and compare with your first-order result.

12-15 Calculate the energy to first order of He^+ in its lowest-energy state. Use the hydrogen atom in its ground state as your zeroth-order approximation. Use atomic units.

12-16 Use simple Hückel MO's for butadiene to calculate to first order the change in π energy that would result in closing *cis*-butadiene to cyclobutadiene **(III)**.

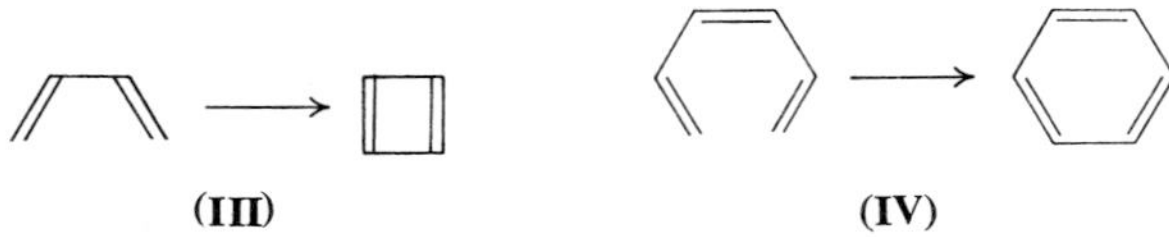

(III) **(IV)**

Repeat the approach for closing hexatriene to benzene. **(IV)**. Which of these two systems benefits most from cyclic as opposed to linear topology? For each system, compare your energy to first order with the actual Hückel energy (see Appendix 6 for data).

12-17 (a) Evaluate $W_2^{(1)}$ for the particle in a box with the perturbing potential shown in Fig. P12-17.

(b) For the perturbation above:

(1) What sign would you expect for $c_{21}^{(1)}$? Describe the effect of this on ϕ_1; on $W_1^{(2)}$.

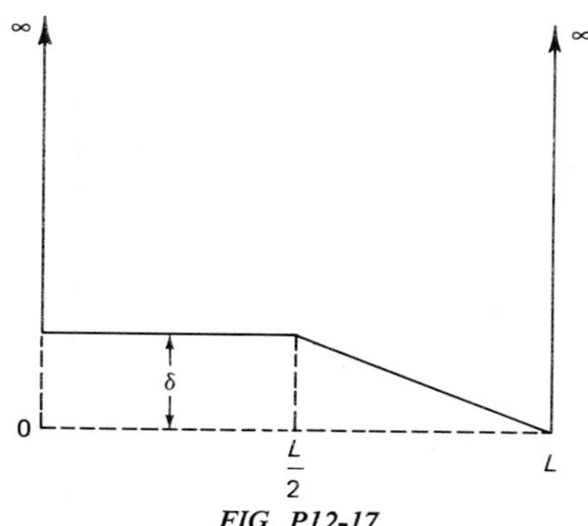

FIG. P12-17

(2) What sign would you expect for $c_{12}^{(1)}$? Describe the effect of this on ϕ_2; on $W_2^{(2)}$.

12-18 An electron is constrained to move in a ring of radius r (Fig. P12-18). The state functions are (Chapter 2)

$$\psi = \begin{Bmatrix} 1/\sqrt{\pi}\,\sin(m\phi) \\ 1/\sqrt{\pi}\,\cos(m\phi) \end{Bmatrix}, \quad m = 1, 2, 3, \ldots; \qquad \psi = 1/\sqrt{2\pi} \quad (m = 0)$$

with $E_m = m^2h^2/8\pi^2I$ (ergs). Assume that the electron is in the $m = 1$ state and that a perturbing magnetic field along the z direction is applied.

(a) What is the essential part of the perturbation hamiltonian H' for this system? (That is, ignore the field strength and polarity.)

(b) Use this operator and the above state functions to find the proper zeroth-order wavefunctions for this energy level.

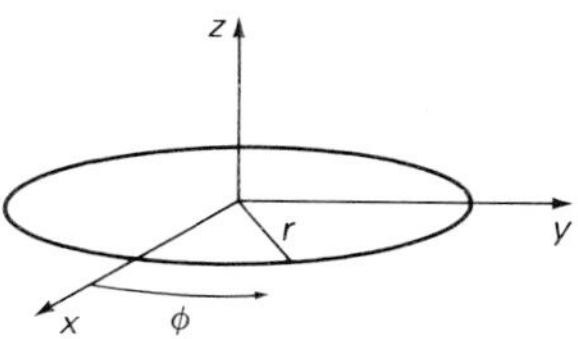

FIG. P12-18

12-19 For the system described in Problem 12-18, r and θ are constant. Therefore the operator $x = r \sin\theta \cos\phi$ behaves as merely $\cos\phi$ in this system. Assuming an initial unperturbed state with quantum number $m\ (\neq 0)$, *derive* the selection rule for the transition to the other states n, induced by x-polarized light, while the system is in the presence of the z-directed magnetic field.

12-20 The benzyl radical, C_7H_7 (V), has the Hückel energies and ground-state configuration given in Table P12-20.

The radical is trapped and oriented in an external reference system as shown. Light polarized in the x direction is beamed on the system, and the frequency varied

(V)

TABLE P12-20[a]

Level	Energy	c_1	c_2	c_3	c_4	c_5	c_6	c_7
7	-2.10β	-0.238	0.500	-0.406	0.354	0.336	0.354	-0.406
6	-1.26β	-0.397	0.500	-0.116	-0.354	0.562	-0.354	-0.116
5	-1.00β	0	0	-0.500	0.500	0	-0.500	0.500
4 ↑	0.00	-0.756	0	0.378	0	-0.378	0	0.378
3 ↑↓	1.00β							
2 ↑↓	1.26β							
1 ↑↓	2.10β							

[a] Coefficients for $2p_z$ basis functions forming the four highest Hückel MOs are listed. Overlap has been assumed to be negligible.

until an absorption is observed. Assuming this to result from excitation of the unpaired electron, to which level has the electron been promoted?

12-21 The simple Hückel energies, occupation numbers, and coefficients for MOs in naphthalene (**VI**) are listed in Table P12-21. Assume that a single crystal of naphthalene is oriented so that each molecule is aligned with respect to an external coordinate system (**VI**).

(a) Light polarized in the x direction is beamed on the crystal. Assuming that the electron is excited from the highest occupied MO, to which empty MOs could it be promoted by the x-polarized light?

(b) Which transitions from the highest occupied MO would be allowed for y-polarized light?

(c) Which ones would be allowed for z-polarized light?

(d) Are any transitions from the highest occupied MO forbidden for nonpolarized light?

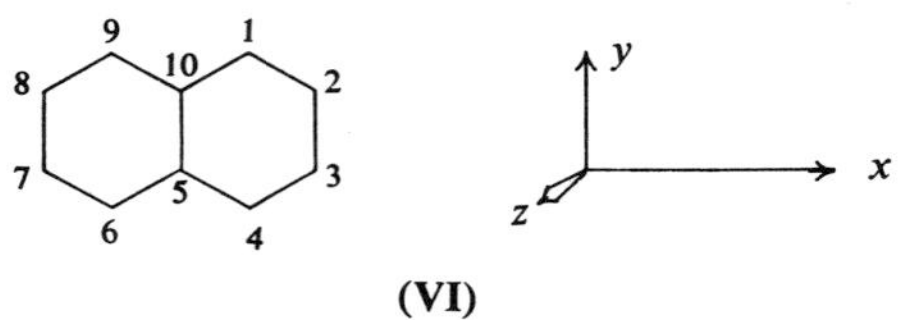

(VI)

12-22 Calculate the dipole moment in the z direction for the states $\phi_{\pm}^{(0)}$ of Eq. (12-81). Now construct a variational function of the form

$$\phi = \cos(\alpha)2s + \sin(\alpha)2p_z$$

TABLE P12-21

Energies $-(\beta)$	Occupation no.	Coefficients									
		atom number									
		1	2	3	4	5	6	7	8	9	10
−2.303	2										
−1.618	2										
−1.303	2										
−1.000	2										
−0.618	2	−0.42	−0.26	0.26	0.42	0	−0.42	−0.26	0.26	0.42	0
+0.618	0	−0.42	0.26	0.26	−0.42	0	0.42	−0.26	−0.26	0.42	0
+1.000	0	0	0.41	−0.41	0	0.41	0	−0.41	0.41	0	−0.41
+1.303	0	0.40	−0.17	−0.17	0.40	−0.35	0.40	−0.17	−0.17	0.40	−0.35
+1.618	0	−0.26	0.42	−0.42	0.26	0	−0.26	0.42	−0.42	0.26	0
+2.303	0	−0.30	0.23	−0.23	0.30	−0.46	0.30	−0.23	0.23	−0.30	0.46

and maximize the z component of the dipole moment as a function of α. Are the states $\phi_{\pm}^{(0)}$ those of maximum dipole magnitude? Discuss why this is reasonable.

REFERENCES

[1] L. Pauling and E. B. Wilson, "Introduction to Quantum Mechanics." McGraw-Hill, New York, 1935.
[2] P. O. Löwdin, *J. Mol. Spectry.* **13**, 326 (1964).
[3] L. I. Schiff, "Quantum Mechanics" (2nd ed.). McGraw-Hill, New York, 1955.
[4] C. W. Scherr and R. E. Knight, *Rev. Mod. Phys.* **35**, 436 (1963).
[5] R. Hoffmann, *Accounts Chem. Res.* **4**, 1 (1971).

CHAPTER 13

GROUP THEORY

13-1 Introduction

It should be evident by this point that symmetry requirements impose important constraints on MOs, and that one can often use symmetry arguments to tell what the MOs of a molecule must look like, in advance of calculation. We have also seen that one can often use symmetry arguments to tell whether or not an integral vanishes. Thus, we have made much use of symmetry already, but in an informal way. The formal use of symmetry, through group theory, will be described in this chapter. Knowledge of group theory augments one's power to use symmetry as a shortcut, and familiarity with formal symmetry notation is necessary to follow the literature of many areas of chemistry, particularly quantum chemistry.

13-2 An Elementary Example

Consider the following four operations, or commands:

(1) Left face (L).
(2) Right face (R).
(3) About face (A).
(4) Remain as you are (E).

These four operations constitute a group in the mathematical sense, and provide a convenient example with which to illustrate some definitions and terminology of group theory. The operations are called the *elements* of the group. Because there are four elements, this group is said to be of *order* four.

How do we know that these four operations constitute a group? Before answering this question, it is necessary to describe what is meant by a *product* of elements. Products of group elements are written in the usual algebraic manner. That is, the symbols are written side by side without an algebraic symbol. Just as xy is understood to be the product of x and y, LR is understood to be the product of "left face" and "right face." But elements of a group need not commute, and so the ordering of symbols in a product is important in group theory. The sequence of operations is understood to read from *right to left* in the product. Thus, LR means "right face" followed by "left face."

If we imagine a drill soldier carrying out the sequence of operations implied by LR, the result is a return of the soldier to his original position. That is, the product of operations LR gives the same result as the single operation E. This is written $LR = E$. It is possible to write similar equations for all the product combinations in our group, and to arrange the results as in Table 13-1. An

TABLE 13-1
Products of Elements in the Group of Four Commands

Second operation \ First operation	*E*	*L*	*R*	*A*
E	*E*	*L*	*R*	*A*
L	*L*	*A*	*E*	*R*
R	*R*	*E*	*A*	*L*
A	*A*	*R*	*L*	*E*

important fact to notice from this *group multiplication table* is that there is no *sequence* of operations in the group that cannot be accomplished by a *single* operation. All the possible positions open to the drill soldier through a sequence of two moves are also achievable through a single move. In other words, no product of elements takes us out of the group—the group exhibits *closure*.

The *reciprocal*, or *inverse* of an operation is that subsequent operation which returns the soldier to his original position. Hence, L is the reciprocal of R, which is expressed as $LR = E$, or $L = R^{-1}$. Examination of Table 13-1 shows that every column has E appearing once, which means that every element of our group has an inverse in the group.

The *associative* law is obeyed if, in general, the sequence of operations $A(BC) = (AB)C$, where the parentheses enclose the pair of elements the product of which is to be evaluated first. We can test whether our elements satisfy this law by trying out all the combinations. For example $L(RA) = LL = A$ and $(LR)A = EA = A$. One can quickly show that this group satisfies the associative law for all combinations of elements.

We are now in a position to define a group. A group is a set of elements which meets the following requirements:

(1) The group contains the identity element (traditionally symbolized E) which corresponds to "make no change."

(2) The group exhibits closure with respect to "multiplication." The product of any two elements in the group is a single element in the group.

(3) There is a reciprocal in the group for every element of the group.
(4) The elements of the group obey the associativity law $(AB)C = A(BC)$.

We mentioned that, in general, group elements need not commute. That is, it is possible that $AB \neq BA$. However, in this example, the elements do all commute. This results in Table 13-1 being symmetric about the main diagonal. Groups in which all the elements commute are called *abelian* groups.

13-3 Symmetry Point Groups

Our example of four operations of a drill soldier differs from the kinds of groups most commonly used in quantum chemistry because it is not a symmetry group. Assuming that the soldier begins by facing north, we are able to *distinguish* four distinct possible subsequent orientations for him (facing the four compass directions). After a *symmetry* operation, an object is understood to be *indistinguishable* from the object before the operation.

Whether or not an operation is a symmetry operation must be decided within the context of the object being operated on. For example, a square (devoid of identifying marks enabling us to distinguish one corner from another; see Fig. 13-1a) may be rotated by 90° about an axis perpendicular to the center (Fig. 13-1b), and be indistinguishable from its starting configuration. However, rotation by 120° does not lead to an indistinguishable configuration (Fig. 13-1c).

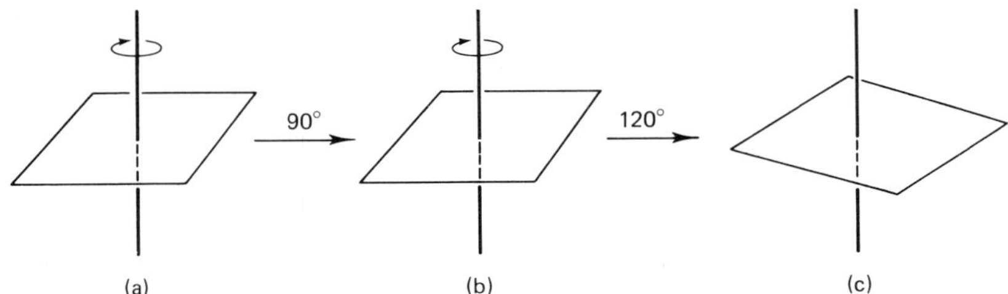

FIG. 13-1 Effects of rotations on a square.

Therefore, rotation by 90° is a symmetry operation for a square, but rotation by 120° is not. However, for an equilateral triangle, rotation by 90° is not a symmetry operation, while rotation by 120° is. For a circle, both rotations are symmetry operations. The only operation that is a symmetry operation for *every* object is the identity operation E.

Another sort of symmetry operation pertains to infinite networks such as occur in idealized models of crystals. Here we can define operations that move an infinite line of cells or atoms to the left or right by a unit number of "steps," producing a configuration indistinguishable from the initial one (Fig. 13-2). Symmetry operations can be usefully categorized into those that leave at least one point in space unmoved (rotations, reflections, inversion) and those that do not (translations). The latter category is of importance in the fields of crystallography and solid-state physics. The former category is useful when we deal with systems that do not undergo periodic repetition in space, and it is with this category that we will be concerned.

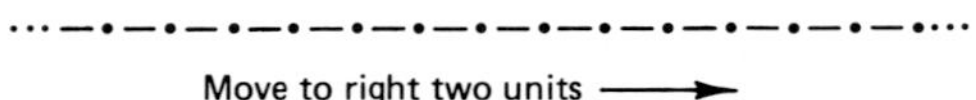

FIG. 13-2 Segment of an infinite repeating sequence of identical "cells" (—·).

If we pick some object or shape of finite size and construct a group from symmetry operations for that shape, we have a *symmetry point group* for that object. We now illustrate how this is done for a ball-and-stick model of the ammonia molecule in its equilibrium nuclear configuration. It is not difficult to find operations that do no more than interchange identical hydrogen nuclei. There are a number of possible rotations about the z axis (Fig. 13-3). One

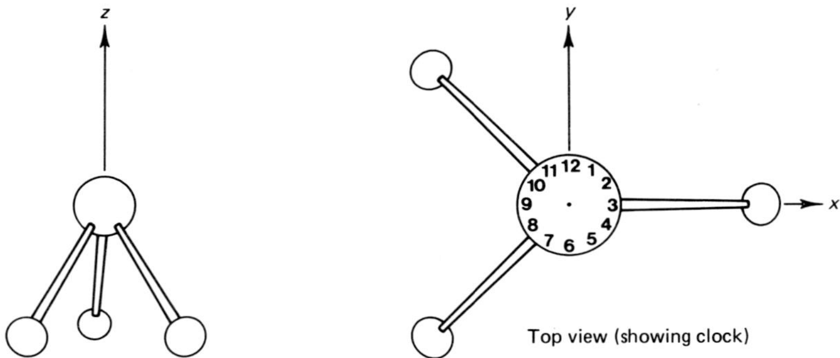

FIG. 13-3 Orientation of a model of ammonia in cartesian space.

could rotate by 120°, 240°, 360°, 480°, etc., either clockwise or counterclockwise. Then there are three reflection planes. One of these is the xz plane (labeled "A" in Fig. 13-4) and the other two are planes containing the z axis and one of the

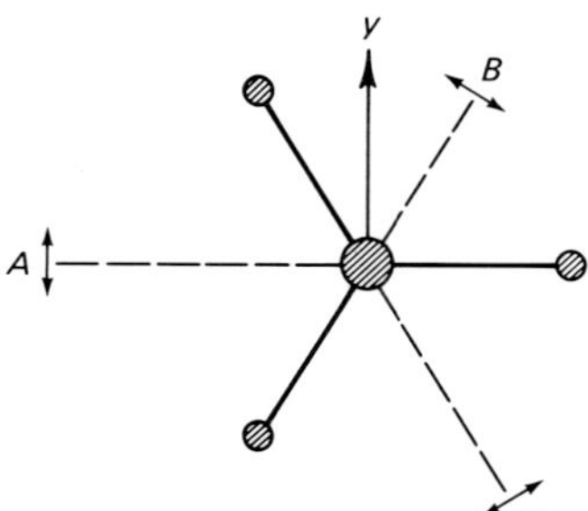

FIG. 13-4 Three symmetry reflection planes for ammonia.

other N–H bonds. Also there is the identity operation E, which we know that we need to satisfy the general requirements for a group.

There is a problem with the rotations, and this is that we could produce an infinite number of them. How do we know when to stop? The answer is that we select only those that avoid "redundancies" among our indistinguishable configurations. Redundancies occur when two operations lead to "identical" indistinguishable configurations. For example, rotation by 360° is redundant with the identity operation because each operation leaves the protons (which we imagine *for the moment* to be distinguishable) in the same locations. Similarly, rotation clockwise by 240° is redundant with rotation counterclockwise by 120° (Fig. 13-5). If we remove all such redundancies, we are left with only two rota-

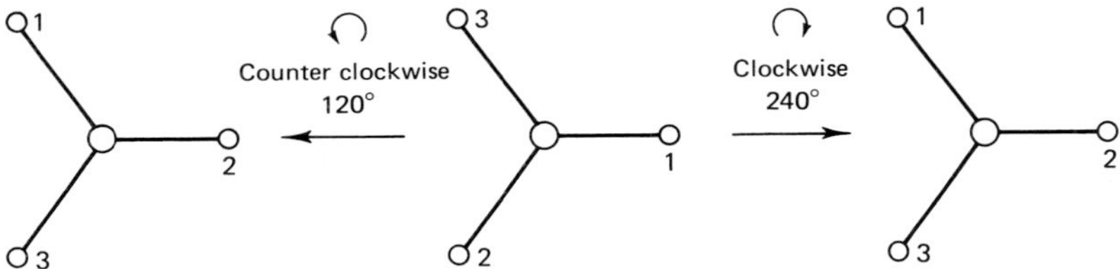

FIG. 13-5 Identical configurations result from the two rotations shown.

tions. There is arbitrariness as to how we wish to describe these. If we let the first be clockwise rotation by 120°, the second could be described as either clockwise rotation by 240° or counterclockwise rotation by 120°. We will use the latter description. (Note that the clock is assumed to face $+\infty$ on the axis about which rotation occurs; see Fig. 13-3.)

Our list of symmetry operations is now as follows:

(1) identity (E);
(2) reflection through xz plane (A);
(3) reflection through plane B (B);
(4) reflection through plane C (C);
(5) 120° clockwise rotation about z axis (D);
(6) 120° counterclockwise rotation about z axis (F).

We now proceed to set up the multiplication table for these operations. It is suggested that the reader do this as an exercise, checking the result against Table 13-2. Construction of the multiplication table is more challenging in this case than in our earlier example.

Let us now use this table to see if the requirements for a group are satisfied by these symmetry elements. Since every product of two operations is equivalent to one of the operations of the set (i.e., since every spot in the table is occupied by one of our six symbols) the set exhibits closure. Also, the identity element is present in the set and occurs once in each column and row (Problem 13-2), and

TABLE 13-2
Multiplication Table for Symmetry Operations of an Ammonia Molecule

Second operation \ First operation	E	A	B	C	D	F
E	E	A	B	C	D	F
A	A	E	D	F	B	C
B	B	F	E	D	C	A
C	C	D	F	E	A	B
D	D	C	A	B	F	E
F	F	B	C	A	E	D

so every element has an inverse in the set. The associative law is satisfied, as one can establish by trying various examples, e.g., $D(CB) = DF = E$, $(DC)B = BB = E$, so that $D(CB) = (DC)B$. [In general, symmetry operations satisfy the associativity law.] Therefore, our set of six symmetry operations constitutes a symmetry point group of order 6.

Inspection of Table 13-2 reveals that it is not symmetric across its principal diagonal. For example, $CF = B$, and $FC = A$; this is not an abelian group.

One might inquire whether this group is the smallest that we can set up for the ammonia model. Inspection of the multiplication table should convince the reader that the following subsets meet the requirements for a group: E; E, D, F; E, A; E, B; E, C. These *subgroups* can be distinguished from the full group by virtue of the fact that none of them exhausts all the possible physically achievable, nonredundant, indistinguishable configurations for the molecule.

13-4 The Concept of Class

Imagine that we are subjecting our ammonia model to the various symmetry operations and that someone in a parallel universe is subjecting his ammonia model to symmetry operations too. Suppose that the parallel universe differs from ours in that everything is reflected through the xz plane. We shall refer to this as "the mirror A universe." We now pose the following problem. Suppose we initially have a particular configuration and our "mirror A" man has the corresponding configuration (achieved by reflecting through plane A) as shown in Fig. 13-6. If the mirror A man now performs some symmetry operation on his model, say, counterclockwise rotation by 120°, F, he ends up with the final configuration shown at the lower right of the figure. (We continue to define "clockwise" from clocks in our universe.) For us to arrive at the *corresponding* final orientation, what operation must we perform? We symbolize

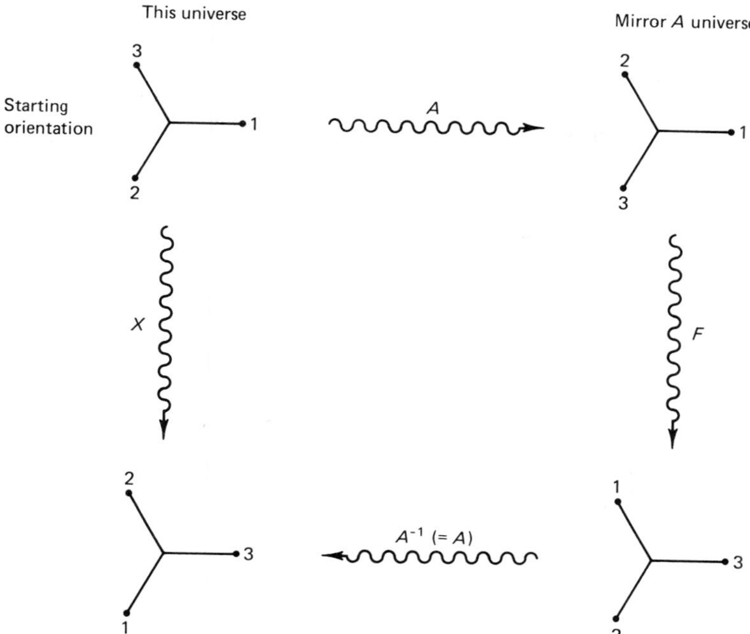

FIG. 13-6 Operation X in this universe parallels operation F in the mirror A universe.

this unknown operation X. We can find out what our final configuration must be by taking the *reciprocal* of reflection A on the mirror man's final configuration. (A takes us from here to there; A^{-1} takes us from there to here.) But $A^{-1} = A$, so we obtain the result at the lower left of the figure. It is evident that X must be D, clockwise rotation by 120°. This is not surprising. It is related to the fact that, when you turn counterclockwise before a mirror, your image appears to turn clockwise.

We can repeat the solution to this problem in a more formal way by requiring that the operation X *followed* by A (into the mirror A universe) bring us to the same configuration as operation A *followed by* F. That is, we seek X such that $AX = FA$. Multiplying both sides from the left by A^{-1} gives $X = A^{-1}FA$. This is merely a mathematical statement of our above discussion. It says, "what operation is equivalent to the process of reflection through plane A followed by counterclockwise rotation by 120° followed by the inverse of reflection through plane A?" Using our multiplication table, we see that $A^{-1} = A$, and so $X = AFA = AB = D$. Therefore, $D = A^{-1}FA$.

We can find the mirror A universe equivalents to all the symmetry operations in the group in a similar way. Thus,

$$A^{-1}EA = E, \qquad A^{-1}AA = A, \qquad A^{-1}BA = C,$$
$$A^{-1}CA = B, \qquad A^{-1}DA = F, \qquad A^{-1}FA = D$$

There is no need to stop here. We can imagine other parallel universes corresponding to reflections B and C and rotations D and F. (The E universe is the one we inhabit.) We can use the same sort of technique to accumulate corresponding operations for all these universes. The results are given in Table 13-3.

TABLE 13-3
$X = Y^{-1}ZY$ as a Function of Y and Z

		Z					
		E	A	B	C	D	F
	E	E	A	B	C	D	F
	A	E	A	C	B	F	D
Y	B	E	C	B	A	F	D
	C	E	B	A	C	F	D
	D	E	C	A	B	D	F
	F	E	B	C	A	D	F

If we examine this table, we note certain patterns. The operation E in our universe corresponds to E in all the universes. The reflections (A, B, and C) always correspond to reflections, and the rotations (D and F) always correspond to rotations. This makes physical sense. If we "do nothing" (E) in our universe, we expect the people in the other universes to do nothing also. If we rotate by 120°, we expect the people to perform rotations by 120° too, although not necessarily always in the same direction. The argument for reflection is the same. These are examples of three *classes* of operation. The formal definition of class is as follows: If P and Q in a group have the property that $X^{-1}PX = P$ or Q and $X^{-1}QX = P$ or Q for all members X in the group, then P and Q belong to the same class. Physically, operations in the same class are of the "same kind"—all reflections, all rotations, etc.

We shall see that classes are important subdivisions of groups. Note, however, that a class need not be a subgroup. For instance, D and F constitute a class, but, as the class does not include E, it is not a subgroup.

In discussing the concept of class, it is unnecessary to postulate parallel universes, and the reader should not be disturbed by this pedagogical device. The people in the "other universes" are merely working with ammonia models that have been reflected or rotated with respect to the model orientation that we chose in Fig. 13-3. Operations in the same class are simply operations that become interchanged if our coordinate system is subjected to one of the symmetry operations of the group.

13-5 Symmetry Elements and Their Notation

There are five kinds of symmetry operations that one can utilize to move an object through a maximum number of indistinguishable configurations. One is the trivial identity operation E. Each of the other kinds of symmetry operation has an associated *symmetry element*[1] in the object. For example, our ammonia model has three reflection operations, each of which has an associated *reflection plane* as its symmetry element. It also has two rotation operations and these are associated with a common *rotation axis* as symmetry element. The axis is said to be *threefold* in this case because the associated rotations are each one-third of a complete cycle. In general, rotation by $2\pi/n$ radians is said to occur about an n-fold axis. Another kind of operation—one we have encountered before—is inversion, and it has a *point of inversion* as its symmetry element. Finally, there is an operation known as *improper rotation.* In this operation, we first rotate the object by some fraction of a cycle about an axis, and then reflect it through a plane perpendicular to the rotation axis. The axis is the symmetry element and is called an *improper* axis.

The following two examples should help clarify the nature of these symmetry elements. Consider first the ethane molecule in its eclipsed conformation

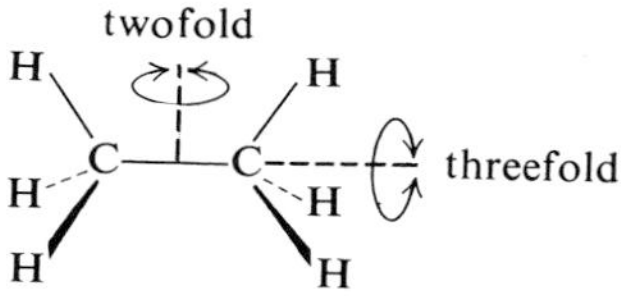

(I)

(I). The following symmetry *elements* can be identified (it is important that you satisfy yourself that you see these elements in the sketch):

(1) one three-fold axis coincident with the C–C bond;

(2) three two-fold axes perpendicular to the C–C bond and intersecting its midpoint;

(3) three reflection planes, each containing the C–C bond and a pair of C–H bonds;

(4) one reflection plane perpendicular to the C–C bond and bisecting it;

(5) no point of inversion;

(6) one three-fold *improper* axis coincident with the C–C bond.

[Note that these operations are to be applied to the *rigid* molecule. Movement of only one methyl group and not the other (i.e., internal rotation) is not allowed.]

[1] This term is not to be confused with a *group element*.

Now let us consider staggered ethane (**II**) (i.e., one methyl group rotated 60° from its eclipsed position). Its symmetry elements are

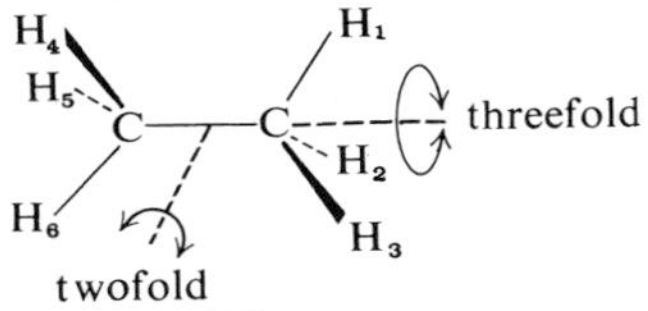

(**II**)

(1) one three-fold axis coincident with the C–C bond;

(2) three two-fold axes perpendicular to the C–C bond and intersecting its midpoint;

(3) three reflection planes, each containing the C–C bond and a pair of C–H bonds;

(4) no reflection plane perpendicular to the C–C bond;

(5) one point of inversion at the midpoint of the C–C bond;

(6) one six-fold *improper* axis coincident with the C–C bond.

In going from the eclipsed to the staggered conformation, we have lost a reflection plane perpendicular to the C–C bond, gained a point of inversion, and changed the order of the improper axis.

Usually it is not difficult to "see" most elements of symmetry in molecules, the exception being improper axes, which tend to be a little tricky. The six-fold improper rotation in staggered ethane is not too hard to envision when it is applied once. If we rotate clockwise by 60° and reflect, H_1 replaces H_5, H_5 replaces H_2, etc. It is a little more difficult when we try to imagine applying this operation twice in succession. The reader should satisfy himself that *two* 60° rotations and *two* reflections result in H_1 replacing H_2, H_2 replacing H_3, H_4 replacing H_5, etc.

A notation for these symmetry elements (and for the operations related to them) has come to be generally accepted in chemistry (exclusive of crystallography, which uses a different notation). This notation is summarized in Table 13-4. The symmetry elements of eclipsed ethane would be, by these conventions, C_3, $3C_2$, σ (perpendicular to C–C), 3σ (containing C–C), S_3. It often occurs that several classes of reflection planes and axes for proper or improper rotations are present in a system. In eclipsed ethane, we can imagine that the three reflection planes containing the C–C bond might all be in the same class, that is, might be interchanged by a symmetry operation. In fact, it is easy to see that they are interchanged by rotations about the threefold axis. However, none of these could ever be equivalent to the reflection perpendicular to the C–C bond because this reflection interchanges the carbons, whereas the others do not. For this reason, we keep separate tally of the different classes of reflection in eclipsed ethane, rather than simply writing "4σ."

TABLE 13-4
Symbols for Symmetry Elements and Operations

Symmetry operation	Symmetry element	Symbol
"Do nothing" (identity)	None	E
Rotation by $2\pi/n$ radians	An n-fold (proper) axis	C_n
Reflection through plane	A plane	σ
Inversion through a point	A point	i
Rotation through $2\pi/n$ radians followed by reflection through a plane perpendicular to the rotation axis	An n-fold (improper) axis	S_n

There is a geometric convention that aids discussion of molecules having axes of rotation. One looks for a unique axis C_n (usually the axis of highest order) and imagines this axis to be vertical (coincident with the z axis). Then a reflection plane perpendicular to this axis is *horizontal* and is labeled σ_h. Planes containing this axis are necessarily vertical and are subdivided into *dihedral* and *vertical* planes. *Dihedral* planes must contain the unique reference axis, C_n, and must also bisect the angles between twofold axes perpendicular to C_n. Such planes are labeled σ_d. Vertical planes that do not bisect twofold axes[2] are labeled σ_v. In eclipsed ethane, the C_3 axis is the principal axis, so the C–C bond is oriented vertically. Therefore, our symmetry *elements* are labeled C_3, $3C_2$, σ_h, $3\sigma_v$, S_3. (The vertical planes are labeled σ_v because they *contain*, rather than bisect, the twofold axes that are perpendicular to the principal axis.) For staggered ethane, we have C_3, $3C_2$, i, $3\sigma_d$, S_6. (Here the vertical planes do *not* contain the twofold axes, but do bisect them. Hence, we label them σ_d. Making a simple sketch will aid in clarifying this distinction.)

Once one has recognized the set of symmetry elements associated with a given object, it is a straightforward matter to list the symmetry *operations* associated with the set. Simplest are the operations associated with elements σ and i, because each such element gives rise to only one operation. Proper and improper axes are somewhat more complicated. Let us return to our ammonia molecule for illustration of this. There we had a threefold axis C_3 and we noted that we could rotate by $2\pi/3$ ($C_3{}^+$) to get one configuration, and $4\pi/3$ ($C_3C_3 = C_3{}^2$) to get another. Alternatively we could choose to rotate by $2\pi/3$ and $-2\pi/3$ ($C_3{}^-$), the latter easily being shown to be equivalent to $C_3{}^2$. But if we rotate by $C_3{}^3$, we return to our original configuration. That is, $C_3{}^3 = E$. Therefore, a C_3 axis produces two unique operations. The reader can easily generalize this to the

[2] In certain cases there will be two geometrically nonequivalent sets of vertical planes and no twofold axes to be bisected. In such cases, one set is labeled σ_d, the other σ_v. The choice is arbitrary, but must be consistent with use of character tables, etc.

statement that a C_n axis yields $n - 1$ unique symmetry operations C_n, C_n^2, $C_n^3, \ldots, C_n^{n-1}$. Benzene has a C_6 axis with five associated nonredundant symmetry operations (C_6, C_6^2, C_6^3, C_6^4, C_6^5). Now C_6^3 is equivalent to a rotation by π radians, an operation we normally write as C_2. Similarly, $C_6^2 = C_3$. The result of such reductions is the set of operations C_6, C_3, C_2, C_3^2, C_6^5 for the C_6 axis of benzene. There are several classes of rotation here. If we use a compressed notation, we can write this set as $2C_6$, $2C_3$, C_2. This indicates that the presence of a sixfold axis implies the existence of coincident twofold and threefold axes. However, these implied elements are not listed for such a system since their operations are all contained in the set of operations of the C_6 axis.

Improper axes can also be associated with several symmetry operations. We noted earlier that S_6, applied twice in succession, results in a simple $2\pi/3$ rotation about the S_6 axis. In other words, we can write the set S_6, S_6^2, S_6^3, S_6^4, S_6^5 as S_6, C_3, S_2, C_3^2. We stop at S_6^5 because $S_6^6 = E$ due to the combination of C_6^6 and an *even* number of reflections. S_6^3 is equivalent to S_2 because it contains three rotations by $2\pi/6$ and an odd number of reflections, and S_2 means one rotation by π and one reflection. The operation S_2, however, is easily shown to be equivalent to an inversion, and so we have, using a compressed notation, $2S_6$, $2C_3$, i associated with the S_6 axis. Since we have already explicitly listed the elements C_3 and i in our set of elements for staggered ethane (or any other system containing an S_6 axis) only the $2S_6$ operations are unique to the S_6 axis. The generalization of this case is that any S_{2n} axis will exist only when the elements C_n and i are also present. Of the $2n - 1$ operations associated with S_{2n}, $n - 1$ are preempted by the C_n axis and 1 by the element i leaving $n - 1$ operations to be attributed to the S_{2n} axis. [If $n = 1$, we have S_2, C_1, and i as elements. But $C_1 = E$, so we ignore it. There is only one operation here ($2 \cdot 1 - 1 = 1$) and it is preempted by i. Therefore, S_2 has no unique operations and it is not listed as a symmetry element.]

In eclipsed ethane, we have the element S_3, which generates operations S_3, S_3^2, S_3^3, S_3^4, S_3^5, $S_3^6, \ldots$. In deciding where to stop here, we note that $S_3^3 \neq E$ because we have here an *odd* number of reflections. Therefore, $S_3^3 = \sigma$, where we understand this to be reflection through the plane perpendicular to the S_3 axis. For eclipsed ethane, this is σ_h. The element S_3^6 has an even number of reflections and is equal to E. How about S_3^4? This has an even number of reflections, so it is identical to C_3^4 which is the same as $C_3^3C_3 = EC_3 = C_3$. Thus, our S_3 element has operations that are consistent with the presence of C_3 and σ_h elements. We note that eclipsed ethane was indeed found to have these elements. Once again, we allow these elements to preempt their operations from S_3. This leaves only two unique operations, S_3 and S_3^5, corresponding to clockwise and counterclockwise improper rotations by $2\pi/3$ radians. In general, S_{2n+1} will occur only when C_{2n+1} and σ (perpendicular to C_{2n+1}) are also present. These preempt a total of $2n + 1$ operations from the total of $2(2n + 1) - 1 = 4n + 1$ we can achieve with S_{2n+1} alone; and we are left with $2n$ operations for S_{2n+1}. The above conclusions are summarized in Table 13-5.

TABLE 13-5
Number of Operations Associated with Symmetry Elements

Element	(Other elements present)	No. operations
i	—	1
σ	—	1
C_n	—	$n - 1$
S_{2n}	(C_n and i present)	$n - 1$
S_{2n+1}	(C_{2n+1} and σ present)	$2n$

The set of symmetry *operations* is contrasted to the set of symmetry *elements* for eclipsed and staggered ethane in Table 13-6. Note that there are 12 symmetry operations in each case. By setting up the multiplication table for either of these sets of 12 operations, we can show that the mathematical requirements for a group are satisfied. Thus, each of these sets of symmetry operations constitutes a separate group of order 12.

TABLE 13-6.
Symmetry Operations and Elements in Ethane

Molecule	Elements	Operations
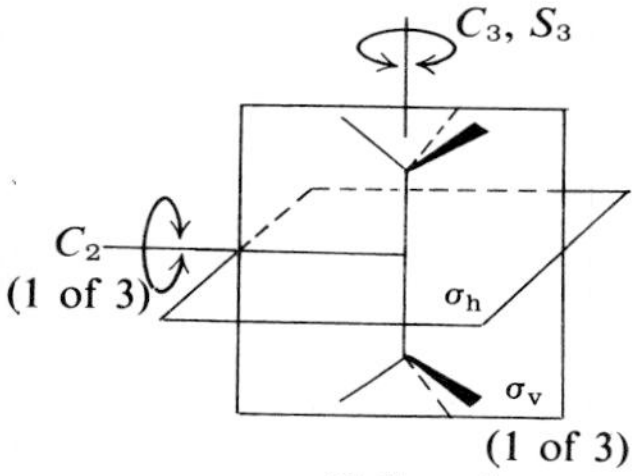 Eclipsed	C_3, $3C_2$, σ_h, $3\sigma_v$, S_3	E, $2C_3$, $3C_2$, σ_h, $3\sigma_v$, $2S_3$; Group order: 12
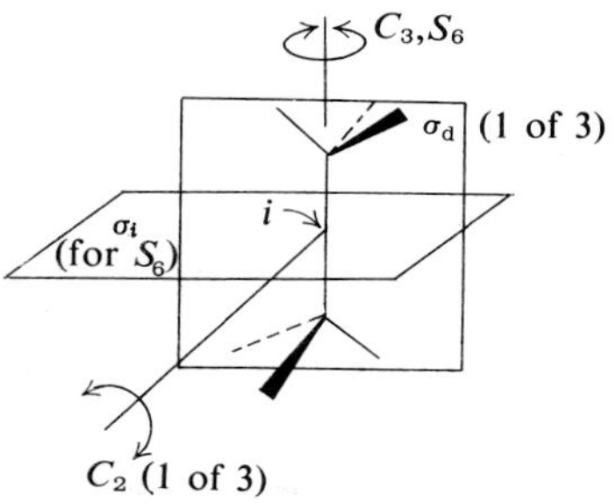 Staggered	C_3, $3C_2$, i, $3\sigma_d$, S_6	E, $2C_3$, $3C_2$, i, $3\sigma_d$, $2S_6$; Group order: 12

The multiplication table for the ammonia model is given in Table 13-7 in terms of the symmetry symbols just described. (A, B, C, are taken to be σ_1, σ_2, σ_3, respectively.)

TABLE 13-7
Multiplication Table for the Ammonia Molecule

Second operation \ First operation	E	σ_1	σ_2	σ_3	C_3^+	C_3^-
E	E	σ_1	σ_2	σ_3	C_3^+	C_3^-
σ_1	σ_1	E	C_3^+	C_3^-	σ_2	σ_3
σ_2	σ_2	C_3^-	E	C_3^+	σ_3	σ_1
σ_3	σ_3	C_3^+	C_3^-	E	σ_1	σ_2
C_3^+	C_3^+	σ_3	σ_1	σ_2	C_3^-	E
C_3^-	C_3^-	σ_2	σ_3	σ_1	E	C_3^+

It would be possible, using what has been described up to this point, to construct a list of symmetry operations for any object we please. Then we could test the set to see if it satisfied the various requirements for a group. In

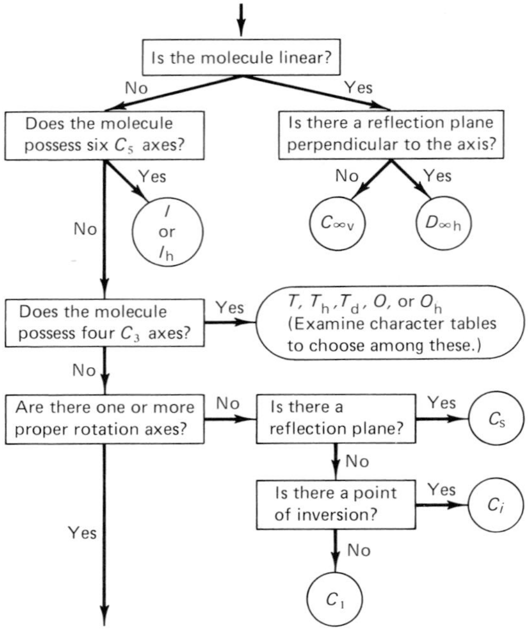

FIG. 13-7 Flow scheme for group symbols.

practice, this is not done. It turns out that (1) only a rather limited number of distinct kinds of symmetry are possible, and (2) in each case, the symmetry operations for the object do form a group. The practical question, then, is, given an object, to which of the known groups does it belong? Once this is settled, we merely look up the tabulated properties of that group and save ourselves the effort of working through all the details.

13-6 Identifying the Point Group of a Molecule

One can decide to which point group a molecule belongs by systematically looking for certain symmetry elements. Each symmetry point group has a unique group symbol, so basically one tries to figure out which group symbol is appropriate for a given molecule. A flowchart which serves this purpose is displayed in Fig. 13-7. As an illustration, we will work out the group symbol for

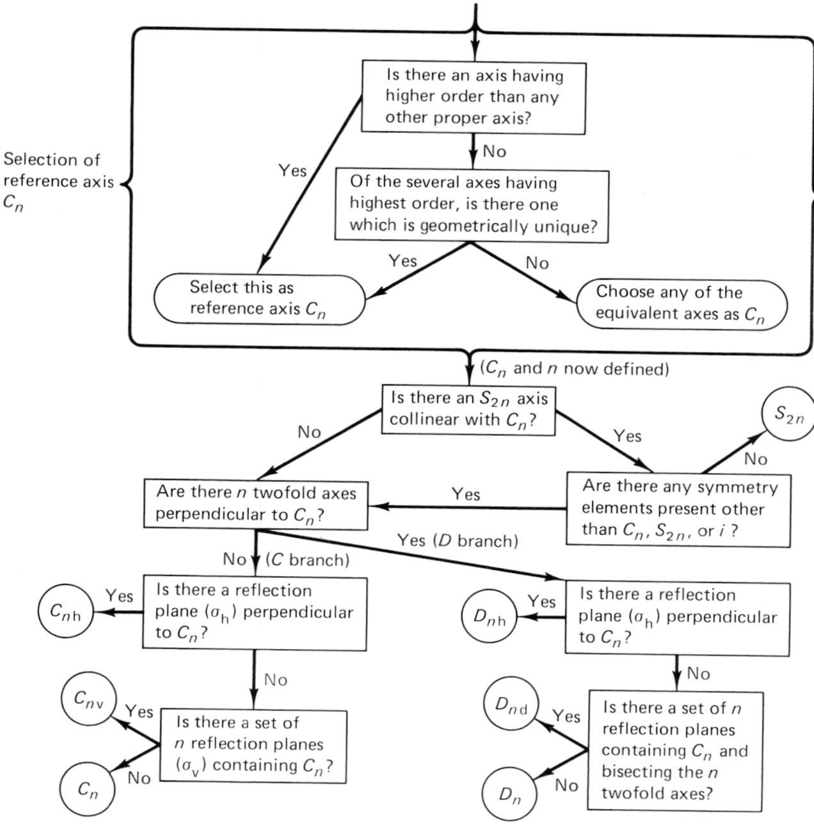

Selection of reference axis C_n
Is there an axis having higher order than any other proper axis?
Yes
No
Of the several axes having highest order, is there one which is geometrically unique?
Yes
No
Select this as reference axis C_n
Choose any of the equivalent axes as C_n
(C_n and n now defined)
Is there an S_{2n} axis collinear with C_n?
No
Yes
S_{2n}
No
Are there any symmetry elements present other than C_n, S_{2n}, or i ?
Yes
Are there n twofold axes perpendicular to C_n?
Yes (D branch)
No (C branch)
Is there a reflection plane (σ_h) perpendicular to C_n?
Yes
C_{nh}
No
Is there a set of n reflection planes (σ_v) containing C_n?
Yes
C_{nv}
No
C_n
Is there a reflection plane (σ_h) perpendicular to C_n?
Yes
D_{nh}
No
Is there a set of n reflection planes containing C_n and bisecting the n twofold axes?
Yes
D_{nd}
No
D_n

FIG. 13-7 (continued)

staggered ethane. The first few questions in the flowchart check to see if the molecule belongs to one of several special groups of very high symmetry. Since staggered ethane is not linear, and since it does not possess the symmetry of any of the regular polyhedra, we move to the question concerning proper rotation axes. We have noted earlier that there are several proper rotation axes in this molecule. We next consider which one should be selected as the reference axis. The axis of highest order is threefold and there is only one of these; therefore, we choose it as our reference axis. This defines n as 3 for the remainder of the flowchart. Next we look to see if there is an S_6 axis coincident with the C_3 axis, and we find that there is. Checking to see if symmetry elements other than C_3, S_6, and i exist, we find that they do indeed, and that among them are three twofold axes perpendicular to the reference axis C_3. This leads us along the "D branch" of the diagram, which means that, whatever else we find, the major symbol for our group will be D. Next we look for a σ_h reflection plane. Finding none, we next seek a set of reflection planes containing C_3 and also bisecting the various C_2 axes. Such dihedral planes are present, so our group symbol is D_{3d} for staggered ethane. The reader may verify that eclipsed ethane follows the same route out to the D branch, but there we *do* find a σ_h plane, and so eclipsed ethane has D_{3h} symmetry. A simple exercise, suggested at this point, is to ascertain the symmetry symbol for ammonia. (The answer is given in the next section.)

13-7 Representations for Groups

We have seen that the group of symmetry operations for the ammonia molecule leads to a particular group table of product operations (Table 13-7). Let us now see if we can assign a *number or matrix* to each symmetry operation such that the products of numbers satisfy the same group multiplication table relationships as do the products of symmetry operations. If we can find such a set of numbers or matrices, we say we have a *representation* for the group.

It is always possible to produce a trivial representation by simply assigning the number $+1$ to each operation. Then any operator relation, such as $\sigma_1\sigma_2 = C_3^+$ is necessarily satisfied by the numbers since $1 \cdot 1 = 1$. Nontrivial representations exist too (except for the C_1 group). For example, the group for molecules

TABLE 13-8
Representations for the C_{3v} Group

	E	σ_1	σ_2
Γ_1	1	1	1
Γ_2	1	-1	-1
Γ_3	$\begin{pmatrix}1 & 0\\0 & 1\end{pmatrix}$	$\begin{pmatrix}1 & 0\\0 & -1\end{pmatrix}$	$\begin{pmatrix}-1/2 & \sqrt{3}/\\ \sqrt{3}/2 & +1/\end{pmatrix}$

(like ammonia) having C_{3v} symmetry can be represented by the set of numbers $+1, -1, -1, -1, +1, +1$, respectively, for the operations $E, \sigma_1, \sigma_2, \sigma_3, C_3^+, C_3^-$ in Table 13-7. Then the relation $\sigma_2 C_3^+ = \sigma_3$ is paralleled by the representation since $(-1)(+1) = -1$, etc. It is also possible to find a representation for the C_{3v} group wherein each operation corresponds to a 2×2 matrix. This is shown in Table 13-8, along with the two other representations already mentioned. The reader is encouraged to test that, for instance, $\sigma_2 C_3^+ = \sigma_3$ in this matrix representation.

The symbol Γ_i is often used to stand for the ith representation of a group. $\Gamma_i(R)$ refers to the representation of the particular operation R in the ith representation. Thus, $\Gamma_2(\sigma_3) = -1$. In our ammonia example, Γ_1 and Γ_2 are *one-dimensional* representations and Γ_3 is *two-dimensional.*

The representation Γ_1 is really the simplest member of a set of equally trivial representations, namely all representations made from unit matrices. Thus, the representation Γ' (Table 13-9) is just as successful a representation as is Γ_1. We could obviously use unit matrices of arbitrary dimension in constructing a representation. We can think of such representations as being "built up" from Γ_1:

$$\Gamma'(R) = \begin{pmatrix} \Gamma_1(R) & 0 \\ 0 & \Gamma_1(R) \end{pmatrix} \qquad \text{etc.}$$

It is possible to extend this approach by building up representations from mixtures of $\Gamma_1, \Gamma_2, \Gamma_3$. Thus,

$$\Gamma''(R) = \begin{pmatrix} \Gamma_2(R) & 0 & 0 & 0 \\ 0 & \Gamma_1(R) & 0 & 0 \\ 0 & 0 & \multicolumn{2}{c}{\multirow{2}{*}{$\Gamma_3(R)$}} \\ 0 & 0 & & \end{pmatrix}$$

would produce the representation given in Table 13-10. It is easy to show that these matrices multiply together in a way that parallels the group table for symmetry operations, since block diagonal matrices always multiply in a block-for-block manner. Hence, the upper left 1×1 blocks (Γ_2) multiply among

σ_3	C_3^+	C_3^-
1	1	1
-1	1	1
$\begin{pmatrix} -1/2 & -\sqrt{3}/2 \\ -\sqrt{3}/2 & 1/2 \end{pmatrix}$	$\begin{pmatrix} -1/2 & \sqrt{3}/2 \\ -\sqrt{3}/2 & -1/2 \end{pmatrix}$	$\begin{pmatrix} -1/2 & -\sqrt{3}/2 \\ \sqrt{3}/2 & -1/2 \end{pmatrix}$

TABLE 13-9
A Two-Dimensional Unit Matrix Representation for the C_{3v} Group

	E	σ_1	σ_2	σ_3	C_3^+	C_3^-
Γ'	$\begin{pmatrix}1 & 0\\0 & 1\end{pmatrix}$	$\begin{pmatrix}1 & 0\\0 & 1\end{pmatrix}$	$\begin{pmatrix}1 & 0\\0 & 1\end{pmatrix}$	$\begin{pmatrix}1 & 0\\0 & 1\end{pmatrix}$	$\begin{pmatrix}1 & 0\\0 & 1\end{pmatrix}$	$\begin{pmatrix}1 & 0\\0 & 1\end{pmatrix}$

themselves, the 1×1 blocks in the 2,2 positions (Γ_1) multiply among themselves, and the 2×2 blocks at the lower right (Γ_3) multiply among themselves. Since each of these sets conforms to the group table, it follows that their composite Γ'' will also. It is evident that there is no limit to the number of representations we could build up in this manner.

Representations like Γ' and Γ'' are called *reducible* representations because they are composites of one or more smaller-dimensional representations and hence can be decomposed into those smaller representations. Any representation that cannot be reduced, or decomposed, into smaller representations is said to be *irreducible*.

How can we tell whether a given representation is reducible or not? If it is already one dimensional, it is obviously irreducible. If it is multidimensional and, like Γ' or Γ'', *uniformly* block diagonalized throughout the whole set of symmetry operations, it is plainly reducible. The trouble comes when it is multidimensional but not block diagonalized, for example, Γ_3. It is sometimes the case that such representations are reducible. To illustrate this point, let us go back to Γ'', which we know is reducible, and imagine transforming this representation by multiplying every matrix from the right by β and from the left β^{-1}, where β is some 4×4 unitary matrix (see Chapter 9). This will give us a new set of six 4×4 matrices that no longer will necessarily be block diagonalized. Yet it is easy to show that these new matrices, Γ^β, are still a representation for our group. We prove this by showing that, if three matrices from Γ'' (call them A'', B'', C'') are related by $A''B'' = C''$, then the corresponding transformed matrices A^β, B^β, C^β, satisfy $A^\beta B^\beta = C^\beta$. If this is true, then the ability of Γ'' to

TABLE 13-10
A C_{3v} Group Representation Built from Other Representations

	E	σ_1	σ_2
$\Gamma''(R)$	$\begin{pmatrix}1 & 0 & 0 & 0\\0 & 1 & 0 & 0\\0 & 0 & 1 & 0\\0 & 0 & 0 & 1\end{pmatrix}$	$\begin{pmatrix}-1 & 0 & 0 & 0\\0 & 1 & 0 & 0\\0 & 0 & 1 & 0\\0 & 0 & 0 & -1\end{pmatrix}$	$\begin{pmatrix}-1 & 0 & 0 & 0\\0 & 1 & 0 & 0\\0 & 0 & -\frac{1}{2} & \sqrt{3}/\\0 & 0 & \sqrt{3}/2 & \frac{1}{2}\end{pmatrix}$

correspond to the group table relationships is retained by Γ^{β}. The proof is as follows:

$$\text{Let} \quad A''B'' = C''.$$
$$\text{Then} \quad A^{\beta}B^{\beta} = \boldsymbol{\beta}^{-1}A''\boldsymbol{\beta}\boldsymbol{\beta}^{-1}B''\boldsymbol{\beta} = \boldsymbol{\beta}^{-1}A''B''\boldsymbol{\beta} = \boldsymbol{\beta}^{-1}C''\boldsymbol{\beta} \equiv C^{\beta}.$$

The point we are trying to make here is that a reducible representation like Γ'' can be put forth in many guises, each corresponding to a different choice of $\boldsymbol{\beta}$, and many of these will not be block diagonal in form. (Representations that differ only by a unitary transformation are said to be *equivalent*. Thus, Γ'' and Γ^{β} are equivalent representations.) To show that such a representation as Γ^{β} is reducible and also to reveal its component representations, we could back-transform it by finding the matrix $\boldsymbol{\beta}$ and calculating

$$\boldsymbol{\beta}\Gamma^{\beta}\boldsymbol{\beta}^{-1} = \boldsymbol{\beta}\boldsymbol{\beta}^{-1}\Gamma''\boldsymbol{\beta}\boldsymbol{\beta}^{-1} = \Gamma''$$

Therefore, deciding whether or not a multidimensional representation is reducible is the same as deciding whether it can be uniformly block-diagonalized through a common unitary transformation. It turns out that there is no single unitary transformation capable of diagonalizing all the 2×2 matrices of Γ_3, and so Γ_3 is an irreducible two-dimensional representation. (We shall show later that this can be established without "trying out" an infinite number of transformations.)

For any group, a goal is to find all the inequivalent, irreducible representations possible. Anything beyond this is superfluous information. For our C_{3v} (ammonia) group, Γ_1, Γ_2, and Γ_3 exhaust the possibilities and constitute a complete set of inequivalent irreducible representations.

13-8 Generating Representations from Basis Functions

The reader may wonder how one goes about discovering nontrivial representations like Γ_3. A convenient way to do this will now be described, and we will show at this stage the connection between quantum mechanics and the group theory of symmetry operations.

σ_3	$C_3{}^{+}$	$C_3{}^{-}$
$\begin{pmatrix} -1 & 0 & 0 & 0 \\ 0 & 1 & 0 & 0 \\ 0 & 0 & -\frac{1}{2} & -\sqrt{3}/2 \\ 0 & 0 & -\sqrt{3}/2 & \frac{1}{2} \end{pmatrix}$	$\begin{pmatrix} 1 & 0 & 0 & 0 \\ 0 & 1 & 0 & 0 \\ 0 & 0 & -\frac{1}{2} & \sqrt{3}/2 \\ 0 & 0 & -\sqrt{3}/2 & -\frac{1}{2} \end{pmatrix}$	$\begin{pmatrix} 1 & 0 & 0 & 0 \\ 0 & 1 & 0 & 0 \\ 0 & 0 & -\frac{1}{2} & -\sqrt{3}/2 \\ 0 & 0 & \sqrt{3}/2 & -\frac{1}{2} \end{pmatrix}$

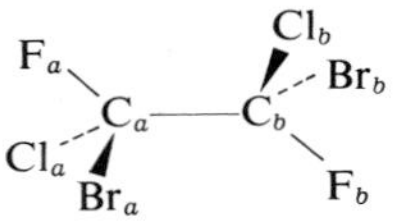

(III)

Consider the molecule shown in (**III**). This molecule has but one nontrivial symmetry element—a point of inversion. According to our flowchart, this places it in the C_i point group. The only symmetry operations here are E and i. Now consider two functions, f_1 and f_2. Let f_1 be located on one end of the molecule. For instance, let f_1 be $1s_{F_a}$, a 1s AO centered on the fluorine atom on the left side of the molecule. Let f_2 be a similar function on the other side of the molecule, $1s_{F_b}$. Now let us see what happens to these functions when they are acted upon by our symmetry operations E and i:

$$Ef_1 = f_1, \qquad Ef_2 = f_2, \qquad if_1 = f_2, \qquad if_2 = f_1$$

We see that f_1 and f_2 are interchanged by inversion. Let us try to find numbers to *represent* these results. Clearly, replacing E by $+1$ will give the correct result. However, to obtain the effect of operation by i we need to *interchange* f_1 and f_2. We cannot achieve this by multiplying by a number, since f_1 and f_2 are linearly independent. If, however, we rewrite the effect of i as

$$i\begin{pmatrix} f_1 \\ f_2 \end{pmatrix} = \begin{pmatrix} f_2 \\ f_1 \end{pmatrix}$$

it becomes clear that i can be represented by the matrix $\left(\begin{smallmatrix} 0 & 1 \\ 1 & 0 \end{smallmatrix}\right)$. Thus, use of the functions $1s_{F_a}$ and $1s_{F_b}$ has generated a two-dimensional representation shown in Table 13-11. (The representation for E has been put into a 2×2 matrix form

TABLE 13-11
A Representation for the C_i Group

C_i	E	i	Basis
Γ	$\begin{pmatrix} 1 & 0 \\ 0 & 1 \end{pmatrix}$	$\begin{pmatrix} 0 & 1 \\ 1 & 0 \end{pmatrix}$	$(1s_{F_a}, 1s_{F_b})$

to be in dimensional agreement with the representation for i.) $1s_{F_a}$ and $1s_{F_b}$ are called a *basis* for Γ. Clearly, any pair of identical functions symmetrically placed with respect to the point of inversion would generate the same two-dimensional representation, and so there is nothing very special about $1s_{F_a}$ and $1s_{F_b}$ as a basis. Is Γ reducible? It is easily argued that it must be. Any unitary 2×2 transformation will have no effect on the matrix for E since $\beta^{-1}1\beta = \beta^{-1}\beta = 1$. We are thus at liberty to look for any unitary transformation β

that diagonalizes the second matrix. Since this is a nonsingular matrix (its determinant is unequal to zero), it should be diagonizable, and it is if we take

$$\begin{pmatrix} 1/\sqrt{2} & 1/\sqrt{2} \\ -1/\sqrt{2} & 1/\sqrt{2} \end{pmatrix}\begin{pmatrix} 0 & 1 \\ 1 & 0 \end{pmatrix}\begin{pmatrix} 1/\sqrt{2} & -1/\sqrt{2} \\ 1/\sqrt{2} & 1/\sqrt{2} \end{pmatrix} = \begin{pmatrix} 1 & 0 \\ 0 & -1 \end{pmatrix}$$

Now that our 2×2 representation has been diagonalized to two 1×1 "blocks," we can rewrite our representations as shown in Table 13-12.

TABLE 13-12
Reduced Representations for the C_i Group

C_i	E	i	Basis
Γ_1	1	1	?
Γ_2	1	−1	?

Our first choice of basis generated a reducible representation. What bases would we need to generate the 1×1 representations Γ_1 and Γ_2? To generate Γ_1, we need a basis function which turns into itself when it is inverted. One possibility is $f_1 = 1s_{F_a} + 1s_{F_b}$. If we sketch this function (Fig. 13-8a), it is evi-

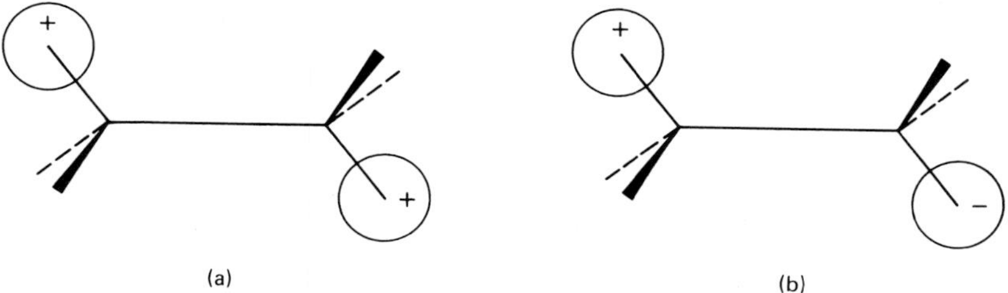

FIG. 13-8 Basis functions for irreducible representations of the C_i group.

dent that it is regenerated unchanged by inversion. The mathematical demonstration is

$$if_1 = i(1s_{F_a} + 1s_{F_b}) = i1s_{F_a} + i1s_{F_b} = 1s_{F_b} + 1s_{F_a} = f_1$$

f_1 is *symmetric* for operations E and i. For Γ_2, we need some function f_2 that turns into *minus* itself upon inversion. $f_2 = 1s_{F_a} - 1s_{F_b}$ would serve, as Fig. 13-8b shows, and as is demonstrated mathematically by

$$if_2 = i(1s_{F_a} - 1s_{F_b}) = i1s_{F_a} - i1s_{F_b} = 1s_{F_b} - 1s_{F_a} = -f_2$$

f_2 is symmetric for E and antisymmetric for i. (Notice that the way in which $1s_{F_a}$ and $1s_{F_b}$ needed to be mixed to produce a diagonal representation is indicated by the coefficients in the *columns* of the matrix we used to diagonalize the original 2×2 representation. The matrix β not only diagonalizes our Γ, it also tells us how to mix the original bases in order to arrive at bases for the irreducible representations.)

This example demonstrates an important fact: *In order to generate a one-dimensional representation for a group, we need a basis function that is either symmetric or antisymmetric for every symmetry operation in the group.* This provides the point of connection with quantum mechanics. We showed much earlier (Chapter 2) that any *nondegenerate* wavefunction (or MO) must be symmetric or antisymmetric for every operation which leaves the hamiltonian unchanged. Since symmetry operations leave the hamiltonian unchanged (they merely interchange identical nuclei), it follows that nondegenerate wavefunctions or orbitals are symmetric or antisymmetric for every operation in the symmetry point group of the molecule. This means that *every nondegenerate wavefunction or orbital is a basis for a one-dimensional representation for its molecular point group.* Indeed, it can be proved that *every wavefunction or orbital, even if degenerate, is a member of a basis for an irreducible representation* for the point group of the molecule. (We indicate how this comes about in a later section.) Therefore, knowing wavefunctions enables one to generate representations. More importantly, knowing representations allows us to say something about wavefunctions. For example, the representation table (Table 13-12) for the C_i group (which is now complete—this group has only two irreducible inequivalent representations) tells us the following:

(1) The molecule FClBrC–CBrClF in the conformation pictured has no degeneracies due to symmetry in its electronic states or in MO energies (if we do a calculation at the MO level). We can tell this because only one-dimensional representations exist for this group.

(2) Every wavefunction for an electronic state or orbital must be either symmetric or antisymmetric for inversion. Therefore, the following AO combinations are feasible for MOs insofar as symmetry is concerned:

$$\begin{aligned}&c(1s_{F_a} - 1s_{F_b}),\\ &c_1(1s_{F_a} + 1s_{F_b}) + c_2(1s_{Cl_a} + 1s_{Cl_b}) + c_3(1s_{Br_a} + 1s_{Br_b})\\ &\quad + c_4(1s_{C_a} + 1s_{C_b}) + c_5(2s_{F_a} + 2s_{F_b}) + \cdots\end{aligned}$$

The following are disallowed:

$$\begin{aligned}&c_1 1s_{F_a},\\ &c_1(2s_{F_a} + 2s_{F_b}) + c_2(2s_{Cl_a} - 2s_{Cl_b})\end{aligned}$$

Our halogenated ethane molecule is a good starting example because it belongs to such a simple group. But let us now return to the C_{3v} group of the ammonia molecule and continue developing the relations between group theory and MO theory. For convenience, the molecule is again sketched (Fig. 13-9) to show its orientation with respect to cartesian axes. (The z coordinate is the principal axis.)

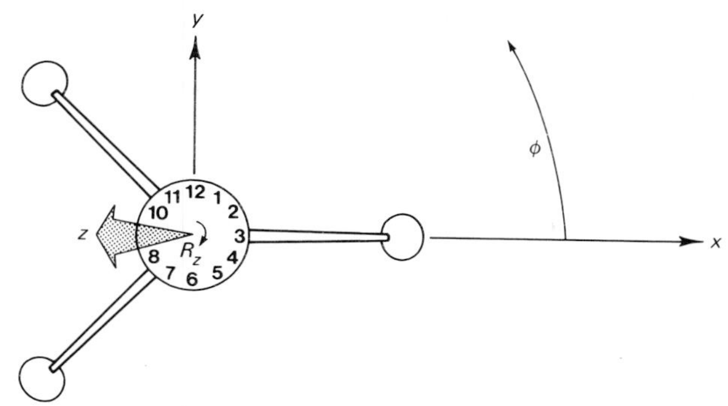

FIG. 13-9 Orientation of a model of ammonia in cartesian space.

The normal practice in group theory is to use cartesian coordinates or linear combinations of such coordinates as basis *functions*[3] for generating many of the representations of a group. Therefore, we begin by examining the z coordinate to see what becomes of it under the various symmetry operations in the C_{3v} group. The results are easily seen to be

$$Ez = +1\,z, \qquad \sigma_1 z = +1\,z, \qquad \sigma_2 z = +1\,z,$$
$$\sigma_3 z = +1\,z, \qquad C_3{}^+ z = +1\,z, \qquad C_3{}^- z = +1\,z$$

Thus, z is a basis for the totally symmetric representation Γ_1 of Table 13-8. The coordinates x and y can also be used as bases. Here things get more complicated. Clockwise rotation of x by $2\pi/3$ radians (to give x') causes it to end up in a position where it must be expressed as a resultant of both x and y (Fig. 13-10). Simple trigonometry requires that, for a general rotation through the

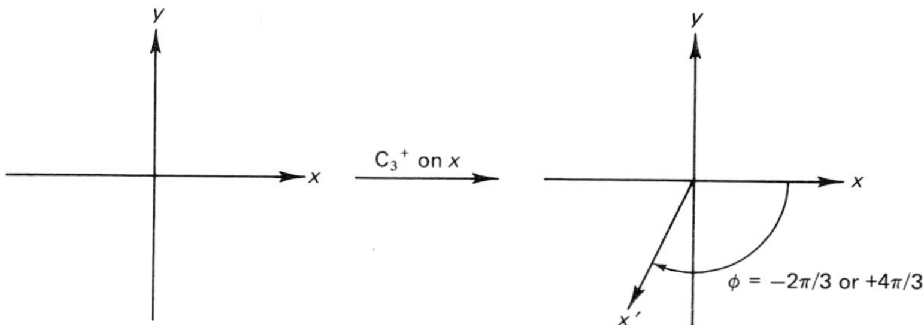

FIG. 13-10 Result of clockwise rotation of x by $2\pi/3$ to produce new vector x'.

[3] The function corresponding to a coordinate is not exactly the same thing as the coordinate itself. The z coordinate is a ray running perpendicular to the xy plane through the coordinate origin. The *function* z is the altitude above (or below) the xy plane at *every* point, regardless of whether it is on the z axis; z^2 is the square of the altitude at every point, etc. The behavior of these functions upon rotation, reflection, etc. is the same as that of the coordinate or product of coordinates.

angle ϕ, the unit vector x' has an x coordinate of $\cos \phi$ and a y coordinate of $\sin \phi$. Similarly, a rotation of y to a new position designated y' must yield a new x coordinate of $-\sin \phi$ and a new y coordinate of $\cos \phi$. Thus, for a rotation through the angle ϕ, we have

$$C_\phi \begin{pmatrix} x \\ y \end{pmatrix} = \begin{pmatrix} x' \\ y' \end{pmatrix} = \begin{pmatrix} x \cos \phi + y \sin \phi \\ -x \sin \phi + y \cos \phi \end{pmatrix}$$

The rotation operator C is thus represented as

$$C_\phi = \begin{pmatrix} \cos \phi & \sin \phi \\ -\sin \phi & \cos \phi \end{pmatrix} \tag{13-1}$$

In the case at hand, *clockwise* rotation by $2\pi/3$ radians is a *decrease* of $2\pi/3$ in ϕ. Substituting $\phi = -2\pi/3$ for $C_3{}^+$ and $\phi = +2\pi/3$ for $C_3{}^-$ gives us the following 2×2 representations:

$$C_3{}^+: \begin{pmatrix} -\frac{1}{2} & +\sqrt{3}/2 \\ -\sqrt{3}/2 & -\frac{1}{2} \end{pmatrix} \qquad C_3{}^-: \begin{pmatrix} -\frac{1}{2} & -\sqrt{3}/2 \\ +\sqrt{3}/2 & -\frac{1}{2} \end{pmatrix}$$

For reflection σ_1, it is easy to see that x is unmoved and y goes into minus itself. Maintaining our dimensionality of two, this gives

$$\sigma_1: \begin{pmatrix} 1 & 0 \\ 0 & -1 \end{pmatrix}$$

For σ_2, x, and y again move into positions x' and y', expressible as resultants of the original x and y vectors (Fig. 13-11). Thus, $x' = -\frac{1}{2}x + (\sqrt{3}/2)y$, $y' =$

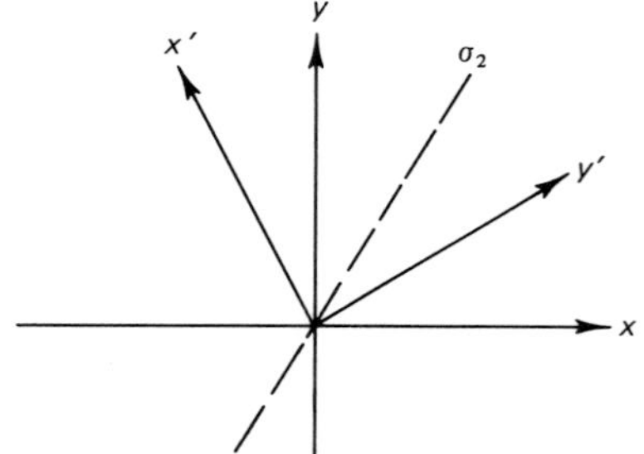

FIG. 13-11 Result of reflection through σ_2 plane of x and y to produce new vectors x' and y'.

$(\sqrt{3}/2)x + \frac{1}{2}y$, and σ_2 has the representation

$$\sigma_2: \begin{pmatrix} -\frac{1}{2} & \sqrt{3}/2 \\ \sqrt{3}/2 & \frac{1}{2} \end{pmatrix}$$

Similarly, σ_3 is easily shown to have the representation

$$\sigma_3: \begin{pmatrix} -\frac{1}{2} & -\sqrt{3}/2 \\ -\sqrt{3}/2 & \frac{1}{2} \end{pmatrix}$$

The operation E does not move either x or y and is represented by the two-dimensional unit matrix. This completes our use of x and y, and we see that together they generate the two-dimensional representation Γ_3. What should we use next? We have not yet generated Γ_2, and so we know that we need to look for another basis. A basis that is frequently employed in group theory is a *direction of rotation* about some symmetry axis. In our case, the symmetry axis is the z axis, and we let R_z stand for a *direction of rotation* about this axis. (*Which* direction we choose, clockwise or counterclockwise, is arbitrary.) Now we consider how R_z is affected by the symmetry operations. $C_3{}^+$ and $C_3{}^-$ have no effect since they merely shift the origin of the ϕ coordinate but do not affect the direction in which ϕ increases or decreases. Put another way, the direction of motion of the hands of a clock is not affected by rotating the clock about an axis perpendicular to its face. However, reflections σ_1, σ_2, and σ_3 *will* cause the direction to be reversed (Fig. 13-12). Therefore,

$$\begin{array}{lll} ER_z = +1\ R_z, & \sigma_1 R_z = -1\ R_z, & \sigma_2 R_z = -1\ R_z \\ \sigma_3 R_z = -1\ R_z & C_3{}^+ R_z = +1\ R_z & C_3{}^- R_z = +1\ R_z \end{array}$$

and we see that R_z is a basis for Γ_2.

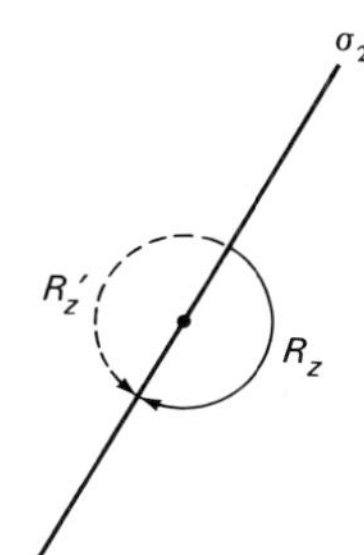

FIG. 13-12 Effect of a reflection on the direction of ϕ.

13-9 Labels for Representations

Thus far, we have labeled our representations Γ_1, Γ_2, etc. We will now describe rules for a more meaningful symbolism—one that has become standard. The rules are as follows:

(1) A one-dimensional representation is given the main symbol A or B. A is used if the representation is symmetric for rotation by $2\pi/n$ about the n-fold principal axis, B if it is antisymmetric. (For C_1, C_s, and C_i groups, which have

no principal axis, the symbol is always A.) A two-dimensional representation has the main symbol E. Three-dimensional representations are symbolized T (or sometimes F), and four-dimensional representations are symbolized G.

(2) Subscripts may be applied as follows. If there are σ_v or σ_d planes, then a subscript 1 means that the basis for the representation is symmetric for such reflections; 2 means it is antisymmetric. If there is an inversion center, subscripts g (*gerade*) and u (*ungerade*) refer to the basis for the representation being respectively symmetric or antisymmetric for inversion.

(3) Superscripts may be applied as follows: If there is a σ_h plane, a single prime means the basis for the representation is symmetric for that reflection; a double prime means it is antisymmetric.

Use of these conventions enables us to write our C_{3v} representation as shown in Table 13-13. (The symbol E in the left-most column of the table should not be confused with the E in the top row. The former labels a two-dimensional representation, the latter refers to the identity operation.) At the right-hand side of the table are listed, for each representation, the bases described above plus a few others. It is convenient for chemical applications to list all cartesian combinations up to the second power, as has been done here. One can go to powers as high as one pleases (z^{99} is a basis for A_1), but first and second powers are of most common practical use in chemistry. The use of parentheses and commas for bases for the E representation [e.g., (xz, yz)] indicate which *pairs* of functions may be selected as bases for this two-dimensional representation.

13-10 Some Connections between the Representation Table and Molecular Orbitals

It is possible, by inspecting Table 13-13, to predict certain properties of MOs or wavefunctions for a molecule having C_{3v} symmetry. Suppose that we did an MO calculation on ammonia. What does this table tell us to expect? In the first place, it tells us that there are only three MO symmetry types possible.

TABLE 13-13

C_{3v}	E	σ_1	σ_2	σ_3
A_1	1	1	1	1
A_2	1	-1	-1	-1
E	$\begin{pmatrix} 1 & 0 \\ 0 & 1 \end{pmatrix}$	$\begin{pmatrix} 1 & 0 \\ 0 & -1 \end{pmatrix}$	$\begin{pmatrix} -\frac{1}{2} & \sqrt{3}/2 \\ \sqrt{3}/2 & \frac{1}{2} \end{pmatrix}$	$\begin{pmatrix} -\frac{1}{2} & -\sqrt{3}/2 \\ -\sqrt{3}/2 & \frac{1}{2} \end{pmatrix}$

We might find nondegenerate MOs having A_1 symmetry (totally symmetric), or A_2 symmetry (antisymmetric for reflections). It is also possible for MOs to exist that form bases for E representations. Since such bases are intermixed by some operations, however, these MOs cannot be either symmetric or antisymmetric for every operation. *Therefore, they must be degenerate.* And, since the intermixing occurs only within pairs of such bases, the MOs must be *doubly* degenerate. Thus, inspection of the representation table tells us at once that nondegenerate and doubly degenerate MOs are possible for ammonia. Since the symmetry requirements apply to wavefunctions as well as to one-electron MOs, the table tells us also that ammonia can have *states* with wavefunctions whose *spatial* symmetries are A_1, A_2, or E. It is conventional to label MOs with lower-case symmetry symbols, a_1, a_2, e, and state functions with upper-case symbols.

The representation table also tells us which basis AOs can appear in the various MOs. For instance, if we used a set of valence AOs for NH_3, we would have a $2p_z$ AO on nitrogen, oriented along the C_3 axis of the molecule, and also $2p_x$ and $2p_y$ AOs perpendicular to C_3. Now $2p_x$, $2p_y$, and $2p_z$ transform like x, y, and z respectively (if they are centered at a common point on the C_3 axis); just as z is symmetric for all symmetry operations of the group, so is $2p_z$. This means that the $2p_z$ AO can be expected to appear only in MOs with a_1 symmetry. $2p_x$ and $2p_y$ must appear together in e-type MOs. What about 2s on nitrogen? Intuitively, we know that it, like $2p_z$, is unaffected by all the operations, and so it should appear only in a_1 MOs. The table indicates this by listing z^2 and $x^2 + y^2$ as bases for the A_1 representation. Since these have the same symmetry, their sum retains the symmetry, and so $x^2 + y^2 + z^2 = r^2$ is also a basis for A_1. Since r^2 is spherically symmetric, this indicates that any spherically symmetric function is a basis for the A_1 representation.

If we were to use an expanded basis set of AOs, including 3d AOs on nitrogen, the group table tells us that $3d_{z^2}$ would appear in the nondegenerate a_1 MOs and that $3d_{x^2-y^2}$, $3d_{xy}$ would appear in degenerate e-type MOs. (Recall that $3d_{z^2}$ is really $3d_{z^2-r^2}$ or $3d_{2z^2-x^2-y^2}$.)

What about the 1s AOs on the H's? Can the representation table tell us in which MOs these will appear? It turns out that it can, and that they go into both

Representation Table for the C_{3v} Group

C_3^+	C_3^-	
1	1	z, $x^2 + y^2$, z^2
1	1	R_z
$\begin{pmatrix} -\frac{1}{2} & \sqrt{3}/2 \\ -\sqrt{3}/2 & -\frac{1}{2} \end{pmatrix}$	$\begin{pmatrix} -\frac{1}{2} & -\sqrt{3}/2 \\ \sqrt{3}/2 & -\frac{1}{2} \end{pmatrix}$	$(x, y)(R_x, R_y)$ $(x^2 - y^2, xy)$ (xz, yz)

a_1- and e-type MOs, but we will defer showing how this can be told from the table until later in the chapter.

The readers may begin to appreciate the usefulness of group theory in quantum chemistry when they consider that, simply by assigning ammonia to the C_{3v} group and looking up the representation table, we are able to say that a minimum-valence basis set MO calculation will produce nondegenerate, totally symmetric (a_1) MOs containing N_{2s}, N_{2p_z}, and H_{1s} AOs, and doubly degenerate (e) MOs containing N_{2p_x}, N_{2p_y}, and H_{1s} AOs. (No a_2 MOs will appear because none of our AOs are a basis for that representation.)

13-11 Representations for Cyclic and Related Groups

Cyclic groups are the groups $C_2, C_3, C_4, \ldots, C_n$ containing only the $n - 1$ rotation operations and the identity operation E. We devote a separate section to these because there are some special problems connected with finding and labeling representations for these groups. (This section is off the mainstream of development of this chapter and may be skipped if desired.)

Let us consider the operations associated with the n-fold proper axis oriented along the z axis and ask what will become of the function $f = \exp(i\phi)$ as it is rotated clockwise about this axis by $2\pi/n$ radians. (We entertain the idea that $\exp(i\phi)$ might be a convenient basis for a representation since such functions were found to be eigenfunctions for the particle-in-a-ring problem in Chapter 2.) Since the clockwise direction is opposite to the normal direction of the ϕ coordinate, the effect of the rotation is to put $f(\phi)$ where $f(\phi - 2\pi/n)$ used to be. To see how the function after rotation compares to that before rotation, we must compare $\exp(i\phi)$ with $\exp[i(\phi - 2\pi/n)]$. That is, the representation R_f, such that $C_n{}^+ \exp(i\phi) = R_f \exp(i\phi)$, is given by $\exp(i\phi)/\exp[i(\phi - 2\pi/n)]$, or $\exp(2\pi i/n)$, which equals $\cos(2\pi/n) + i \sin(2\pi/n)$. For various fractions of a cycle (i.e., various n), R_f takes on different values:

n:	1	2	3	4	5	6	7	8
R_f:	1	-1	$\exp(2\pi i/3)$	i	$\exp(2\pi i/5)$	$\exp(\pi i/3)$	$\exp(\pi i/7)$	$\exp(\pi i/4)$

The important point here is that $f = \exp(i\phi)$ is a basis for a one-dimensional representation for C_n since a rotation turns f into a constant times f and not into some other function. For the C_3 group, then, we could write a partial representation table as shown in Table 13-14a. Now $\exp(4\pi i/3)$ is equal to

TABLE 13-14a
Partial Representation for the C_3 Group

C_3	E	C_3	$C_3{}^2$	
A	1	1	1	z, R_z
	1	$\exp(2\pi i/3)$	$\exp(4\pi i/3)$	$\exp(i\phi)$

$\exp(-2\pi i/3)$, and $\exp(-2\pi i/3)$ is the complex conjugate of $\exp(2\pi i/3)$. If we let $\epsilon \equiv \exp(2\pi i/3)$, we can write the table as shown in Table 13-14b. If $f = \exp(i\phi)$ is a satisfactory basis, $f^* = \exp(-i\phi)$ is also acceptable, since it is linearly

TABLE 13-14b
Partial Representation for the C_3 Group

C_3	E	C_3	C_3^2	$\epsilon = \exp(2\pi i/3)$
A	1	1	1	z, R_z
	1	ϵ	ϵ^*	$\exp(i\phi)$

independent of f. If one calculates the representations for $n = 1, 2, 3, \ldots$ as before, one finds that the numbers R_{f^*} are the complex conjugates of R_f. Therefore, we can immediately expand our table as shown in Table 13-14c.

TABLE 13-14c
Representation for the C_3 Group

C_3	E	C_3	C_3^2	$\epsilon = \exp(2\pi i/3)$
A	1	1	1	z, R_z
E	$\{1$	ϵ	$\epsilon^*\}$	$\exp(i\phi)$
	$\{1$	ϵ^*	$\epsilon\}$	$\exp(-i\phi)$

Since the existence of $\exp(i\phi)$ as a basis for a one-dimensional representation always implies that $\exp(-i\phi)$ exists as a basis, these sorts of one-dimensional representations always occur in pairs. *It is conventional* to combine these with braces and refer to them with the symbol E, which we claimed earlier is reserved for two-dimensional representations. Note, however, that *a pair of one-dimensional representations is not the same as a two-dimensional representation*, and we must broaden our definition of the symbol E to include both types of situation.

Our representation table for the C_3 group now looks almost the way one would find it in a standard tabulation. However, instead of listing $\exp(i\phi)$ and $\exp(-i\phi)$ as bases, the convention is to list x and y. In relating cartesian to spherical polar coordinates, $x = r \sin\theta \cos\phi$ and $y = r \sin\theta \sin\phi$. When we are concerned only with changes in ϕ, x goes as $\cos\phi$, y as $\sin\phi$, and, since $\sin\phi$ and $\cos\phi$ are expressible as linear combinations of $\exp(i\phi)$ and $\exp(-i\phi)$, it follows that x and y are *equivalent* to $\exp(\pm i\phi)$ as bases. If we had started out with x and y as bases, we would have found that, for rotations, these are intermixed, leading to a truly two-dimensional representation. In fact, the effects of C_3 and C_3^2 on x and y were worked out earlier for the C_{3v} group. There we found that C_3 and C_3^2 ($= C_3^-$) were represented by the two-dimensional matrices shown in Table 13-15. But this E representation is reducible to the two one-dimensional representations through the unitary matrix

$$\mathsf{U} = \frac{1}{\sqrt{2}}\begin{pmatrix} 1 & i \\ i & 1 \end{pmatrix}$$

TABLE 13-15
Representations for the C_3 Group

C_3	E	C_3	C_3^2	
A	1	1	1	z, R_z
E	$\begin{pmatrix} 1 & 0 \\ 0 & 1 \end{pmatrix}$	$\begin{pmatrix} -\frac{1}{2} & \sqrt{3}/2 \\ -\sqrt{3}/2 & -\frac{1}{2} \end{pmatrix}$	$\begin{pmatrix} -\frac{1}{2} & -\sqrt{3}/2 \\ \sqrt{3}/2 & -\frac{1}{2} \end{pmatrix}$	(x, y)

The resulting block-diagonalized representation is

$$\begin{matrix} E & C_3 & C_3^2 \\ \begin{pmatrix} 1 & 0 \\ 0 & 1 \end{pmatrix} & \begin{pmatrix} -\frac{1}{2} - (i\sqrt{3}/2) & 0 \\ 0 & -\frac{1}{2} + (i\sqrt{3}/2) \end{pmatrix} & \begin{pmatrix} -\frac{1}{2} + (i\sqrt{3}/2) & 0 \\ 0 & -\frac{1}{2} - (i\sqrt{3}/2) \end{pmatrix} \end{matrix}$$

which can be separated into two one-dimensional representations:

$$\begin{matrix} E & C_3 & C_3^2 \\ 1 & -\frac{1}{2} - (i\sqrt{3}/2) & -\frac{1}{2} + (i\sqrt{3}/2) \\ 1 & -\frac{1}{2} + (i\sqrt{3}/2) & -\frac{1}{2} - (i\sqrt{3}/2) \end{matrix}$$

Since $\epsilon = \exp(2\pi i/3) = \cos(2\pi/3) + i\sin(2\pi/3) = -\frac{1}{2} + (i\sqrt{3}/2)$, we recognize that this pair of one-dimensional representations is the same as the pair we found earlier. Furthermore, we note that U is precisely the transformation that turns x (i.e., $\cos\phi$) and y (i.e., $\sin\phi$) back into $\exp(\pm i\phi)$ (to within a constant multiplier):

$$\mathsf{U}\begin{pmatrix} x \\ y \end{pmatrix} = \frac{1}{\sqrt{2}}\begin{pmatrix} 1 & i \\ i & 1 \end{pmatrix}\begin{pmatrix} \cos\phi \\ \sin\phi \end{pmatrix} = \frac{1}{\sqrt{2}}\begin{pmatrix} \cos\phi + i\sin\phi \\ i\cos\phi + \sin\phi \end{pmatrix} = \begin{pmatrix} (1/\sqrt{2})\exp(i\phi) \\ (-i/\sqrt{2})\exp(-i\phi) \end{pmatrix}$$

Thus, (x, y) produce a *reducible*, two-dimensional representation *equivalent* to the *irreducible* representation given by $\exp(\pm i\phi)$. The reason for listing (x, y) as bases is simply that most applications of the table are made to real functions (e.g., chemists usually prefer to work with $2p_x$ and $2p_y$ AOs rather than with $2p_{+1}$ and $2p_{-1}$). Our final form for the table, then, is that shown in Table 13-16, where additional bases have been listed.

The preceding discussion has been within the context of the C_n groups. One might ask what sort of symmetry operation is needed to make it impossible for $\exp(i\phi)$ to be a basis for a one-dimensional representation. The answer is,

TABLE 13-16
Irreducible Representations for the C_3 Group

C_3	E	C_3	C_3^2		$\epsilon = \exp(2\pi i/3)$
A	1	1	1	z, R_z	$z^2, x^2 + y^2, x^2 - y^2, xy$
E	$\begin{Bmatrix} 1 \\ 1 \end{Bmatrix}$	$\begin{matrix} \epsilon \\ \epsilon^* \end{matrix}$	$\begin{matrix} \epsilon^* \\ \epsilon \end{matrix}$	(x, y) (R_x, R_y)	(yz, xz)

any operation that causes a reversal in the direction of the coordinate ϕ. For then, $\exp(i\phi) \rightarrow \exp(-i\phi)$, and our basis function has turned into another independent function rather than into a constant times itself. Therefore, the presence of any symmetry operation that reverses the direction of motion of the hands of a clock will suffice to prevent representations of the ϵ, ϵ^* sort. Operations that reverse clock direction are σ_d, σ_v, and C_2' (perpendicular to the principal axis). Clock direction is unaffected by σ_h, i, and S_n. Therefore, we can expect ϵ, ϵ^* types of representations to occur in groups of types C_n, C_{nh}, S_n, all of which have a C_n axis but no σ_d, σ_v, or C_2' elements.

13-12 Orthogonality in Irreducible Inequivalent Representations

We come now to a very important point regarding representations. We will illustrate our arguments with the representation table (Table 13-13) for the C_{3v} group. Notice the following features of that table:

(a) If we choose the A_1 representation, square all the numbers, and sum over all six symmetry operations, we get 6 as a result.

(b) If we do the same thing with the A_2 representation, we get the same result.

(c) If we do the same thing for the upper left-hand elements (the 1, 1 elements) of the E representation, we get 3 as a result.

(d) If we do the same thing for each of the other positions in the E representation, the result is 3 each time.

In general, the result of this procedure for any irreducible representation in any group will be the order of the group divided by the dimension of the representation. That is, if h is the order of the group, l_i is the dimension of representation Γ_i, and $\Gamma_i^{(j,k)}(R)$ is the number in the (j, k) position of the matrix representing symmetry operation R, then the mathematical formula that corresponds to our general statement is

$$\sum_R |\Gamma_i^{(j,k)}(R)|^2 = h/l_i \qquad (13\text{-}2)$$

Note that the *absolute* square is used to accommodate the ϵ, ϵ^* type representations of cyclic groups.

We can conceive of the set of six numbers for A_1 as being a vector of six elements. The six numbers of A_2 constitute a second vector, and E provides four more six-dimensional vectors. If each such vector is multiplied by $\sqrt{l_i/h}$, then each vector is normalized.

Now let us examine these vectors regarding their orthogonality. If we take the scalar product of vectors A_1 and A_2, the result is zero:

$$\underbrace{(1 \quad 1 \quad 1 \quad 1 \quad 1 \quad 1)}_{A_1} \underbrace{\begin{Bmatrix} 1 \\ -1 \\ -1 \\ -1 \\ 1 \\ 1 \end{Bmatrix}}_{A_2} = 0$$

The reader may quickly verify that the scalar product of any two *different* vectors from among the set of six in the C_{3v} representation table is zero. Thus these six vectors are orthogonal. Once again, this result always holds between "representation vectors" in irreducible inequivalent representations for any group. Combining this orthogonality property with the normality property mentioned earlier, we have

$$\sum_R [\sqrt{l_i/h}\Gamma_i^{(k,l)}(R)]^*[\sqrt{l_j/h}\Gamma_j^{(m,n)}(R)] = \delta_{ij}\,\delta_{k,m}\,\delta_{l,n} \tag{13-3}$$

where Γ_i and Γ_j are understood to be irreducible and, if $i \neq j$, inequivalent. This relation, sometimes called "the great orthogonality theorem," is of central importance in group theory. Its essence is captured by the statement that "irreducible inequivalent representations are comprised of orthogonal vectors." We do not prove the theorem in this book,[4] but we do make considerable use of Eq. (13-3).

One immediate result of the relation is that it enables us to tell when we have completed the task of finding all the inequivalent irreducible representations of a group. If we consider the C_{3v} group, for example, we note that it is of order six, since there are six symmetry operations. This means that each "representation vector" will have six elements, i.e., is a vector in six-dimensional space. The maximum number of orthogonal vectors we can have in six-dimensional space is six. Therefore, the number of representation vectors cannot exceed the order of the group. Furthermore, since the number of vectors provided by an n-dimensional representation is n^2 (e.g., E is two-dimensional and gives four vectors), we can state that *the sum of the squares of the dimensions of the inequivalent irreducible representations of a group cannot exceed the order of the group.*

[4] See Bishop [1] or Eyring *et al.* [2, Appendix VI].

In fact, it can be proved[4] that this sum of squares of dimensions must *equal* the order of the group when all such representations are included. That is,

$$\sum_{i}^{\substack{\text{all inequivalent} \\ \text{irreducible representations}}} l_i^2 = h \tag{13-4}$$

Thus, the fact that the squares of the dimensions of the A_1, A_2, and E representations for the C_{3v} group add up to six, which is the order of the group, indicates that no more irreducible representations exist (except those that are equivalent to those we already have).

13-13 Characters and Character Tables

Thus far, we have defined representations and shown how they may be generated from basis functions. We have distinguished between reducible and irreducible representations and have indicated that there is an unlimited number of *equivalent* representations corresponding to any given two- or higher-dimensional representation. An example of a pair of equivalent, reducible, two-dimensional representations, derived in Section 13-11, is given in Table 13-17. Equivalent representations are related through unitary transformations,

TABLE 13-17
Equivalent Representations for the C_3 Group

C_3	E	C_3	C_3^2
$\Gamma_{x,y}$	$\begin{pmatrix} 1 & 0 \\ 0 & 1 \end{pmatrix}$	$\begin{pmatrix} -\frac{1}{2} & -\sqrt{3}/2 \\ \sqrt{3}/2 & -\frac{1}{2} \end{pmatrix}$	$\begin{pmatrix} -\frac{1}{2} & \sqrt{3}/2 \\ -\sqrt{3}/2 & -\frac{1}{2} \end{pmatrix}$
$\Gamma_{\exp(\pm\phi)}$	$\begin{pmatrix} 1 & 0 \\ 0 & 1 \end{pmatrix}$	$\begin{pmatrix} -\frac{1}{2} - i\sqrt{3}/2 & 0 \\ 0 & -\frac{1}{2} + i\sqrt{3}/2 \end{pmatrix}$	$\begin{pmatrix} -\frac{1}{2} + i\sqrt{3}/2 & 0 \\ 0 & -\frac{1}{2} - i\sqrt{3}/2 \end{pmatrix}$

which are a special kind of similarity transformation (see Chapter 9), and two matrices that differ only by a similarity transformation have the same *trace*, or *character* (Problem 9-7), which is defined as the sum of the diagonal elements of a matrix. The matrices in Table 13-17 exemplify this fact, their characters being respectively 2, -1, -1 for E, C_3, and C_3^2 in both representations. The generally accepted symbol for the character of operation R in representation Γ_i is $\chi_i(R)$, and the mathematical definition is

$$\chi_i(R) = \sum_j \Gamma_i^{j,j}(R) \tag{13-5}$$

In practice, it is the *characters* of irreducible representations that are used in most chemical applications of group theory. This means that one needs only the *character table* for a group, rather than the whole representation table. For the C_{3v} group, the character table is displayed in Table 13-18. Comparison with Table 13-13 will make clear that the character is merely the sum of diagonal elements. (For one-dimensional representations, the character and the representation are identical.) Since the representation for the *identity operation* is always a unit matrix, the character for this operation is always the same as the dimension of the representation. Hence, the first character in a row tells us the dimension of the corresponding representation.

TABLE 13-18
Characters for the C_{3v} Group

C_{3v}	E	σ_1	σ_2	σ_3	C_3^+	C_3^-	
A_1	1	1	1	1	1	1	$z, x^2 + y^2, z^2$
A_2	1	-1	-1	-1	1	1	R_z
E	2	0	0	0	-1	-1	$(x, y)(R_x, R_y)$ $(x^2 - y^2, xy)(xz, yz)$

An immediate consequence of the orthogonality theorem for representations is that the vectors resulting from *characters* are orthogonal too. This is trivially obvious for characters of one-dimensional representations. For multi-dimensional representations, the character vector is simply the sum of the representation vectors in diagonal positions. If a given vector (say, the A_1 vector) is orthogonal to each of these (say, E_{11} and E_{22}), then it is orthogonal to their sum; that is, in terms of the vector notation of Chapter 9, if $\tilde{\mathsf{a}}_1\mathsf{e}_{11} = 0$ and $\tilde{\mathsf{a}}_1\mathsf{e}_{22} = 0$, then $\tilde{\mathsf{a}}_1(\mathsf{e}_{11} + \mathsf{e}_{22}) = 0$.

Inspection of Table 13-18 reveals a curious thing. For any given row of characters, *all operations in the same class have the same character*. There is a fairly simple reason for this. We have indicated already that operations in the same class are operations that can be interchanged merely by group reflections, rotations, etc., of the symmetry elements in the group, but we have seen that such changes are mathematically effected through *similarity transformations*. This means that representations for operations in the same class are interchangeable via similarity transformations. That is, the matrix representing, say, σ_1 (in the E representation of C_{3v}) can be made equal to the matrix representing σ_2 through a similarity transformation:

$$\mathsf{T}^{-1}\sigma_1\mathsf{T} = \sigma_2 \tag{13-6}$$

(From our group Table 13-7, we can ascertain that T must be the matrix representing σ_3.) Now, the two sides of Eq. (13-6) must have the same character since they are identical 2×2 matrices, but the left-hand side must have the same character as σ_1 since character is unchanged by a similarity transformation. Therefore, σ_1 and σ_2 have the same character.

We can take advantage of the above rule to write our character table in abbreviated form, illustrated for the C_{3v} group in Table 13-19. This is the standard form for character tables. A collection of such tables appears in Appendix 13.

TABLE 13-19
The Standard Short-Form Character Table for the C_{3v} Group

C_{3v}	E	3σ	$2C_3$	
A_1	1	1	1	$z, x^2 + y^2, z^2$
A_2	1	-1	1	R_z
E	2	0	-1	$(x, y)(R_x, R_y)(x^2 - y^2, xy)(xz, yz)$

That characters must be equal in the same class is a restriction on our character vectors. In Table 13-19 it is made evident that, in the C_{3v} group, our vectors really only have three independent variables each, one for each class. These are properly thought of, then, as vectors in three-dimensional space (with weighting factors 1, 3, and 2 for E, σ, and C_3, respectively). There can be no more than three such vectors that are orthogonal, and so we are left with the result that the number of inequivalent irreducible representations in a group cannot exceed (and is in fact equal to[5]) the number of classes in the group. This result, together with the fact that the sum of squares of dimensions of inequivalent irreducible representations must equal the order of the group, often suffices to tell us in advance how many representations there are and what their dimensions are. For our C_{3v} group, the order is six and there are three classes. Hence, we know that there are three representations and that the squares of their dimensions sum to six. The problem reduces to: "What three positive integers squared, sum to six?" There is only one answer: 1, 1, and 2. The fact that there will *always* be a totally symmetric one-dimensional representation also helps pin down the possibilities. For example, can one have a group of order eight and only two classes? There is no way this can happen. Two classes would mean two representations. If both were E type, their dimensions squared would indeed sum to eight. But one of them must be one-dimensional, and there is no way the other can square to seven.

Our collected list of conditions that the characters in a completed table must satisfy is as follows:

(1) There must be a one-dimensional representation having all characters equal to $+1$.

(2) The leading character in each row (i.e., the character for operation E) must equal the dimension of the representation.

[5] See Bishop [1].

(3) The sum of the squares of the leading characters must equal the order of the group.

(4) The number of rows in the character table must equal the number of classes in the group.

(5) The absolute squares of the characters in a given row (times the weighting factor for each class if the abbreviated form is used) equals the order of the group. (Character vectors are normalized.) This results directly from Eq. (13-2).

(6) The character vectors are orthogonal (again, using weighting factors, if appropriate).

This is a fairly large number of restrictions, and may suffice to allow one to produce the character table for a group without ever actually producing representations. For example, consider the C_{4v} group, which has the operations E, $2C_4$, C_2, $2\sigma_v$, and $2\sigma_d$. The group thus has order eight and five classes. There must be five representations, and the only way their dimensions can square to eight is if four of them are one-dimensional and one is two-dimensional. This already enables us to write Table 13-20. It is not difficult to find a way to make

TABLE 13-20
Partial C_{4v} Character Table

C_{4v}	E	$2C_4$	C_2	$2\sigma_v$	$2\sigma_d$
A_1	1	1	1	1	1
Γ_1	1				
Γ_2	1				
Γ_3	1				
E	2				

Γ_1 orthogonal to A_1. We simply place -1 in some places to produce four products of -1 and four of $+1$. Three possibilities are shown in Table 13-21. These are orthogonal not only to A_1, but to each other as well, and so we have found the characters for Γ_1, Γ_2, and Γ_3. The characters for the E representation must have squares that sum to eight and also be orthogonal to all four one-dimensional representation vectors. One possibility is fairly obvious. Since the

TABLE 13-21
Partial C_{4v} Character Table

E	$2C_4$	C_2	$2\sigma_v$	$2\sigma_d$
1	1	1	-1	-1
1	-1	1	1	-1
1	-1	1	-1	1

characters for operations E and C_2 are $+1$ in all the one-dimensional representations, we could take the characters for the E representaton to be

E	$2C_4$	C_2	$2\sigma_v$	$2\sigma_d$
2	0	-2	0	0

Other cases which meet the normality condition are

2	± 1	0	± 1	0
2	0	0	± 1	± 1
2	± 1	0	0	± 1

But none of these is orthogonal to all the one-dimensional sets. Therefore, the complete character table (except for the basis functions) for the C_{4v} group is shown in Table 13-22, where the symbols A_2, B_1, B_2 are consistent with symmetry or antisymmetry for C_4 and σ_v as described in Section 13-9.

TABLE 13-22
Completed C_{4v} Character Table

C_{4v}	E	$2C_4$	C_2	$2\sigma_v$	$2\sigma_d$
A_1	1	1	1	1	1
A_2	1	1	1	-1	-1
B_1	1	-1	1	1	-1
B_2	1	-1	1	-1	1
E	2	0	2	0	0

13-14 Using Characters to Resolve Reducible Representations

It was pointed out earlier that several irreducible representations can be combined into a larger-dimensional reducible representation. Our example was

$$\begin{pmatrix} \Gamma_2 & 0 & 0 \\ 0 & \Gamma_1 & 0 \\ 0 & 0 & \Gamma_3 \end{pmatrix} \equiv \begin{pmatrix} A_2 & 0 & 0 \\ 0 & A_1 & 0 \\ 0 & 0 & E \end{pmatrix} = \Gamma'$$

which is a four-dimensional representation (since Γ_3 is two-dimensional). A matrix built up in this way is symbolized $A_2 \oplus A_1 \oplus E$. It is easy to see that the characters of the reducible representation Γ' are simply the *sums of characters* for the individual irreducible component representations (since the diagonal elements of A_2, A_1, and E all lie on the diagonal of Γ'). Thus, the characters of Γ' are

	E	3σ	$2C_3$
Γ':	4	0	1

Furthermore, no matter how Γ' is disguised by a similarity transformation, its character vector is unchanged. Now, suppose you were given the representation

Γ', disguised through some similarity transformation so as to be nonblock diagonal, and asked to tell which irreducible representations were present. How could you do it? One way would be to find the similarity transformaton that would return the representation to block diagonal form. But there is a much simpler way. We can test to see if the character vector of Γ' is orthogonal to the character vectors of each of our irreducible representations. For instance, if Γ' contained only A_2 and E, its character vector would be orthogonal to A_1 because A_2 and E have character vectors orthogonal to A_1. If A_1 is present in Γ', then Γ' and A_1 character vectors are not orthogonal. Indeed, the *amount of* A_1, A_2, or E present can be found by making use of the character vector normality relation. This is illustrated for Γ' by the following equations:

$$\begin{aligned} A_1&: \tfrac{1}{6}(1\cdot 4 + 3\cdot 1\cdot 0 + 2\cdot 1\cdot 1) = 1 \\ A_2&: \tfrac{1}{6}(1\cdot 4 + 3\cdot -1\cdot 0 + 2\cdot 1\cdot 1) = 1 \\ E&: \tfrac{1}{6}(2\cdot 4 + 3\cdot 0\cdot 0 + 2\cdot -1\cdot 1) = 1 \end{aligned}$$

In general, for $\Gamma' = c_1\Gamma_1 \oplus c_2\Gamma_2 \oplus \cdots \oplus c_i\Gamma_i \oplus \cdots$

$$c_i = (1/h) \sum_R \chi_i(R)\chi'(R) \qquad (13\text{-}7)$$

where h is the order of the group. This technique for resolving a reducible representation into its component irreducible representations is very useful in quantum chemistry, as we shall see shortly.

13-15 Identifying Molecular Orbital Symmetries

We stated earlier that any MO must be a basis for an irreducible representation. Given a set of computed MOs, how does one decide which representation each MO is a basis for? One does this by comparing the MO's with the characters in the character table. Some examples will make this clear. In Table 13-23 are extended Hückel data for NH_3, oriented as shown in Fig. 13-13. The minimal valence basis set of seven AOs leads to seven MOs. Notice that MOs 5 and 6 and also 2 and 3 are degenerate. Therefore, these MOs must be bases for two-dimensional representations, and are assigned the symbol e (lower case for MOs). The other MOs are all given the main symbol a. There are two possibilities for these MOs—a_1 or a_2. These differ in their characters for reflection, a_1 being symmetric, and a_2 antisymmetric. If we look at the eigenvectors for MOs 1, 4, and 7, we see that they contain the 1s AOs on each hydrogen with equal sign and magnitudes. Since reflection always interchanges two hydrogens, these MOs are clearly all symmetric for reflection, and so we label them all a_1. Our result, then, is

MO:	1	2	3	4	5	6	7
Symmetry:	a_1	e	e	a_1	e	e	a_1

Next, consider staggered ethane, which we have earlier assigned to the D_{3d}

TABLE 13-23
Extended Hückel Data for NH_3

MO no.	MO energy (a.u.)	MO occupancy
1	0.7494	0
2	0.1279	0
3	0.1279	0
4	−0.4964	2
5	−0.5955	2
6	−0.5955	2
7	−1.0178	2

	Eigenvectors						
AO\MO	1	2	3	4	5	6	7
N(2s)	1.2946	0.0000	0.0000	−0.1715	0.0000	0.0000	0.7387
$N(2p_z)$	−0.4369	0.0000	0.0000	−0.9628	0.0000	0.0000	0.0214
$N(2p_x)$	0.0000	1.0275	0.0000	0.0000	0.6498	0.0000	0.0000
$N(2p_y)$	0.0000	0.0000	−1.0275	0.0000	0.0000	0.6498	0.0000
$H_1(1s)$	−0.7166	−1.0399	0.0000	0.0656	0.4422	0.0000	0.1561
$H_2(1s)$	−0.7166	0.5200	0.9006	0.0656	−0.2211	0.3829	0.1561
$H_3(1s)$	−0.7166	0.5200	−0.9006	0.0656	−0.2211	−0.3829	0.1561

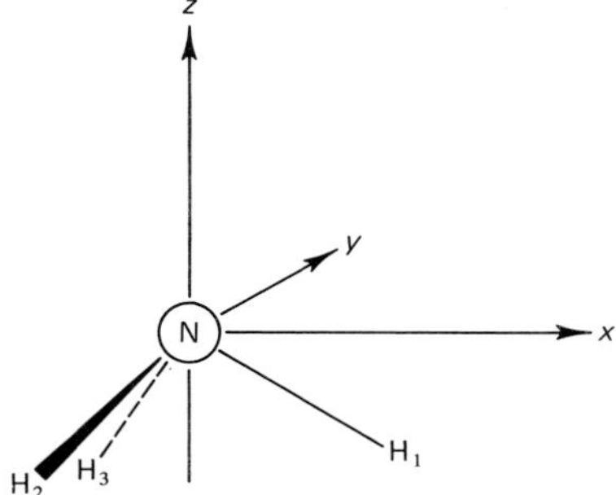

FIG. 13-13 Orientation of ammonia with respect to cartesian axes.

point group. Orbital energy levels and sketches of the MOs appear in Fig. 13-14. The character table for the D_{3d} group is given in Table 13-24.

As before, we observe that certain of the orbitals have the same energies, so we assign such doubly degenerate MOs the main symbol e. These MOs are either symmetric or antisymmetric for inversion and are accordingly subscripted g or u, respectively. All of the nondegenerate MOs must have the main symbol a, since b does not appear in the D_{3d} table. The character table indicates that a_1 and a_2 differ in that they are respectively symmetric and antisymmetric for two-fold rotations that switch the molecule end for end. The u, g subscripts again

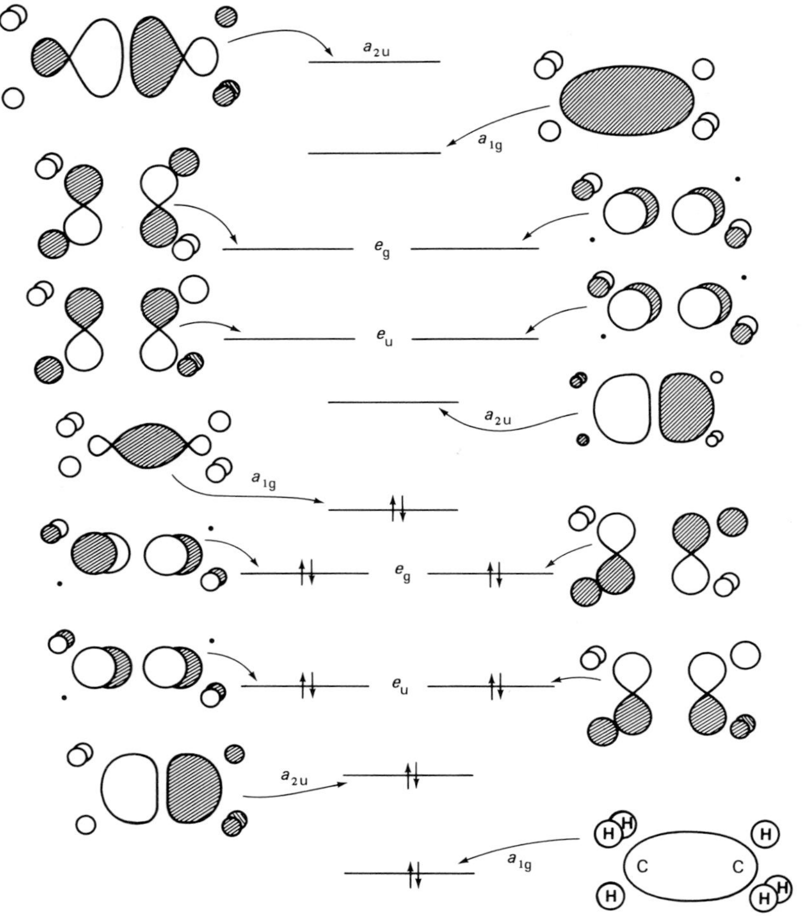

FIG. 13-14 Valence MOs for staggered ethane. The energy level spacings have been altered for convenience. The hatched areas have a negative sign.

TABLE 13-24
Characters for the D_{3d} Point Group

D_{3d}	E	$2C_3$	$3C_2$	i	$2S_6$	$3\sigma_d$
A_{1g}	1	1	1	1	1	1
A_{2g}	1	1	-1	1	1	-1
E_g	2	-1	0	2	-1	0
A_{1u}	1	1	1	-1	-1	-1
A_{2u}	1	1	-1	-1	-1	1
E_u	2	-1	0	-2	1	0

refer to inversion. Inspection of the figures enables us to decide which symbols are appropriate in each case. The resulting symmetry designations are included in Fig. 13-14.

13-16 Determining in Which Molecular Orbital an Atomic Orbital Will Appear

Earlier, we noted that the $2p_z$ AO in ammonia will contribute to a_1 MOs because $2p_z$ transforms like z, and z is listed as a basis for the a_1 representation. If the basis functions were not listed, we could have reached the same conclusion simply by taking $2p_z$ and putting it through all the symmetry operations to produce a representation:

$$\begin{aligned} E2p_z &= +1\ 2p_z \\ \sigma_i 2p_z &= +1\ 2p_z, \qquad i = 1, 2, 3 \\ C_3{}^{\pm}2p_z &= +1\ 2p_z \end{aligned}$$

The representation contains only +1, so $2p_z$ obviously "has" a_1 symmetry.

When we come to the 1s AOs on hydrogens in NH_3, we cannot use the list of basis functions. It includes only coordinates originating on the principal axis, and the hydrogens are not on that axis. Here we *must* generate a representation. Let us try to do this by putting one of the hydrogen atoms, H_1, through the various symmetry operations (also see Fig. 13-15):

$$\begin{aligned} EH_1 &= +1\ H_1 \\ \sigma_1 H_1 &= +1\ H_1 \\ \sigma_2 H_1 &= H_3 \\ \sigma_3 H_1 &= H_2 \\ C_3{}^+ H_1 &= H_2 \\ C_3{}^- H_1 &= H_3 \end{aligned}$$

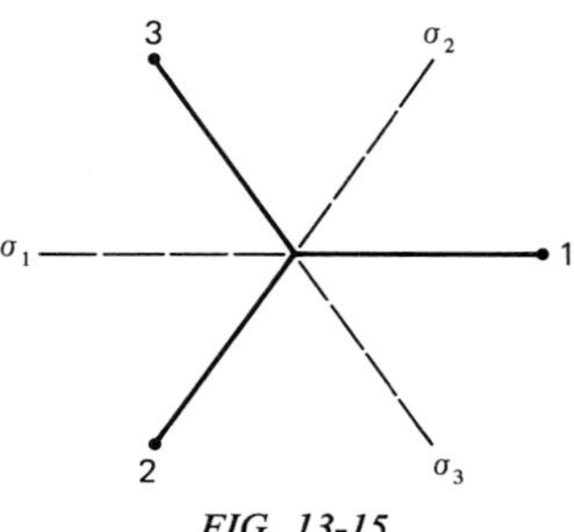

FIG. 13-15

Since some of these operations interchange H_1 with H_2 or H_3, we are not achieving a one-dimensional representation. We must take all three functions together and work out a three-dimensional representation. Thus,

$$E\begin{pmatrix} H_1 \\ H_2 \\ H_3 \end{pmatrix} = \begin{pmatrix} H_1 \\ H_2 \\ H_3 \end{pmatrix}, \qquad E: \begin{pmatrix} 1 & 0 & 0 \\ 0 & 1 & 0 \\ 0 & 0 & 1 \end{pmatrix}, \qquad \chi(E) = 3$$

$$\sigma_1 \begin{pmatrix} H_1 \\ H_2 \\ H_3 \end{pmatrix} = \begin{pmatrix} H_1 \\ H_3 \\ H_2 \end{pmatrix}, \qquad \sigma_1\colon \begin{pmatrix} 1 & 0 & 0 \\ 0 & 0 & 1 \\ 0 & 1 & 0 \end{pmatrix}, \qquad \chi(\sigma_1) = 1$$

$$C_3{}^+ \begin{pmatrix} H_1 \\ H_2 \\ H_3 \end{pmatrix} = \begin{pmatrix} H_2 \\ H_3 \\ H_1 \end{pmatrix}, \qquad C_3{}^+\colon \begin{pmatrix} 0 & 1 & 0 \\ 0 & 0 & 1 \\ 1 & 0 & 0 \end{pmatrix}, \qquad \chi(C_3{}^+) = 0$$

and similarly for σ_2, σ_3, and $C_3{}^-$. But we are only going to use the characters χ, and we know that σ_2 and σ_3 must have the same character as σ_1 (i.e., 1) and $C_3{}^-$ must have the same character as $C_3{}^+$ (i.e., 0). Our character table for the representation resulting from the basis of three hydrogen 1s AOs then, is

C_{3v}	E	3σ	$2C_3$	
Γ_{3H}	3	1	0	(H_1, H_2, H_3)

Notice that a "one" on the diagonal of a 3×3 representation matrix has the effect of keeping a hydrogen 1s AO in place. Thus, the E operation keeps all three H's unmoved, has three "ones" on the diagonal, and has a character of 3. The σ operations each leave but one hydrogen unmoved, have a single "one" on the diagonal, and have a character of 1. C_3 leaves no hydrogen unmoved and has a character of zero. *In general, the characters of such representations are the numbers of functions not moved by the various operations.* Thus, we could have written down the above characters for Γ_{3H} without figuring out the representation matrices.

It is evident that Γ_{3H} must be reducible, since it is of higher dimension than anything in the C_{3v} character table. To resolve Γ_{3H} into its irreducible components, we use the relation (13-7):

$$\begin{aligned} A_1&: \ \tfrac{1}{6}[1\cdot 3\cdot 1 + 3\cdot 1\cdot 1 + 2\cdot 0\cdot 1] = 1 \\ A_2&: \ \tfrac{1}{6}[1\cdot 3\cdot 1 + 3\cdot 1\cdot -1 + 2\cdot 0\cdot 1] = 0 \\ E&: \ \tfrac{1}{6}[1\cdot 3\cdot 2 + 3\cdot 1\cdot 0 + 2\cdot 0\cdot -1] = 1 \end{aligned}$$

Therefore, $\Gamma_{3H} = A_1 \oplus E$. We conclude from this that hydrogen 1s AOs can appear in MOs having a_1 or e symmetry. Table 13-23 indicates that this is correct.

13-17 Generating Symmetry Orbitals

Consider the lowest-energy extended Hückel MO for NH_3. It is

$$\phi_7 = 0.7387N_{2s} + 0.0214N_{2p_z} + 0.1561\ 1s_1 + 0.1561\ 1s_2 + 0.1561\ 1s_3$$

We see that the hydrogen AOs all have the same sign and magnitude in this MO. In fact, we noted above that this *must* happen in all a_1 MOs of NH_3 for reasons of symmetry. If an MO is to be symmetric for all the reflection and rotation operations of the C_{3v} group, there is no other combination which will be adequate. When we have several equivalent atoms, and symmetry forces their AOs to appear in MOs in certain combinations, we refer to those combinations as *symmetry orbitals*. Thus, $\phi_{a_1}^H = N(1s_1 + 1s_2 + 1s_3)$ is the a_1 symmetry orbital for the hydrogens in ammonia (N is a normalizing constant).

One can use the character table to generate symmetry orbitals. This is done by picking any one of the AOs, say $1s_2$, and operating on it with each symmetry operation *times the character for each operation* in the representation of interest. The sum of all these operations is an unnormalized symmetry orbital. Thus, for the a_1 representation in NH_3,

$$\begin{aligned}\phi_{a_1}^H &= E\cdot 1\cdot 1s_1 + \sigma_1\cdot 1\cdot 1s_1 + \sigma_2\cdot 1\cdot 1s_1 + \sigma_3\cdot 1\cdot 1s_1 + C_3{}^+\cdot 1\cdot 1s_1 + C_3{}^-\cdot 1\cdot 1s_1\\ &= 1s_1 + 1s_1 + 1s_3 + 1s_2 + 1s_2 + 1s_3\\ &= 2(1s_1 + 1s_2 + 1s_3)\end{aligned}$$

If we normalize (ignoring overlap between 1s AOs on different centers), we obtain

$$\phi_{a_1}^H = (1/\sqrt{3})(1s_1 + 1s_2 + 1s_3)$$

To generate symmetry orbitals of e symmetry is a little more involved. First we pick a 1s AO and do just as before, using now the characters for e rather than a_1:

$$\begin{aligned}\phi_e{}^H &= E\cdot 2\cdot 1s_1 + 0\cdot\text{all reflections} + (-1)\cdot C_3{}^+\cdot 1s_1 + (-1)\cdot C_3{}^- 1s_1\\ &= 2\,1s_1 - 1s_2 - 1s_3\end{aligned}$$

Normalization yields

$$\phi_e{}^H = (1/\sqrt{6})(2\,1s_1 - 1s_2 - 1s_3)$$

Because e symmetry is manifested by doubly degenerate MOs, we need to find a mate for $\phi_e{}^H$. We can try to do this by repeating the above procedure except operating on $1s_2$ instead of $1s_1$. This yields

$$\psi_e{}^H = (1/\sqrt{6})(2\,1s_2 - 1s_1 - 1s_3)$$

But this function is not orthogonal to $\phi_e{}^H$. (The overlap is $-\frac{1}{2}$.) To achieve orthogonality, we resort to Schmidt orthogonalization (Chapter 6):

$$\psi_e^{H'} = \psi_e{}^H - S\phi_e{}^H$$

Upon expansion and renormalization, this gives

$$\psi_e^{H'} = (1/\sqrt{2})(1s_2 - 1s_3)$$

The data in Table 13-23 show that the e-type MOs do contain the hydrogen 1s AOs in just the manner prescribed by symmetry. For example, MO 5 has hydrogen 1s coefficients 0.4422, −0.2211, −0.2211, a combination similar to that in $\phi_e{}^H$. The degenerate mate, MO 6, has hydrogen coefficients of 0.0000, 0.3829, −0.3829, similar to $\psi_e^{H'}$.

Chemists who have had some experience in these matters are likely to prefer thinking in terms of symmetry orbitals. Thus, in thinking of ammonia, they are likely to take as a minimal valence basis set the functions: N_{2s}, N_{2p_x}, N_{2p_y}, N_{2p_z}, $(1/\sqrt{3})(1s_1 + 1s_2 + 1s_3)$, $(1/\sqrt{6})(2\,1s_1 - 1s_2 - 1s_3)$, $(1/\sqrt{2})(1s_2 - 1s_3)$. (We continue to ignore overlap between 1s AOs.) Since they know that it is not possible for bases of different symmetries to mix (it would produce an MO of mixed symmetry), they know at once that they can have a_1 MOs from mixtures of N_{2s}, N_{2p_z} and $(1/\sqrt{3})(1s_1 + 1s_2 + 1s_3)$ and e-type MOs from the remaining functions. In effect, they have used symmetry to partition their functions into two subsets that do not interact with each other. This means that, in the MO calculation, the hamiltonian matrix will have no mixing elements between members of different subsets. This is indicated schematically in Fig. 13-16.

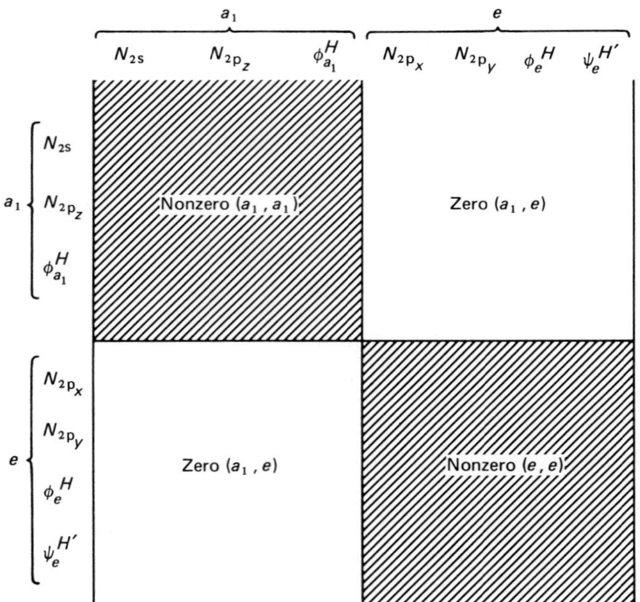

FIG. 13-16 Partitioned hamiltonian matrix.

They also know in advance that there will be *three* MOs of a_1 symmetry (since only three basis functions have that symmetry) and *four* of e symmetry (two degenerate pairs). It is interesting to see how strongly symmetry controls the nature of NH_3 MOs.

The fact that symmetry orbitals can be used to block diagonalize the hamiltonian was referred to in connection with homonuclear diatomic molecules

(Chapter 7). Here we have shown how character tables can be used to guide one in choosing basis orbitals.

Because symmetry orbitals depend on symmetry and not on finer details of molecular structure, they recur again and again in molecules of similar symmetry. For instance, the a_1 and e combinations of hydrogen coefficients discussed above for ammonia will be found for hydrogen AOs in staggered or eclipsed ethane (see the drawings in Fig. 13-14, for instance) and for carbon AOs in MOs for cyclopropenyl (Chapter 8). Because symmetry requirements transcend the differences between various approximate methods for solving the Schrödinger equation, we expect these symmetry patterns to appear in MOs for, say, ammonia, at extended Hückel, CNDO, INDO, MINDO, or *ab initio* levels of computation.

13-18 Hybrid Orbitals and Localized Orbitals

The concept of a *hybridized orbital* is often encountered in the literature, especially in introductory discussions of bonding theory. While this concept is not essential to MO theory, it is used enough to justify a brief discussion.

In the previous section, we showed how one could transform from a basis set of STOs to a basis set of symmetry orbitals. Since these two sets are related through a unitary transformation, they are *equivalent* and must lead to the same MOs when we do a linear variation calculation. However, there are an infinite number of unitary transformations available, and so the set of symmetry orbitals is only one of an infinite number of possible equivalent bases. Of course, this set has the unique advantage of being a set of bases for representations of the symmetry group, which makes it easy to work with. Another set of equivalent basis functions are the *hybrid orbitals*. These have the distinction of being the functions that are concentrated along the directions of bonds in the system.

Consider, for example, methane, which was discussed in detail in Chapter 10. The minimal basis set of valence STOs on carbon can be transformed to form four tetrahedrally directed hybrids:

$$\phi_1 = \tfrac{1}{2}(\mathrm{s} + \mathrm{p}_x - \mathrm{p}_y + \mathrm{p}_z), \qquad \phi_2 = \tfrac{1}{2}(\mathrm{s} - \mathrm{p}_x + \mathrm{p}_y + \mathrm{p}_z)$$

$$\phi_3 = \tfrac{1}{2}(\mathrm{s} - \mathrm{p}_x - \mathrm{p}_y - \mathrm{p}_z), \qquad \phi_4 = \tfrac{1}{2}(\mathrm{s} + \mathrm{p}_x + \mathrm{p}_y - \mathrm{p}_z)$$

One of these hybrids, ϕ_4, is shown in Fig. 13-17 and can be seen to point toward one of the hydrogen atoms. Because the square of each hybrid consists of one part s AO to three parts p AO, these are called sp^3 hybrids. The reason for focusing on sp^3 hybrids in this case is that they have physical appeal since they point along the C–H bonds and therefore seem to have a more natural relation to the electron-pair bond approach of G. N. Lewis. This is deceptive, however, because the set of four carbon sp^3 orbitals is completely equivalent to the set of four carbon STOs. The sum of squares of the hybrids is spherically symmetric

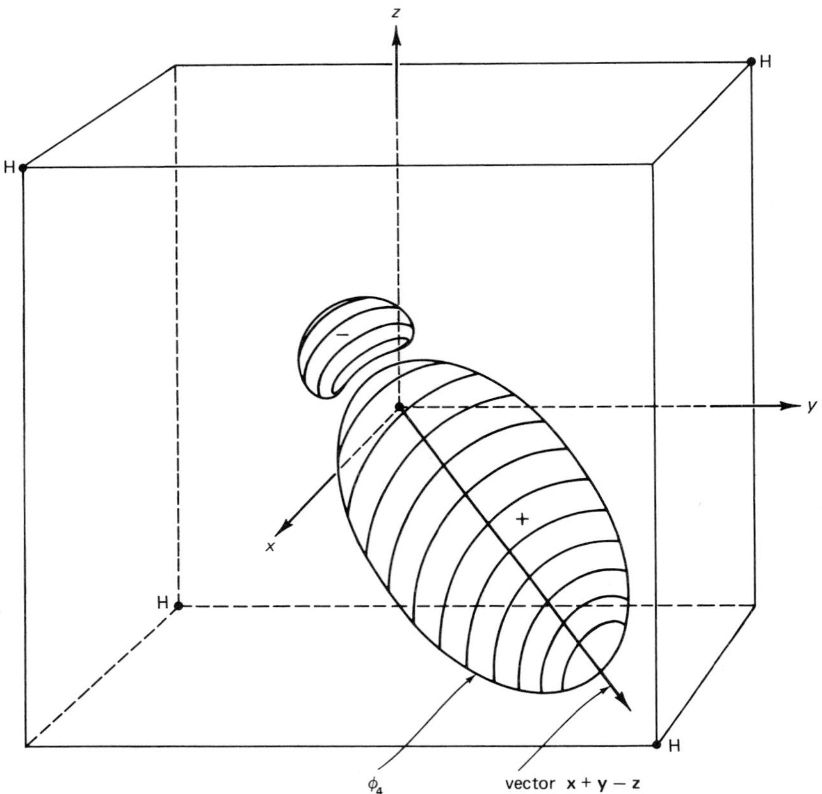

FIG. 13-17 A sketch of the hybrid $\sigma_4 = \frac{1}{2}(s + p_x + p_y - p_z)$. The direction of the hybrid is coincident with that of a vector having the same x, y, z dependence as ϕ_4. The other three hybrids are identical except that they point toward the other three H atoms. (The coordinate system here is rotated with respect to that used in Chapter 10.)

just as is the sum of squares of STOs. Thus, even though each hybrid is directed toward a hydrogen, the electron density due to all four occupied hybrids is spherically symmetric. Furthermore, after the linear variation is performed, the MOs that are produced contain *mixtures* of hybrids to give us the exact same delocalized MOs produced from STOs. No single MO consists of just one hybrid and one hydrogen 1s AO, and therefore no single MO can be identified with one C–H bond. We conclude then that hybrid orbitals are one of an infinite number of choices of basis, that they have an appealing appearance because of their concentration in bond regions, but that no concentration of charge in the molecule results as a consequence of using hybrids rather than STOs. (Some concentration of charge in the bonds does result from overlap between basis functions on carbon and those on hydrogens, but this occurs to exactly the same degree for the various equivalent basis sets.)

Another example is planar $CH_3^+(D_{3h})$. As before, we can mix our minimal valence STOs on carbon to produce hybrids pointing toward the hydrogens. If one hydrogen is on the $+y$ axis, the hybrids are

$$\psi_1 = (1/\sqrt{3})\mathrm{s} + (\sqrt{2}/\sqrt{3})\mathrm{p}_y,$$

$$\psi_2 = (1/\sqrt{3})\mathrm{s} + (1/\sqrt{2})\mathrm{p}_x - (1/\sqrt{6})\mathrm{p}_y,$$

$$\psi_3 = (1/\sqrt{3})\mathrm{s} - (1/\sqrt{2})\mathrm{p}_x - (1/\sqrt{6})\mathrm{p}_y$$

Each of these hybrids, when squared, is one part s to two parts p and is called an sp^2 hybrid. The coefficients for the p AOs are determined from simple vector considerations: One merely calculates how x and y vectors must be combined to produce resultant vectors pointing toward the corners of an equilateral triangle. The resulting hybridized basis set for CH_3^+ is ψ_1, ψ_2, ψ_3, plus the $2p_z$ STO on carbon and a 1s STO on each hydrogen. As before, the sum of the squares of ψ_1, ψ_2, ψ_3, and $2p_z$ is spherically symmetric.

We turn now to *localized orbitals*. We have been emphasizing that one can subject *basis sets* to unitary transformations without making any physical difference. A similar rule applies for *filled molecular orbitals* in a determinantal wavefunction. These too can be subjected to unitary transformations without affecting the *total* energy or *total* electronic distribution for the system. (We have encountered this fact before. See, for instance, Appendix 7.) Thus, we have the capability of altering the appearance of the individual orbitals in the wavefunction without affecting the wavefunction itself. Chemists tend to think of the electrons in molecules as being paired in bond regions, lone pairs, and inner shells, but MOs are delocalized and do not reflect this viewpoint. But by carrying out unitary transformations, we can attempt to produce orbitals that are more localized without sacrificing any of the properties of the overall wavefunction. For methane, we could mix our four delocalized occupied MOs together to try to produce four new orbitals, each one concentrated in a different C–H bond region. One can do this, but it is important to realize that these localized orbitals are not eigenfunctions of an energy operator, for they have been produced by mixing eigenfunctions of different energy. Furthermore, the localization is never complete in any system of physical interest. Each localized orbital always contributes at least slightly to charge buildup in regions outside that of its primary localization. For instance, a localized $C–H_1$ orbital in methane will have small "residual" components at H_2, H_3, and H_4.

What we have been discussing in this section are various kinds of *equivalent* orbitals. At the level of *basis sets*, we have indicated that a minimal valence basis set of STOs is equivalent to a set of symmetry orbitals and also to a set of hybrid orbitals (as well as an infinite number of other possibilities). At the level of *molecular orbitals* we have indicated that the set of occupied delocalized MOs is equivalent to an infinity of transformed sets, some of which will tend to be localized in regions chemists associate with bonds, lone pairs, or inner shells.

One's choice among the possibilities for *basis* is a matter of taste. However, at the MO level, the *delocalized* MOs have two features that are sometimes advantageous. The first is that their energies are eigenvalues for some energy operator (the Fock operator in SCF theory). These are related in a simple way to ionization potentials and electron affinities via Koopman's theorem. Hence, delocalized MOs are more appropriate when considering photoelectron spectra, etc. The second advantage of delocalized MOs is that they display in a clear way the symmetry requirements on the system because they are bases for representations. Hence, these MOs are the most appropriate to use when one is using MO phase relations to infer the nature of certain intra- or intermolecular interactions. (See Chapter 14 for examples.) When delocalized MOs are mixed to form localized orbitals, these energy and symmetry features become partially disguised.

13-19 Symmetry and Integration

Throughout this book, the usefulness of symmetry to determine whether an integral vanishes has been emphasized. It should come as no surprise, therefore, that the formal mathematics of symmetry—group theory—is also useful for this purpose.

The basic idea we have used all along is that, if an integrand is antisymmetric for any symmetry operation, it must have equal positive and negative regions, which cancel on integration. If there is *no* symmetry operation for which the integrand is antisymmetric, then the integral need not vanish. (It still might vanish, but not because of symmetry.) The group theoretical equivalent of this is as follows. Suppose that we have an integral over the integrand f:

$$\int f\,dv = ?$$

The function f is identified as being related to some symmetry point group. (Examples are given shortly.) We want to know what representation f is a basis for. If f produces a representation containing A_1, then f has some totally symmetric character and the integral need not vanish. But if f is devoid of A_1 character, the integral vanishes by symmetry. Our problem, therefore, is to decide which irreducible representations are present in the representation that is produced by the integrand f.

In quantum chemistry, the integrand of interest is often a product of wavefunctions (or orbitals) and operators. For example, the hamiltonian matrix H contains integrals of the form

$$H_{ij} = \int \psi_i{}^* \hat{H} \psi_j \, d\tau$$

We know that $\hat{H}$ is invariant for any symmetry operation of the group, and so $\hat{H}$ has A_1 symmetry. ψ_i and ψ_j are assigned symmetries by comparing their behaviors under various operations with the group character table, as illustrated earlier. Thus, it is fairly easy to ascertain the symmetries of the various *parts* of the integrand. The problem is to determine the symmetry of the *product* $\psi_i{}^*\hat{H}\psi_j$.

To develop a rule for products, let us consider the simplest case—the one-dimensional representations. Suppose that ψ_1 and ψ_2 are bases for one-dimensional representations Γ_1 and Γ_2. Then, for some symmetry operation R

$$R\psi_1 = \chi_1(R)\psi_1, \qquad R\psi_2 = \chi_2(R)\psi_2$$

where χ is a character ($1, -1, \epsilon$, or ϵ^*). If we operate on the *product* $\psi_1\,\psi_2$ with R, we obtain[6]

$$R\psi_1\psi_2 = (R\psi_1)(R\psi_2) = \chi_1(R)\psi_1\chi_2(R)\psi_2 = \chi_1(R)\chi_2(R)\psi_1\psi_2$$

That is, *the characters for the product $\psi_1\psi_2$ are equal to the products of the characters for ψ_1 and ψ_2*. We have demonstrated the rule for one-dimensional representations, but it can be proved for higher-dimensional cases as well. In group theory, the product of two functions, like $\psi_1\psi_2$, is referred to as a *direct product* to distinguish it from a product of symmetry operations, like $\sigma_3 C_3{}^+$. The symbol for a direct product is $\otimes$.

For the C_{3v} group, the characters for some direct products of bases for

TABLE 13-25
Characters for Direct Products of Bases for Irreducible Representations of C_{3v}

C_{3v}	E	3σ	$2C_3$		
A_1	1	1	1	z	$x^2 + y^2, z^2$
A_2	1	-1	1	R_z	
E	2	0	-1	$(x, y)(R_x, R_y)$	$(x^2 - y^2, xy)(xz, yz)$
$E \otimes E$	4	0	1	$x^2 \quad y^2 \quad x^2z^2 \quad xy$	
$A_2 \otimes E$	2	0	-1	$R_zx \quad R_zy$	
$A_2 \otimes A_2$	1	1	1	$R_z{}^2$	
$A_1 \otimes A_2 \otimes E$	2	0	-1	zR_zx	

irreducible representations are shown in Table 13-25. The direct product x^2 has as characters the product of characters of E times itself. These characters (4, 0, 1) do not agree with any of the irreducible representation character sets, and so $E \otimes E$ is reducible. We can tell, in fact, that $E \otimes E$ is four-dimensional from the leading character. To resolve $E \otimes E$, we employ the formula (13-7), which gives $E \otimes E = A_1 \oplus A_2 \oplus E$, and fits the observation that $E \otimes E$ is four-dimensional. The other direct products listed in Table 13-25 (R_zx, $R_z{}^2$,

[6] That $R\psi_1\psi_2 = (R\psi_1)(R\psi_2)$ is not always obvious to the student, but it should be evident that operating on (say reflecting) the function $\psi_1\psi_2$ gives the same result as reflecting ψ_1 and ψ_2 separately and then taking the product.

zR_zx, etc.) all give character sets indicative of irreducible representations. We see that $A_2 \otimes E = E$, $A_2 \otimes A_2 = A_1$, $A_2 \otimes A_1 \otimes E = E$.

There is a general rule that is illustrated by these examples. *A direct product of bases for two irreducible representations contains A_1 character if and only if the two irreducible representations are the same.* That is, if f_i is a basis for Γ_i and f_j is a basis for Γ_j, and $f_i f_j$ is a basis for $\Gamma_{i,j}$, where

$$\Gamma_{i,j} \equiv \Gamma_i \otimes \Gamma_j = c_1 A_1 \oplus c_2 \Gamma_2 \oplus \cdots \oplus c_i \Gamma_i \oplus c_j \Gamma_j \oplus \cdots$$

then $c_1 \neq 0$ if and only if $\Gamma_i = \Gamma_j$.

Another rule is that, if Γ_i is A_1, then $\Gamma_{i,j} = \Gamma_j$; that is, multiplying a function f_2 by a totally symmetric function f_1 gives a product with the symmetry of f_2.

Now we are in a position to decide whether the integral of a product of functions and operators will vanish. For our examples, we will continue to use orbitals, operators, and coordinates from the ammonia molecule. Some of these quantities, segregated according to symmetry, are given in Table 13-26.

TABLE 13-26
Operators and Orbitals for Ammonia Classified by Symmetry

a_1	e
N_{2s}	N_{2p_x}
$N2_{p_z}$	N_{2p_y}
$(1/\sqrt{3})(1s_1 + 1s_2 + 1s_3)$	$(1/\sqrt{6})(2 \cdot 1s_1 - 1s_2 - 1s_3)$
ϕ_1 } MOs (see Table 13-23)	
ϕ_4 }	$(1/\sqrt{2})(1s_2 - 1s_3)$
ϕ_7 }	ϕ_2 } MOs
$\hat{H}$	ϕ_3 }
z	ϕ_5 }
	ϕ_6 }
	x
	y

Example 1 $\int N_{2p_z} \hat{H} N_{2p_x}\, dv$ The symmetries of the three functions in the integrand are respectively A_1, A_1, E. The direct product has symmetry E. There is no A_1. The integral vanishes.

Example 2 $\int N_{2p_x} \hat{H} (1/\sqrt{2})(1s_2 - 1s_3)\, dv$ The symmetries are E, A_1, E. The direct product is therefore $E \otimes E \otimes A_1 = A_1 \oplus A_2 \oplus E$. Since A_1 is present, the integral need not vanish.

These two examples are related to the block diagonalization of the matrix H, discussed in a previous section. The zero blocks in that matrix correspond to integrals between functions of different symmetry. Since $\hat{H}$ is of A_1 symmetry, it has no influence on the symmetry of the integrand. If ψ_i and ψ_j have different symmetries, their direct product cannot contain A_1 symmetry and the integral over $\psi_i \hat{H} \psi_j$ must vanish. The reader can now understand how the computational procedure guarantees MOs of "pure" symmetry (i.e., bases of irreducible representations). If two basis functions ψ_i and ψ_j differ in symmetry, there will be a zero value for H_{ij}. A zero H_{ij} means that mixing ψ_i and ψ_j will produce no energy lowering. Hence, the variation procedure will not mix these functions together in the same MO, so the MO will not be of mixed symmetry.

Example 3 $\int \phi_1 x \phi_4 \, dv$ Integrals of this sort are involved in calculating spectral intensities. The symmetries are $A_1 \otimes E \otimes A_1 = E$ and the integral vanishes. This means a transition between states corresponding to an electron going from ϕ_1 to ϕ_4 (or ϕ_4 to ϕ_1) is forbidden for x-polarized light and an oriented molecule (see Section 12-9).

Example 4 $\int \phi_3 y \phi_5 \, dv$ The symmetry here is $E \otimes E \otimes E$, which gives characters 8, 0, -1. This resolves into $A_1 \oplus A_2 \oplus 3E$ and the integral need not vanish. Corresponding transitions are "y allowed."

In this chapter we have seen how formal group theory can be used to characterize MO symmetries, construct symmetry orbitals, and indicate whether integrals vanish by symmetry. It is true that one can perform MO calculations and get correct results without explicitly considering symmetry or group theory, since the computational procedures satisfy symmetry considerations automatically. But group theory allows a much deeper understanding of the constraints that symmetry places on a problem and often leads to significant shortcuts in computation.

A notable feature of group theory is its hierarchy of concepts. At the lowest level are the symmetry operations and the basis functions they operate on. At the intermediate level are the representations for the group, produced from the basis functions. At the highest level are the characters, produced from the representations. The characters provide the "handles" that we actually work with, but our interest is often focused on the basis functions to which they are related. This tends to lend an air of unreality to the use of group theory. An aim of this chapter has been to avoid this feeling of unreality by dispensing with formal proofs, and instead illustrating relationships through investigation of examples. Further insight should come from solving the problems at the end of this chapter.

PROBLEMS

13-1 Do the following operations constitute a group?
"come 90° to port" (*P*) "come 90° to starboard" (*S*) "steady as she goes" (*E*).

13-2 The text indicates that every element in the group has an inverse if *E* appears in each column of the multiplication table. But E also appears once in each row. What does this mean?

13-3 Consider the group of four operations of the drill soldier (Section 13-2).

(a) To which symmetry point group is this set of four operations isomorphic (i.e., which group has the same product relationship)?

(b) Based on the *mathematical* definition of class and Table 13-1, how many classes are there in this group?

(c) Based on your physical intuition about kinds of operation, how many classes would you have anticipated for this group? If there is a discrepancy between (b) and (c), try to explain it.

13-4 The C_{3v} (ammonia) group is of order six. This is the same as the number of ways one can place three hydrogens at the three corners of an equilateral triangle $(3 \cdot 2 \cdot 1)$. When we consider the C_{4v} group, we have 24 ways we can place four hydrogens at the corners of a square $(4 \cdot 3 \cdot 2 \cdot 1)$. But the C_{4v} group only has order eight. Explain.

13-5 For each of the molecules (IV)–(VII),

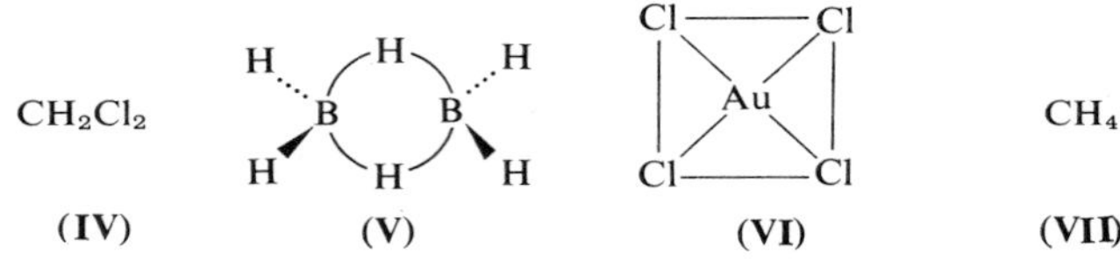

(a) list the symmetry elements,
(b) calculate the number of symmetry operations for each element,
(c) obtain the order of the group,
(d) determine the group symmetry symbol,
(e) check your results for (a)–(c) against the appropriate character table in Appendix 13.

13-6 (a) Demonstrate that U is a unitary matrix.
(b) Demonstrate that $U^\dagger A U$ is diagonal.

$$U = \begin{pmatrix} 1/\sqrt{2} & -1/\sqrt{2} \\ 1/\sqrt{2} & 1/\sqrt{2} \end{pmatrix}, \qquad A = \begin{pmatrix} 0 & 1 \\ 1 & 0 \end{pmatrix}$$

13-7 Assign the following molecules to point groups, look up their character tables, and indicate in each case whether one could expect doubly degenerate MOs.

(a) C_6H_6 (b) CH_2Cl_2 (c) B_2H_6 (see Problem 13-5)
(d) staggered C_2H_6 (e) staggered CH_3CCl_3

13-8 Consider the planar molecule CO_3^{2-} (VIII). The oxygen atoms are at the

(VIII)

corners of an equilateral triangle.

(a) What is the point group of this molecule?

(b) Using the appropriate character table, assign a symmetry symbol to each of MOs (IX)–(XII).

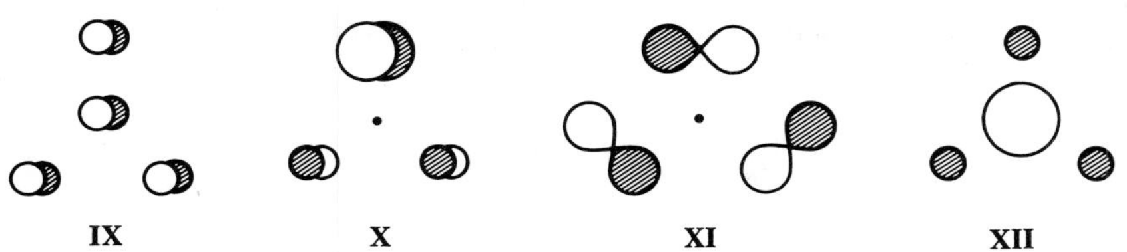

13-9 Table P13-9 gives the eigenvalues and eigenvectors resulting from an extended Hückel calculation of the allene molecule (**XIII**). The molecule is aligned as shown with respect to cartesian axes. Ascertain the point group for this molecule. Using the character table for this group, assign a symmetry symbol to each MO. Is a transition from the highest occupied MO level to the lowest unoccupied level allowed by symmetry for any direction of polarization?

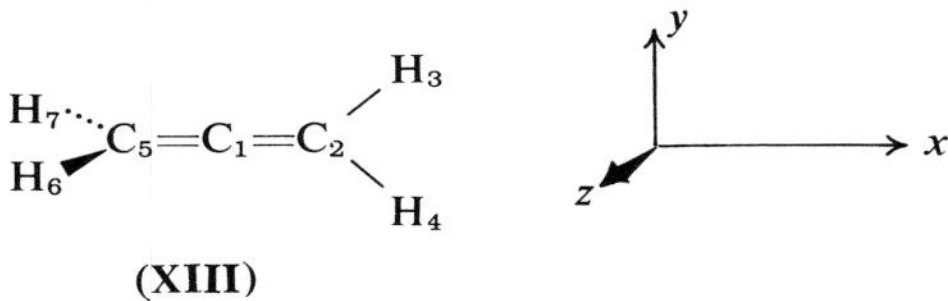

(XIII)

13-10 Consider the water molecule, oriented as shown in Fig. P13-10 with the y axis perpendicular to the molecular plane and the z axis bisecting the H–O–H angle.

(a) Figure out as many nonredundant symmetry operations for this molecule as you can, and set up their multiplication table. Ascertain that you have a *group* of operations by checking closure, etc.

(b) Use the functions z, R_z, x, and y as bases to set up a character table for this group.

(c) Use the resulting table to find out the symmetries of all MOs that can contain 1s AOs on the hydrogens.

(d) Produce the symmetry combinations of these AOs that can appear in the MOs of water.

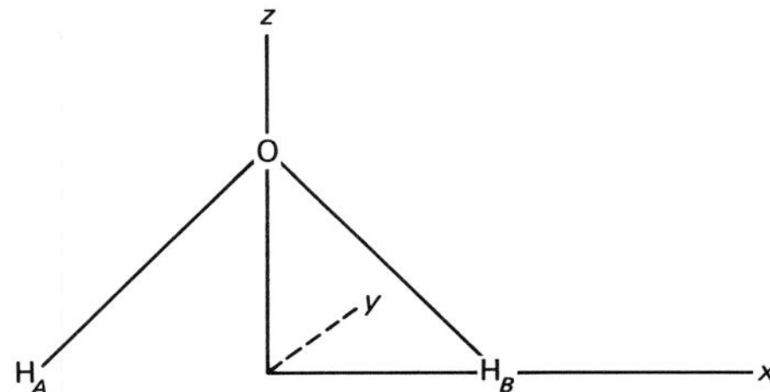

FIG. P13-10 Relation of the water molecule to cartesian axes.

TABLE P13-9
Extended Hückel Molecular Orbitals for Allene

MO no.	Energy (a.u.)	C_1 2s	C_1 $2p_z$	C_1 $2p_x$	C_1 $2p_y$	C_2 2s	C_2 $2p_z$
1	1.7868	0	0	1.58	0	−1.23	0
2	1.4916	1.52	0	0	0	−1.01	0
3	0.4927	−0.54	0	0	0	−0.51	0
4	0.3681	0	0	0.67	0	0.36	0
5	0.3231	0	0	0	−0.34	0	0
6	0.3231	0	0.34	0	0	0	−0.11
7	−0.2619	0	0	0	0.85	0	0
8	−0.2619	0	0.85	0	0	0	−0.78
9	−0.4326	0	0.56	0	0	0	0.67
10	−0.4326	0	0	0	−0.56	0	0
11	−0.4881	0	0	−0.49	0	−0.08	0
12	−0.5558	0	−0.16	0	0	0	−0.04
13	−0.5558	0	0	0	0.16	0	0
14	−0.6221	0.43	0	0	0	−0.14	0
15	−0.8102	0	0	−0.13	0	−0.44	0
16	−0.9363	0.47	0	0	0	0.36	0

13-11 Consider the *trans*-chlorobromotetramine cobalt(III) ion (**XIV**).

(**XIV**)

(a) Find the appropriate symmetry elements for this molecule and set up their group multiplication table. (Ignore the hydrogens on the ammonias.) Check the multiplication table to be sure all requirements for a mathematical group are satisfied.

(b) Use the following as bases for representations: z, R_z, x, y, $x^2 - y^2$, xy. Make sure you get all the inequivalent irreducible representations allowed in the group by checking $\Sigma_i\ l_i^2 = h$.

(c) Set up the character table. Now ascertain which symmetry orbitals contain 2s orbitals of nitrogen. Give the symmetry combinations of those AOs that appear in these symmetry orbitals.

13-12 Use the relationships that must exist among characters to complete the

	Atomic Orbital Coefficients				C_5			
$2p_y$	h_3	h_4	2s	$2p_z$	$2p_x$	$2p_y$	h_6	h_7
0	0.30	0.30	1.23	0	0.58	0	−0.30	−0.30
0	0.24	0.24	−1.01	0	−0.57	0	0.24	0.24
0	0.61	0.61	−0.51	0	0.75	0	0.61	0.61
0	−0.58	−0.58	−0.36	0	0.83	0	0.58	0.58
.27	−0.88	0.88	0	0	0	0.11	0	0
0	0	0	0	−1.27	0	0	0.88	−0.88
0.01	−0.21	0.21	0	0	0	−0.78	0	0
0	0	0	0	0.01	0	0	−0.21	0.21
0	0	0	0	−0.10	0	0	−0.16	0.16
0.10	0.16	−0.16	0	0	0	−0.68	0	0
0	0.17	0.17	0.08	0	0.41	0	−0.17	−0.17
0	0	0	0	−0.48	0	0	−0.44	0.44
0.48	−0.44	0.44	0	0	0	−0.04	0	0
0	−0.24	−0.24	−0.14	0	0.32	0	−0.24	−0.24
0	−0.18	−0.18	0.44	0	−0.02	0	0.18	0.18
0	0.07	0.07	0.36	0	0.02	0	0.07	0.07

following tables. Include proper symbols for the representations, but do not include bases.

(a)

	E	C_2	σ_v	σ_v'

(b)

	E	$2C_3$	$3C_2$	σ_h	$2S_3$	$3\sigma_v$

13-13 The D_5 group has four classes of operation and has order ten. How many inequivalent irreducible representations are there and what are their dimensions?

13-14 Consider the structure shown in Fig. P13-14.

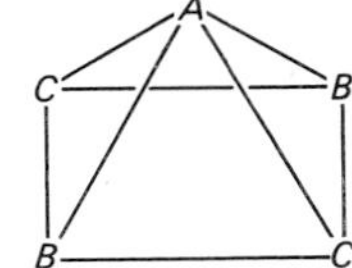

FIG. P13-14 Square pyramid.

(a) Figure out the symmetry elements and operations for this molecule.

(b) What is the group order and number of classes?

(c) How many inequivalent irreducible representations are there and what are their dimensions?

(d) Ascertain the group symbol and compare your answers with the character table in Appendix 13.

13-15 A group has the following representations: A_1, A_2, B_1, B_2, E_1, E_2. What is the group order and how many classes are there?
13-16 Find the matrices that transform s and p STOs into sp^3 and sp^2 hybrids (Section 13-18). Demonstrate that these are unitary matrices.
13-17 It has been argued (Section 13-18) that sp^2 hybrid orbitals are appropriate basis functions for $CH_3^+(D_{3d})$. Could one use a basis set of sp^3 hybrid orbitals for this system?
13-18 In each of the following cases, resolve the given character set. If these were characters of integrands, would the integral vanish by symmetry? For example,

C_{3v}: 4 0 1 $\qquad A_1 \oplus A_2 \oplus E \qquad$ No.

(a) C_{2v}: 5 -1 1 1 -3
(b) D_{2h}: 3 -1 -1 3 -1 3 3 -1
(c) D_{3d}: 8 2 0 0 0 0

13-19 Referring to the data in Problem 13-9, which integrals below must vanish by symmetry?
(a) $\int \phi_6 x \phi_{10}\, dv$ (b) $\int \phi_6 y \phi_{10}\, dv$ (c) $\int \phi_1 x \phi_2\, dv$
(d) $\int \phi_3 x \phi_{14}\, dv$ (e) $\int \phi_2 z \phi_4\, dv$

13-20 Consider the possible electronic excitations of staggered ethane from its occupied 1 e_g MO to the various empty MOs of symmetry a_{1g}, a_{2u}, e_g, and e_u. Which of these are symmetry allowed and how are they polarized?
13-21 Referring to the data in Problem 12-20, which transitions from MO 4 can be induced by y-polarized light? (*Note*: the molecular y axis is coincident with the symmetry z axis.)

REFERENCES

[1] D. M. Bishop, "Group Theory in Chemistry." Oxford Univ. Press, London and New York, 1973.
[2] H. Eyring, J. Walter, and G. E. Kimball, "Quantum Chemistry." Wiley, New York, 1944.

CHAPTER 14

QUALITATIVE MOLECULAR ORBITAL THEORY

14-1 The Need for a Qualitative Theory

Ab initio and semiempirical computational methods have proved extremely useful. But also needed is a simple conceptual scheme that enables one to predict the broad outlines of a calculation in advance, or else to rationalize a computed result in a fairly simple way. Chemistry requires conceptual schemes, simple enough to carry around in one's head, with which new information can be evaluated and related to other information. Such a theory has developed alongside the mathematical methods described in earlier chapters. We shall refer to it as qualitative molecular orbital theory (QMOT). In this chapter we describe selected aspects of this many-faceted subject and illustrate QMOT applications to questions of molecular shape and conformation, and reaction stereochemistry.

14-2 Hierarchy in Molecular Structure and in Molecular Orbitals

We seek a simple qualitative approach to the question, "How does the total energy of a system change as we move the nuclei with respect to each other?" This question is very broad, encompassing the phenomena of molecular structure and chemical reactivities.

It is useful to distinguish three kinds of process that can occur as nuclei are moved. One of these is the process in which two nuclei move closer together or farther apart, with their separation being somewhere around 1 or 2 Å (i.e., about one bond length) either at the outset or the conclusion of the motion (or both). This process includes the breaking or forming of bonds and also the stretching or compressing of bonds. It also includes the forcing together of two species that will not bond (e.g., He with He). Let us refer to this as a *nearest-neighbor* interaction, even though the two nuclei need not be bonded in the usual chemical sense. The second process is the changing of the bond angle between two nuclei bonded to a third. The changing of the H–O–H angle in water is an example. A necessary consequence of such a change in angle is a change in distance between the two nuclei being moved (here H---H). In geometries normally of interest, however, this distance is somewhat greater than a typical bond length throughout the entire process. We refer to this process as *bond-angle change*. The third process is the rotation of one part of a system with respect to the other about some axis (usually a single bond in the system). An example is rotation of one methyl group in ethane with respect to the other. We refer to this process as a *torsional angle change*, or an internal rotation. Such a change will produce changes in distances between nuclei located on opposite ends of the torsional axis, but these distances typically remain several times as great as a bond length throughout the entire process.

Chemists have long recognized that the energies associated with these three kinds of change fall into a loose hierarchy, with nearest-neighbor interactions having the greatest effect on energy, bond-angle changes having a smaller effect, and torsional angle changes the least. Indeed, for this reason spectral transitions corresponding to stretching, bending, and torsional modes are found in different regions of the electromagnetic spectrum.

Most nearest-neighbor interactions are a consequence of the *connectedness*, or *topology* of a molecule. This aspect of molecular structure, sometimes called the *first-order*, or *primary* structure, is the first aspect one considers when establishing structure, and it is the first aspect that chemists became aware of, historically. The *second-order* aspect of structure concerns the bond angles. Once those are at least roughly known, one can go on to consider the *third-order*, or *tertiary* structure resulting from torsional energetics. The last aspect is usually referred to as the *conformation* of the system.

It is advantageous to discuss MOs from a similar viewpoint. If we wish to guess the nature of the MOs of a system (i.e., where they have their nodes) and the MO energy order, we first consider the topology of the system. (Recall that this is the *only* thing that the simple Hückel method considers.) Elementary arguments lead to a fair approximation of the appearance and relative energies of the MOs. Next, we can consider bending the system, bending the MOs along with it. By judging whether MO energies will rise or fall in this process, we shall show that one can often predict whether the molecule will be linear or bent. Finally, when we know the second-order structure, we can imagine the various conformational possibilities, allowing the MOs to be carried along with the nuclei. Again, by judging how the MO energies respond, it is possible to make predictions as to which conformation is most stable.

In order to formulate rules for QMOT, we will return to the H_2^+ molecule ion and the H_2 molecule. Then, using insights gained there, we shall consider more complicated systems.

14-3 H_2^+ Revisited

In Chapter 7 we used the linear variation method to solve the minimal basis H_2^+ problem. However, symmetry conditions alone suffice to force the solutions to be

$$\psi_{\sigma_g} = [1/\sqrt{2(1+S)}](1s_a + 1s_b), \qquad E_g(\text{el}) = (H_{aa} + H_{ab})/(1+S) \quad (14\text{-}1)$$

$$\psi_{\sigma_u} = [1/\sqrt{2(1-S)}](1s_a - 1s_b), \qquad E_u(\text{el}) = (H_{aa} - H_{ab})/(1-S) \quad (14\text{-}2)$$

where H_{aa} and H_{ab} are negative energies, and S is the (positive) overlap integral between 1s AOs on nuclei a and b. The energies E_g(el) and E_u(el) are upper bounds for the *electronic* energy of the σ_g and σ_u states. The total energies are obtained by adding the internuclear repulsion energy $1/R$ a.u., where R is the internuclear distance in atomic units.

It is instructive to consider the total energies, E_g(tot) and E_u(tot) as the result of an artificial step-by-step procedure as indicated in Fig. 14-1. We begin

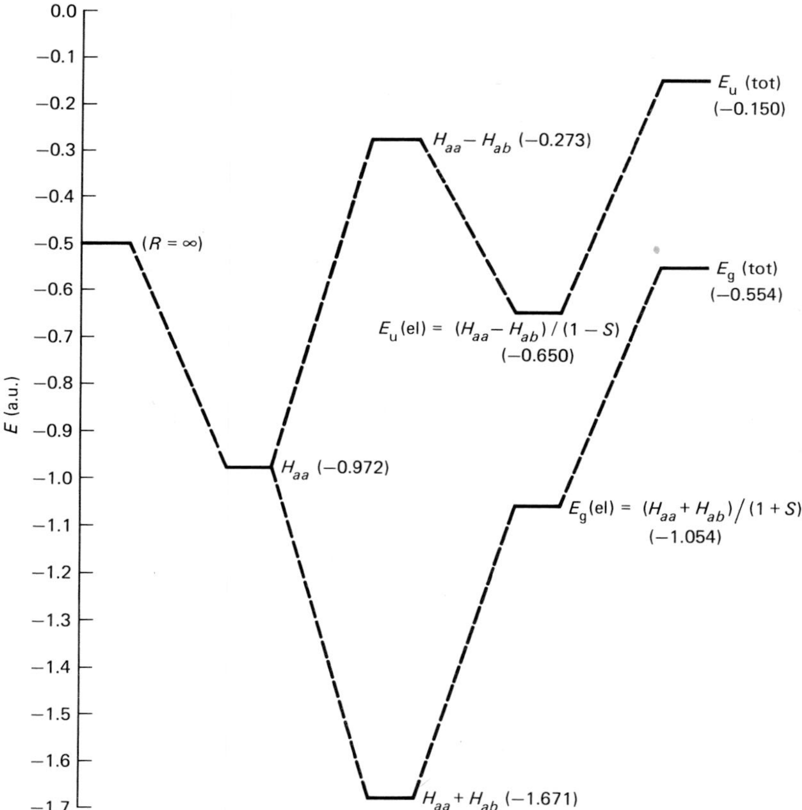

FIG. 14-1 Steps in compiling total energies for minimal basis LCAO–MO calculation on $H_2{}^+$ at $R = 2$ a.u.

with a 1s AO on nucleus a at $E = -\frac{1}{2}$ a.u. If we now bring proton b up to a distance of 2 a.u., but do not allow the 1s AO to respond, we get an energy lowering due to the increased nuclear attraction now felt by the electron in $1s_a$. At $R = 2$ a.u., this additional attraction lowers the energy by 0.472 a.u., giving $H_{aa} = -0.972$ a.u. Let us refer to this as the *frozen AO in molecule* energy. (It may be thought of as the energy to first order due to a "perturbation" caused by the approach of proton b, although this is hardly a small perturbation.) As our next step, we include H_{ab}. This term equals -0.699 a.u., and it splits the energy evenly around H_{aa}, as shown in the figure. The resulting energies are the expectation values for the electronic energies of the *unnormalized* (due to omission of overlap) functions $2^{-1/2}(1s_a \pm 1s_b)$. Two things have happened in this step. The electronic charge has become delocalized over both centers, and *it has changed in amount so that we no longer have one electron in each MO*. Because the overlap term S (equal to 0.586 at $R = 2$ a.u.) has not yet come into the calculation, we have here the energies due to $1 + S$, or 1.586 electron in the σ_g MO, and $1 - S$, or 0.414 electron in the σ_u MO.

Before proceeding to the next step, let us examine the two energies at this point to see how they compare for equal amounts of charge. The 0.414 electronic charge in σ_u is associated with an energy of -0.273 a.u., whereas the 1.586 charge in σ_g corresponds to -1.671 a.u. It is clear that the σ_g MO is *inherently* of lower energy (relative to $E = 0$) per unit charge, due to the detailed nature of kinetic and nuclear electronic energies. (We will not concern ourselves with these detailed aspects, however.)

Our next step is to normalize the charges by dividing by $1 \pm S$. This essentially adds 0.586 electron to σ_u and subtracts 0.586 from σ_g. From the figure, we see that this lowers the energy of σ_u and raises that of σ_g. This is reasonable. Adding more charge to an MO of negative energy should make its energy contribution more negative, removal of charge should make it less negative. A very important fact, though, is that σ_g rises more than σ_u goes down. This simply reflects our observation in the preceding paragraph that σ_g charge "has lower energy per unit charge," so removal of it "costs more" than is gained by putting it into σ_u. A useful summary of the effect of renormalization is: Renormalization tends to cancel the energy level changes due to nuclear motion. The higher an energy level is, the less effective is this cancellation. Therefore, net energy changes (due to nuclear motion) tend to be greatest for the antibonding member of a bonding–antibonding pair of levels, and, in general, greater for a higher-energy MO (bonding or antibonding) than for a lower-energy MO.

The final step is to add the internuclear repulsion energy of 1/2 a.u. to each level. It is important to notice that the final *total* energy levels are related to the initial H atom energies in almost the identical way that $E_g(\mathrm{el})$ and $E_u(\mathrm{el})$ are related to the "atom-in-molecule" energy H_{aa} (see Fig. 14-2) because the energy lowering due to the original $1s_a$ electron being attracted by proton b (-0.472 a.u. at $R = 2$ a.u.) is fairly close in magnitude to the repulsion between the protons ($+0.5$ a.u.). We expect this near cancellation to hold as long as R is large enough that proton b is "outside" the charge cloud due to the $1s_a$ electron. In other words, the *total* energies should lie above or below the *separated-atom energy* in much the same way that the *electronic energies* lie above or below the "*atom-in-molecule*" *energy, if the internuclear separation is not too small.* [We know that, as R approaches zero, the internuclear repulsion approaches infinity,

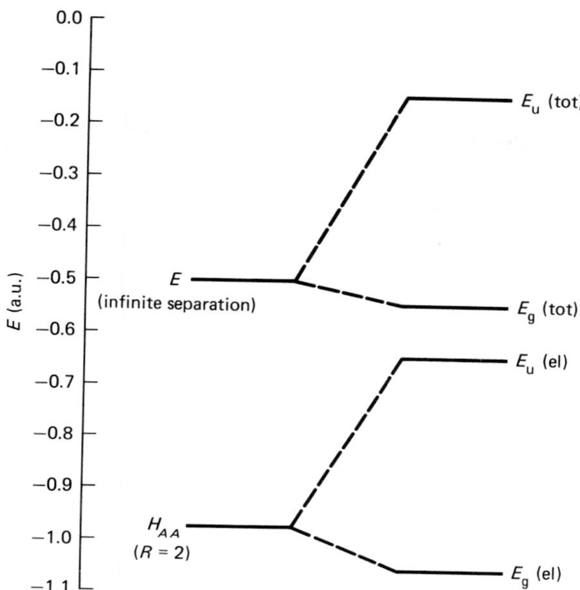

FIG. 14-2 Total and electronic energies for bonding and antibonding states of H_2^+ compared to appropriate reference energies.

whereas the exact values of E_g(el) and E_u(el) respectively, approach the united atom He^+ energies of -2 a.u. (1s) and -0.5 a.u. ($2p_\sigma$), and the cancellation ultimately breaks down.]

From this discussion of H_2^+, the following ideas emerge:

(1) The energy of an MO is lowered by bonding interactions, raised by antibonding interactions, relative to the appropriate reference energy.

(2) Antibonding interactions are inherently more destabilizing than bonding interactions are stabilizing.

(3) A parallel exists between electronic energy change and total energy change if we are careful about reference energies and internuclear distances.

But H_2^+ is atypical of the systems we will be interested in treating by QMOT. We will usually be considering neutral, many-electron systems, and H_2^+ is a charged, one-electron system. Therefore, we turn next to the molecule H_2 to consider how well the above ideas carry over to a more typical system.

14-4 H_2: Comparisons with H_2^+

We first consider the ramifications of the neutrality and nonpolarity of H_2. Imagine that we have a ground-state hydrogen atom H_a and we allow another similar atom, H_b, to approach it. At values of R in excess of, say, 2 a.u., we expect the perturbation felt by H_a to be much smaller than was the case in our H_2^+ discussion. This is because, where before we had approach by a *charged* particle, here we have approach by a neutral atom. The attraction between the electron on H_a and the proton on H_b is counterbalanced by repulsion between the electron on H_a and that on H_b. This means that the frozen atom-in-molecule energy for H_2 is fairly close to the energy of the isolated atom. This simplifies our qualitative treatment for neutral molecules since it means we can meaningfully compare molecular electronic energies directly with unperturbed atomic electronic energies.

We now come to a consideration of the orbital energies of H_2. Here we will find that there are important differences between a one-electron system like H_2^+ and multielectronic systems. Consider the lowest ($1\sigma_g$) MO of H_2. According to the description of *ab initio* theory in Chapter 11, the "energy of" this MO at some internuclear separation R [call it $E_{1\sigma_g}(R)$] is equal to the energy of an electron *in* this MO (i.e., the orbital energy is equal to the one-electron energy). This energy results from kinetic and nuclear attraction components and from repulsion for the other electron. *But where is this other electron*? If we are considering the ground state of H_2, it is in the $1\sigma_g$ MO also. That gives us an energy we might call $E_{1\sigma_g}(R, 1\sigma_g^2)$. However, we might instead be considering an excited state of H_2, perhaps with the configuration $1\sigma_g 1\sigma_u$. Depending on whether we choose the symmetric or antisymmetric combination for the spatial part of the wavefunction, we shall be considering an excited singlet or triplet state. In each case, repulsion for the $1\sigma_g$ electron will be different. Thus, we already have three orbital energies for this lowest MO, and we could continue getting more by considering other excited states of H_2. Clearly, the orbital energies in a multielectronic molecule are dependent on the state being considered.

Another important feature of one-electron energies in multielectronic systems is that they do not add up to the total electronic energy. That is, $2E_{1\sigma_g}(R, 1\sigma_g^2)$ is not equal to the electronic energy of H_2 at R. As pointed out in Chapter 11, this is because $E_{1\sigma_g}(E, 1\sigma_g^2)$ includes the interelectronic repulsion, so $2E_{1\sigma_g}(R, 1\sigma_g^2)$ counts the interelectronic repulsion twice.

One might imagine that, since MO energies in multielectronic systems are state-dependent and cannot be simply summed to give the electronic energy, it is hopeless to use them as a basis for explanation or prediction. However, this would be too pessimistic. It turns out that the *qualitative* features of MO energies are not all that sensitive to change of state (see Fig. 14-3) and, besides, we are usually concerned with the ground state or with excited states wherein most of the electrons remain in orbitals occupied in the ground state. Also, the extra measure of interelectronic repulsion that is included in the sum of one-electron energies can sometimes be expected to compensate roughly for the as yet unincluded internuclear repulsion energy. This rough equality requires that our system be neutral (so that the total number of repelling negative charges is equal

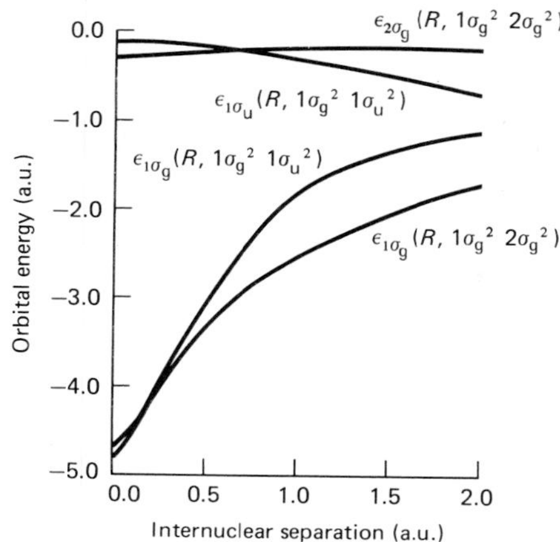

FIG. 14-3 Orbital energies as function of internuclear separation for He_2. The two curves for $E_{1\sigma_g}$ are qualitatively similar, although far from identical. (From Yarkony and Schaefer [1].)

to the total amount of positive charge) and nonpolar (so that the loci of charge are similar). We expect the equality to be quite good at large internuclear separation, where the electrons of each atom repel those of others as though they were centered on the nuclei, and to become progressively poorer as the atoms get closer together and undergo interpenetration of charge clouds. If we accept this rough equality, then we are permitted to approximate the change in *total* energy of the system (when the nuclei move), as equal to the change in the sum of one-electron energies.[1]

14-5 Rules for Qualitative Molecular Orbital Theory

The considerations discussed in the two preceding sections provide a rather loose justification for the following QMOT rules related to *total energy changes when nuclei are moved.*

(1) An increase in overlap population between two AOs tends to lower the energy of an MO; a decrease tends to raise it.

(2) The effects of a given amount of orbital overlap population change on orbital energy are much more pronounced for higher-energy MOs. A corollary is: The destabilizing effect of an antibonding relation between two AOs tends to be greater than the stabilizing effect of a bonding relation, other factors (AO identities, distances) being equal.

(3) The sum of changes of one-electron energies should approximately equal the *total* energy change if we are treating a neutral, nonpolar system and if

[1] For recent comments on this point, see Ruedenberg [2].

the nuclei that are moving with respect to each other are separated by a distance of a normal bond length or more.

Rule (2) and its corollary are due to the different effect of renormalization on orbitals of different energy. Note that rule three refers only to energy *changes*. We do *not* expect the sum of one-electron energies to equal the total energy. This becomes obvious in the limit of infinite separation of atoms (e.g., in CO_2) in which there is no internuclear repulsion, but interelectron repulsion *within* each atom is still being counted twice.

These rules are normally applied only to MOs made from valence-shell AOs. Inner-shell electrons are only very weakly perturbed in normal nuclear motions. The resulting small changes, while detectable and useful for analytical purposes, are inconsequential compared with valence electron effects.

14-6 Application of QMOT Rules to Homonuclear Diatomic Molecules

If we apply our rules from the preceding section to the motion of a pair of identical nuclei, each carrying a 1s AO, we obtain the orbital energy versus *R* curve shown in Fig. 14-4. The σ_g MO energy is predicted to drop as overlap

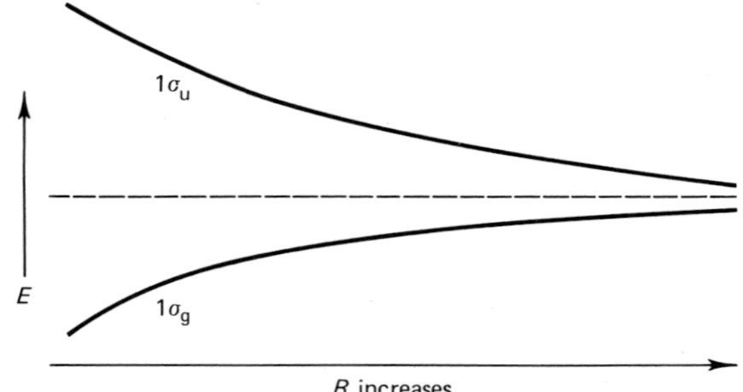

FIG. 14-4 Energy versus internuclear separation *R* for two nuclei with 1s AOs derived from QMOT rules.

population increases, the σ_u to rise as out-of-phase overlap increases, and σ_u rises faster than σ_g drops. In QMOT, we argue from this figure that one-, two-, or three-electron homonuclear diatomic molecules should be stable (H_2^+, H_2, H_2^-, He_2^+) and that four-electron molecules (He_2) should be unstable. Since a similar figure holds for molecules in which the valence orbital is 2s, 3s, etc., we might also expect systems like Li_2^+, Li_2, Li_2^-, Be_2^+, Na_2^+, Na_2, Na_2^-, Mg_2^+ to exist, but not Be_2 or Mg_2. This set of predictions is a reasonable starting point, and in many cases agrees with observation (see e.g., Table 7-2). By the time we get to the Na–Mg series, however, the energy difference between 3s and 3p AOs is so small that it is unrealistic to treat these as "pure" 3s cases. Consequently, we must put less faith in simple predictions for those molecules. The comparison between our QMOT guess about these molecules and experimental or *ab initio* observation is shown in Table 14-1.

TABLE 14-1
Stability of Some Homonuclear Diatomics as Predicted by QMOT and as Observed from Experiment or ab Initio *Calculation*

Molecule	QMOT	Experimental or *ab initio*	Molecule	QMOT	Experimental or *ab initio*
H_2^+	Stable	Stable	Be_2^+	Stable	Stable
H_2	Stable	Stable	Be_2	Not stable	Not stable
H_2^-	Stable	Stable[a]	Na_2^+	Stable	Stable
He_2^+	Stable	Stable	Na_2	Stable	Stable
He_2	Not stable	Not stable	Na_2^-	Stable	?
Li_2^+	Stable	Stable	Mg_2^+	Stable	?
Li_2	Stable	Stable	Mg_2	Not stable	Stable (?)
Li_2^-	Stable	Stable			

[a] This molecule–ion is unstable with respect to losing an electron and forming this neutral molecule at its lowest energy, but it is stable with respect to dissociation into a neutral atom and a negative ion in their ground states.

The reader may have noticed that we have violated one of our QMOT conditions by considering nonneutral systems. One is presumably less safe in including such systems, although several of them have been studied and found to fit the QMOT prediction. Apparently, if one is concerned only with the question of the presence or absence of a valley in the total energy curve (and not with relative depths of valleys or relative R_e values), deviation from neutrality by *one* electron is not too damaging. However, for doubly positive diatomics, like He_2^{2+}, the internuclear repulsion dominates so that there is no stable species.

One can add p-type AOs to the two nuclei and expand the orbital energy plot, as illustrated in Fig. 14-5. Filling in the orbital levels with electrons leads to the prediction that B_2 is singly bonded, C_2 is doubly bonded, N_2 triply bonded, O_2 doubly bonded, F_2 singly bonded, and Ne_2 not bonded. These systems, with their singly charged relatives, have been described in Chapter 7, and we will say no more about them here except that the agreement between QMOT rules and observations is quite respectable (see Fig. 14-6).

An important distinction exists between the energy versus R curves drawn in Fig. 14-5 and those in Fig. 7-17. The latter set was constructed by sketching orbital energies for the united-atom and separated-atom limits, and linking these energies together using symmetry agreement and the noncrossing rule. The former set was constructed by sketching orbital energies for the separated atoms, and then using QMOT rules to decide which curves go up, and which go

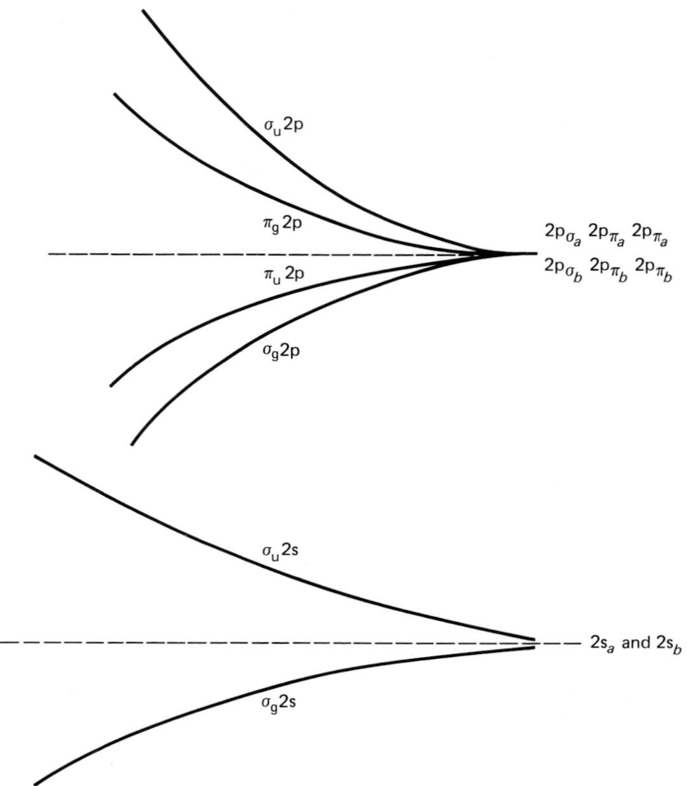

FIG. 14-5 Qualitative sketches of homonuclear diatomic MO energies as a function of *R* based on QMOT rules.

down in energy as *R* decreases. When we wish to emphasize this distinction, we will refer to these as *two-sided* and *one-sided* correlation diagrams, respectively.

According to the simple QMOT viewpoint, we should expect a bonding MO to be lower in energy than the AOs that comprise it. Likewise, an antibonding MO should be higher in energy. We can test this by comparing first ionization potentials (IPs) for molecules against those for the constituent atoms. (Recall that Koopmans' theorem equates orbital energy to ionization potential.) If the highest occupied MO (HOMO) of the molecule is bonding, the IP for the molecule should be greater than that for the atom. If it is antibonding, the IP of the molecule should be smaller. Strictly speaking, the HOMO of the molecule may consist of mixtures of AOs on each atom. In that case, we should compute a "valence state ionization potential" for the atom. Also, for heteronuclear molecules AB, we need to know what percentage of the HOMO to identify

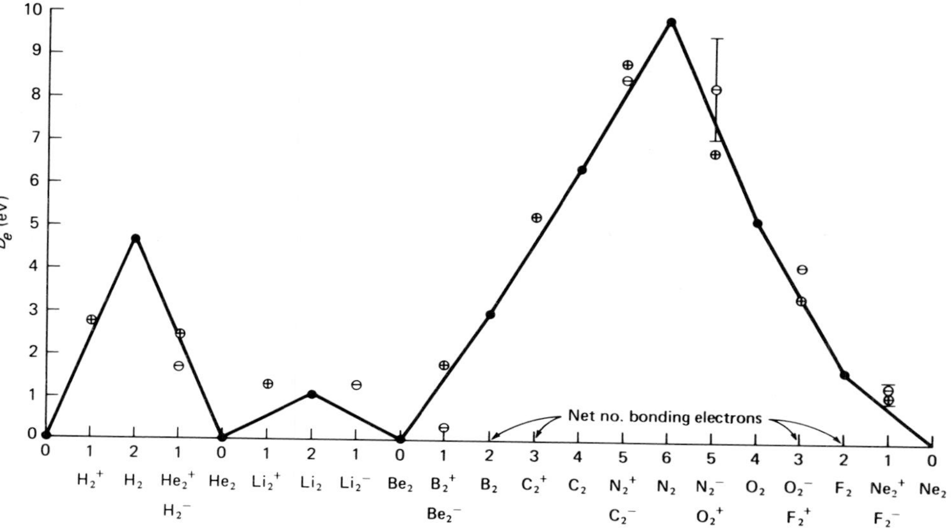

FIG. 14-6 D_e versus *aufbau* sequence for homonuclear diatomic molecules and ions. The tendency for systems having more net bonding electrons to have a greater D_e is adhered to fairly well (see Table 7-2 for data).

with each atom in order to obtain a suitable average atomic IP to compare with the IP of the molecule. Even if we ignore these corrections, however, and simply compare experimental IPs, the anticipated behavior is shown nicely by diatomic molecules, as indicated in Table 14-2.

There is much similarity between the QMOT rules and the assumptions inherent in the extended Hückel method described in Chapter 10. There, also, a bonding interaction is equated with energy lowering and an antibonding interaction with an energy rise. Furthermore, the sum of orbital energies is assumed to change in parallel with the *total* energy change, even though the internuclear repulsion is not included. We noted that this assumption limits the range of validity for EHMO calculations to relative nuclear motions at distances that are on the order of a bond length or greater. The EHMO method is, in essence, the numerical equivalent to the qualitative MO approach, and such calculations can serve as a guide for developing qualitative explanations in complicated situations or for producing numbers which enable one to compare QMOT with experimental or *ab initio* results.

14-7 Shapes of Polyatomic Molecules: Walsh Diagrams

In this section we will describe how the rules and concepts of QMOT enable one to rationalize and predict molecular shapes. The earliest systematic

TABLE 14-2

Comparison of Molecular and Atomic First Ionization Potentials[a]

Molecule	HOMO bonding (b) or antibonding (a)	IP (eV)	IP of molecule expected $>$ or $<$ than atomic average	IP atoms	Does experiment agree with theory?
H_2	b	15.427	$>$	13.598	Yes
He_2	a	~22.0	$<$	24.46	Yes
Li_2	b	5.12	$>$	5.363	No
B_2	b	~ 9.5	$>$	8.257	Yes
C_2	b	12.0 ± 0.6	$>$	11.267	Yes
N_2	b	15.576	$>$	14.549	Yes
O_2	a	12.06	$<$	13.618	Yes
F_2	a	15.7	$<$	17.426	Yes
Ne_2	a	20.1	$<$	21.47	Yes
Si_2	b	7.4 ± 0.3	$>$	8.15	No
Cl_2	a	11.48 ± 0.1	$<$	13.02	Yes
Br_2	a	10.53	$<$	11.85	Yes
I_2	a	9.3	$<$	10.457	Yes
CN	b	14.5 ± 0.5	$>$	11.27 (C), 14.55 (N)	Yes
NO	a	9.25	$<$	13.62 (O), 14.55 (N)	Yes
CO	b	14.013	$>$	13.62 (O), 11.27 (C)	Yes
CS	b	11.8, 11.9	$>$	11.27 (C), 10.36 (S)	Yes
ICl	a	10.3	$<$	10.46 (I), 13.02 (Cl)	Yes
IBr	a	9.98	$<$	10.46 (I), 11.85 (Br)	Yes

[a] Data are from [3] or from Table 7-2.

treatment of this problem was given by Walsh,[2] whose approach has been extended by others, particularly Gimarc [6].[3]

We begin by considering the symmetric triatomic class of molecules HAH, where A is any atom. Such molecules can be linear or bent. Walsh's approach predicts which are linear, which are bent, and sometimes which of two bent molecules is more bent.

We approach the problem in the following way. First we sketch the valence MOs for the generalized linear molecule HAH, deciding which is lowest, second lowest, etc. in energy. Then we imagine bending the molecule and argue whether each MO should go up or down in energy on the basis of our QMOT rules. This produces a chart of orbital energies versus bond angle—a one-sided correlation diagram. Finally, we use this diagram to argue that HAH will be linear or bent, depending on how many valence electrons HAH has and on how they are distributed among the MOs.

The first problem is to sketch the MOs for linear HAH and decide their energy order. Probably the simplest way to do this is through use of symmetry and perturbation arguments. We know that the linear molecule belongs to the $D_{\infty h}$ point group, possessing a center of inversion and a reflection plane through the central atom and perpendicular to the HAH axis. Therefore, the two hydrogen 1s AOs ($1s_1$ and $1s_2$) will appear in MOs in the symmetry combinations $\phi_g = 1s_1 + 1s_2$, $\phi_u = 1s_1 - 1s_2$, where g and u stand for *gerade* and *ungerade*, respectively (see Chapters 7 and 13 for a background discussion). Therefore, we will consider which MOs will result from interactions between the valence AOs on atom A and the symmetry orbitals ϕ_g and ϕ_u. A perturbation-type diagram for this appears in Fig. 14-7. We have assumed that only the valence s and p AOs on A are involved in bonding. Extension to include d AOs is possible.

On the right side of Fig. 14-7, the symmetry orbitals ϕ_g and ϕ_u are shown to be slightly split. This reflects the greater stability of the in-phase, or bonding, combination. However, the splitting is slight because the hydrogen atoms are quite far apart (so that atom A can fit between them). These two levels sandwich the separated-atom limit of $-\frac{1}{2}$ a.u. or -13.6 eV.

The AOs of atom A are sketched on the left. Their energies are arranged so that the 2p energies are about the same as the ϕ_g, ϕ_u symmetry orbital energies on the left. (For example, AO energies used for nitrogen in EHMO calculations are: 2s ~ -25 eV, 2p ~ -13 eV.) For the linear molecule, we can label the s and p AOs as σ or π and g or u.

To generate the MO energy level pattern from the interactions between these AOs on A and ϕ_g, ϕ_u, we use the following rules from perturbation theory (see Chapter 12):

(1) interactions occur only between orbitals of identical symmetry,

[2] See Walsh [4] and the papers immediately following. See also Mulliken [5].

[3] For a critical review of the theoretical validity of Walsh's method, see Buenker and Peyerimhoff [7].

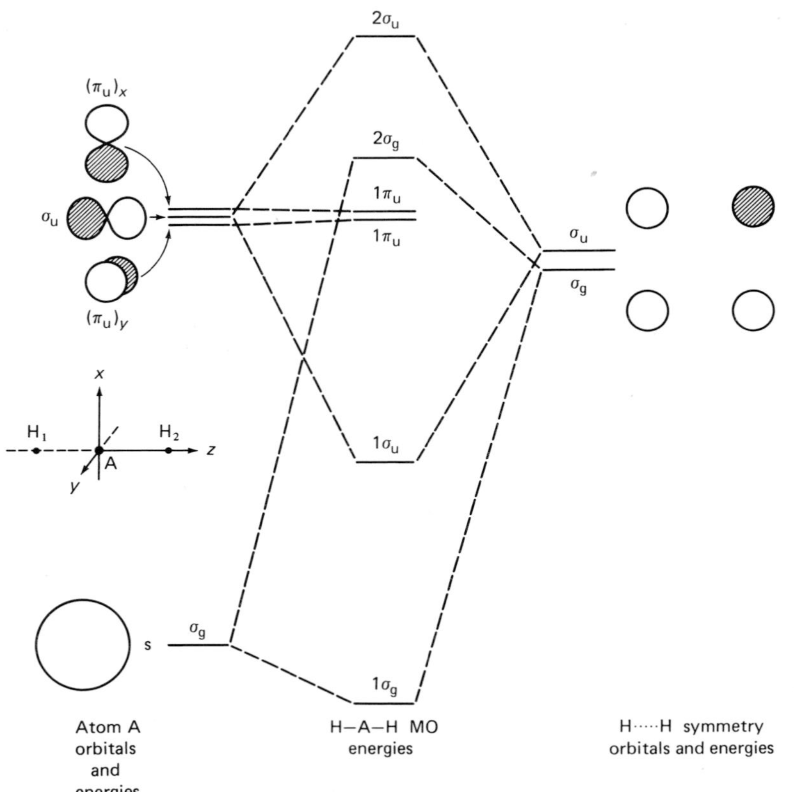

FIG. 14-7 Orbital energies of MOs formed by interaction of σ_u and σ_g symmetry orbitals on $H_1 \cdots H_2$ with valence s and p AOs on central atom A.

(2) interactions lead to larger splittings if the interacting orbitals are closer in energy (overlap considerations being equal).

The resulting energy levels appear in the central column of Fig. 14-7.

We need sketches of the MOs whose energy level pattern we have just approximated. We can guess the qualitative appearance of these by recalling that, when two orbitals interact to give splitting, the lower energy corresponds to a bonding interaction, the higher energy to antibonding. Thus, for example, Fig. 14-7 indicates that the $1\sigma_g$ MO is a bonding combination of the 2s AO on A and the σ_g symmetry orbital, whereas $2\sigma_g$ is the antibonding combination. The π_u MOs are simply the p_π AOs on A, since there is nothing of the same symmetry for them to interact with. The six MOs for the HAH molecule are sketched in Fig. 14-8a.

Before proceeding, notice that the lowest two MOs are A–H bonding,

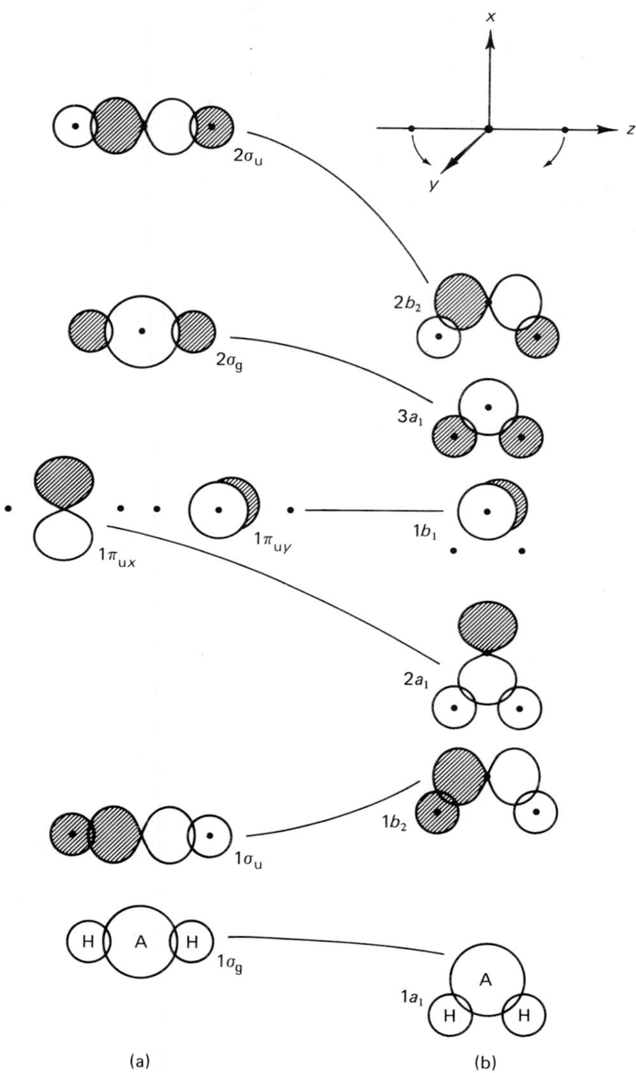

FIG. 14-8 The Walsh-type correlation diagram for HAH: (a) linear $D_{\infty h}$; (b) bent C_{2v}. The cross-hatched parts of MOs have opposite sign from open parts.

the next two are nonbonding, the highest two are antibonding. This is an example of the way in which topological, or nearest-neighbor, interactions govern the gross features of energy ordering. In fact, we could have generated this same set of MOs and energy order by simply sketching all of the MOs we could think of that were symmetric or antisymmetric for relevant symmetry operations and then putting the bonding ones lowest (with s lower than p), nonbonding next, and antibonding highest (again recognizing that greater s character should yield lower energy). (Note that the nonbonding MOs are not symmetric or antisymmetric for arbitrary rotations about the C_∞ axis. Hence, they must form a basis for a representation of dimension greater than one. Hence, they are degenerate. See Chapter 13 for detailed discussion.) Electrons in the two lowest MOs produce A–H bonding. Electrons in the next two MOs have little effect on A–H bonding and, in fact, constitute what a chemist normally thinks of as lone pairs. Electrons in the two highest MOs tend to weaken the A–H bonds. We normally do not worry about questions of shape for systems where these highest two MOs are filled because such an HAH system is not even bonded (i.e., we do not worry about second-order structure if there is no stable first-order structure). Consequently, these two highest MOs will be omitted in many energy-versus-angle diagrams, although there are certain cases where they can be useful (e.g., in singly excited configurations) (see Problem 14-5).

We now consider how the MO energies change upon bending the molecule. As $1\sigma_g$ is bent, the two hydrogen AOs move closer together. Because they have the same phase, this leads to an overlap increase, but it occurs over a fairly long distance, being a second-nearest neighbor interaction. Therefore, there is an energy lowering, but it is not very large. Bending $1\sigma_u$ leads to two changes. First, the 1s AOs move away from the axis of maximum concentration of the 2p AO. This causes a substantial loss of overlap and a substantial increase in energy. Second, the 1s AOs move closer to each other. They disagree in phase, and this also tends to increase the energy, although it is a relatively small effect because it occurs between second-nearest neighbors. In the linear molecule, $1\pi_{ux}$ and $1\pi_{uy}$ MOs contained no contribution from hydrogen 1s because the hydrogens are in a nodal plane in each case. If we imagine that, in bending the molecule, we keep the hydrogens in the xz plane, then we see that the hydrogens are remaining in the nodal plane for $1\pi_{uy}$, but have moved away from the nodal plane of $1\pi_{ux}$. Once this happens, the 1s AOs are no longer forbidden by symmetry from contributing to the π_x MO, and a "growing in" of 1s AOs occurs, leading to an MO like the $2a_1$ MO drawn in Fig. 14-8. This behavior is more complicated than we observed for the lower-energy MOs because it involves more than a mere distortion of an existing MO. With a little experience, this additional complication is easily predicted (or, one can do an EHMO calculation and "peek" at the answer by sketching out the MOs contained in the output; see Problem 14-6). The effect on the energy is quite large because several things happen, all of which are energy lowering:

(1) For a given amount of 1s AO, the bonding overlap with 2p increases with bending.

(2) For a given amount of 1s AO, the bonding overlap between the two hydrogens increases with bending.

(3) Since the amount of 1s AO present is not constant, but increases with bending (from zero in the linear configuration) the rate of energy lowering due to (1) and (2) is further augmented.

Also, this is a fairly high-energy MO, and QMOT rule (3) tells us to expect such MOs to respond more dramatically to overlap changes. Finally, the overlap of a 1s AO with a 2p AO on another nucleus varies as $\cos\theta$, where θ is zero when the 2p AO points directly at the 1s AO. This means that the *rate of change of overlap with angle* is much greater around $\theta = 90°$ than at $\theta = 0°$ (see Problem 14-8). This is another reason for thinking that $1\pi_{ux} \rightarrow 2a_1$ will drop in energy much faster than $1\sigma_u \rightarrow 1b_2$ will rise.

The other π MO, $1\pi_{uy}$, undergoes no changes in overlap since the hydrogen atoms remain in the nodal plane throughout the bending process. Therefore, QMOT arguments do not predict any energy change for this MO.

The highest two MOs change in energy in ways that should be obvious to the reader, based on the above examples. Since these are the highest-energy MOs, they should show further enhanced sensitivity to overlap changes.

The MOs for the bent form are labeled in accordance with the symmetry notation for the C_{2v} point group, with a and b meaning symmetric and antisymmetric, respectively, for rotation about the twofold axis and 1 and 2 being analogous symbols for reflection in the plane containing the C_2 axis and perpendicular to the molecular plane. The lowest valence MO of each symmetry type is numbered "1" despite the fact that lower-energy inner-shell orbitals exist.

Because of the very qualitative nature of the arguments leading to Fig. 14-8, no effort is made to attach a numerical scale, either for energy or angle.

We are now in a position to see how predictions based on our Walsh-type correlation diagram compare with experimental data. For molecules having only one or two valence electrons, we expect the preferred shape in the ground state to be bent. Examples are H_3^+ and LiH_2^+, both of which have been shown by experiment and/or accurate calculation to be bent. Molecules with three or four valence electrons should be linear, since the $1\sigma_u - 1b_2$ energy rise is much greater than the change in the lower MO. Examples are BeH_2^+, BeH_2, and BH_2^+, which are indeed linear. Addition of one or two more electrons now brings the $1\pi_u - 2a_1$ MO into play, and we have already argued that the energy change of this MO should be considerably greater than that of $1\sigma_u - 1b_2$. Basically we have here a competition between a filled MO that favors the linear form and a higher, partially or completely filled MO favoring the bent form. We therefore might reasonably expect molecules in which $2a_1$ is *singly* occupied to be bent, and molecules in which it is *doubly* occupied to be *more* bent. Occupancy of the $1\pi_u - 1b_1$ MO should have no effect on angle. Thus, that a molecule like $BH_2(1a_1)^2(1b_2)^2(2a_1)$ has an equilibrium bond angle of 131°, whereas $SiH_2(1a_1)^2(1b_2)^2(2a_1)^2$ has an angle of 97°, $NH_2(1a_1)^2(1b_2)^2(2a_1)^2(1b_1)$ has 103°

and $H_2O(1a_1)^2(1b_2)^2(2a_1)^2(1b_1)^2$ has 105° is in pleasing accord with these simple ideas.

Changes of angle upon electronic excitation also agree well with the correlation diagram. The triplet state of SiH_2 resulting from the $2a_1 \rightarrow 1b_1$ excitation has a wider angle (124°) than does the ground state (97°). The excited singlet corresponding to the same excitation has a comparable angle (126°). NH_2, when excited from $\ldots(2a_1)^2(1b_1)$ to $(2a_1)(1b_1)^2$ opens from 103 to 144°. The isoelectronic PH_2, under similar excitation, opens from 92 to 123°. There are other examples to support the validity of the HAH diagram, but these suffice to illustrate that this qualitative approach has considerable generality and utility. Note again that singly charged cations appear to fit QMOT predictions despite the fact that there is less theoretical basis for success here.

Walsh-type correlation diagrams have been constructed and discussed for many systems, among them AH_3, HAB, HAAH, BAAB, H_2AAH_2, B_2AAB_2, H_3AAH_3.[4] It is not appropriate that these all be described here. We will briefly discuss two more cases that bring in some additional features.

Molecules with HAB configuration lack the high symmetry of HAH, and this means that the MOs are not as highly symmetry determined as in HAH. Probably the simplest way to arrive at sketches for linear HAB MOs is to start with AB MOs (similar to A_2 MOs) and add the 1s AO of H in bonding and antibonding modes to form linear MOs. The results for the seven lowest-energy MOs (all A–H bonding or nonbonding) are seen at the left side of Fig. 14-9. (Diatomic MOs were discussed in Chapter 7.)

We now imagine the hydrogen atom to move away from the AB axis, as shown, and use our QMOT rules to decide whether the energies should rise or fall. As before, we expect overlap changes between H and A (nearest neighbors) to have a greater effect on energy than those between H and B.

The bent molecule has only one symmetry element, namely a reflection plane containing the nuclei. An a' MO is symmetric under this reflection, a'' is antisymmetric. This paucity of symmetry types means that many of the correlation lines in the diagram refer to the same symmetry. Hence, it is not too surprising that some of our correlations run into conflict with the noncrossing rule. In Fig. 14-9, dashed lines are drawn from 3σ to $4a'$ and from $1\pi_x$ to $3a'$. These dashed lines connect the MO drawings in the manner expected if we ignore the noncrossing rule and simply bend the MOs along with the molecule. They are, as it were, *intended* correlations. But these lines are associated with the same symmetry a' and hence cannot cross. Instead we have an *avoided* crossing, as 3σ switches course and connects with $3a'$ and $1\pi_x$ goes to $4a'$ (solid lines in Fig. 14-9). Avoided crossings are not uncommon in quantum chemistry, and they occur in curves referring to *state energy* as well as orbital energy. A generalized sketch exemplifying the idea is shown in Fig. 14-10. The actual energy change

[4] See Gimarc [6].

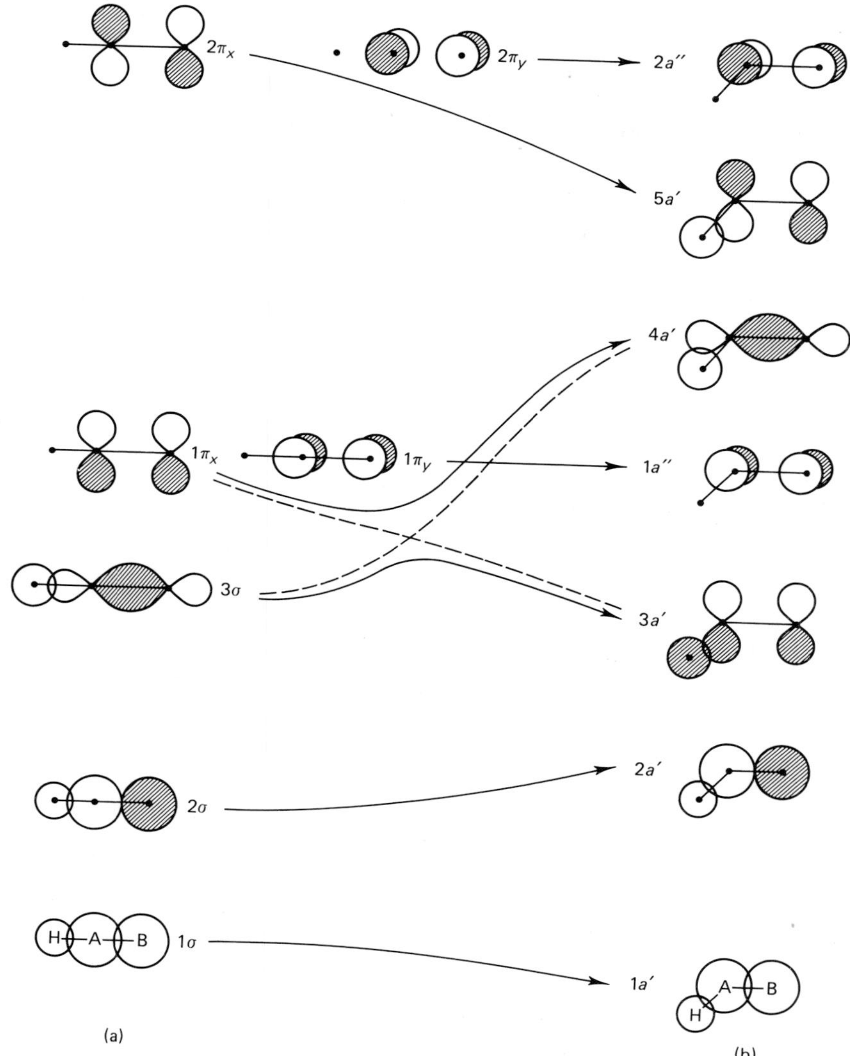

FIG. 14-9 The Walsh-type diagram for the HAB system: (a) linear $C_{\infty v}$; (b) bent C_s. (After Gimarc [6].) Reprinted with permission from *Accounts Chem. Res.* **7**, 384 (1974). Copyright by the American Chemical Society.

(as a function of bond length, angle change, or whatever process is occurring) may show an intermediate maximum or minimum as a result of the avoided crossing. (The dashed lines are energies we predict by "forgetting" to allow the two functions of the same symmetry to be mixed in the variational procedure. The error involved in this is small if the two functions are of dissimilar energy.

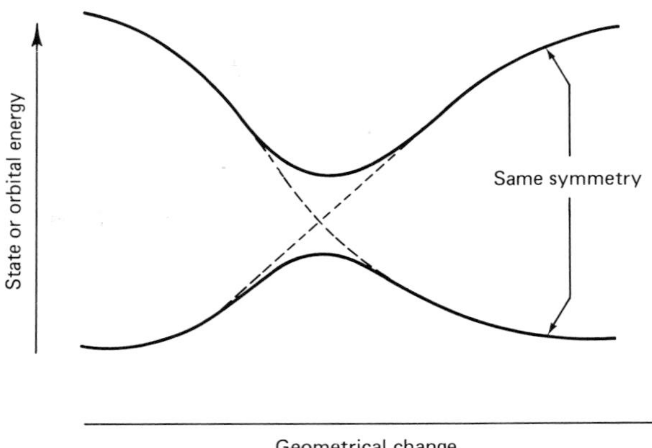

FIG. 14-10 Intended (dotted lines) and actual correlations between orbitals or states having the same symmetry.

As they grow closer in energy, the error grows worse, and the deviation between solid and dashed lines gets bigger as the dashed lines converge.)

A classic example of such an intermediate maximum is seen in an excited state of H_2, illustrated in Fig. 14-11. Such minima are important in understanding high-energy processes because they provide a means for some molecules to exist in bound vibrational states even while unstable with respect to dissociation products. Such states are called *metastable* states.

The HAB Walsh diagram of Fig. 14-9 rationalizes the fact that the ten-valence electron HCN is linear in the ground state (due to $1\pi_x - 4a'$) but bent in the first excited state. Such molecules as HNO, HNF, and HOCl, with 12–14 electrons, are bent in both ground and excited states because there is always at least one electron in the $5a'$ level.

The final system we shall consider is the H_3AAH_3 system. We will show how QMOT can be used to understand why diborane (B_2H_6) has a bridged structure whereas ethane (C_2H_6) does not, why ethane prefers to be staggered (D_{3d}) rather than eclipsed (D_{3h}), and what geometry changes we might expect if ethane is forced into the eclipsed conformation.

Gimarc's diagram relating MOs for A_2H_6 in D_{3d} staggered and D_{2h} bridged shapes is shown in Fig. 14-12. The MOs on the left are all A–H bonding and are arranged pretty much in the order one would expect on the basis of the A–A bonding. The lowest two are composed mainly of valence s AOs on atoms A. Next come the π bonding combinations, then the p_σ bond, followed finally by the π antibonds. The $1e_u$ π bonding levels lie below the $2a_{1g}p_\sigma$ bonding level because the former have greater ability to overlap with the hydrogens.

There are only two MOs that show much energy change as we distort from D_{3d} to D_{2h} geometry. These are the $2a_{1g} \rightarrow 2a_g$ and the $1e_g \rightarrow 1b_{2g}$. In the

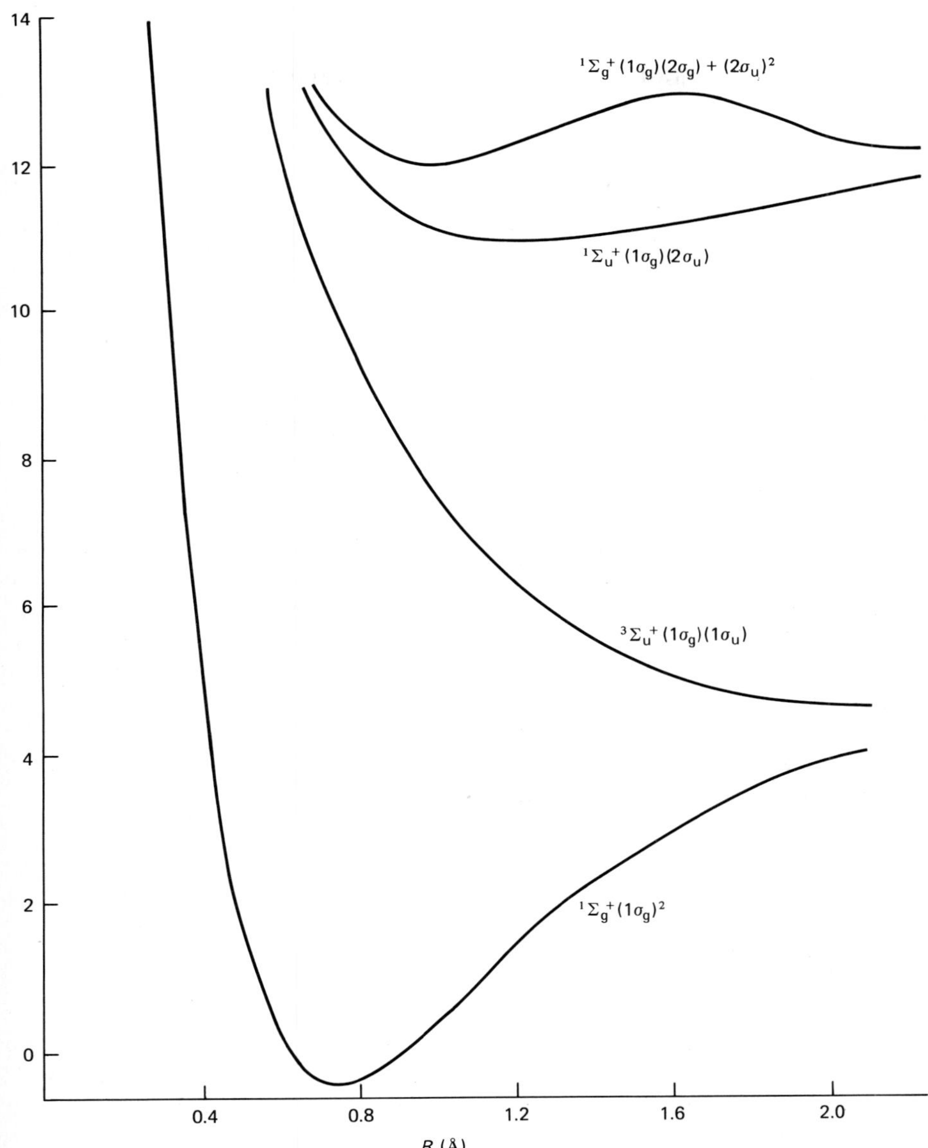

FIG. 14-11 The four lowest states of H_2. Note the curve for the first excited $^1\Sigma_g{}^+$ state. This shape results from an avoided crossing. (From Sharp [8].)

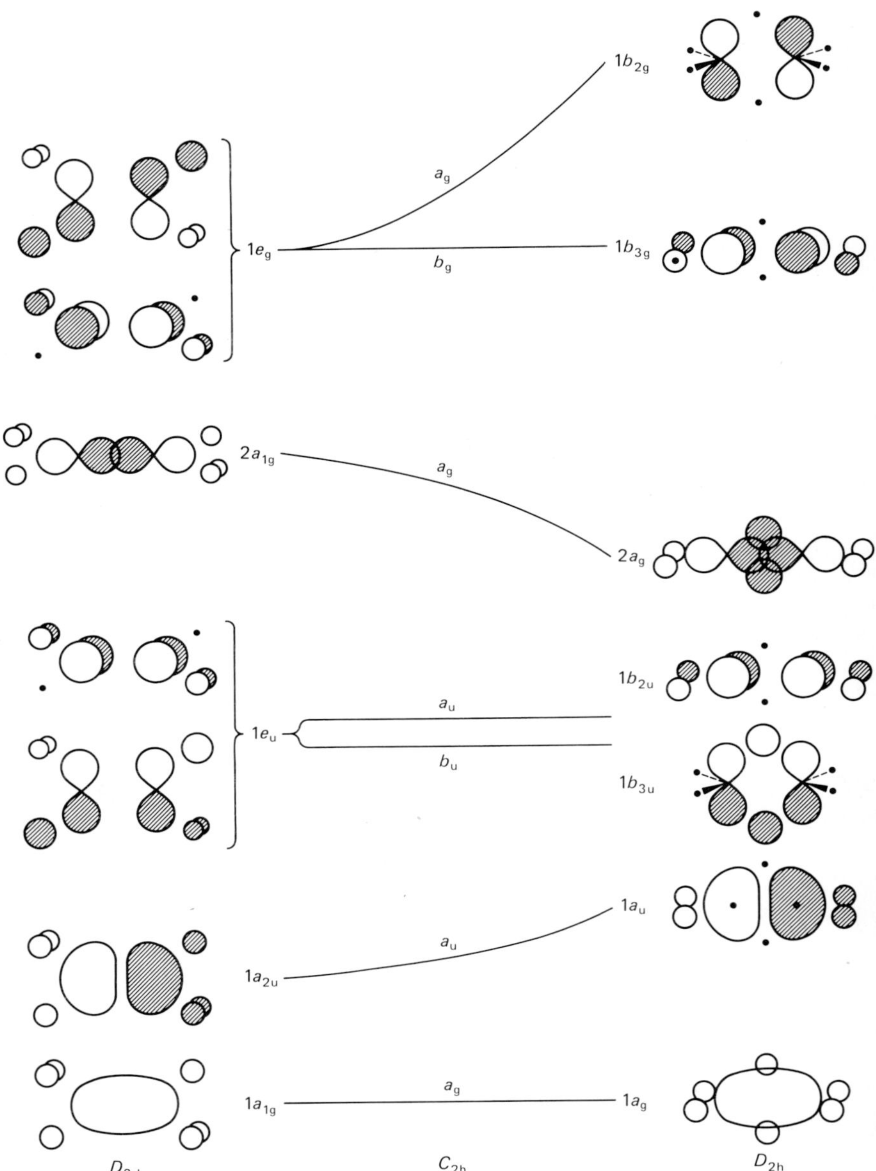

FIG. 14-12 Walsh-type correlation diagram for D_{3d}–D_{2h} shapes of H_3AAH_3. (After Gimarc [6].) Reprinted with permission from *Accounts Chem. Res.* **7**, 384 (1974). Copyright by the American Chemical Society.

former case, the energy drops because two hydrogens have moved from positions off-axis of one p lobe into positions off axis of two p lobes, thereby increasing the total amount of overlap. The energy in the latter case rises very markedly because the change in geometry places all six hydrogens into nodal planes, greatly reducing the overlap.

The prediction is that a 10- or 12-valence electron A_2H_6 system should favor a bridged D_{2h} geometry over D_{3d} but a 14-valence electron system should prefer D_{3d} over D_{2h}. Diborane (12 valence electrons) and ethane (14) have structures consistent with this.

In structural problems such as this, one must be careful that, when comparing two possible molecular shapes, one is not overlooking other possibilities that might be even more stable. For instance, even though the diagram in Fig. 14-12 indicates that ethane should prefer D_{3d} geometry to D_{2h}, it says nothing about D_{3d} relative to D_{3h}, the open, eclipsed form. For this we must construct another diagram, shown in Fig. 14-13. Here the principal energy changes occur in the doubly degenerate *e*-type MOs. Recall that degenerate MOs need not be symmetric or antisymmetric for all symmetry operations of the molecular point group. This results, in this case, in the *e*-type MOs being much more unbalanced, or lopsided, than the nondegenerate *a*-type MOs. As a result, the overlap population changes upon rotation are much bigger for *e*- than for *a*-type MOs. The higher-energy $e_g - e''$ set of MOs dominates the lower energy $e_u - e'$ set for two reasons; it is at higher energy and hence more sensitive to overlap change, and the coefficients on the hydrogens are bigger due to the central nodal plane, which reduces the size of the MO in the A–A bond, forcing it to be larger elsewhere. In sum, a 14-valence electron A_2H_6 molecule prefers the staggered (D_{3d}) form because the long-range H····H antibonding in $1e''$ dominates the long range bonding in $1e'$. We can describe this as "nonbonded repulsion" between hydrogens at opposite ends of the molecule.

The energy changes in Fig. 14-12 are much larger than those in Fig. 14-13. In the former, we are charting energy changes associated with changes in bond angle and even molecular topology. Overlap changes are large and occur between nearest neighbors. In Fig. 14-13 we are charting energy changes associated with internal rotation. Here the overlap changes occur between third-nearest neighbors and are very small. The order in which the possibilities have been examined —D_{3d} versus D_{2h} followed by D_{3d} versus D_{3h}—is thus sensible in that we are considering the grosser energy changes first.

One can go even further and guess the qualitative changes in C–C, C–H distances and C–C–H angle if ethane is forced into the eclipsed conformation. We argue that the $1e_g \rightarrow 1e''$ pair of MOs suffer the greatest overlap change, losing population between the vicinal hydrogens. We must renormalize the MO to compensate for this loss, just as we had to in H_2^+, discussed earlier. To renormalize, the MO $1e''$ is multiplied by a factor slightly greater than unity. This magnifies the π antibond between the carbons and the C–H bonding in this

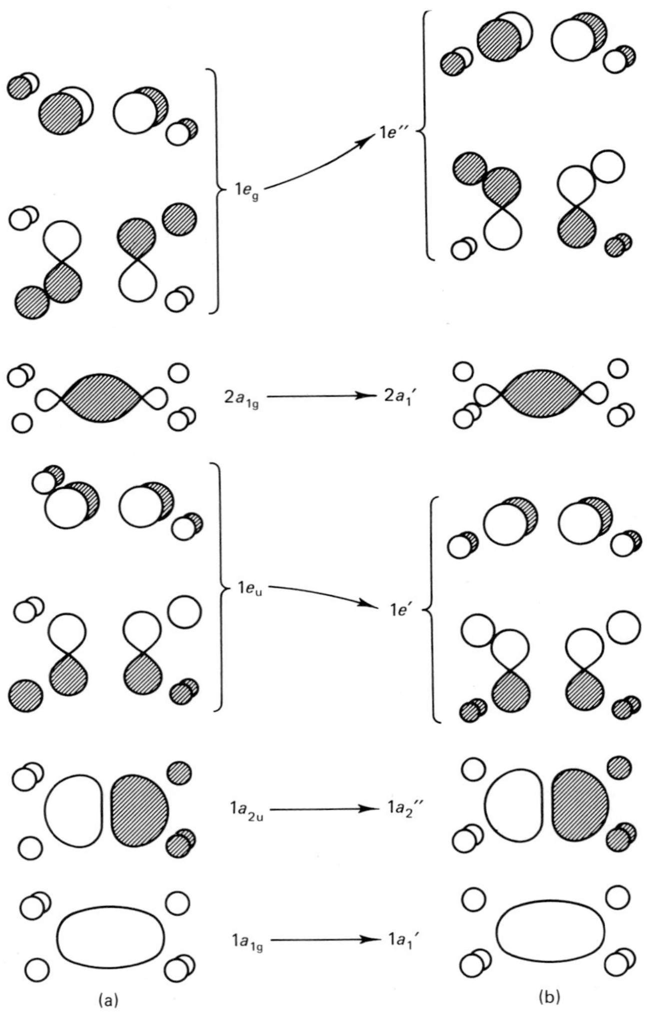

FIG. 14-13 Walsh-type diagram for D_{3d}–D_{3h} A_2H_6: (a) D_{3d} (staggered); (b) D_{3h} (eclipsed). Note that the *e*-type MOs for the two forms do not turn into each other by rotating about the C–C bond. This is really a two-sided correlation diagram, the high symmetry of each form determining the MOs. Then QMOT rules are used to decide how similar MOs on the two sides should relate in energy. (See Lowe [9].)

MO. Thus, we expect eclipsed ethane to have a slightly lengthened C–C bond, slightly shorter C–H bonds, and a larger C–C–H angle (the latter presumably mainly due to the increased vicinal repulsion brought about by overlap changes in the original rotation). *Ab initio* calculations[5] support these conclusions.

14-8 Frontier Orbitals

We have indicated that higher-energy MOs tend to undergo more pronounced energy changes upon overlap change due to distortion of the nuclear frame. This fact has led to a shortcut method for guessing the results of full orbital correlation diagrams of the sort we have already discussed. One merely considers what the energy behavior will be for the highest occupied MO (HOMO) and bases the prediction entirely on that MO, ignoring all the others. Fukui[6] was the first to draw attention to the special importance of the HOMO. He also noted that, in certain reactions in which the molecule in question acted as an electron acceptor, the lowest unfilled MO (LUMO) of the molecule (before it has accepted the electrons) is the important one. These two MOs are called the *frontier* MOs. It sometimes happens that the second-highest-energy occupied MO undergoes a much bigger overlap change than the HOMO does, and therefore dominates the process. Recognition of this fact has led to a special name for the MOs just below the HOMO and just above the LUMO. They are called *subjacent* and *superjacent* MOs (see Fig. 14-14).

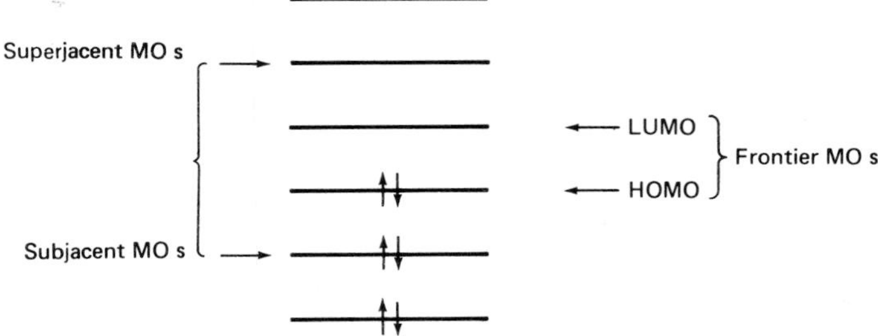

FIG. 14-14 HOMO and LUMO frontier MOs and subjacent and superjacent MOs.

An example of the frontier MO approach is provided by reconsidering the staggered versus eclipsed conformation for ethane. We expect the highest-energy, lopsided MO to be the π antibonding $e_g - e''$ degenerate pair. Qualitative molecular orbital theory rules lead us to expect this pair to have higher energy in the eclipsed form. Therefore, we expect ethane to be staggered.

The same approach can be used to predict the conformation of dimethylacetylene, $H_3C{-}C{\equiv}C{-}CH_3$. The HOMO is again a degenerate pair of π-type

[5] Stevens [10] finds that the C–C distance increases by 0.01 Å, the C–H distance decreases by 0.001 Å, and the C–C–H angle opens by 0.3°.

[6] See Fujimoto and Fukui [11].

MOs. (Generally speaking, one assumes that occupied π MOs are higher in energy than occupied σ MOs, and this is often true. Even when it is not, however, the π-type MOs often tend to be more lopsided and hence to dominate because their overlap changes are greater.) The two degenerate HOMOs are delocalized over the entire molecule and can be expected to have the following characteristics:

(1) They will be orthogonal to each other.

(2) They will be bonding in the central C≡C region, helping to establish multiple bond character there.

(3) They will be antibonding in the C—C single bond regions, thereby cancelling out double-bond character from a lower set of π-type MOs.

(4) They will be C–H bonding.

(Use of rules (2)–(4) often suffices to establish the qualitative nature of HOMOs of hydrocarbons.) The results of all these conditions are the MOs sketched in Fig. 14-15. Observe that the end-to-end hydrogen overlap is most positive in the

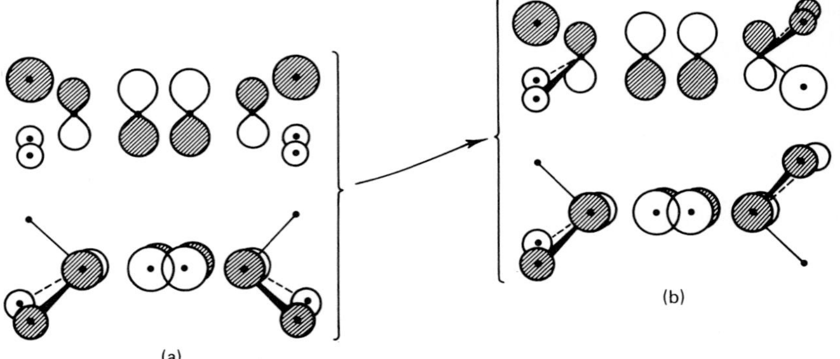

FIG. 14-15 Degenerate HOMOs for dimethylacetylene, (a) eclipsed, (b) staggered, lead to the prediction that this molecule should prefer the eclipsed conformation.

eclipsed conformation. This leads to the prediction that this molecule is more stable in the eclipsed conformation. Since the hydrogens are so far apart, the overlap change is expected to be very small. *Ab initio* calculations indicate that dimethylacetylene is more stable in the eclipsed form and that it has a barrier of less than 0.02 kcal/mole.

As another example of frontier orbital usage, consider the methyl rotation barrier in propene, H_3C—CH=CH_2. Here the HOMO should be π-bonding in the double bond, antibonding in the single bond, and C–H bonding in the methyl group. This MO is sketched in Fig. 14-16 for the two possible conformations. The end-to-end antibonding in this MO is greatest for case (b), and so conformation (a) is favored. Indeed, it has been observed that, *in general*, a threefold rotor attached to a double bond prefers to eclipse the double bond. A

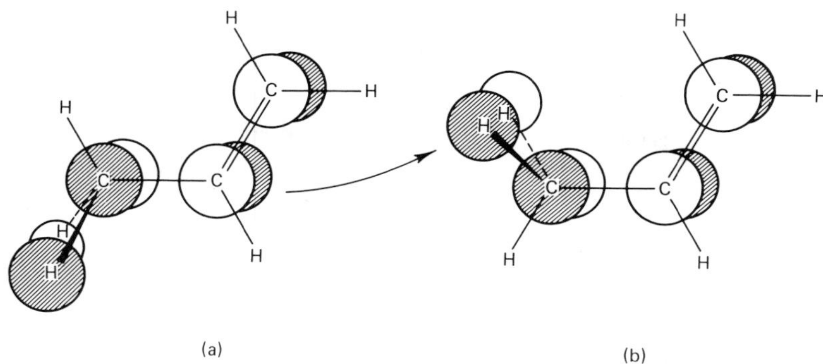

FIG. 14-16 HOMO of propene in two conformations. Methyl group (a) eclipses and (b) staggers the double bond. The energy is lower in (a).

few examples are acetaldehyde ($H_3C—CH{=}0$), *N*-methylformaldimine ($H_3C—N{=}CH_2$), nitrosomethane ($H_3C—N{=}O$), and vinyl silane ($H_3Si—CH{=}CH_2$).

Notice that the HOMO of Fig. 14-16 is qualitatively similar to one of the $1e_g - 1e''$ HOMOs of ethane. The QMOT frontier orbital argument for the stability of staggered ethane is basically the same as that for the stability of form (a) in propene. Observe that this MO also resembles the HOMO of 1,3-butadiene, and would lead to the prediction that the trans form of this molecule is more stable than the cis. This is, in fact, observed to be the case.

It is important to bear in mind that the frontier orbital approach is an approximation to an approximation. It is not always easy to know when one is on safe ground. Of the examples mentioned here, ethane and dimethylacetylene are safest because the overlap changes are small. Hence, the perturbation is slight, and our assumption that the MOs of the two forms are essentially identical, except for AO overlap changes, is quite accurate. Also, symmetry is high, and so we know that σ MO overlap changes will be smaller than lopsided π MO overlap changes. Propene and butadiene are risky. Here the whole molecular framework is lopsided, so overlap changes are large in σ as well as in π MOs. Indeed, if one performs EHMO calculations on these molecules, one finds that σ-type MO energies change much more than does the π HOMO energy. This comes about because of the fairly close approach by some of the hydrogens in these molecules. Much of this σ energy change cancels out among the several σ MOs. In propene, the cancellation is so complete that the π HOMO energy change is almost the same as the total EHMO energy change. In butadiene, however, the π HOMO accounts for only about one-third of the total. Even though the frontier orbital method has an astonishing range of qualitative usefulness (we shall see more applications shortly), it is clear that caution is needed.

14-9 Qualitative Molecular Orbital Theory of Reactions

It has been found possible to extend and amplify QMOT procedures so that they apply to chemical reactions. One of the most striking examples of this was application to unimolecular cyclization of an open conjugated molecule (e.g., *cis*-1,3-butadiene, closing to cyclobutene). This type of reaction is called an *electrocyclic* reaction. The details of the electrocyclic closure of *cis*-1,3-butadiene are indicated in Fig. 14-17.

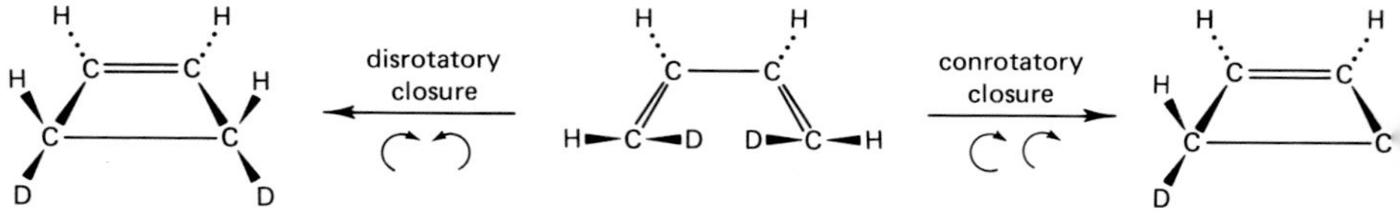

disrotatory closure

conrotatory closure

FIG. 14-17 Two idealized modes of electrocyclic closure of *cis*-1,3-butadiene.

If we imagine that we can keep track of the terminal hydrogens in butadiene (perhaps by deuterium substitution as indicated in the figure) then we can distinguish between two products. One of them is produced if the two terminal methylene groups have rotated in the same sense, either both clockwise or both counterclockwise, to put the two inside atoms of the reactant (here D atoms) on opposite sides of the plane of the four carbon atoms in the product. This is called a *conrotatory* (cŏn′·rō·tā′·tory) closure. The other mode rotates the methylenes in opposite directions (*distotatory*) to give a product wherein the inside atoms appear on the same side of the C_4 plane.

A priori, we do not know whether the reaction follows either of these two paths. Figure 14-17 depicts processes where both methylene groups rotate by equal amounts as the reaction proceeds. This is an extreme case of what is known as a *concerted* process. The two processes occur together, or in concert. The opposite extreme is a *nonconcerted*, or *stepwise* process, wherein one methylene group would rotate all the way (90°) and only after this was completed would the other group begin to rotate. This process would lead to an intermediate having a plane of symmetry (ignoring the difference between D and H), which means that the second methylene group would be equally likely to rotate either way, giving a 50–50 mixture of the two products pictured in Fig. 14-17.

One can make a case for the reaction having some *substantial degree of concertedness* (by which we mean that the second methylene should be partly rotated before the first one is finished rotating). The reaction involves destruction of a four-center conjugated π system and formation of an isolated π bond and a new C–C σ bond. Energy is lost in the dissolution of the old bonds, and gained in formation of the new ones. Therefore, we expect the lowest-energy path between reactants and products to correspond to a reaction coordinate wherein the new bonds start to form before the old ones are completely broken. But the new σ bond cannot form to any significant extent until *both* methylene groups have undergone some rotation. Thus, concertedness in breaking old bonds and forming new ones is aided by some concertedness in methylene group rotations. (Note that concertedness does not necessarily imply absence of an intermediate. If the reaction surface had a local minimum at a point at which both methylenes were rotated by 45°, it would not affect the argument at all.)

Because they knew that many electrocyclic reactions are observed to be *stereospecific* (i.e., give ~100% of one product or the other in a reaction like that in Fig. 14-17), Woodward and Hoffmann [12] sought an explanation of a qualitative MO nature. They used frontier orbitals and argued how their energies would change with a con- or disrotatory motion, due to changes in overlap. For butadiene in its ground state, the HOMO is the familiar π MO shown in the center of Fig. 14-18. The figure indicates that the interaction

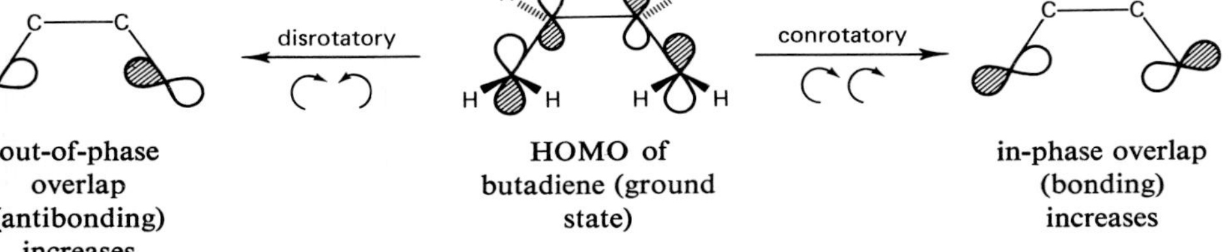

FIG. 14-18 The HOMO of ground state *cis*-1,3-butadiene as it undergoes concerted closure by either mode.

between p–π AOs on terminal carbons is favorable for bonding in the region of the incipient σ bond only in the conrotatory case. Therefore, the prediction is that, for concerted electrocyclic closure, butadiene in the ground state should prefer to go by a conrotatory path. When the reaction is carried out by heating butadiene (thermal reaction), which means that the reactant is virtually all in the ground electronic state, the product is indeed purely that expected from conrotatory closure.

One can also carry out electrocyclic reactions photochemically. The excited butadiene now has an electron in a π MO that was empty in the ground state. This MO was the lowest unoccupied MO (LUMO) of ground-state butadiene, pictured in Fig. 14-19. One can see that the step to the next-higher MO of butadiene has just introduced one more node, reversing the phase relation between terminal π AOs, and reversing the predicted path from con- to disrotatory. Experimentally, the photochemical reaction is observed to give purely the product corresponding to disrotatory closure. (It is not always obvious which empty MO becomes occupied in a given photochemical experiment. One assumes that the LUMO of the ground state is the one to use, but there is some risk here.)

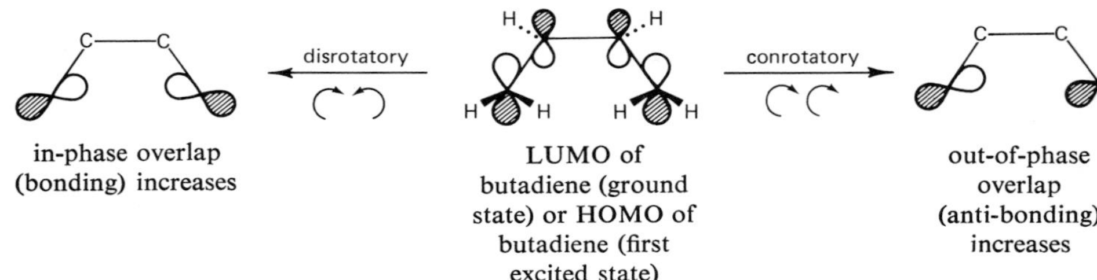

FIG. 14-19 The HOMO of the first excited state of *cis*-1,3-butadiene as it undergoes closure by either mode.

One might worry about the fact that we are looking at only a part of one MO, thereby ignoring a great deal of change in other MOs and other parts of the molecule. However, much of this other change, while large, is expected to be about the same for either of the two paths being compared. The large overlap changes between p–π AOs on terminal and inner carbon atoms, for instance, are about the same for either mode of rotation. This approach, then, is focused first on the frontier orbitals, which are guessed as being most likely to dominate the energy change, and second on those changes in the frontier orbitals that will differ in the two paths.

This method is trivially extendable to longer systems. Hexatriene closes to cyclohexadiene in just the manner predicted by the frontier orbitals. The only significant change in going from butadiene to hexatriene is that we go from four to six π electrons. This means that the HOMO for hexatriene has one more node than that for butadiene (or, the HOMO for a $2n$ π-electron system is like the LUMO for a $2n - 2$ π-electron system insofar as end-to-end phase relations are concerned). The net effect is that the predictions for hexatriene are just the reverse of those for butadiene. That is, hexatriene closes thermally by the disrotatory mode and photochemically by the conrotatory mode. The general rule, called a *Woodward–Hoffmann rule*, is this: the thermal electrocyclic reactions of a k π-electron system will be disrotatory for $k = 4q + 2$, conrotatory for $k = 4q$ ($q = 0, 1, 2, \ldots$); in the first excited state these relationships are reversed.[7]

It is possible to treat electrocyclic reactions in another way, namely, via a two-sided correlation diagram approach. This was first worked out by Longuet-Higgins and Abrahamson [14]. Only orbitals (occupied *and* unoccupied) that are involved in bonds being made or broken during the course of the reaction are included in the diagram. For butadiene, these are the four π MOs already familiar from simple Hückel theory. For cyclobutene, they are the two π MOs associated with the isolated 2-center π bond and the two σ MOs associated with the new C–C σ bond. These orbitals and their energies are shown in Fig. 14-20.

[7] See Woodward and Hoffmann [13, p. 45].

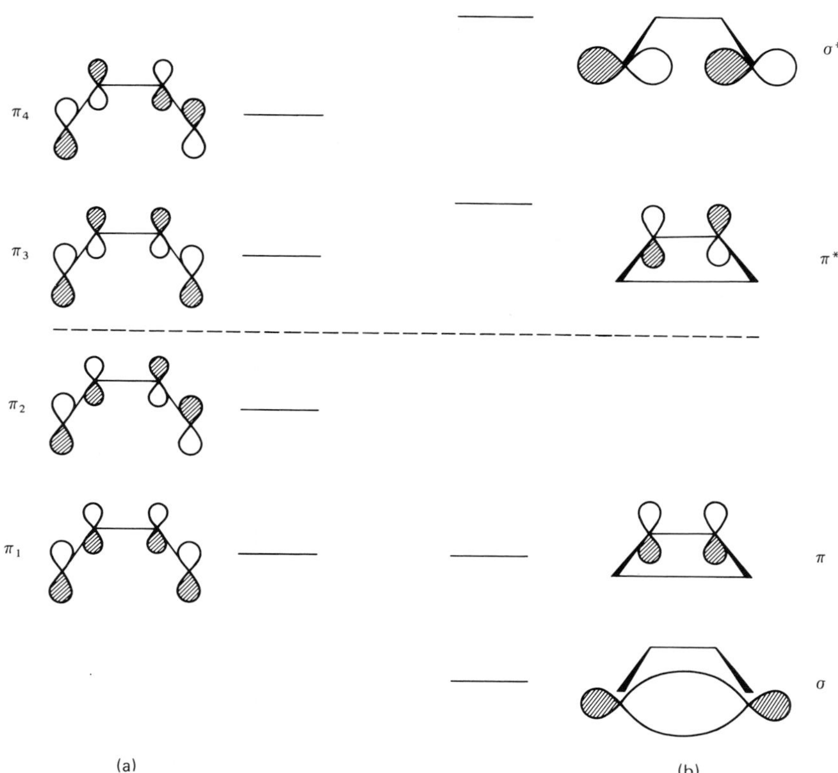

FIG. 14-20 MOs associated with bonds being broken or formed in the electrocyclic closure of (a) *cis*-1,3-butadiene to (b) cyclobutene.

In cyclobutene, the σ and σ^* MOs are assumed to be more widely split than the π and π^* because the p_σ AOs overlap more strongly. Also, the σ MO is assumed lower than π_1 of butadiene. However, these details are not essential. All we have to be certain of is that we have correctly divided the occupied from the unoccupied MOs on the two sides. The dashed line in Fig. 14-20 separates these sets.

Next we must decide which symmetry elements are preserved throughout the idealized reactions we wish to treat. Let us consider first the reactants and products. These have C_{2v} symmetry, that is, a twofold rotational axis, C_2, and two reflection planes σ_1 and σ_2 containing the C_2 axis (see Fig. 14-21). A conrotatory twist preserves C_2, but, during the intermediate stages between reactant and product, σ_1 and σ_2 are lost as symmetry operations. A disrotatory twist preserves σ_1 but destroys C_2 and σ_2. Therefore, when we connect energy levels together for the disrotatory mode, we must connect levels of the same symmetry for σ_1, but for the conrotatory mode, they must agree in symmetry

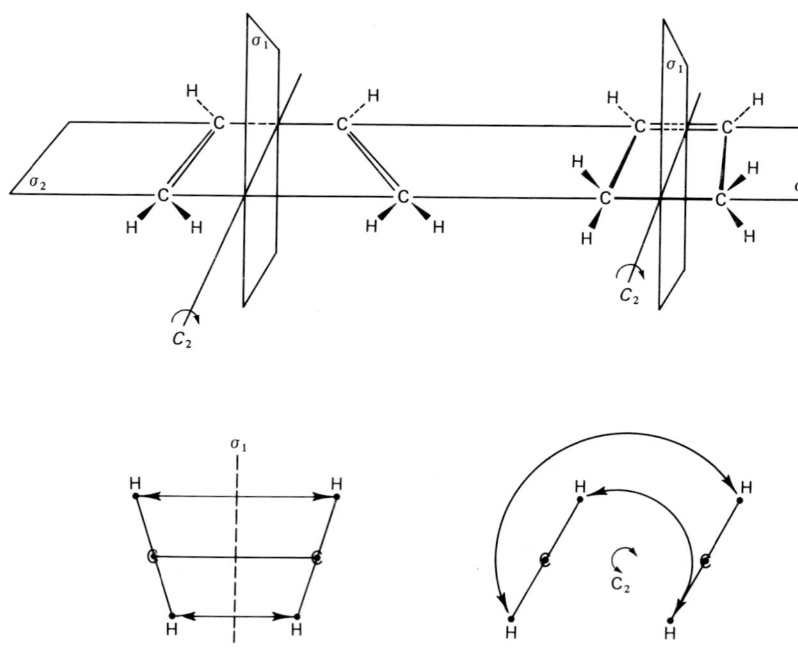

FIG. 14-21 Sketches illustrating that the conrotatory mode (b) preserves the C_2 axis while the disrotatory mode (a) preserves the reflection plane σ_1.

for C_2. The σ_2 plane applies to neither mode and is therefore ignored. The symmetries for each MO are easily determined from examination of the sketches in Fig. 14-20, and are given in Table 14-3. These assignments lead to two different correlation diagrams, one for each mode. It is conventional to arrange these as shown in Fig. 14-22.

There is curve crossing in these diagrams, but it is always lines of different symmetry that cross, and so no violation of the noncrossing rule occurs.

TABLE 14-3
Symmetries for C_{2v} MOs

MO	σ_1	C_2	MO	σ_1	C_2
Butadiene			Cyclobutene		
π_1	S[a]	A	σ	S	S
π_2	A	S	π	S	A
π_3	S	A	π^*	A	S
π_4	A	S	σ^*	A	A

[a] S is symmetric; A antisymmetric.

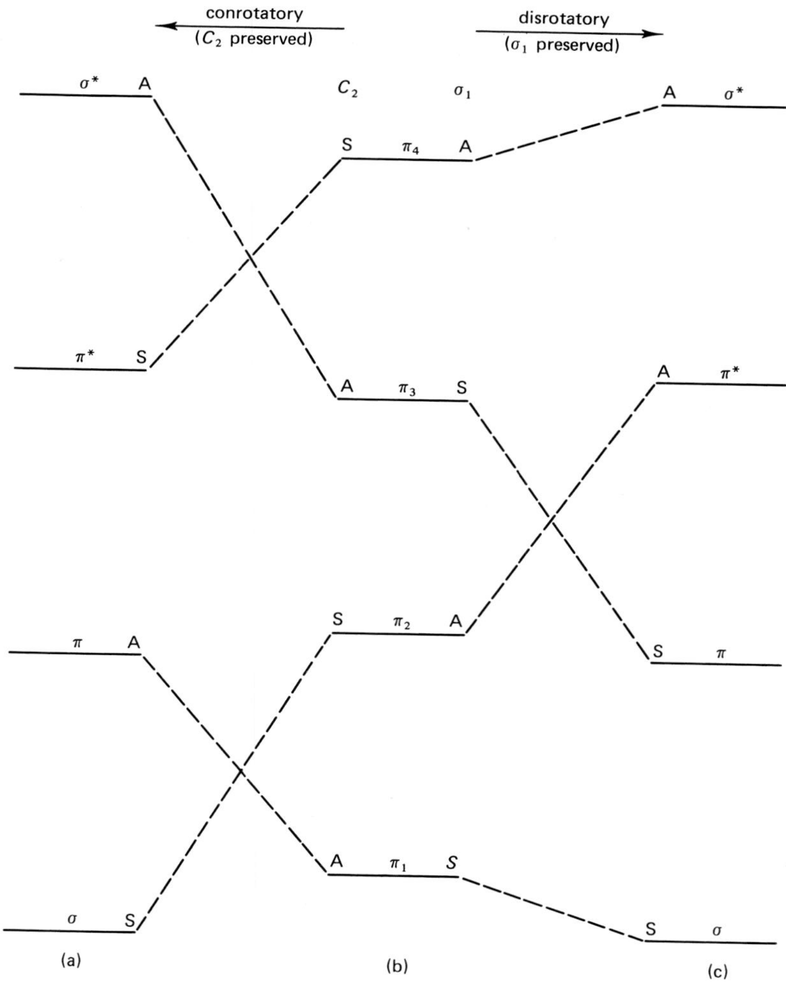

FIG. 14-22 A pair of two-sided correlation diagrams (one for each mode) for the electrocyclic reactions of *cis*-1,3-butadiene: (a) cyclobutene; (b) butadiene; (c) cyclobutene.

If we are considering a thermal reaction, the lowest two π MOs of butadiene are occupied. These correlate with the lowest two MOs of cyclobutene if the conrotatory mode is followed, and the thermal conversion of *cis*-butadiene to cyclobutene by a conrotatory closure is said to be *symmetry allowed.* The other mode correlates π_2 with an empty cyclobutene MO (π^*). Taking this route moves the reactant toward doubly excited cyclobutene. (Even though we might anticipate deexcitation somewhere along the way, the energy required in early stages would still be much higher than would be needed for the symmetry-allowed mode.) This is said to be a *symmetry-forbidden* reaction.

If we now imagine photoexcitation of *cis*-butadiene to have generated a state associated with the configuration $\pi_1{}^2\pi_2\pi_3$, and trace the fate of this species for the two modes of reaction, we note that the disrotatory route leads to cyclobutene in the configuration $\sigma^2\pi\pi^*$ while the conrotatory mode gives $\sigma\pi^2\sigma^*$. Both of these are excited, but the former corresponds to the lowest excited configuration ($\pi \rightarrow \pi^*$) while the second corresponds to a very high-energy excitation ($\sigma \rightarrow \sigma^*$). Therefore, the former is "allowed" (since it goes from lowest excited reactant to lowest excited product) and the latter is "forbidden."

The two-sided correlation diagrams of Fig. 14-22 thus lead to the same predictions as the frontier orbital maximization of overlap approach. The difference between these approaches is as follows: The frontier-orbital approach requires sketching the HOMO and then judging overlap changes upon nuclear motion using QMOT reasoning. The two-sided correlation diagram approach requires sketching all the MOs (occupied and unoccupied) of both reactant and product involved in bonds breaking or forming, ordering the corresponding energy levels, and finding symmetry elements preserved throughout the reaction. Once all this is done, the levels are connected by correlation lines *without* reliance on QMOT reasoning. Some qualitative reasoning enters in the ordering of energy levels (levels with more nodes have higher energy), but the two-sided correlation diagram technique is the more rigorous method of the two and tends to be preferred whenever the problem has enough symmetry to make it feasible. Reliance on frontier orbitals is more common for processes of lower symmetry.

Concern is sometimes expressed about the apparent restrictions resulting from use of symmetry in correlation diagram arguments. One can imagine the butadiene cyclization occurring with less-than-perfect concertedness, the two methylene groups rotating by different amounts as the reaction proceeds. But that would destroy all symmetry elements. Will our symmetry-based arguments still pertain to such an imperfectly concerted reaction coordinate? Again, if we label certain sites by substituting deuteriums for hydrogens as shown in Fig. 14-17, the symmetry will be destroyed. Do our predictions still apply? One can answer these questions affirmatively by reasoning in the following way. If we had a collection of nuclei and electrons, and we could move the nuclei about in arbitrary ways and study the ground-state energy changes, experience tells us that the energy would be found to change in a smooth and continuous way. We can think of the energy as a hypersurface, with hyperdimensional "hills," "valleys," and "passes." Now, in a few very special nuclear configurations, identical nuclei would be interelated by symmetry operations, and we would be able to make deductions on group-theoretical grounds. Such deductions would only strictly apply to those symmetric configurations, but they would serve as indicators of what the energy is like in nearby regions of configuration space. Thus, the correlation diagram indicates that a *perfectly* concerted thermal electrocyclic reaction of butadiene will require much less energy to go conrotatory as opposed to disrotatory. The inference that a less-perfectly concerted reaction will have a similar preference is merely an assumption that it is easier to pass through the mountains *in the vicinity* of a low pass than a high one. Experience also leads us to expect that substituting for H a D (or even a CH_3) will have little effect on the MOs, even though, strictly speaking, symmetry is lost. In essence, we work with an ideal model and use chemical sense to extend the results to less ideal situations, just as we do when, in applying the ideal gas equation of state to real gases, we avoid the high-pressure, low-temperature conditions under which we know the oversimplifications in the ideal gas model will lead to *significant* error.

It is possible to combine information on *orbital* symmetries and energies to arrive at *state* symmetries and energies. Then one can construct a correlation diagram for states.[8] We now demonstrate this for the dis- and conrotatory reactions just considered.

Each orbital occupation scheme is associated with a net symmetry for any given symmetry operation. Character tables could be used to assign these symmetries, but this is not necessary. All we need to use is the fact that, in multiplying functions together, symmetries follow the rules: $S \times S = S$, $A \times A = S$, $S \times A = A$. Thus, any *doubly* occupied MO in a configuration will contribute symmetrically to the final result. To ascertain the net symmetry, then, we focus on the partly filled MOs. The symmetries for C_2 and σ_1 of ground and some excited configurations of butadiene and cyclobutene are listed in Table 14-4. Included are the cyclobutene configurations that result from intended correlations of various butadiene configurations. (For instance, $\pi_1{}^2\pi_2{}^2$ butadiene has an intended correlation with $\sigma^2\pi^{*2}$ cyclobutene if the disrotatory mode is followed. This is inferred from the *orbital* correlation diagram, Fig. 14-22.)

Assuming that the energies of states associated with these configurations fall into groups roughly given by sums of orbital energies, we obtain the two-sided diagram shown in Fig. 14-23. Only a few of the configurations are interconnected, to keep the diagram simple. Note that the ground-state configuration of butadiene correlates directly with the ground state of cyclobutene for conrotatory closure, but has an intended correlation with a doubly excited configuration in the disrotatory mode. This intended correlation would violate the noncrossing rule by crossing another line of S symmetry, so that the actual curve turns around and joins onto the ground state level for cyclobutene. The effect of the intended correlation with a high-energy state is to produce a significant barrier to reaction. The figure shows that, for the first excited configuration, the high-energy barrier occurs for the opposite mode of reaction. State correlation diagrams thus convert a "symmetry-forbidden" orbital correlation

[8] Actually, we shall be looking at simple products of MOs, or *configurations*. Each configuration is associated with one or more states and gives the proper symmetry for these states as well as an approximate average energy of all the associated states. Hence, the treatment described here gives a sort of *average* state correlation diagram. It might be more accurately called a *configuration* correlation diagram.

TABLE 14-4
Symmetries and Intended Correlations of Some Configurations of Butadiene and Cyclobutene

	Symmetry for		Cyclobutene "intended" configuration	
Configuration	σ_1	C_2	Con	Dis
Butadiene				
$\pi_1^2\pi_2^2$	S[a]	S	$\pi^2\sigma^2$	$\sigma^2\pi^{*2}$
$\pi_1^2\pi_2\pi_3$	A	A	$\pi^2\sigma\sigma^*$	$\sigma^2\pi^*\pi$
$\pi_1^2\pi_2\pi_4$	S	S	$\pi^2\sigma\pi^*$	$\sigma^2\pi^*\sigma^*$
$\pi_1\pi_2^2\pi_3$	S	S	$\pi\sigma^2\sigma^*$	$\sigma\pi^{*2}\pi$
$\pi_1\pi_2^2\pi_4$	A	A	$\pi\sigma^2\pi^*$	$\sigma\pi^*\sigma^{*2}$
$\pi_1^2\pi_3^2$	S	S	$\sigma^2\sigma^{*2}$	$\sigma^2\pi^2$
⋮				
Cyclobutene				
$\sigma^2\pi^2$	S	S		
$\sigma^2\pi\pi^*$	A	A		
$\sigma\pi^2\pi^*$	A	S		
$\sigma\pi^2\pi^*$	A	S		
$\sigma\pi^2\sigma^*$	A	A		
$\sigma^2\pi^{*2}$	S	S		
$\sigma^2\pi^*\sigma^*$	S	A		
⋮				

[a] S is symmetric; A antisymmetric.

diagram into a high-activation-energy barrier: the conclusions are the same using either diagram.

Another kind of reaction that is formally closely related to the electrocyclic reaction is the *cycloaddition* reaction, exemplified by the Diels–Alder reaction between ethylene and butadiene to give cyclohexene (**I**). Such reactions are

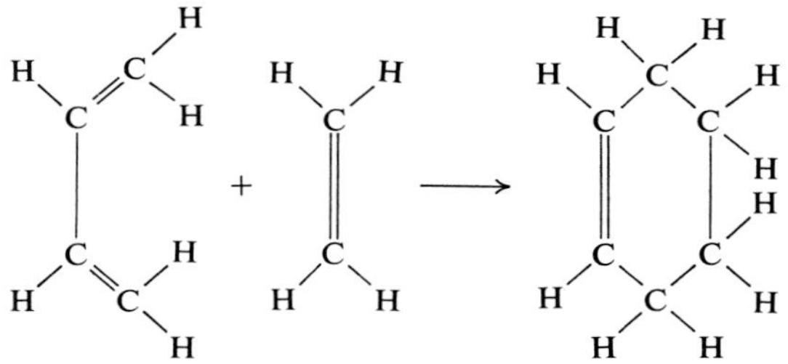

(**I**)

classified in terms of the number of centers between the points of connection. Thus, the Diels–Alder reaction is a [4 + 2] cycloaddition reaction. One can conceive of several distinct geometrical possibilities for a concerted mechanism

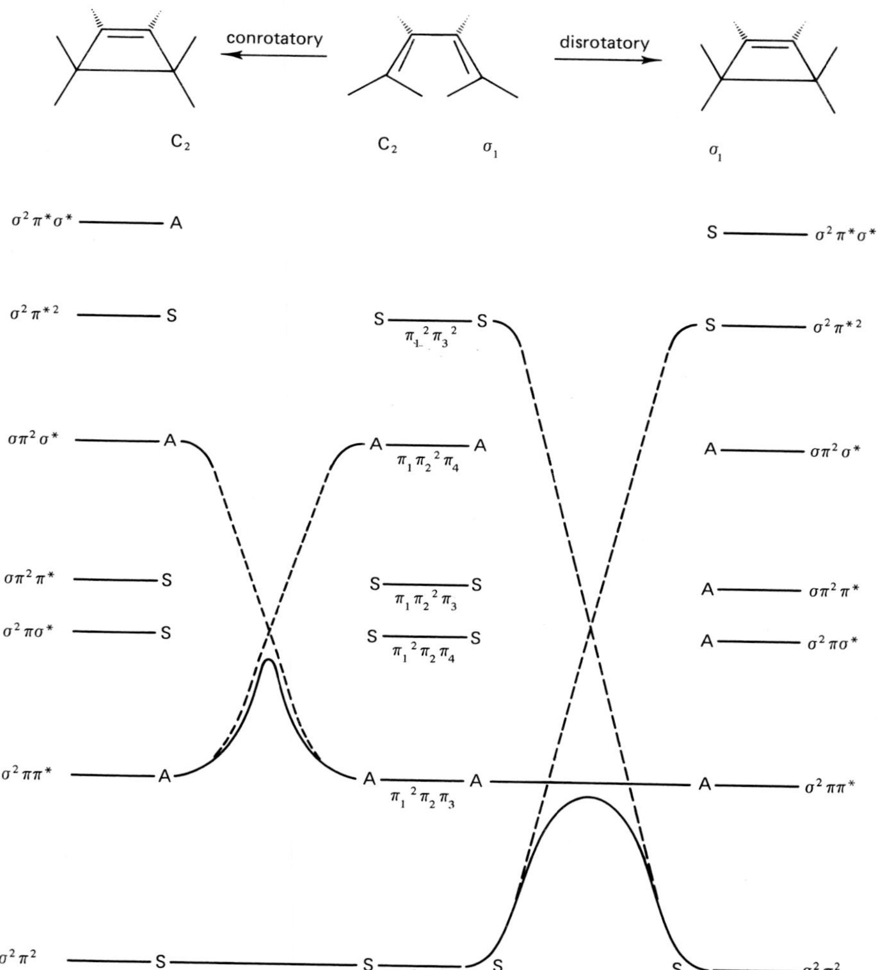

FIG. 14-23 A *state* or *configuration* correlation diagram for the electrocyclic closure of *cis*-1,3-butadiene.

for such a reaction. The two new σ bonds can be envisioned as being formed on the same face (suprafacial) (**II**) or opposite faces (antarafacial) (**III**) of each of the two reactants. The various possibilities are illustrated in Fig. 14-24. Qualitative MO theory is used to judge which process is energetically most favorable.

(**II**) (**III**)

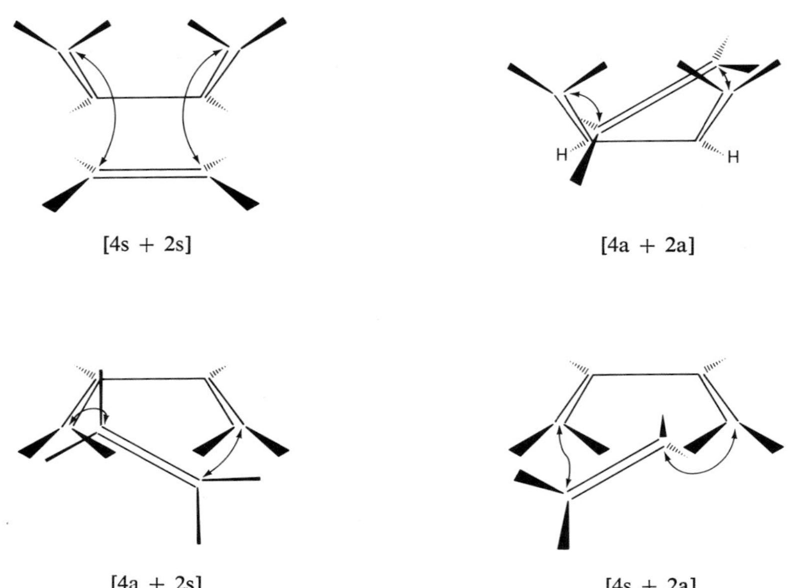

FIG. 14-24 Four suprafacial–antarafacial combinations possible for the Diels–Alder [2 + 4] cycloaddition reaction.

One has a choice between the two-sided correlation diagram and the frontier orbital approach. We demonstrate the latter[9] since it is simpler. Both methods lead to the same conclusion. In the course of this reaction, electrons become shared between the π systems of butadiene and ethylene. This is accomplished, to a rough approximation, by interaction between the HOMO of butadiene and the LUMO of ethylene and also between the LUMO of butadiene and the HOMO of ethylene. Let us consider the former interaction. The MOs are shown in Fig. 14-25 and the overlapping regions are indicated for the four geometric possibilities. Inspection of the sketches indicates that the two MOs have positive overlap in the regions of *both* incipient σ bonds only for the [4s + 2s] and [4a + 2a] modes. Therefore, the prediction is that these modes proceed with less activation energy and are favored. Now let us turn to the other pair of MOs, namely the LUMO of butadiene (**IV**) and the HOMO of ethylene (**V**). Note

[9] See Hoffmann and Woodward [15].

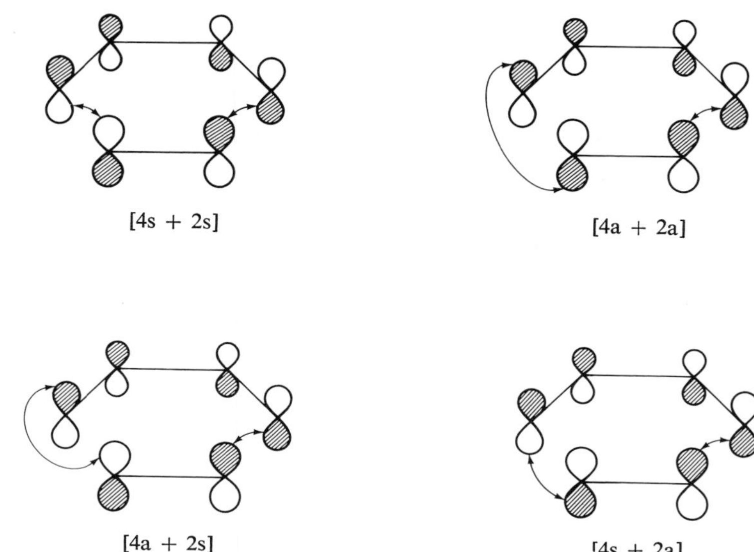

FIG. 14-25 Overlaps between HOMO of butadiene and LUMO of ethylene resulting from four interactive modes pictured in Fig. 14-24. The geometries for the four modes would all differ. These drawings are highly stylized.

that, for each MO, the end-to-end phase relationship is reversed from what it was before. Two symmetry reversals leave us with no net change in the intermolecular phase relations. It is easy to see, therefore, that these MOs also favor the [s, s] and [a, a] modes. In cycloaddition reactions of this sort, one need analyze only one HOMO–LUMO pair in order to arrive at a prediction. Extension to longer molecules or to photochemical cycloadditions proceeds by the same kinds of arguments presented for the electrocyclic reactions.

Another type of reaction to which qualitative MO theory has been applied is the *sigmatropic shift* reaction, where a hydrogen migrates from one carbon to another and simultaneously a shift in the double bond system occurs. An example is given in Fig. 14-26.

The usual treatment of this reaction[10] involves examining the HOMO for the system at some intermediate stage in the reaction where the hydrogen has lost much of its bonding to its original site and is trying to bond onto its new site. At this stage, the HOMO of the molecule approaches that of the nonbonding MO of an odd alternant hydrocarbon (Fig. 14-27) with a slightly bound hydrogen on one end. The suprafacial mode is favored in this particular case because the hydrogen can maintain positive overlap simultaneously with its old and new sites—the new bond can form as the old bond breaks. This is not possible

[10] See Woodward and Hoffmann [16].

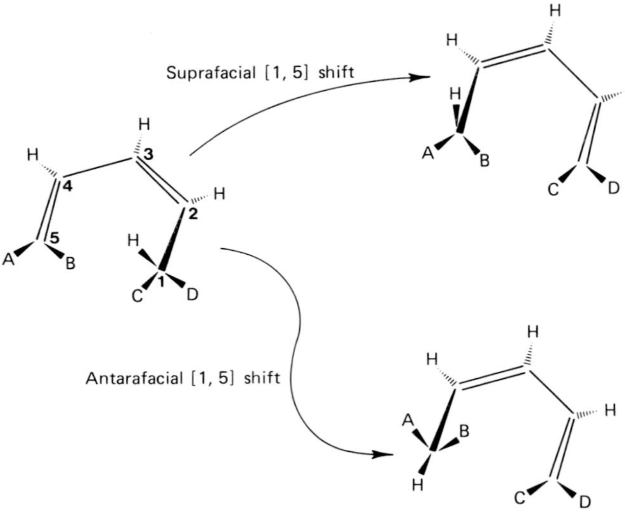

FIG. 14-26 The two possible distinct products resulting from a shift of a hydrogen from position 1 to position 5 in a substituted 1,3-pentadiene. Groups A, B, C, D are deuterium atoms, methyl groups, etc., enabling us to distinguish the products.

for the antarafacial [1, 5] shift. However, the [1, 7] shift prefers the antarafacial mode.

Many other types of chemical reaction have been rationalized using qualitative MO theory. The association of S_N2 reactions with Walden inversion (i.e., the adding group attacks the opposite side of an atom from the leaving group)

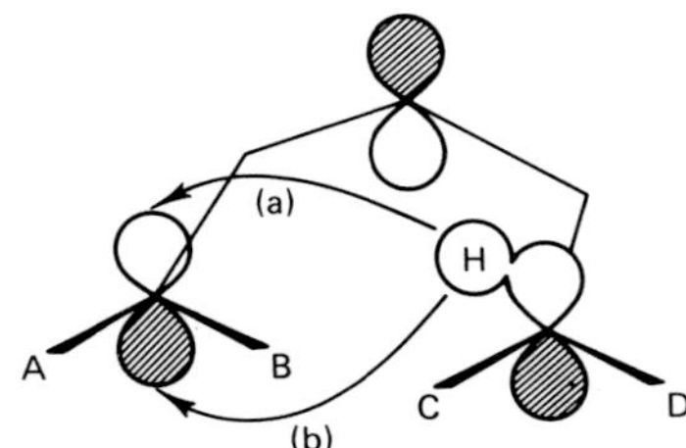

FIG. 14-27 Phase relations in HOMO for (a) suprafacial and (b) antarafacial [1, 5] sigmatropic shifts.

is rationalized by arguing that an approaching nucleophile will donate electrons into the LUMO of the substrate. The LUMO for CH_3Cl is shown in Fig. 14-28. A successful encounter between CH_3Cl and a base results in a bond between the base and the carbon atom, so the HOMO of the base needs to overlap the p AO of carbon in the LUMO of Fig. 14-28a. Attack at the position marked "1" in the figure is unfavorable because any base MO would be near a nodal surface, yielding poor overlap with the LUMO. Therefore, attack at site 2 is favored. As the previously empty LUMO of CH_3Cl becomes partially occupied,

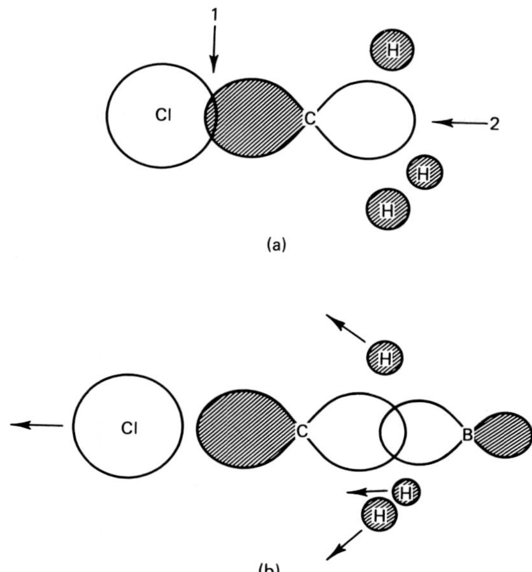

FIG. 14-28 (a) The LUMO of CH_3Cl. (b) Positive overlap between HOMO of base B and LUMO of CH_3Cl increases antibonding between C and Cl and also repels H atoms from their original positions.

we expect a loss of bonding between C and Cl. Also, negative overlap between the forming C-base bond and the three "backside" hydrogens should encourage the latter to migrate away from the attacked side, as indicated in Fig. 14-28b.

The tendency of a high-energy, occupied MO of the base to couple strongly with the LUMO of a molecule like CH_3Cl depends partly on the energy agreement between these MOs. If they are nearly isoenergetic, they mix much more easily and give a bonded combination of much lower energy. Molecules where the HOMO is high tend to be polarizable bases. A high-energy HOMO means that the electrons are not very well bound and will easily shift about to take advantage of perturbations. Such bases react readily with molecules having a low-energy LUMO (Fig. 14-29a). This corresponds to a "soft-base–soft-acid" interaction in the approach of Pearson [17]. When the HOMO and LUMO are in substantial energy disagreement, orbital overlap becomes less important as a controlling mechanism, and simple electrostatic interactions may dominate. This is a "hard-acid–hard-base" situation. Thus, we expect QMOT rules to apply to soft–soft, rather than hard–hard interactions.

Yet another variant of qualitative MO theoretical prediction of reaction stereochemistry has been described by Liotta [18]. This is basically a frontier orbital approach, but the orbital is allowed to distort as the reaction proceeds. One assumes that this distortion will occur so as to minimize out-of-phase

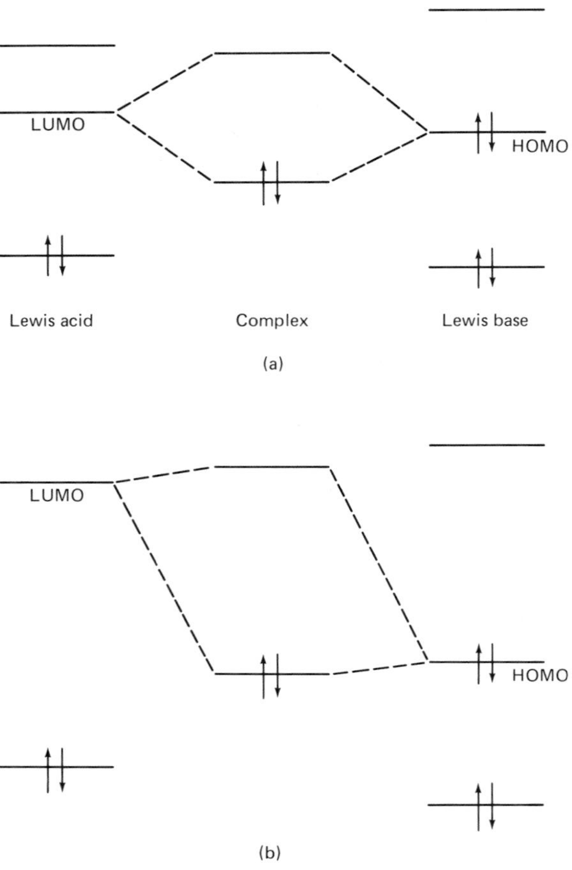

FIG. 14-29 **LUMO–HOMO interactions and splitting for (a) nearly degenerate levels, (b) well-separated levels.**

overlaps and maximize in-phase overlaps. An example helps to clarify the idea. Consider the displacement of some leaving group X from the molecule (**VI**). If attack by a nucleophile Y^- occurs at C_1, we have an S_N2 reaction. Attack by a nucleophile at C_3 can also displace X as indicated in (VII). Such a displacement is labeled S_N2'. The question arises as to whether Y attacks C_3 suprafacially or antarafacially with respect to the leaving group X. One first draws the LUMO

(VI)

Y^- + $H_2C_3{=}C_2H{-}C_1H_2X \longrightarrow YH_2C_3{-}C_2H{=}C_1H_2$ + X^-

(VII)

for the substrate (Fig. 14-30a). This is antibonding between C_2 and C_3, bonding between C_1 and C_2, antibonding between C_1 and X. [The X AO is shown to be of s type. It would be some mixture of s and p, depending on which atom or group of atoms X is. One can obtain the LUMO in a molecule of this sort from a semiempirical calculation such as EHMO (Chapter 10), CNDO (Chapter 11), etc.] Now one imagines σ–π mixing to occur in this MO (as it becomes occupied) so as to minimize the antibonding between C_1 and X (Fig. 14-30b). Next, one carries the σ–π mixing on down the molecule, always keeping the in-phase overlaps maximized and out-of-phase minimized, but maintaining the basic nodal structure of the original LUMO (Fig. 14-30c). Since the MO at C_3 bulges out on the same side of the molecular plane as X, attack is favored in a suprafacial mode (Fig. 14-30d). Liotta cites experimental results to support predictions made in this way. Note that the method also predicts that ordinary S_N2 reactions should proceed with attack from the backside of C_1, just as does our earlier LUMO analysis. Basically, Liotta's approach finds which of two possible modes allows for the existence of the lower-energy HOMO of the intermediate complex.

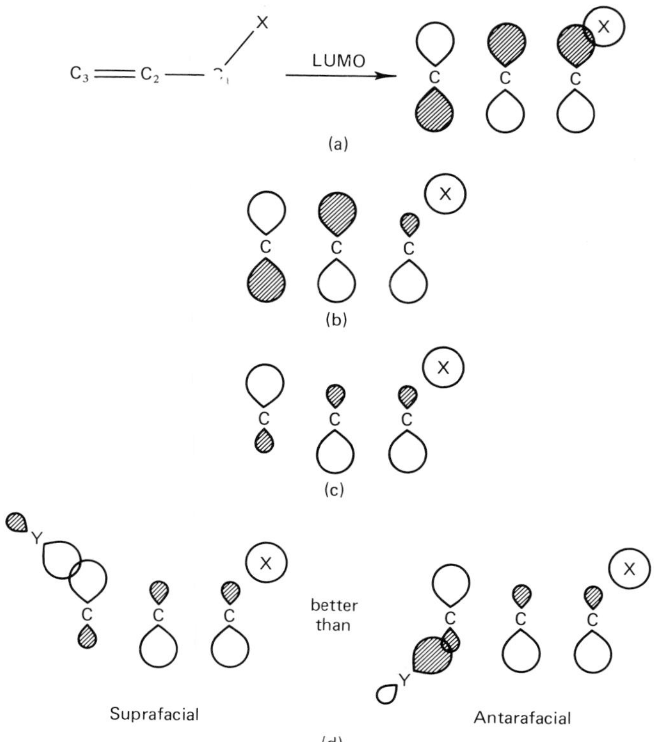

FIG. 14-30

The reader may, by this time, begin to appreciate the very wide scope of QMOT and the large number of variations of a common theme which have been used. In this chapter we have given only a few representative examples. We have not described all the variations or all types of application. For fuller treatment, the reader should consult specialized books on this subject, some of which have been referred to in this chapter [19].

PROBLEMS

14-1 Calculate to first order the electronic energy of a hydrogen atom in its 1s state and in the presence of an additional proton at a distance of 2 a.u. What is the *total* energy to first order? Repeat for distances of 1 and 3 a.u.

14-2 Evaluate and graph the effects of dividing $H_{aa} \pm H_{ab}$ by $1 \pm S$ for each of the following cases: $H_{aa} = 0, -5, -10, +10, -20$. In each case, let $H_{ab} = -5$, $S = 0.5$. Does the QMOT rule that antibonding interactions are more destabilizing than bonding interactions are stabilizing apply in all cases? Is the bonding level always the lower of the two? Does the QMOT expectation appear to be better followed by very low-energy levels, or by higher-energy levels?

14-3 Table P14-3 is a list of electron affinities (in electron volts) of certain molecules and atoms. Can you rationalize the molecular values relative to the atomic values using QMOT ideas?

TABLE P14-3
Atomic and Molecular Electron Affinities (in electron volts)

H (0.75)	Cl (3.61)	C_2 (3.5)	O_2 (0.43)	Cl_2 (2.32)
C (1.27)	Br (3.36)	CN (3.8 or 3.2)	F_2 (2.9)	Br_2 (2.5)
N (0.0 ± 0.2)	I (3.06)	N_2 (−1.6)	S_2 (1.66)	I_2 (2.6)
O (1.46)	S (2.08)	CO (< -1.8)	SO (1.09)	ICl (1.43)
F (3.40)	H_2 (~ -2)	CS (<1.2)	FCl (1.5)	IBr (2.7)

14-4 For some time, it was uncertain whether the ground states of CH_2 and NH_2^+ are singlets $(2a_1)^2$ or triplets $(2a_1)(1b_1)$. The ground-state geometries of these systems have HAH angles of 136° (CH_2) and 140–150° (NH_2^+). Based on other data described in the text for HAH systems, would you say these angles are more consistent with a singlet or a triplet ground state? Assuming that the first excited state is the other multiplicity, should the first excited state be more or less bent than the ground state?

14-5 Based on Fig. 14-8, what should happen to the geometry of H_2O upon $1b_1 \rightarrow 3a_1$ excitation?

14-6 Carry out EHMO calculations for CH_2 at HCH angles of 180, 150, 120, and 90°. (Use a constant C–H bond distance of about 1Å in all cases.) From an examination of the MO coefficients, sketch and assign symmetry symbols to each MO. Plot the energies versus angle. Critically discuss your computed results compared to Fig. 14-8. If there are differences, try to rationalize them. (Remember that any EHMO orbital energy change can be analyzed in terms of Mulliken population changes, as discussed in Chapter 10.)

14-7 Using the EHMO energy formula [Eq. (10-25)], analyze the contributions to the orbital energy change between 180 and 120° that you calculated for the $1b_2$ MO in Problem 14-6. What percentage of the energy change comes from loss of overlap between 1s and 2p AOs? From antibonding between hydrogens? Compare this with the discussion in the text.

14-8 If overlap between an s AO and a p AO goes as cos θ (for constant and finite R) (Fig. P14-8), what is the mathematical expression for the rate of change of overlap with angle? Calculate the effect on overlap of a 30° shift, starting from $\theta = 0$. Calculate the effect of a 30° shift from $\theta = 90°$.

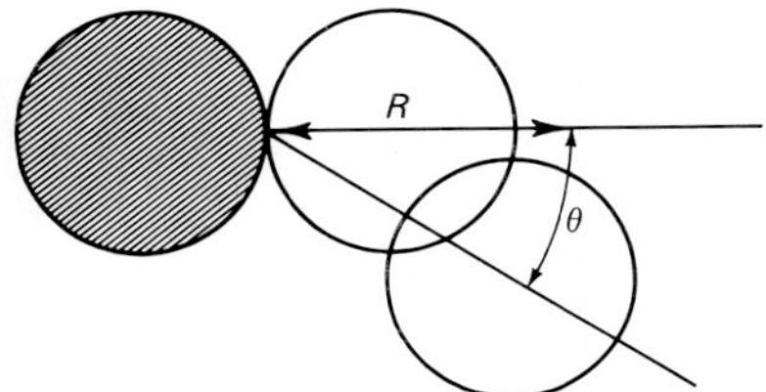

FIG. P14-8

14-9 Use symmetry to help establish an energy level pattern and MO sketches for planar AH_3 (equilateral triangular). Use QMOT rules to produce the correlation diagram for planar versus pyramidal AH_3. Based on your reasoning, which of the following should be planar? BH_3, CH_3^+, BeH_3^-, NH_3, PH_3, H_3O^+, CH_3^-. Can you think of any other shapes that might be examined as possibilities for AH_3 systems?

14-10 Use an EHMO program to generate MOs for CO_2 at 180, 150, 120, and 90°. Sketch the MOs, characterize their symmetries, and construct an orbital energy correlation diagram for this molecule. Indicate what causes each MO energy to rise or fall. Based on your figure, would you expect the following molecules to be linear or bent? $BeCl_2$, C_3, CO_2, N_3^-, NO_2, O_3, F_2O.

14-11 Should a $\pi_g \rightarrow \pi_u$ electronic transition for ozone cause the O–O–O angle to increase or decrease according to Walsh-type arguments? Sketch the MOs and indicate your reasoning. [The notation π_g and π_u refers to the MOs in the linear molecule. For the equilibrium bent structure, these MOs are: $\pi_g \rightarrow a_2, b_2$; $\pi_u \rightarrow a_1, b_1$.]

14-12 Consider the electrocyclic reaction wherein the allyl *anion* closes to form a cyclopropenyl π anion (**VIII**). (The negative charge in the cyclopropyl anion may be thought of as resulting from double occupancy of a p–π AO on the singly protonated carbon.) Sketch the orbitals being formed or destroyed in this process. Determine

(VIII)

the orbital symmetries for the symmetry operations conserved in conrotatory and disrotatory modes of closure. Set up an orbital correlation diagram and decide which mode is more likely for thermal and photochemical reactions.

14-13 Construct an orbital correlation diagram for the "broadside" 2 + 2 cyclo-

(IX)

addition of two acetylenes to form cyclobutadiene (**IX**). Is the reaction likely to proceed through an intermediate of square planar geometry? Assuming this geometry, would reaction be easier thermally or photochemically?

14-14 For a system having no symmetry elements (except E), what is the result of the noncrossing rule?

14-15 (a) Construct an orbital correlation diagram for the [2 + 4] cycloaddition (Diels–Alder) reaction discussed in the text.

(b) Construct a *state* correlation diagram for this reaction.

14-16 Based on the orbital relations discussed in the text and extensions of these relations to other cases, formulate generalized verbal rules (Woodward–Hoffmann rules) for cycloadditions and sigmatropic shift reactions.

REFERENCES

[1] D. R. Yarkony and H. F. Schaefer, III, *J. Chem. Phys.* **61**, 4921 (1974).
[2] K. Ruedenberg, *J. Chem. Phys.* **66**, 375 (1977).
[3] Ionization potentials, appearance potentials, and heats of formation of gaseous positive ions, NSRDS-NBS 26, Nat'l. Bur. Stand. (1969).
[4] A. D. Walsh, *J. Chem. Soc.* p. 2260 (1953).
[5] R. S. Mulliken, *Rev. Mod. Phys.* **14**, 204 (1942).
[6] B. M. Gimarc, *Accounts Chem. Res.* **7**, 384 (1974).
[7] R. J. Buenker and S. D. Peyerimhoff, *Chem. Rev.* **74**, 127 (1974).
[8] T. E. Sharp, *Atomic Data* **2**, 119 (1971).
[9] J. P. Lowe, *J. Am. Chem. Soc.* **92**, 3799 (1970).
[10] R. M. Stevens, *J. Chem. Phys.* **52**, 1397 (1970).
[11] H. Fujimoto and K. Fukui, *in* "Chemical Reactivity and Reaction Paths" (G. Klopman, ed.). Wiley (Interscience), New York, 1974.
[12] R. B. Woodward and R. Hoffmann, *J. Am. Chem. Soc.* **87**, 395 (1965).
[13] R. B. Woodward and R. Hoffmann, "The Conservation of Orbital Symmetry." Academic Press, New York, 1970.
[14] H. C. Longuet-Higgins and E. W. Abrahamson, *J. Am. Chem. Soc.* **87**, 2045 (1965).
[15] R. Hoffmann and R. B. Woodward, *J. Am. Chem. Soc.* **87**, 2046 (1965).
[16] R. B. Woodward and R. Hoffmann, *J. Am. Chem. Soc.* **87**, 2511 (1965).
[17] R. G. Pearson, ed., "Hard and Soft Acids and Bases." Dowden, Hutchison, and Ross, Stroudsburg, Pennsylvania, 1973.
[18] C. L. Liotta, *Tetrahedron Lett.* **8**, 519, 523 (1975).
[19] B. M. Gimarc, "Qualitative Molecular Orbital Theory." Academic Press, New York (to be published).

APPENDIX 1

USEFUL INTEGRALS

$$\int x^n e^{ax}\,dx = (x^n e^{ax}/a) - (n/a)\int x^{n-1}e^{ax}\,dx$$

$$\int_0^\infty x^n e^{-ax}\,dx = (n!/a^{n+1}) = \Gamma_{n+1}(a), \qquad n > -1, a > 0$$

$$\int_0^\infty e^{-ax^2}\,dx = \tfrac{1}{2}\sqrt{\pi/a}$$

$$\int_0^\infty xe^{-ax^2}\,dx = 1/2a$$

$$\int_0^\infty x^2 e^{-ax^2}\,dx = \tfrac{1}{4}\sqrt{\pi/a^3}$$

$$\int_0^\infty x^3 e^{-ax^2}\,dx = 1/2a^2$$

$$\int_0^\infty x^{2n} e^{-ax^2}\,dx = \frac{1\cdot 3\cdot \cdots \cdot(2n-1)}{2^{n+1}}\sqrt{\frac{\pi}{a^{2n+1}}}$$

$$\int_0^\infty x^{2n+1} e^{-ax^2}\,dx = n!/2a^{n+1}$$

$$\int_1^\infty e^{-ax}\,dx = e^{-a}/a$$

$$\int_0^1 e^{-ax}\,dx = (1/a)(1 - e^{-a})$$

$$\int_1^\infty xe^{-ax}\,dx = (e^{-a}/a^2)(1 + a)$$

$$\int_0^1 xe^{-ax}\,dx = (1/a^2)[1 - e^{-a}(1 + a)]$$

$$\int_1^\infty x^2 e^{-ax}\,dx = (2e^{-a}/a^3)(1 + a + a^2/2)$$

$$\int_0^1 x^2 e^{-ax}\,dx = (2/a^3)[1 - e^{-a}(1 + a + a^2/2)]$$

$$\int_1^\infty x^n e^{-ax}\,dx = (n!e^{-a}/a^{n+1}) \sum_{k=0}^{n} a^k/k! \equiv A_n(a)$$

$$\int_y^\infty x^n e^{-ax}\,dx = (n!e^{-ay}/a^{n+1}) \sum_{k=0}^{n} (ay)^k/k!$$

$$\int_{-1}^{+1} e^{-ax}\,dx = (1/a)(e^a - e^{-a})$$

$$\int_{-1}^{+1} x e^{-ax}\,dx = (1/a^2)[e^a - e^{-a} - a(e^a + e^{-a})]$$

$$\int_{-1}^{+1} x^n e^{-ax}\,dx = (-1)^{n+1}A_n(-a) - A_n(a)$$

$$\int_{-1}^{+1} x^n\,dx = \begin{cases} 0\ , & n = 1, 3, 5, \ldots \\ 2/(n+1), & n = 0, 2, 4, \ldots \end{cases}$$

APPENDIX 2

DETERMINANTS

A determinant is a scalar calculated from an ordered set of elements according to a specific evaluation recipe. The elements are ordered in a square array of rows and columns, bounded at left and right by straight vertical lines. For instance, (A2-1) is a 2×2 determinant:

$$\begin{vmatrix} x & -i \\ 2 & y^2 \end{vmatrix} \tag{A2-1}$$

The recipe for evaluating a 2×2 determinant is: From the product of the elements on the principal diagonal (upper left to lower right) subtract the product of the other two elements. Thus, (A2-1) has the value $xy^2 + 2i$.

Larger determinants are evaluated by a process that reduces them step by step to a linear combination of smaller determinants until, finally, they are all 2×2's, which are then evaluated as above. The process of reduction involves the concept of a *cofactor*. As our example, we use the 4×4 determinant (A2-2), symbolized $|M|$, where M is the array of elements within the vertical bars:

$$|M| = \begin{vmatrix} a_{11} & a_{12} & a_{13} & a_{14} \\ a_{21} & a_{22} & a_{23} & a_{24} \\ a_{31} & a_{32} & a_{33} & a_{34} \\ a_{41} & a_{42} & a_{43} & a_{44} \end{vmatrix} \tag{A2-2}$$

The elements are numbered so that the first index tells which row, and the second index which column, the element is in. The cofactor of element a_{11} is defined as the determinant obtained by removing the row and column containing a_{11}. We see in (A2-2) that striking out row 1 and column 1 gives us a 3×3 determinant (dotted outline) as cofactor of a_{11}. Symbolize this cofactor as $|A_{11}|$.

To evaluate the determinant $|M|$, we expand in terms of cofactors. We begin by choosing any row or column of M. (We will choose row 1.) Then we write a linear combination containing every element in this row or column times its cofactor:

$$|M| = a_{11}|A_{11}| - a_{12}|A_{12}| + a_{13}|A_{13}| - a_{14}|A_{14}| \tag{A2-3}$$

The sign of each term in the linear combination is determined as follows. If the sum of row and column indices is even, the sign is plus. If the sum is odd, the sign is minus. Since the indices of a_{12} and a_{14} sum to odd numbers, they are minus in (A2-3).

The method of expanding in cofactors is successively applied until a large determinant is reduced to 3×3's or 2×2's that can be evaluated directly (see Problem A2-1). Thus, a 5×5 is first expanded to five 4×4's and each 4×4 expanded to four 3×3's giving a total of 20 3×3's. This method becomes extremely clumsy for large determinants.

Some useful properties of determinants, symbolized $|M|$, are stated below without proof. The reader should verify that these are true using 2×2 or 3×3 examples, or by examining Eq. (A2-3).

(1) Multiplying every element in *one* row or *one* column of M by the constant c multiplies the value of $|M|$ by c.

(2) If every element in a row or column of M is zero, then $|M| = 0$.

(3) Interchanging two rows or columns of M to produce M' results in $|M'| = -|M|$; i.e., it reverses the sign of $|M|$.

(4) Adding to any row (column) of M the quantity c times any other row (column) of M does not affect the value of the determinant.

(5) If two rows or columns of M differ only by a constant multiplier then $|M| = 0$.

Use of Determinants in Linear Homogeneous Equations

Suppose that we seek a nontrivial solution for the following set of linea[r] homogeneous equations:

$$a_1x + b_1y + c_1z = 0 \tag{A2-4}$$

$$a_2x + b_2y + c_2z = 0 \tag{A2-5}$$

$$a_3x + b_3y + c_3z = 0 \tag{A2-6}$$

Here, x, y, and z are unknown and the coefficients a_i, b_i, c_i are given. Let u[s] collect the coefficients into a determinant $|M|$,

$$|M| = \begin{vmatrix} a_1 & b_1 & c_1 \\ a_2 & b_2 & c_2 \\ a_3 & b_3 & c_3 \end{vmatrix} \tag{A2-7}$$

As before, let $|A_1|$ be the cofacter of a_1, etc. Now, multiply Eq. (A2-4) by $|A_1|$ (since $|A_1|$ is a determinant, it is just a number, and so this is a scalar multiplica[-]tion), Eq. (A2-5) by $-|A_2|$, and Eq. (A2-6) by $|A_3|$ and add the results to ge[t]

$$x(a_1|A_1| - a_2|A_2| + a_3|A_3|) + y(b_1|A_1| - b_2|A_2| + b_3|A_3|) \\ + z(c_1|A_1| - c_2|A_2| + c_3|A_3|) = 0 \tag{A2-8}$$

The coefficient of x is just $|M|$. The coefficients of y and z correspond to determinants having two identical rows and hence are zero. Therefore,

$$|M|x = 0 \tag{A2-9}$$

In order for x to be nonzero (i.e., nontrivial) it is necessary that $|M| = 0$. This is a result that is very useful. *The condition that must be met by the coefficients of a set of linear homogeneous equations in order that nontrivial solutions exist is that their determinant vanish.*

PROBLEMS

A2-1 Expand the 3 × 3 determinant (Fig. PA2-1), by cofactors and show that this result is equivalent to the direct evaluation of the 3 × 3 by summing the three products parallel to the main diagonal (solid arrows) and subtracting the three products parallel to the other diagonal (dashed arrows).

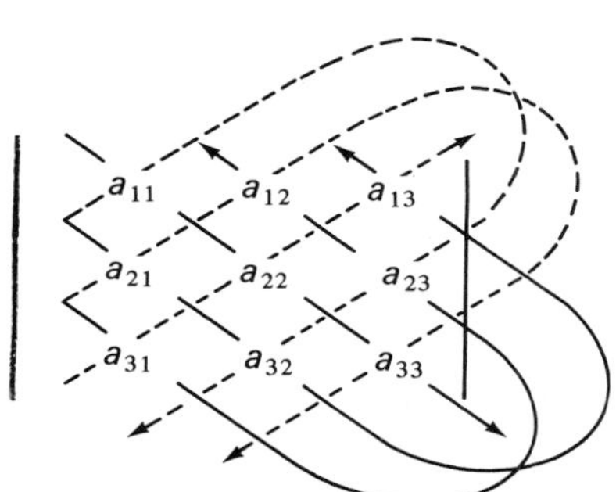

FIG. PA2-1

A2-2 Evaluate

(a) $\begin{vmatrix} 0 & 1 \\ 2 & 1 \end{vmatrix}$ (b) $\begin{vmatrix} 1 & 1 & 0 \\ 0 & 1 & 1 \\ 1 & 1 & 1 \end{vmatrix}$ (c) $\begin{vmatrix} 1 & 2 & 0 & 1 \\ 3 & 0 & 1 & 4 \\ 1 & 1 & 0 & 1 \\ 0 & 2 & 1 & 1 \end{vmatrix}$

(d) $\begin{vmatrix} x & 2 \\ 1 & x \end{vmatrix} = 0$ for x

A2-3 Verify that the coefficient of y in Eq. (A2-8) is zero.

A2-4 Consider the following set of linear homogeneous equations:

$$4x + 2y - z = 0, \qquad 3x - y - 2z = 0, \qquad 2y + z = 0$$

Do nontrivial roots exist?

A2-5 Find a value for c which allows nontrivial solutions for the equations

$$cx - 2y + z = 0, \qquad 4x + cy - 2z = 0, \qquad -8x + 5y - cz = 0$$

A2-6 Five properties of determinants have been listed in this appendix.

(a) Prove statement (5) is true assuming statements (1)–(4) are true.

(b) Demonstrate statements (1)–(4) using simple examples.

APPENDIX 3

EVALUATION OF THE COULOMB REPULSION INTEGRAL OVER 1s AOs

Evaluation of

$$\iint 1s(1)1s(2)(1/r_{12})1s(1)1s(2)\,dv(1)\,dv(2) \tag{A3-1}$$

where

$$1s(1) = \sqrt{\xi^3/\pi}\exp(-\xi r) \tag{A3-2}$$

may be carried out in two closely related ways.[1] Each method is instructive and sheds light on the other, and so we will give both of them here.

The first method works from a physical model and requires knowledge of two features of situations governed by the $1/r^2$ force law (e.g., electrostatics, gravitation). Suppose that there exists a spherical shell in which charge or mass is distributed uniformly, like the soap solution in a soap bubble. The first feature is that a point charge or mass *outside* the sphere has a potential due to attraction (or repulsion) by the sphere that is identical to the potential produced if the sphere collapsed to a point at its center (conserving mass or charge in the process). Thus, the electrostatic interaction between two *separated* spherical charge distributions may be calculated as though all the charge were concentrated at their centers. The second feature is that the potential is identical for all points *inside* the spherical shell; that is, if the core of the earth were hollow, a person would be weightless there. There would be no tendency for that person to drift toward a wall or toward the center.

Armed with these facts, we can evaluate the integral. First, we remark that all the functions in the integrand commute. This enables us to write Eq. (A3-1) as

$$\iint 1s^2(1)(1/r_{12})1s^2(2)\,dv(1)\,dv(2) \tag{A3-3}$$

[1] Other methods, not discussed here, also exist. See, for example, Margenau and Murphy [1, pp. 382–383].

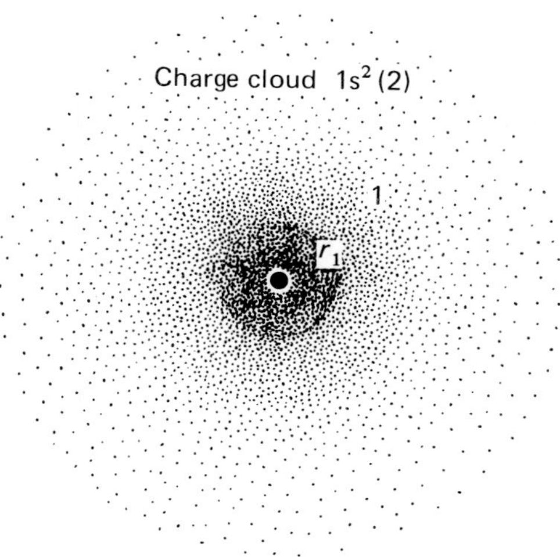

FIG. A3-1 Sketch of spherical charge cloud $1s^2(2)$ with electron 1 at a distance r_1 from the nucleus.

The functions $1s^2(1)$ and $1s^2(2)$ are just charge clouds for electrons 1 and 2, and the integral is evidently just the energy of repulsion between the clouds. Suppose (see Fig. A3-1) that, at some instant, electron 1 is at a distance r_1 from the nucleus. What is its energy of repulsion with the charge cloud of electron 2? The charge cloud of electron 2 can be divided into two parts: the charge inside a sphere of radius r_1 and the charge outside that sphere. From what we just said, electron 1 experiences a repulsion due to the cloud *inside* the sphere that is the same as the repulsion it would feel if that part of the cloud were collapsed to the center. We can calculate the energy due to this repulsion (call it the "inner repulsion energy") by dividing the product of charges by the distance between them:

$$\text{inner repulsion energy} = (\text{fraction of charge cloud 2 inside } r_1) \times 1/r_1$$

$$= 4\pi \int_0^{r_1} 1s^2(2) r_2^{\,2}\, dr_2 \times 1/r_1 \qquad \text{(A3-4)}$$

where the factor 4π comes from integrating over θ_2, ϕ_2. Electron 1 also experiences repulsion from charge cloud 2 *outside* the sphere of radius r_1. But, from what we said above, electron 1 would experience this same "outer repulsion" no matter where it was inside the inner sphere. Therefore we will calculate the energy due to this repulsion as though electron 1 were at the center, since this preserves spherical symmetry and simplifies the calculation. It follows that all the charge in a thin shell of radius r_2 repels electron 1 through an effective distance of r_2. Integrating over all such shells gives

$$\text{outer repulsion energy} = 4\pi \int_{r_1}^{\infty} (1/r_2) 1s^2(2) r_2^2 \, dr_2 \tag{A3-5}$$

The total energy of repulsion between charge cloud 2 and electron 1 at r_1 is the sum of inner and outer repulsive energies. But electron 1 is not always at r_1. Therefore, we must finally integrate over all positions of electron 1, weighted by the frequency of their occurrence:

$$\text{repulsive energy} = 16\pi^2 \int_0^{\infty} 1s^2(1) \left\{ (1/r_1) \int_0^{r_1} 1s^2(2) r_2^2 \, dr_2 + \int_{r_1}^{\infty} 1s^2(2) r_2 \, dr_2 \right\} r_1^2 \, dr_1 \tag{A3-6}$$

The inner integrals contain but one variable, r_2, and can be evaluated with the help of Appendix 1. After they are performed, the integrand depends only on r_1 and this is also easily integrated yielding $5\xi/8$ as the result. A positive value is necessary since a net repulsion exists between two clouds of like charge.

The second method of evaluation is more mathematical and more general. The function $1/r_{12}$ is expressible[2] as a series of terms involving associated Legendre functions:

$$\frac{1}{r_{12}} = \sum_{l=0}^{\infty} \sum_{m=-l}^{+l} \frac{(l-|m|)!}{(l+|m|)!} \frac{r_<^l}{r_>^{l+1}} P_l^{|m|}(\cos\theta_1) P_l^{|m|}(\cos\theta_2) \exp[im(\phi_1 - \phi_2)] \tag{A3-7}$$

This infinite series will give the distance between particles 1 and 2 located at positions r_1, θ_1, ϕ_1 and r_2, θ_2, ϕ_2 (Fig. A3-2). All we need to do is pick the

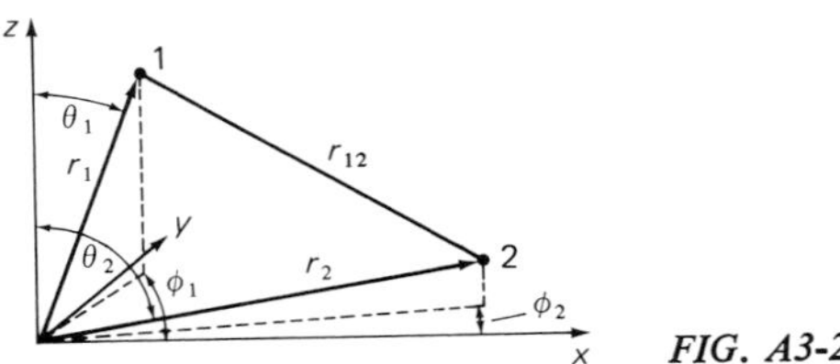

FIG. A3-2

larger of r_1 and r_2 and call that $r_>$, the other being $r_<$, and substitute those numbers into the formula. We also need all the Legendre functions for cos θ_1 and cos θ_2, and values of $\exp[im(\phi_1 - \phi_2)]$ for all integral values of m. Puttin

[2] See Eyring *et al.* [2, Appendix 5].

all this together as indicated by Eq. (A3-7) would give a series of numbers whose sum would converge to the value of $1/r_{12}$. While this is an exceedingly cumbersome way to calculate the distance between two points, it turns out that use of the formal expression (A3-7) enables us to integrate Eq. (A3-1). This comes about because the Legendre functions satisfy the relation

$$\int_0^\pi P_l^{|m|}(\cos\theta)P_{l'}^{|m|}(\cos\theta)\sin\theta\,d\theta = \frac{2}{2l+1}\frac{(l+|m|)!}{(l-|m|)!}\delta_{ll'} \qquad \text{(A3-8)}$$

The first Legendre polynomial P_0 is equal to unity. Therefore, 1s(i), which has no θ dependence, can be written

$$1s(i) = (\xi^3/\pi)^{1/2}\exp(-\xi r_i)P_0(\cos\theta_i) \qquad \text{(A3-9)}$$

Thus, in the integral (A3-1) there will be an integration over θ_1 of the form

$$\int_0^\pi P_0(\cos\theta_1)P_l^{|m|}(\cos\theta_1)P_0(\cos\theta_1)\sin\theta_1\,d\theta_1 \qquad \text{(A3-10)}$$

for each term in the sum (A3-7) (and a similar integral over θ_2). However, since $1^2 = 1$, $[P_0(\cos\theta_1)]^2 = P_0(\cos\theta_1)$, and integral (A3-10) becomes [by Eq. (A3-8)]

$$\int_0^\pi P_0(\cos\theta_1)P_l^{|m|}(\cos\theta_1)\sin\theta_1\,d\theta_1 = 2\delta_{0l} \qquad \text{(A3-11)}$$

[m must equal zero here, otherwise the integral over ϕ will vanish.] In other words, all terms of the sum over l and m vanish except the first term, for which $l = m = 0$. This gives that the $1/r_{12}$ operator is equal to $1/r_>$. Hence, the repulsion integral is

$$16\pi^2\int_0^\infty\int_0^\infty\left(\frac{1s^2(1)1s^2(2)r_1^2r_2^2}{r_>}\right)dr_2\,dr_1 \qquad \text{(A3-12)}$$

where $r_>$ is the greater of r_1, r_2. Suppose that we integrate over r_2 first. As r_2 changes value, it is sometimes smaller, sometimes larger than a particular value of r_1. When it is larger, $r_>$ is r_2. When it is smaller, $r_>$ is r_1. Putting this argument into mathematical form gives

$$16\pi^2\int_0^\infty\left\{\int_0^{r_1}\frac{1s^2(1)1s^2(2)r_1^2r_2^2\,dr_2}{r_1} + \int_{r_1}^\infty\frac{1s^2(1)1s^2(2)r_1^2r_2^2\,dr_2}{r_2}\right\}dr_1$$

(A3-13)

Since the variable of integration in the two inner integrals is r_2, the quantities $1s^2(1)$, r_1^2, and r_1 may be brought outside these inner integrals, giving us the same equation (A3-6) that we obtained by the first method. This second method is more generally useful because it can be used when repulsions involving p, d, etc. charge clouds are calculated. In these cases, terms involving $l = 1, 2$, etc., become nonvanishing, but the series generally truncates after a few terms.

REFERENCES

[1] H. Margenau and D. M. Murphy, "The Mathematics of Physics and Chemistry." Van Nostrand-Reinhold, Princeton, New Jersey, 1956.

[2] H. Eyring, J. Walter, and G. E. Kimball, "Quantum Chemistry." Wiley, New York, 1944.

APPENDIX 4

SOME CHARACTERISTICS OF SOLUTIONS OF THE LINEAR VARIATION PROCEDURE

In this appendix, we shall show that:

(1) the nondegenerate approximate eigenfunctions obtained by the linear variation procedure are orthogonal, and

(2) the nth lowest root is never lower than the nth exact eigenvalue of the hamiltonian.

We follow the approach of MacDonald [1]. The original proof of point (2) above was given by Hylleraas and Undheim [2].

Let us begin with a basis set of n linearly independent functions $\chi_1, \chi_2, \ldots, \chi_n$. For convenience, they are assumed to be orthonormal:

$$\chi_k{}^*\chi_l \, d\tau = \delta_{kl} \tag{A4-1}$$

These will be mixed by our variational procedure to form *approximate* eigenfunctions,

$$\phi_i = \sum_{k=1}^{n} c_{ki}\chi_k \tag{A4-2}$$

and *real* approximate eigenvalues

$$W_i = \int \phi_i{}^*\hat{H}\phi_i \, d\tau \tag{A4-3}$$

We symbolize the *exact* eigenfunctions and eigenvalues ψ_i and E_i, respectively. The coefficients in Eq. (A4-2) are assumed to be scaled to normalize the approximate eigenfunctions:

$$\int \phi_i{}^*\phi_i \, d\tau = 1 \tag{A4-4}$$

The process of linear variation is designed to find values of W that are stationary for infinitesimal variations in the approximate eigenfunctions. That is,

$$\delta W_i = \delta \int \phi_i{}^*\hat{H}\phi_i \, d\tau = 0 \tag{A4-5}$$

In Chapter 7 it is shown that this leads to a set of simultaneous homogeneous linear equations:

$$\int \chi_k^*(\hat{H} - W_i)\phi_i \, d\tau \equiv \sum_{l=1}^{n} (H_{kl} - W_i \, \delta_{kl})c_{li} = 0, \qquad i = 1, 2, \ldots, n \tag{A4-6}$$

where

$$H_{kl} = \int \chi_k^* \hat{H} \chi_l \, d\tau \tag{A4-7}$$

With this background of equations and definitions, we now show that the nondegenerate *approximate* eigenfunctions ϕ_i and ϕ_j are orthogonal. That

$$\int \phi_j^*(\hat{H} - W_i)\phi_i \, d\tau = 0 \tag{A4-8}$$

is easily seen since ϕ_j is a sum over χ's [Eq. (A4-2)], and Eq. (A4-8) becomes a sum of integrals, all of which have the form on the left of Eq. (A4-6) and all of which are therefore equal to zero. Similarly, since $\hat{H}$ is hermitian, we have [from Eq. (A4-8)]

$$\int \phi_i(\hat{H} - W_i)^*\phi_j^* \, d\tau = 0 \tag{A4-9}$$

The difference between an integral of the form (A4-8) (but with the i and j indices interchanged) and the integral (A4-9) must vanish:

$$\begin{aligned} \int [\phi_i^*(\hat{H} - W_j)\phi_j - \phi_i(\hat{H} - W_i)^*\phi_j^*] \, d\tau &= 0 \\ = (W_i^* - W_j) \int \phi_i^*\phi_j \, d\tau &+ \int \phi_i^* \hat{H} \phi_j \, d\tau - \int \phi_j \hat{H}^* \phi_i^* \, d\tau \\ = (W_i - W_j) \int \phi_i^* \phi_j \, d\tau & \end{aligned} \tag{A4-10}$$

where we have employed the facts that $\hat{H}$ is hermitian and W_i is real. Hence, if $W_i \neq W_2$, the integral must vanish and ϕ_i and ϕ_j are orthogonal.

We now consider the behavior of the roots W_i as more and more basis functions are added to the set. Suppose that we have solved the determinantal equation for our basis set of n functions, obtaining n approximate eigenfunctions ϕ_i and eigenvalues W_i. If we were to repeat the calculation using these newly found ϕ's as our basis set, the corresponding determinantal equation would be

$$D_n(W) = \begin{vmatrix} W_1 - W & 0 & 0 & \cdots & 0 \\ 0 & W_2 - W & 0 & \cdots & 0 \\ 0 & 0 & W_3 - W & \cdots & 0 \\ & & \vdots & & \vdots \\ 0 & 0 & 0 & \cdots & W_n - W \end{vmatrix} = 0 \tag{A4-11}$$

That is, if our basis set is identical to our solution set, there are no off-diagonal elements and no mixing among the basis functions occurs. The value of $D_n(W)$ in this form is simply the product of the diagonal elements

$$D_n(W) = \prod_{i=1}^{n} (W_i - W)$$

and it is easy to see that $D_n(W)$ vanishes whenever $W = W_1, W_2, \ldots, W_n$.

For convenience, we will assume that we have numbered the W_i's in order of increasing energy, so that $W_1 \leq W_2 \leq W_3 \leq \cdots \leq W_n$.

Suppose that we keep these ϕ's as our basis (they span the same function space as the χ's but do not give off-diagonal elements) and now we add one more function, χ_{n+1}, which is orthogonal to all the ϕ's and is normalized. This new basis set gives the following determinantal equation:

$$D_{n+1}(W) = \begin{vmatrix} W_1 - W & 0 & \cdots & 0 & H_{1,n+1} \\ 0 & W_2 - W & \cdots & 0 & H_{2,n+1} \\ \vdots & \vdots & & \vdots & \vdots \\ 0 & 0 & \cdots & W_n - W & H_{n,n+1} \\ H_{n+1,1} & H_{n+1,2} & \cdots & H_{n+1,n} & H_{n+1,n+1} - W \end{vmatrix} = 0 \tag{A4-12}$$

where $H_{n+1,i} = \int \chi_{n+1}^* \hat{H} \phi_i \, d\tau$.

Off-diagonal elements now appear in the row and column associated with the new basis function. This determinant can be expanded and shown to satisfy the equation

$$D_{n+1}(W) = \left[(H_{n+1,n+1} - W)\prod_{i=1}^{n}(W_i - W)\right] - \left[\sum_{k=1}^{n} |H_{k,n+1}|^2 \prod_{i=1,i\neq k}^{n} (W_i - W)\right] \tag{A4-13}$$

The value of $D_{n+1}(W)$ will vary with W and may be positive, negative, or zero. Values of W giving zero are our new approximate eigenvalues. To distinguish these new roots from the old, we label them W_1', W_2', $\ldots$, W_n', W_{n+1}'. We can say something about how these new roots W' are related to the old roots by seeing what value the new determinant $D_{n+1}(W)$ will have when W is set equal to one of the old roots W_j. In this case, the first bracket part in Eq. (A4-13) vanishes. Also, the second bracket part must vanish except when the jth term is omitted from the product. Hence,

$$D_{n+1}(W_j) = -|H_{j,n+1}|^2 \prod_{i=1,i\neq j}^{n} (W_i - W_j) \tag{A4-14}$$

The terms in the product are positive or zero when $i > j$, negative or zero when $i < j$, due to our earlier ordering of W's by energy. Hence, if j is an odd number, there is an even number of i's less than j, so the product is zero or positive, and so $D_{n+1}(W_j)$ is zero or negative. Continuing this argument gives the result

$$D_{n+1}(W_j)\begin{cases} \leq 0, & j \text{ odd} \\ \geq 0, & j \text{ even} \end{cases} \tag{A4-15}$$

[The zeros result if we have degeneracy such that several W_i equal W_j. Also if $H_{j,n+1}$ vanishes, $D_{n+1}(W_j)$ equals zero. The latter corresponds to no mixing because the interaction element is zero.]

Let us also check the behavior of $D_{n+1}(W)$ as W goes lower than W_1, toward $-\infty$, and higher than W_n, toward $+\infty$. Inspection of Eq. (A4-13) indicates that the first bracket term dominates the second because it increases like W^{n+1} as $W \to \pm\infty$ compared to W^{n-1} for the second bracket term. As W approaches $-\infty$, all the terms in the product are positive, and so $D_{n+1}(W)$ approaches $+\infty$. As W approaches $+\infty$, the product terms are negative, and the product sign depends on whether there is an even or an odd number of terms. As a result of these considerations, we have

$$D_{n+1}(W)\begin{cases} \to +\infty & \text{as} \quad W \to -\infty \\ \to (-1)^{n+1}\infty & \text{as} \quad W \to +\infty \end{cases} \tag{A4-16}$$

The results of Eqs. (A4-15)–(A4–16) tell us a great deal about how $D_{n+1}(W)$ varies with W. Consider a case in which we go from four basis functions to five. For simplicity, assume all roots to be nondegenerate. We start with four roots, W_1–W_4, located at W values that cause $D_4(W)$ to vanish. The situation is sketched in Fig. A4-1. We know that $D_5(W)$ will be positive at $W = W_2$ and

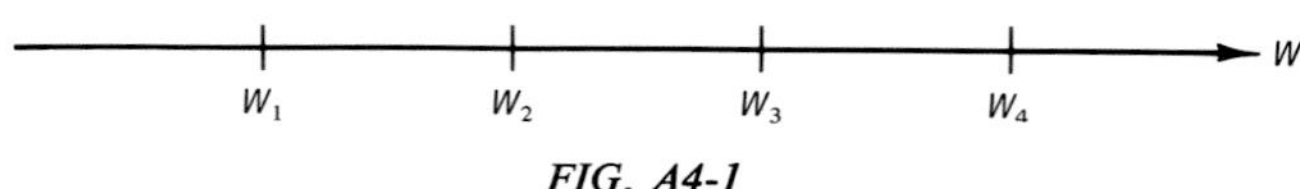

FIG. A4-1

W_4, and negative at $W = W_1$ and W_3. Also, we can say that $D_5(W)$ approaches $+\infty$ as $W \to -\infty$, and $-\infty$ as $W \to +\infty$. These conclusions are indicated in Fig. A4-2. We also know that $D_5(W)$ is a continuous function [since Eq. (A4-13)

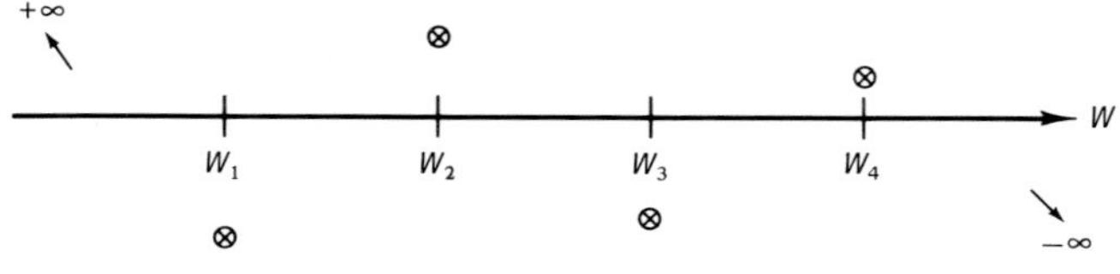

FIG. A4-2

is just a polynomial in powers of W] and that it can cross the $D_5(W) = 0$ axis no more than five times (since we are limited to five roots for a five-by-five determinant). This is sufficient to force the curve for $D_5(W)$ to behave *qualitatively* like the dashed line sketched in Fig. A4-3. Thus, our knowledge about

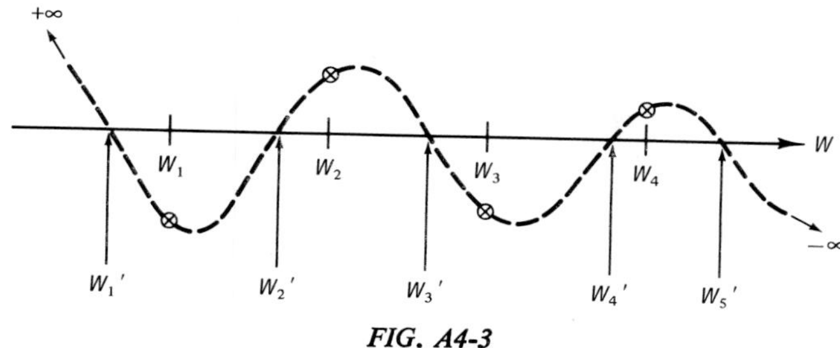

FIG. A4-3

$D_{n+1}(W)$ is sufficient to require that the old roots W be sandwiched between the new roots W' in a one-to-one ratio of roots to spaces. It is apparent from our last sketch that adding new basis functions can only cause a given root (e.g., the fourth lowest) to become even lower or perhaps remain unshifted. This means that the kth lowest root for a given calculation is an upper bound for the kth lowest root for any calculation having an even larger basis set (which includes the smaller basis set). If we go to an infinite and complete basis set, we obtain exact eigenvalues and eigenfunctions E and ψ. Therefore, we can conclude that, for a linear variation calculation, the kth lowest root is an upper bound for the kth lowest eigenvalue E_k of the hamiltonian.

REFERENCES

[1] J. K. L. MacDonald, *Phys. Rev.* **43**, 830 (1933).
[2] E. A. Hylleraas and B. Undheim, *Z. Physik* **65**, 759 (1930).

APPENDIX 5

THE PAIRING THEOREM[1]

A5-1 Pairing of Roots and Relation between Coefficients for Alternant Systems

The HMO assumptions are

$$H_{ij} = \begin{cases} \alpha & \text{if} \quad i = j \\ \beta & \text{if} \quad i \neq j \quad \text{are bonded together} \\ 0 & \text{if} \quad i \neq j \quad \text{are not bonded together} \end{cases} \tag{A5-1}$$

$$S_{ij} = \delta_{ij} \tag{A5-2}$$

$$\phi_k = \sum_i c_{ik}\chi_i \tag{A5-3}$$

where χ_i is a $2p_\pi$ AO on carbon i.

An alternant hydrocarbon can be labeled with asterisks to demonstrate the existence of two sets of carbon centers in the molecule such that no two atoms in the same set are nearest neighbors (see Chapter 8, Section 9). The following discussion pertains to alternant systems.

The simultaneous equations leading to Hückel energies and coefficients are of the form

$$c_i x + c_j + c_k + c_l + \cdots = 0 \tag{A5-4}$$

where $x = (\alpha - E)/\beta$. Atoms j, k, l must be bonded to atom i if c_j, c_k, c_l are to be unequal to zero. Hence, atoms j, k, and l belong to one set of atoms, and atom i belongs to the other set.

If we have already found a value of x and a set of coefficients satisfying the simultaneous equations (A5-4), it is easy to show that these equations will also be satisfied if we insert $-x$ and also reverse the signs of the coefficients for one set of centers *or* the other. If we reverse the coefficient signs for the set j, k, l, we obtain, on the left-hand side

$$c_i(-x) - c_j - c_k - c_l - \cdots \tag{A5-5}$$

[1] See Coulson and Rushbrooke [1].

which is the negative of Eq. (A5-4) and hence still equals zero. If we reverse the sign of c_i, we have

$$-c_i(-x) + c_j + c_k + c_l + \cdots \tag{A5-6}$$

which is identical to Eq. (A5-4).

This proves that each root of an alternant hydrocarbon at x ($\neq 0$) has a mate at $-x$ and that their associated coefficients differ only in sign between one or the other sets of atoms.

Note that, if $x = 0$, the c_i term vanishes, leaving coefficients for only one set of centers. Reversing all signs in this case corresponds to multiplying the *entire* MO by -1, which does not generate a new (linearly independent) function. Thus, it is possible for an alternant system to have a single, unpaired root at $x = 0$. It is *necessary* for odd alternants to have such a root. An even alternant may have a root at $x = 0$, but, if it has one such root, it must have another since, in the end, there must be an even number of roots.

A5-2 Demonstration That Electron Densities Are Unity in Ground States of Neutral Alternant Hydrocarbons

From n AOs result n MOs. The AOs as well as the MOs can be assumed normalized and (in the HMO method) orthogonal. If each AO contains one electron, the electron density at each AO is unity. If these AOs are combined to form MOs, and *each MO* has one electron, each AO electron density would still be unity, since the set of all singly occupied MOs is just a unitary transformation of the set of all singly occupied AOs.

(The matrix equivalent of these statements is

$$\mathsf{C}^{\dagger}\mathsf{C} = \mathsf{1} = \mathsf{C}\mathsf{C}^{\dagger} \tag{A5-7}$$

The left equality means that the sum of squares (absolute) of coefficients over *all atoms* in *one* MO is unity, so the MO is normalized. The right equality means that the sum of squares of coefficients over *one* atom in *all* MOs is unity.)

For an alternant hydrocarbon, however, the *squares* of coefficients in an MO at $E = \alpha + k\beta$ are identical to those in the MO at $E = \alpha - k\beta$. Therefore, no change in electron density will result if each electron in the upper half of our MO energy spectrum is shifted to its lower-energy mate. Thus, the resulting state, which is the neutral ground state, still has unit electron density at each AO.

REFERENCE

[1] C. A. Coulson and G. S. Rushbrooke, *Proc. Cambridge Phil. Soc.* **36**, 193 (1940).

APPENDIX 6

HÜCKEL MOLECULAR ORBITAL ENERGIES, COEFFICIENTS, ELECTRON DENSITIES, AND BOND ORDERS FOR SOME SIMPLE MOLECULES

Each molecule is labeled as alternant or nonalternant. For alternants, only the occupied MO data is tabulated since the remainder may be generated by use of the pairing theorem (see Appendix 5). Bond orders are tabulated for only one bond from each symmetry equivalent set in a molecule.

- x HMO root $= (\alpha - E)/\beta$
- n number of electrons in MO when molecule is in neutral ground state
- c_i LCAO–MO coefficient of AO at atom i
- q_i π-electron density on atom i
- p_{ij} π-bond order between atoms i and j
- E_π total π energy of the molecule $=$ sum of π-electron energies

Molecules in this tabulation are grouped according to the number of centers in the conjugated system.

Index of Systems Tabulated

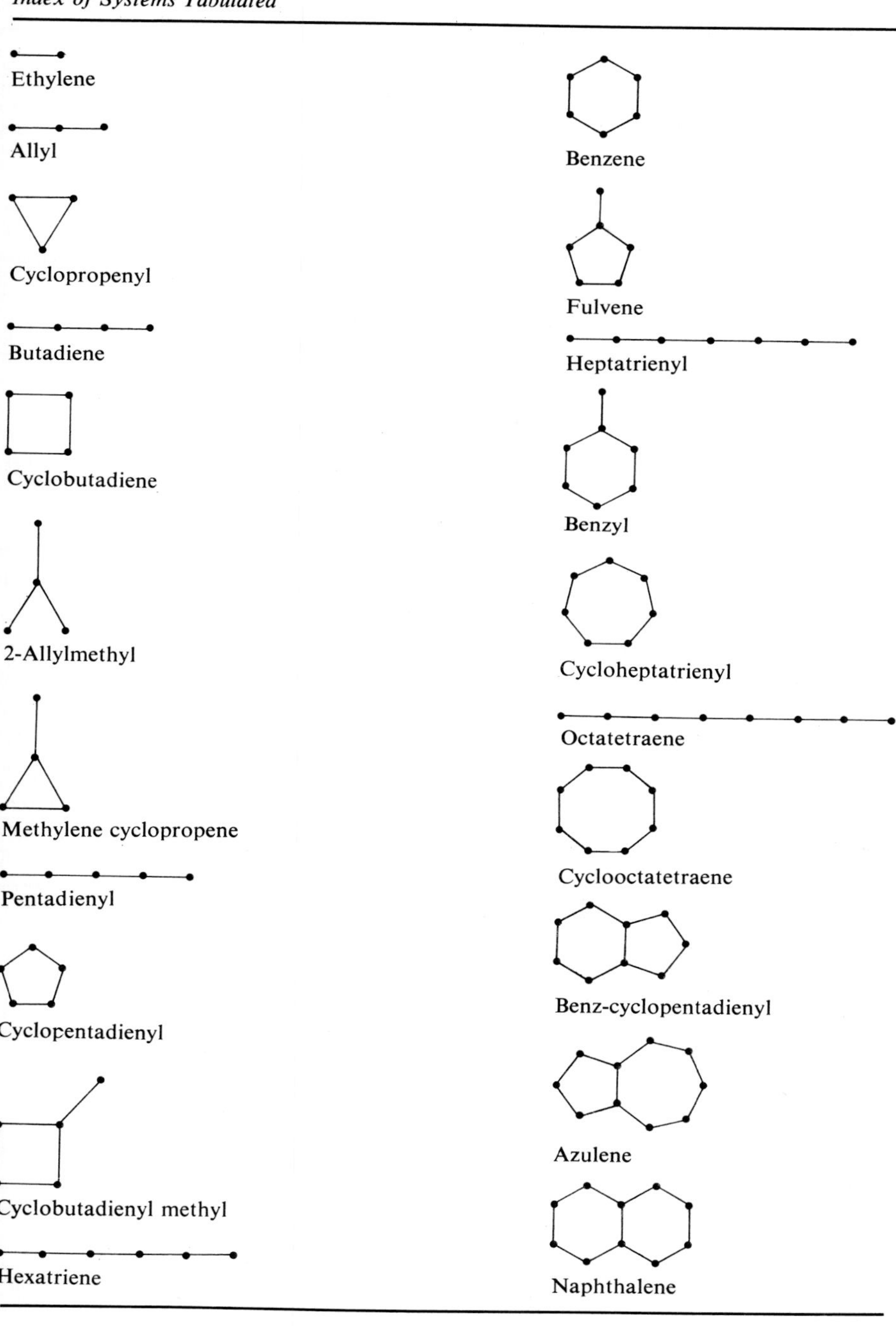
Ethylene
Allyl
Cyclopropenyl
Butadiene
Cyclobutadiene
2-Allylmethyl
Methylene cyclopropene
Pentadienyl
Cyclopentadienyl
Cyclobutadienyl methyl
Hexatriene
Benzene
Fulvene
Heptatrienyl
Benzyl
Cycloheptatrienyl
Octatetraene
Cyclooctatetraene
Benz-cyclopentadienyl
Azulene
Naphthalene

Two Centers

Ethylene (alternant) C_2H_2

1 2

all q = 1.0, p_{12} = 1.
E_π = 2α +

n	x	c_1	c_2
2	−1.000	0.7071	0.707

Three Centers

Allyl radical (alternant) C_3H_5

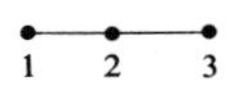

all q = 1.0, p_{12} = 0.70
E_π = 3α + 2.828

n	x	c_1	c_2	c_3
2	−1.4142	0.5000	0.7071	0.50
1	0.0000	0.7071	0.0000	−0.70

Cyclopropenyl radical (nonalternant) C_3H_3

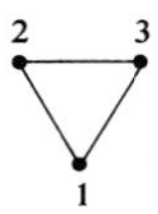

all q = 1.0, p_{12} = 0.
E_π = 3α + 3.000

n	x	c_1	c_2	c_3
2	−2.0000	0.5774	0.5774	0.57
$\frac{1}{2}$	1.0000	−0.8165	0.4082	0.40
$\frac{1}{2}$	1.0000	0.0000	0.7071	−0.70

Four Centers

Butadiene (alternant) C_4H_6

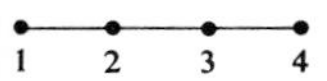

all $q = 1.0, p_{12} = 0.8944, p_{23} = 0.4472,$
$E_\pi = 4\alpha + 4.4721\beta$

n	x	c_1	c_2	c_3	c_4
2	−1.6180	0.3718	0.6015	0.6015	0.3718
2	−0.6180	0.6015	0.3718	−0.3718	−0.6105

Cyclobutadiene (alternant) C_4H_4

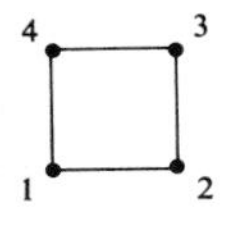

all $q = 1.0, p_{12} = 0.5, E_\pi = 4\alpha + 4.000\beta$

n	x	c_1	c_2	c_3	c_4
2	−2.0000	0.5000	0.5000	0.5000	0.5000
2	0.0000	0.5000	0.5000	−0.5000	−0.5000

2-Allylmethyl (alternant) C_4H_6

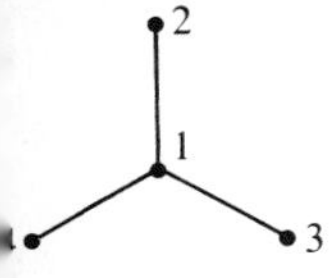

all $q = 1.0, p_{12} = 0.5774, E_\pi = 4\alpha + 3.4641\beta,$

n	x	c_1	c_2	c_3	c_4
2	−1.7320	0.7071	0.4082	0.4082	0.4082
1	0.0	0.0000	0.7071	−0.7071	0.0000
1	0.0	0.0000	0.4082	0.4082	−0.8165

Methylene cyclopropene C_4H_4 (nonalternant)

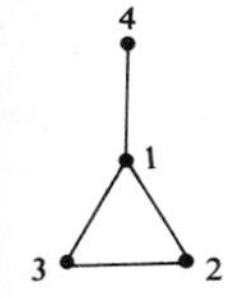

$E_\pi = 4\alpha + 4.9624\beta, p_{12} = 0.4527,$
$p_{23} = 0.8176, p_{14} = 0.7583$

n	x	c_1	c_2	c_3	c_4
2	−2.1701	0.6116	0.5227	0.5227	0.2818
2	−0.3111	0.2536	−0.3682	−0.3682	0.8152
0	1.0000	0.0000	0.7071	−0.7071	0.0000
0	1.4812	0.7494	−0.3020	−0.3020	−0.5059
	$q_i =$	0.8768	0.8176	0.8176	1.4881

Five Centers

Pentadienyl radical (alternant) C_5H_7

all q = 1.0, p_{12} = 0.7887, p_{23} = 0.577
E_π = 5α + 5.464

n	x	c_1	c_2	c_3	c_4	c_5
2	−1.7320	0.2887	0.5000	0.5774	0.5000	0.28
2	−1.0000	0.5000	0.5000	0.0000	−0.5000	−0.50
1	0.0000	0.5774	0.0000	−0.5774	0.0000	0.57

Cyclopentadienyl radical (nonalternant) C_5H_5

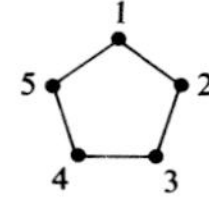

all q = 1.0, p_{12} = 0.5854, E_π = 5α+5.854

n	x	c_1	c_2	c_3	c_4	c_5
2	−2.0000	0.4472	0.4472	0.4472	0.4472	0.44
$\frac{3}{2}$	−0.6180	0.6325	0.1954	−0.5117	−0.5117	0.19
$\frac{3}{2}$	−0.6180	0.0000	−0.6015	−0.3718	0.3718	0.60
0	1.6180	0.6325	−0.5117	0.1954	0.1954	−0.51
0	1.6180	0.0000	0.3718	−0.6015	0.6015	−0.37

Cyclobutadienylmethyl radical (alternant) C_5H_5

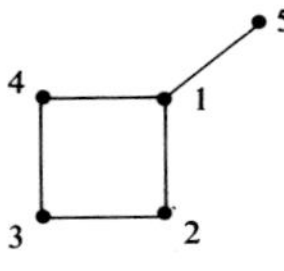

all q = 1.0, p_{12} = 0.3574, p_{23} = 0.61
p_{15} = 0.8628, E_π = 5α + 5.595

n	x	c_1	c_2	c_3	c_4	c_5
2	−2.1358	0.5573	0.4647	0.4351	0.4647	0.26
2	−0.6622	−0.4351	0.1845	0.5573	0.1845	−0.65
1	0.0000	0.0000	−0.7071	0.0000	0.7071	0.00

Six Centers

Hexatriene (alternant) C_6H_8

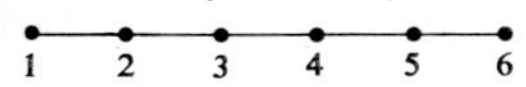

all $q = 1.0$, $p_{12} = 0.8711$, $p_{23} = 0.4834$, $p_{34} = 0.7848$, $E_\pi = 6\alpha + 6.9879\beta$

n	x	c_1	c_2	c_3	c_4	c_5	c_6
2	−1.8019	0.2319	0.4179	0.5211	0.5211	0.4179	0.2319
2	−1.2470	0.4179	0.5211	0.2319	−0.2319	−0.5211	−0.4179
2	−0.4450	0.5211	0.2319	−0.4179	−0.4179	0.2319	0.5211

Benzene (alternant) C_6H_6

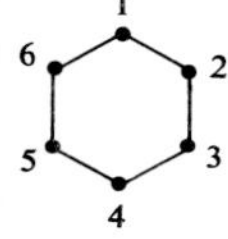

all $q = 1.0$, $p_{12} = 0.6667$, $E_\pi = 6\alpha + 8\beta$

n	x	c_1	c_2	c_3	c_4	c_5	c_6
2	−2.0000	0.4082	0.4082	0.4082	0.4082	0.4082	0.4082
2	−1.0000	0.0000	0.5000	0.5000	0.0000	−0.5000	−0.5000
2	−1.0000	0.5774	0.2887	−0.2887	−0.5774	−0.2887	0.2887

Fulvene (nonalternant) C_6H_6

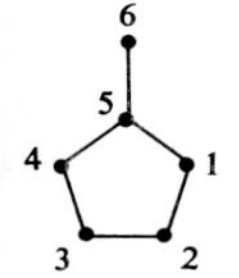

$E_\pi = 6\alpha + 7.4659\beta$, $p_{12} = 0.7779$, $p_{23} = 0.5202$, $p_{45} = 0.4491$, $p_{56} = 0.7586$

n	x	c_1	c_2	c_3	c_4	c_5	c_6
2	−2.1149	0.4294	0.3851	0.3851	0.4294	0.5230	0.2473
2	−1.0000	0.0000	0.5000	0.5000	0.0000	−0.5000	−0.5000
2	−0.6180	0.6015	0.3718	−0.3718	−0.6015	0.0000	0.0000
0	0.2541	−0.3505	0.2795	0.2795	−0.3505	−0.1904	0.7495
0	1.6180	−0.3718	0.6015	−0.6015	0.3718	0.0000	0.0000
0	1.8608	−0.4390	0.1535	0.1535	−0.4390	0.6635	−0.3566
	$q_i =$	1.0923	1.0730	1.0730	1.0923	1.0470	0.6223

Seven Centers

Heptatrienyl radical (alternant) C_7H_9

1 2 3 4 5 6 7

all $q = 1.0$, $E_\pi = 7\alpha + 8.0547\beta$,
$p_{12} = 0.8155$, $p_{23} = 0.5449$, $p_{34} = 0.6533$

n	x	c_1	c_2	c_3	c_4	c_5	c_6	c_7
2	−1.8478	0.1913	0.3536	0.4619	0.5000	0.4619	0.3536	0.1913
2	−1.4142	0.3536	0.5000	0.3536	0.0000	−0.3536	−0.5000	−0.3536
2	−0.7654	0.4619	0.3536	−0.1913	−0.5000	−0.1913	0.3536	0.4619
1	0.0000	−0.5000	0.0000	0.5000	0.0000	−0.5000	0.0000	0.5000

Benzyl radical (alternant) C_7H_7

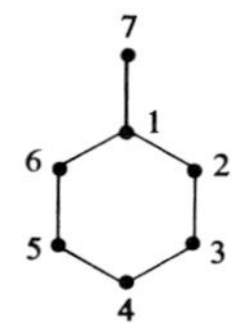

all $q = 1.0$, $p_{12} = 0.5226$, $p_{23} = 0.7050$,
$p_{34} = 0.6350$, $p_{17} = 0.6350$, $E_\pi = 7\alpha + 8.7206\beta$

n	x	c_1	c_2	c_3	c_4	c_5	c_6	c_7
2	−2.1010	0.5000	0.4063	0.3536	0.3366	0.3536	0.4063	0.2380
2	−1.2593	−0.5000	−0.1163	0.3536	0.5615	0.3536	−0.1163	−0.3970
2	−1.0000	0.0000	0.5000	0.5000	0.0000	−0.5000	−0.5000	0.0000
1	0.0000	0.0000	−0.3780	0.0000	0.3780	0.0000	−0.3780	0.7560

Cycloheptatrienyl radical (nonalternant) C_7H_7

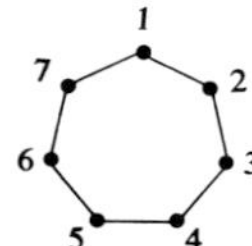

all $q = 1.0$, $p_{12} = 0.6102$, $E_\pi = 7\alpha + 8.5429\beta$

n	x	c_1	c_2	c_3	c_4	c_5	c_6	c_7
2	−2.0000	0.3780	0.3780	0.3780	0.3780	0.3780	0.3780	0.3780
2	−1.2470	−0.5345	−0.3333	0.1189	0.4816	0.4816	0.1189	−0.3333
2	−1.2470	0.0000	−0.4179	−0.5211	−0.2319	0.2319	0.5211	0.4179
$\frac{1}{2}$	0.4450	0.5345	−0.1189	−0.4816	0.3333	0.3333	−0.4816	−0.1189
$\frac{1}{2}$	0.4450	0.0000	0.5211	−0.2319	−0.4180	0.4180	0.2319	−0.5211
0	1.8019	−0.5345	0.4816	−0.3333	0.1189	0.1189	−0.3333	0.4816
0	1.8019	0.0000	0.2319	−0.4179	0.5211	−0.5211	0.4179	−0.2319

ight Centers

ctatetraene (alternant) C_8H_{10}

1 2 3 4 5 6 7 8

all $q = 1.0, p_{12} = 0.8621, p_{23} = 0.4948,$
$p_{34} = 0.7581, p_{45} = 0.5288, E_\pi = 8\alpha + 9.5175\beta$

x	c_1	c_2	c_3	c_4	c_5	c_6	c_7	c_8
−1.8794	0.1612	0.3030	0.4082	0.4642	0.4642	0.4082	0.3030	0.1612
−1.5321	0.3030	0.4642	0.4082	0.1612	−0.1612	−0.4082	−0.4642	−0.3030
−1.0000	−0.4082	−0.4082	0.0000	0.4082	0.4082	0.0000	−0.4082	−0.4082
−0.3473	0.4642	0.1612	−0.4082	−0.3030	0.3030	0.4082	−0.1612	−0.4642

yclooctatetraene (alternant) C_8H_8

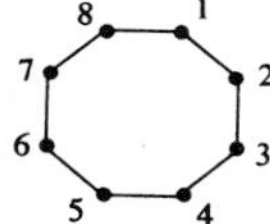

all $q = 1.0, p_{12} = 0.6035, E_\pi = 8\alpha + 9.6568\beta$

x	c_1	c_2	c_3	c_4	c_5	c_6	c_7	c_8
−2.0000	0.3536	0.3536	0.3536	0.3536	0.3536	0.3536	0.3536	0.3536
−1.4142	0.3536	0.0000	−0.3536	−0.5000	−0.3536	0.0000	0.3536	0.5000
−1.4142	0.3536	0.5000	0.3536	0.0000	−0.3536	−0.5000	−0.3536	0.0000
0.0000	0.3536	0.3536	−0.3536	−0.3536	0.3536	0.3536	−0.3536	−0.3536
0.0000	0.3536	−0.3536	−0.3536	0.3536	0.3536	−0.3536	−0.3536	0.3536

ne Centers

nzcyclopentadienyl radical (nonalternant) C_9H_7

7 1 8 2 9 3 4

$p_{12} = 0.6592, p_{49} = 0.6608, p_{56} = 0.7301,$
$p_{18} = 0.3921, p_{45} = 0.5494, p_{89} = 0.5374,$
$E_\pi = 9\alpha + 11.5808\beta$

n	x	c_1	c_2	c_3	c_4	c_5	c_6	c_7	c_8	c_9
2	−2.3226	0.3203	0.2758	0.3203	0.2988	0.2259	0.2259	0.2988	0.4681	0.4681
2	−1.5450	−0.3114	−0.4031	−0.3114	0.2689	0.4934	0.4934	0.2689	−0.0780	−0.0780
2	−1.1935	0.2992	0.0000	−0.2992	−0.4841	−0.2207	0.2207	0.4841	0.3571	−0.3571
2	−0.7293	−0.2054	−0.5634	−0.2054	0.0935	−0.3454	−0.3454	0.0935	0.4136	0.4136
1	−0.2950	0.5428	0.0000	−0.5428	0.3355	0.2591	−0.2591	−0.3355	0.1601	−0.1601
0	0.9016	0.1548	−0.3434	0.1548	−0.5424	0.2852	0.2852	−0.5424	0.2038	0.2038
0	1.2950	−0.2591	0.0000	0.2591	−0.1601	0.5428	−0.5428	0.1601	0.3355	−0.3355
0	1.6952	0.4840	−0.5711	0.4840	0.1884	−0.0699	−0.0699	0.1884	−0.2495	−0.2495
0	2.1935	−0.2207	0.0000	0.2207	0.3571	−0.2992	0.2992	−0.3571	0.4841	−0.4841
	$q_i =$	0.6625	1.1119	0.6625	0.8092	0.9249	0.9249	0.8092	1.0474	1.0474

Ten Centers

Azulene (nonalternant) $C_{10}H_8$

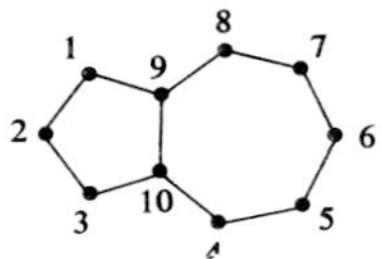

$p_{12} = 0.6560, p_{4,10} = 0.5858, p_{56} = 0.638$
$p_{19} = 0.5956, p_{45} = 0.6640, p_{9,10} = 0.400$
$E_\pi = 10\alpha + 13.3635$

n	x	c_1	c_2	c_3	c_4	c_5	c_6	c_7	c_8	c_9	c_{10}
2	−2.3103	0.3233	0.2799	0.3233	0.2886	0.1998	0.1730	0.1998	0.2886	0.4670	0.46
2	−1.6516	−0.2678	−0.3243	−0.2678	0.1909	0.4333	0.5247	0.4333	0.1909	−0.1180	−0.11
2	−1.3557	0.2207	0.0000	−0.2207	−0.4841	−0.3571	0.0000	0.3571	0.4841	0.2992	−0.29
2	−0.8870	−0.2585	−0.5829	−0.2585	0.2186	−0.1598	−0.3603	−0.1598	0.2186	0.3536	0.35
2	−0.4773	0.5428	0.0000	−0.5428	0.1601	0.3355	0.0000	−0.3355	−0.1601	0.2591	−0.25
0	0.4004	−0.0632	0.3158	−0.0632	0.4699	0.1023	−0.5109	0.1023	0.4699	−0.2904	−0.29
0	0.7376	−0.2992	0.0000	0.2992	−0.3571	0.4841	0.0000	−0.4841	0.3571	0.2207	−0.22
0	1.5792	0.4364	−0.5527	0.4364	−0.0844	0.2697	−0.3416	0.2697	−0.0844	−0.1365	−0.13
0	1.8692	−0.2500	0.2675	−0.2500	−0.3233	0.4045	−0.4328	0.4045	−0.3233	0.1998	0.19
0	2.0953	−0.2591	0.0000	0.2591	0.3355	−0.1601	0.0000	0.1601	−0.3355	0.5428	−0.54
	$q_i =$	1.1729	1.0466	1.1729	0.8550	0.9864	0.8700	0.9864	0.8550	1.0274	1.02

Naphthalene (alternant) $C_{10}H_8$

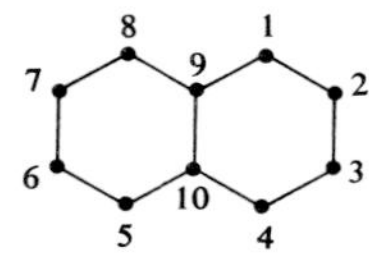

all $q = 1.0$, $E_\pi = 10\alpha + 13.6832$
$p_{12} = 0.7246, p_{23} = 0.6032, p_{19} = 0.5547, p_{9,10} = 0.518$

n	x	c_1	c_2	c_3	c_4	c_5	c_6	c_7	c_8	c_9	c_{10}
2	−2.3028	0.3006	0.2307	0.2307	0.3006	0.3006	0.2307	0.2307	0.3006	0.4614	0.461
2	−1.6180	0.2629	0.4253	0.4253	0.2629	−0.2629	−0.4253	−0.4253	−0.2629	0.0000	0.000
2	−1.3028	0.3996	0.1735	−0.1735	−0.3996	−0.3996	−0.1735	0.1735	0.3996	0.3470	−0.347
2	−1.0000	0.0000	−0.4082	−0.4082	0.0000	0.0000	−0.4082	−0.4082	0.0000	0.4082	0.408
2	−0.6180	0.4253	0.2629	−0.2629	−0.4253	0.4253	0.2629	−0.2629	−0.4253	0.0000	0.000

APPENDIX 7

DERIVATION OF THE HARTREE–FOCK EQUATION

This appendix is divided into two parts. In the first section we develop the formula for the expectation value $\bar{E} = \langle\psi|H|\psi\rangle$ for the case in which ψ is a single determinantal wavefunction over MOs. In the second section we derive the Hartree–Fock equation by requiring $\bar{E}$ to be stationary with respect to variations in ψ.

A7-1 The Expansion of $\bar{E}$ in Terms of Integrals over MOs

We limit discussion to the case in which ψ is a single, closed-shell determinant. We will develop our arguments by referring to a four-electron example:

$$\psi_4 = (4!)^{-1/2}|\phi_1(1)\bar{\phi}_1(2)\phi_2(3)\bar{\phi}_2(4)| \tag{A7-1}$$

Recall that this is the shorthand formula for a Slater determinant. Each ϕ is a normalized MO, the MOs are assumed to be orthogonal, and a bar signifies that an electron possesses β spin.

As we develop our arguments within the context of ψ, we will generalize them to apply to the general $2n$ electron closed-shell wavefunction

$$\psi_{2n} = [(2n)!]^{-1/2}|\phi_1(1)\bar{\phi}_1(2)\phi_2(3)\bar{\phi}_2(4)\cdots\phi_n(2n-1)\bar{\phi}_n(2n)| \tag{A7-2}$$

When ψ_4 is expanded according to the rule for determinants (Appendix 2), we obtain 4! products. We note the following features of the expanded form.

(1) There is one product, occurring with coefficient $+1$, which is identical to the product appearing in the shorthand form of Eq. (A7-1). We refer to this as the "leading term."

(2) An equivalent way of expressing a Slater determinant is via the expression (for ψ_4)

$$\psi_4 = (4!)^{-1/2}\sum_P(-1)^pP(\phi_1(1)\bar{\phi}_1(2)\phi_2(3)\bar{\phi}_2(4)) \tag{A7-3}$$

Here P stands for all the sequences of permutations of electron labels that lead to different products (i.e., P is a permutation *operator*), and p is the number of pairwise permutations in a given sequence. For ψ_4 there are 4! sequences P, the simplest being "no permutations" (hence, $p = 0$) which produces the leading term. Then there are single permutations, such as $P_{1,2}$ (with $p = 1$), which produces the term $-\phi_1(2)\bar{\phi}_1(1)\phi_2(3)\bar{\phi}_2(4)$. There are also double permutations, etc. According to Eq. (A7-3), any term differing from the leading term by an odd number of permutations will appear with coefficient -1. We will be particularly concerned with products that differ from the leading term by a single permutation.

(3) A single permutation may be made to occur between electrons in MO's with the same spins or different spins. In the latter case, two electrons in the singly permuted product will disagree in spin with their counterparts in the leading term. In the former case, no such spin disagreement will exist.

(4) Terms also appear in ψ_4 corresponding to more than a single permutation of electron indices.

It is useful to pick a representative example of each type of product mentioned above. For ψ_4, we have the following:

Leading term: $\phi_1(1)\bar{\phi}_1(2)\phi_2(3)\bar{\phi}_2(4)$
Singly permuted term: $\phi_1(1)\bar{\phi}_1(4)\phi_2(3)\bar{\phi}_2(2)$; Spin agreement: $(P_{2,4})$
Singly permuted term: $\phi_1(2)\bar{\phi}_1(1)\phi_2(3)\bar{\phi}_2(4)$; Spin disagreement: $(P_{1,2})$
Doubly permuted term: $\phi_1(2)\bar{\phi}_1(4)\phi_2(3)\bar{\phi}_2(1)$; $(P_{1,2}P_{1,4})$

Upon expanding $\langle\psi_4|\hat{H}|\psi_4\rangle$, we obtain a set of 4! products on both the left- and right-hand sides of $\hat{H}$:

$$\begin{aligned}\bar{E} = (4!)^{-1}\int &\{\phi_1{}^*(1)\bar{\phi}_1{}^*(2)\phi_2{}^*(3)\bar{\phi}_2{}^*(4) - \phi_1{}^*(1)\bar{\phi}_1{}^*(4)\phi_2{}^*(3)\bar{\phi}_2{}^*(2) - \cdots\} \\ &\times \hat{H}(1,2,3,4)\{\phi_1(1)\bar{\phi}_1(2)\phi_2(3)\bar{\phi}_2(4) - \phi_1(1)\bar{\phi}_1(4)\phi_2(3)\bar{\phi}_2(2) - \cdots\}\, d\tau\end{aligned} \tag{A7-4}$$

This can be expanded into a set of integrals, one for each term on the left:

$$\begin{aligned}\bar{E} = (4!)^{-1}\Big\{\int &\phi_1{}^*(1)\bar{\phi}_1{}^*(2)\phi_2{}^*(3)\bar{\phi}_2{}^*(4)\hat{H}(1,2,3,4)[\phi_1(1)\bar{\phi}_1(2)\phi_2(3)\bar{\phi}_2(4) \\ &- \phi_1(1)\bar{\phi}_1(4)\phi_2(3)\bar{\phi}_2(2) - \phi_1(2)\bar{\phi}_1(1)\phi_2(3)\bar{\phi}_2(4) - \cdots]\, d\tau \\ &- \int \phi_1{}^*(1)\bar{\phi}_1{}^*(4)\phi_2{}^*(3)\bar{\phi}_2{}^*(2)\hat{H}(1,2,3,4)[\phi_1(1)\bar{\phi}_1(2)\phi_2(3)\bar{\phi}_2(4) \\ &- \phi_1(1)\bar{\phi}_1(4)\phi_2(3)\bar{\phi}_2(2) - \phi_1(2)\bar{\phi}_1(1)\phi_2(3)\bar{\phi}_2(4) - \cdots]\, d\tau\Big\}\end{aligned} \tag{A7-5}$$

etc. In Eq. (A7-5), $\bar{E}$ is a sum of 4! integrals, each containing one term from the set on the left of $\hat{H}$ and all 4! from the set on the right.

At first, it might seem that we must evaluate all of the 4! integrals in Eq. (A7-5). But it can be shown that these integrals, times their $+1$ or -1 coefficients, are all equal to each other, enabling us to write $\bar{E}$ as 4! times the first integral:

$$\begin{aligned}\bar{E} = \int &\phi_1{}^*(1)\bar{\phi}_1{}^*(2)\phi_2{}^*(3)\bar{\phi}_2{}^*(4)\hat{H}(1,2,3,4) \\ &\sum_P (-1)^p P(\phi_1(1)\bar{\phi}_1(2)\phi_2(3)\bar{\phi}_2(4))\, d\tau\end{aligned} \tag{A7-6}$$

The demonstration that the various integrals in Eq. (A7-5), times their coefficients, are equal to each other is as follows. Consider the second integral in Eq. (A7-5). Note that, if we permute electrons 2 and 4 in that integral, we restore the term on the left of $\hat{H}$ to its original "leading term" order, thereby making that product identical to its counterpart in the first integral. Furthermore, if we carry out this permutation throughout the whole of the integrand of integral number 2 (i.e., in $\hat{H}$, in all 4! products to the right of $\hat{H}$, and in $d\tau$), we will not affect the value of the integral. (Recall that, for example,

$$\int_0^1 x^2\,dx \int_1^2 y^3\,dy \equiv \int_0^1 y^2\,dy \int_1^2 x^3\,dx)$$

The result of this permutation $P_{2,4}$ on the second integral in Eq. (A7-5) is

$$\int \phi_1{}^*(1)\bar{\phi}_1{}^*(2)\phi_2{}^*(3)\bar{\phi}_2{}^*(4)\hat{H}(1, 4, 3, 2)[\phi_1(1)\bar{\phi}_1(4)\phi_2(3)\bar{\phi}_2(2) - \phi_1(1)\bar{\phi}_1(2)\phi_2(3)\bar{\phi}_2(4) - \cdots]\,d\tau \tag{A7-7}$$

Now $\hat{H}$ is invariant under exchange of electron indices, and the set of products to the right of $\hat{H}$ in Eq. (A7-7) is the same set we had before, but their order is changed, and the whole product evidently differs by a factor of -1 from the set in the first integral. Therefore, we can say that the first and second integrals of Eq. (A7-5) have the same absolute value but different signs. However, the fact that these integrals contribute to $\bar{E}$ with opposite signs cancels the sign disagreement. In this way, every integral in Eq. (A7-5) can be compared to the leading integral and Eq. (A7-6) verified. This much simplified expression for $\bar{E}$ is, for the $2n$-electron case

$$\bar{E} = \int \phi_1{}^*(1)\bar{\phi}_1{}^*(2)\cdots\phi_n{}^*(2n-1)\bar{\phi}_n{}^*(2n)\hat{H}(1, 2, \ldots, 2n) \left[\sum_P (-1)^p P(\phi_1(1)\bar{\phi}_1(2)\cdots\phi_n(2n-1)\bar{\phi}_n(2n))\right] d\tau \tag{A7-8}$$

At this point we write out $\hat{H}$ more explicitly. It is, in atomic units,

$$\hat{H}(1, 2, \ldots, 2n) = \sum_{i=1}^{2n}\left(-\tfrac{1}{2}\nabla_i{}^2 - \sum_{\mu}^{\text{nuclei}} Z_\mu/r_{\mu i}\right) + \sum_{i=1}^{2n-1}\sum_{j=i+1}^{2n} 1/r_{ij} \tag{A7-9}$$

$$= \sum_{i=1}^{2n} H_{(i)}^{\text{core}} + \sum{}' \, 1/r_{ij} \tag{A7-10}$$

Here, $\sum'$ is a shorthand symbol for the double sum in Eq. (A7-9). We see that $\hat{H}$ is comprised of one-electron operators, $H_{(i)}^{\text{core}}$, which deal with the kinetic and nuclear-electron attraction energies for electron i, and two-electron operators for interelectronic repulsion. The internuclear repulsion is omitted since, for a given nuclear configuration, it is simply a constant that can be added to the electronic energy. Note for future reference that $\hat{H}$ has no dependence on electron spin coordinates.

If we insert the expression (A7-10) for $\hat{H}$ into Eq. (A7-6) for $\bar{E}$, it is easy to to see that we can expand the result into separate sets of integrals over one- and two-electron operators. We consider first the one-electron integrals. For ψ_4, these are

$$\int (\phi_1{}^*(1)\bar{\phi}_1{}^*(2)\phi_2{}^*(3)\bar{\phi}_2{}^*(4)) \times \sum_{i=1}^{4} H_{(i)}^{\text{core}} [\phi_1(1)\bar{\phi}_1(2)\phi_2(3)\bar{\phi}_2(4) - \phi_1(1)\bar{\phi}_1(4)\phi_2(3)\phi_2(2) - \cdots] \, d\tau \tag{A7-11}$$

Upon expanding this, the first set of integrals we obtain is

$$\int \phi_1{}^*(1)\bar{\phi}_1{}^*(2)\phi_2{}^*(3)\bar{\phi}_2{}^*(4)[H_{(1)}^{\text{core}} + H_{(2)}^{\text{core}} + H_{(3)}^{\text{core}} + H_{(4)}^{\text{core}}] \phi_1(1)\bar{\phi}_1(2)\phi_2(3)\bar{\phi}_2(4) \, d\tau \tag{A7-12}$$

This can be expanded again. The first integral contains the operator $H_{(1)}^{\text{core}}$, which does not act on electrons 2–4. This allows a separation into a product of integrals as follows:

$$\int \phi_1{}^*(1)\bar{\phi}_1{}^*(2)\phi_2{}^*(3)\bar{\phi}_2{}^*(4)H_{(1)}^{\text{core}}\phi_1(1)\bar{\phi}_1(2)\phi_2(3)\bar{\phi}_2(4) \, d\tau \tag{A7-13}$$

$$= \int \phi_1{}^*(1)H_{(1)}^{\text{core}}\phi_1(1) \, d\tau_1 \int \bar{\phi}_1{}^*(2)\bar{\phi}_1(2) \, d\tau_2 \int \phi_2{}^*(3)\phi_2(3) \, d\tau_3 \int \bar{\phi}_2{}^*(4)\bar{\phi}_2(4) \, d\tau_4 \tag{A7-14}$$

The last three integrals are overlap integrals and are all unity by virtue of normality of the MOs. The first integral, a "core integral," is normally symbolized H_{11}. Here the subscripts refer to the MO index, not the electron index:

$$H_{ii} = \int \phi_i{}^*(1)H_{(1)}^{\text{core}}\phi_i(1) \, d\tau_1 \tag{A7-15}$$

Therefore, Eq. (A7-13) equals H_{11}. By continued expansion, Eq. (A7-12) can be shown to be equal to $H_{11} + H_{11} + H_{22} + H_{22} = 2(H_{11} + H_{22})$. In this case, we have been dealing with identical MO products on the two sides of the operator.

As we continue evaluating the expansion of Eq. (A7-12), we next encounter an integral in which the products differ by a permutation, namely,

$$-\int \phi_1{}^*(1)\bar{\phi}_1{}^*(2)\phi_2{}^*(3)\bar{\phi}_2{}^*(4)[H_{(1)}^{\text{core}} + H_{(2)}^{\text{core}} + H_{(3)}^{\text{core}} + H_{(4)}^{\text{core}}]\phi_1(1)\bar{\phi}_1(4)\phi_2(3)\bar{\phi}_2(2) \, d\tau \tag{A7-16}$$

Again, for $H^{\text{core}}(1)$, this may be written

$$-\int \phi_1{}^*(1)H_{(1)}^{\text{core}}\phi_1(1) \, d\tau_1 \int \bar{\phi}_1{}^*(2)\bar{\phi}_2(2) \, d\tau_2 \times \int \phi_2{}^*(3)\phi_2(3) \, d\tau_3 \int \bar{\phi}_2{}^*(4)\bar{\phi}_1(4) \, d\tau_4 \tag{A7-17}$$

Orbital orthogonality will cause the second and fourth integrals to vanish. In general, if the two products differ by one or more permutations, they will have two or more sites of disagreement. Upon expansion, at least one disagreement will occur in an overlap integral, causing the integral to vanish. Thus, except for the integral involving identical products [Eq. (A7-12)], all the integrals obtained by expansion of Eq. (A7-11) vanish. Our result, generalized to the $2n$-electron case, is (see Appendix 11 for bra–ket notation)

$$\left\langle \psi_{2n} \right| \sum_{i=1}^{2n} H_{(i)}^{\text{core}} \left| \psi_{2n} \right\rangle = \sum_{i=1}^{n} 2H_{ii} \tag{A7-18}$$

We now turn to integrals containing two-electron operators. Consider, for example, an integral that has products differing in two places,

$$-\langle \phi_1(1)\bar{\phi}_1(2)\phi_2(3)\bar{\phi}_2(4)|1/r_{13}|\phi_1(3)\bar{\phi}_1(2)\phi_2(1)\bar{\phi}_2(4)\rangle \tag{A7-19}$$

This can be partly separated into a product of integrals over different electron coordinates.

$$(\text{A7-19}) = -\langle \phi_1(1)\phi_2(3)|1/r_{13}|\phi_1(3)\phi_2(1)\rangle\langle \bar{\phi}_1(2)|\bar{\phi}_1(2)\rangle\langle \bar{\phi}_2(4)|\bar{\phi}_2(4)\rangle \tag{A7-20}$$

Observe that the two disagreements are inside the two-electron integral, and that the overlap terms both show complete internal agreement and are therefore equal to unity. It is clear that, if our two products differed in *more* than two places, at least one such disagreement would appear in an overlap integral, causing the whole integral to vanish. Therefore, two-electron integrals need be considered only if they involve products differing by zero or one permutations. Let us consider these two possibilities separately.

If there are no disagreements, we have for ψ_4,

$$\begin{aligned}
&\left\langle \phi_1(1)\bar{\phi}_1(2)\phi_2(3)\bar{\phi}_2(4) \middle| \sum{}' 1/r_{ij} \middle| \phi_1(1)\bar{\phi}_1(2)\phi_2(3)\bar{\phi}_2(4) \right\rangle \\
&\quad = \langle \phi_1(1)\bar{\phi}_1(2)|1/r_{12}|\phi_1(1)\bar{\phi}_1(2)\rangle + \langle \phi_1(1)\phi_2(3)|1/r_{13}|\phi_1(1)\phi_2(3)\rangle \\
&\quad\quad + \langle \phi_1(1)\bar{\phi}_2(4)|1/r_{14}|\phi_1(1)\bar{\phi}_2(4)\rangle + \langle \bar{\phi}_1(2)\phi_2(3)|1/r_{23}|\bar{\phi}_1(2)\phi_2(3)\rangle \\
&\quad\quad + \langle \bar{\phi}_1(2)\bar{\phi}_2(4)|1/r_{24}|\bar{\phi}_1(2)\bar{\phi}_2(4)\rangle + \langle \phi_2(3)\bar{\phi}_2(4)|1/r_{34}|\phi_2(3)\bar{\phi}_2(4)\rangle
\end{aligned} \tag{A7-21}$$

These integrals give the coulombic repulsion between electrons in MOs. They are symbolized J_{ij}, where

$$J_{ij} = \langle \phi_i(1)\phi_j(2)|1/r_{12}|\phi_i(1)\phi_j(2)\rangle \equiv \langle ij|ij\rangle \tag{A7-22}$$

Here ϕ_i and ϕ_j may be associated with either spin. Because the operator and MOs commute, the integrand can be rearranged to give

$$J_{ij} = \int \phi_i^*(1)\phi_i(1)(1/r_{12})\phi_j^*(2)\phi_j(2)\, d\tau_1\, d\tau_2 \equiv (ii|jj) \tag{A7-23}$$

Some people prefer this form because it places the two mutually repelling charge clouds on the two sides of the operator. It is important to realize that the parenthetical expression $(ii|jj)$ and the bra–ket shorthand $\langle ij|ij\rangle$ correspond to *different conventions* for electron index order, and are really the same integral.

Returning to Eq. (A7-21), we see that it is equal to

$$J_{11} + J_{12} + J_{12} + J_{12} + J_{12} + J_{22} = \sum_{i=1}^{2} \Big(J_{ii} + \sum_{j\neq i} 2J_{ij}\Big) \qquad \text{(A7-24)}$$

We must now consider the case where the products differ by a single permutation, hence in two places. An example has been provided in Eq. (A7-19). We noted that, when the operator $1/r_{ij}$ corresponds to electrons i and j in the positions of disagreement, the overlap integrals are all unity. Otherwise, at least one overlap integral vanishes. An integral like that in Eq. (A7-20) is called an exchange integral.

Exchange integrals can occur only when the product on the right of the operator differs from the leading term by a single permutation. Hence, exchange integrals always enter with a coefficient of -1.

We noted earlier that two classes of singly permuted products exist. One class involves permutations between electrons of like spin. In such a case, ϕ_i and ϕ_j appear throughout the integral K_{ij} with spin agreement. For cases where electrons of different spin have been permuted, spin disagreement forces the exchange integral to vanish. (Since $1/r_{ij}$ is not a spin operator, the integration over spin coordinates factors out and produces a vanishing integral if spins disagree.)

The result of all this is that each singly permuted product can give $-K_{ij}$ if the permutation is between electrons of like spin in MOs ϕ_i and ϕ_j, and zero otherwise. For ψ_4, the acceptable permutations can be seen to be electron 1 with 3 and electron 2 with 4, both of these occurring between ϕ_1 and ϕ_2 space MOs. Hence, the contribution to E is $-2K_{12}$. Combining this with J terms gives

$$\Big\langle\psi_4\Big|\sum{}' 1/r_{ij}\Big|\psi_4\Big\rangle = J_{11} + 4J_{12} - 2K_{12} + J_{22} \qquad \text{(A7-25)}$$

From the definitions of J and K, it is apparent that

$$J_{ij} = J_{ji}, \qquad K_{ij} = K_{ji}, \qquad K_{ii} = J_{ii}$$

This allows us to rewrite Eq. (A7-25) as

$$2J_{11} - K_{11} + 2J_{12} - K_{12} + 2J_{21} - K_{21} + 2J_{22} - K_{22}$$
$$= \sum_{i=1}^{2} \sum_{j=1}^{2} (2J_{ij} - K_{ij}) \qquad \text{(A7-26)}$$

Generalizing to the $2n$-electron, closed-shell case and adding in our one-electron contribution,

$$\bar{E} = \langle\psi_{2n}|\hat{H}|\psi_{2n}\rangle = 2\sum_{i=1}^{n} H_{ii} + \sum_{i=1}^{n}\sum_{j=1}^{n} (2J_{ij} - K_{ij}) \qquad \text{(A7-27)}$$

This is the desired expression for $\bar{E}$ in terms of integrals over MOs ϕ_i, for a single-determinantal, closed-shell wavefunction.

A7-2 Derivation of the Hartree–Fock Equations

To find the "best" MOs, we seek those that minimize $\bar{E}$, that is, those MOs ϕ for which $\bar{E}$ is stationary to small variations $\delta\phi$. But there is a restriction in the variations $\delta\phi$. The MOs can only be varied in ways that do not destroy their orthonormality, since this property was assumed in deriving Eq. (A7-27). This means that, for proper variations $\delta\phi$ at the minimum $\bar{E}$, both $\bar{E}$ and all the MO overlap integrals $S_{ij} \equiv \langle\phi_i|\phi_j\rangle$ must remain constant. (S_{ij} must equal unity when $i = j$, zero otherwise.) If $\bar{E}$ and S_{ij} are constant, any linear combination of them is constant too. Thus, we may write that, at the minimum $\bar{E}$,

$$c_0\bar{E} + \sum_i \sum_j c_{ij}S_{ij} = \text{constant} \tag{A7-28}$$

for our restricted type of $\delta\phi$. This equation will hold for *any* set of coefficients c as long as $\delta\phi$ is of the proper *restricted* nature. However, it is possible to show that, for a particular set of coefficients, Eq. (A7-28) is satisfied at minimum $\bar{E}$ for *any* small variations $\delta\phi$. The particular coefficients are called Lagrangian multipliers. They are of undetermined value thus far, but their values will become known in the course of solving the problem. The technique, known as "Lagrange's method of undetermined multipliers" is from the calculus of variations.[1]

The Lagrangian multipliers will ultimately turn out to be essentially the MO energies. For future convenience we write Eq. (A7-28) in the form

$$\bar{E} - 2\sum_i \sum_j \epsilon_{ij}S_{ij} = \text{constant for} \quad \delta\phi \tag{A7-29}$$

where we now understand $\delta\phi$ to be unrestricted and ϵ_{ij} to be some unknown special set of constants.

The stability of the quantity on the left-hand side of Eq. (A7-29) may be expressed as follows:

$$\delta E - 2\delta \sum_i \sum_j \epsilon_{ij}S_{ij} = 0 \tag{A7-30}$$

or, expanding $\bar{E}$,

$$2\sum_{i=1}^{n} \delta H_{ii} + \sum_{i=1}^{n}\sum_{j=1}^{n} (2\,\delta J_{ij} - \delta K_{ij}) - 2\sum_{i=1}^{n}\sum_{j=1}^{n} \epsilon_{ij}\,\delta S_{ij} = 0 \tag{A7-31}$$

The variations occur in the MOs ϕ, and so

$$\delta S_{ij} = \int \delta\phi_i{}^*(1)\phi_j(1)\,d\tau_1 + \int \phi_i{}^*(1)\,\delta\phi_j(1)\,d\tau_1 \tag{A7-32}$$

[1] For an introduction to this topic, see Margenau and Murphy [1].

$$\delta H_{ii} = \int \delta\phi_i^*(1) H_{(1)}^{\text{core}} \phi_i(1)\, d\tau_1 + \int \phi_i^*(1) H_{(1)}^{\text{core}}\, \delta\phi_i(1)\, d\tau_1 \tag{A7-33}$$

$$\delta J_{ij} = \int \delta\phi_i^*(1)\phi_j^*(2)(1/r_{12})\phi_i(1)\phi_j(2)\, d\tau_1\, d\tau_2$$
$$+ \int \phi_i^*(1)\, \delta\phi_j^*(2)(1/r_{12})\phi_i(1)\phi_j(2)\, d\tau_1\, d\tau_2 + \text{complex conjugates} \tag{A7-34}$$

It is convenient to define a coulomb operator $\hat{J}_i(1)$ as

$$\hat{J}_i(1) = \int \phi_i^*(2)(1/r_{12})\phi_i(2)\, d\tau_2 \tag{A7-35}$$

Using this definition we can rewrite Eq. (A7-34) as

$$\delta J_{ij} = \int \delta\phi_i^*(1)\hat{J}_j(1)\phi_i(1)\, d\tau_1 + \int \delta\phi_j^*(1)\hat{J}_i(1)\phi_j(1)\, d\tau_1 + \text{complex conjugates} \tag{A7-36}$$

In the same spirit, we define an exchange operator $\hat{K}_i$, which, because it involves an orbital exchange, must be written in the context of an orbital being operated on:

$$\hat{K}_i(1)\phi_j(1) = \int \phi_i^*(2)(1/r_{12})\phi_j(2)\, d\tau_2 \phi_i(1) \tag{A7-37}$$

This enables us to write δK_{ij}

$$\delta K_{ij} = \int \delta\phi_i^*(1)\hat{K}_j(1)\phi_i(1)\, d\tau_1 + \int \delta\phi_j^*(1)\hat{K}_i(1)\phi_j(1)\, d\tau_1$$
$$+ \text{complex conjugates}$$

Employing the operators $\hat{J}$ and $\hat{K}$, Eq. (A7-31) can be written as follows:

$$2\sum_i \int \delta\phi_i^*(1)\Big[H_{(1)}^{\text{core}}\phi_i(1) + \sum_j (2\hat{J}_j(1) - \hat{K}_j(1))\phi_i(1) - \sum_j \epsilon_{ij}\phi_j(1)\Big]\, d\tau_1$$
$$+ 2\sum_i \int \delta\phi_i(1)\Big[H_{(1)}^{\text{core}*}\phi_i^*(1) + \sum_j (2\hat{J}_j^*(1) - \hat{K}_j^*(1))\phi_i^*(1)$$
$$- \sum_j \epsilon_{ij}^*\phi_j^*(1)\Big]\, d\tau_1 = 0 \tag{A7-38}$$

Here we have made use of the hermitian properties of H^{core}, $\hat{J}$, and $\hat{K}$, and also the relation $\epsilon_{ji}\int \delta\phi_j(1)\phi_i^*(1)\, d\tau_1 = \epsilon_{ij}\int \delta\phi_i(1)\phi_j^*(1)\, d\tau_1$, which is merely an index interchange.

Since the variations $\delta\phi_i^*$ and $\delta\phi_i$ are independent, each half of Eq. (A7-38) must independently equal zero. Hence, we can select either half for further development. We will select the first half. This equation indicates that the sum of integrals equals zero. Either the integrals are all individually equal to zero or else they are finite but cancel. However the latter possibility is ruled out because the variations $\delta\phi_i{}^*$ are arbitrary. By appropriately picking $\delta\phi_i{}^*$, we could always spoil cancellation if the various integrals for different i were nonzero. But the equation states that the sum vanishes for every $\delta\phi_i{}^*$. Therefore, we are forced to conclude that each integral vanishes.

Continuing in the same spirit, we can conclude that the term in brackets in the integrand is zero. For the integral to vanish requires the integrand either to be identically zero or else to have equal positive and negative parts. If the latter were true for some choice of $\delta\phi_i{}^*$, it would be possible to change $\delta\phi_i{}^*$ so as to unbalance the cancellation and produce a nonzero integral. Since the integral is zero for all $\delta\phi_i{}^*$, it must be that the bracketed term vanishes identically. Thus,

$$\left[H_{(1)}^{\text{core}} + \sum_j (2\hat{J}_j(1) - \hat{K}_j(1))\right]\phi_i(1) = \sum_j \epsilon_{ij}\phi_j(1) \tag{A7-39}$$

for all $i = 1$ to n and for a certain set of constants ϵ_{ij}.

The original development of SCF equations was performed by Hartree for simple product wavefunctions. Fock later extended the approach to apply to antisymmetrized wavefunctions. For this reason, the collection of operators in brackets in Eq. (A7-39) is called the Fock operator, symbolized $\hat{F}$, and Eq. (A7-39) becomes

$$\hat{F}(1)\phi_i(1) = \sum_j \epsilon_{ij}\phi_j(1) \tag{A7-40}$$

Equation (A7-40) is a differential equation for each MO ϕ_i. But as it stands it is not an eigenvalue equation because, instead of regenerating ϕ_i, we obtain a sum of functions ϕ_j times the various unknown constants ϵ_{ij}. However, there remains a degree of freedom in the problem that can be used to throw Eq. (A7-40) into eigenvalue form.

It is pointed out in Appendix 2 that the value of a determinant is unchanged if any row or column, multiplied by a constant, is added to any other row or column. This means that a Slater determinant of "best" MOs is unaffected by such internal rearrangements. In other words, if we were to solve Eq. (A7-40) for a set of "best" MOs, $\phi_i{}^{\text{b}}$, we could form various new orthonormal MOs, (e.g., $\phi_i{}^{\text{b}} + \lambda_{ik}\phi_k{}^{\text{b}}$, $\phi_k{}^{\text{b}} - \lambda_{ki}\phi_i{}^{\text{b}}$) by mixing them together, and our wavefunction ψ, and all values of observables predicted from ψ, including $\bar{E}$, would be precisely the same.

A transformation that mixes the MOs ϕ without affecting the property of orthonomality is called a unitary transformation (see Chapter 9). Letting U stand for such a transformation, we have that a transformed set of ϕ's, called ϕ', is given by

$$\phi_i' = \sum_j U_{ji}\phi_j, \qquad i = 1, \ldots, n \tag{A7-41}$$

In matrix notation, this is

$$\tilde{\phi}' = \tilde{\phi}\mathsf{U} \tag{A7-42}$$

where $\tilde{\phi}'$ and $\tilde{\phi}$ are row vectors, viz.

$$\tilde{\phi}' = (\phi_1'\phi_2'\cdots\phi_n'), \tag{A7-43}$$

and U is an $n \times n$ matrix, with

$$\mathsf{U}\mathsf{U}^\dagger = \mathsf{U}^\dagger\mathsf{U} = \mathsf{1} \tag{A7-44}$$

In terms of these matrices, Eq. (A7-40) is

$$\hat{F}\tilde{\phi} = \tilde{\phi}\mathsf{E} \tag{A7-45}$$

where E is an $n \times n$ matrix. If we multiply this from the right by U, we obtain

$$\hat{F}\tilde{\phi}\mathsf{U} = \tilde{\phi}\mathsf{E}\mathsf{U} \tag{A7-46}$$

Inserting $\mathsf{1}$ (in the form $\mathsf{U}\mathsf{U}^\dagger$) between $\tilde{\phi}$ and E gives

$$\hat{F}\tilde{\phi}\mathsf{U} = \tilde{\phi}\mathsf{U}\mathsf{U}^\dagger\mathsf{E}\mathsf{U} \tag{A7-47}$$

or

$$\hat{F}\tilde{\phi}' = \tilde{\phi}'\mathsf{U}^\dagger\mathsf{E}\mathsf{U} \tag{A7-48}$$

We can now require that the matrix U be such that $\mathsf{U}^\dagger\mathsf{E}\mathsf{U}$ is a diagonal matrix E'. (This requires that E be a hermitian matrix, which can be shown to be the case.[2])

This requirement defines U, and we have

$$\hat{F}\tilde{\phi}' = \tilde{\phi}'\mathsf{E}' \tag{A7-49}$$

which corresponds to

$$\hat{F}\phi_i' = \epsilon_i'\phi_i', \qquad i = 1, 2, \ldots, n \tag{A7-50}$$

This equation has the desired eigenvalue form, and is commonly referred to as the Hartree–Fock equation. It is discussed at length in Chapter 11.

It is important to bear in mind that our transformation U is for mathematical convenience and has no physical effect. We may imagine that our original basis set spans a certain function space, and that solution of Eq. (A7-50) produces a set of occupied MOs ϕ_i' that span a "best" subspace. Transformations by unitary matrices produce new sets of MOs ϕ'' but these still span the same subspace as ϕ'. However, they are generally not eigenfunctions of $\hat{F}$, and satisfy the less convenient Eq. (A7-40). Nonetheless, there are occasions when it is useful to use some set of MOs other than ϕ', and we can always do this without having to worry about introducing physical changes as long as our converted MO's are related to ϕ' by a unitary transformation.

[2] See Roothaan [2].

The Hartree–Fock equation is ordinarily used in quantum chemistry in connection with a basis set of AOs, and it is possible to carry through a derivation of the Hartree–Fock equation for this type of basis. Detailed treatments of this derivation may be found in the paper by Roothaan [2] and in the book by Pople and Beveridge [3].

REFERENCES

[1] H. Margenau and G. M. Murphy, "The Mathematics of Physics and Chemistry." Van Nostrand-Reinhold, Princeton, New Jersey, 1956.
[2] C. C. J. Roothaan, *Rev. Mod. Phys.* **23**, 69 (1951).
[3] J. A. Pople and D. L. Beveridge, "Approximate Molecular Orbital Theory." McGraw-Hill, New York, 1970.

APPENDIX 8

THE VIRIAL THEOREM FOR ATOMS AND DIATOMIC MOLECULES

A8-1 Atoms

In Chapter 3 it was shown that, for the ground state of the quantum-mechanical harmonic oscillator, the average value of the kinetic energy is equal to the average value of the potential energy. We now consider how the average electronic kinetic and potential energies are related in an atom. We begin by deriving a rather general expression, and then we discuss how it applies to different levels of calculation.

As our first step, we examine the effects of *coordinate scaling* on average values. In order to follow this discussion, it is useful to recall that one can manipulate variables and limits in an integral as follows:

$$\int_a^b f(x)\,dx = \int_a^b f(y)\,dy = \int_a^b f(\eta x)\,d(\eta x) = \eta\int_{a/\eta}^{b/\eta} f(\eta x)\,dx \qquad \text{(A8-1)}$$

Let $\psi(\mathbf{r}_1, \mathbf{r}_2, \ldots, \mathbf{r}_n)$ be a normalized function of the space coordinates of n electrons. Let

$$\bar{T} = \langle\psi|\hat{T}|\psi\rangle \qquad \text{(A8-2)}$$

$$\bar{V} = \langle\psi|\hat{V}|\psi\rangle \qquad \text{(A8-3)}$$

where $\hat{T}$ and $\hat{V}$ are, respectively, the kinetic and potential energy operators for some system, and are independent of spin.

We introduce a scale factor η into ψ. This factor affects the lengths of the vectors $\mathbf{r}_i$ but not their directions. That is,

$$\psi_\eta \equiv \psi(\eta\mathbf{r}_1, \eta\mathbf{r}_2, \ldots, \eta\mathbf{r}_n) \qquad \text{(A8-4)}$$

If $\eta > 1$, ψ_η is more contracted in $3n$-dimensional space than ψ. For $\eta < 1$, ψ_η is more diffuse.

We must check to see if our scaled function ψ_n is normalized. We know that

$$1 = \int \psi^*(\mathbf{r}_1, \ldots, \mathbf{r}_n)\psi(\mathbf{r}_1, \ldots, \mathbf{r}_n)\,dv$$
$$= \int \psi^*(\eta\mathbf{r}_1, \ldots, \eta\mathbf{r}_n)\psi(\eta\mathbf{r}_1, \ldots, \eta\mathbf{r}_n)\,d(\eta v) \qquad \text{(A8-5)}$$

because we have simply relabeled all variables $\mathbf{r}$ by $\eta\mathbf{r}$, including the volume element, just as in Eq. (A8-1). We now factor η out of the volume element and divide the limits of integration by η, just as in Eq. (A8-1). However, the limits are zero and infinity, so they are unaffected. The volume element $d(\eta v)$ is given by

$$d(\eta v) = (\eta r_1)^2 \sin\theta_1\, d(\eta r_1)\, d\theta_1\, d\phi_1 (\eta r_2)^2 \sin\theta_2\, d(\eta r_2)\, d\theta_2\, d\phi_2 \cdots \tag{A8-6}$$

and so η^3 appears for each electron. Thus, we are led to

$$1 = \eta^{3n} \int \psi_\eta^* \psi_\eta\, dv \tag{A8-7}$$

Therefore, our normalization constant for ψ_η is $\eta^{3n/2}$, and our *normalized*, scaled function is

$$\psi_\eta = \eta^{3n/2} \psi(\eta\mathbf{r}_1, \eta\mathbf{r}_2, \ldots, \eta\mathbf{r}_n) \tag{A8-8}$$

[Compare this with the specific example encountered in Eq. (7-7).]

We now inquire as to the values of $\bar{V}_\eta$ and $\bar{T}_\eta$, where

$$\bar{T}_\eta = \langle\psi_\eta|\hat{T}|\psi_\eta\rangle \tag{A8-9}$$

$$\bar{V}_\eta = \langle\psi_\eta|\hat{V}|\psi_\eta\rangle \tag{A8-10}$$

For an n-electron atom,

$$\hat{T} = -\tfrac{1}{2} \sum_{i=1}^{n} \nabla_i^2 \tag{A8-11}$$

$$\hat{V} = -\sum_{i=1}^{n} (Z/r_i) + \sum_{i=1}^{n-1} \sum_{j=i+1}^{n} 1/r_{ij} \tag{A8-12}$$

Therefore

$$\bar{V}_\eta = \eta^{3n} \int \psi^*(\eta\mathbf{r}_1, \ldots) \left[\sum_{i=1}^{n} (-Z/r_i) + \sum_{i=1}^{n-1} \sum_{j=i+1}^{n} 1/r_{ij} \right] \psi(\eta\mathbf{r}_1, \ldots)\, dv \tag{A8-13}$$

We could make the integral equal to $\bar{V}$ if we could get the scale factor into all the r terms in the operator and also into dv. The volume element dv requires η^{3n}, which is already present in Eq. (A8-13) from the normalization constants. To get η into the operator, we need to multiply the operator by η^{-1}. Multiplying Eq. (A8-13) by $\eta\eta^{-1}$ gives, then

$$\bar{V}_\eta = \eta \int \psi^*(\eta\mathbf{r}_1, \ldots) \left[\sum_{i=1}^{n} (-Z/\eta r_i) + \sum_{i=1}^{n-1} \sum_{j=i+1}^{n} 1/\eta r_{ij} \right] \psi(\eta\mathbf{r}_1, \ldots)\, d(\eta v) \tag{A8-14}$$

or

$$\bar{V}_\eta = \eta \bar{V} \tag{A8-15}$$

The same approach to $\bar{T}_\eta$ gives

$$\bar{T}_\eta = \eta^2 \bar{T} \tag{A8-16}$$

This arises from the fact that

$$\nabla^2 = \frac{1}{r^2}\frac{\partial}{\partial r}\left(r^2 \frac{\partial}{\partial r}\right) + \frac{1}{r^2 \sin\theta}\frac{\partial}{\partial\theta}\left(\sin\theta \frac{\partial}{\partial\theta}\right) + \frac{1}{r^2 \sin^2\theta}\frac{\partial^2}{\partial\phi^2} \tag{A8-17}$$

and scaling the r terms here requires multiplying by η^{-2}. Hence, the integral is multiplied by $\eta^2\eta^{-2}$ in the final step.

The *general* result is that, for any quantum-mechanical system where

$$\hat{V} = f(r^{-v}) \tag{A8-18}$$

scaling results in

$$\bar{T}_\eta = \eta^2 \bar{T}, \qquad \bar{V}_\eta = \eta^v \bar{V} \tag{A8-19}$$

For atoms, $\hat{V}$ contains r as r^{-1}. For all systems, $\hat{T}$ involves ∇^2, which contains r to the net power of -2.

We can now write the expression for the total energy of the atom as given by the scaled function

$$\bar{E}_\eta = \bar{T}_\eta + \bar{V}_\eta = \eta^2 \bar{T} + \eta \bar{V} \tag{A8-20}$$

Now we can seek the best value of the scale factor. We do this by minimizing $\bar{E}_\eta$ with respect to variations in η:

$$\partial \bar{E}\eta / \partial \eta = 2\eta \bar{T} + \bar{V} = 0 \tag{A8-21}$$

($\bar{T}$ and $\bar{V}$ are independent of η.)

We are now in a position to make some statements about the average values of $\hat{T}$ and $\hat{V}$ for certain wavefunctions. Let us consider first the *exact* values of $\bar{T}$ and $\bar{V}$. We know that, if ψ were an exact eigenfunction, no further energy lowering would result from rescaling. That is, η equals unity in Eq. (A8-21). As a result,

$$2\bar{T} + \bar{V} = 0 \tag{A8-22}$$

or

$$\bar{V} = -2\bar{T} \tag{A8-23}$$

or, since $\bar{T} + \bar{V} = \bar{E}$,

$$E = -\bar{T} = \tfrac{1}{2}\bar{V} \tag{A8-24}$$

Thus, for an atom, we know that the *exact* nonrelativistic energy is equal to minus the *exact* average kinetic energy and is equal to one half the exact potential energy. Knowing that the exact energy of the ground-state neon atom is -128.925 a.u. enables us to say that $\bar{T} = +128.925$ a.u. and $\bar{V} = -257.850$

a.u. without actually knowing ψ. Moreover, the same relation holds for *any* stable state of an atom.

This same argument holds, not only for exact solutions, but for any trial function that has already been energy optimized with respect to a scale factor. For then a new scaling parameter η gives no improvement, $\eta = 1$, and all is as above. Thus, any *nonlinear* variation scheme consistent with uniform scaling should ultimately lead to the relations [Eqs. (A8-22)–(A8-24)]. Satisfying these relations is frequently referred to as satisfying the virial relation. Completely optimized single-ζ and double-ζ functions satisfy the virial relation.

It follows that Hartree–Fock atomic wavefunctions must satisfy the virial relation. Such solutions are, by definition, the *best* (lowest energy) attainable in a single determinantal form. "Best" includes all conceivable variation, linear or nonlinear, so all improvements achievable by scale factor variation are already present at the Hartree–Fock level, and $\eta = 1$.

In the event that $\bar{E}$ *can* be lowered by scaling, it is possible to evaluate the optimum η from Eq. (A8-21), which gives

$$\eta = -\bar{V}/2\bar{T} \tag{A8-25}$$

One of the useful applications of the virial theorem is as an indicator of closeness of approach to the Hartree–Fock solution for an atom. If the calculation involves nonlinear variation (uniformly applied to all r coordinates), then the resulting wavefunction will satisfy the virial relations no matter how deficient it is as an approximation to the true eigenfunction. However, if the calculation involves only linear variation, as for example, when a linear combination of gaussian functions is used to approximate an AO, then there is no guarantee that the virial relation will be satisfied. If the basis set is extensive enough, however, the Hartree–Fock limit will be approached, and $\bar{V}/\bar{T}$ will approach -2. Strictly speaking, a linear variation calculation on an atom that gives $\bar{V}/\bar{T} = -2$ is simply one that cannot be improved by uniform scaling. Therefore, approach to -2 is not a guarantee of approach to the Hartree–Fock limit. It is a necessary but not a sufficient condition.

A8-2 Diatomic Molecules

The treatment here is very similar to that for atoms. We make the Born–Oppenheimer approximation by assuming that ψ depends parametrically on the internuclear separation R:

$$\psi = \psi(\mathbf{r}_1, \mathbf{r}_2, \ldots, \mathbf{r}_n, R) \tag{A8-26}$$

When we scale $\mathbf{r}_i$, we scale R as well:

$$\psi_\eta = \psi(\eta\mathbf{r}_1, \eta\mathbf{r}_2, \ldots, \eta\mathbf{r}_n, \eta R) \tag{A8-27}$$

Henceforth, we let $\eta R \equiv \rho$. Performing the same variable manipulations as in Section A8-1, we find

$$\bar{T}_\eta \equiv \bar{T}(\eta, \rho) = \eta^2 \bar{T}(1, \rho) \tag{A8-28}$$

$$\bar{V}_\eta \equiv \bar{V}(\eta, \rho) = \eta \bar{V}(1, \rho) \tag{A8-29}$$

Here, $\hat{V}$ may or may not include the internuclear repulsion term. This gives, for the total energy,

$$\bar{E}_\eta = \eta^2 \bar{T}(1, \rho) + \eta \bar{V}(1, \rho) \tag{A8-30}$$

Upon taking the derivative with respect to η, we obtain

$$\frac{\partial \bar{E}_\eta}{\partial \eta} = 2\eta \bar{T}(1, \rho) + \bar{V}(1, \rho) + \eta^2 \frac{\partial \bar{T}(1, \rho)}{\partial \eta} + \eta \frac{\partial \bar{V}(1, \rho)}{\partial \eta} = 0 \tag{A8-31}$$

This differs from the atomic case in that $\bar{V}(1, \rho)$ and $\bar{T}(1, \rho)$ depend on η through ρ. But

$$\frac{\partial}{\partial \eta} = \left(\frac{\partial}{\partial \rho}\right)\left(\frac{\partial \rho}{\partial \eta}\right) = \left(\frac{\partial}{\partial \rho}\right) R \tag{A8-32}$$

and so Eq. (A8-31) becomes

$$\frac{\partial \bar{E}_\eta}{\partial \eta} = 0 = 2\eta \bar{T}(1, \rho) + \eta \bar{V}(1, \rho) + \eta^2 R \frac{\partial \bar{T}(1, \rho)}{\partial \rho} + \eta R \frac{\partial \bar{V}(1, \rho)}{\partial \rho} \tag{A8-33}$$

If we assume that ψ is the exact eigenfunction, then $\eta = 1$, and

$$2\bar{T} + \bar{V} + R\,(\partial \bar{E}/\partial R) = 0 \tag{A8-34}$$

Indeed, this relation holds for any case in which all improvement in the nature of a scale factor variation has been made, such as, for example, the Hartree–Fock limit. Note that, if $\bar{V}$ contains internuclear repulsion, $\bar{E}$ is the total energy. If not, $\bar{E}$ is the electronic energy.

PROBLEMS

A8–1 Use the methods outlined in this appendix to show that $\bar{V} = \bar{T}$ for any stationary state of the quantum mechanical harmonic oscillator.

A8–2 Evaluate $\bar{V}$ and $\bar{T}$ with $\psi = 1/\sqrt{\pi}\exp(-r)$ for the Li^{2+} ion. From these, establish the optimum scale factor η and write down the expression for the normalized optimized ψ_η and the optimized energy E_η. Compare these results with the eigenfunction for Li^{2+}.

APPENDIX 9

DETAILS[1] OF THE SOLUTION OF THE MATRIX EQUATION HC=SCE

A9-1 Finding the Matrix A Such That $A^{\dagger}SA = 1$ by the Schmidt Procedure.

Let the original, *non*orthonormal linearly independent basis functions $f_1, f_2, \ldots, f_n$ be collected into a vector

$$f = \begin{pmatrix} f_1 \\ f_2 \\ \vdots \\ f_n \end{pmatrix} \quad \text{(A9-1)}$$

Since we are dealing here with a vector of *functions* instead of numbers, we must concern ourselves with the details of multiplying such vectors together. A function of one continuous variable (say, r) may itself be considered a vector, each element of the vector being the value of the function at a different value of r. Since the continuous variable r has infinitely many values separated by the infinitesimal increment dr, the vector will have an infinite number of elements. Thus, we can imagine the vector for the function $f(r)$ to have the form

$$f(r) = (f(0)f(dr)f(2dr)f(3dr)\cdots) \quad \text{(A9-2)}$$

(For reasons that will become apparent, it is convenient to express the function as a row, rather than a column, vector.) With this view of a function in mind, it becomes evident that the vector of functions [Eq. (A9-1)] is a semiinfinite matrix having n rows and an infinite number of "columns."

We now consider the result of "scalar multiplying" an infinite row vector corresponding to the function $f_1(r)$ times the infinite column vector corresponding to $f_2^{\dagger}(r)$. Sweeping across the row and down the column and summing products would give

$$f_1(r)f_2^{\dagger}(r) = f_1(0)f_2^*(0) + f_1(dr)f_2^*(dr) + \cdots \equiv \int f_1(r)f_2^*(r)\,dr \quad \text{(A9-3)}$$

Hence, when dealing with functions in this way, we produce *integrals of products*.

[1] See Chapter 9, Section 4.

If the original functions have several variables, e.g., $f(r, \theta, \phi)$, then the "scalar product" becomes the integral over all the variables.

As a result of all this, we can write

$$\mathsf{ff}^\dagger = \begin{pmatrix} f_1 \\ f_2 \\ \vdots \\ f_n \end{pmatrix} (f_1^\dagger, f_2^\dagger, \ldots, f_n^\dagger)$$

$$= \begin{pmatrix} \int f_1 f_1^* \, d\tau & \int f_1 f_2^* \, d\tau & \cdots & \int f_1 f_n^* \, d\tau \\ \vdots & & & \\ \int f_n f_1^* \, d\tau & & \cdots & \int f_n f_n^* \, d\tau \end{pmatrix} = \mathsf{S} \qquad \text{(A9-4)}$$

We are seeking a transformation matrix A which will mix the functions f_i to form an orthonormal set of functions g_i. In matrix notation, we seek A such that

$$\mathsf{f}^\dagger \mathsf{A} = (f_1^\dagger f_2^\dagger \cdots f_n^\dagger) \begin{pmatrix} a_{11} \cdots a_{1n} \\ \vdots \quad\quad \vdots \\ a_{n1} \cdots a_{nn} \end{pmatrix} = (g_1^\dagger g_2^\dagger \cdots g_n^\dagger) = \mathsf{g}^\dagger \qquad \text{(A9-5)}$$

where

$$\mathsf{gg}^\dagger = 1 \qquad \text{(A9-6)}$$

As a result of these definitions, the relation (9-27) used in Chapter 9 is easily demonstrated:

$$1 = \mathsf{gg}^\dagger = (\mathsf{f}^\dagger \mathsf{A})^\dagger \mathsf{f}^\dagger \mathsf{A} = \mathsf{A}^\dagger \mathsf{ff}^\dagger \mathsf{A} = \mathsf{A}^\dagger \mathsf{SA} \qquad \text{(A9-7)}$$

The matrix A is not unique. Different procedures generate different matrices A, which, in turn, generate different sets of orthonormal vectors g. In the Schmidt procedure, the basic idea is to let g_1 be f_1 (normalized), g_2 be the normalized part of f_2 orthogonal to g_1, g_3 be the normalized part of f_3 orthogonal to g_1 and g_2, etc. As a result of this procedure, g_i is a linear combination of $f_1, f_2, \ldots, f_i$, but does not include any f_k's with $k > i$. This means that A is an upper triangular matrix:

$$(f_1, f_2, f_3, \ldots) \begin{pmatrix} a_{11} & a_{12} & a_{13} & \cdots \\ 0 & a_{22} & a_{23} & \cdots \\ 0 & 0 & a_{33} & \cdots \end{pmatrix}$$
$$= (\underbrace{a_{11} f_1}_{g_1} \; \underbrace{a_{12} f_1 + a_{22} f_2}_{g_2} \; \underbrace{a_{13} f_1 + a_{23} f_2 + a_{33} f_3}_{g_3} \cdots) \qquad \text{(A9-8)}$$

Our problem is to find the numbers a_{ij} from the known numbers S_{ij}. Since the purpose of a_{11} is only to normalize, we have at once that $a_{11} = S_{11}^{-1/2}$. In order to produce equations for the other a_{ij}, we will work out the expressions for a_{13}, a_{23}, a_{33} assuming a_{11}, a_{12}, and a_{22} are already known (i.e., g_1 and g_2 are found), and then generalize. For simplicity, we assume all our functions to be real.

According to the Schmidt procedure, described in Chapter 6, the component of f_3 which is orthogonal to g_1 and g_2 is given by

$$g_3' = f_3 - Ov_{31}g_1 - Ov_{32}g_2 \tag{A9-9}$$

where Ov_{ij} is the overlap between f_i and g_j:

$$Ov_{ij} = \int f_i g_j \, d\tau \tag{A9-10}$$

The prime on g_3' means that the function is as yet unnormalized. We will now expand Ov_{31} and Ov_{32} with the aid of Eq. (A9-8):

$$Ov_{31} = \int f_3 g_1 \, d\tau = \int f_3 a_{11} f_1 \, d\tau = a_{11} S_{31} \tag{A9-11}$$

$$Ov_{32} = \int f_3 g_2 \, d\tau = \int f_3(a_{12}f_1 + a_{22}f_2) \, d\tau = a_{12}S_{31} + a_{22}S_{32} \tag{A9-12}$$

Generalizing, we have that

$$Ov_{ij} = \sum_{k=1}^{j} a_{kj} S_{ik} \tag{A9-13}$$

In order to make use of our expression for Ov_{ij}, we must convert Eq. (A9-9) into the form shown for g_3 in Eq. (A9-8). We do this by expanding g_1 and g_2 in terms of f_1 and f_2, viz.

$$g_3' = f_3 - Ov_{31}a_{11}f_1 - Ov_{32}(a_{11}f_1 + a_{22}f_2) \tag{A9-14}$$

or, rearranging,

$$g_3' = f_3 - Ov_{32}a_{22}f_2 - (Ov_{31}a_{11} + Ov_{32}a_{12})f_1 \tag{A9-15}$$

We are almost finished because we have found matrix elements (call them a_{13}', a_{23}', a_{33}'), which produce the unnormalized vector g_3', which is orthogonal to g_1 and g_2, that is,

$$g_3' = a_{13}'f_1 + a_{23}'f_2 + a_{33}'f_3 \tag{A9-16}$$

where a_{33}' equals unity and

$$a_{13}' = -(Ov_{31}a_{11} + Ov_{32}a_{12}) \tag{A9-17}$$

$$a_{23}' = -Ov_{32}a_{22} \tag{A9-18}$$

Generalizing these results gives

$$a_{ji}' = -\sum_{k=j}^{i-1} Ov_{ik}a_{jk}, \qquad a_{ii}' = 1 \tag{A9-19}$$

To normalize, we must compute

$$g_3 = g_3' l_3^{-1/2} \tag{A9-20}$$

where

$$l_3 = \int g_3' g_3' \, d\tau = a_{13}'^2 S_{11} + a_{23}'^2 S_{22} + a_{33}'^2 S_{33} + 2(a_{13}' a_{23}' S_{12} + a_{13}' a_{33}' S_{13} + a_{23}' a_{33}' S_{23}) \tag{A9-21}$$

or, in general,

$$l_i = \sum_{k=1}^{i} a_{ki}'^2 S_{kk} + 2 \sum_{k=1}^{i-1} \sum_{l=k+1}^{i} a_{ki}' a_{li}' S_{kl} \tag{A9-22}$$

The computational scheme, then, is as follows:

(1) Read in or compute the overlap matrix.
(2) Set $a_{11} = S_{11}^{-1/2}$.
(3) For each successive column i of A:
  (a) calculate the functions Ov_{ij} according to Eq. (A9-13):
  (b) calculate the elements a_{ji}' according to Eq. (A9-19);
  (c) calculate l_i according to Eq. (A9-22);
  (d) calculate the elements a_{ji} by multiplying a_{ji}' by $l_i^{-1/2}$.

The Schmidt method is the most commonly used orthogonalization technique in quantum chemistry. Other techniques that offer special advantages are available,[2] but they generally are slower.

A FORTRAN listing of a Schmidt orthogonalization program is given in Appendix 10.

A9-2 Finding the Orthogonal Matrix C, Such That $\tilde{\mathsf{C}}\mathsf{HC} = \mathsf{E}$, by the Jacobi Method

The Jacobi method is used in many quantum-chemical programs chiefly for two reasons: it has been known for a long time and it is easy to program. A characteristic of this method is that it calculates all the elements of E and C simultaneously. This is wasteful if one is interested in only a few values of E and a few columns of C. An alternative method that gets around this limitation is described in the following section.

Our problem is, given a known real symmetric matrix H, to find the orthogonal matrix C such that $\tilde{\mathsf{C}}\mathsf{HC}$ is diagonal. (This is a subclass of the more general problem where H is *hermitian*, C is a *unitary* matrix, and $\mathsf{C}^\dagger \mathsf{HC}$ is diagonal. Most quantum-chemical calculations fall into this subclass.)

For purposes of argument, suppose H is a 4×4 matrix, and a search of the off-diagonal elements reveals H_{13} to be the largest in magnitude. The Jacobi

[2] See, for example, Löwdin [1].

procedure corresponds to constructing an orthogonal matrix O_1 having the form

$$\mathsf{O}_1 = \begin{pmatrix} \cos\alpha & 0 & \sin\alpha & 0 \\ 0 & 1 & 0 & 0 \\ -\sin\alpha & 0 & \cos\alpha & 0 \\ 0 & 0 & 0 & 1 \end{pmatrix} \tag{A9-23}$$

Note that the 1, 3 and 3, 1 off-diagonal positions are nonzero, in consequence to these same positions in H being largest. Also, the 1, 1 and 3, 3 positions have the value $\cos\alpha$. The remainder of O_1 is of the same form as a unit matrix.

We allow this matrix O_1 to transform H, and we will fix the value of α to force the 1, 3 and 3, 1 positions of the *transformed* matrix to be zero, that is,

$$\tilde{\mathsf{O}}_1\mathsf{H}\mathsf{O}_1 = \mathsf{A} \tag{A9-24}$$

where $a_{13} = a_{31} = 0$. This transformation will also change the values of all the elements in rows 1 and 3 and columns 1 and 3 of H, but not elsewhere.

The next step is to find the largest off-diagonal elements in A and construct a matrix O_2 to zero these via the transformation

$$\tilde{\mathsf{O}}_2\mathsf{A}\mathsf{O}_2 = \mathsf{B} \tag{A9-25}$$

This process is continued until a matrix is produced with no off-diagonal elements larger than a preselected value (e.g., 10^{-8}). This final matrix is taken to be E. Since this is generated by the process

$$\tilde{\mathsf{O}}_n \cdot \cdots \tilde{\mathsf{O}}_2\tilde{\mathsf{O}}_1\mathsf{H}\mathsf{O}_1\mathsf{O}_2 \cdots \mathsf{O}_n = \mathsf{E} \tag{A9-26}$$

it is clear that the accumulated product $\mathsf{O}_1\mathsf{O}_2 \cdots \mathsf{O}_n$ is the coefficient matrix C.

The fact that each matrix O_i corresponds to a rotation of axes by α in two dimensions (see Chapter 9) leads to the term "rotation" matrix for O_i.

The number of "rotations" n required to diagonalize H is generally much larger than the number of off-diagonal elements. This comes about because an element that is made to vanish in one rotation will be unzeroed in a later rotation that involves that same row or column.

In order to obtain equations for elements of the transformed matrix A, we expand $\tilde{\mathsf{O}}\mathsf{H}\mathsf{O}$ explicitly. Let the zeroed elements be a_{ij} and a_{ji}. Then, using trigonometric identities, it is possible to show that

$$a_{ij} = a_{ji} = 0 = \tfrac{1}{2}(H_{ii} - H_{jj}) \sin 2\alpha + H_{ij} \cos 2\alpha \tag{A9-27}$$

$$a_{ii} = \tfrac{1}{2}(H_{ii} + H_{jj}) + \tfrac{1}{2}(H_{ii} - H_{jj}) \cos 2\alpha - H_{ij} \sin 2\alpha \tag{A9-28}$$

$$a_{jj} = \tfrac{1}{2}(H_{ii} + H_{jj}) - \tfrac{1}{2}(H_{ii} - H_{jj}) \cos 2\alpha + H_{ij} \sin 2\alpha \tag{A9-29}$$

$$a_{ik}\ (k \neq i, j) = H_{ik} \cos\alpha - H_{jk} \sin\alpha = a_{ki} \tag{A9-30}$$

$$a_{jk}\ (k \neq i, j) = H_{ik} \sin\alpha + H_{jk} \cos\alpha = a_{kj} \tag{A9-31}$$

To evaluate these terms requires knowledge of sin 2α, cos 2α, sin α, and cos α. These are obtained by starting with Eq. (A9-27), which may be written

$$\tan 2\alpha = 2H_{12}/(H_{22} - H_{11}) \tag{A9-32}$$

We could evaluate α via an arctangent program, and then compute sine and cosine functions from α, but this is computationally inefficient. Instead we shall develop expressions for all our trigonometric quantities in terms of elements of H. Equation (A9-32) is equivalent to[3]

$$\cos^2 2\alpha = (H_{22} - H_{11})^2/[(H_{22} - H_{11})^2 + 4H_{12}] \tag{A9-33}$$

We must pause here to consider the range of α. From Eq. (A9.32) we see that tan 2α can be positive or negative, and so for 2α we select the range $-\pi/2$ to $\pi/2$. Over this range tan 2α goes from $-\infty$ to $+\infty$ and is single valued. Then α lies between $\pm\pi/4$, so cos α and cos 2α are always positive, while sin α and sin 2α have the same sign as tan α. Therefore, we should take the positive root of $\cos^2 2\alpha$:

$$\cos 2\alpha = |H_{22} - H_{11}|/R \tag{A9-34}$$

where

$$R = [(H_{22} - H_{11})^2 + 4H_{12}]^{1/2} \tag{A9-35}$$

and R is taken to be positive.

From Eq. (A9-32) we can obtain

$$\sin 2\alpha = \text{Sign } 2H_{12}/R \tag{A9-36}$$

where

$$\text{Sign} = \begin{Bmatrix} +1 \\ -1 \end{Bmatrix} \quad \text{if} \quad (H_{22} - H_{11})\begin{cases} > 0 \\ < 0 \end{cases} \tag{A9-37}$$

Finally, we have

$$\cos \alpha = [\tfrac{1}{2}(\cos 2\alpha + 1)]^{1/2} \tag{A9-38}$$

$$\sin \alpha = \sin 2\alpha/(2 \cos \alpha) \tag{A9-39}$$

In addition to their use in Eqs. (A9-30)–(A9-31), sin α and cos α are also necessary in order to calculate new elements in the accumulating product $\mathsf{O}_i \cdots \mathsf{O}_3\mathsf{O}_2\mathsf{O}_1$.

One fairly time consuming step in the Jacobi method is the search for the largest off-diagonal element preceding each rotation. In an effort to speed this up, some programs store the locations of several of the largest elements found in a search. After each rotation a check is made to see which of these remaining

[3] $\tan^2 2\alpha = 4H_{12}^2/(H_{22} - H_{11})^2 = \sin^2 2\alpha/\cos^2 2\alpha$; $4H_{12}^2 \cos^2 2\alpha = (H_{22} - H_{11})^2 \sin^2 2\alpha = (H_{22} - H_{11})^2(1 - \cos^2 2\alpha)$.

elements have been altered. Those not so altered remain candidates for the next rotation. This procedure results in a search being required much less frequently.

The computing procedure, then, is as follows:

(1) Search one off-diagonal triangle of H for the largest element H_{ij} (or several largest elements).

(2) Test H_{ij} to see if it exceeds a preselected small value. If it does not, H is diagonal and the process should be terminated.

(3) Use H_{ii}, H_{jj}, and H_{ij} to calculate cos 2α, sin 2α, cos α, and sin α according to Eqs. (A9-34)–(A9-39).

(4) Set a_{ij} and a_{ji} to zero and calculate all other elements in rows and columns i and j according to Eqs. (A9-28)–(A9-31). Store these in vectors as they are found. After they are all calculated, put them into H.

(5) Use sin α and cos α to calculate new elements in rows and columns i and j of the accumulating product matrix **C**.

(6) Return to step 1.

A FORTRAN listing of the Jacobi procedure is given in Appendix 10.

A9-3 Finding Eigenvalues and Eigenvectors of a Symmetric Matrix via Transformation to Tridiagonal Form

A more efficient and flexible procedure for finding eigenvalues and eigenvectors of a symmetric matrix has been devised.[4] First, the matrix is transformed to tridiagonal (or codiagonal) form. [All elements zero except those on the main diagonal and on the diagonals immediately adjacent (above and below) the main diagonal.] This process is performed in a relatively small number of steps. Next, any desired eigenvalues are found, independently of each other, using a simple algorithm. Once an eigenvalue is known, its eigenvector may be computed if desired. Such eigenvectors, which refer to the tridiagonal matrix, are then transformed back into the basis of the original matrix. An outline of the basic formulas is given below.

A. Matrix Tridiagonalization

Reduction of a real symmetric matrix A to tridiagonal form is most efficiently done by the method of Householder. This method uses an orthogonal transformation that zeros the starting matrix an entire row and column at a time.

Householder's transformation matrix is defined by

$$\mathsf{T} = 1 - 2\mathsf{w}\mathsf{w}^{\dagger} \tag{A9-40}$$

[4] See Wilkinson [2], Givens [3], and Ortega [4].

w is a column vector; therefore, $\mathsf{ww}^\dagger$ is a matrix and T is symmetric. The restriction that the scalar product $\mathsf{w}^\dagger\mathsf{w} = 1$ makes T orthogonal ($\mathsf{T}^{-1} = \mathsf{T}$).

For any given intermediate stage of computation where the $(r - 1)$th row and column are to be appropriately zeroed, the corresponding vector w_r is defined to have $r - 1$ leading zeros:

$$\mathsf{w}_r{}^\dagger = (0, 0, \ldots, 0, x_r, x_{r+1}, \ldots, x_n) \tag{A9-41}$$

With $\mathsf{w}^\dagger\mathsf{w} = 1$ this gives $x_r{}^2 + x_{r+1}^2 \cdots + x_n{}^2 = 1$. It follows from this that the matrix T is simply the unit matrix down to and including the row and column being zeroed. The situation when $r = 2$ is

$$\underset{\mathsf{T}_2}{\begin{pmatrix} 1 & 0 & 0 & 0 \\ 0 & & \cdots & \\ 0 & & \cdots & \\ 0 & & \cdots & \end{pmatrix}} \underset{\mathsf{A}_1}{\begin{pmatrix} a_{11} & a_{12} & a_{13} & a_{14} \\ a_{21} & a_{22} & a_{23} & a_{24} \\ a_{31} & a_{32} & a_{33} & a_{34} \\ a_{41} & a_{42} & a_{43} & a_{44} \end{pmatrix}} \underset{\mathsf{T}_2}{\begin{pmatrix} 1 & 0 & 0 & 0 \\ 0 & & \cdots & \\ 0 & & \cdots & \\ 0 & & \cdots & \end{pmatrix}} = \underset{\mathsf{A}_2}{\begin{pmatrix} \alpha_1 & \beta_1 & 0 & 0 \\ \beta_1 & & \cdots & \\ 0 & & \cdots & \\ 0 & & \cdots & \end{pmatrix}} \tag{A9-42}$$

T_2 operating on the matrix $(\mathsf{A}_1\mathsf{T}_2)$ cannot change the first row or column of $(\mathsf{A}_1\mathsf{T}_2)$. Therefore, any zeros introduced into the first row or column of A must arise from the operation $\mathsf{A}_1\mathsf{T}_2$. This leads us at once to equations for the nonzero elements of w. We require the matrix

$$\mathsf{A}_1\mathsf{T}_2 = \mathsf{A}_1(1 - 2\mathsf{w}_2\mathsf{w}_2{}^\dagger) = \mathsf{A}_1 - 2\mathsf{A}_1\mathsf{w}_2\mathsf{w}_2{}^\dagger$$

to have zeros in the appropriate row and column. For row $r - 1$, this is $n - r$ elements, giving $n - r$ equations. The normalization requirement gives the remaining equation needed to solve for the $n - r + 1$ elements of w_r. The results are, for the general case,

$$x_r{}^2 = \tfrac{1}{2}[1 + (A_{r-1,r}\cdot\text{Sign})/S^{1/2}] \tag{A9-43}$$

$$x_{r+i} = (A_{r-1,r+i}\cdot\text{Sign})/2x_rS^{1/2} \tag{A9-44}$$

where

$$\text{Sign} = \text{sign of } A_{r-1,r} \tag{A9-45}$$

$$S = \sum_{i=r}^{n} A_{r-1,i}^2 \tag{A9-46}$$

Furthermore, it follows that

$$\alpha_{r-1} = A_{r-1,r-1} \tag{A9-47}$$

$$\beta_{r-1} = -\text{Sign}\cdot S^{1/2} \tag{A9-48}$$

For the new elements of TAT, we have

$$\begin{aligned} \mathsf{TAT} &= (1 - 2\mathsf{ww}^\dagger)\mathsf{A}(1 - 2\mathsf{ww}^\dagger) \\ &= \mathsf{A} - 2\mathsf{ww}^\dagger\mathsf{A} - 2\mathsf{Aww}^\dagger + 4\mathsf{w}(\mathsf{w}^\dagger\mathsf{Aw})\mathsf{w}^\dagger \\ &= \mathsf{A} - 2\mathsf{w}[\mathsf{w}^\dagger\mathsf{A} - (\mathsf{w}^\dagger\mathsf{Aw})\mathsf{w}^\dagger] - 2[\mathsf{Aw} - \mathsf{w}(\mathsf{w}^\dagger\mathsf{Aw})]\mathsf{w}^\dagger \end{aligned} \tag{A9-49}$$

If we let

$$\mathsf{p} = \mathsf{Aw} \tag{A9-50}$$

$$Z = \mathsf{w}^\dagger\mathsf{Aw} = \mathsf{w}^\dagger\mathsf{p} \qquad \text{(a scalar)} \tag{A9-51}$$

$$\mathsf{q} = \mathsf{Aw} - (\mathsf{w}^\dagger\mathsf{Aw})\mathsf{w} = \mathsf{p} - Z\mathsf{w} \tag{A9-52}$$

then

$$\mathsf{TAT} = \mathsf{A} - 2\mathsf{wq}^\dagger - 2\mathsf{qw}^\dagger \tag{A9-53}$$

The program scheme will be to compute:

(1) x's from Eqs. (A9-43)–(A9-44) and form w;
(2) p from Eq. (A9-50);
(3) Z from Eq. (A9-51);
(4) q from Eq. (A9-52);
(5) $-2(\mathsf{wq}^\dagger - \mathsf{qw}^\dagger)$;
(6) TAT from Eq. (A9-53);
(7) α and β from Eq. (A9-47)–(A9-48).

If one wishes to extract eigenvectors, then the elements of w must be saved. Assume that the eigenvalues and eigenvectors of the tridiagonal matrix have been found. In order to recover the eigenvectors v of the original matrix, we must carry the eigenvectors p of the tridiagonal matrix back through the transformations T that interconvert the matrices:

$$\mathsf{v} = \mathsf{T}_2\mathsf{T}_3\cdots\mathsf{T}_{n-1}\mathsf{p} \tag{A9-54}$$

The product may be accumulated by taking

$$\begin{aligned} \mathsf{p}_{n-1} &= \mathsf{T}_{n-1}\mathsf{p} \\ \mathsf{p}_{n-2} &= \mathsf{T}_{n-2}\mathsf{p}_{n-1} \\ &\vdots \\ \mathsf{v} = \mathsf{p}_2 &= \mathsf{T}_2\mathsf{p}_3 \end{aligned} \tag{A9-55}$$

Furthermore, by using

$$\mathsf{T}_r\mathsf{p}_{r+1} = (1 - 2\mathsf{w}_r\mathsf{w}_r^\dagger)\mathsf{p}_{r+1} = \mathsf{p}_{r+1} - 2\mathsf{w}_r\mathsf{w}_r^\dagger\mathsf{p}_{r+1} = \mathsf{p}_{r+1} - 2(\mathsf{w}_r^\dagger\mathsf{p}_{r+1})\mathsf{w}_r \tag{A9-56}$$

(since $\mathsf{w}_r^\dagger\mathsf{p}_{r+1}$ is a scalar) we see that we need not construct and store matrices, but merely carry out some simple vector operations.

The computation scheme that emerges is as follows:

(1) Select a starting p from the matrix of eigenvectors of the tridiagonal matrix.

(2) Compute the scalar product $\mathsf{w}_r^\dagger\mathsf{p}$.

(3) Multiply w_r by this scalar, subtract the result from p, and store the final result in p.

(4) Repeat this sequence for all w_r.

B. Finding Eigenvalues and Eigenvectors of a Tridiagonal Matrix

(*a*) *Eigenvalues* An algorithm is known for finding the eigenvalues of an $n \times n$ tridiagonal matrix A. Consider a sequence of functions of some argument Z, $f_i(Z)$ ($i = 0, 1, 2, \ldots, n$). For any real Z, $f_i(Z)$ may be zero, negative, or positive in value. We define another function SIG$[f_i(Z)]$ as

$$\mathrm{SIG}[f_i(Z)] = \begin{cases} +1 \cdots f_i(Z) > 0 \\ -1 \cdots f_i(Z) < 0 \\ \mathrm{SIG}[f_{i-1}(Z)] \cdots f_i(Z) = 0 \end{cases} \tag{A9-57}$$

We may assume $f_0(Z) > 0$ for unambiguous definition. Once we choose a definition of $f_i(Z)$ and pick some value for Z, it is apparent that we will generate an ordered sequence of plus and minus unities.

It turns out that, if we define the f_i in terms of the elements of a tridiagonal matrix in a certain way, the sequence of plus and minus unities gives us information about the position of Z with respect to the eigenvalues scattered along the real number axis.

The tridiagonalized matrix is

$$\begin{pmatrix} a_1 & b_2 & 0 & 0 & \cdots \\ b_2 & a_2 & b_3 & 0 & \cdots \\ 0 & b_3 & a_3 & b_4 & \cdots \\ \vdots & \vdots & \vdots & \vdots & \end{pmatrix} \tag{A9-58}$$

In terms of these elements, the functions $f_i(Z)$ are defined as

$$f_{i\neq 0}(Z) = \begin{cases} (a_i - Z)\,\mathrm{SIG}[f_{i-1}(Z)] \cdots b_{i-1} = 0 \\ (a_i - Z)\cdot f_{i-1}(Z) - b_{i-1}^2 \cdot \mathrm{SIG}[f_{i-2}(Z)] \cdots b_{i-2} = 0, \qquad b_{i-1} \neq 0 \\ (a_i - Z)\cdot f_{i-1}(Z) - b_{i-1}^2 f_{i-2}(Z) \cdots \qquad \text{otherwise} \end{cases} \tag{A9-59}$$

$$f_0(Z) = 1 \tag{A9-60}$$

In the trivial case where all b's are zero and a's are therefore the eigenvalues, the first definition for $f_i(Z)$ holds for all i. If Z is algebraically less than or equal to all a, then $(a_i - Z)$ will be positive and SIG$[f_i(Z)]$ will be $+1$ for all i. As soon as Z exceeds an eigenvalue, say a_k, all SIG values up through SIG$[f_{k-1}(Z)]$ will be $+1$ and all those following will be -1. Thus, crossing one eigenvalue is signaled by one reversal of sign in the sequence, (e.g., $+ + - -$). If Z exceeds two eigenvalues, two reversals occur (e.g., $+ - + +$). (This can be demonstrated with some simple examples.)

In general, when the b's are nonzero, this property is maintained. A given value of Z will produce an ordered sequence of plus and minus ones. The number of agreements in sign between neighbors is equal to the number of eigenvalues greater than or equal to Z. Hence, we can always tell how many eigenvalues lie between two values of Z, and how many lie above or below both values of Z.

Such an algorithm enables us to pin down any one or more eigenvalues to within any desired degree of accuracy by systematic variation of Z.

In programming such a scheme, we might ask how we can tell what the upper and lower limits of useful Z values are. Since the norm (square root of sum of squares of all elements) must be conserved in an orthogonal transformation, it follows that no eigenvalue can exceed in absolute value the norm. Hence, as a first step, one can take the sum of the squares of the elements of the tridiagonal matrix. The positive and negative roots of this quantity define the limits of Z.

(*b*) *Eigenvectors* We begin with a tridiagonal matrix A for which we have one or more accurate eigenvalues λ_i. We desire the corresponding eigenvectors p_i so that

$$\mathsf{A}\mathsf{p}_i = \lambda_i \mathsf{p}_i$$

is solved exactly. If, instead of p_i, we use some arbitrary vector x, and an approximate eigenvalue Z_i, then

$$(\mathsf{A} - Z_i\mathsf{1})\mathsf{x} = \mathsf{d} \tag{A9-61}$$

We may, if we wish, regard x as defined by d. Then, d is an arbitrary vector in the space of the eigenvector p_i so that

$$\mathsf{d} = \sum_{i=1}^{n} r_i \mathsf{p}_i \tag{A9-62}$$

Substitution gives

$$(\mathsf{A} - Z_i\mathsf{1})\mathsf{x} = \sum_{i=1}^{n} r_i \mathsf{p}_i \tag{A9-63}$$

Multiplying from the left by $(\mathsf{A} - Z_i\mathsf{1})^{-1}$ gives

$$\mathsf{x} = \sum_{i=1}^{n} r_i (\mathsf{A} - Z_i\mathsf{1})^{-1} \mathsf{p}_i \tag{A9-64}$$

$$\mathsf{x} = \sum_{i=1}^{n} r_1 [1/(\lambda_i - Z_i)] \mathsf{p}_i \tag{A9-65}$$

When Z_i is very close to λ_i, the term in parentheses becomes very large, and x approaches $\mathsf{p}_i \cdot c$, where c is a constant.

Writing out the equations in $(\mathsf{A} - Z\mathsf{1})\mathsf{x} = \mathsf{d}$ explicitly, we obtain [assuming that A has the form (A9–58)]

$$
\begin{aligned}
(a_1 - Z)x_1 + b_2x_2 &= d_1 && (1) \\
b_2x_1 + (a_2 - Z)x_2 + b_3x_3 &= d_2 && (2) \\
b_3x_2 + (a_3 - Z)x_3 + b_4x_4 &= d_3 && (3) \\
&\vdots && \vdots \\
b_{n-1}x_{n-2} + (a_{n-1} - Z)x_{n-1} + b_nx_n &= d_{n-1} && (n-1) \\
b_nx_{n-1} + (a_n - Z)x_n &= d_n && (n)
\end{aligned}
\qquad \text{(A9-66)}
$$

If we can find the x's in Eqs. (A9-66), we should have a vector that is proportional to the eigenvector p_i. Furthermore, this should be true no matter what we choose for the elements of d, as long as d contains a significant contribution from p_i [i.e., r_i in Eq. (A9-62) is not zero]. The procedure is as follows:

(1) Eliminate the variables in Eqs. (A9-66) in their natural order. (For each variable being eliminated, e.g., x_1, let the larger of the two coefficients, say b_2, define the row that is to be multiplied and subtracted. In this example, we would multiply the left-hand side of the second row in Eqs. (A9-66) by $(a_1 - Z)/b_2$, and subtract the result from the first row. This gives us a new equation which we will call $1'$. Now we renumber the equations so that $2 \rightarrow 1$ and $1 \rightarrow 2$. Next we repeat the procedure with x_2, etc.)

(2) Set the right-hand side of the resulting n equations equal to unity. (We have not yet defined d since it should not affect our results. Here we are choosing d to be "that vector which, after the manipulations described above, gives us unity on the right-hand side of each equation.")

(3) Solve for the x's, working backward from x_n along the set of simultaneous equations. Normalize the result to obtain p_i. (If higher accuracy is desired, this first p_i may be used as a new guess for d and the whole elimination procedure repeated, this time carrying both sides of the equations along and not setting the right-hand side equal to unity at the end.)

(4) Any two eigenvectors corresponding to degenerate eigenvalues should be Schmidt orthogonalized.

For a more extensive discussion of this admittedly complicated eigenvalue–eigenvector procedure, see the papers by Wilkinson [2].

A FORTRAN listing of a program for computing selected eigenvalues and eigenvectors by the above procedures is given in Appendix 10.

REFERENCES

[1] P.-O. Löwdin, *J. Chem. Phys.* **18**, 365 (1950).
[2] J. H. Wilkinson, *Comput. J.* **3**, 23 (1960); **1**, 90 (1958).
[3] W. Givens, *Appl. Math. Ser. U.S. Bur. Std.* **29**, 117 (1953).
[4] J. M. Ortega, *Applied Mathematics and Statistics Laboratories, Stanford Univ. Tech. Rep. No. 4*, Stanford, California, 1960.

APPENDIX 10

COMPUTER PROGRAM LISTINGS

A10-1 Simple Hückel Program

The following main program, together with the subsequently listed subroutine (JACOBI), performs simple, noniterative Hückel calculations. Details are given in comments in the main program. This program runs on an IBM 360 computer and requires about 40K core.

```
C   PROGRAM FOR FINDING ENERGIES, BOND ORDERS, ELECTRON DENSITIES,
C   POLARIZABILITIES FOR HOMO AND HETERONUCLEAR CONJUGATED MOLECULES
C   BY THE SIMPLE HUCKEL METHOD.  BOND LENGTHS AND FREE VALENCES ARE
C   CALCULATED FOR HOMONUCLEAR SYSTEMS ONLY.
C   JOHN P. LOWE  -  PENN STATE UNIVERSITY.
C   PROGRAMMED IN FORTRAN IV, DOUBLE PRECISION.
C   FIRST CARD IS TITLE (80 CHARACTERS, 1 IN FIRST SPACE).
C   NEXT CARD CONTAINS FOUR NUMBERS IN 4I2 FORMAT.
C   FIRST NUMBER IS NUMBER OF ATOMS IN CONJUGATED SYSTEM.
C   SECOND NUMBER IS NUMBER OF BONDS.
C   THIRD IS NUMBER OF ELECTRONS. (LIMITED MOLECULAR CHARGE...+2, +1, 0,
C   -1, -2.)
C   FOURTH IS NUMBER OF MATRIX ELEMENTS YOU WISH TO MODIFY IN TOPOLOGICAL
C   MATRIX TO HANDLE HETEROATOMS.
C   THE NEXT CARD IS A BOND NUMBERING SEQUENCE CARD (FORMAT=40I2).
C   CONNECTED SEQUENCE OF ATOMS IS LISTED AS A LIST OF NUMBERS.
C   (E.G. BENZENE =  1 2 3 4 5 6 1). TO AFFIX OTHER ATOMS, SKIP TWO
C   SPACES AND CONTINUE NUMBERING (E.G. TRIMETHYLENE METHANE =
C    1 2 3   2 4).
C   NUMBERING SCHEME FOR MOLECULE IS ARBITRARY.
C   (E.G. BENZENE = 1 4 3 2 6 5 1).
C   IF NHETRO = 0, NEXT CARD IS TITLE CARD FOR A NEW MOLECULE.
C   OTHERWISE, NEXT NHETRO CARDS HAVE ROW AND COLUMN INDICES OF MATRIX
C   ELEMENT TO BE REVISED AND NEW MATRIX ELEMENT IN FORMAT 2I2,F15.5
C   EACH I,J MODIFICATION IS AUTOMATICALLY MADE AT I,J AND J,I.
C   THIS PROGRAM WILL COMPUTE POLARIZABILITIES ONLY FOR CLOSED
C   SHELL MOLECULES.
C   MAXIMUM CAPACITY = 30 ATOMS.
      IMPLICIT REAL*8 (A-H,O-Z)
      DIMENSION NUMBER(40),A(30,30),ORTHO(30,30),NN(30),NP(30),
     1 TOPA(40),BOTA(40),SORTA(30),INDEX(30),ELECNO(30),KEEP(40,2),
     2 FREEVA(30)
    1 FORMAT (80H
     1                                                            )
    2 FORMAT(4I2)
3     FORMAT(1H0 ,19X22HNUMBER OF ROTATIONS = ,I4,//20X18HNUMBER OF ATOM
     1S = ,I2,//20X18HNUMBER OF BONDS = ,I2,//20X22HNUMBER OF ELECTRONS
     2= ,I2,//20X25HBOND NUMBERING SEQUENCE  ,40I2,//)
5     FORMAT(1H0,  8HENERGIES,4X4HOCC.,46X12HCOEFFICIENTS,/8H  (BETA),5X
     13HNO.,47X11HATOM NUMBER,/22X1H1,9X1H2,9X1H3,9X1H4,9X1H5,9X1H6,9X1H
     27,9X1H8,9X1H9,8X2H10,/21X2H11,8X2H12,8X2H13,8X2H14,8X2H15,8X2H16,8
     3X2H17,8X2H18,8X2H19,8X2H20,/)
7     FORMAT(1H0,F8.5,4XI1,4X10(2X,F8.5)/(16X10(2X,F8.5)))
    8 FORMAT(1H0,//1X18HELECTRON DENSITIES,10(3X,F7.4)/(16X10(3X,F7.4)))
```

```
9      FORMAT(1H0,10X4HBOND,11X5HORDER, 9X6HLENGTH)
   13 FORMAT(40I2)
99     FORMAT(1H0,16HFREE VALENCES    ,10(3X,F7.4)/(16X10(3X,F7.4)))
1000   FORMAT(1H ,  9XI2,1H-,I2,10XF7.4,8XF5.3)
  702 FORMAT(2I2,F15.5)
704    FORMAT(1H  25HCORRECTED MATRIX ELEMENT I2,1H,I2,3H = F10.5)
  753 FORMAT(7XI2,9X10(2XF8.5)/(16X10(2XF8.5)))
 3333 FORMAT(1H0,15HTOTAL ENERGY = ,F11.4,5H BETA)
1111   READ(5,1,END=99999)
       READ(5,2)  NATOMS,NBONDS,NELEC,NHETRO
       READ(5,13) (NUMBER(I),I=1,40)
       WRITE(6,1)
       DO 23  I=1,NATOMS
       DO 23  J=1,NATOMS
   23 A(I,J) = 0.0D0
C  INDEX SCHEME IS NOW USED TO SET UP HUCKEL ENERGY MATRIX.
       LOOP=0
        MMM=0
       DO 215 K=1,40
       LOOP=LOOP+1
       L=K+1
       IF(NUMBER(K))211,216,211
211    MA=NUMBER(K)
       IF(NUMBER(L))217,213,217
217    MB=NUMBER(L)
       MMM = MMM+1
       KEEP(MMM,1) = MA
       KEEP(MMM,2) = MB
       A(MA,MB)=-1.0D0
       A(MB,MA)=-1.0D0
       GO TO 215
213    IF(NUMBER(K))215,214,215
216    IF(NUMBER(L))215,214,215
215    CONTINUE
C  EXTRA OR REVISED VALUES FOR HETEROATOMS ARE NOW INSERTED.
  214 IF(NHETRO)701,700,701
  701 DO 703 K=1,NHETRO
       READ(5,702)I,J,X
       WRITE(6,704) I,J,X
       A(I,J) = -X
  703 A(J,I) = -X
  700 LTEST=0
C  THE MATRIX WILL NOW BE DIAGONALIZED.
       CALL JACOBI (NATOMS,A,ORTHO,LTEST,SORTA,ELECNO)
  709 WRITE(6,3) LTEST,NATOMS,NBONDS,NELEC,(NUMBER(K),K=1,LOOP)
       IF(NHETRO) 721,720,721
  721 WRITE(6,722)
  722 FORMAT(1X  96HTHIS MATRIX HAS BEEN MODIFIED TO ACCOUNT FOR HETERO-
      1ATOMS.  SEE CORRECTED MATRIX ELEMENTS ABOVE.  )
C  THE EIGENVALUES ARE NEXT SORTED AND STORED IN BOTA AND TOPA.
  720 IND1=0
       IND2=0
       DO 12  K=1,NATOMS
       IF(A(K,K)) 10,11,11
10     IND1=IND1+1
       NN(IND1)=K
       BOTA(IND1)=DABS(A(K,K))
       GO TO 12
11     IND2=IND2+1
       NP(IND2)=K
       TOPA(IND2)=A(K,K)
12     CONTINUE
C  NOW EACH SUBCLASS IS RANKED NUMERICALLY AND ALL ARE STORED IN
C  SORTA.  INDICES FOR THEIR ORIGINAL ORDER WILL BE STORED IN INDEX.
       DO 38  K1=1,IND1
       DUMMY=0.0D0
       DO 30  K2=1,IND1
       IF(DUMMY-BOTA(K2)) 31,30,30
31     DUMMY=BOTA(K2)
       MN=K2
30     CONTINUE
```

```
      SORTA(K1)=-DUMMY
      INDEX(K1)=NN(MN)
38    BOTA(MN)=0.0D0
      DO 48  K1=1,IND2
      DUMMY=0.0D0
      DO 40  K2=1,IND2
      IF(DUMMY-TOPA(K2)) 41,41,40
41    DUMMY=TOPA(K2)
      MM=K2
40    CONTINUE
      MARK=NATOMS-K1+1
      SORTA(MARK)=DUMMY
      INDEX(MARK)=NP(MM)
48    TOPA(MM)=-1.0D0
C  THE NO. OF ELECTRONS IN EACH MO WILL NOW BE COMPUTED.
      DO 50  K=1,NATOMS
50    ELECNO(K)=0.0D0
      NAA=1
      DO 51  K=1,NELEC
53    IF(ELECNO(NAA)-1.0D0) 54,55,55
54    ELECNO(NAA)=1.0D0
      GO TO 51
55    NBB=NAA+1
      DEL=SORTA(NBB)-SORTA(NAA)
      IF(DEL-0.00001) 56,56,57
56    IF(ELECNO(NBB)-1.0D0) 58,57,57
58    ELECNO(NBB)=1.0D0
      GO TO 51
57    ELECNO(NAA)=2.0D0
52    NAA=NAA+1
51    CONTINUE
      WRITE(6,5)
      DO 89  K=1,NATOMS
      NUMEL=ELECNO(K)
      ENERGY = -SORTA(K)
      K2=INDEX(K)
89    WRITE(6,7) ENERGY  ,NUMEL,(ORTHO(K1,K2),K1=1,NATOMS)
C  NEXT, ELECTRON DENSITIES ARE CALCULATED AND STORED IN TOPA.
      DO 65  K1=1,NATOMS
      SUM=0.0D0
      DO 63  K2=1,NATOMS
      LA=INDEX(K2)
      CONTR=ELECNO(K2)*ORTHO(K1,LA)**2
63    SUM=SUM+CONTR
   65 TOPA(K1) = SUM
C  BOND ORDERS ARE STORED IN BOTA.
      DO 75 K=1,MMM
        K1=KEEP(K,1)
      K2=KEEP(K,2)
71    SUM=0.0D0
      DO 73 K3=1,NATOMS
      NA=INDEX(K3)
      CONTR=ELECNO(K3)*ORTHO(K1,NA)*ORTHO(K2,NA)
73    SUM=SUM+CONTR
      BOTA(K)=SUM
75    CONTINUE
C  NEXT, COMPUTE TOTAL ENERGY.
      SUM=0.0D0
      DO 141  K=1,NATOMS
      X=SORTA(K)*ELECNO(K)
141   SUM=SUM+X
      TOTALE =-SUM
      WRITE(6,3333) TOTALE
C  NEXT, COMPUTE FREE VALENCES.
      DO 21 K=1,NATOMS
      SUM=0.0D0
      DO 22 L=1,MMM
      IF(KEEP(L,1).EQ.K) SUM=SUM+BOTA(L)
   22 IF(KEEP(L,2).EQ.K) SUM=SUM+BOTA(L)
   21 FREEVA(K) = 1.732D0-SUM
C  NOW TEST WILL BE MADE TO SEE IF DEGENERATE LEVELS ARE ONLY PARTLY
```

```
C  FILLED.  IF SO, ELECTRON DENSITIES, BOND ORDERS, AND FREE VALENCES
C  ARE AVERAGED.  (THIS ASSUMES DEGENERACY FOR REASONS OF SYMMETRY ONLY)
      KKAP=NELEC/2
      IF(2*KKAP-NELEC)601,604,604
601   DEL1=SORTA(KAP+2)-SORTA(KAP+1)
      DEL2=SORTA(KAP+1)-SORTA(KAP)
      IF(DEL1-0.0000010D0)603,603,602
602   IF(DEL2-0.0000010D0) 603,603,604
  603 SUM2=0.0D0
      EN = DFLOAT(NATOMS)
      ENBOND=DFLOAT(NBONDS)
      AV1=NELEC/EN
      DO 605  J=1,NATOMS
  605 SUM2=SUM2+FREEVA(J)
      AV2=SUM2/EN
      SUM2=0.0D0
      DO 607 J=1,MMM
  607 SUM2=SUM2+BOTA(J)
      AV3=SUM2/ENBOND
      DO 606  J=1,NATOMS
      TOPA(J) = AV1
  606 FREEVA(J)=AV2
      DO 608 K=1,MMM
  608 BOTA(K)=AV3
      WRITE(6,142)
  142 FORMAT(' PARTIALLY OCCUPIED DEGENERATE MO-S FOUND.  ELECTRON DENSI
     1TIES, BOND ORDERS AND LENGTHS, ' /' AND FREE VALENCES HAVE BEEN AV
     2ERAGED.' )
  604 WRITE (6,8)(TOPA(K),K=1,NATOMS)
       IF(NHETRO) 2000,2001,2000
 2001 WRITE(6,99) (FREEVA(K),K=1,NATOMS)
C  A TEST IS NOW MADE TO SEE IF THE MOLECULE HAS ALL MO'S EITHER
C  DOUBLY OCCUPIED OR COMPLETELY EMPTY.  IF NOT, THE POLARIZABILITY
C  CALCULATION IS SKIPPED.
 2000 DO 708 I=1,NATOMS
      IF(ELECNO(I)-1.0D0) 708,705,707
  707 NHIGH = I
  708 CONTINUE
      NUNOCC = NHIGH + 1
      DO 710 L=1,NATOMS
      DO 710 K=1,NATOMS
      SUM = 0.0D0
      DO 711 I=1,NHIGH
      KI=INDEX(I)
      DO 711 J=NUNOCC,NATOMS
      KJ=INDEX(J)
711   SUM=SUM+ORTHO(L,KI)*ORTHO(K,KI)*ORTHO(L,KJ)*ORTHO(K,KJ)/(SORTA(I)
     1 -SORTA(J))
  710 A(L,K)=4.0D0*SUM
  750 WRITE(6,751)
  751 FORMAT(1X//5X33HATOM-ATOM MUTUAL POLARIZABILITIES  //)
      DO 752 I=1,NATOMS
  752 WRITE(6,753)I,(A(I,K),K=1,NATOMS)
C  BOND LENGTHS ARE NOW COMPUTED FROM BOND ORDERS.
  705 WRITE(6,9)
      DO 90 J=1,MMM
      K=KEEP(J,1)
      L=KEEP(J,2)
      X=1.54D0-0.2D0/(1.0D0+0.765D0*(1.0D0-BOTA(J))/BOTA(J))
      IF(NHETRO.NE.0) X=0.0D0
      WRITE(6,1000)K,L,BOTA(J),X
90    CONTINUE
      GO TO 1111
99999 STOP
      END
C
C
      SUBROUTINE JACOBI (NATOMS,A,ORTHO,LTEST,V1,V2)
C     DIAGONALIZES MATRIX A AND RETURNS EIGENVECTORS IN ORTHO.
      IMPLICIT REAL*8(A-H,O-Z)
```

```
      DIMENSION A(30,30),ORTHO(30,30),V1(30),V2(30)
      DO 22 I=1,NATOMS
      DO 23 J=1,NATOMS
   23 ORTHO(I,J)=0.0D0
   22 ORTHO(I,I)=1.0D0
110   DUMMY=0.0D0
      DO 111 J=2,NATOMS
      IND=J-1
      DO 111  I=1,IND
      POS=DABS(A(I,J))
      IF(DUMMY-POS)112,111,111
112   DUMMY=POS
      MAXROW=I
      MAXCOL=J
111   CONTINUE
      IF (DUMMY-1.0D-06) 131,131,113
113   I=MAXROW
      J=MAXCOL
      DIFF=A(J,J)-A(I,I)
      ELEM=A(I,J)
      RSQ=DIFF*DIFF+4.0D0*ELEM*ELEM
      R=DSQRT(RSQ)
      COSINE=DABS(DIFF)/R
      IF ( DIFF) 114,115,115
114   SINE=-2.0D0*ELEM/R
      GO TO 116
115   SINE= 2.0D0*ELEM/R
116   ARG=0.50D0*(1.0D0+COSINE)
      COS=DSQRT(ARG)
      SIN=0.5D0*SINE/COS
      SUM=A(I,I)+A(J,J)
      DO 121  K=1,NATOMS
      V1(K)=A(K,I)*COS-A(K,J)*SIN
121   V2(K)=A(K,I)*SIN+A(K,J)*COS
      DO 122 K=1,NATOMS
      A(K,I)=V1(K)
      A(I,K)=V1(K)
      A(K,J)=V2(K)
  122 A(J,K)=V2(K)
          A(I,I)=0.50D0*SUM-0.50D0*DIFF*COSINE-ELEM*SINE
          A(J,J)=0.50D0*SUM+0.50D0*DIFF*COSINE+ELEM*SINE
          A(I,J)=0.0D0
          A(J,I)=0.0D0
      DO 125 K=1,NATOMS
      V1(K) = ORTHO(K,I)*COS-ORTHO(K,J)*SIN
  125 ORTHO(K,J)=ORTHO(K,I)*SIN + ORTHO(K,J)*COS
      DO 126 K=1,NATOMS
  126 ORTHO(K,I)=V1(K)
      LTEST=LTEST+1
      GO TO 110
  131 RETURN
      END
```

A10-2 Program for Solving HC = SCE

The main program and subroutines listed below solve the above matrix equation given H and S. (Subroutine SCHMID performs the Schmidt orthogonalization. This subroutine was written by Professor A. A. Frost, of Northwestern University.) The program can handle matrices of dimension up to 50 × 50 and is programmed for an IBM 360 computer.

```
C       MAIN PROGRAM FOR COMPUTING EIGENVALUES AND EIGENVECTORS OF
C       REAL SYMMETRIC MATRIX, WITH OR WITHOUT INCLUSION OF OVERLAP.
C
C       PROGRAMMED BY J.P. LOWE IN FORTRAN IV, DOUBLE PRECISION.
C       N = DIMENSION OF MATRIX.
```

```
C       NROOTS = NUMBER OF EIGENVALUES DESIRED.
C       NCHOIS = 0 IF EIGENVECTORS NOT DESIRED.
C       NORTHO = 0 IF BASIS ALREADY ORTHOGONAL (S=1).
C       NPRINT = 1 IF FOLLOWING INTERMEDIATE OUTPUT DESIRED - -
C       SCHMIDT TRANSFORMATION MATRIX, TRANSFORMED OVERLAP MATRIX
C       (I.E., UNIT MATRIX), TRANSFORMED HAMILTONIAN, TRIDIAGONALIZED
C       MATRIX, EIGENVECTORS OF TRIDIAGONALIZED MATRIX.  OTHERWISE,
C       NPRINT = 0.
C       ZLOWER AND ZUPPER DEFINE THE LIMITS OF SEARCH FOR EIGENVALUES.
C       ACC IS ACCURACY TO WHICH EIGENVALUES WILL BE DETERMINED.
C       ABOVE IN FORMAT 5I2,2F10.5,D10.2
C       THEN OVERLAP (NCHOIS=1) MATRIX IS READ IN, UPPER TRIANGLE ONLY,
C       ELEMENTS PUCHED IN FORMAT 4F20.8 UNTIL UPPER TRIANGLE ALL IN.
C       HAMILTONIAN MATRIX FED IN IN THE SAME MANNER.
      IMPLICIT REAL*8(A-H,O-Z)
      DIMENSION A(50,50),P(50,50),V(50),T(50,50)
C       INPUT FORMATS
   10  FORMAT (5I2,2F10.5,D10.2)
   20 FORMAT (7F10.6)
   30 FORMAT (72H
     1                  )
C       OUTPUT FORMATS
   40 FORMAT (1H016X98HEIGENVALUE(S) AND EIGENVECTOR(S) OF REAL SYMMETRI
     1C MATRIX BY METHODS OF HOUSEHOLDER AND WILKINSON.)
   50 FORMAT (1H0///52X27HSTARTING HAMILTONIAN MATRIX)
   60 FORMAT (1H0///58X14HOVERLAP MATRIX)
   70 FORMAT (1H1///11X29HSCHMIDT TRANSFORMATION MATRIX)
   80 FORMAT (1H1///5X40HHAMILTONIAN IN TERMS OF ORTHOGONAL BASIS)
   90 FORMAT (1H1///54X23H TRIDIAGONALIZED MATRIX/48X36H(LOWER TRIANGLE
     1CONTAINS W VECTORS).)
  100 FORMAT (1H0//10X31H EIGENVECTOR(S) NOT CALLED FOR.)
  110 FORMAT (1H1//10X20H LIST OF EIGENVALUES/)
  120 FORMAT (15XF12.8)
  130 FORMAT (1H1//50X55HORDERED MATRIX OF EIGENVECTORS FOR ORIGINALHAMI
     1LTONIAN./)
  140 FORMAT (1H150X34HEIGENVECTORS OF TRIDIAGONAL MATRIX/)
  150 FORMAT (51X29HIN TERMS OF ORTHOGONAL BASIS.//)
  160 FORMAT (1H013(2X8F15.8/))
  170 FORMAT (51X27HIN TERMS OF ORIGINAL BASIS.//)
  180 FORMAT (1H0//10X37HTIME REQUIRED FOR ORTHOGONALIZATION =F9.2,1X8HS
     1ECONDS.)
  190 FORMAT (1H0//10X39HTIME REQUIRED FOR TRIDIAGONALIZATION = F9.2,1X8
     1HSECONDS.)
  200 FORMAT (1H0///10X36HTIME REQUIRED TO FIND EIGENVALUES = F9.2,1X8HS
     1ECONDS.)
  210 FORMAT (1H0///10X37HTIME REQUIRED TO FIND EIGENVECTORS = F9.2,1X8H
     1SECONDS.)
  220 READ (5,30)
      WRITE (6,30)
      WRITE (6,40)
       READ(5,10) N,NROOTS,NCHOIS,NORTHO,NPRINT,ZLOWER,ZUPPER,ACC
      NZERO=0
      NTWO=2
      NMIN=-1
      READ (5,240) ((A(I,J),J=I,N),I=1,N)
  240 FORMAT (4F20.8)
      IF (NORTHO)  250,280,250
  250 WRITE (6,60)
      CALL MATRIX(N,NZERO,A)
      CALL TIMUSE (JZZ)
      CALL SCHMID(A,T,V,N)
      CALL TIMUSE (JXX)
      B=DFLOAT (JXX-JZZ)
      CALL TAT(N,A,T)
       IF(NPRINT) 1000,1001,1000
 1000 WRITE (6,260)
  260 FORMAT (1H150X27HTRANSFORMED OVERLAP MATRIX.//)
      CALL MATRIX(N,NZERO,A)
      WRITE (6,180) B
 1001 READ (5,240) ((A(I,J),J=I,N),I=1,N)
```

```
  280 WRITE (6,50)
      CALL MATRIX(N,NZERO,A)
      IF (NORTHO)  290,300,290
  290 CALL TAT(N,A,T)
       IF(NPRINT)1002,1003,1002
 1002 WRITE (6,70)
      CALL MATRIX(N,NTWO,T)
      WRITE (6,80)
      CALL MATRIX(N,NTWO,A)
 1003 CALL TIMUSE (JAA)
  300 CALL TRIDIH(N,A,V)
      CALL TIMUSE (JBB)
      B=DFLOAT(JBB-JAA)
       IF(NPRINT) 1004,1005,1004
 1004 WRITE (6,90)
      CALL MATRIX(N,NTWO,A)
      WRITE (6,190) B
 1005 CALL VALUE(N,NROOTS,A,V,ACC,ZLOWER,ZUPPER)
      CALL TIMUSE (JCC)
      B=DFLOAT(JCC-JBB)
      WRITE (6,110)
      DO 320 J=1,NROOTS
  320 WRITE (6,120) V(J)
      WRITE (6,200) B
      IF (NCHOIS)  340,330,340
  330 WRITE (6,100)
      GO TO 220
  340 CALL TRIVEC(N,NROOTS,A,V,P)
       IF(NPRINT)1006,1007,1006
 1006 WRITE (6,140)
      IF (NORTHO)  350,360,350
  350 WRITE (6,150)
  360 DO 370 I=1,N
  370 WRITE (6,160) (P(I,J),J=1,NROOTS)
 1007 CALL EIGVEC(N,NROOTS,A,V,P)
      CALL ORTHOG(N,NROOTS,A,V,P)
      CALL TIMUSE (JDD)
      B=DFLOAT (JDD-JCC)
       IF(NPRINT) 1008,1009,1008
 1008 WRITE (6,130)
      IF (NORTHO)  380,390,380
  380 WRITE (6,150)
  390 DO 400 I=1,N
  400 WRITE (6,160) (P(I,J),J=1,NROOTS)
      WRITE (6,210) B
 1009 IF (NORTHO)  410,430,410
  410 CALL MLTPLY(N,NROOTS,T,P)
      WRITE (6,130)
      WRITE (6,170)
      DO 420 I=1,N
  420 WRITE (6,160) (P(I,J),J=1,NROOTS)
  430 GO TO 220
      END
C
C
      SUBROUTINE TRIDIH(N,A,V)
      IMPLICIT REAL*8(A-H,O-Z)
C      TRIDIAGONALIZES A REAL, SYMMETRIC MATRIX BY METHOD OF HOUSEHOLDER
C      SEE REFERENCE - J. H. WILKINSON, THE COMPUTER JOURNAL,3,23(1960).
C      N IS ORDER OF MATRIX.  MAX N = 50
C      A IS MATRIX TO BE TRANSFORMED.
C      OUTPUT A HAS W VECTORS STORED COLUMNWISE BELOW THE DIAGONAL.
C      PROGRAMMED IN FORTRAN II, DOUBLE PRECISION, BY JOHN P. LOWE,
C      NOVEMBER , 1964.
      DIMENSION A(50,50),V(50)
C      FIRST SET UP MASTER DO-LOOP (CORRESPONDS TO INDEX R ) TO RUN
C      FROM 2 TO N-1.
      MAX=N-1
      DO 140 I=2,MAX
      IR=I-1
```

```
C       COMPUTE ELEMENTS OF VECTOR W.  THESE ARE STORED IN LOWER A.
C       HENCE, IN COMPUTING AW, ONLY UPPER TRIANGLE OF A CAN BE USED.
C       COLUMN INDEX OF A FOR STORING W IS IR.
C       FIRST FIND SGN.
      IF (A(IR,I))  10,20,20
   10 SGN=-1.0D0
      GO TO 30
   20 SGN=1.0D0
C       Z IS S**0.5 OF THEORY.
   30 Z=0.0D0
      DO 40 K=I,N
   40 Z=Z+A(IR,K)*A(IR,K)
      Z=DSQRT(Z)
      IF (Z)  50,50,60
   50 A(I,IR)=1.0D0
      GO TO 70
   60 A(I,IR)=DSQRT(0.5D0*(1.0D0+SGN*A(IR,I)/Z))
   70 IND=I+1
      DO 80 K=IND,N
   80 A(K,IR)=SGN*A(IR,K)/(2.0D0*A(I,IR)*Z)
C       SAVE THIS Z.
      V(1)=Z
C       IT IS NOW NECESSARY TO FIND P=AW.  THIS VECTOR WILL BE STORED
C       IN V.  ONLY ELEMENTS IND TO N ARE NEEDED.
      DO 100 K=I,N
      V(K)=0.0D0
      DO 90 L=I,K
   90 V(K)=V(K)+A(L,K)*A(L,IR)
      KP=K+1
      IF (KP-N) 101,101,100
  101 DO 100 L=KP,N
      V(K)=V(K)+A(K,L)*A(L,IR)
  100  CONTINUE
C       NEXT COMPUTE Z OF THEORY (WILKINSON CALLS IT K).
      Z=0.0D0
      DO 110 K=I,N
  110 Z=Z+A(K,IR)*V(K)
C       NEXT COMPUTE Q VECTOR = P-ZW.
C       STORE Q ON P IN V.
C       SINCE FIRST IR TERMS OF W ARE ZERO, ONLY LATER TERMS NEED BE
C       COMPUTED.
      DO 120 K=I,N
  120 V(K)=V(K)-Z*A(K,IR)
C       TO COMPUTE TAT, ADJUST INDICES SO THAT ONLY UPPER TRIANGLE OF
C       TRANSFORMED SECTION IS CALLED.  TRANSFORMED SQUARE IS ROW AND
C       COLUMN I TO N.
      DO 130 K=I,N
      DO 130 L=K,N
C       NOW FIND CORRESPONDING VALUE OF 2*(WQ-QW) AND STORE IN Z.
      Z=2.0D0*(A(K,IR)*V(L)+V(K)*A(L,IR))
  130 A(K,L)=A(K,L)-Z
C       INSERT BETA ABOVE DIAGONAL AND ZERO PROPER ELEMENTS.
      A(IR,I)=-SGN*V(1)
      DO 140 K=IND,N
  140 A(IR,K)=0.0D0
      RETURN
      END
C
C
      SUBROUTINE ORTHOG(N,NROOTS,A,V,P)
      IMPLICIT REAL*8(A-H,O-Z)
      DIMENSION A(50,50),V(50),P(50,50)
      IF (NROOTS-1)  100,100,10
   10 J=0
      DO 90 I=2,NROOTS
      IND=I-1
      IF (V(I)-V(IND)-1.0D-6)  20,20,30
   20 J=J+1
      IF (I-NROOTS)  90,40,40
   30 IF (J)  90,90,50
```

```
   40 IND=IND+1
   50 K=IND-J
      K1=K+1
      DO 80 L1=K1,IND
      KM=L1-1
      DO 80 L2=K,KM
      C=0.0D0
      DO 60 L3=1,N
   60 C=C+P(L3,L1)*P(L3,L2)
      Z=0.0D0
      DO 70 L3=1,N
      P(L3,L1)=P(L3,L1)-C*P(L3,L2)
   70 Z=Z+P(L3,L1)**2
      Z=DSQRT(Z)
      DO 80 L3=1,N
   80 P(L3,L1)=P(L3,L1)/Z
      J=0
   90 CONTINUE
  100 RETURN
      END
C
C
      SUBROUTINE SCHMID(S,R,RS,NDIM)
      IMPLICIT REAL*8(A-H,O-Z)
C       S IS MATRIX OF OVERLAPS - (THE METRIC MATRIX).
C       R IS THE TRANSFORMATION MATRIX.
C       S MAY BE UPPER TRIANGULAR.
C       PROGRAMMED BY A. A. FROST - NORTHWESTERN UNIVERSITY
C       FORTRAN II  -  DOUBLE PRECISION.
      DIMENSION RS(50),S(50,50),R(50,50)
      NMIN=1
      NMAX=NDIM
      IF (S(1,1))  120,120,10
C       SET UNIT MATRIX IN R AND FILL IN LOWER S.
   10 DO 30 J=NMIN,NMAX
      JM=J-1
      DO 20 I=NMIN,JM
      S(J,I)=S(I,J)
      R(J,I)=0.0D0
   20 R(I,J)=0.0D0
   30 R(J,J)=1.0D0
      R(NMIN,NMIN)=1.0D0/DSQRT(S(NMIN,NMIN))
      NMINP=NMIN+1
      DO 110 M=NMINP,NMAX
C       CALCULATE EACH SUCCESSIVE COLUMN OF R.
      MM1=M-1
      DO 40 J=NMIN,MM1
      RS(J)=0.0D0
      DO 40 I=NMIN,J
   40 RS(J)=RS(J)+R(I,J)*S(I,M)
C       CALCULATE NEW VECTOR M.
      DO 60 I=NMIN,MM1
      RIM=0.0D0
      DO 50 J=NMIN,MM1
   50 RIM=RIM-RS(J)*R(I,J)
   60 R(I,M)=RIM
C       CALCULATE SQUARE OF VECTOR M.
      SUM=S(NMIN,NMIN)*R(NMIN,M)**2
      DO 80 L=NMINP,M
      SUMRS=0.0D0
      LM1=L-1
      DO 70 K=NMIN,LM1
   70 SUMRS=SUMRS+R(K,M)*S(K,L)
   80 SUM=SUM+2.0D0*SUMRS*R(L,M)+S(L,L)*R(L,M)**2
      IF (SUM)  120,120,90
C       NORMALIZE VECTOR M.
   90 SQRTSM=DSQRT(SUM)
      DO 100 J=NMIN,M
  100 R(J,M)=R(J,M)/SQRTSM
  110 CONTINUE
```

```
      RETURN
  120 WRITE (6,130)
  130 FORMAT (70H  S MATRIX APPARENTLY NOT POSITIVE DEFINITE.  CALCULATI
     1ON TERMINATED. )
      STOP
      END
C
C
      SUBROUTINE MLTPLY(N,NROOTS,T,P)
      IMPLICIT REAL*8(A-H,O-Z)
C       MULTIPLIES N X NROOTS MATRIX P BY N X N MATRIX T.
C       RESULT STORED IN P.
      DIMENSION T(50,50),P(50,50),V(50)
      DO 30 I=1,NROOTS
      DO 20 J=1,N
      SUM=0.0D0
      DO 10 K=1,N
   10 SUM=SUM+T(J,K)*P(K,I)
   20 V(J)=SUM
      DO 30 K=1,N
   30 P(K,I)=V(K)
      RETURN
      END
C
      SUBROUTINE TAT(N,A,T)
      IMPLICIT REAL*8(A-H,O-Z)
C       CARRIES OUT A CONGRUENT TRANSFORMATION T TRANSPOSE A T WHERE A IS
C       SYMMETRICAL AND T IS UPPER TRIANGULAR.
C       TRANSPOSED A RETURNED IN A.  T IS SAVED.
C       FILLS IN LOWER A IN CASE IT IS NOT ALREADY SYMMETRICAL.
C       DOUBLE PRECISION  -  FORTRAN II.
C       PROGRAMMED BY A. A. FROST.
      DIMENSION A(50,50),T(50,50)
      DO 10 I=2,N
      DO 10 J=1,I
   10 A(I,J)=A(J,I)
      NP=N+1
      DO 30 JR=1,N
      J=NP-JR
      DO 30 I=1,N
      SUM=0.0D0
      DO 20 K=1,J
   20 SUM=SUM+A(I,K)*T(K,J)
   30 A(I,J)=SUM
      DO 50 IR=1,N
      I=NP-IR
      DO 50 J=1,N
      SUM=0.0D0
      DO 40 K=1,I
   40 SUM=SUM+T(K,I)*A(K,J)
   50 A(I,J)=SUM
      RETURN
      END
C
C
      SUBROUTINE MATRIX(NDIM,NTRI,A)
      IMPLICIT REAL*8(A-H,O-Z)
C       WRITES OUT NDIM X NDIM MATRIX A AND TRACE.
C       IF NTRI IS
C       NEGATIVE  -  ONLY UPPER TRIANGLE, LEFT ADJUSTED, IS WRITTEN.
C       ZERO  -  FILLS IN LOWER TRIANGLE AND WRITES ENTIRE MATRIX.
C       POSITIVE  -  WRITES ENTIRE MATRIX.
C       FORTRAN II  -  DOUBLE PRECISION.
      DIMENSION A(50,50)
   10 FORMAT (1H013(2X8F15.8/))
   20 FORMAT (1H01X9H TRACE = F15.8)
      TRACE=0.0D0
      IF (NTRI)  30,50,70
   30 DO 40 I=1,NDIM
```

```
      TRACE=TRACE+A(I,I)
   40 WRITE (6,10) (A(I,J),J=I,NDIM)
      WRITE (6,20) TRACE
      RETURN
   50 DO 60 J=2,NDIM
      K=J-1
      DO 60 I=1,K
   60 A(J,I)=A(I,J)
   70 DO 80 I=1,NDIM
      TRACE=TRACE+A(I,I)
   80 WRITE (6,10) (A(I,J),J=1,NDIM)
      WRITE (6,20) TRACE
      RETURN
      END
C
C
      SUBROUTINE EIGVEC(N,NROOTS,A,V,P)
      IMPLICIT REAL*8(A-H,O-Z)
      DIMENSION A(50,50),V(50),P(50,50)
      DO 20 I=1,NROOTS
      M=N-1
      DO 20 J=2,M
      KR=N+1-J
      KC=N-J
      Z=0.0D0
      DO 10 L=1,J
      KRR=KR+L-1
   10 Z=Z+A(KRR,KC)*P(KRR,I)
      DO 20 L=1,J
      KRR=KR+L-1
   20 P(KRR,I)=P(KRR,I)-2.0D0*Z*A(KRR,KC)
      RETURN
      END
C
C
      SUBROUTINE TRIVEC(N,NROOTS,A,V,P)
      IMPLICIT REAL*8(A-H,O-Z)
C      COMPUTES EIGENVECTORS OF TRIDIAGONAL, N X N, MATRIX A WITH
C      EIGENVALUES V.  RETURNS VECTORS IN MATRIX P.
C      SET UP DO-LOOP WHICH SELECTS EIGENVALUE AND EIGENVECTOR.
      DIMENSION A(50,50),V(50),P(50,50),WORKV(50,3)
      DO 80 I=1,NROOTS
      Z=V(I)
C      TRANSFER COEFFICIENTS OF STARTING EQNS. INTO WORKV.
      WORKV(1,1)=0.0D0
      WORKV(1,2)=A(1,1)-Z
      WORKV(1,3)=A(1,2)
      M=N-1
      DO 10 J=2,M
      WORKV(J,1)=A(J-1,J)
      WORKV(J,2)=A(J,J)-Z
   10 WORKV(J,3)=A(J,J+1)
      WORKV(N,1)=A(N-1,N)
      WORKV(N,2)=A(N,N)-Z
      WORKV(N,3)=0.0D0
C      TEST COEFFICIENTS FOR VARIABLE I TO FIND WHICH IS LARGER.
      DO 60 J=1,M
      X=DABS(WORKV(J,2))
      Y=DABS(WORKV(J+1,1))
      IF (X-Y) 40,20,20
C      IF X LARGER, MLTPLY EQN J BY WORKV(J+1,1)/WORKV(J,2) AND
C      SUBTRACT FROM EQN J+1.  EQN J, LEFT ADJUSTED, BECOMES
C      WORKV(J) AND NEW EQN BECOMES WORKV(J+1).
   20 FACTOR=WORKV(J+1,1)/WORKV(J,2)
      DO 30 K=1,2
      Z=WORKV(J+1,K)-WORKV(J,K+1)*FACTOR
      WORKV(J,K)=WORKV(J,K+1)
   30 WORKV(J+1,K)=Z
      WORKV(J,3)=0.0D0
      GO TO 60
C      IF Y EXCEEDS X, MLTPLY EQN (J+1) BY WORKV(J,2)/WORKV(J+1,1)
```

```
C       AND SUBTRACT FROM EQN J.  EQN J+1 BECOMES WORKV(J) AND NEW
C       EQN BECOMES WORKV(J+1,1).
   40 FACTOR=WORKV(J,2)/WORKV(J+1,1)
      DO 50 K=2,3
      Z=WORKV(J,K)-WORKV(J+1,K-1)*FACTOR
      WORKV(J,K-1)=WORKV(J+1,K-1)
   50 WORKV(J+1,K-1)=Z
      WORKV(J,3)=WORKV(J+1,3)
      WORKV(J+1,3)=-WORKV(J+1,3)*FACTOR
   60 CONTINUE
C       ELIMINATED EQNS ARE NOW COMPLETE.  SOLVE IN REVERSE ORDER.
C       AS SOLUTIONS ARE FOUND, STORE THEM IN COLUMN I OF MATRIX P.
      P(N,I)=1.0D0/WORKV(N,2)
      DO 70 J=2,M
      K=N+1-J
      KP1=K+1
      KM1=K-1
      WORKV(K,2)=WORKV(K,2)*P(KP1,I)
      WORKV(KM1,3)=WORKV(KM1,3)*P(KP1,I)
   70 P(K,I)=(1.0D0-WORKV(K,2)-WORKV(K,3))/WORKV(K,1)
      WORKV(1,2)=WORKV(1,2)*P(2,I)
   80 P(1,I)=(1.0D0-WORKV(1,2)-WORKV(1,3))/WORKV(1,1)
C       SCALE THE VECTORS.
      DO 100 I=1,NROOTS
      Z=0.0D0
      DO 90 K=1,N
   90 Z=Z+P(K,I)
      Z=1.0D0/Z
      DO 100 K=1,N
  100 P(K,I)=Z*P(K,I)
C       NORMALIZE THE VECTORS.
      DO 120 I=1,NROOTS
      Z=0.0D0
      DO 110 J=1,N
  110 Z=Z+P(J,I)*P(J,I)
      Z=1.0D0/DSQRT(Z)
      DO 120 J=1,N
  120 P(J,I)=Z*P(J,I)
      RETURN
      END
C
C
      SUBROUTINE SCALE(N,A,V,I,ZUPPER,ZLOWER,ADJUST)
      IMPLICIT REAL*8(A-H,O-Z)
      DIMENSION A(50,50),V(50)
      FI=I
      P=37.0D0/FI
      ADJUST=10.0D0**P
      DO 10 K=1,N
      V(K)=V(K)/ADJUST
      DO 10 J=1,N
   10 A(J,K)=A(J,K)/ADJUST
      ZUPPER=ZUPPER/ADJUST
      ZLOWER=ZLOWER/ADJUST
      RETURN
      END
C
C
      SUBROUTINE NUMBER(Z,M,N,A,V,NTEST,MTEST,ADJUST,BDJUST,ZUPPER,ZLOWE
     1R)
      IMPLICIT REAL*8(A-H,O-Z)
C       FINDS NUMBER, M, OF EIGENVALUES OF TRIDIAGONAL N X N MATRIX A
C       (WITH BETAS IN V) WHICH ARE GREATER THAN OR EQUAL TO Z.
C       DEFINE F1 = F(I-1), F2 = F(I-2), F = F(I).
C       DEFINE SIG1, SIG2, AND SIG ANALOGOUSLY.
   10 FORMAT (42H0 PROGRAM HAS RESCALED MATRIX.  DIVISOR = D20.8,/40H AL
     1L OUTPUT DATA IS FOR ORIGINAL MATRIX.)
      DIMENSION A(50,50),V(50)
      F1=1.0D0
      SIG1=1.0D0
      M=0
```

```
      DO 150 I=1.N
C       TEST TO SEE IF PRECEDING BETA IS ZERO.
      IF (V(I))  30.20.30
   20 F=(A(I.I)-Z)*SIG1
      GO TO 60
   30 K=I-1
      IF (V(K))  50.40.50
   40 F=(A(I.I)-Z)*F1-V(I)*V(I)*SIG2
      GO TO 60
   50 F=(A(I.I)-Z)*F1-V(I)*V(I)*F2
   60 IF (F-1.0D+37)  80.70.70
   70 NTEST=1
      MTEST=1
      CALL SCALE(N.A.V.I.ZUPPER.ZLOWER.ADJUST)
      WRITE (6.10) ADJUST
      ADJUST=ADJUST*BDJUST
      BDJUST=ADJUST
      GO TO 160
   80 IF (F)  90.100.110
   90 SIG=-1.0D0
      GO TO 120
  100 SIG=SIG1
      GO TO 120
  110 SIG=1.0D0
  120 F2=F1
      F1=F
      IF (SIG*SIG1-0.5D0)  140.140.130
  130 M=M+1
  140 SIG2=SIG1
  150 SIG1=SIG
  160 RETURN
      END
C
C
      SUBROUTINE VALUE(N.NROOTS.A.V.ACC.ZLOWER.ZUPPER)
      IMPLICIT REAL*8(A-H.O-Z)
C       COMPUTES NROOTS LOWEST EIGENVALUES OF REAL. SYMMETRIC
C       TRIDIAGONAL N X N MATRIX A TO WITHIN ACC. AND STORES THEM IN V.
C       FIRST TRANSFER BETAS TEMPORARILY TO V.  (LAST ALPHA MUST ALSO
C       BE MOVED TO AVOID DESTRUCTION.)
      DIMENSION A(50.50).V(50)
      ADJUST=1.0D0
      BDJUST=1.0D0
      NTEST=0
      MTEST=0
      IF (ACC)  20.10.20
   10 ACC=1.0D-6
   20 X=A(N.N)
      V(1)=0.0D0
      K=N-1
      DO 30 I=1.K
      K1=I+1
   30 V(K1)=A(I.K1)
      ZSAVE=ZUPPER
      Z=ZLOWER
      Y=V(N)
C       AT START WE KNOW THAT NO. OF EIGENVALUES EXCEEDING ZLOWER IS
C       EQUAL TO N.
      M1=N
      CALL NUMBER(Z.M.N.A.V.NTEST.MTEST.ADJUST.BDJUST.ZUPPER.ZLOWER)
      IF (MTEST)  60.60.50
   50 MTEST=0
      GO TO 20
   60 IF (M-N)  70.200.200
   70 WRITE (6.80) Z.M
   80 FORMAT (1H15X32HBEGINING Z VALUE TOO HIGH.   Z = D20.8./35X3HM =I3/
     1/10X10HREADJUST Z)
      PART=(ZUPPER-ZLOWER)/100.0D0
      Z=ZLOWER-10.0D0*PART
      CALL NUMBER(Z.M.N.A.V.NTEST.MTEST.ADJUST.BDJUST.ZUPPER.ZLOWER)
      IF (MTEST)  100.100.90
```

```
   90 MTEST=0
      GO TO 20
  100 IF (M-N)  120.110.110
  110 ZLOWER=Z
      GO TO 200
  120 WRITE (6.130) Z.M
  130 FORMAT (10X29HDOWNWARD TEST FAILED - - Z = D20.8.2X4HM = I3)
      Z=ZLOWER
      DO 170 LL=1.50
      Z=Z+PART
      CALL NUMBER(Z.M.N.A.V.NTEST.MTEST.ADJUST.BDJUST.ZUPPER.ZLOWER)
      IF (MTEST)  150.150.140
  140 MTEST=0
      GO TO 20
  150 IF (M-N)  170.160.160
  160 ZLOWER=Z
      GO TO 200
  170 WRITE (6.180) LL.Z.M
  180 FORMAT (10X16HUPWARD TEST NO. I2.2X4HZ = D20.8.2X4HM = I3)
      WRITE (6.190)
  190 FORMAT (5X//10X74HADJUSTMENTS OF INITIAL Z VALUE LISTED ABOVE FAIL
     1 TO ALLEVIATE THE PROBLEM./10X16HPROGRAM RETURNS./10X40HDISREGARD
     1FURTHER OUTPUT ON THIS MATRIX.)
      RETURN
  200 SIGN=1.0D0
C       WE HOP TO NEW POSITION AND FIND NEW NO. OF EIGENVALUES.
      I=1
  210 Z=Z+SIGN*(ZUPPER-ZLOWER)/2.0D0
      CALL NUMBER(Z.M.N.A.V.NTEST.MTEST.ADJUST.BDJUST.ZUPPER.ZLOWER)
      IF (MTEST)  230.230.220
  220 MTEST=0
      GO TO 20
C       TEST TO SEE IF WE HAVE CROSSED EIGENVALUES.
  230 IF (M1-M)  240.240.250
C       IF NONE CROSSED. HOP UPFIELD AGAIN.  HOP 1/2 DISTANCE
C       FROM PRESENT Z TO ZUPPER.
  240 ZLOWER=Z
      SIGN=1.0D0
      GO TO 210
C       IF WE HIT 22. WE HAVE CROSSED VALUES BY MOVING UPFIELD.
C       HENCE WE MUST SAVE NEW AND OLD Z POSITIONS AND HOP DOWNFIELD.
C       BUT FIRST TEST TO SEE IF VALUE HAS BEEN SUFFICIENTLY PINNED
C       DOWN.
  250 SIGN=-1.0D0
      IF ((Z-ZLOWER)-ACC)  260.290.290
  260 L=M1-M
C       (THIS MEASURES DEGENERACY)
      DO 270 K=1.L
      ZK=K
      A(I.N)=(Z-0.5D0*(Z-ZLOWER)+ZK*ACC/10.0D0)*ADJUST
  270 I=I+1
C       TEST TO SEE IF ALL DESIRED ROOTS ARE FOUND YET.
      IF (M-(N-NROOTS))  300.300.280
  280 M1=M
      ZLOWER=Z
      ZUPPER=ZSAVE
      SIGN=1.0D0
      GO TO 210
  290 ZUPPER=Z
      GO TO 210
  300 DO 310 K=1.N
  310 V(K)=A(K.N)
      A(N.N)=X
      A(N-1.N)=Y
      IF (NTEST)  340.340.320
  320 DO 330 I=1.N
      DO 330 J=1.N
  330 A(I.J)=A(I.J)*ADJUST
  340 RETURN
      END
```

APPENDIX 11

BRA–KET NOTATION

Bra–ket, or Dirac, notation is frequently used in the literature because of its economical form. Perhaps the best way to learn how this notation is used is by studying its use in a few familiar relations and proofs. Accordingly, we have outlined a few of these uses. The applications and subtleties of this notation go considerably beyond the treatment summarized here.[1]

"Usual" notation		Dirac notation
$\int \phi_m{}^* \phi_n \, d\tau$	$\equiv$	$\underbrace{\langle \phi_m \vert}_{\text{bra}} \underbrace{\vert \phi_n \rangle}_{\text{ket}} \equiv \langle m \vert n \rangle$ (A11-1)
$\int \phi_m{}^* A \phi_n \, d\tau$	$\equiv$	$\langle \phi_m \vert A \vert \phi_n \rangle \equiv \langle m \vert A \vert n \rangle \equiv A_{mn}$ (A11-2)
$\left[\int \phi_m{}^* \phi_n \, d\tau \right]^* = \int \phi_n{}^* \phi_m \, d\tau$		$\langle \phi_m \vert \phi_n \rangle^* = \langle \phi_n \vert \phi_m \rangle$
	or	(A11-3)
		$\langle m \vert n \rangle^* = \langle n \vert m \rangle$

For hermitian operator A:

$$\int \phi_m{}^* A \phi_n \, d\tau = \int \phi_n (A \phi_m)^* \, d\tau = \left[\int \phi_n{}^* A \phi_m \, d\tau \right]^* \qquad \langle m \vert A \vert n \rangle = \langle n \vert A \vert m \rangle^* \tag{A11-4}$$

[1] Strictly speaking, for instance, $\langle \phi_m \vert \phi_n \rangle$ and $\langle m \vert n \rangle$ are not identical in meaning. The former refers to specific functions, ϕ_m and ϕ_n, which represent state vectors in a specific representation. The latter refers to the state vectors in *any* representation and hence is a more general expression. Distinctions such as this will not be necessary at the level of this text.

Any function ψ can be written as a sum of a complete set of orthonormal functions ϕ:

$$\psi = \sum_m c_m\phi_m \qquad |\psi\rangle = \sum_m c_m|\phi_m\rangle \equiv \sum_m c_m|m\rangle$$

$$\int \phi_n^*\psi\, d\tau = \sum_m c_m \int \phi_n^*\phi_m\, d\tau = c_n \qquad \langle n|\psi\rangle = \sum_m c_m\langle n|m\rangle = c_n$$

$$c_n = \int \phi_n^*\psi\, d\tau \qquad c_n = \langle n|\psi\rangle$$

$$\psi = \sum_m c_m\phi_m = \sum_m \int \phi_m^*\psi\, d\tau\phi_m \qquad |\psi\rangle = \sum_m \langle m|\psi\rangle|m\rangle = \sum_m |m\rangle\langle m|\psi\rangle$$

Example of Use Proof that eigenvalues of A (hermitian) are real.

$$A|m\rangle = a_m|m\rangle \tag{A11-5}$$

$$\langle m|A|m\rangle = a_m\underbrace{\langle m|m\rangle}_{\neq 0,\ \neq\infty}, \tag{A11-6}$$

$$\langle m|A|m\rangle^* = a_m^*\langle m|m\rangle \tag{A11-7}$$

Combining Eqs. (A11-4), (A11-6), and (A11-7), we have

$$(a_m - a_m^*) = 0 \qquad \text{Q.E.D.}$$

APPENDIX 12

VALUES OF SOME USEFUL CONSTANTS AND CONVERSION FACTORS

Values of Some Useful Constants[a]

Quantity	Symbol and/or formula[c]	Value			Un-certainty (ppm)
		Atomic units	SI units	Other units	
(a) Fundamental constants					
Planck's constant	h	2π	6.626176×10^{-34} J sec	4.135701×10^{-15} eV sec	5.4
Planck's constant $h/2\pi$	$\hbar$	1	$1.0545887 \times 10^{-34}$ J sec	6.582173×10^{-16} eV sec	5.4
Rest mass of electron	m_e	1	9.109534×10^{-31} kg	9.109534×10^{-28} gm	5.1
Charge of electron	$-e$	-1	-1.602189×10^{19} C	$-4.803242 \times 10^{-10}$ esu	2.9
Rest mass of proton	m_p	1.83615×10^3	$1.6726485 \times 10^{-27}$ kg	$1.6726485 \times 10^{-24}$ gm	5.1
Rest mass of neutron	m_n	1.83868×10^3	$1.6749543 \times 10^{-27}$ kg	$1.6749543 \times 10^{-24}$ gm	5.1
Speed of light in vacuum	c	137.039	2.99792458×10^8 m sec^{-1}	$2.99792458 \times 10^{10}$ cm sec^{-1}	0.004
Avogadro's number[b]	N_A	—	6.0220943×10^{23} mol^{-1}	—	1.05
(b) Derived quantities					
Bohr radius	a_0	1	$5.2917706 \times 10^{-11}$ m	0.52917706 Å	0.82

Twice the ionization potential of the hydrogen atom with infinite nuclear mass	$E_a = e^2/a_0$	1	4.359814×10^{-18} J	27.21161 eV; 2 rydbergs	6.6
Electric field strength one bohr radius from proton	e/a_0^2	1	5.1423×10^{11} V m^{-1}	1.715270×10^{10} esu cm^{-2}	4.4
Polarizability (of a molecule)	$\alpha = e^2 a_0^2/E_a$	1	1.648776×10^{-41} C^2 m^2 J^{-1}	1.481846×10^{-25} esu^2 cm^2 erg^{-1}	1.4
Bohr magneton	$\mu_B = e\hbar/2m_e$	$\frac{1}{2}$	9.274078×10^{-24} J T^{-1}	5.788378×10^{-9} eV G^{-1}	3.9
Nuclear magneton	$\mu_N = e\hbar/2m_p$	2.723087×10^{-4}	5.050824×10^{-27} J T^{-1}	$3.1524515 \times 10^{-12}$ eV G^{-1}	3.9
Electric dipole moment of electron–proton separated by one Bohr radius	ea_0	1	8.478418×10^{-30} C m	2.541765×10^{-20} esu m = 2.541765 debyes	3.8
Time for 1s electron in hydrogen atom to travel one bohr radius	$t = \hbar/E_a$	1	2.41888×10^{-17} sec	—	12
Atomic unit of velocity	a_0/t	1	2.18769×10^{6} m sec^{-1}	2.18767×10^{8} cm sec^{-1}	13
Atomic unit of volume	a_0^3	1	1.481846×10^{-31} m^3	0.14818 Å^3	2.0
Atomic unit of probability density	a_0^{-3}	1	6.748340×10^{30} m^{-3}	6.748340 Å^{-3}	3.0

[a] From Cohen and Taylor [1]. C = coulomb, J = joule, V = volt, T = tesla, G = gauss, Å = angstrom.

[b] See Ref. [2].

[c] Formula appropriate for atomic units.

Energy Conversion Factors[a]

	eV	joule[b]	kcal/mole
eV	1	$1.6021892 \times 10^{-19}$	23.060362
joule[b]	6.2414601×10^{18}	1	1.4393033×10^{20}
kcal/mole	4.336445×10^{-2}	6.947805×10^{-21}	1
Hz	$4.1357012 \times 10^{-15}$	$6.6261759 \times 10^{-34}$	$9.5370770 \times 10^{-14}$
m^{-1}	1.239852×10^{-6}	1.986477×10^{-25}	2.859144×10^{-5}
°K	8.617347×10^{-5}	1.380662×10^{-23}	1.987191×10^{-3}
a.u.	27.21161	4.359816×10^{-18}	6.275098×10^{2}

[a] To convert *from* units in the left hand column *to* units in the top row, multiply by the

[b] 1 joule = 10^7 erg.

REFERENCES

[1] E. R. Cohen and B. N. Taylor, *J. Phys. Chem. Ref. Data* **2**, No. 4, 663 (1973).
[2] A. L. Robinson, *Science*, **185**, 1037 (1974).

Hz	m^{-1}	°K	a.u.
2.4179696×10^{14}	8.065479×10^{5}	1.160450×10^{4}	3.674901×10^{-2}
1.5091661×10^{33}	5.034037×10^{24}	7.242902×10^{22}	2.293675×10^{17}
1.0485393×10^{13}	3.497551×10^{4}	5.032223×10^{2}	1.593601×10^{-3}
1	3.3356412×10^{-9}	4.799274×10^{-11}	1.519829×10^{-16}
2.9979243×10^{8}	1	1.438786×10^{-2}	4.556333×10^{-8}
2.083648×10^{10}	6.950303×10^{1}	1	3.166790×10^{-6}
6.579686×10^{15}	2.194747×10^{7}	3.157772×10^{5}	1

factor in the row–column position, e.g., 1 kcal/mole = 1.0485393×10^{13} Hz.

APPENDIX 13

GROUP THEORETICAL CHARTS AND TABLES

A13-1 Flow Scheme for Group Symbols

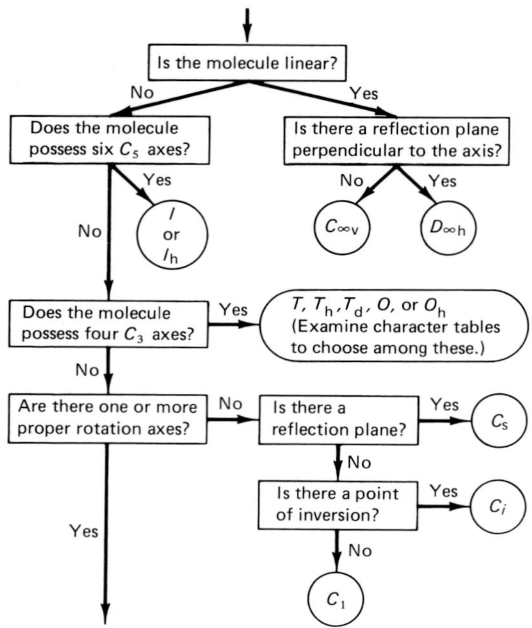

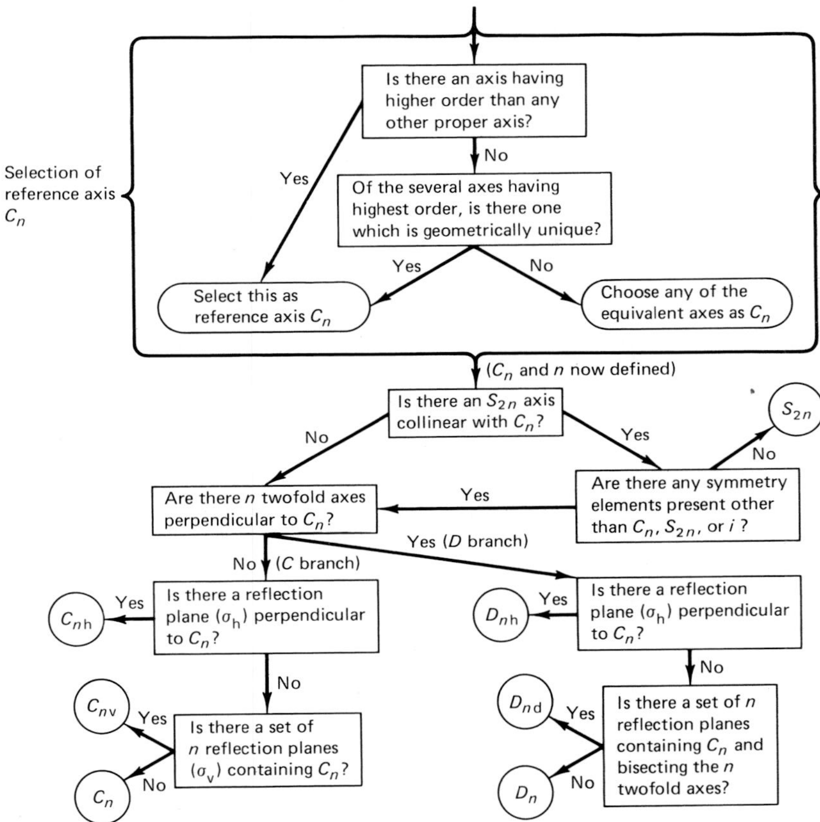

Selection of reference axis C_n
Is there an axis having higher order than any other proper axis?
No
Yes
Of the several axes having highest order, is there one which is geometrically unique?
Yes
No
Select this as reference axis C_n
Choose any of the equivalent axes as C_n
(C_n and n now defined)
Is there an S_{2n} axis collinear with C_n?
No
Yes
S_{2n}
No
Are there n twofold axes perpendicular to C_n?
Yes
Are there any symmetry elements present other than C_n, S_{2n}, or i?
Yes (D branch)
No (C branch)
C_{nh}
Yes
Is there a reflection plane (σ_h) perpendicular to C_n?
D_{nh}
Yes
Is there a reflection plane (σ_h) perpendicular to C_n?
No
No
C_{nv}
Yes
Is there a set of n reflection planes (σ_v) containing C_n?
No
C_n
D_{nd}
Yes
Is there a set of n reflection planes containing C_n and bisecting the n twofold axes?
No
D_n

A13-2 Meaning of Labels for Representations

Symbol	Interpretation
Main Symbol	
A	One-dimensional representation symmetric for rotation by $2\pi/n$ about principal axis. (For c_1, c_s, c_i, which have no principal axis, this symbol merely means a one-dimensional representation.)
B	One-dimensional representation but antisymmetric for rotation by $2\pi/n$ about principal axis
E	Two-dimensional representation
T (or F)	Three-dimensional representation
G	Four-dimensional representation

Subscripts

1	Symmetric for σ_v or σ_d reflections
2	Antisymmetric for σ_v or σ_d reflections
g	Symmetric for inversion
u	Antisymmetric for inversion

Superscripts

′	Symmetric for σ_h reflection
″	Antisymmetric for σ_h reflection

A13-3 Character Tables

A. Special High-Symmetry Groups: $C_{\infty v}$, $D_{\infty h}$, I, I_h, T, T_h, T_d, O, O_h,

$C_{\infty v}$	E	$2C_\infty^\Phi$	···	$\infty\sigma_v$		
$A_1 \equiv \Sigma^+$	1	1	···	1	z	x^2+y^2, z^2
$A_2 \equiv \Sigma^-$	1	1	···	−1	R_z	
$E_1 \equiv \Pi$	2	$2\cos\Phi$	···	0	$(x, y); (R_x, R_y)$	(xz, yz)
$E_2 \equiv \Delta$	2	$2\cos 2\Phi$	···	0		(x^2-y^2, xy)
$E_3 \equiv \Phi$	2	$2\cos 3\Phi$	···	0		
···	···	···	···	···		

$D_{\infty h}$	E	$2C_\infty^\Phi$	···	$\infty\sigma_v$	i	$2S_\infty^\Phi$	···	∞C_2		
Σ_g^+	1	1	···	1	1	1	···	1		x^2+y^2, z^2
Σ_g^-	1	1	···	−1	1	1	···	−1	R_z	
Π_g	2	$2\cos\Phi$	···	0	2	$-2\cos\Phi$	···	0	(R_x, R_y)	(xz, yz)
Δ_g	2	$2\cos 2\Phi$	···	0	2	$2\cos 2\Phi$	···	0		(x^2-y^2, xy)
···	···	···	···	···	··	···	···	···		
Σ_u^+	1	1	···	1	−1	−1	···	−1	z	
Σ_u^-	1	1	···	−1	−1	−1	···	1		
Π_u	2	$2\cos\Phi$	···	0	−2	$2\cos\Phi$	···	0	(x, y)	
Δ_u	2	$2\cos 2\Phi$	···	0	−2	$-2\cos 2\Phi$	···	0		
···	···	···	···	···	···	···	···	···		

I	E	$12C_5$	$12C_5^2$	$20C_3$	$15C_2$		
A	1	1	1	1	1		$x^2+y^2+z^2$
T_1	3	$\frac{1}{2}(1+\sqrt{5})$	$\frac{1}{2}(1-\sqrt{5})$	0	−1	$(x, y, z)(R_x, R_y, R_z)$	
T_2	3	$\frac{1}{2}(1-\sqrt{5})$	$\frac{1}{2}(1+\sqrt{5})$	0	−1		
G	4	−1	−1	1	0		
H	5	0	0	−1	1		$(2z^2-x^2-y^2,$ $x^2-y^2, xy, yz, zx)$

I_h	E	$12C_5$	$12C_5^2$	$20C_3$	$15C_2$	i	$12S_{10}$	$12S_{10}^3$	$20S_6$	15σ		
A_g	1	1	1	1	1	1	1	1	1	1		$x^2 + y^2 + z^2$
T_{1g}	3	$\frac{1}{2}(1 + \sqrt{5})$	$\frac{1}{2}(1 - \sqrt{5})$	0	−1	3	$\frac{1}{2}(1 - \sqrt{5})$	$\frac{1}{2}(1 + \sqrt{5})$	0	−1	(R_x, R_y, R_z)	
T_{2g}	3	$\frac{1}{2}(1 - \sqrt{5})$	$\frac{1}{2}(1 + \sqrt{5})$	0	−1	3	$\frac{1}{2}(1 + \sqrt{5})$	$\frac{1}{2}(1 - \sqrt{5})$	0	−1		
G_g	4	−1	−1	1	0	4	−1	−1	1	0		
H_g	5	0	0	−1	1	5	0	0	−1	1		$(2z^2 - x^2 - y^2,$ $x^2 - y^2,$ $xy, yz, zx)$
A_u	1	1	1	1	1	−1	−1	−1	−1	−1		
T_{1u}	3	$\frac{1}{2}(1 + \sqrt{5})$	$\frac{1}{2}(1 - \sqrt{5})$	0	−1	−3	$-\frac{1}{2}(1 - \sqrt{5})$	$-\frac{1}{2}(1 + \sqrt{5})$	0	1	(x, y, z)	
T_{2u}	3	$\frac{1}{2}(1 - \sqrt{5})$	$\frac{1}{2}(1 + \sqrt{5})$	0	−1	−3	$-\frac{1}{2}(1 + \sqrt{5})$	$-\frac{1}{2}(1 - \sqrt{5})$	0	1		
G_u	4	−1	−1	1	0	−4	1	1	−1	0		
H_u	5	0	0	−1	1	−5	0	0	1	−1		

T	E	$4C_3$	$4C_3^2$	$3C_2$		$\epsilon = \exp(2\pi i/3)$
A	1	1	1	1		$x^2 + y^2 + z^2$
E	$\begin{cases}1 \\ 1\end{cases}$	ϵ ϵ^*	ϵ^* ϵ	$\begin{matrix}1 \\ 1\end{matrix}\}$		$(2z^2 - x^2 - y^2,$ $x^2 - y^2)$
T	3	0	0	-1	(R_x, R_y, R_z); (x, y, z)	(xy, xz, yz)

T_h	E	$4C_3$	$4C_3^2$	$3C_2$	i	$4S_6$	$4S_6^5$	$3\sigma_h$		$\epsilon = \exp(2\pi i/3)$
A_g	1	1	1	1	1	1	1	1		$x^2 + y^2 + z^2$
A_u	1	1	1	1	-1	-1	-1	-1		
E_g	$\begin{cases}1 \\ 1\end{cases}$	ϵ ϵ^*	ϵ^* ϵ	1 1	1 1	ϵ ϵ^*	ϵ^* ϵ	$\begin{matrix}1 \\ 1\end{matrix}\}$		$(2z^2 - x^2 - y^2,$ $x^2 - y^2)$
E_u	$\begin{cases}1 \\ 1\end{cases}$	ϵ ϵ^*	ϵ^* ϵ	1 1	-1 -1	$-\epsilon$ $-\epsilon^*$	$-\epsilon^*$ $-\epsilon$	$\begin{matrix}-1 \\ -1\end{matrix}\}$		
T_g	3	0	0	-1	1	0	0	-1	(R_x, R_y, Rz)	(xz, yz, xy)
T_u	3	0	0	-1	-1	0	0	1	(x, y, z)	

T_d	E	$8C_3$	$3C_2$	$6S_4$	$6\sigma_d$		
A_1	1	1	1	1	1		$x^2 + y^2 + z^2$
A_2	1	1	1	-1	-1		
E	2	-1	2	0	0		$(2z^2 - x^2 - y^2,$ $x^2 - y^2)$
T_1	3	0	-1	1	-1	(R_x, R_y, R_z)	
T_2	3	0	-1	-1	1	(x, y, z)	(xy, xz, yz)

O	E	$6C_4$	$3C_2(=C_4^2)$	$8C_3$	$6C_2$		
A_1	1	1	1	1	1		$x^2 + y^2 + z^2$
A_2	1	-1	1	1	-1		
E	2	0	2	-1	0		$(2z^2 - x^2 - y^2,$ $x^2 - y^2)$
T_1	3	1	-1	0	-1	(R_x, R_y, R_z); (x, y, z)	
T_2	3	-1	-1	0	1		(xy, xz, yz)

O_h	E	$8C_3$	$6C_2$	$6C_4$	$3C_2$ $(=C_4^2)$	i	$6S_4$	$8S_6$	$3\sigma_h$	$6\sigma_d$		
A_{1g}	1	1	1	1	1	1	1	1	1	1		$x^2 + y^2 + z^2$
A_{2g}	1	1	-1	-1	1	1	-1	1	1	-1		
E_g	2	-1	0	0	2	2	0	-1	2	0		$(2z^2 - x^2 - y^2,$ $x^2 - y^2)$
T_{1g}	3	0	-1	1	-1	3	1	0	-1	-1	(R_x, R_y, R_z)	
T_{2g}	3	0	1	-1	-1	3	-1	0	-1	1		(xz, yz, xy)
A_{1u}	1	1	1	1	1	-1	-1	-1	-1	-1		
A_{2u}	1	1	-1	-1	1	-1	1	-1	-1	1		
E_u	2	-1	0	0	2	-2	0	1	-2	0		
T_{1u}	3	0	-1	1	-1	-3	-1	0	1	1	(x, y, z)	
T_{2u}	3	0	1	-1	-1	-3	1	0	1	-1		

B. *Groups with No Axis of Symmetry:* C_1, C_i, C_s

C_1	E
A	1

C_s	E	σ_h		
A'	1	1	x, y, R_z	x^2, y^2, z^2, xy
A''	1	−1	z, R_x, R_y	yz, xz

C_i	E	i		
A_g	1	1	R_x, R_y, R_z	$x^2, y^2, z^2, xy, xz, yz$
A_u	1	−1	x, y, z	

C. *The* S_{2n} *Groups*

S_4	E	S_4	C_2	S_4^3		
A	1	1	1	1	R_z	$x^2 + y^2, z^2$
B	1	−1	1	−1	z	$x^2 - y^2, xy$
E	$\begin{Bmatrix} 1 \\ 1 \end{Bmatrix}$	$\begin{matrix} i \\ -i \end{matrix}$	$\begin{matrix} -1 \\ -1 \end{matrix}$	$\begin{matrix} -i \\ i \end{matrix}$	(x, y); (R_x, R_y)	(xz, yz)

S_6	E	C_3	C_3^2	i	S_6^5	S_6		$\epsilon = \exp(2\pi i/3)$
A_g	1	1	1	1	1	1	R_z	$x^2 + y^2, z^2$
E_g	$\begin{Bmatrix} 1 \\ 1 \end{Bmatrix}$	$\begin{matrix} \epsilon \\ \epsilon^* \end{matrix}$	$\begin{matrix} \epsilon^* \\ \epsilon \end{matrix}$	$\begin{matrix} 1 \\ 1 \end{matrix}$	$\begin{matrix} \epsilon \\ \epsilon^* \end{matrix}$	$\begin{matrix} \epsilon^* \\ \epsilon \end{matrix}$	(R_x, R_y)	$(x^2 - y^2, xy)$; (xz, yz)
A_u	1	1	1	−1	−1	−1	z	
E_u	$\begin{Bmatrix} 1 \\ 1 \end{Bmatrix}$	$\begin{matrix} \epsilon \\ \epsilon^* \end{matrix}$	$\begin{matrix} \epsilon^* \\ \epsilon \end{matrix}$	$\begin{matrix} -1 \\ -1 \end{matrix}$	$\begin{matrix} -\epsilon \\ -\epsilon^* \end{matrix}$	$\begin{matrix} -\epsilon^* \\ -\epsilon \end{matrix}$	(x, y)	

S_8	E	S_8	C_4	S_8^3	C_2	S_8^5	C_4^3	S_8^7		$\epsilon = \exp(2\pi i/8)$
A	1	1	1	1	1	1	1	1	R_z	$x^2 + y^2, z^2$
B	1	−1	1	−1	1	−1	1	−1	z	
E_1	$\begin{Bmatrix} 1 \\ 1 \end{Bmatrix}$	$\begin{matrix} \epsilon \\ \epsilon^* \end{matrix}$	$\begin{matrix} i \\ -i \end{matrix}$	$\begin{matrix} -\epsilon^* \\ -\epsilon \end{matrix}$	$\begin{matrix} -1 \\ -1 \end{matrix}$	$\begin{matrix} -\epsilon \\ -\epsilon^* \end{matrix}$	$\begin{matrix} -i \\ i \end{matrix}$	$\begin{matrix} \epsilon^* \\ \epsilon \end{matrix}$	(x, y); (R_x, R_y)	
E_2	$\begin{Bmatrix} 1 \\ 1 \end{Bmatrix}$	$\begin{matrix} i \\ -i \end{matrix}$	$\begin{matrix} -1 \\ -1 \end{matrix}$	$\begin{matrix} -i \\ i \end{matrix}$	$\begin{matrix} 1 \\ 1 \end{matrix}$	$\begin{matrix} i \\ -i \end{matrix}$	$\begin{matrix} -1 \\ -1 \end{matrix}$	$\begin{matrix} -i \\ i \end{matrix}$		$(x^2 - y^2, xy)$
E_3	$\begin{Bmatrix} 1 \\ 1 \end{Bmatrix}$	$\begin{matrix} -\epsilon^* \\ -\epsilon \end{matrix}$	$\begin{matrix} -i \\ i \end{matrix}$	$\begin{matrix} \epsilon \\ \epsilon^* \end{matrix}$	$\begin{matrix} -1 \\ -1 \end{matrix}$	$\begin{matrix} \epsilon^* \\ \epsilon \end{matrix}$	$\begin{matrix} i \\ -i \end{matrix}$	$\begin{matrix} -\epsilon \\ -\epsilon^* \end{matrix}$		(xz, yz)

D. *The* C_n *Groups*

C_2	E	C_2		
A	1	1	z, R_z	x^2, y^2, z^2, xy
B	1	−1	x, y, R_x, R_y	yz, xz

C_3	E	C_3	C_3^2		$\epsilon = \exp(2\pi i/3)$
A	1	1	1	z, R_z	$x^2 + y^2, z^2$
E	1	ϵ	ϵ^*	$(x, y)(R_x, R_y)$	$(x^2 - y^2, xy)(yz, xz)$
	1	ϵ^*	ϵ		

C_4	E	C_1	C_2	C_4^3		
A	1	1	1	1	z, R_z	$x^2 + y^2, z^2$
B	1	-1	1	-1		$x^2 - y^2, xy$
E	1	i	-1	$-i$	$(x, y)(R_x, R_y)$	(yz, xz)
	1	$-i$	-1	i		

C_5	E	C_5	C_5^2	C_5^3	C_5^4		$\epsilon = \exp(2\pi i/5)$
A	1	1	1	1	1	z, R_z	$x^2 + y^2, z^2$
E_1	1	ϵ	ϵ^2	ϵ^{2*}	ϵ^*	$(x, y)(R_x, R_y)$	(yz, xz)
	1	ϵ^*	ϵ^{2*}	ϵ^2	ϵ		
E_2	1	ϵ^2	ϵ^*	ϵ	ϵ^{2*}		$(x^2 - y^2, xy)$
	1	ϵ^{2*}	ϵ	ϵ^*	ϵ^2		

C_6	E	C_6	C_3	C_2	C_3^2	C_6^5		$\epsilon = \exp(2\pi i/6)$
A	1	1	1	1	1	1	z, R_z	$x^2 + y^2, z^2$
B	1	-1	1	-1	1	-1		
E_1	1	ϵ	$-\epsilon^*$	-1	$-\epsilon$	ϵ^*	(x, y)	(xz, yz)
	1	ϵ^*	$-\epsilon$	-1	$-\epsilon^*$	ϵ	(R_x, R_y)	
E_2	1	$-\epsilon^*$	$-\epsilon$	1	$-\epsilon^*$	$-\epsilon$		$(x^2 - y^2, xy)$
	1	$-\epsilon$	$-\epsilon^*$	1	$-\epsilon$	$-\epsilon^*$		

C_7	E	C_7	C_7^2	C_7^3	C_7^4	C_7^5	C_7^6		$\epsilon = \exp(2\pi i/7)$
A	1	1	1	1	1	1	1	z, R_z	$x^2 + y^2, z^2$
E_1	1	ϵ	ϵ^2	ϵ^3	ϵ^{3*}	ϵ^{2*}	ϵ^*	(x, y)	(xz, yz)
	1	ϵ^*	ϵ^{2*}	ϵ^{3*}	ϵ^3	ϵ^2	ϵ	(R_x, R_y)	
E_2	1	ϵ^2	ϵ^{3*}	ϵ^*	ϵ	ϵ^3	ϵ^{2*}		$(x^2 - y^2, xy)$
	1	ϵ^{2*}	ϵ^3	ϵ	ϵ^*	ϵ^{3*}	ϵ^2		
E_3	1	ϵ^3	ϵ^*	ϵ^2	ϵ^{2*}	ϵ	ϵ^{3*}		
	1	ϵ^{3*}	ϵ	ϵ^{2*}	ϵ^2	ϵ^*	ϵ^3		

C_8	E	C_8	C_4	C_2	C_4^3	C_8^3	C_8^5	C_8^7		$\epsilon = \exp(2\pi i/8)$
A	1	1	1	1	1	1	1	1	z, R_z	$x^2 + y^2, z^2$
B	1	-1	1	1	1	-1	-1	1		
E_1	1	ϵ	i	-1	$-i$	$-\epsilon^*$	$-\epsilon$	ϵ^*	(x, y)	(xz, yz)
	1	ϵ^*	$-i$	-1	i	$-\epsilon$	$-\epsilon^*$	ϵ	(R_x, R_y)	
E_2	1	i	-1	1	-1	$-i$	i	$-i$		$(x^2 - y^2, xy)$
	1	$-i$	-1	1	-1	i	$-i$	i		
E_3	1	$-\epsilon$	i	-1	$-i$	ϵ^*	ϵ	$-\epsilon^*$		
	1	$-\epsilon^*$	$-i$	-1	i	ϵ	ϵ^*	$-\epsilon$		

E. *The C_{nv} Groups*

C_{2v}	E	C_2	$\sigma_v(xz)$	$\sigma_v'(yz)$		
A_1	1	1	1	1	z	x^2, y^2, z^2
A_2	1	1	-1	-1	R_z	xy
B_1	1	-1	1	-1	x, R_y	xz
B_2	1	-1	-1	1	y, R_x	yz

C_{3v}	E	$3\sigma_v$	$2C_3$		
A_1	1	1	1	z	$x^2 + y^2, z^2$
A_2	1	-1	1	R_z	
E	2	0	-1	$(x, y)(R_x, R_y)$	$(x^2 - y^2, xy)(xz, yz)$

C_{4v}	E	$2C_4$	C_2	$2\sigma_v$	$2\sigma_d$		
A_1	1	1	1	1	1	z	$x^2 + y^2, z^2$
A_2	1	1	1	-1	-1	R_z	
B_1	1	-1	1	1	-1		$x^2 - y^2$
B_2	1	-1	1	-1	1		xy
E	2	0	-2	0	0	$(x, y)(R_x, R_y)$	(xz, yz)

C_{5v}	E	$2C_5$	$2C_5^2$	$5\sigma_v$		
A_1	1	1	1	1	z	$x^2 + y^2, z^2$
A_2	1	1	1	-1	R_z	
E_1	2	$2 \cos 72°$	$2 \cos 144°$	0	$(x, y)(R_x, R_y)$	(xz, yz)
E_2	2	$2 \cos 144°$	$2 \cos 72°$	0		$(x^2 - y^2, xy)$

C_{6v}	E	$2C_6$	$2C_3$	C_2	$3\sigma_v$	$3\sigma_d$		
A_1	1	1	1	1	1	1	z	$x^2 + y^2, z^2$
A_2	1	1	1	1	-1	-1	R_z	
B_1	1	-1	1	-1	1	-1		
B_2	1	-1	1	-1	-1	1		
E_1	2	1	-1	-2	0	0	$(x, y)(R_x, R_y)$	(xz, yz)
E_2	2	-1	-1	2	0	0		$(x^2 - y^2, xy)$

F. *The C_{nh} Groups*

C_{2h}	E	C_2	i	σ_h		
A_g	1	1	1	1	R_z	x^2, y^2, z^2, xy
B_g	1	-1	1	-1	R_x, R_y	xz, yz
A_u	1	1	-1	-1	z	
B_u	1	-1	-1	1	x, y	

C_{3h}	E	C_3	C_3^2	σ_h	S_3	S_3^5		$\epsilon = \exp(2\pi i/3)$
A'	1	1	1	1	1	1	R_z	$x^2 + y^2, z^2$
E'	$\begin{cases}1\\1\end{cases}$	$\begin{matrix}\epsilon\\\epsilon^*\end{matrix}$	$\begin{matrix}\epsilon^*\\\epsilon\end{matrix}$	$\begin{matrix}1\\1\end{matrix}$	$\begin{matrix}\epsilon\\\epsilon^*\end{matrix}$	$\begin{matrix}\epsilon^*\\\epsilon\end{matrix}\Big\}$	(x, y)	$(x^2 - y^2, xy)$
A''	1	1	1	-1	-1	-1	z	
E''	$\begin{cases}1\\1\end{cases}$	$\begin{matrix}\epsilon\\\epsilon^*\end{matrix}$	$\begin{matrix}\epsilon^*\\\epsilon\end{matrix}$	$\begin{matrix}-1\\-1\end{matrix}$	$\begin{matrix}-\epsilon\\-\epsilon^*\end{matrix}$	$\begin{matrix}-\epsilon^*\\-\epsilon\end{matrix}\Big\}$	(R_x, R_y)	(xz, yz)

C_{4h}	E	C_4	C_2	C_4^3	i	S_4^3	σ_h	S_4		
A_g	1	1	1	1	1	1	1	1	R_z	$x^2 + y^2, z^2$
B_g	1	-1	1	-1	1	-1	1	-1		$x^2 - y^2, xy$
E_g	$\begin{cases}1\\1\end{cases}$	$\begin{matrix}i\\-i\end{matrix}$	$\begin{matrix}-1\\-1\end{matrix}$	$\begin{matrix}-i\\i\end{matrix}$	$\begin{matrix}1\\1\end{matrix}$	$\begin{matrix}i\\-i\end{matrix}$	$\begin{matrix}-1\\-1\end{matrix}$	$\begin{matrix}-i\\i\end{matrix}\Big\}$	(R_x, R_y)	(xz, yz)
A_u	1	1	1	1	-1	-1	-1	-1	z	
B_u	1	-1	1	-1	-1	1	-1	1		
E_u	$\begin{cases}1\\1\end{cases}$	$\begin{matrix}i\\-i\end{matrix}$	$\begin{matrix}-1\\-1\end{matrix}$	$\begin{matrix}-i\\i\end{matrix}$	$\begin{matrix}-1\\-1\end{matrix}$	$\begin{matrix}-i\\i\end{matrix}$	$\begin{matrix}1\\1\end{matrix}$	$\begin{matrix}i\\-i\end{matrix}\Big\}$	(x, y)	

C_{5h}	E	C_5	C_5^2	C_5^3	C_5^4	σ_h	S_5	S_5^7	S_5^3	S_5^9		$\epsilon = \exp(2\pi i/5)$
A'	1	1	1	1	1	1	1	1	1	1	R_z	$x^2 + y^2, z^2$
E_1'	$\begin{cases}1\\1\end{cases}$	$\begin{matrix}\epsilon\\\epsilon^*\end{matrix}$	$\begin{matrix}\epsilon^2\\\epsilon^{2*}\end{matrix}$	$\begin{matrix}\epsilon^{2*}\\\epsilon^2\end{matrix}$	$\begin{matrix}\epsilon^*\\\epsilon\end{matrix}$	$\begin{matrix}1\\1\end{matrix}$	$\begin{matrix}\epsilon\\\epsilon^*\end{matrix}$	$\begin{matrix}\epsilon^2\\\epsilon^{2*}\end{matrix}$	$\begin{matrix}\epsilon^{2*}\\\epsilon^2\end{matrix}$	$\begin{matrix}\epsilon^*\\\epsilon\end{matrix}\Big\}$	(x, y)	
E_2'	$\begin{cases}1\\1\end{cases}$	$\begin{matrix}\epsilon^2\\\epsilon^{2*}\end{matrix}$	$\begin{matrix}\epsilon^*\\\epsilon\end{matrix}$	$\begin{matrix}\epsilon\\\epsilon^*\end{matrix}$	$\begin{matrix}\epsilon^{2*}\\\epsilon^2\end{matrix}$	$\begin{matrix}1\\1\end{matrix}$	$\begin{matrix}\epsilon^2\\\epsilon^{2*}\end{matrix}$	$\begin{matrix}\epsilon^*\\\epsilon\end{matrix}$	$\begin{matrix}\epsilon\\\epsilon^*\end{matrix}$	$\begin{matrix}\epsilon^{2*}\\\epsilon^2\end{matrix}\Big\}$		$(x^2 - y^2, xy)$
A''	1	1	1	1	1	-1	-1	-1	-1	-1	z	
E_1''	$\begin{cases}1\\1\end{cases}$	$\begin{matrix}\epsilon\\\epsilon^*\end{matrix}$	$\begin{matrix}\epsilon^2\\\epsilon^{2*}\end{matrix}$	$\begin{matrix}\epsilon^{2*}\\\epsilon^2\end{matrix}$	$\begin{matrix}\epsilon^*\\\epsilon\end{matrix}$	$\begin{matrix}-1\\-1\end{matrix}$	$\begin{matrix}-\epsilon\\-\epsilon^*\end{matrix}$	$\begin{matrix}-\epsilon^2\\-\epsilon^{2*}\end{matrix}$	$\begin{matrix}-\epsilon^{2*}\\-\epsilon^2\end{matrix}$	$\begin{matrix}-\epsilon^*\\-\epsilon\end{matrix}\Big\}$	(R_x, R_y)	(xz, yz)
E_2''	$\begin{cases}1\\1\end{cases}$	$\begin{matrix}\epsilon^2\\\epsilon^{2*}\end{matrix}$	$\begin{matrix}\epsilon^*\\\epsilon\end{matrix}$	$\begin{matrix}\epsilon\\\epsilon^*\end{matrix}$	$\begin{matrix}\epsilon^{2*}\\\epsilon^2\end{matrix}$	$\begin{matrix}-1\\-1\end{matrix}$	$\begin{matrix}-\epsilon^2\\-\epsilon^{2*}\end{matrix}$	$\begin{matrix}-\epsilon^*\\-\epsilon\end{matrix}$	$\begin{matrix}-\epsilon\\-\epsilon^*\end{matrix}$	$\begin{matrix}-\epsilon^{2*}\\-\epsilon^2\end{matrix}\Big\}$		

C_{6h}	E	C_6	C_3	C_2	C_3^2	C_6^5	i	S_3^5	S_6^5	σ_h	S_6	S_3		$\epsilon = \exp(2\pi i/$
A_g	1	1	1	1	1	1	1	1	1	1	1	1	R_z	$x^2 + y^2, z^2$
B_g	1	-1	1	-1	1	-1	1	-1	1	-1	1	-1		
E_{1g}	$\begin{cases}1\\1\end{cases}$	$\begin{matrix}\epsilon\\\epsilon^*\end{matrix}$	$\begin{matrix}-\epsilon^*\\-\epsilon\end{matrix}$	$\begin{matrix}-1\\-1\end{matrix}$	$\begin{matrix}-\epsilon\\-\epsilon^*\end{matrix}$	$\begin{matrix}\epsilon^*\\\epsilon\end{matrix}$	$\begin{matrix}1\\1\end{matrix}$	$\begin{matrix}\epsilon\\\epsilon^*\end{matrix}$	$\begin{matrix}-\epsilon^*\\-\epsilon\end{matrix}$	$\begin{matrix}-1\\-1\end{matrix}$	$\begin{matrix}-\epsilon\\-\epsilon^*\end{matrix}$	$\begin{matrix}\epsilon^*\\\epsilon\end{matrix}\Big\}$	(R_x, R_y)	(xz, yz)
E_{2g}	$\begin{cases}1\\1\end{cases}$	$\begin{matrix}-\epsilon^*\\-\epsilon\end{matrix}$	$\begin{matrix}-\epsilon\\-\epsilon^*\end{matrix}$	$\begin{matrix}1\\1\end{matrix}$	$\begin{matrix}-\epsilon^*\\-\epsilon\end{matrix}$	$\begin{matrix}-\epsilon\\-\epsilon^*\end{matrix}$	$\begin{matrix}1\\1\end{matrix}$	$\begin{matrix}-\epsilon^*\\-\epsilon\end{matrix}$	$\begin{matrix}-\epsilon\\-\epsilon^*\end{matrix}$	$\begin{matrix}1\\1\end{matrix}$	$\begin{matrix}-\epsilon^*\\-\epsilon\end{matrix}$	$\begin{matrix}-\epsilon\\-\epsilon^*\end{matrix}\Big\}$		$(x^2 - y^2, xy$
A_u	1	1	1	1	1	1	-1	-1	-1	-1	-1	-1	z	
B_u	1	-1	1	-1	1	-1	-1	1	-1	1	-1	1		
E_{1u}	$\begin{cases}1\\1\end{cases}$	$\begin{matrix}\epsilon\\\epsilon^*\end{matrix}$	$\begin{matrix}-\epsilon^*\\-\epsilon\end{matrix}$	$\begin{matrix}-1\\-1\end{matrix}$	$\begin{matrix}-\epsilon\\-\epsilon^*\end{matrix}$	$\begin{matrix}\epsilon^*\\\epsilon\end{matrix}$	$\begin{matrix}-1\\-1\end{matrix}$	$\begin{matrix}-\epsilon\\-\epsilon^*\end{matrix}$	$\begin{matrix}\epsilon^*\\\epsilon\end{matrix}$	$\begin{matrix}1\\1\end{matrix}$	$\begin{matrix}\epsilon\\\epsilon^*\end{matrix}$	$\begin{matrix}-\epsilon^*\\-\epsilon\end{matrix}\Big\}$	(x, y)	
E_{2u}	$\begin{cases}1\\1\end{cases}$	$\begin{matrix}-\epsilon^*\\-\epsilon\end{matrix}$	$\begin{matrix}-\epsilon\\-\epsilon^*\end{matrix}$	$\begin{matrix}1\\1\end{matrix}$	$\begin{matrix}-\epsilon^*\\-\epsilon\end{matrix}$	$\begin{matrix}-\epsilon\\-\epsilon^*\end{matrix}$	$\begin{matrix}-1\\-1\end{matrix}$	$\begin{matrix}\epsilon^*\\\epsilon\end{matrix}$	$\begin{matrix}\epsilon\\\epsilon^*\end{matrix}$	$\begin{matrix}-1\\-1\end{matrix}$	$\begin{matrix}\epsilon^*\\\epsilon\end{matrix}$	$\begin{matrix}\epsilon\\\epsilon^*\end{matrix}\Big\}$		

G. *The D_n Groups*

D_2	E	$C_2(z)$	$C_2(y)$	$C_2(x)$		
A	1	1	1	1		x^2, y^2, z^2
B_1	1	1	-1	-1	z, R_z	xy
B_2	1	-1	1	-1	y, R_y	xz
B_3	1	-1	-1	1	x, R_x	yz

D_3	E	$2C_3$	$3C_2$		
A_1	1	1	1		$x^2 + y^2, z^2$
A_2	1	1	-1	z, R_z	
E	2	-1	0	$(x, y)(R_x, R_y)$	$(x^2 - y^2, xy)(xz, yz)$

D_4	E	$2C_4$	$C_2(= C_4^2)$	$2C_2'$	$2C_2''$		
A_1	1	1	1	1	1		$x^2 + y^2, z^2$
A_2	1	1	1	-1	-1	z, R_z	
B_1	1	-1	1	1	-1		$x^2 - y^2$
B_2	1	-1	1	-1	1		xy
E	2	0	-2	0	0	$(x, y)(R_x, R_y)$	(xz, yz)

D_5	E	$2C_5$	$2C_5^2$	$5C_2$		
A_1	1	1	1	1		$x^2 + y^2, z^2$
A_2	1	1	1	-1	z, R_z	
E_1	2	2 cos 72°	2 cos 144°	0	$(x, y)(R_x, R_y)$	(xz, yz)
E_2	2	2 cos 144°	2 cos 72°	0		$(x^2 - y^2, xy)$

D_6	E	$2C_6$	$2C_3$	C_2	$3C_2'$	$3C_2''$		
A_1	1	1	1	1	1	1		$x^2 + y^2, z^2$
A_2	1	1	1	1	-1	-1	z, R_z	
B_1	1	-1	1	-1	1	-1		
B_2	1	-1	1	-1	-1	1		
E_1	2	1	-1	-2	0	0	$(x, y)(R_x, R_y)$	(xz, yz)
E_2	2	-1	-1	2	0	0		$(x^2 - y^2, xy)$

H. The D_{nd} Groups

D_{2d}	E	$2S_4$	C_2	$2C_2'$	$2\sigma_d$		
A_1	1	1	1	1	1		x^2+y^2, z^2
A_2	1	1	1	−1	−1	R_z	
B_1	1	−1	1	1	−1		x^2-y^2
B_2	1	−1	1	−1	1	z	xy
E	2	0	−2	0	0	(x, y); (R_x, R_y)	(xz, yz)

D_{3d}	E	$2C_3$	$3C_2$	i	$2S_6$	$3\sigma_d$		
A_{1g}	1	1	1	1	1	1		x^2+y^2, z^2
A_{2g}	1	1	−1	1	1	−1	R_z	
E_g	2	−1	0	2	−1	0	(R_x, R_y)	(x^2-y^2, xy), (xz, yz)
A_{1u}	1	1	1	−1	−1	−1		
A_{2u}	1	1	−1	−1	−1	1	z	
E_u	2	−1	0	−2	1	0	(x, y)	

D_{4d}	E	$2S_8$	$2C_4$	$2S_8{}^3$	C_2	$4C_2'$	$4\sigma_d$		
A_1	1	1	1	1	1	1	1		x^2+y^2, z^2
A_2	1	1	1	1	1	−1	−1	R_z	
B_1	1	−1	1	−1	1	1	−1		
B_2	1	−1	1	−1	1	−1	1	z	
E_1	2	$\sqrt{2}$	0	$-\sqrt{2}$	−2	0	0	(x, y)	
E_2	2	0	−2	0	2	0	0		(x^2-y^2, xy)
E_3	2	$-\sqrt{2}$	0	$\sqrt{2}$	−2	0	0	(R_x, R_y)	(xz, yz)

D_{5d}	E	$2C_5$	$2C_5{}^2$	$5C_2$	i	$2S_{10}^3$	$2S_{10}$	$5\sigma_d$		
A_{1g}	1	1	1	1	1	1	1	1		x^2+y^2, z^2
A_{2g}	1	1	1	−1	1	1	1	−1	R_z	
E_{1g}	2	2 cos 72°	2 cos 144°	0	2	2 cos 72°	2 cos 144°	0	(R_x, R_y)	(xz, yz)
E_{2g}	2	2 cos 144°	2 cos 72°	0	2	2 cos 144°	2 cos 72°	0		$(x^2-y^2, x$
A_{1u}	1	1	1	1	−1	−1	−1	−1		
A_{2u}	1	1	1	−1	−1	−1	−1	1	z	
E_{1u}	2	2 cos 72°	2 cos 144°	0	−2	−2 cos 72°	−2 cos 144°	0	(x, y)	
E_{2u}	2	2 cos 144°	2 cos 72°	0	−2	−2 cos 144°	−2 cos 72°	0		

D_{6d}	E	$2S_{12}$	$2C_6$	$2S_4$	$2C_3$	$2S_{12}^5$	C_2	$6C_2'$	$6\sigma_d$		
A_1	1	1	1	1	1	1	1	1	1		x^2+y^2, z^2
A_2	1	1	1	1	1	1	1	−1	−1	R_z	
B_1	1	−1	1	−1	1	−1	1	1	−1		
B_2	1	−1	1	−1	1	−1	1	−1	1	z	
E_1	2	$\sqrt{3}$	1	0	−1	$-\sqrt{3}$	−2	0	0	(x, y)	
E_2	2	1	−1	−2	−1	1	2	0	0		(x^2-y^2, xy)
E_3	2	0	−2	0	2	0	−2	0	0		
E_4	2	−1	−1	2	−1	−1	2	0	0		
E_5	2	$-\sqrt{3}$	1	0	−1	$\sqrt{3}$	−2	0	0	(R_x, R_y)	(xz, yz)

I. *The D_{nh} Groups*

E	$C_2(z)$	$C_2(y)$	$C_2(x)$	i	$\sigma(xy)$	$\sigma(xz)$	$\sigma(yz)$		
1	1	1	1	1	1	1	1		x^2, y^2, z^2
1	1	−1	−1	1	1	−1	−1	R_z	xy
1	−1	1	−1	1	−1	1	−1	R_y	xz
1	−1	−1	1	1	−1	−1	1	R_x	yz
1	1	1	1	−1	−1	−1	−1		
1	1	−1	−1	−1	−1	1	1	z	
1	−1	1	−1	−1	1	−1	1	y	
1	−1	−1	1	−1	1	1	−1	x	

E	$2C_3$	$3C_2$	σ_h	$2S_3$	$3\sigma_v$		
1	1	1	1	1	1		$x^2 + y^2, z^2$
1	1	−1	1	1	−1	R_z	
2	−1	0	2	−1	0	(x, y)	$(x^2 - y^2, xy)$
1	1	1	−1	−1	−1		
1	1	−1	−1	−1	1	z	
2	−1	0	−2	1	0	(R_x, R_y)	(xz, yz)

E	$2C_4$	C_2	$2C_2'$	$2C_2''$	i	$2S_4$	σ_h	$2\sigma_v$	$2\sigma_d$		
1	1	1	1	1	1	1	1	1	1		$x^2 + y^2, z^2$
1	1	1	−1	−1	1	1	1	−1	−1	R_z	
1	−1	1	1	−1	1	−1	1	1	−1		$x^2 - y^2$
1	−1	1	−1	1	1	−1	1	−1	1		xy
2	0	−2	0	0	2	0	−2	0	0	(R_x, R_y)	(xz, yz)
1	1	1	1	1	−1	−1	−1	−1	−1		
1	1	1	−1	−1	−1	−1	−1	1	1	z	
1	−1	1	1	−1	−1	1	−1	−1	1		
1	−1	1	−1	1	−1	1	−1	1	−1		
2	0	−2	0	0	−2	0	2	0	0	(x, y)	

E	$2C_5$	$2C_5^2$	$5C_2$	σ_h	$2S_5$	$2S_5^3$	$5\sigma_v$		
1	1	1	1	1	1	1	1		$x^2 + y^2, z^2$
1	1	1	−1	1	1	1	−1	R_z	
2	2 cos 72°	2 cos 144°	0	2	2 cos 72°	2 cos 144°	0	(x, y)	
2	2 cos 144°	2 cos 72°	0	2	2 cos 144°	2 cos 72°	0		$(x^2 - y^2, xy)$
1	1	1	1	−1	−1	−1	−1		
1	1	1	−1	−1	−1	−1	1	z	
2	2 cos 72°	2 cos 144°	0	−2	−2 cos 72°	−2 cos 144°	0	(R_x, R_y)	(xz, yz)
2	2 cos 144°	2 cos 72°	0	−2	−2 cos 144°	−2 cos 72°	0		

D_{6h}	E	$2C_6$	$2C_3$	C_2	$3C_2'$	$3C_2''$	i	$2S_3$	$2S_6$	σ_h	$3\sigma_d$	$3\sigma_v$		
A_{1g}	1	1	1	1	1	1	1	1	1	1	1	1		$x^2 + y^2, z^2$
A_{2g}	1	1	1	1	−1	−1	1	1	1	1	−1	−1	R_z	
B_{1g}	1	−1	1	−1	1	−1	1	−1	1	−1	1	−1		
B_{2g}	1	−1	1	−1	−1	1	1	−1	1	−1	−1	1		
E_{1g}	2	1	−1	−2	0	0	2	1	−1	−2	0	0	(R_x, R_y)	(xz, yz)
E_{2g}	2	−1	−1	2	0	0	2	−1	−1	2	0	0		$(x^2 - y^2, x$
A_{1u}	1	1	1	1	1	1	−1	−1	−1	−1	−1	−1		
A_{2u}	1	1	1	1	−1	−1	−1	−1	−1	−1	1	1	z	
B_{1u}	1	−1	1	−1	1	−1	−1	1	−1	1	−1	1		
B_{2u}	1	−1	1	−1	−1	1	−1	1	−1	1	1	−1		
E_{1u}	2	1	−1	−2	0	0	−2	−1	1	2	0	0	(x, y)	
E_{2u}	2	−1	−1	2	0	0	−2	1	1	−2	0	0		

D_{8h}	E	$2C_8$	$2C_8^3$	$2C_4$	C_2	$4C_2'$	$4C_2''$	i	$2S_8$	$2S_8^3$	$2S_4$	σ_h	$4\sigma_d$	$4\sigma_v$		
A_{1g}	1	1	1	1	1	1	1	1	1	1	1	1	1	1		$x^2 + y^2, z^2$
A_{2g}	1	1	1	1	1	−1	−1	1	1	1	1	1	−1	−1	R_z	
B_{1g}	1	−1	−1	1	1	1	−1	1	−1	−1	1	1	1	−1		
B_{2g}	1	−1	−1	1	1	−1	1	1	−1	−1	1	1	−1	1		
E_{1g}	2	$\sqrt{2}$	$-\sqrt{2}$	0	−2	0	0	2	$\sqrt{2}$	$-\sqrt{2}$	0	−2	0	0	(R_x, R_y)	(xz, yz)
E_{2g}	2	0	0	−2	2	0	0	2	0	0	−2	2	0	0		$(x^2 - y^2, xy)$
E_{3g}	2	$-\sqrt{2}$	$\sqrt{2}$	0	−2	0	0	2	$-\sqrt{2}$	$\sqrt{2}$	0	−2	0	0		
A_{1u}	1	1	1	1	1	1	1	−1	−1	−1	−1	−1	−1	−1		
A_{2u}	1	1	1	1	1	−1	−1	−1	−1	−1	−1	−1	1	1	z	
B_{1u}	1	−1	−1	1	1	1	−1	−1	1	1	−1	−1	−1	1		
B_{2u}	1	−1	−1	1	1	−1	1	−1	1	1	−1	−1	1	−1		
E_{1u}	2	$\sqrt{2}$	$-\sqrt{2}$	0	−2	0	0	−2	$-\sqrt{2}$	$\sqrt{2}$	0	2	0	0	(x, y)	
E_{2u}	2	0	0	−2	2	0	0	−2	0	0	2	−2	0	0		
E_{3u}	2	$-\sqrt{2}$	$\sqrt{2}$	0	−2	0	0	−2	$\sqrt{2}$	$-\sqrt{2}$	0	2	0	0		

APPENDIX 14

HINTS FOR SOLVING SELECTED PROBLEMS

CHAPTER 1

1-1 Use Eq. (1-25).

1-7 P.E. $(t) = -\int_0^{\psi(x,t)} m[\partial^2\Psi(x, t)/\partial t^2]\, d\Psi(x, t) = \frac{1}{2}m\omega^2\psi^2(x, t)$
Next integrate P.E. (t) over one complete cycle $(0 - t')$.

CHAPTER 2

2-3 $\sin x \cos y = \frac{1}{2}[\cos(x - y) - \cos(x + y)]$.

2-7 What kind of function has $\lambda_{II} = \infty$? When could such a function join smoothly onto a sine function in region I?

CHAPTER 3

3-1 Imagine an auto runs from A to B at 30 mph and from B to C at 60 mph. Sketch the distribution function for the auto. Then reason how you arrived at this function and apply similar reasoning to the harmonic oscillator.

3-6 Consider how the solutions for the harmonic oscillator would meet the condition imposed by this new potential.

CHAPTER 4

4-2 The classical turning point occurs when the total energy equals the potential energy.

4-9 Ignore all but the θ and ϕ dependences in Eq. (4-30). Do not forget to *square* these dependences, and do not forget to include the $3^{1/2}$ term of $3d_{z^2}$.

4-10 The asymptotic solution is $\exp(i\sqrt{2E}x)$, which decays with increasing x for $E < 0$. Then take $\psi = f(x)\exp(i\sqrt{2E}x)$ and substitute into the Schrödinger equation, etc.

4-12 $x = r \sin\theta \cos\phi$.

4-13 Do not forget to include θ dependence of dv.

CHAPTER 5

5-4 Square ψ and integrate, using the fact that 1s, 2s are orthonormal.

CHAPTER 6

6-11 Use the Schmidt orthogonalization method.

CHAPTER 7

7-3 Do not forget that overlap between ϕ_a and ϕ_b must enter normality condition: $c_a^2 + c_b^2 + 2c_ac_bS = 1$.

7-4 Note that ψ_+ and ψ_- are degenerate at $R = \infty$.

7-6 Use the Schmidt orthogonalization procedure (Chapter 6) to construct 2s′.
7-7 (b) Take limit as $F \to 0$ rather than simply evaluating at $F = 0.1$. Note that $(1 + x)^m = 1 + mx + [m(m - 1)/2!]\, x^2 + \cdots$.
7-10 $\int \phi^2(-1/r_a)\, dv = 1 - (\xi + 1)\exp(-2\xi)$ using the method of Appendix 3.
7-12 In the limit of $R \to 0$, H_{AA} is indeterminate. Use l'Hospital's rule (i.e., take d/dR on the numerator and denominator and evaluate at $R = 0$). Alternatively, you can expand $\exp(-2R)$ in powers of R and evaluate at $R = 0$.
7-19 Note that (f) and (g) have both AOs on center a. When $\hat{H}$ is present in the integral, you are restricted to considering symmetry operations that do not affect $\hat{H}$.
7-20 Use the fact that $\phi = \sum_i c_i\psi_i$ and $\bar{E} = \sum_i c_i^* c_i E_i$.
7-22 (a) Note that, for symmetric ψ_n, $\int \psi\phi\, dx = 2\int_0^{L/2} \psi_n\phi\, dx$. For antisymmetric ψ_n, the integral can be evaluated by inspection. A useful integral is: $\int x \sin x\, dx = \sin x - x\cos x$.

(c) Use the fact that $\bar{E} = \sum_n c_n^2 E_n$. The series can be estimated with a small calculator (tedious) or else by summing the first few terms and integrating over a function that envelopes the higher terms.

CHAPTER 8

8-15 (b) Simply note where HOMO is bonding, antibonding, nonbonding, and recognize that some of the effect of this MO will be lost upon ionization.

CHAPTER 12

12-6 Recall that perturbation should be greatest for states with ψ^2 largest in region of perturbation.
12-15 To evaluate the first-order correction to the energy, you can recognize that $\langle 1s| -1/r|1s\rangle$ is identical to the potential energy of the H atom. The virial theorem tells you the value of this quantity at once.
12-16 Use the fact that $E_\pi = \alpha \sum_i^{\text{MOs}} n_i + 2\beta \sum_i^{\text{MOs}} \sum_{k<l}^{\text{neighbors}} p_{kl}$.

CHAPTER 13

13-9 Notice which MOs are degenerate when assigning symmetries. For the final part of the question, notice that the molecular x axis corresponds to the group theoretic z axis.

CHAPTER 14

14-13 Do not forget that the cyclobutadiene molecule differs from two acetylenes in both π and σ systems. There are a total of eight orbitals to be sketched for each side of this reaction.

APPENDIX 15

ANSWERS TO SELECTED PROBLEMS[1]

CHAPTER 1

1-1 [See Hint.] $(A + B + C)\cos(kx) + (B + iC - iD)\sin(kx)$.

1-2 $\psi(x)$ = same as Eq. (1-32) except cos instead of sin when n is odd.

1-3 $\alpha^2 = \beta^2 = (2\pi/\lambda)^2$.

1-4 Work functions: Cs = 1.9 eV, Zn = 3.7 eV. $h = 4.13 \times 10^{-15}$ eV sec.

1-5 (a) 0.055 nm. (b) 3.31×10^{-25} nm.

1-6 Yes. $AB = BA = 2x^2(d^2/dx^2) + x^3(d^3/dx^3)$.

1-7 [See Hint.] Integrating $\mathrm{PE}(t) = \frac{1}{2}m\omega^2\Psi^2(x,t)$ over a cycle and dividing by t' to give average PE per unit time gives $\mathrm{PE} = m\omega^2\psi^2(x)/4$. [$m$ is really $\rho\,dx$.] An identical result comes from integrating $\mathrm{KE}(t) = \frac{1}{2}m\omega^2\psi^2(x)\sin^2(\omega t)$ over the same cycle.

1-8 (a) No. Becomes infinite at $x = \pm\infty$. (b) Same as (a). (c) Yes.
(d) No. Becomes infinite at $x = -\infty$. (e) Yes.

1-9 $\psi = \sin x$ or $\cos x$ are examples.

1-10 We need establish only one of the extreme profiles for the string. Then, as $\cos(\omega t)$ oscillates between $+1$ and -1, the string oscillates between the two extremes. In other words, $\sin(x)$ and $-\sin(x)$ are the same solution at different times. (They differ by a phase factor.)

1-11 Only (d) and (f). [The latter is most easily seen after recognizing that the function equals $\exp(4x)$.]

CHAPTER 2

2-1 $\mathrm{J^2\,sec^2\,kg^{-1}\,m^{-2} = (kg\,m^2\,s^{-2})^2\,sec^2\,kg^{-1}\,m^{-2} = kg\,m^2\,sec^{-2} = J}$.

2-2
$$A = \left[\frac{L}{n\pi}\int_0^L \sin^2\left(\frac{n\pi x}{L}\right) d\left(\frac{n\pi x}{L}\right)\right]^{-1/2}$$
$$= \left[\frac{L}{n\pi}\int_0^{n\pi} \sin^2 y\, dy\right]^{-1/2} = \left[\frac{L}{n\pi}\cdot\frac{n\pi}{2}\right]^{-1/2} = \sqrt{\frac{2}{L}}$$
or else recognize that, since $\sin^2 + \cos^2 = 1$, $\int_0^L (\sin^2 + \cos^2)\,dx = L$, and so $\int_0^L \sin^2 = L/2$.

2-3 [See Hint.] $(2/L)\int_0^L \sin(n\pi x)\sin(m\pi x)\,dx$ = (using Hint) $(1/\pi)\int_0^\pi \{\cos[(n-m)y] - \cos[(n+m)y]\}\,dy = 0$, for n and m integers and $n \neq m$.

2-4 (a) S. (b) −A. (c) SS. (d) AA. (e) −AS. (f) AASASSA. (g) −AASASAA.

Rule: Product antisymmetric when *odd* number of antisymmetric functions is present.

[1] Hints for some of these are given in Appendix 14.

2-5 All are zero by symmetry except (d), (e), (h).
2-6 If $U \rightarrow \infty$, $\lambda_{\text{II}} \rightarrow i \cdot 0$, $\psi_{\text{II}} \rightarrow \exp(-\infty) \rightarrow 0$.
2-7 [See Hint.] $\lambda_{\text{II}} = \infty$, and so ψ_{II} is a constant. A constant has a zero derivative, and ψ_{I} must arrive at $x = L$ with zero derivative if successful junction is to be made. This requires that an odd number of quarter-waves fit between 0 and L (so wave arrives with either a peak or a valley at $x = L$). This requires that $[(2n + 1)/4]\lambda_{\text{I}} = L$; $\lambda_{\text{I}} = 4L/(2n + 1) = h/\sqrt{2mU}$; $U = (2n + 1)^2h^2/32mL^2$ is the relation between U and L that is required for a state to exist at $E = U$. (Strictly speaking, one can only approach $\lambda = \infty$ as a limit, and this problem is physically meaningless. However, it makes a good exercise.)
2-8 0.6089, 0.1955, $\frac{1}{3}$.
2-9 $\lambda_1 = 1.24 \times 10^8$ Å, $\lambda_2 = 2.78 \times 10^6$ Å.
2-10 Given that $H\psi_1 = E_1\psi_1$, $H\psi_2 = E_2\psi_2$, $E_1 = E_2 = E$ and $\phi = c_1\psi_1 + c_2\psi_2$. Then $H\phi = c_1H\psi_1 + c_2H\psi_2 = c_1E_1\psi_1 + c_2E_2\psi_2 = E(c_1\psi_1 + c_2\psi_2) = E\phi$. Q.E.D.
2-11 $\exp(i\sqrt{2}\phi)$ does not join onto itself when $\phi \rightarrow \phi + 2\pi$.
2-12 (a) ψ should oscillate on right with same λ as on left.
(b) ψ should be symmetric or antisymmetric (and λ should be same in each side).
(c) ψ should be smooth (i.e., have no cusp) at finite barrier.
(d) ψ should be a decaying exponential at right.
(e) Same as (d). ψ should not become infinite.
2-13 Both $3h^2/4mL_x^2$. Accidental degeneracy is one not forced by symmetry.
2-14 $\Delta E = [(6 + n)^2 - (5 + n)^2]h^2/8mL^2$

$$\lambda = (8mcl^2/h)(2n + 10^2)/(2n + 11) = 637(2n + 10)^2/(2n + 11) \text{ Å}$$

n:	0	1	2	3
λ:	5791	7056	8323	9592

CHAPTER 3

3-1 [See Hint.] $P(x)$ is proportional to $1/v(x)$, which is $[dx(t)/dt]^{-1}$, which is $[-\sqrt{k/m}L\sin(\sqrt{k/m}t)]^{-1}$. This is proportional to

$$[\sin^2(\sqrt{k/m}t)]^{-1/2} = [1 - \cos^2(\sqrt{k/m}t)]^{-1/2} = [1 - x^2/L^2]^{-1/2}$$

The *normalized* probability distribution function is $(\pi\sqrt{L^2 - x^2})^{-1}$.
3-2, 3 $H_2(y) = 4y^2 - 2$.
3-4 The first function is asymmetric; the second becomes infinite in both limits of y.
3-5 Zero point energy $= \frac{3}{2}h\nu$; 10; 3.
3-6 [See Hint.] The barrier requires $\psi = 0$ at $x \leq 0$ but does not affect $\hat{H}$ at $x > 0$. Therefore, antisymmetric solutions of harmonic oscillator are still good. Results are

$$\psi_{x>0} = \sqrt{2} \times \psi_{\text{harm, osc.}}, \quad n = 1, 3, 5, \ldots, \quad \text{and} \quad E = (n + \tfrac{1}{2})h\nu, \quad n = 1, 3, 5, \ldots$$

$$\psi_{x \leq 0} = 0$$

CHAPTER 4

4-1 $E_2 - E_1 = \frac{3}{8}$ a.u. $= 2.467382 \times 10^{15}$ Hz using m_e. Use of μ gives 0.999455 times this value.
4-2 [See Hint.] $E_{1s} = -\frac{1}{2}$ a.u. $V(r) = -1/r$ a.u. Equal when $r = 2$ a.u. $\int_2^\infty \psi^2\,dv = 0.238$, and so 23.8%.
4-3 (a) $1/Z$ a.u. (b) $3/2Z$ a.u. (c) 0 a.u. (by inspection of ψ^2).

4-4 (a) 4 a.u. (b) 5 a.u. (c) 2 a.u.
4-5 $(1/\sqrt{2})\int_0^\infty \exp(-r)(2 - r)\exp(-r/2)r^2\,dr = \cdots 0$. (Do not forget r^2 from dv.)
4-6 $(-1/r)_{\text{av}} = \int (1s)^2(-1/r)\,dv = -1$ a.u., which is double the total energy of $-\frac{1}{2}$ a.u. r_{av} for 1s is $\frac{3}{2}$ a.u., and so $-1/r_{\text{av}} = -\frac{2}{3}$ a.u., which disagrees with $(-1/r)_{\text{av}}$.

For the $2p_0$ electron $(-1/r)_{\text{av}} = -\frac{1}{4}$, which again is double the total energy of $-\frac{1}{8}$ a.u.

r_{av} for $2p_0$ is 5 a.u., and $-1/r_{\text{av}} = -\frac{1}{5}$ a.u., which disagrees with $(-1/r)_{\text{av}}$. These disagreements simply illustrate that an average of reciprocals is not equal to the reciprocal of the average. (Taking a reciprocal is a nonlinear operation.)
4-7 $\pi^{-1/2}$ is the normalizing factor.
4-8 For reflection in the xy plane, $2p_z$ is antisymmetric, and $3d_{xy}$ is symmetric.
4-9 [See Hint.] The sum of squares of angular dependencies equals $\frac{4}{3}$.
4-10 [See Hint.] $f'' + 2i\sqrt{2E}f' + 2f/x = 0$. Let $f = \sum_{i=0}^{\infty} c_i x^i$. Gives

$$c_0 = 0, \qquad c_{n+2} = -[2i\sqrt{2E}(n + 1) + 2]c_{n+1}/(n + 1)(n + 2)$$

Comparing this with asymptotic solution indicates that the wavefunction will explode at large x unless the series for f is truncated. [The f series behaves at large n like $\exp(-2i\sqrt{2E}x)$.] If c_{n+1} is the highest nonzero term, obtain $2i\sqrt{2E}(n + 1) + 2 = 0$, or $E = -1/2(n + 1)^2$. Results (ψ not normalized) are

$n = 0,\quad E = -\frac{1}{2}$ a.u., $\quad \psi_{x\geq 0} = x\exp(-x), \quad \psi_{x\leq 0} = \pm x\exp(x)$ [2 sol'ns]
$n = 1,\quad E = -\frac{1}{8}$ a.u., $\quad \psi_{x\geq 0} = (x - x^2/2)\exp(-x/2)$, etc. [2 sol'ns]
$n = 2,\quad E = -\frac{1}{18}$ a.u., $\quad \psi_{x\geq 0} = (x - (2x^2/3) + 2x^3/27)\exp(-x/3)$, etc. [2 sol'ns]

4-11 See Appendix 12.
4-12 [See Hint.] $\int 1s^2 r \sin\theta\cos\phi\,dv = 0$ (because $\cos\phi$ antisymmetric in each subrange $0 - \pi$, $\pi - 2\pi$). The average value of x *should* be zero because electron equally likely to be found at equal $\pm x$ positions due to the spherical symmetry of ψ^2.
4-13 [See Hint.] $\theta_{mp} = 35°\ 15'$, $144°\ 45'$.
4-14 $\bar{x} = \int_{-\infty}^{+\infty} \psi^2 x\,dx$. ψ^2 is symmetric, x is antisymmetric, and $\bar{x} = 0$.
4-15

$$\begin{aligned}\hat{L}_x 2p_0 &= \hat{L}_x R(r)\cos\theta = -iR(r)\sin\theta\cos\phi \neq \text{constant} \times 2p_0\\ \hat{L}_y 2p_0 &= iR(r)\sin\theta\sin\phi \neq \text{constant} \times 2p_0\\ \hat{L}_x 1s &= 0 = \hat{L}_y 1s = \hat{L}_z 1s = \hat{L}^2 1s \cdots = 0 \times 1s\end{aligned}$$

Since the vector has zero length, its x, y, z components must also have zero length. The question of vector orientation becomes meaningless.
4-16 $[-1/(\sin\theta)(d/d\theta)\sin\theta\, d/d\theta]R(r)\cos\theta = 2R(r)\cos\theta$, $l(l + 1) = 2$, $l = 1$.
4-17 6.998×10^9 Hz, 2.8 ppm.

CHAPTER 5

5-1 $-\frac{1}{2}(\nabla_1^2 + \nabla_2^2 + \nabla_3^2) - 3/r_1 - 3/r_2 - 3/r_3 + 1/r_{12} + 1/r_{23} + 1/r_{13}$.
5-2 $\bar{r}_{1s} = 3/2Z =$ (for He^+) $\frac{3}{4}$ a.u.; $\bar{r}_{2s} = 6/Z =$ (for He^+) 3 a.u.
5-3 $E = 2.343 \times 10^5$ eV compared with an IP of 13.6 eV.
5-4 [See Hint.] $\int \psi^2\,dv = \frac{1}{2}\int (1s^2 + 2(1s2s) + 2s^2)\,dv = \frac{1}{2}(1 + 0 + 1) = 1$.
5-5 $\psi_a(2 \leftrightarrow 1) = (1/\sqrt{2})[1s(2)2s(1) - 2s(2)1s(1)] = -\psi_a$.
5-6 Upon substitution and expansion, complete cancellation occurs.

5-7 $(1/\sqrt{6})[1s2p1s(\alpha\beta\beta - \beta\beta\alpha) + 1s1s2p(\beta\alpha\beta - \alpha\beta\beta) + 2p1s1s(\beta\beta\alpha - \beta\alpha\beta)]$.

5-8 $\int 1s^*2s\, dv \int 1s^*1s\, dv \int 2s^*1s\, dv \int \alpha^*\alpha\, d\omega \int \beta^*\alpha\, d\omega \int \alpha^*\beta\, d\omega = 0\cdot1\cdot0\cdot1\cdot0\cdot0 = 0$.

5-9 For $r_1 = 1$, $r_2 = 2$, $r_3 = 0$ get

$$\psi(1, 2, 0) = (1/\sqrt{6})[1\bar{s}(r = 1)2p_z(r = 2)1s(r = 0) + 2p_z(r = 1)1s(r = 2)1\bar{s}(r = 0) - 2p_z(r = 1)1\bar{s}(r = 2)1s(r = 0) - 1s(r = 1)2p_z(r = 2)1\bar{s}(r = 0)]$$

The other cases are the same except for factor of -1. Thus, ψ^2 is identical for all three cases, and no physical distinction exists.

5-10 See the discussion following Eq. (5-54).

5-11 $\bar{T} = -\bar{E}$, $\bar{V} = 2\bar{E}$, $\bar{V} = -2\bar{T}$.

5-12 F, $1s^22s^22p^5$, $Z = 9$, $\xi_{1s} = 8.7$, $\xi_{2s} = \xi_{2p} = 2.6$.

5-13 Let $\hat{A}\phi = a\phi$ and $\int \phi^*\phi\, d\tau = 1$. $(\hat{A})_{av} = \int \phi^*\hat{A}\phi\, d\tau = \int \phi^* a\phi\, d\tau = a\int \phi^*\phi\, d\tau = a$.

5-14 Li^{2+} is a hydrogenlike ion, and hence should have all states of same n degenerate. Li differs in that potential seen by electron is not of form $-Z/r$, due to screening of nucleus by other electrons. Hence, degeneracy is lost. The 2s AO of Li is lower than the 2p due to the fact that the 2s electron spends a larger fraction of time near nucleus where it experiences full nuclear charge.

5-15 $\frac{1}{2}(\frac{1}{2} + 1) = \frac{3}{4}$.

5-16 For a given number of α and β spins, only one independent symmetric combination exists. (Convince yourself of this.) For n electrons, we can start with all α spins (one symmetric spin state), change one α to β (one symmetric spin state), change another α to β (one symmetric state), etc. until all spins are β. This exhausts the possible symmetric spin states. For n electrons, then, the possibilities are: no changes, one change, two changes, ..., n changes. This is $n + 1$ cases, and so degeneracy is $n + 1$.

CHAPTER 6

6-1 $\int_{-\infty}^{\infty} \psi^*(d^2/dx^2)\phi\, dv \overset{?}{=} \int_{-\infty}^{\infty} \phi(d^2/dx^2)\psi^*\, dv$. Use $\int_{-\infty}^{\infty} v\, du = uv|_{-\infty}^{\infty} - \int_{-\infty}^{\infty} u\, dv$. On the left, let $v = \psi^*$, $u = d\phi/dx$, $du = d^2\phi/dx^2$, $dv = d\psi^*/dx$. On the right, let $v = \phi$, $u = d\psi^*/dx$, etc. The uv term vanishes since ψ^* and ϕ each vanish at limits. The remaining integrals are identical.

6-2 Each equals $-4\sqrt{8}/27$.

6-3 $\int \psi^*\psi\, dv = 1$, $\int \chi_i^*\chi_j\, dv = \delta_{i,j}$, $\psi = \sum_i c_i\chi_i$. Then

$$\int \psi^*\psi\, dv = 1 = \int \textstyle\sum_i c_i^*\chi_i^* \sum_j c_j\chi_j\, dv = \sum_i\sum_j c_i^*c_j\delta_{ij} = \sum_i c_i^*c_i. \quad \text{Q.E.D.}$$

6-4 $\psi = \sum_i c_i\mu_i$, $\int \mu_i^*\mu_j\, dv = \delta_{i,j}$, want c_k:

$$\int \mu_k^*\psi\, dv = \int \mu_k^* \textstyle\sum_i c_i\mu_i\, dv = \sum_i c_i \int \mu_k^*\mu_i\, dv = \sum_i c_i\delta_{k,i} = c_k$$

6-5 (a)

$$(1/\pi)\int_0^{2\pi} \cos 2\phi(\hbar/i)(d/d\phi)\cos 2\phi\, d\phi = -(2/\hbar\pi i)'\int_0^{2\pi} \cos 2\phi \sin 2\phi\, d\phi$$

$$\propto \int_0^{2\pi} \text{sym}\cdot\text{antisym} = 0$$

(b)

$$\psi = (1/\sqrt{2})[(1/\sqrt{2\pi})\exp(2i\phi)] + (1/\sqrt{2})[(1/\sqrt{2\pi})\exp(-2i\phi)]$$

Terms in [ ] are normalized eigenfunctions of $\hat{p}_\phi$ with eigenvalues of $+2\hbar$ and $-2\hbar$. So $(\hat{p}_\phi)_{av} = (1/\sqrt{2})^2(2\hbar) + (1/\sqrt{2})^2(-2\hbar) = 0$.

6-6

$$[x, p_x] = [x(\hbar/i)(d/dx) - (\hbar/i)(d/dx)x]f(x) = (\hbar/i)(xf' - f - xf') = -(\hbar/i)f$$
$$\Delta x \cdot \Delta p_x \geq \tfrac{1}{2}|\int \psi^*(-\hbar/i)\psi\, d\tau| = |-\hbar/2i| = \hbar/2$$

6-7 ϕ must be identical to the eigenfunction ψ_0.

6-8 No. The existence of *some* real eigenvalues does not guarantee that the operator satisfies the definition of hermiticity:

$$(d/dr)\exp(-ar) = -a\exp(-ar)$$

but

$$\int_0^\infty \exp(-ar)(d/dr)\exp(-br)r^2\,dr \neq \int_0^\infty \exp(-br)(d/dr)\exp(-ar)r^2\,dr \qquad \text{if} \quad a \neq b$$

6-9 Each side equals $-(1/2\sqrt{2})\psi_{1s}\exp(it/2) - (1/8\sqrt{2})\psi_{2p_0}\exp(it/8)$.

6-10 $(1 - S^2)^{-1/2}$

6-11 [See Hint.] $S = \sqrt{3}/2$, and so $\phi = (2/\sqrt{3\pi})(r - \tfrac{3}{2})\exp(-r)$.

CHAPTER 7

7-1 Normalizing factor $= (2\alpha/\pi)^{3/4}$; $\bar{E} = (3\alpha/2) - 2\sqrt{2\alpha}/\sqrt{\pi}$; $\alpha = 8/9\pi$; $\bar{E}(\min) = -4/3\pi = -0.4244$ a.u.; $\bar{r} = 1.5$ a.u.; $r_{\mathrm{mp}} = \sqrt{9\pi}/4 = 1.329$ a.u. (For ψ_{exact}, $E = -0.5$ a.u., $\bar{r} = 1.5$ a.u., $r_{\mathrm{mp}} = 1.0$ a.u.)

7-2 (a) and (b) See text and Eqs. (7-16)–(7-20). (c) $\alpha = \tfrac{5}{3}$, $\bar{E} = -0.370$ a.u.

7-3 [See Hint.] $\bar{E}$(lowest) $= -2.030$ a.u. $\psi = 1.045\,\phi_a - 0.179\,\phi_b$.

7-4 [See Hint.] Since they are degenerate, ψ_+ and ψ_- may be mixed. The sum gives $1s_a$, describing the case in which electron is at a. The difference gives $1s_b$.

7-5 For He_2, the second MO ($\sigma_u 1s$) correlates with third united atom AO ($2p_\sigma$). For LiH, the second MO (σ) correlates with second united atom AO (2s). Thus, this MO is less antibonding in heteronuclear case.

7-6 [See Hint.] $2s' = 1.0295\ 2s - 0.2447\ 1s$; $2\sigma_g = 0.0136\ 1s_A - 0.6523\ 2s_A' - -0.0854\ 2p_{\sigma,A}$ and similarly for B.

7-7 (a) $S_{11} = 1$, $S_{12} = 0$, $S_{22} = 1$, $H_{11} = -\tfrac{1}{2}$, $H_{12} = -F$, $H_{22} = 0$. $\bar{E} = -\tfrac{1}{4} - \tfrac{1}{4}\sqrt{1 + 16F^2}$; for $F = 0.1$, $\bar{E} = -0.51926$ a.u. This trial form is superior because $z \cdot \psi_{1s}$ is more contracted than ψ_{2p_z}, closer in size to ψ_{1s}, hence interferes constructively and destructively with ψ_{1s} more effectively.

(b) [See Hint.] lim($F \to 0$) of $\sqrt{1 + 16F^2} = 1 + 8F^2$; In lim, $\bar{E} = -\tfrac{1}{2} - 2F^2$, $-\tfrac{1}{2}\alpha F^2 = -2F^2$; $\alpha = 4$. $E(e^2/a_0) \leftrightarrow \alpha F^2$ (α units)$\cdot(e/a_0{}^2)^2$, α units $= a_0{}^3$. (See Appendix 12.)

7-8 Since 2s is isoenergetic with 2p states, these should mix freely in response to field. Hence, 2s is more polarizable.

7-9 $\int \psi^2\,dv = c_1{}^2 S_{AA} + 2c_1c_2S_{AB} + c_2{}^2 S_{BB}$. But $S_{AA} = S_{BB} = 1$, and $S_{AB} = 0$ by symmetry; so $= c_1{}^2 + c_2{}^2$.

7-10 [See Hint.] $\bar{E}_{\mathrm{elec}} = (\xi^2/2) - 2 + 2(\xi + 1)\exp(-2\xi)$; $\xi_{\mathrm{best}} = 0.9118$, $\bar{E}_{\mathrm{elec}} = -0.9668$ a.u.; $\bar{E}_{\mathrm{elec}} + 1/R = \bar{E}_{\mathrm{tot}} = -0.4668$ a.u. Since this energy exceeds that of $H + H^+$ (-0.5 a.u. at $R = \infty$), this function does not demonstrate the existence of a bound state.

7-11 k must be greater than S.

7-12 [See Hint.] Both equal $-\tfrac{3}{2}$ a.u. This is higher than the lowest He^+ eigenvalue because these are hydrogen atom 1s functions instead of He^+ functions.

7-13 $\bar{E}(\min) = -12/5 = -2.4$ a.u. $\psi = \sqrt{2/5}(\phi_a + \phi_b)$.

7-14 $c_1 = \sqrt{0.4} = 0.632$, $c_3 = 0$ by symmetry.

7-15 (a) $\hat{H} = -\frac{1}{2}\nabla^2 - (1/r_{\mathrm{H}}) - 2/r_{\mathrm{He}}$.

(b) Separated atoms: lowest energy for $\mathrm{H}^+ + \mathrm{He}^+(1s) =$ united atom; $\mathrm{Li}^{2+}(1s) = -4.5$ a.u.

7-16 (a) 4. (b) 3 (a triplet). (c) (1) increase, (2) decrease. (d)

7-17

$1s\sigma_g$	$2p_z\sigma_u$	$3p_y\pi_u$	$3d_{xy}\delta_g$
$2s\sigma_g$	$2p_x\pi_u$	$3d_{z^2}\sigma_g$	$3d_{xz}\pi_g$

7-18 (a) Antibonding. (b) Bonding. (c) Bonding.

7-19 [See Hint.] The integrals that vanish by symmetry are (b), (c), (e), and (f); (g) does not vanish. The AOs are orthogonal due to different symmetry for reflection in the xy plane at a. But $\hat{H}$ is not invariant to this reflection. In (f), the relevant reflection is through the xz plane; $\hat{H}$ is invariant to this one.

7-20 [See Hint.] The energy $\bar{E} = -0.375$ a.u. $= (0.9775)^2(-\frac{1}{2}$ a.u.$)$ + higher-energy contributions. But this leading term equals -0.478 a.u., and so the net value of the higher energy terms must be positive. Therefore, at least one of them must correspond to a state with positive energy—a continuum state.

7-21 Slater's rules give $\zeta = 1.7$, whereas the variation method gives $\zeta = 27/16 = 1.6875$.

7-22 (a) [See Hint.] For $n =$ odd,

$$c_n = 2\int_0^{L/2} \phi\psi\, dx = \pm\frac{4\sqrt{6}}{n^2\pi^2}\begin{cases} + \text{ for } n = 1, 5, 9, 13, \ldots \\ - \text{ for } n = 3, 7, 11, 15, \ldots \end{cases}$$

For $n =$ even, $c_n = 0$ (by symmetry) (i.e., ϕ is symmetric and so contains only symmetric ψ_n).

(b)

$$\phi_{\text{approx}}(x = L/2) = \sum_{n=1}^{m} c_n\psi_n(x = L/2) = (4\sqrt{6}/\pi^2)\sqrt{2/L}\sum_{n=1\,(\text{odd})}^{m}(1/n^2)$$

m:	1	3	5	7	9	...	135
$\sqrt{L}\phi_{\text{approx}}(x = L/2)$:	1.40395	1.55994	1.61609	1.64475	1.66208		1.72689

$\sqrt{L}\phi(x = L/2) = \sqrt{3} = 1.73205$.

(c) [See Hint.]

$$\begin{aligned}\bar{E} &= \sum_{\text{odd } n}(4\sqrt{6}/n^2\pi^2)^2(n^2h^2/8mL^2) = (12h^2/\pi^4mL^2)\sum_{\text{odd } n}(1/n^2)\\ &\leq (12h^2/\pi^4mL^2)\left[\sum_{\text{odd } n=1}^{m}(1/n^2) + \tfrac{1}{2}\int_{m+1}^{\infty}(1/x^2)\,dx\right]\\ &= [(h^2/8mL^2)(96/\pi^4)(1.23386)]_{m=9}\\ &= [1.21602(h^2/8mL^2)]_{m=9}; \qquad [1.21432(h^2/8mL^2)]_{m=135}\end{aligned}$$

CHAPTER 8

8-1 For ψ_{prod}, $E = E_1 + E_2 + E_3$. For ψ_{det}, $E = \frac{1}{6}(E_1 + E_2 + E_3$ six times). Energies of products in ψ are $E_1 + E_2 + E_3$ and $E_1 + E_2 + E_4$. These can be factored out to give $\hat{H}\psi = E\psi$ only if $E_3 = E_4$.

2

(a)

$$\longrightarrow \begin{vmatrix} x & 1 & 0 & 0 & 0 & 0 \\ 1 & x & 1 & 0 & 1 & 0 \\ 0 & 1 & x & 1 & 0 & 0 \\ 0 & 0 & 1 & x & 1 & 0 \\ 0 & 1 & 0 & 1 & x & 1 \\ 0 & 0 & 0 & 0 & 1 & x \end{vmatrix}$$

(b)

$$\longrightarrow \begin{vmatrix} x & 1 & 1 & 0 & 0 & 0 \\ 1 & x & 1 & 0 & 0 & 0 \\ 1 & 1 & x & 1 & 0 & 0 \\ 0 & 0 & 1 & x & 1 & 1 \\ 0 & 0 & 0 & 1 & x & 1 \\ 0 & 0 & 0 & 1 & 1 & x \end{vmatrix}$$

(c) $\begin{vmatrix} x & 1 \\ 1 & x \end{vmatrix}$ (only 2 unsaturated carbons, so the same as ethylene).

(d) Same as (c). Same as *two* ethylenes since the two π systems are noninteracting due to spatial separation.

(e) Same as (c). Same as *two* ethylenes since the two π systems are orthogonal and noninteracting.

8-3

$$\begin{vmatrix} x & 1 & 1 & 1 \\ 1 & x & 0 & 0 \\ 1 & 0 & x & 0 \\ 1 & 0 & 0 & x \end{vmatrix} = 0, \qquad x^4 - 3x^2 = 0$$

See Appendix 6 for results.

8-4 $\frac{1}{3}$, since only χ_3 is common to both MOs.

8-5 There is no way to construct a circular sequence of alternating sign having an *odd* number of members.

8-6 The probability of finding electron 1 in dv is $\int_2 \int_3 \psi_\pi^2(1, 2, 3)\, dv(2)\, dv(3)\, dv = \phi_1^2\, dv$. For electron 2 it is $\phi_1^2\, dv$, and for electron 3 it is $\phi_2^2\, dv$. For *an* electron it is the sum of these. Hence, the electron density function is Eq. (8-44). For the determinantal form, expansion leads to six terms. ψ^2 gives 36 terms, but disagreements between spin or space functions cause integrals over cross products to vanish. Each of the six self products leads to the same net result as above. The determinantal normalizing factor squares to $\frac{1}{6}$ to produce a final result as given by Eq. (8-44).

8-7 $E = \alpha + 2\beta(\sqrt{2}/3\sqrt{3} + 0 + 0 + 0) = \alpha + 0.544\beta.$

8-8 See Appendix 6 for coefficients.

8-9 $q = 1$ at all centers in an HMO calculation on an alternant. This *result* is consistent with the *initial assumption* that all carbons are equally attractive to an electron.

8-12 Bond orders: CH_2–CH, $0.8944 \rightarrow 0.6708$; CH–CH, $0.4472 \rightarrow 0.5854$.

Bond lengths (Eq. 8-61): CH_2–CH, 1.354 → 1.392; CH–CH, 1.436 → 1.408; ΔCH_2–CH = +0.038 Å, ΔCH–CH = −0.028 Å.

8-13 For benzene, $c_{\mu i}$ should be taken as $1/\sqrt{6}$ since all carbons are equivalent.

8-14 Only fluoranthene deviates markedly because it is nonalternant. Hence, its LUMO and HOMO energies are not symmetrically disposed about $E = \alpha$.

8-15 (a) Oxidation potential ~0.97 V, reduction potential ~1.41 V. (b) [See Hint]. To shorten: 4–10, 9–10, 8–9; to lengthen: 3–10, 1–9, 4–5, 7–8; otherwise no change.

8-16 $E = 18\alpha + 21.877\beta$. Error $= 0.0015\beta$ per π electron.

8-17 (a) Naphthalene; E_π (from Table 8-2) $= 10\alpha + 13.1325\beta$, from HMO $= 10\alpha + 13.6832\beta$. The difference $= 0.055\beta$ per π electron, aromatic. Perylene; E_π (Table 8-2) $= 20\alpha + 27.2796\beta$, E_π(HMO) $= 20\alpha + 28.2453\beta$; $\Delta E_\pi = 0.048\beta$ per π electron, aromatic.

(b) *RE* for perylene is slightly less than double that for naphthalene. The central ring does not appear to be contributing.

(c) These two bonds are single in all formal (nonpolar) structures.

(d) The calculated length = 1.443 Å. The HMO length is too short. The actual length is more consistent with these being "truly" single bonds.

8-18 The fourth molecule in Fig. 8-24 should strive for six electrons in each ring. This would make the left side (i.e., the seven-membered ring) net positive. The other two molecules become net negative on the left. Electron densities corroborate this. For the fourth molecule, charge densities exceed unity in the five-membered ring and are less elsewhere. The fifth molecule has only one π electron density less than unity, and this is for the methylene carbon.

8-19 (a) 9. (b) 10. (c) 4. (d) 6. (e) 10.

8-20 Since the formal structure always shows C–O single bonds, $C_1{=}C_2$ and $C_3{=}C_4$ double bonds, and $C_2{-}C_3$ as single, we can use the single-, double-bond distinctions of Table 8-3. These give

$$\begin{vmatrix} x & 1.1 & 0 & 0 & 0.8 & 0 & 0 & 0 \\ 1.1 & x & 0.9 & 0 & 0 & 0.3 & 0 & 0 \\ 0 & 0.9 & x-0.1 & 1.1 & 0 & 0 & 0.8 & 0 \\ 0 & 0 & 1.1 & x & 0.8 & 0 & 0 & 0 \\ 0.8 & 0 & 0 & 0.8 & x+2.0 & 0 & 0 & 0 \\ 0 & 0.3 & 0 & 0 & 0 & x+1.5 & 0 & 0 \\ 0 & 0 & 0.8 & 0 & 0 & 0 & x-0.1 & 3.0 \\ 0 & 0 & 0 & 0 & 0 & 0 & 3.0 & x-0.5 \end{vmatrix}$$

Otherwise, the positions with 1.1 and 0.9 become 1.0.

8-21 (a) Left. (b) Left. (c) Right.

8-22 $q_r = 1$ at all centers, and so it does not predict some centers best for nucleophilic, and hence worst for electrophilic substitution. Since the HOMO and LUMO have identical absolute coefficients (by the pairing theorem), the same site is most favored for both nucleophilic and electrophilic substitution. L_r must be identical for nucleophilic, radical, or electrophilic substitution because an interrupted even alternant produces an odd alternant, for which cationic, neutral, and anionic π

energies (β part) are the same. Of the four indices, only L_r is relevant to free radical substitution.

8-23 No. Both types should prefer the most polarizable site, since that is site to which charge is most easily attracted or from which it is most easily repelled.

8-24 (a) $F_1 = 0.0684$, $F_2 = 0.4618$, $F_4 = 0.9737$.

(b)

Index	Values		Preferred site
q_r	$q_2 = 0.818$	$q_4 = 1.488$	4
HOMO	$c_2{}^2 = 0.1356$	$c_4{}^2 = 0.2559$	4
$L_r{}^+$	$L_2^+ = 2.134\beta$	$L_4^+ = 0.962\beta$	4
π_{rr}	$\pi_{22} = -0.4340$	$\pi_{44} = -0.4019$	2

(c) Only protons on C_2 and C_3 will produce ESR splitting in simplest theory, since singly occupied MO of radical anion is zero elsewhere.

(d) Net bonding, because energy is below $E = \alpha$ and this happens only when bonding interactions dominate.

8-25 The correlation is fairly good except for styrene, which is way off. But styrene is the only member of the set where addition is not occurring at a ring position. Because the geometric constraints are so different, the relation between free valence and transition-state energy is presumably rather different for styrene.

CHAPTER 9

9-1 (a) 212 (b) $\begin{pmatrix} 6a & 6b & 6c \\ 7a & 7b & 7c \end{pmatrix}$ (c) $\begin{pmatrix} 25 & 13 \\ i-7 & 18 \end{pmatrix}$ (d) $\begin{pmatrix} 1 & 0 \\ 0 & 1 \end{pmatrix}$

(e) $\begin{pmatrix} 3i+16 & 2i+28 \\ 31 & 51 \\ -12 & -21 \end{pmatrix}$ (f) product not defined (g) 1

9-2 H is defined to be hermitian if $H_{ij} = H_{ji}^*$. $H_{ji} = \int \chi_j{}^* \hat{H} \chi_i \, d\tau$, and so $H_{ji}^* = \int \chi_j \hat{H}^* \chi_i{}^* \, d\tau$. But if $\hat{H}$ is hermitian, this must equal $\int \chi_i{}^* \hat{H} \chi_j \, d\tau \equiv H_{ij}$. Therefore, $H_{ji}^* = H_{ij}$ and H is hermitian.

9-4 $\mathsf{AC} = \widetilde{\mathsf{CA}}$. But $\widetilde{\mathsf{CA}} = \tilde{\mathsf{A}}\tilde{\mathsf{C}}$, so $\mathsf{AC} = \tilde{\mathsf{A}}\tilde{\mathsf{C}}$. This must be true in this example because A and C are symmetric. That is, $\mathsf{A} = \tilde{\mathsf{A}}$, $\mathsf{C} = \tilde{\mathsf{C}}$.

9-5 (a)

$$\begin{aligned} |\mathsf{B} - \lambda_i \mathsf{1}| &= |\mathsf{T}^{-1}\mathsf{AT} - \lambda_i \mathsf{1}| = |\mathsf{T}^{-1}\mathsf{AT} - \lambda_i \mathsf{T}^{-1}\mathsf{1T}| = |\mathsf{T}^{-1}(\mathsf{A} - \lambda_i \mathsf{1})\mathsf{T}| \\ &= |\mathsf{T}^{-1}|\,|\mathsf{A} - \lambda_i \mathsf{1}|\,|\mathsf{T}| = |\mathsf{TT}^{-1}(\mathsf{A} - \lambda_i \mathsf{1})| = |\mathsf{A} - \lambda_i \mathsf{1}| \end{aligned}$$

(b) For diagonal B, value of $|\mathsf{B} - \lambda_i \mathsf{1}|$ is product of diagonal elements. For this to vanish, at least one such element must vanish. This will occur whenever λ_i equals a diagonal element of B. Therefore, the latent roots are the diagonal values.

9-6 If a latent root is zero, then the product of latent roots is zero. But this product is the value of the determinant of the matrix. If the determinant of the matrix is zero, there is no inverse.

9-7 (a)

$$\begin{aligned}\mathrm{tr(ABC)} &= \sum_{i=1}^{n} (\mathrm{ABC})_{ii} = \sum_i \sum_j \sum_k a_{ij}b_{jk}c_{ki} \\ &= \sum_i \sum_j \sum_k c_{ki}a_{ij}b_{jk} \qquad \left[\text{which is } \sum_k (\mathrm{CAB})_{kk} = \mathrm{tr(CAB)}\right] \\ &= \sum_i \sum_j \sum_k b_{jk}c_{ki}a_{ij} \qquad \left[\text{which is } \sum_j (\mathrm{BCA})_{jj} = \mathrm{tr(BCA)}\right] \\ &= \sum_i \sum_j \sum_k (c_{ki}b_{jk}a_{ij}) \qquad \left[\text{which is } \textit{not} \sum_i (\mathrm{CBA})_{ii}, \text{ hence } \neq \mathrm{tr(CBA)}\right].\end{aligned}$$

(b) $\mathrm{tr(T^{-1}AT) = tr(TT^{-1}A) = tr(A)}$.

9-8

$$\begin{aligned}(\text{norm } \tilde{\mathrm{T}}\mathrm{AT})^2 &= \sum_{i,j} (\tilde{\mathrm{T}}\mathrm{AT})_{ij}\widetilde{(\tilde{\mathrm{T}}\mathrm{AT})}_{ji} = \sum_{i,j} (\tilde{\mathrm{T}}\tilde{\mathrm{A}}\mathrm{T})_{ij}(\tilde{\mathrm{T}}\mathrm{AT})_{ji} \\ &= \sum_{i,j,k,l} (\tilde{\mathrm{T}})_{ik}(\tilde{\mathrm{A}})_{kl}(\mathrm{T})_{lj}(\tilde{\mathrm{T}})_{jl}(\mathrm{A})_{lk}(\mathrm{T})_{ki} \\ &= \sum_{k,l} \Big[(\tilde{\mathrm{A}})_{kl}(\mathrm{A})_{lk} \underbrace{\sum_i (\tilde{\mathrm{T}})_{ik}(\mathrm{T})_{ki}}_{1} \underbrace{\sum_j (\mathrm{T})_{lj}(\tilde{\mathrm{T}})_{jl}}_{1}\Big] \\ &= \sum_{k,l} (\tilde{\mathrm{A}})_{kl}(\mathrm{A})_{lk} = (\text{norm A})^2\end{aligned}$$

9-9 (a) tr = 0, det = 2, norm = $\sqrt{6}$; therefore, $a + b + c = 0$, $abc = 2$, $a^2 + b^2 + c^2 = 6$; solutions: 2, −1, −1. (b) Solutions 1, 1, −1. (c) 0, $1 + \sqrt{3}$, $1 - \sqrt{3}$.

9-10 Both vectors transform to $\binom{3\cos\theta}{-3\sin\theta}$. Hence, reversal is not possible and transformation is singular. This is verified by fact that the determinant vanishes.

9-11 The matrix is already diagonalized. This means the eigenvector matrix is the 3 × 3 unit matrix.

9-12 Let $\mathrm{T^{-1}AT = D_A}$ (diagonal) and $\mathrm{T^{-1}BT = D_B}$ (diagonal). Then $\mathrm{D_AD_B = D_BD_A}$ (diagonal matrices commute); $\mathrm{T^{-1}ATT^{-1}BT = T^{-1}BTT^{-1}AT}$; $\mathrm{T^{-1}ABT = T^{-1}BAT}$; $\mathrm{TT^{-1}ABTT^{-1} = TT^{-1}BATT^{-1}}$; AB = BA.

9-13 In the second case, C is not unitary, since $\mathrm{C^{\dagger}SC = 1}$. The ordinary procedures for diagonalizing H have *built in* the requirement that $\mathrm{C^{\dagger}C = 1}$. The problem would be to find a matrix C that simultaneously diagonalizes H and satisfies $\mathrm{C^{\dagger}SC = 1}$.

9-14

$$\int \alpha^{\dagger}\beta\, d\omega \to (1 \quad 0)\begin{pmatrix}0\\1\end{pmatrix} = 0; \qquad \int \alpha^{\dagger}\alpha\, d\omega \to (1 \quad 0)\begin{pmatrix}1\\0\end{pmatrix} = 1$$

$$\hat{S}_z\alpha = \tfrac{1}{2}\begin{pmatrix}1 & 0\\0 & -1\end{pmatrix}\begin{pmatrix}1\\0\end{pmatrix} = \tfrac{1}{2}\begin{pmatrix}1\\0\end{pmatrix} = \tfrac{1}{2}\alpha$$

CHAPTER 10

10-1

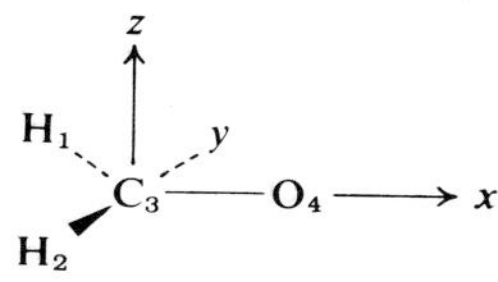

10-2

AO no.	Atom	AO type	AO no.	Atom	AO type
1	H_1	1s	6	C_3	$2p_y$
2	H_2	1s	7	O_4	2s
3	C_3	2s	8	O_4	$2p_z$
4	C_3	$2p_z$	9	O_4	$2p_x$
5	C_3	$2p_x$	10	O_4	$2p_y$

10-3 $E = -0.756$ a.u.; MO 9

$$\phi_9 = -0.27\ 1s_1 - 0.27\ 1s_2 - 0.49\ 2s_C + 0.22\ 2p_{xC} + 0.31\ 2s_O + 0.33\ 2p_{xO}$$

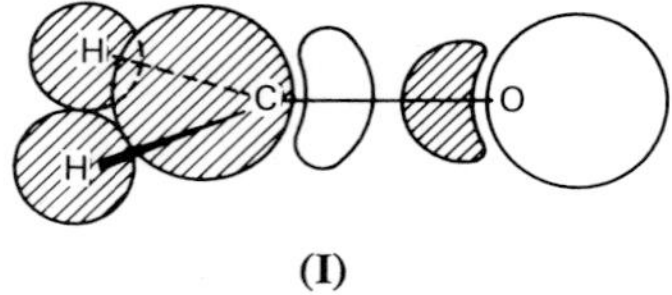

(I)

Aσ MO, mainly C–H_2 bonding and lone pair (nonbonding) on oxygen. Shows some C–O antibonding character [see (**I**)].

$E = -0.611$ a.u.; MO 8

$$\phi_8 = -0.21\ 1s_1 + 0.21\ 1s_2 - 0.32\ 2p_{yC} - 0.76\ 2p_{yO}$$

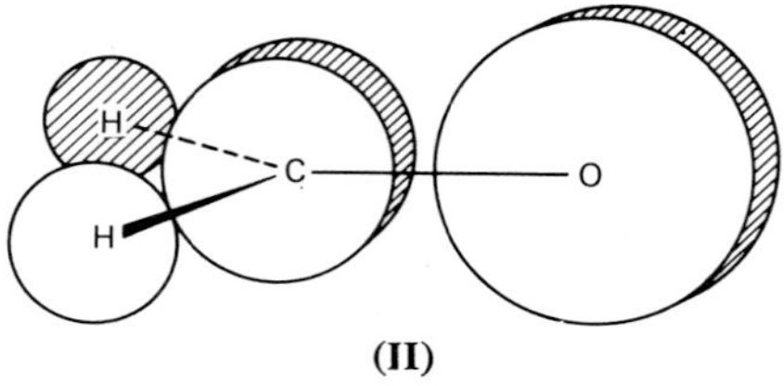

(II)

A σ MO, CH_2 and C–O bonding [see (**II**)].

$E = -0.597$ a.u.; MO no. 7

$$\phi_7 = 0.24\ 2p_{zC} + 0.92\ 2p_{zO}$$

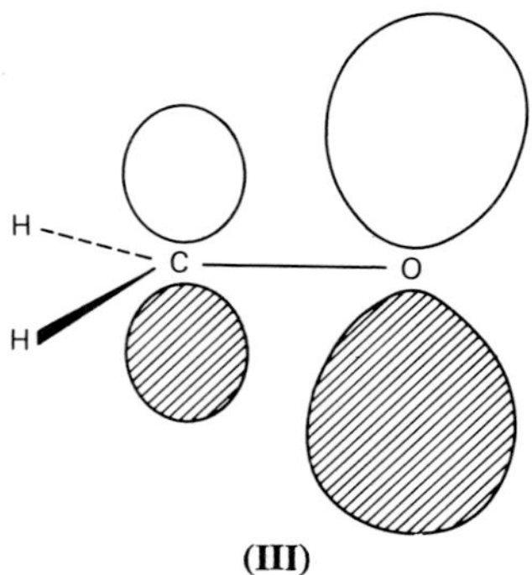

(III)

A π MO, mostly on oxygen, but somewhat delocalized to give some C–O bonding [see (**III**)].

10-4 The π MOs are 4 and 7. All others are σ.
10-5 C and O $2p_\pi$ AOs are 4 and 8. The 4, 8 overlap population is seen from the data to be 0.1936. Since MO 7 is C–O bonding, loss of an electron should cause the C–O bond to lengthen.
10-6

$$\begin{aligned} E_7 &= (0.2456)^2(-10.67 \text{ eV}) + (0.9181)^2(-15.85 \text{ eV}) \\ &\quad + 2(0.2456)(0.9181)(1.75)(0.2146)(-10.67 \text{ eV} - 15.85 \text{ eV})/2 \\ &= -16.25 \text{ eV} = -0.5972 \text{ a.u.} \end{aligned}$$

10-7 The sum of the elements in the upper triangle = 12. (Use of *all* elements would count overlap populations twice.)
10-8 If column 7 is the gross populations of MO no. 7, then it should turn out that $0.2175 = 2[c_{47}^2 + (0.5)(2)c_{47}c_{87}S_{48}]$: $2[(0.2456)^2 + (0.2456)(0.9181)(0.2146)] = 0.2175$. Q.E.D.
10-9 These must be AOs because MO charges must be 0, 1, or 2. AO 4, for example, gets its charge from MO 7. We have just seen (previous problem) that this is 0.2175. (AO 4 also appears in MO 4, and the "charge matrix" gives a value of 1.7825 for this. But this does not appear in the gross population because MO no. 4 is unoccupied in the ground state configuration.)
10-10 The net charges are the AO charges plus the nuclear charges (after cancellation of some nuclear charge by inner-shell electrons). These results indicate high polarity, with oxygen being the negative end of the dipole. The predicted polarity is unrealistically high because EHMO neglects interelectronic repulsion which would tend to counteract such extreme charge imbalance.
10-11 Number MOs = number AOs = 1 on each H and 4 (valence) on each $C = 22$.

CHAPTER 11

11-1

	Koopmans	ΔSCF	Experiment
2s → 2p	1.0800	1.0830	0.989
1s → 2p	31.9220	31.1921	31.19

11-2

	Koopmans–SCF (eV) (electron relaxation)	SCF − observed (eV) (electron correlation)
$^2B_1$	2.71	−1.54
$^2A_1$	2.52	−1.40
$^2B_2$	1.86	−0.90

11-3 For electron affinities, these errors should reinforce, rather than cancel, because adding an electron should *increase* electron correlation.
11-4 $ad - cb + \lambda(af - be) = ad + \lambda af - bc - \lambda be$.
11-5 Neither ψ_1 nor ψ_2 is already the best function in our function space. Hence, we cannot argue that mixing will bring no improvement.
11-6 This must be true to enable a_1 to be factored from the expanded form of $\hat{A}\psi$.

11-7 For a given choice of basis functions, there are two integrals:

$$\langle \chi_a(1)\chi_b(2)|\chi_c(1)\chi_d(2)\rangle \qquad \text{and} \qquad \langle \chi_a(1)\chi_b(2)|\chi_d(1)\chi_c(2)\rangle$$

There are five ways to choose a function for each position. Thus, the number of integrals is $2 \times 5^4 = 31{,}250$.
11-8 (a) and (c) would be prevented from contributing.
11-9

$$\hat{H} = -\tfrac{1}{2}\sum_{i=1}^{10} \nabla_i^2 - \sum_{i=1}^{10}\left(\frac{1}{r_{i,\mathrm{H}_1}} + \frac{1}{r_{i,\mathrm{H}_2}} + \frac{8}{r_{i,\mathrm{O}}}\right) + \sum_{i=1}^{9}\sum_{j=i+1}^{10}\frac{1}{r_{ij}}$$

CHAPTER 12
12-1 (a)

$$\langle\psi|H|\phi\rangle = \langle\psi|H_0 + H'|\phi\rangle = \langle\psi|H_0|\phi\rangle + \langle\psi|H'|\phi\rangle$$
$$\langle\phi|H|\psi\rangle^* = \langle\phi|H_0|\psi\rangle^* + \langle\phi|H'|\psi\rangle^*$$

If H and H_0 are hermitian, $\langle\psi|H|\phi\rangle = \langle\phi|H|\psi\rangle^*$, $\langle\psi|H_0|\phi\rangle = \langle\phi|H_0|\psi\rangle^*$. Therefore, $\langle\psi|H'|\phi\rangle = \langle\phi|H'|\psi\rangle^*$, and so H' is hermitian.

(b) $\langle\psi_j|H'|\psi_i\rangle = \langle\psi_i|H'|\psi_j\rangle^*$; therefore, the numerator of Eq. (12-21) equals $\langle\psi_i|H'|\psi_j\rangle\langle\psi_i|H'|\psi_j\rangle^*$.

(c)

$$\langle\psi_i|\phi_i^{(1)}\rangle = \left\langle\psi_i\Big|\sum_{i\neq j} c_{ji}\psi_j\right\rangle = \sum_{j\neq i} c_{ji}\langle\psi_i|\psi_j\rangle = \sum_{j\neq i} c_{ji}\delta_{ij} = 0$$

$$\langle\phi_i^{(1)}|H_0|\psi_i\rangle = \langle\phi_i^{(1)}|E_i\psi_i\rangle = E_i\langle\phi_i^{(1)}|\psi_i\rangle = 0$$

(d) $N = \left(1 + \sum_{j\neq i} c_{ji}^2\right)^{-1/2}$.

12-2 $E_0 + W_0^{(1)} = \langle\psi|H_0|\psi\rangle + \langle\psi|H'|\psi\rangle = \langle\psi|H|\psi\rangle \geq E_0$.
12-3 (a) δ. (b) δ. (c) $-\delta/2$. (d) $\delta/2$. (e) $-\delta/2$. (f) 0.
12-4 $E_\pi = 4\alpha + 4.9624\beta + (0.1)(q_4)$; $q_4 = 1.4881$; $E_\pi = 4\alpha + 5.1112\beta$.
12-5 The effect is least at C_6 since q_6 is smallest.
12-6 [See Hint.] $E_1^{(1)} > E_3^{(1)} > E_2^{(1)}$.
12-7 (a)

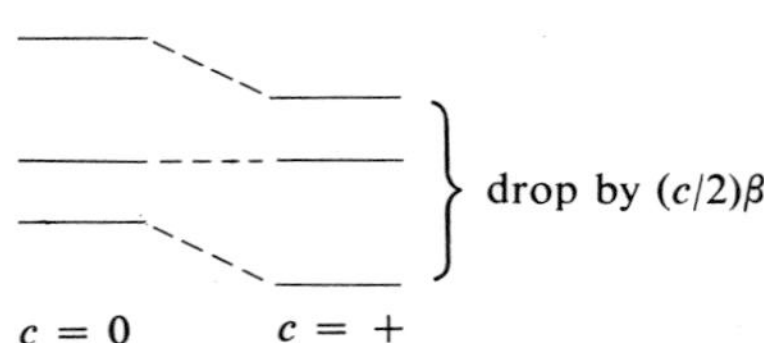

(b)

$$\phi_1^{(1)} = \frac{\langle\psi_2|H'|\psi_1\rangle}{E_1 - E_2}\psi_2 + \frac{\langle\psi_3|H'|\psi_1\rangle}{E_1 - E_3}\psi_3$$

Since H' depends only on density at C_2, it comes out of the integral. [See (IV).]

$$\phi_1^{(1)} = 0 + (-\tfrac{1}{2}c\beta/2\sqrt{2}\beta)\psi_3 = -0.1768c\psi_3, \qquad \phi_2^{(1)} = 0$$
$$\phi_3^{(1)} = +0.1768c\psi_1$$

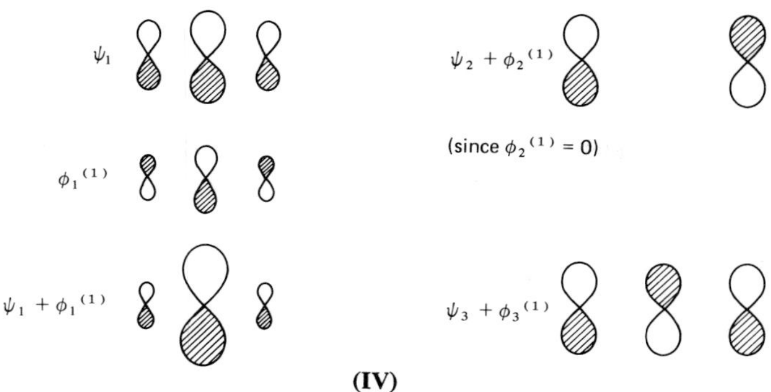

(IV)

Thus, $\psi_1 + \phi_1^{(1)}$ has more density at C_2 than did ψ_1, $\psi_2 + \phi_2^{(1)}$ is identical to ψ_2, and $\psi_3 + \phi_3^{(1)}$ has lost density at C_2.

12-8

$$c_{41}^{(1)} = \frac{\langle\psi_1|H'|\psi_4\rangle}{E_1 - E_4} = \frac{(2/L)\int_0^L \sin(\pi x/L)(Ux/L)\sin(4\pi x/L)\,dx}{-15\pi^2/2L^2} = \frac{64UL^2}{15^3\pi^4}$$

$$c_{21}^{(1)} = \frac{32UL^2}{27\pi^4}, \qquad \frac{c_{41}^{(1)}}{c_{21}^{(1)}} = \frac{2}{125} = 1.6\%$$

12-9 (a) Nondegenerate MO, $\phi_1 = (1/\sqrt{3})(\chi_1 + \chi_2 + \chi_3)$ is already correct. The correct zeroth-order degenerate MOs must give zero interaction element with H'. For this H', this means that the overlap between these MOs must be zero at C_2. Thus, one MO must have a node at C_2 [$\phi_2 = (1/\sqrt{2})(\chi_1 - \chi_3)$] and the other must be orthogonal to it [$\phi_3 = (1/\sqrt{6})(2\chi_2 - \chi_1 - \chi_3)$].

If one uses data from Appendix 6, one obtains, for degenerate MOs, $\psi_1 = -0.8165\chi_1 + 0.4082\chi_2 + 0.4082\chi_3$, and $\psi_2 = 0.7071\chi_2 - 0.7071\chi_3$. These give $H'_{11} = 0.1666c\beta$, $H'_{22} = 0.5c\beta$, $H'_{12} = 0.2886c\beta$. Since $H'_{12} \neq 0$, one knows ψ_1 and ψ_2 are not correct zeroth-order wavefunctions. Solving the determinantal equation gives $E_1 = 0$, $E_2 = 0.6666c\beta$. These are the first-order corrections to the energies of the two upper levels. Solving for coefficients gives, for $E = 0$, $c_1 = -0.866$, $c_2 = 0.500$, and so the proper zeroth-order wavefunction having a zero first-order correction is $\phi_1^{(0)} = -0.866\psi_1 + 0.500\psi_2 = 0.7071\chi_1 - 0.7071\chi_3$. For $E = 0.6666c\beta$, $c_1 = 0.500$, $c_2 = 0.866$, and so $\phi_2^{(0)} = -0.4082\chi_1 + 0.8165\chi_2 - 0.4082\chi_3$. These are the same functions arrived at intuitively above.

(b) For the above zeroth-order MOs, the densities at C_2 are respectively $\frac{1}{3}$, 0, $\frac{2}{3}$. Therefore, the energy of the lowest level drops by $c\beta/3$, that for one of the originally degenerate levels drops by $2c\beta/3$, and the other level is unaffected (to first order).

12-10 An s function has no planar nodes, but $3d_{xy}$, $3d_{yz}$, and $3d_{xz}$ each have two nodal cartesian axis planes. For these cases, the integral $\langle 2s|x, y, \text{ or } z|3d\rangle$ will always have at least one plane of antisymmetry and will vanish. The $3d_{z^2}$ and $3d_{x^2-y^2}$ functions are symmetric for reflection in all three Cartesian planes. Therefore such integrals as $\langle 2s|x, y, \text{ or } z|3d_{z^2}\rangle$ are always antisymmetric because x, y, and z are antisymmetric. Since all these integrals vanish, all integrals between 2s and any linear combinations of 3d AOs must vanish, and the transition is forbidden.

12-11 The field polarizes the atom, which means that the 2s state acquires 2p character. But the 2p → 1s transition is allowed, and so the atom now relaxes to the 1s state.

12-12 $\pi_{1,2} = -0.1768\beta^{-1}$; $\pi_{1,3} = -0.265\beta^{-1}$. Both atoms 2 and 3 lose charge, but atom 3 loses more than atom 2.

12-13 The effect is zero, to first order, because ψ^2 is symmetric for every state and the perturbation is antisymmetric.

12-14 First-order result: $E = 6\alpha + 7.777\beta$. Computed result: $E = 6\alpha + 7.8546\beta$.

12-15 [See Hint.] $E = E_0 + E_1 = -\frac{1}{2}$ a.u. $+ \langle 1s|-1/r|1s\rangle = -\frac{3}{2}$ a.u.

12-16 [See Hint.] For butadiene: $\Delta E_\pi = 2\beta[(0.3718)^2 - (0.6105)^2] = -0.469\beta$.

For hexatriene: $\Delta E_\pi = 2\beta[(0.2319)^2 - (0.4179)^2 + (0.5211)^2] = 0.543\beta$. The energy of hexatriene is lowered, that of butadiene is raised, and so hexatriene benefits.

For cyclobutadiene: $E_0 + E^{(1)} = 4\alpha + 4.0031\beta$, E (Hückel) $= 4\alpha + 4.000\beta$.

For benzene: $E_0 + E^{(1)} = 6\alpha + 7.531\beta$, E (Hückel) $= 6\alpha + 8.000\beta$.

12-17 (a) $W_2^{(1)} = 3\delta/4$.

(b-1) Expect $c_{21}^{(1)}$ to cause ψ_1 to shift to right. Since ψ_2 is positive on left of box, negative on right, $c_{21}^{(1)}$ should be negative. Since ψ_2 is above ψ_1, it should cause energy to be depressed, and $c_{21}^{(1)}$ leads to a negative contribution to $W_1^{(2)}$.

(b-2) Because $c_{ij}^{(1)} = -c_{ji}^{(1)}$, $c_{12}^{(1)}$ must be positive, giving a $\phi_2^{(1)}$ that causes charge to shift left and a contribution to $W_2^{(2)}$ that is positive.

12-18 (a) The magnetic field interacts with the orbital magnetic moment, which is proportional to angular momentum. Hence, the essential part of H' is $(1/i)\, \partial/\partial\phi$.

(b) Diagonalize the perturbation matrix. $H_{11} = 0$, $H_{22} = 0$, $H_{12} = -i$, $H_{21} = i$, $E^2 - 1 = 0$, $E = \pm 1$,

$$\phi_+ = (1/\sqrt{2})(\sin\phi + i\cos\phi) = (i/\sqrt{2})\exp(-i\phi)$$
$$\phi_- = (1/\sqrt{2})(\sin\phi - i\cos\phi) = (-i/\sqrt{2})\exp(i\phi)$$

12-19 You must ascertain whether $\langle\psi_m|x|\psi_n\rangle = 0$

$$(1/2\pi)\int_0^{2\pi} \exp(-im\phi)\cos\phi\exp(in\phi)\,d\phi$$
$$= (1/2\pi)\int_0^{2\pi}\left\{\exp[i(n - m + 1)\phi] + \exp[i(n - m - 1)\phi]\right\}d\phi = 0$$

unless a term in brackets vanishes. Therefore, $\langle\psi_m|x|\psi_n\rangle$ vanishes unless $n - m + 1 = 0$, or $n - m - 1 = 0$, that is, unless $n = m \pm 1$. Therefore, allowed transitions have $\Delta m = \pm 1$.

12-20 Since, for MO 4, $c_3 = c_7$, this MO is symmetric for reflection through the yz plane. The operator x is antisymmetric for this reflection. Therefore, if integral $\langle\phi_4|x|\phi_?\rangle$ is to be nonzero, $\phi_?$ must be antisymmetric for this reflection. Of the empty MOs shown, only ϕ_5 satisfies this requirement. There is no other symmetry operation present which will independently cause the integral to vanish, and $\phi_4 \to \phi_5$ is likely to be the observed transition.

12-21 (a) The HOMO is antisymmetric for reflection through the yz plane. (Assume that the coordinate origin is in the center of the 5–10 bond.) The x operator is also antisymmetric. Therefore, the allowed transition should be to an MO that is symmetric for this reflection. There are three such MOs, at energies of $+1.000$, $+1.303$, $+2.303$ in units of $-\beta$. But the middle of these disagrees in symmetry with the HOMO for reflection through the xz plane. Therefore, only the other two transitions are allowed.

(b) Here, the integrals containing y will vanish by symmetry except for transitions to $+0.618$ and $+1.303$, but the latter state disagrees in symmetry with the HOMO for the yz plane reflection. Hence, only $-0.618 \rightarrow +0.618$ is y allowed.

(c) No π–π transition is z allowed.

(d) Transitions to 1.303 and 1.618 are not allowed for any polarization.

12-22 $\langle\phi_{\pm}^{(0)}|-z|\phi_{\pm}^{(0)}\rangle = \pm\langle 2s|r \cos\theta|2p_z\rangle = \pm 3$ a.u. For $\phi = \cos(\alpha)$ 2s + $\sin(\alpha)$ $2p_z$, maximum dipole occurs when $\cos\alpha = 1/\sqrt{2}$, $\sin\alpha = \pm 1/\sqrt{2}$, that is, when $\phi = \phi_{\pm}^{(0)}$. This is reasonable since the mixing of degenerate states like these requires no energy "expense" in terms of the unperturbed hamiltonian. As soon as the slightest external field appears, the mixing will occur to the above extent to produce maximum dipoles.

CHAPTER 13

13-1 No. "Come about 180°" is needed for closure.

13-2 It means that for each operation there is a right inverse as well as a left inverse. If $AB = E$, then A is the inverse of B *and* B is the inverse of A.

13-3 (a) C_4. (b) 4. (c) Probably only three, since one tends to think of left face and right face as being in same class. However, in the C_4 group they are not, because there is no operation in the group to interchange them (such as reflection through a plane containing the z axis).

13-4 There are many possible arrangements counted in 4! which are not physically achievable through operations in the group. For example,

$$\begin{array}{ccc} 1-2 & & 1-4 \\ |\quad | & \not\longrightarrow & |\quad | \\ 4-3 & & 3-2 \end{array}$$

For C_{3v}, all possible arrangements are accessible.

13-5 (a) C_{2v}. (b) D_{2h}. (c) D_{4h}. (d) T_d.

13-6 (a) $U^{\dagger}U = UU = 1$ (upon explicit multiplication).

(b) Upon explicit multiplication, $U^{\dagger}AU = \begin{pmatrix} 1 & 0 \\ 0 & -1 \end{pmatrix}$.

13-7 (a) D_{6h} (yes). (b) C_{2v} (no). (c) D_{2h} (no). (d) D_{3d} (yes). (e) C_{3v} (yes).

13-8 (a) D_{3h}. (b) (1) a_2''; (2) e''; (3) a_2'; (4) a_1'.

13-9 [See Hint.] D_{2d},

MO number:	1	2	3	4	5 6	7 8	9 10	11	12 13	14	15	16
MO symmetry:	b_2	a_1	a_1	b_2	e	e	e	b_2	e	a_1	b_2	a_1

The highest occupied MO is 9, 10; the lowest empty MO is 8, 7, and so the transition is $e \rightarrow e$.

$$\langle\phi_9|x \text{ or } y|\phi_8\rangle = \int e \otimes e \otimes e = \int e \oplus e \oplus e \oplus e = 0$$

$$\langle\phi_9|z|\phi_8\rangle = \int e \otimes b_2 \otimes e = \int a_1 \oplus a_2 \oplus b_1 \oplus b_2 \neq 0$$

Transition is allowed for (group theory) z polarized light. This means x polarized for the coordinate system shown.

13-10 (a) and (b) can be checked against C_{2v} character table. (c) Hydrogens generate characters 2 0 2 0, which is $a_1 \oplus b_1$. (d) The unnormalized symmetry combinations are: a_1, $1s_A + 1s_B$; b_1, $1s_A - 1s_B$.

13-11 (a) and (b) can be checked against the C_{4v} character table.

(c) Hydrogens generate characters 4 0 0 2 0 or 4 0 0 0 2, depending on how σ_v and σ_d are selected. Assuming that σ_v contains corner ammonia molecules gives the former set. This resolves to $a_1 \oplus b_1 \oplus e$. (The other choice gives b_2 instead of b_1, but reversal of choice of σ_v and σ_d has the effect of interchanging the symbols b_1 and b_2, and there is no real difference involved in this choice.)

(d) For a situation where the nitrogens are numbered as shown in the figure, the unnormalized symmetry orbitals are: a_1, $2s_1 + 2s_2 + 2s_3 + 2s_4$; b_1, $2s_1 - 2s_2 + 2s_3 - 2s_4$; e, $2s_1 - 2s_3$ and $2s_2 - 2s_4$; or $2s_1 + 2s_2 - 2s_3 - 2s_4$ and $2s_1 - 2s_2 - 2s_3 + 2s_4$. (Other combinations are also possible, but these two sets are the most convenient.)

13-12 (a) Four operations means order 4. Four classes means four representations. Hence, each representation must be one dimensional, therefore having character $+1$ or -1 for every operation. One of these must be $+1$ everywhere (A_1). The others must all have $+1$ in the first column and -1 in two of the other three columns. The result is as given in Appendix 13 for C_{2v}.

(b) Twelve operations gives order twelve. Six classes means six representations. This must mean two 2×2 and four 1×1. There is but one unique set of orthonormal character vectors that fit this framework. Check against the D_{3h} character table.

13-13 Two two-dimensional representations and two one-dimensional representations.

13-14 Check against C_{2v}.

13-15 Order = 12. There are six classes.

13-16

$$\frac{1}{2}\begin{pmatrix} 1 & 1 & -1 & 1 \\ 1 & -1 & 1 & 1 \\ 1 & -1 & -1 & -1 \\ 1 & 1 & 1 & -1 \end{pmatrix}\begin{pmatrix} \mathrm{s} \\ \mathrm{p}_x \\ \mathrm{p}_y \\ \mathrm{p}_z \end{pmatrix} = \mathrm{sp}^3 \text{ set}$$

$$\begin{pmatrix} 1/\sqrt{3} & 0 & \sqrt{2}/\sqrt{3} & 0 \\ 1/\sqrt{3} & 1/\sqrt{2} & -1/\sqrt{6} & 0 \\ 1/\sqrt{3} & -1/\sqrt{2} & -1/\sqrt{6} & 0 \\ 0 & 0 & 0 & 1 \end{pmatrix}\begin{pmatrix} \mathrm{s} \\ \mathrm{p}_x \\ \mathrm{p}_y \\ \mathrm{p}_z \end{pmatrix} = \mathrm{sp}^2 \text{ set}$$

For each matrix T, $\mathsf{T}^{\dagger}\mathsf{T} = 1$.

13-17 Yes. Since various hybridized sets are equivalent, the final result of the calculation is independent of one's choice.

13-18 (a) $A_2 \oplus 2B_1 \oplus E$. Yes. (b) $A_g \oplus 2B_{3u}$. No.
(c) $A_{1g} \oplus A_{2g} \oplus E_g \oplus A_{1u} \oplus A_{2u} \oplus E_u$. No.

13-19 (a) $e \otimes b_2 \otimes e = a_1 \oplus a_2 \oplus b_1 \oplus b_2$. Need not vanish.
(b) $e \otimes e \otimes e = e \oplus e \oplus e \oplus e$. Must vanish.
(c) $a_1 \otimes b_2 \otimes b_2 = a_1$. Need not vanish.
(d) $a_1 \otimes b_2 \otimes a_1 = b_2$. Must vanish.
(e) $a_1 \otimes e \otimes b_2 = e$. Must vanish.

13-20 $e_g \rightarrow a_{2u}$, e_u are x, y allowed. $e_g \rightarrow e_u$ is z allowed.

13-21 The symmetry of the molecule is C_{2v}. All π MOs are antisymmetric for C_2 so must be bases for b_1 or b_2 representations. The function y (for the molecule) is z (in the table), and so it is a basis for the a_1 representation. For the product $\phi_4 y \phi_n$ to contain a_1 symmetry, it is necessary, then, that ϕ_n have the same symmetry as ϕ_4. ϕ_6 and ϕ_7 do have same symmetry; therefore, $\phi_4 \rightarrow \phi_6, \phi_7$ are y allowed (where y is coincident with the symmetry axis).

CHAPTER 14

14-1 $\langle 1s_A | \hat{H}_{\text{hyd}} - 1/r_B | 1s_A \rangle = -\frac{1}{2} - (1/R) + [(1/R) + 1] \exp(-2R)$ where R is distance between nuclei. For $R = 2$ a.u., $E_{\text{elec}} = -0.9725$ a.u., $E_{\text{tot}} = -0.4725$ a.u. $R = 1$ a.u., $E_{\text{elec}} = -1.2293$ a.u., $E_{\text{tot}} = -0.2293$ a.u. $R = 3$ a.u., $E_{\text{elec}} = -0.8300$ a.u., $E_{\text{tot}} = -0.4967$ a.u.

14-2 Expected QMOT behavior is reversed for very low H_{AA}. The "antibonding" MO is lower than the "bonding" for $H_{AA} = -20$. This happens because the loss of energy involved in removing charge from the atoms is not compensated by that gained by putting the charge in the bond region.

14-3 The molecular electron affinities tend to be greater than for the atoms when the extra molecular electron goes into a bonding MO, smaller if into an antibonding MO. QMOT leads us to expect the MO energy to be lowered (raised) from separated atom levels if the interaction is bonding (antibonding). Koopmans' theorem then leads to predictions in qualitative agreement with these data.

14-4 The observed ground-state angles are more consistent with the triplet-state configuration. The first excited state should then be a singlet and have a smaller angle.

14-5 It should become more bent. (Also, the O–H bonds should lengthen, although this is not the kind of geometric change which the figure explicitly treats.)

14-6 The computed results will largely agree with QMOT ideas. However, it is possible that the $1\sigma_g$–$1a_1$ level will rise where Walsh's rules predict it will fall. [Whether this occurs depends upon details of EHMO parameter choices.] Upon analysis, this turns out to result from a situation similar to that examined in Problem 14-2. That is, the increase in H–H overlap population comes at the expense of population elsewhere. If the energy associated with this "population elsewhere" is low (i.e., if the original MO energy is low enough) the energy cost is greater than the gain due to increased H–H overlap population. This inversion of behavior for low levels is ignored in the Walsh approach. However, it does not occur for a given MO until it is fairly deeply buried under higher filled MOs. Also, since the higher MOs dominate the behavior of the molecule anyway, the inversion does not affect our prediction.

14-7 Since the exact answer depends on details of your EHMO program, allow me to take this opportunity to toast your good health.

14-8 If $S = S_0 \cos\theta$, $dS/d\theta = -S_0 \sin\theta$. ΔS for $\theta = 0$ to $\theta = 30°$ equals $-(1 - 0.866)S_0 = -0.134S_0$; for 90–60°, $\Delta S = -S_0(0 - 0.5) = 0.5S_0$.

14-9 For a diagram and discussion, see Gimarc [1]. Those with six valence electrons (the first three in the list) are planar. Those with eight electrons (the last four) are pyramidal.

14-10 Sketches and discussions of AB_2 molecules may be found in the literature [2, 3]. Molecules with 16 or fewer valence electrons ($BeCl_2$, C_3, CO_2, N_3^-) should be linear. Those with more than 16 should be bent (NO_2, O_3, F_2O).

14-11 Bending should increase end-to-end antibonding. These MOs favor the linear form [see (**V**)].

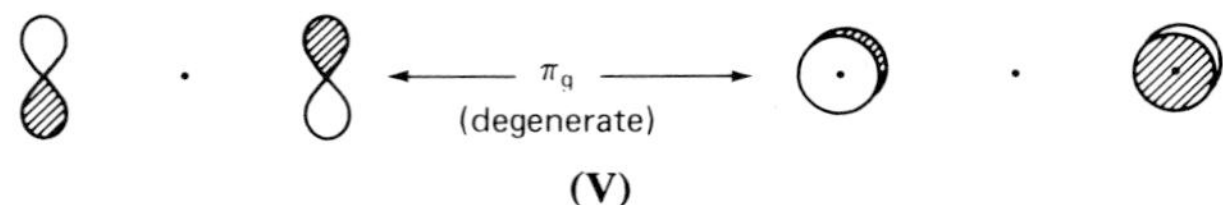

(V)

Bending should increase end-to-end bonding. These MOs favor the bent form [see (**VI**)].

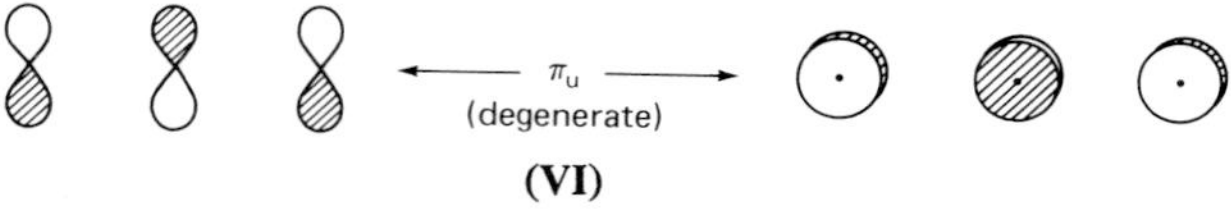

(VI)

Therefore, $\pi_g \rightarrow \pi_u$ should make molecule more bent.

14-12 For allyl, draw the three π MOs. For the cyclic molecule, draw a C–C bond (lowest in energy), a single p–π AO on the negative carbon (intermediate energy) and the C–C antibond (high energy). Conrotary motion preserves a C_2 axis, disrotatory preserves a reflection plane. For the C_2 axis, the allyl MO symmetries are (in order of increasing energy) A, S, A. For the cyclopropenyl anion, they are S, A, A. For the reflection plane, the same MOs have symmetries S, A, S; and S, S, A. The resulting predictions for the four-electron anion are that thermal closure goes conrotatory, photochemical goes disrotatory.

14-13 [See Hint.] The diagram is given in (**VII**). σ and π refer to symmetry (S or A) for reflection through the molecular plane. The second symmetry symbol refers to reflections through a plane between the two acetylenes. The third symbol refers to a reflection orthogonal to the first two (i.e., bisecting both acetylenes at their bond midpoints). The reaction does not appear favorable for a thermal mode. Photochemically it is less unfavorable, but still corresponds to a rather highly excited product. A square planar intermediate is unlikely for either mode.

14-14 No states can differ in symmetry in this case, and no crossings should occur.

14-15 See Woodward and Hoffmann [4, pp. 23, 24].

14-16 See Woodward and Hoffmann [4, pp. 70, 117].

APPENDIX 2

A2-2 (a) -2. (b) 1. (c) 0. (d) $x = \pm\sqrt{2}$.

A2-4 Determinant of coefficients vanishes, and so nontrivial roots *do* exist.

A2-5 $c = 2, -1 \pm \sqrt{7}$ are the roots.

A2-6 (a) If two rows or columns differ by factor c, then multiplication of the

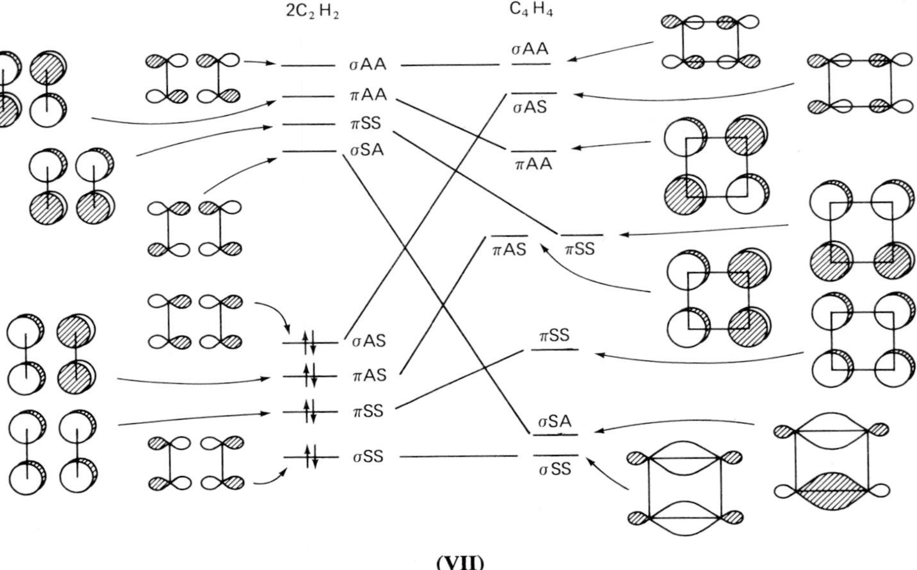

(VII)

smaller row or column gives $|M'| = c|M|$ (by rule 1), and M' has two identical rows or columns. Interchanging these gives M'', and $|M'| = -|M''|$. But $M'' = M'$ because the interchanged rows or columns are identical. Therefore, $|M'| = -|M'|$, and $|M'| = 0$. Therefore, $|M| = c|M'| = 0$.

APPENDIX 8

A8-1 $\hat{T} = -\frac{1}{2}\, d^2/dx^2$, $\hat{V} = \frac{1}{2}\, kx^2$. Equation (A8-19) gives $\bar{E}\eta = \eta^2\bar{T} + \eta^{-2}\bar{V}$. $\partial\bar{E}/\partial\eta = 0 = 2\eta\bar{T} - 2\eta^{-3}\bar{V}$. For an exact solution, $\eta = 1$, and $\bar{T} = \bar{V}$.
A8-2 $\bar{V} = -3$ a.u., $\bar{T} = \frac{1}{2}$ a.u., $\eta = -\bar{V}/2\bar{T} = 3$, $\psi_\eta = \sqrt{\eta^3/\pi}\exp(-\eta r) = \sqrt{27/\pi}$ $\exp(-3r)$, $E_\eta = \eta^2\bar{T} + \eta\bar{V} = \frac{9}{2} - 9 = -4.5$ a.u.

REFERENCES

[1] B. M. Gimarc, *Accounts Chem. Res.* **7**, 384 (1974).
[2] R. S. Mulliken, *Rev. Mod. Phys.* **4**, 1 (1932).
[3] A. D. Walsh, *J. Chem. Soc.* 2260 (1953).
[4] R. B. Woodward and R. Hoffmann, "The Conservation of Orbital Symmetry." Academic Press, New York, 1970.

INDEX

A

Abelian group, 383
Ab initio calculation, 309–342, *see also* Hartree–Fock equation
Allyl radical, 205
Alternant hydrocarbon, 220, 498
Angular momentum, 51, 97
  eigenvalues, 101
  of gyroscope, 98
  operators, 99–100
  vector diagram, 100–101
Antibonding orbital, 178
Aromaticity, 239, 241
Associativity, in group, 382
Atomic orbitals, 108
Atomic units, 96
Atom–atom polarizability, 362
Aufbau principle, 132
Average value, 73, 83, 139, 145

B

Barrier penetration, 42, 47, 65, 80
Basis, 192, 284, 311, 315
  balance, 174, 194
  for representation, 400
Benzene, 225
Binding energy, 197
Bohr magneton, 102
Bohr radius, 80
Bond–atom polarizability, 364
Bond–bond polarizability, 364
Bonding orbital, 178
Bond integral, *see* Resonance integral
Bond length, 228, 333–337
Bond order, 217
Born–Oppenheimer approximation, 168
Boson, 116
Boundary conditions, 7, 8, 29, 43
Bra-ket notation, 350, 552–553
Brillouin's theorem, 326
Butadiene, 223

C

Character tables, 413, 560–571
Charge distribution, 214
Class, 386, 414
Closed shell, 113, 311
Closure, in group, 382
Cofactor, 485
Commutator, 143, 146
Completeness, 67
Complex conjugate, 21, 87
Concerted reaction, 464
Configuration interaction, 322–327
Conjugate variables, 19
Constant of motion, 31, 43, 97
  and sharp values, 50
Continuity, of wavefunction, 23
Conversion factors, *table*, 556–557
Correlation, of electrons, 180
Correlation diagram, 47, 191, 446, 466, 471
Correlation energy, 319
Correspondence principle, 31, 35
Coulomb hole, 126
Coulomb integral, 122, 207, 488–492
Coulomb operator, 312, 516
Cyclic group, 408
Cycloaddition reaction, 472
Cyclobutadiene, 224

D

de Broglie wavelength, 15–16, 20, 33, 42
Degeneracy, 32, 80, 211
Delocalization, 224
  energy, 239
Density function, 136, 215
Determinants, 485–487
Diagonal matrix, 271
Diffraction, of electrons, 16
Dimension, of representation, 397
Dipole moment, 140
  ab initio, 336
  induced, 367
  permanent, 367
Dirac delta function, 139, 146
Dissociation energy, 197
Double-zeta basis, 316

E

Eigenfunction, 21
  of commuting operators, 143
  completeness, 144
  of hermitian operator, 142
  physical meaning, 33
Eigenvalue, 21, 287, *see also* Energy level
  of hermitian operator, 141
  matrix, 276
Eigenvector, 276, 287
Einstein, A., 13, 15
Electrocyclic reaction, 464
Electromagnetic radiation, *see* Light
Electron densities, 215
  and electron spin resonance, 231
Electronic configuration, 109
Element, of group, 381
Energy, classical particle, 20
Energy level
  harmonic oscillator, 31, 70
  hydrogen atom, 31
  hydrogenlike ion, 78
  particle in box, 31
  particle in ring, 52
Equivalent representation, 399
Ethylene, 222
Exchange integral, 122
Exchange operator, 312, 516
Excited states of helium, 119–127
Exclusion principle, 116, 147

F

Fermi hole, 126
Fermion, 116
First-order correction, 348, 351, 355
Free particle, 49
Free valence, 253
Frontier orbitals, 253, 461

G

Gaussian function, 317
Generating function, 71
Group multiplication table, 382

H

Hamiltonian matrix, 285
Hamiltonian operator, 20, 107, 310
Harmonic oscillator
  classical, 60–61
  quantum mechanical, 63
Hartree–Fock equation, 312, 509–519
Hartree–Fock limit, 318
Heisenberg uncertainty principle, *see* Uncertainty principle
Heisenberg, W., 19, 32
Hermite polynomial, 71
Hermitian operator, 136, 140
Helium atom, 119–127
Heliumlike system, 359
Heteroatom Hückel parameter, 245
Homogeneous equation, 160, 164
Homonuclear diatomic molecule, 181, 444
Hooke's law, 60
Hückel determinant, 205
Hund's rule, 126, 187
Hybrid orbital, 425
Hydrogen molecule ion, 167–181, 438–441
Hydroxyl radical, 331

I

Identity element, 382
Improper rotation, 389
Independent electron approximation, 108, 129, 204
Inverse, of operation, 382

Inversion, 389
Ionization potential, 236, 448
Irreducible representation, 398

J

Jacobi method, 528–531
Jahn–Teller distortion, 216

K

Koopmans' theorem, 320
Kronecker delta, 37–38, 72

L

Laguerre polynomial, 95
Laplacian, 7
Legendre polynomial, 94, 490
Light, 9–11
Linear combination, 7
  of atomic orbitals, 167
Linear dependence, 8, 28, 67
Linear homogeneous equation, 486
Linear variation, 493–497
  matrix formulation, 275
Localization energy, 254
Localized orbital, 425

M

Matrix, 267
  commutation, 270
  complex conjugate, 269
  hermitian adjoint, 269
  inverse, 271
  latent roots, 281
  multiplication, 269
  nonsingular, 275
  norm, 281
  orthogonal, 277
  product, 271
  trace, 281
  transpose, 269
  tridiagonalization, 280, 531–534
  unitary, 277
Measurement, 138, 146
  and average values, 145
  and eigenvalues, 138
Methane, 283–300
Minimal basis, 169
Molecular orbital, 169, 209
Momentum, 20, 50, *see also* Angular momentum
Mulliken population, 295–301

N

Newton's second law, 6
Node, 4, 54, 85
Noncrossing rule, 187, 191
Normalization, 22, 49, 210

O

Operator, 20, 136
  commutation, 21
Order, of group, 381
Orthogonality, 37, 85, *see also* Schmidt orthogonalization
  in groups, 411
Orthogonal transformation, 274–275
Orthonormality, 37, 72
  spin functions, 115
Overlap, 159
Overlap integral, 207
Overlap matrix, 285
Oxidation–reduction potential, 234

P

Pairing theorem, 221, 498–499
Particle in box
  with finite central barrier, 44–48
  one-dimensional, 27–38
  with one finite wall, 38–44
  perturbed, 352–359, 375
  three-dimensional, 52–56
Particle in ring, 50–52
Partitioning, determinantal equation, 184
Pauli principle, 119
Pauli spin matrix, 282
Perturbation theory
  for degenerate states, 364
  for nondegenerate states, 347–364

Photoelectric effect, 11
Photon, 13
Pi orbital, 203
Point group, 383
Polarizability, 252
  excited hydrogen atom, 365–368
  hydrogen atom, 157–166
Polarization function, 317
Postulates of quantum mechanics, 135–140, 145, 147
Power series, 67
Probability density, 14, 80
  anticlassical, 35, 65
Product, in group, 381
Pyridine, 245
Pyrrole, 246

Q

Quantum number, 31, 84

R

Reaction
  energies, 340
  indices, 250–257
  qualitative theory, 464
Recursion relation, 68
Reduced mass, 77
Reducible representation, 398, 417
Reflection, 389
Representation, 396
Resonance integral, 207
Rotation, 389

S

Schmidt orthogonalization, 143, 278, 525–528
Schrödinger, E., 20
Schrödinger equation, 19, 20, 30, 76
  matrix form, 525–537
  physical meaning, 23
Screening constant, 130
Second-order correction, 351, 357
Secular determinant, 160
Secular equation, 160
Selection rule, 371
Self-consistent field, 129, 309–344
Self-consistent Hückel calculation, 248
Semiempirical method, 205
Separated atom, 168
Separated-atom basis, 169
Separation of variables, 53, 55, 92
Sigma–pi separability, 202
Sigmatropic shift reaction, 475
Similarity transformation, 275
Simultaneous equations, 210
Single-center basis, 169
Single valuedness, 22
Slater determinant, 118, 120
Slater, J., 117
Slater-type orbital, 130, 315
Slater's rules, 130
Spherical harmonics, 97
Spherical polar coordinate, 77
Spin, 102, 112
  multiplicity, 123
  orbital, 114
  vector diagram, 123, 124
Square integrability, 23, 30
Stark effect, 366
State function, *see* Wavefunction
Stationary state, 30
Symmetry
  electron exchange, 111
  element, 389
  of hamiltonian operator, 35, 111
  and integration, 37, 354, 428
  operator, 35, 383
  of wavefunction, 35, 111, 115, 174, 288, 418
Symmetry orbital, 182, 422

T

Time dependence, 137
Topological determinant, 208
Tunneling, *see* Barrier penetration

U

Uncertainty principle, 19, 32, 101, 146–147
Unitary transformation, 274–275
United atom, 168

V

Valence state ionization potential, 286
Variation method, 150

excited states, 165, 176
linear, 157
nonlinear, 151
Variation principle, 145
Vector, 267
Virial theorem, 520–524
Virtual orbital, 323

W

Walsh diagram, 447
Wave, 1
energy storage, 4
harmonic, 2
standing, 3, 7
Wave equation
classical, 5
quantum mechanical, *see* Schrödinger equation
Wave nature of matter, *see* de Broglie wavelength
Wavefunction, 21, 135
asymptotic behavior, 65, 69
conditions, 21
Wolfsberg–Helmholtz relation, 286
Woodward–Hoffmann rule, 466

Z

Zeeman splitting, 102
Zero differential overlap, 343
Zero point energy, 32, 64, 70, 79